COMPREHENSIVE RENEWABLE ENERGY

COMPREHENSIVE RENEWABLE ENERGY

EDITOR-IN-CHIEF
Ali Sayigh
Chairman of WREC, Director General of WREN, and Chairman of IEI, Brighton, UK

VOLUME 2
WIND ENERGY

VOLUME EDITOR
John K. Kaldellis
Technological Education Institute of Piraeus, Athens, Greece

ELSEVIER

AMSTERDAM BOSTON HEIDELBERG LONDON NEW YORK OXFORD
PARIS SAN DIEGO SAN FRANCISCO SINGAPORE SYDNEY TOKYO

Elsevier
Radarweg 29, PO Box 211, 1000 AE Amsterdam, The Netherlands
The Boulevard, Langford Lane, Kidlington, Oxford OX5 1GB, UK
225 Wyman Street, Waltham, MA 02451, USA

Copyright © 2012 Elsevier Ltd. All rights reserved.

4.04   Hydrogen Safety Engineering: The State-of-the-Art and Future Progress
Copyright © 2012 V Molkov

5.16   Renewable Fuels: An Automotive Perspective
Copyright © 2012 Lotus Cars Limited

The following articles are US Government works in the public domain and not subject to copyright:
1.19   Cadmium Telluride Photovoltaic Thin Film: CdTe
1.37   Solar Power Satellites
4.02   Current Perspective on Hydrogen and Fuel Cells
5.02   Historical Perspectives on Biofuels

No part of this publication may be reproduced, stored in a retrieval system or transmitted in any form or by any means electronic, mechanical, photocopying, recording or otherwise without the prior written permission of the publisher

Permissions may be sought directly from Elsevier's Science & Technology Rights Department in Oxford, UK: phone (+44) (0) 1865 843830; fax (+44) (0) 1865 853333; email: permissions@elsevier.com. Alternatively you can submit your request online by visiting the Elsevier web site at http://elsevier.com/locate/permissions, and selecting *Obtaining permission to use Elsevier material*

Notice
No responsibility is assumed by the publisher for any injury and/or damage to persons or property as a matter of products liability, negligence or otherwise, or from any use or operation of any methods, products, instructions or ideas contained in the material herein. Because of rapid advances in the medical sciences, in particular, independent verfication of diagnoses and drug dosages should be made.

British Library Cataloguing in Publication Data
A catalogue record for this book is available from the British Library

The Library of Congress Control Number: 2012934547

ISBN: 978-0-08-087872-0

For information on all Elsevier publications
visit our website at books.elsevier.com

Printed and bound in Italy

11 12 13 14   10 9 8 7 6 5 4 3 2 1

Working together to grow
libraries in developing countries

www.elsevier.com | www.bookaid.org | www.sabre.org

ELSEVIER   BOOK AID International   Sabre Foundation

Editorial: Gemma Mattingley, Joanne Williams
Production: Edward Taylor, Maggie Johnson

EDITOR-IN-CHIEF

Professor Ali Sayigh, BSc, DIC, PhD, CEng, a British citizen, graduated from Imperial College London and the University of London in 1966. He is a fellow of the Institute of Energy, a fellow of the Institution of Electrical Engineers, and is a chartered engineer.

From 1966 to 1985, Prof. Sayigh taught in the College of Engineering at the University of Baghdad and at King Saud University, Saudi Arabia, as a full-time professor, and also at Kuwait University as a part-time professor. From 1981 to 1985, he was Head of the Energy Department at the Kuwait Institute for Scientific Research (KISR) and expert in renewable energy at the Arab Organization of Petroleum Exporting Countries (AOPEC), Kuwait.

He started working in solar energy in September 1969. In 1984, he established links with Pergamon Press and became Editor-in-Chief of his first international journal, *Solar & Wind Technology*. Since 1990 he has been Editor-in-Chief of *Comprehensive Renewable Energy* incorporating *Solar & Wind Technology*, published by Elsevier Science Ltd., Oxford, UK. He is the editor of several international journals published in Morocco, Iran, Bangladesh, and Nigeria.

He has been a member of the International Society for Equitation Science (ISES) since 1973, founder and chairman of the ARAB Section of ISES since 1979, chairman of the UK Solar Energy Society for 3 years, and consultant to many national and international organizations, among them, the British Council, the Islamic Educational, Scientific and Cultural Organization (ISESCO), the United Nations Educational, Scientific and Cultural Organization (UNESCO), the United Nations Development Programme (UNDP), the Economic and Social Commission for Western Asia (ESCWA), and the United Nations Industrial Development Organization (UNIDO).

Since 1977 Prof. Sayigh has founded and directed several renewable energy conferences and workshops in the International Centre for Theoretical Physics (ICTP) – Trieste, Italy, Canada, Colombia, Algeria, Kuwait, Bahrain, Malaysia, Zambia, Malawi, India, the West Indies, Tunisia, Indonesia, Libya, Taiwan, UAE, Oman, the Czech Republic, Germany, Australia, Poland, the Netherlands, Thailand, Korea, Iran, Syria, Saudi Arabia, Singapore, China, the United States, and the United Kingdom.

In 1990 he established the World Renewable Energy Congress (WREC) and, in 1992, the World Renewable Energy Network (WREN), which hold their Congresses every 2 years, attracting more than 100 countries each time. In 2000, he and others in UAE, Sharjah, founded the Arab Science and Technology Foundation (ASTF) and regional conferences have been held in Sweden, Malaysia, Korea, Indonesia, Australia, UAE, and Libya, to name but a few. Prof. Sayigh has been running an annual international seminar on all aspects of renewable energy since 1990 in the United Kingdom and abroad. In total, 85 seminars have been held.

Prof. Sayigh supervised and graduated more than 34 PhD students and 64 MSc students at Reading University and the University of Hertfordshire when he was a professor from 1986 to 2004.

He has edited, contributed, and written more than 32 books and published more than 500 papers in various international journals and conferences.

In 2000–09, he initiated and worked closely with Sovereign Publication Company to produce the most popular magazine at annual bases called *Renewable Energy*, which was distributed freely to more than 6000 readers around the world. Presently, he is the editor-in-chief of *Comprehensive Renewable Energy*, coordinating 154 top scientists', engineers', and researchers' contributions in eight volumes published by Elsevier Publishing Company, Oxford, UK.

VOLUME EDITORS

Dr. Wilfried G. J. H. M. van Sark graduated from Utrecht University, the Netherlands, with an MSc in experimental physics in 1985, and with an MSc thesis on measurement and analysis of I–V characteristics of c-Si cells. He received his PhD from Nijmegen University, the Netherlands; the topic of his PhD thesis was III–V solar cell development, modeling, and processing. He then spent 7 years as a postdoc/senior researcher at Utrecht University and specialized in a-Si:H cell deposition and analysis. He is an expert in plasma chemical vapor deposition, both radio frequency and very high frequency. After an assistant professor position at Nijmegen University, where he worked on III–V solar cells, he returned to Utrecht University, with a focus on (single-molecule) confocal fluorescence microscopy of nanocrystals. In 2002, he moved to his present position as assistant professor at the research group Science, Technology and Society of the Copernicus Institute at Utrecht University, the Netherlands, where he performed and coordinated research on next-generation photovoltaic devices incorporating nanocrystals; for example, luminescent solar concentrators, as well as photovoltaic performance, life cycle analysis, socioeconomics, and policy development. He is member of the editorial board of Elsevier's scientific journal *Renewable Energy*, and member of various organizing committees of the European Union, the Institute of Electrical and Electronics Engineers (IEEE), and the SPIE PV conferences. He is author or coauthor of over 200 peer-reviewed journal and conference paper publications and book chapters. He has (co-)edited three books, including the present one.

Professor John K. Kaldellis holds a mechanical engineering degree from the National Technical University of Athens (NTUA) and a business administration diploma from the University of Piraeus. He obtained his PhD from NTUA (Fluid Sector) sponsored by Snecma–Dassault, France, and Bodossakis Foundation, Greece. He is currently the head of the Mechanical Engineering Department and since 1991 the director of the Soft Energy Applications and Environmental Protection Laboratory of the Technological Education Institute (TEI) of Piraeus. Prof. Kaldellis is also the scientific director (for TEI of Piraeus) of the MSc in Energy program organized by Heriot-Watt University and TEI of Piraeus. His scientific expertise is in the fields of energy and the environment. His research interests include feasibility analysis of energy sector applications; technological progress in wind, hydro, and solar energy markets; hybrid energy systems; energy storage issues; social attitudes toward renewable energy applications; and environmental technology–atmospheric pollution. He has participated in numerous research projects, funded by the European Union, European/Greek Industries, and the Greek State. Prof. Kaldellis has published six books concerning renewable energy applications and environmental protection. He is also the author of more than 100 scientific/research papers in international peer-reviewed journals and more than 300 papers for international scientific conferences. During the last decade, he was also a member of the Scientific Committee of the Hellenic Society of Mechanical–Electrical Engineers as well as a member of the organizing and scientific committee of several national and international conferences. He is currently a member of the editorial board of the *Renewable Energy International* journal and reviewer in more than 40 international journals in the energy and environment sector. He is the editor of the book *Stand-Alone and Hybrid Wind Energy Systems: Technology, Energy Storage and Applications* that has recently been published.

Dr. Soteris A. Kalogirou is a senior lecturer at the Department of Mechanical Engineering and Materials Science and Engineering at the Cyprus University of Technology, Limassol, Cyprus. He received his Higher Technical Institute (HTI) degree in mechanical engineering in 1982, his MPhil in mechanical engineering from the Polytechnic of Wales in 1991, and his PhD in mechanical engineering from the University of Glamorgan in 1995. In June 2011, he received the title of DSc from the University of Glamorgan.

For more than 25 years, he has been actively involved in research in the area of solar energy and particularly in flat-plate and concentrating collectors, solar water heating, solar steam generating systems, desalination, and absorption cooling. Additionally, since 1995, he has been involved in pioneering research dealing with the use of artificial intelligence methods, such as artificial neural networks, genetic algorithms, and fuzzy logic, for the modeling and performance prediction of energy and solar energy systems.

He has 29 books and book contributions and published 225 papers, 97 in international scientific journals and 128 in refereed conference proceedings. To date he has received more than 2550 citations on this work. He is Executive Editor of *Energy*, Associate Editor of *Renewable Energy*, and Editorial Board Member of another 11 journals. He is the editor of the book *Artificial Intelligence in Energy and Renewable Energy Systems*, published by Nova Science Inc.; coeditor of the book *Soft Computing in Green and Renewable Energy Systems*, published by Springer; and author of the book *Solar Energy Engineering: Processes and Systems*, published by Academic Press of Elsevier.

He has been a member of the World Renewable Energy Network (WREN) since 1992 and is a member of the Chartered Institution of Building Services Engineers (CIBSE), the American Society of Heating Refrigeration and Air-Conditioning Engineers (ASHRAE), the Institute of Refrigeration (IoR), and the International Solar Energy Society (ISES).

Dr. Andrew Cruden, a British citizen, was born in 1968. He obtained his BEng, MSc, and PhD in electrical engineering from the University of Strathclyde and CEng, MIEE Dr. Cruden is a past member of BSI GEL/105 Committee on Fuel Cells and Committee member of the IET Scotland Power Section. He is Director of the Scottish Hydrogen and Fuel Cell Association (SHFCA; www.shfca.org.uk) and Director of Argyll, Lomond and the Islands Energy Agency (www.alienergy.org.uk).

Dr. Cruden has been active in the field of hydrogen and fuel cells since 1995, when he acted as a consultant for Zevco Ltd., providing assistance with power electronic interfaces for early fuel cell systems. Later in 1998, he helped found the Scottish Fuel Cell Consortium (SFCC), supported by the Scottish Enterprise Energy Team, which ultimately developed a battery/fuel cell hybrid electric vehicle based on an AC Cobra kit car. The experience and contacts from the SFCC eventually gave rise to the formation of the Scottish Hydrogen and Fuel Cell Association (SHFCA), a trade body for the industry to promote and commercialize Scottish expertise in this field. Dr. Cruden was the founding chairman of the SHFCA.

Dr. Cruden is currently investigating alkaline electrolyzers in terms of improving their part load efficiency and lifetime when powered by variable renewable power sources, for example, wind turbines, as part of a £5 million EPSRC Supergen project on the 'Delivery of Sustainable Hydrogen' (EP/G01244X/1). He is also working with a colleague within Electronic and Electrical Engineering (EEE) at Strathclyde, studying the concept of vehicle-to-grid energy storage, as a mechanism not only to allow controlled load leveling on the power system, but also to potentially 'firm' up renewable energy generation. This work is supported by two research grants, an international E.On Research Initiative 2007 award and an ESPRC grant (EP/F062133/1).

Dr. Cruden is a senior lecturer within the Department of Electronic and Electrical Engineering at the University of Strathclyde. His current fields of research are modeling fuel cell and electrolyzer systems, fuel cell combined heat and power (CHP) systems, power electronic devices for interfacing both vehicular and stationary fuel cell systems, condition monitoring systems for renewable energy sources (i.e., wind turbines as part of EPSRC Supergen on Wind Energy Technologies, EP/D034566/1), and energy management systems for hybrid electric vehicles.

His areas of expertise include hydrogen-powered fuel cells and electrolyzers, energy storage for electric vehicles, and renewable energy generation.

Professor Dermot J. Roddy, BSc, PhD, CEng, FIET, joined Newcastle University as Science City Professor of Energy in 2008 after a period of some 20 years in the energy industry and petrochemical sectors. He is also Director of the Sir Joseph Swan Centre for Energy Research, which integrates energy research across Newcastle University and links with a powerful external industrial base in the energy sector. Outside of the university he is Chairman of Northeast Biofuels, Finance Director of the UK Hydrogen Association, and Vice-President of the Northern England Electricity Supply Companies Association. Prior to coming to Newcastle University, he was Chief Executive of Renew Tees Valley Ltd. – a company which he set up in 2003 to create a viable and vibrant economy in the Tees Valley based on renewable energy and recycling – where he was instrumental in a wide range of major renewable energy and low-carbon projects relating to biomass, biofuels, hydrogen, carbon capture and storage, wind, and advanced waste processing technologies. From 1998 to 2002, he ran the crude oil refinery on Teesside as a site director for a $5 billion turnover facility before moving to the Netherlands to work on Petroplus' international growth plans. Roddy's experience in the petrochemical industry began in 1985, involving a variety of UK and international roles in operations, engineering, and technology with ICI and others. Prior to that he developed leading-edge technology at Queen's University, Belfast, for optimization and control in aerospace applications.

André G. H. Lejeune was born on 2 August 1942 in Belgium. He was graduated in 1967 as a civil engineer, in 1972 as doctor in applied sciences (PhD), and in 1973 as master in oceanography in the University of Liège in Belgium. He was appointed full-time professor in the same university in 1976, and was visitor professor at the UNESCO–IHE Institute for Water Education in the Netherlands and Ecole Polytechnique Fédérale de Lausanne (EPFL) in Switzerland. Within the framework of his activities of professor, director of the Hydraulic Constructions and Hydraulic Research Laboratory, and expert, he took part in studies of dams and hydraulic structures and went on site in more than 90 countries of the world. In particular, he was for the last 6 years the chairman of the Technical Committee on Hydraulics for Dams in ICOLD (International Commission of Large Dams). He is a member of the Belgian Royal Academy of Sciences. He made his PhD thesis in hydraulic numerical modelization. This thesis received the Lorenz G. Straub Award in Minneapolis, USA (H. Einstein Jr. was a member of the Jury), and was used in particular by Chinese colleagues in the Three Gorges Project. Due to his practice and experience, he has a very complete knowledge of the hydraulic phenomena modelizations through both numerical and physical means.

With his wife, he has 3 children and 11 grandchildren. He likes books, tennis, and diving.

Thorsteinn I. Sigfusson is an internationally recognised physicist, educated in Copenhagen, Denmark, and Cambridge, UK. He is Director-General of the Innovation Center, Iceland and Professor of physics at the University of Iceland. He has been a visiting professor at Columbia University, New York, and he is currently the lead scientist in a prize-winning energy technology project performed at Tomsk Polytechnic University in Tomsk, Russia.

He has been a key figure in the introduction of new ideas and opportunities in the further greening of Icelandic society through the energy industry, and instrumental in the challenge of saving imported hydrocarbons by focusing on hydrogen from renewable energy.

He has started over a dozen start-up companies from research in Iceland and chaired various international societies in alternative energy. Among his achievements in geothermal energy is the construction of the world's largest solid-state thermoelectric generator powered with geothermal steam in southern Iceland. At the Innovation Center, Iceland, efforts are made to develop materials to withstand erosion in geothermal environments.

 AbuBakr S. Bahaj is Professor of Sustainable Energy at the University of Southampton. After completing his PhD, he was employed by the University, progressing from a researcher to a personnel chair of Sustainable Energy. Over the past 20 years, Prof. Bahaj has established the energy theme within the University and directed his Sustainable Energy Research Group (SERG, www.energy.soton.ac.uk), which is now considered to be one of the United Kingdoms's leading university-based research groups in renewable energy and energy in buildings. He initiated and managed research in ocean energy conversion (resources, technologies, and impacts), photovoltaics, energy in buildings, and impacts of climate change on the built environment in the University. This work has resulted in over 230 articles published in academic refereed journals and conference series of international standing (see www.energy.soton.ac.uk).

Prof. Bahaj is the head of the Energy and Climate Change Division (ECCD) within the highly rated Faculty of Engineering and the Environment – Civil Engineering and the Environment – (www.civil.soton.ac.uk/research/divisions/divlist.asp?ResearchGroupID=1) (second in the United Kingdom, Research Assessment Exercise in 2008, with 80% of research judged to be either 'World Leading' or 'Internationally Excellent'). The aims of the Division and SERG are to promote and execute fundamental and applied research and preindustrial development in the areas of energy resources, technologies, energy efficiency, and the impact of climate change.

Prof. Bahaj is an experienced research team director and has many internationally focused research projects including collaborative projects in China, the European Union, the Middle East, and Africa. He also coordinated (2006–10) the United Kingdom's Engineering and Physical Sciences Research Council (EPSRC), Ecoregion Research Networks that aim to develop research themes and projects to study eco-city development encompassing resource assessment, technology pathways for the production and conservation of energy, planning, and social and economic studies required in establishing eco-regions in China and elsewhere (http://www.eco-networks.org). He is a founding member of the Sino-UK Low Carbon City Development Cooperation (LCCD) which aims to promote and undertake research into pathways for low-carbon development in Chinese cities. His work also encompasses an ongoing multimillion pound program in Africa, 'Energy for Development' for promoting and implementing village electrification systems, addressing villager's needs, and establishing coherent approaches to the commercial sustainability of the projects. This program is funded by the Research Councils and the UK Department for International Development (DFID; www.energyfordevelopment.net).

Prof. Bahaj is the editor-in-chief of the *International Journal of Sustainable Energy* and associate Editor of the *Renewable & Sustainable Energy Review*. He was on the editorial boards of the journals *Sustainable Cities and Society* and *Renewable Energy* (2005–11), and the United Kingdom's Institute of Civil Engineering journal *Energy* (2006–09). He was a member of the Tyndall Centre for Climate Change Research Supervisory Board (2005–10), and from 2001 to 2007 he was a member of the UK Government Department of Business, Enterprise and Regulatory Reform (now Department for Business Innovations and Skills, BIS), Technology Programmes Panels on Water (including ocean energy) and Solar Energy, now being administered by the Technology Strategy Board (TSB). Prof. Bahaj was the chair of the Technical Committees of the World Renewable Energy Congress – held in Glasgow (July 2008) and in Abu Dhabi (September 2010). He was a member of the Technical Committee of the 27th International Conference on Offshore Mechanics and Arctic Engineering (OMAE, 2008), a member of the management and technical committees of the European Wave and Tidal Energy Conferences (EWTEC, Porto, Portugal, September 2007; and Uppsala, Sweden, September 2009). He is also a member of the British Standards Institution (BSI) Committee GEL/82 on PV Energy Systems. Recently, at the invitation of the International Energy Agency, he has completed the 2008 status report on tidal stream energy conversion and in September 2009 was elected to chair the next EWTEC conference in the series – EWTEC2011 which was held in Southampton, 5–9 September 2011, and attended by around 500 participants.

To address training in the areas of energy and climate change Prof. Bahaj has coordinated and developed a set of MSc programs under the banner 'Energy and Sustainability' that address Energy Resources and Climate Change and Energy, Environment and Buildings.

CONTRIBUTORS FOR ALL VOLUMES

P Agnolucci
Imperial College London, London, UK

EO Ahlgren
Chalmers University of Technology, Gothenburg, Sweden

D Aklil
Pure Energy Center, Unst, Shetland Isles, UK

D-C Alarcón Padilla
Centro de Investigaciones Energéticas Medioambientales y Tecnológicas (CIEMAT), Plataforma Solar de Almeria, Almeria, Spain

K Alexander
University of Canterbury, Christchurch, New Zealand

S Alexopoulos
Aachen University of Applied Sciences, Jülich, Germany

A Altieri
UNICA – Brazilian Sugarcane Industry Association, São Paulo, Brazil

A Anthrakidis
Aachen University of Applied Sciences, Jülich, Germany

E Antolín
Universidad Politécnica de Madrid, Madrid, Spain

P Archambeau
University of Liège, Liège, Belgium

H Ármannsson
Iceland GeoSurvey (ISOR), Reykjavík, Iceland

MF Askew
Wolverhampton, UK

A Athienitis
Concordia University, Montreal, QC, Canada

G Axelsson
University of Iceland, Reykjavik, Iceland

V Badescu
Polytechnic University of Bucharest, Bucharest, Romania

AS Bahaj
The University of Southampton, Southampton, UK

P Banda
Instituto de Sistema Fotovoltaicos de Concentración (ISFOC), Puertollano, Spain

VG Belessiotis
'DEMOKRITOS' National Center for Scientific Research, Athens, Greece

P Berry
ADAS High Mowthorpe, Malton, UK

F Bidault
Imperial College London, London, UK

D Biro
Fraunhofer Institute for Solar Energy Systems, Freiburg, Germany

G Boschloo
Uppsala University, Uppsala, Sweden

C Boura
Aachen University of Applied Sciences, Jülich, Germany

E Bozorgzadeh
Iran Water and Power Resources Development Company (IWPCO), Tehran, Iran

CE Brewer
Iowa State University, Ames, IA, USA

M Börjesson
Chalmers University of Technology, Gothenburg, Sweden

RC Brown
Iowa State University, Ames, IA, USA

F Bueno
University of Burgos, Burgos, Spain

K Burke
NASA Glenn Research Center, Cleveland, OH, USA

LF Cabeza
GREA Innovació Concurrent, Universitat de Lleida, Lleida, Spain

L Candanedo
Dublin Institute of Technology, Dublin, Ireland

YG Caouris
University of Patras, Patras, Greece

UB Cappel
Uppsala University, Uppsala, Sweden

JA Carta
Universidad de Las Palmas de Gran Canaria, Las Palmas de Gran Canaria, Spain

P Chen
Dalian Institute of Chemical Physics, Dalian, China

DG Christakis
Wind Energy Laboratory, Technological Educational Institute of Crete, Crete, Greece

DA Chwieduk
Warsaw University of Technology, Warsaw, Poland

J Clark
University of York, York, UK

G Conibeer
University of New South Wales, Sydney, NSW, Australia

AJ Cruden
University of Strathclyde, Glasgow, UK

MC da Silva

B Davidsdottir
University of Iceland, Reykjavík, Iceland

O de la Rubia
Instituto de Sistema Fotovoltaicos de Concentración (ISFOC), Puertollano, Spain

E Despotou
Formerly of the European Photovoltaic Industry Association, Brussels, Belgium

BJ Dewals
University of Liège, Liège, Belgium

AL Dicks
The University of Queensland, Brisbane, QLD, Australia

R DiPippo
University of Massachusetts Dartmouth, Dartmouth, MA, USA

E Dunlop
European Commission DG Joint Research Centre, Ispra, Italy

NM Duteanu
Newcastle University, Newcastle upon Tyne, UK;
University 'POLITEHNICA' Timisoara, Timisoara, Romania

LM Eaton
Oak Ridge National Laboratory, Oak Ridge, TN, USA

H-J Egelhaaf
Konarka Technologies GmbH, Nürnberg, Germany

T Ehara
Mizuho Information & Research Institute, Tokyo, Japan

B Erable
Newcastle University, Newcastle upon Tyne, UK;
CNRS-Université de Toulouse, Toulouse, France

S Erpicum
University of Liège, Liège, Belgium

G Evans
NNFCC, Biocentre, Innovation Way, Heslington, York, UK

AFO Falcão
Instituto Superior Técnico, Technical University of Lisbon, Lisbon, Portugal

G Faninger
University of Klagenfurt, Klagenfurt, Austria; Vienna University of Technology, Vienna, Austria

GA Florides
Cyprus University of Technology, Limassol, Cyprus

ÓG Flóvenz
Iceland GeoSurvey (ISOR), Reykjavík, Iceland

RN Frese
VU University Amsterdam, Amsterdam, The Netherlands

Þ Friðriksson
Iceland GeoSurvey (ISOR), Reykjavík, Iceland

VM Fthenakis
Columbia University, New York, NY, USA; Brookhaven National Laboratory, Upton, NY, USA

M Fuamba
École Polytechnique de Montréal, Montreal, QC, Canada

A Fuller
University of Canterbury, Christchurch, New Zealand

LMC Gato
Instituto Superior Técnico, Technical University of Lisbon, Lisbon, Portugal

R Gazey
Pure Energy Center, Unst, Shetland Isles, UK

TA Gessert
National Renewable Energy Laboratory (NREL), Golden, CO, USA

MM Ghangrekar
*Newcastle University, Newcastle upon Tyne, UK;
Indian Institute of Technology, Kharagpur, India*

M Giannouli
University of Patras, Patras, Greece

EA Gibson
University of Nottingham, Nottingham UK

A Gil
Hydropower Generation Division of Iberdrola, Salamanca, Spain

SW Glunz
Fraunhofer Institute for Solar Energy Systems, Freiburg, Germany

JC Goldschmidt
Fraunhofer Institute for Solar Energy Systems ISE, Freiburg, Germany

R Gottschalg
Loughborough University, Leicestershire, UK

MA Green
The University of New South Wales, Sydney, NSW, Australia

J Göttsche
Aachen University of Applied Sciences, Jülich, Germany

J Guo
China Institute of Water Resources and Hydropower Research (IWHR), Beijing, China

A Hagfeldt
Uppsala University, Uppsala, Sweden

B Hagin
Ingénieur-Conseil, Lutry, Switzerland

K Hall
Technology Transition Corporation, Ltd., Tyne and Wear, UK

O Hamandjoda
University of Yaounde, Yaounde, Republic of Cameroon

AP Harvey
Newcastle University, Newcastle upon Tyne, UK

JA Hauch
Konarka Technologies GmbH, Nürnberg, Germany

D Heinemann
University of Oldenburg, Oldenburg, Germany

V Heller
Imperial College London, London, UK

GP Hersir
Iceland GeoSurvey (ISOR), Reykjavík, Iceland

T Heyer
Technical University of Dresden, Dresden, Germany

P Hilger
Aachen University of Applied Sciences, Jülich, Germany

B Hillring
Swedish University of Agricultural Sciences, Skinnskatteberg, Sweden

T Hino
CTI Engineering International Co., Ltd., Chu-o-Ku, Japan

LC Hirst
Imperial College London, London, UK

B Hoffschmidt
Aachen University of Applied Sciences, Jülich, Germany

H Horlacher
Technical University of Dresden, Dresden, Germany

N Hughes
Imperial College London, London, UK

SL Hui
Bechtel Civil Company, San Francisco, CA, USA

D Husmann
University of Wisconsin–Madison, Madison, WI, USA

JTS Irvine
University of St Andrews, St Andrews, UK

D Jacobs
Freie Universität Berlin, Berlin, Germany

Y Jestin
Advanced Photonics and Photovoltaics Group, Bruno Kessler Foundation, Trento, Italy

A Jäger-Waldau
Institution for Energy Transport, Ispra, Italy

S Jianxia
Design and Research Institute, Yangzhou City, Jiangsu Province, China

E Johnson
Pure Energy Center, Unst, Shetland Isles, UK

HF Kaan
TNO Energy, Comfort and Indoor Quality, Delft, The Netherlands

JK Kaldellis
Technological Education Institute of Piraeus, Athens, Greece

SA Kalogirou
Cyprus University of Technology, Limassol, Cyprus

HD Kambezidis
Institute of Environmental Research and Sustainable Development, Athens, Greece

M Kapsali
Technological Education Institute of Piraeus, Athens, Greece

M Karimirad
Norwegian University of Science and Technology, Trondheim, Norway

T Karlessi
National and Kapodistrian University of Athens, Athens, Greece

SN Karlsdóttir
Innovation Center Iceland, Iceland

D Al Katsaprakakis
Wind Energy Laboratory, Technological Educational Institute of Crete, Crete, Greece

O Kaufhold
Aachen University of Applied Sciences, Jülich, Germany

CA Kaufmann
Helmholtz Zentrum für Materialien und Energie GmbH, Berlin, Germany

KA Kavadias
Technological Education Institute of Piraeus, Athens, Greece

LL Kazmerski
National Renewable Energy Laboratory, Golden, CO, USA

A Kazmi
University of York, York, UK

K Kendall
University of Birmingham, Birmingham, UK

J Kenfack
University of Yaounde, Yaounde, Republic of Cameroon

R Kenny
European Commission DG Joint Research Centre, Ispra, Italy

HC Kim
Brookhaven National Laboratory, Upton, NY, USA

L Kloo
KTH—Royal Institute of Technology, Stockholm, Sweden

G Knothe
USDA Agricultural Research Service, Peoria, IL, USA

FR Kogler
Konarka Technologies GmbH, Nürnberg, Germany

D Kolokotsa
Technical University of Crete, Crete, Greece

K Komoto
Mizuho Information & Research Institute, Tokyo, Japan

E Kondili
Technological Education Institute of Piraeus, Athens, Greece

H Kristjánsdóttir
University of Iceland, Reykjavík, Iceland

LA Lamont
Petroleum Institute, Abu Dhabi, UAE

GA Landis
NASA Glenn Research Center, Cleveland, OH, USA

JGM Lee
Newcastle University, Newcastle upon Tyne, UK

G Leftheriotis
University of Patras, Patras, Greece

A Lejeune
University of Liège, Liège, Belgium

T Leo
FuelCell Energy Inc., Danbury, CT, USA

E Lester
The University of Nottingham, Nottingham, UK

E Lorenz
University of Oldenburg, Oldenburg, Germany

JW Lund
Geo-Heat Center, Oregon Institute of Technology, Klamath Falls, OR, USA

A Luque
Universidad Politécnica de Madrid, Madrid, Spain

BP Machado
Intertechne, Curitiba, PR, Brazil

EBL Mackay
GL Garrad Hassan, Bristol, UK

T-F Mahdi
École Polytechnique de Montréal, Montreal, QC, Canada

GG Maidment
London South Bank University, London, UK

A Malmgren
BioC Ltd, Cirencester, UK

C Manson-Whitton
Progressive Energy Ltd., Stonehouse, UK

Á Margeirsson
Magma Energy Iceland, Reykjanesbaer, Iceland

A Martí
Universidad Politécnica de Madrid, Madrid, Spain

M Martinez
Instituto de Sistema Fotovoltaicos de Concentración (ISFOC), Puertollano, Spain

S Mathew
University of Brunei Darussalam, Gadong, Brunei Darussalam

PH Middleton
University of Agder, Grimstad, Norway

R Mikalsen
Newcastle University, Newcastle upon Tyne, UK

D Milborrow
Lewes, East Sussex, UK

H Müllejans
European Commission DG Joint Research Centre, Ispra, Italy

V Molkov
University of Ulster, Newtownabbey, Northern Ireland, UK

M Moner-Girona
Joint Research Centre, European Commission, Institute for Energy and Transport, Ispra, Italy

PE Morthorst
Technical University of Denmark, Roskilde, Denmark

N Mortimer
North Energy Associates Ltd, Sheffield, UK

E Mullins
Teagasc, Oak Park Crops Research Centre, Carlow, Republic of Ireland

P Mulvihill
Pioneer Generation Ltd., Alexandra, New Zealand

DR Myers
National Renewable Energy Laboratory, USA

D Nash
University of Strathclyde, Glasgow, UK

GF Nemet
University of Wisconsin–Madison, Madison, WI, USA

H Nfaoui
Mohammed V University, Rabat, Morocco

T Nikolakakis
Columbia University, New York, NY, USA

X Niu
Changjiang Institute of Survey, Planning, Design and Research, Wuhan, China

B Norton
Dublin Institute of Technology, Dublin, Ireland

A Nuamah
The University of Nottingham, Nottingham, UK; RWE npower, Swindon, UK

B O'Connor
Aachen University of Applied Sciences, Jülich, Germany

O Olsson
Swedish University of Agricultural Sciences, Skinnskatteberg, Sweden

V Ortisi
Pure Energy Center, Unst, Shetland Isles, UK

H Ossenbrink
European Commission DG Joint Research Centre, Ispra, Italy

AG Paliatsos
Technological Education Institute of Piraeus, Athens, Greece

A Pandit
VU University Amsterdam, Amsterdam, The Netherlands

E Papanicolaou
'DEMOKRITOS' National Center for Scientific Research, Athens, Greece

A Paurine
London South Bank University, London, UK

N Pearsall
Northumbria University, Newcastle, UK

RJ Pearson
Lotus Engineering, Norwich, UK

RD Perlack
Oak Ridge National Laboratory, Oak Ridge, TN, USA

H Pettersson
Swerea IVF AB, Mölndal, Sweden

GS Philip
KCAET, Malapuram, Kerala, India

S Pillai
The University of New South Wales, Sydney, NSW, Australia

M Pirotton
University of Liège, Liège, Belgium

BG Pollet
University of Birmingham, Birmingham, UK

D Porter
Association of Electricity Producers, London, UK

A Pouliezos
Technical University of Crete, Hania, Greece

R Preu
Fraunhofer Institute for Solar Energy Systems, Freiburg, Germany

CM Ramos

C Rau
Aachen University of Applied Sciences, Jülich, Germany

AA Refaat
Cairo University, Giza, Egypt

TH Reijenga
BEARiD Architecten, Rotterdam, The Netherlands

AHME Reinders
Delft University of Technology, Delft, The Netherlands; University of Twente, Enschede, The Netherlands

G Riley
RWE npower, Swindon, UK

DJ Roddy
Newcastle University, Newcastle upon Tyne, UK

S Rolland
Alliance for Rural Electrification, Brussels, Belgium

A Roskilly
Newcastle University, Newcastle upon Tyne, UK

F Rubio
Instituto de Sistema Fotovoltaicos de Concentración (ISFOC), Puertollano, Spain

F Rulot
University of Liège, Liège, Belgium

L Rybach
GEOWATT AG, Zurich, Switzerland

M Santamouris
National and Kapodistrian University of Athens, Athens, Greece

J Sattler
Aachen University of Applied Sciences, Jülich, Germany

M Sauerborn
Aachen University of Applied Sciences, Jülich, Germany

TW Schmidt
The University of Sydney, Sydney, NSW, Australia

N Schofield
University of Manchester, Manchester, UK

REI Schropp
Utrecht University, Utrecht, The Netherlands

K Scott
Newcastle University, Newcastle upon Tyne, UK

SP Sen
NHPC Ltd., New Delhi, India

TI Sigfusson
Innovation Center, Reykjavik, Iceland

L Sims
Konarka Technologies GmbH, Nürnberg, Germany; Universität Augsburg, Augsburg, Germany

C Smith
NNFCC, Biocentre, Innovation Way, Heslington, York, UK

K Sæmundsson
Iceland GeoSurvey (ISOR), Reykjavík, Iceland

BK Sovacool
Vermont Law School, South Royalton, VT, USA

J Spink
Teagasc, Oak Park Crops Research Centre, Carlow, Republic of Ireland

JN Sørensen
Technical University of Denmark, Lyngby, Denmark

T Stallard
The University of Manchester, Manchester, UK

GS Stavrakakis
Technical University of Crete, Chania, Greece

R Steim
Konarka Technologies GmbH, Nürnberg, Germany

BJ Stokes
CNJV LLC, Washington, DC, USA

L Sun
KTH—Royal Institute of Technology, Stockholm, Sweden; Dalian University of Technology (DUT), Dalian, China

L Suo
Science and Technology Committee of the Ministry of Water Resources, Beijing, China

DT Swift-Hook
Kingston University, London, UK; World Renewable Energy Network, Brighton, UK

A Synnefa
National and Kapodistrian University of Athens, Athens, Greece

S Szabo
Joint Research Centre, European Commission, Institute for Energy and Transport, Ispra, Italy

MJY Tayebjee
The University of Sydney, Sydney, NSW, Australia

A Tesfai
University of St Andrews, St Andrews, UK

P Thornley
The University of Manchester, Manchester, UK

Y Tripanagnostopoulos
University of Patras, Patras, Greece

L Tsakalakos
General Electric – Global Research Center, New York, NY, USA

JWG Turner
Lotus Engineering, Norwich, UK

E Tzen
Centre for Renewable Energy Sources and Saving (CRES), Pikermi, Attica, Greece

T Unold
Helmholtz Zentrum für Materialien und Energie GmbH, Berlin, Germany

J van der Heide
imec vzw, Leuven, Belgium

P van der Vleuten
Free Energy Consulting, Eindhoven, The Netherlands

F Van Hulle
XP Wind Consultancy, Leuven, Belgium

GC van Kooten
University of Victoria, Victoria, BC, Canada

WGJHM van Sark
Utrecht University, Utrecht, The Netherlands

I Waller
FiveBarGate Consultants Ltd, Cleveland, UK

I Walsh
Opus International Consultants Ltd., New Zealand

Y Wang
Newcastle University, Newcastle upon Tyne, UK

T Wizelius
Gotland University, Visby, Sweden; Lund University, Lund, Sweden

LL Wright
University of Tennessee, Knoxville, TN, USA

H Xie
Changjiang Institute of Survey, Planning, Design and Research, Wuhan, China

M Yamaguchi
Toyota Technological Institute, Tempaku, Nagoya, Japan

P Yianoulis
University of Patras, Patras, Greece

EH Yu
Newcastle University, Newcastle upon Tyne, UK

H Yu
Newcastle University, Newcastle upon Tyne, UK

DP Zafirakis
Technological Education Institute of Piraeus, Athens, Greece

G Zaragoza
Centro de Investigaciones Energéticas Medioambientales y Tecnológicas (CIEMAT), Plataforma Solar de Almeria, Almeria, Spain

M Zeman
Delft University of Technology, Delft, The Netherlands

PREFACE

Comprehensive Renewable Energy is the only multivolume reference work of its type at a time when renewable energy sources are increasingly in demand and realistically sustainable, clean, and helping to combat climate change and global warming. Renewable energy investment has exceeded US$10 billion per year during the past 5 years. The World Renewable Energy Network (WREN) predicts that this figure is set to increase to US$20 billion per year by 2015.

As Editor-in-Chief, I have assembled an impressive world-class team of 154 volume editors and contributing authors for the eight volumes. They represent policy makers, researchers, industrialists, financiers, and heads of organizations from more than 80 countries to produce this definitive complete work in renewable energy covering the past, explaining the present, and giving the ideas and prospects of development for the future. There are more than 1000 references from books, journals, and the Internet within the eight volumes. *Comprehensive Renewable Energy* is full of color charts, illustrations, and photographs of real projects and research results from around the world. Each chapter has been painstakingly reviewed and checked for consistent high quality. The result is an authoritative overview that ties the literature together and provides the user with reliable background information and a citation resource.

The field of renewable energy research and development is represented by many journals that are directly and indirectly concerned with the field. But no reference work encompasses the entire field and unites the different areas of research through in-depth foundational reviews. *Comprehensive Renewable Energy* fills this vacuum, and is the definitive work for this subject area. It will help users apply context to diverse journal literature, aiding them in identifying areas for further research and development.

Research into renewable energy is spread across a number of different disciplines and subject areas. These areas do not always share a unique identifying factor or subject themselves to clear and concise definitions. This work unites the different areas of research and allows users, regardless of their background, to navigate through the most essential concepts with ease, saving them time and vastly improving their understanding so that they can move forward, whether in their research, development, manufacturing, or purchase of renewable energy.

The first volume is devoted to Photovoltaic Technology and is edited by Mr. Wilfried G. J. H. M. van Sark from the Netherlands. It consists of 38 chapters, written by 41 authors from Europe, the United States, Japan, China, India, Africa, and the Middle East. The topics covered range from the smallest applications to MW projects. A brief introduction and history is followed by chapters on finance and economics, solar resources, up- and downconversion, crystalline photovoltaic (PV) cells, luminescent concentrators, thin-film and multiple-junction plastic solar cells, dye-sensitized solar cells, bio-inspired converters, application of micro- and nanotechnology, building integrated photovoltaics (BIPV) application in architecture, and very large-scale PV systems. Without doubt, this is an impressive tour of an immense field.

Volume 2 is devoted to Wind Energy and is edited by Professor John K. Kaldellis from Greece. It consists of 22 chapters written by 22 authors, again from various parts of the world, covering all aspects of wind energy from small wind mills to very large wind farms. The volume includes chapters on the history of wind power, the potential of wind power, wind turbine development, aerodynamic analysis, mechanical and electrical loads, control systems, noise and testing, onshore and offshore wind systems, policy, industry, and special wind power applications.

Volume 3 is devoted to Solar Thermal Applications and the editor is Professor Soteris A. Kalogirou from Cyprus. It consists of 19 chapters written by 17 authors. All aspects of solar thermal energy and its applications are covered. The volume begins with solar energy as a source of heat and goes on to describe the history of thermal applications, low-temperature and high-temperature storage systems, selective coating, glazing, modeling and simulation, hot water systems, space heating and cooling, water desalination, industrial and agricultural applications, concentration power, heat pumps, and passive solar architecture. The authors have looked at the Sun from the thermal energy aspect and put together a very informative and up-to-date volume from which every interested person, no matter what their level of knowledge, can benefit.

Volume 4 is on Fuel Cells and Hydrogen Technology and is edited by Dr. Andrew Cruden from the United Kingdom. It consists of 14 chapters covering the following topics: introduction and perspectives on hydrogen and fuel cells; theory and application of alkaline fuel cells; application of proton exchange membrane (PEM) fuel cells; molten carbonate fuel cells; solid oxide fuel cells; microbial and biological fuel cells; storage of compressed gas and hydrogen; the economy and policy of hydrogen technology; hydrogen safety engineering and future progress; the use of hydrogen for transport; and hydrogen and fuel cell power electronics. The 14 chapters were written by 16 authors. All aspects of practice, innovative technology, and future guidelines for researchers and industry have been addressed in this definitive volume.

Volume 5 deals with the huge field of Biomass and Biofuels and is edited by Professor Dermot J. Roddy from the United Kingdom. This work consists of 21 chapters written by 23 authors, again covering all aspects of biomass and biofuels, including their past, present, and future. The volume explains the history and prospective future of biofuels; bioethanol development in Brazil; power generation from biomass; biomass co-firing stations; biomass world market; a critical assessment of biomass – combined heat and power (CHP) energy systems; the ethics of biofuel production – issues, constraints, and limitations; greenhouse gases life cycle analysis; six different solutions from gasification and pyrolysis; new processes in biomass-to-liquid technology; new processes in biofuel production; biofuels from waste materials; novel feedstocks and woody biomass; feedstocks with the potential of yield improvement; renewable fuels – an automotive prospective; and novel use of biofuels in a range of engine configurations. Under Expanding the Envelope, there are chapters on biochar, extracting additional value from biomass, and biomass to chemicals. Finally, the chapter on bioenergy policy development concludes the volume.

Volume 6 is concerned with Hydro Power and is edited by Professor André G. H. Lejeune from Belgium. This is the oldest of all the renewable energy applications and has progressed over the ages from pico-hydro of a few hundred watts to large- and mega-scale dams generating more than 3000 MW with innovative civil engineering capability. This volume consists of 18 chapters prepared by 21 authors. It contains introduction – benefits and constraints of hydropower, recent developments and achievements in hydraulic research in China, and the management of hydropower and its impacts through construction and operation. The volume then assesses nine hydropower schemes around the world: the Three Gorges Project in China; large hydropower plants of Brazil; hydropower in Iran – vision and strategy; the recent trend in developing hydropower in India; the evolution of hydropower in Spain; hydropower in Japan; hydropower in Canada; an overview of institutional structure reform of the Cameroon power sector and assessment; and hydropower reliability in Switzerland. Other important issues are covered: pumped storage power plants; simplified generic axial-flow microhydro turbines; the development of a small hydroelectric scheme at Horseshoe Bend, Teviot River, New Zealand; concrete durability in dam design structure; and long-term sediment management for sustainable hydropower.

Volume 7 deals with Geothermal Energy. The editor of this volume is Professor Thorsteinn I. Sigfusson from Iceland. The volume consists of 10 chapters, which are written by 15 different authors. It covers the following areas: introduction and the physics of geothermal resources and management during utilization; geothermal shallow systems – heat pumps; geothermal exploration techniques; corrosion, scaling, and material selection in geothermal power production; direct heat utilization of geothermal energy; geothermal power plants; geochemical aspects of geothermal utilization; geothermal cost and investment factors; and the role of sustainable geothermal development.

Volume 8 is devoted to Generating Electricity from the Oceans, edited by Professor AbuBakr S. Bahaj from the United Kingdom. It consists of six chapters written by five authors. The volume covers the historical aspects of wave energy conversion, resource assessment for wave energy, development of wave devices from initial conception to commercial demonstration, air turbines, and the economics of ocean energy.

One chapter is totally devoted to Renewable Energy Policy and Incentives. It is included in the first volume only. The author of this chapter is Mr. David Porter, Chief Executive of the Association of Electricity Producers in the United Kingdom, an author who has had vast experience of dealing with electricity generation in the United Kingdom over many years. He has advised the British Government on how to meet supply and demand of electricity and coordinate with all electricity producers regarding their sources and supply. The chapter outlines the types of mechanisms used to promote renewable energy and their use, the impact on their deployment, ensuring investor certainty, the potential for harmonizing support schemes, and the conclusion.

In short, my advice to anyone who wants to acquire comprehensive knowledge concerning renewable energy, no matter which subject or application, is that they should acquire this invaluable resource for their home, research center and laboratory, company, or library.

Professor Ali Sayigh BSc, DIC, PhD, FIE, FIEE, CEng
Chairman of WREC (World Renewable Energy Congress)
Director General of WREN (World Renewable Energy Network)
Chairman of IEI (The Institution of Engineers (India))
Editor-in-Chief of *Renewable Energy*
Editor-in-Chief of *Renewable Energy Magazine*

CONTENTS

Editor-in-Chief v
Volume Editors vii
Contributors for All Volumes xi
Preface xix

Volume 1 Photovoltaic Solar Energy

Renewable Energy

1.01 Renewable Energy Policy and Incentives 1
D Porter

Photovoltaic Solar Energy

1.02 Introduction to Photovoltaic Technology 5
WGJHM van Sark

1.03 Solar Photovoltaics Technology: No Longer an Outlier 13
LL Kazmerski

1.04 History of Photovoltaics 31
LA Lamont

Economics and Environment

1.05 Historical and Future Cost Dynamics of Photovoltaic Technology 47
GF Nemet and D Husmann

1.06 Feed-In Tariffs and Other Support Mechanisms for Solar PV Promotion 73
D Jacobs and BK Sovacool

1.07 Finance Mechanisms and Incentives for Photovoltaic Technologies in Developing Countries 111
M Moner-Girona, S Szabo, and S Rolland

1.08 Environmental Impacts of Photovoltaic Life Cycles 143
VM Fthenakis and HC Kim

1.09 Overview of the Global PV Industry 161
A Jäger-Waldau

1.10 Vision for Photovoltaics in the Future 179
E Despotou

1.11	Storage Options for Photovoltaics *VM Fthenakis and T Nikolakakis*	199

Resource and Potential

1.12	Solar Radiation Resource Assessment for Renewable Energy Conversion *DR Myers*	213
1.13	Prediction of Solar Irradiance and Photovoltaic Power *E Lorenz and D Heinemann*	239

Basics

1.14	Principles of Solar Energy Conversion *LC Hirst*	293
1.15	Thermodynamics of Photovoltaics *V Badescu*	315

Technology

1.16	Crystalline Silicon Solar Cells: State-of-the-Art and Future Developments *SW Glunz, R Preu, and D Biro*	353
1.17	Thin-Film Silicon PV Technology *M Zeman and REI Schropp*	389
1.18	Chalcopyrite Thin-Film Materials and Solar Cells *T Unold and CA Kaufmann*	399
1.19	Cadmium Telluride Photovoltaic Thin Film: CdTe *TA Gessert*	423
1.20	Plastic Solar Cells *L Sims, H-J Egelhaaf, JA Hauch, FR Kogler, and R Steim*	439
1.21	Mesoporous Dye-Sensitized Solar Cells *A Hagfeldt, UB Cappel, G Boschloo, L Sun, L Kloo, H Pettersson, and EA Gibson*	481
1.22	Multiple Junction Solar Cells *M Yamaguchi*	497
1.23	Application of Micro- and Nanotechnology in Photovoltaics *L Tsakalakos*	515
1.24	Upconversion *TW Schmidt and MJY Tayebjee*	533
1.25	Downconversion *MJY Tayebjee, TW Schmidt, and G Conibeer*	549
1.26	Down-Shifting of the Incident Light for Photovoltaic Applications *Y Jestin*	563
1.27	Luminescent Solar Concentrators *JC Goldschmidt*	587
1.28	Thermophotovoltaics *J van der Heide*	603
1.29	Intermediate Band Solar Cells *E Antolín, A Martí, and A Luque*	619
1.30	Plasmonics for Photovoltaics *S Pillai and MA Green*	641
1.31	Artificial Leaves: Towards Bio-Inspired Solar Energy Converters *A Pandit and RN Frese*	657

Applications

1.32	Design and Components of Photovoltaic Systems *WGJHM van Sark*	679
1.33	BIPV in Architecture and Urban Planning *TH Reijenga and HF Kaan*	697
1.34	Product-Integrated Photovoltaics *AHME Reinders and WGJHM van Sark*	709
1.35	Very Large-Scale Photovoltaic Systems *T Ehara, K Komoto, and P van der Vleuten*	733
1.36	Concentration Photovoltaics *M Martinez, O de la Rubia, F Rubio, and P Banda*	745
1.37	Solar Power Satellites *GA Landis*	767
1.38	Performance Monitoring *N Pearsall and R Gottschalg*	775
1.39	Standards in Photovoltaic Technology *H Ossenbrink, H Müllejans, R Kenny, and E Dunlop*	787

Volume 2 Wind Energy

2.01	Wind Energy – Introduction *JK Kaldellis*	1
2.02	Wind Energy Contribution in the Planet Energy Balance and Future Prospects *JK Kaldellis and M Kapsali*	11
2.03	History of Wind Power *DT Swift-Hook*	41
2.04	Wind Energy Potential *H Nfaoui*	73
2.05	Wind Turbines: Evolution, Basic Principles, and Classifications *S Mathew and GS Philip*	93
2.06	Energy Yield of Contemporary Wind Turbines *DP Zafirakis, AG Paliatsos, and JK Kaldellis*	113
2.07	Wind Parks Design, Including Representative Case Studies *D Al Katsaprakakis and DG Christakis*	169
2.08	Aerodynamic Analysis of Wind Turbines *JN Sørensen*	225
2.09	Mechanical-Dynamic Loads *M Karimirad*	243
2.10	Electrical Parts of Wind Turbines *GS Stavrakakis*	269
2.11	Wind Turbine Control Systems and Power Electronics *A Pouliezos*	329
2.12	Testing, Standardization, Certification in Wind Energy *F Van Hulle*	371
2.13	Design and Implementation of a Wind Power Project *T Wizelius*	391
2.14	Offshore Wind Power Basics *M Kapsali and JK Kaldellis*	431

2.15	Wind Energy Economics *D Milborrow*	469
2.16	Environmental-Social Benefits/Impacts of Wind Power *E Kondili and JK Kaldellis*	503
2.17	Wind Energy Policy *GC van Kooten*	541
2.18	Wind Power Integration *JA Carta*	569
2.19	Stand-Alone, Hybrid Systems *KA Kavadias*	623
2.20	Wind Power Industry and Markets *PE Morthorst*	657
2.21	Trends, Prospects, and R&D Directions in Wind Turbine Technology *JK Kaldellis and DP Zafirakis*	671
2.22	Special Wind Power Applications *E Kondili*	725

Volume 3 Solar Thermal Systems: Components and Applications

Solar Thermal Systems

3.01	Solar Thermal Systems: Components and Applications – Introduction *SA Kalogirou*	1
3.02	Solar Resource *HD Kambezidis*	27
3.03	History of Solar Energy *VG Belessiotis and E Papanicolaou*	85

Components

3.04	Low Temperature Stationary Collectors *YG Caouris*	103
3.05	Low Concentration Ratio Solar Collectors *SA Kalogirou*	149
3.06	High Concentration Solar Collectors *B Hoffschmidt, S Alexopoulos, J Göttsche, M Sauerborn, and O Kaufhold*	165
3.07	Thermal Energy Storage *LF Cabeza*	211
3.08	Photovoltaic/Thermal Solar Collectors *Y Tripanagnostopoulos*	255
3.09	Solar Selective Coatings *P Yianoulis, M Giannouli, and SA Kalogirou*	301
3.10	Glazings and Coatings *G Leftheriotis and P Yianoulis*	313
3.11	Modeling and Simulation of Passive and Active Solar Thermal Systems *A Athienitis, SA Kalogirou, and L Candanedo*	357

Applications

3.12	Solar Hot Water Heating Systems *G Faninger*	419
3.13	Solar Space Heating and Cooling Systems *SA Kalogirou and GA Florides*	449
3.14	Solar Cooling and Refrigeration Systems *GG Maidment and A Paurine*	481
3.15	Solar-Assisted Heat Pumps *DA Chwieduk*	495
3.16	Solar Desalination *E Tzen, G Zaragoza, and D-C Alarcón Padilla*	529
3.17	Industrial and Agricultural Applications of Solar Heat *B Norton*	567
3.18	Concentrating Solar Power *B Hoffschmidt, S Alexopoulos, C Rau, J Sattler, A Anthrakidis, C Boura, B O'Connor, and P Hilger*	595
3.19	Passive Solar Architecture *D Kolokotsa, M Santamouris, A Synnefa, and T Karlessi*	637

Volume 4 Fuel Cells and Hydrogen Technology

4.01	Fuel Cells and Hydrogen Technology – Introduction *AJ Cruden*	1
4.02	Current Perspective on Hydrogen and Fuel Cells *K Burke*	13
4.03	Hydrogen Economics and Policy *N Hughes and P Agnolucci*	45
4.04	Hydrogen Safety Engineering: The State-of-the-Art and Future Progress *V Molkov*	77
4.05	Hydrogen Storage: Compressed Gas *D Nash, D Aklil, E Johnson, R Gazey, and V Ortisi*	111
4.06	Hydrogen Storage: Liquid and Chemical *P Chen*	137
4.07	Alkaline Fuel Cells: Theory and Application *F Bidault and PH Middleton*	159
4.08	PEM Fuel Cells: Applications *AL Dicks*	183
4.09	Molten Carbonate Fuel Cells: Theory and Application *T Leo*	227
4.10	Solid Oxide Fuel Cells: Theory and Materials *A Tesfai and JTS Irvine*	241
4.11	Biological and Microbial Fuel Cells *K Scott, EH Yu, MM Ghangrekar, B Erable, and NM Duteanu*	257
4.12	Hydrogen and Fuel Cells in Transport *K Kendall and BG Pollet*	281
4.13	H_2 and Fuel Cells as Controlled Renewables: FC Power Electronics *N Schofield*	295
4.14	Future Perspective on Hydrogen and Fuel Cells *K Hall*	331

Volume 5   Biomass and Biofuel Production

Biomass and Biofuels

5.01	Biomass and Biofuels – Introduction *DJ Roddy*	1
5.02	Historical Perspectives on Biofuels *G Knothe*	11

Case Studies

5.03	Bioethanol Development in Brazil *A Altieri*	15
5.04	Biomass Power Generation *A Malmgren and G Riley*	27
5.05	Biomass Co-Firing *A Nuamah, A Malmgren, G Riley, and E Lester*	55

Issues, Constraints & Limitations

5.06	A Global Bioenergy Market *O Olsson and B Hillring*	75
5.07	Biomass CHP Energy Systems: A Critical Assessment *M Börjesson and EO Ahlgren*	87
5.08	Ethics of Biofuel Production *I Waller*	99
5.09	Life Cycle Analysis Perspective on Greenhouse Gas Savings *N Mortimer*	109

Technology Solutions – New Processes

5.10	Biomass Gasification and Pyrolysis *DJ Roddy and C Manson-Whitton*	133
5.11	Biomass to Liquids Technology *G Evans and C Smith*	155
5.12	Intensification of Biofuel Production *AP Harvey and JGM Lee*	205
5.13	Biofuels from Waste Materials *AA Refaat*	217

Technology Solutions – Novel Feedstocks

5.14	Woody Biomass *LL Wright, LM Eaton, RD Perlack, and BJ Stokes*	263
5.15	Potential for Yield Improvement *J Spink, E Mullins, and P Berry*	293

Technology Solutions – Novel End Uses

5.16	Renewable Fuels: An Automotive Perspective *RJ Pearson and JWG Turner*	305
5.17	Use of Biofuels in a Range of Engine Configurations *A Roskilly, Y Wang, R Mikalsen, and H Yu*	343

Expanding the Envelope

5.18	Biochar *CE Brewer and RC Brown*	357
5.19	Extracting Additional Value from Biomass *MF Askew*	385
5.20	Biomass to Chemicals *A Kazmi and J Clark*	395
5.21	Bioenergy Policy Development *P Thornley*	411

Volume 6 Hydro Power

Hydro Power

6.01	Hydro Power – Introduction *A Lejeune*	1

Constraints of Hydropower Development

6.02	Hydro Power: A Multi Benefit Solution for Renewable Energy *A Lejeune and SL Hui*	15
6.03	Management of Hydropower Impacts through Construction and Operation *H Horlacher, T Heyer, CM Ramos, and MC da Silva*	49

Hydropower Schemes Around the World

6.04	Large Hydropower Plants of Brazil *BP Machado*	93
6.05	Overview of Institutional Structure Reform of the Cameroon Power Sector and Assessments *J Kenfack and O Hamandjoda*	129
6.06	Recent Hydropower Solutions in Canada *M Fuamba and TF Mahdi*	153
6.07	The Three Gorges Project in China *L Suo, X Niu, and H Xie*	179
6.08	The Recent Trend in Development of Hydro Plants in India *SP Sen*	227
6.09	Hydropower Development in Iran: Vision and Strategy *E Bozorgzadeh*	253
6.10	Hydropower Development in Japan *T Hino*	265
6.11	Evolution of Hydropower in Spain *A Gil and F Bueno*	309
6.12	Hydropower in Switzerland *B Hagin*	343

Design Concepts

6.13	Long-Term Sediment Management for Sustainable Hydropower *F Rulot, BJ Dewals, S Erpicum, P Archambeau, and M Pirotton*	355
6.14	Durability Design of Concrete Hydropower Structures *S Jianxia*	377
6.15	Pumped Storage Hydropower Developments *T Hino and A Lejeune*	405

6.16	Simplified Generic Axial-Flow Microhydro Turbines *A Fuller and K Alexander*	435
6.17	Development of a Small Hydroelectric Scheme at Horseshoe Bend, Teviot River, Central Otago, New Zealand *P Mulvihill and I Walsh*	467
6.18	Recent Achievements in Hydraulic Research in China *J Guo*	485

Volume 7   Geothermal Energy

7.01	Geothermal Energy – Introduction *TI Sigfusson*	1
7.02	The Physics of Geothermal Energy *G Axelsson*	3
7.03	Geothermal Energy Exploration Techniques *ÓG Flóvenz, GP Hersir, K Sæmundsson, H Ármannsson, and Þ Friðriksson*	51
7.04	Geochemical Aspects of Geothermal Utilization *H Ármannsson*	95
7.05	Direct Heat Utilization of Geothermal Energy *JW Lund*	169
7.06	Shallow Systems: Geothermal Heat Pumps *L Rybach*	187
7.07	Geothermal Power Plants *R DiPippo*	207
7.08	Corrosion, Scaling, and Material Selection in Geothermal Power Production *SN Karlsdóttir*	239
7.09	Geothermal Cost and Investment Factors *H Kristjánsdóttir and Á Margeirsson*	259
7.10	Sustainable Energy Development: The Role of Geothermal Power *B Davidsdottir*	271

Volume 8   Ocean Energy

8.01	Generating Electrical Power from Ocean Resources *AS Bahaj*	1
8.02	Historical Aspects of Wave Energy Conversion *AFO Falcão*	7
8.03	Resource Assessment for Wave Energy *EBL Mackay*	11
8.04	Development of Wave Devices from Initial Conception to Commercial Demonstration *V Heller*	79
8.05	Air Turbines *AFO Falcão and LMC Gato*	111
8.06	Economics of Ocean Energy *T Stallard*	151
Index		171

2.01 Wind Energy – Introduction

JK Kaldellis, Technological Education Institute of Piraeus, Athens, Greece

© 2012 Elsevier Ltd. All rights reserved.

2.01.1	Introduction	1
2.01.2	Pros and Cons of Wind Energy	3
2.01.3	Brief Content Presentation	5
2.01.4	Conclusions	8
References		9
Further Reading		10
Relevant Websites		10

Glossary

Aeolus According to Greek mythology, Aeolus was the ruler of winds.

Calm spell The period of time during which wind speed takes values lower than a predefined value. Normally calm spells are considered to occur when the appearing wind speed is lower than 2 ms^{-1}, although in the case of wind turbines, calm spells may be considered as corresponding to the periods that wind speed is lower than the wind speed required for the machine to start operating.

Capacity factor The capacity factor of a wind turbine refers to the ratio of actual energy production of the machine for a given time period to the respective potential energy production of the same machine if it had operated at its rated power for the entire time period.

Energy pay-back period The period of time required for the entire amount of energy embedded in a system (during its life span) to be compensated by the system's energy production.

Feed-in tariff Feed in tariff refers to a policy mechanism developed for the support of renewable energy technologies, through the award of a certain payment per kWh for electricity produced by a renewable resource and fed into the grid. Feed in tariffs may vary on the basis of technology, geographical location and installation site.

Life-cycle Life-cycle refers to the period of time capturing all stages involved in a project, including energy projects as well. Regarding an energy plant (e.g., a wind farm), life-cycle concerns the stages of equipment manufacturing, transportation, installation, operation and decommissioning.

Neural network The term actually refers to artificial neural networks composed by artificial interconnected neurons which are used to mimic properties of biological neurons, in order to solve artificial intelligence problems.

R&D The term is used to describe research and development, and refers to creative work undertaken on a systematic basis in order to increase the stock of knowledge, and the use of this stock of knowledge to devise new applications.

Technical availability Technical availability is configured by the hours of operation of a given wind turbine or a given wind farm, by subtracting the time period that the machine is kept out of operation due to, e.g., scheduled maintenance, unforeseen faults of the machine, etc.

Wind energy The kinetic energy carried by a wind stream of certain characteristics (e.g., wind speed and air density).

Wind farm-wind park A group of wind turbines installed within the boundaries of a given area (either onshore or offshore) for the purpose of massive power generation.

Wind hybrid stand-alone system A power configuration that is used for the electrification of consumers that are not interconnected to an electricity grid and that combines two or more energy conversion systems – with one of them being a wind turbine (or a wind farm) – with an energy storage device.

Wind power The conversion of wind energy to useful forms of energy, i.e. mechanical work.

Wind turbine A man-made machine used to exploit the kinetic energy of wind so as to produce wind power in the form of electricity.

2.01.1 Introduction

Ever since the early days of mankind, wind was viewed as one of the most arresting natural phenomena. In fact, according to Greek mythology, humans worshipped the wind god Aeolus, who along with his eight assisting gods, that is, the so-called Anemoi, each assigned with one wind direction (Boreas (N), Kaikias (NE), Eurus (E), Apeliotes (SE), Notus (S), Livas (SW), Zephyrus (W), and Skiron (NW)) (**Figure 1**), was considered as the ruler of the winds, thus underlining the importance of wind energy for the economic and production activities during even this early historic period.

In this context, wind energy was initially exploited for the navigation of ships (**Figure 2**), while further, the first relatively simple applications of wind energy exploitation for the production of mechanical work appeared. At the same time of course, in order for their constantly increasing needs to be satisfied, people had to exploit other energy sources as well. However, despite the existence of alternative energy sources, wind machines were found to comprise a rather useful solution for the grinding of grains and other

Figure 1 The tower of winds, situated in Athens (shown are Boreas and Skiron).

Figure 2 Greek stamp demonstrating the Argo sailing ship.

Figure 3 Aspects of a medieval-type windmill for grinding grain and an American-type windmill used for water pumping.

production activities up until Medieval times [1], while a great number of multiblade wind machines installed mainly in the United States during the nineteenth century were used for water pumping purposes [2] (**Figure 3**).

Although acknowledging the importance of these early stages of wind energy history, it is believed that true and actual interest in wind energy grew during and after the end of the two world wars and wind energy was established after the consecutive energy crises between 1970 and 1980 [3]. More specifically, in the early 1980s, contemporary power generating wind turbines of 15–100 kW first

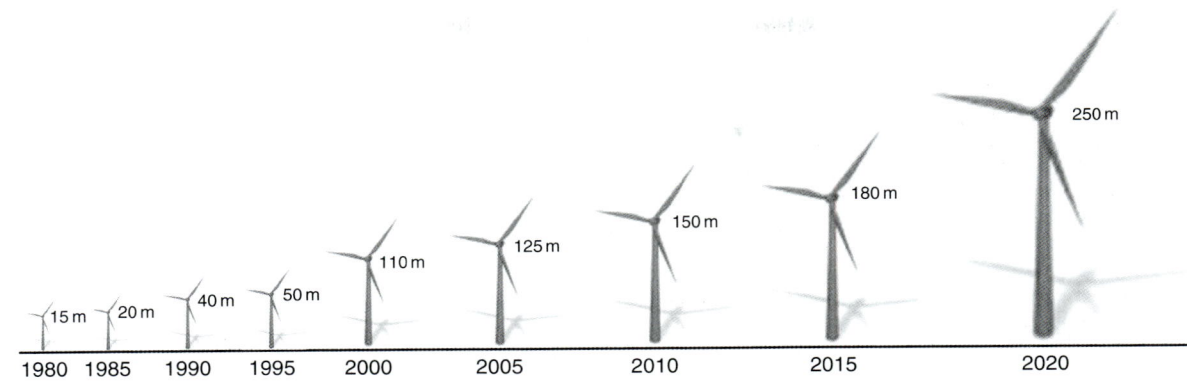

Figure 4 Time evolution of contemporary wind turbine size. Based on data from European Wind Energy Association (2009) Wind energy the facts, technology, wind turbine technology. http://www.wind-energy-the-facts.org/en/factsheets.html (accessed September 2011) [4].

appeared, followed by machines of somewhat greater power of around 300 kW. Accordingly, up until the mid-1990s, the rated power of wind turbines was in the order of 600–1000 kW, while nowadays, the market of modern wind turbines is dominated by multimegawatt machines, with rotor diameters even exceeding 150 m (**Figure 4**) [4]. In this context, current short-term realistic targets in terms of rated power are elevated to machines of 10 MW, destined mainly to serve offshore wind energy applications [5, 6], although future innovative concepts will increase machine capacity even more [7].

As a result of these constant developments, the global installed capacity of wind turbines has nowadays exceeded 200 GW (**Figure 5**) [8], with the contribution of wind energy to the local electrical energy balance of certain countries even exceeding 10% (**Figure 6**) [9]. At the same time, based on future plans and announcements made by the authorities of the most developed countries, wind energy applications are expected to develop even further, with a target of 1000 GW installed wind power to be achieved by 2030 (**Figure 7**) [10]. Considering the situation encountered so far, efforts are undertaken in this introductory chapter of the encyclopedia in order to first present the most important pros and cons of wind energy and to then provide a short summary of the following 21 chapters comprising the wind energy volume.

2.01.2 Pros and Cons of Wind Energy

Wind energy, which is explicitly the exploitation of the kinetic energy of wind, has attracted the interest of people since the early days of history. Note that the global wind potential is configured mainly by the absorbance of only a small proportion (~0.2%) of the incident solar energy on the various regions of the planet, which eventually leads to the development of climate.

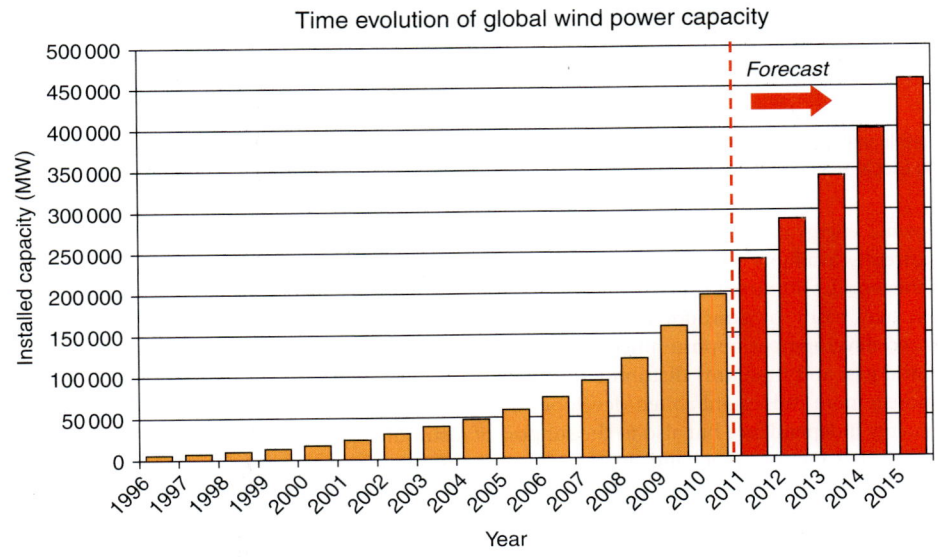

Figure 5 Time evolution and prediction of global wind power installed capacity. Based on data from Global Wind Energy Council (2011) Global wind report 2010. http://www.gwec.net (accessed September 2011) [8].

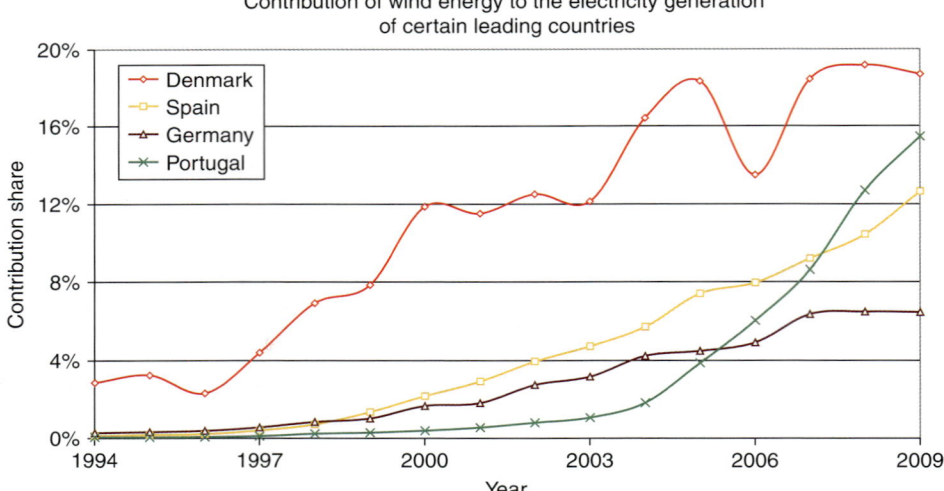

Figure 6 Wind energy contribution in the electrical energy balance of representative countries. Based on data from Energy Information Administration (2011) International energy statistics. http://www.eia.gov/ (accessed September 2011) [9].

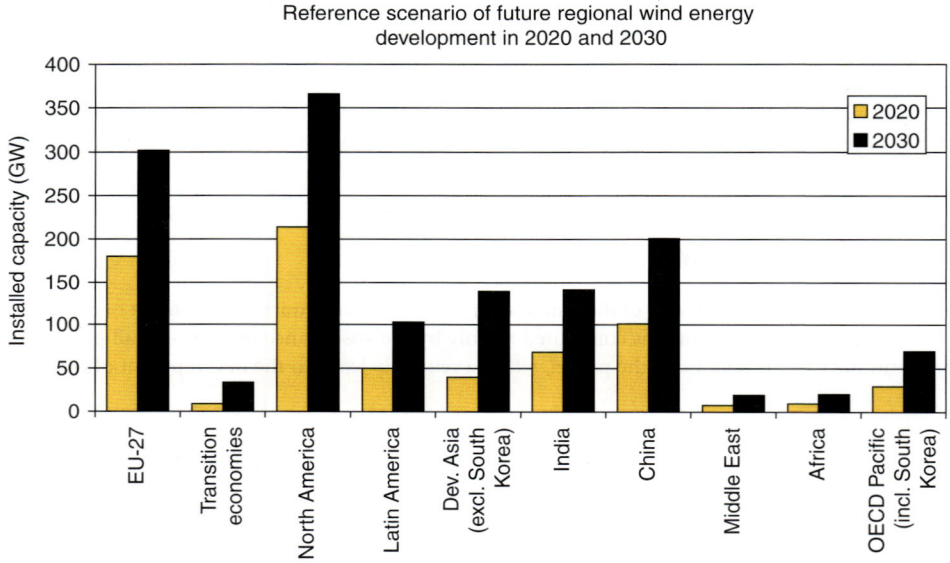

Figure 7 Regional development of wind energy according to the reference scenario of the Global Wind Energy Council. Based on data from Global Wind Energy Council (2011) Global wind power outlook 2010. http://www.gwec.net (accessed September 2011) [10].

In this context, wind energy comprises a nonfinite renewable energy source with a vast potential that is, however, only partly exploited by the currently available wind energy technology [11, 12]. In parallel, it should also be noted that wind potential is distributed across the world, without of course neglecting the fact that in some areas, local wind potential may be of higher/lower quality. Thus, as it may easily be concluded, the availability of wind energy throughout the planet contributes remarkably in providing balanced development opportunities all over the world [13], regardless of the existence of other fossil fuel reserves (e.g., oil, coal, natural gas, and uranium) distributed unevenly [14]. Finally, given also the fact that wind energy is normally of higher quality in more remote and less inhabited/developed areas, efforts for exploiting the local wind potential contribute not only to the increase of energy independence but also to the support of distributed generation patterns [15, 16] and the electrification of isolated consumers [17, 18]. On the other hand, apart from its expansion to the most remote areas, wind energy has recently entered the urban environment as well, with concepts of building integrated wind turbines aspiring to contribute remarkably to the future electrification of urban consumers [19–21].

At the same time, given the severe environmental problems of our planet, exploitation of wind energy may be determined as an environmentally friendly way of covering energy needs, with minimum, local-character environmental impacts involved [22, 23] being at least two orders less severe than that caused by conventional energy sources such as nuclear, coal, and oil [24]. In addition, installation and operation of wind parks may be considered as of low risk, with accidents recorded being minimum, while additionally, the impacts of natural disasters (e.g., fires, floods, and earthquakes) are also not considerable in the inhabited surroundings of operating wind farms. For this purpose, wind energy is established as a clean (green) energy source, which is also determined by a rather low energy payback period of less than 1 year, reflecting the contribution of the respective technology to sustainable development as well [25, 26].

On the other hand, wind energy is not always available, meaning that it is based on noncontrollable natural phenomena, which are responsible for the so-called intermittency of wind energy production [27]. However, despite the stochastic nature of wind energy, there are numerous advanced calculation tools that can provide reliable prediction of wind speeds [28–31], although due to the fact that wind energy exploitation is limited within a specific range of wind speeds (usually between 3–4 and 25–30 m s^{-1}), the possibility of long-term periods during which no energy production is encountered (i.e., either calm spells or extreme wind speeds) should also be considered. As a result, when considering wind energy, it is imperative to also consider a reserve energy source such as backup conventional power stations, energy storage systems [32–36], and hybrid units [37–40], which can be used to complement any energy deficit caused by the intermittency of the primary wind energy system. In addition, intense variation of the wind speed may also cause severe impacts on the quality of the electricity produced (e.g., voltage and frequency issues) [41–44], which requires installation of additional cost compensation mechanisms in order to provide consumers with the appropriate quality of electricity.

Finally, given the fact that the energy density of wind is relatively low, the per unit area maximum exploitation of wind energy by contemporary wind turbines ranges mainly between 150 and 300 W m^{-2}. This fact along with the technological status of modern wind machines imposes the need to operate a significant number of large-scale wind turbines in order for sufficient energy production to be achieved. For example, a modern wind turbine of 3 MW has a rotor diameter of around 100 m and a swept area of around 8000 m^2, while providing an annual energy production in the order of 7500 MWh$_e$. Furthermore, due to the considerable size of modern machines and the fact that they may operate in highly visible areas, the visual impact perception by the local inhabitants found in the proximity of a given wind farm suggests one of the major issues concerning wind energy [45, 46]. Similarly, the issues of noise production and impacts on local ecosystems (mainly bird collision) caused by the operation of wind farms are also of major importance [47–49]. In this context, it should be noted that although such issues should always be taken into account when considering installation and operation of a new wind farm, they usually influence relatively restricted areas in the surroundings of wind farms and are normally the subject of detailed and analytical studies carried out by wind energy developers [50, 51].

Synopsizing, by considering the pros and cons of wind energy, which will be further analyzed and elaborated in the following chapters, it is the opinion of the current volume's editorial team that wind energy suggests a renewable, widely distributed, and environmentally friendly energy source, applications of which are determined by high-quality technological standards and contribute considerably to the satisfaction of constantly increasing energy needs and the protection of the environment. In this context, it is expected that the development rate of such applications shall persist at high levels encountered so far, aiming to contribute more than 15% to the planet's electrical energy needs within the next 20 years.

2.01.3 Brief Content Presentation

Chapter 2.02 provides a thorough view of wind energy issues. A review of the past and current energy status on a global level is first undertaken, analyzing in detail the major energy trends as well as the contribution of fossil fuels and renewable energy sources. According to the existing official data, the current contribution of wind energy is rather limited, although increased wind energy participation should be expected in the future fuel mix of our planet. In this context and through the determination of the current wind power status and the evaluation of long-term wind energy developments, predictions concerning future prospects of wind energy appear to be rather encouraging. Thus, Chapter 2.02 clarifies the present role and future prospects of wind energy in the energy balance of the planet, giving at the same time a rather enlightening picture of the global energy market.

Accordingly, an overview of wind energy history starting from ancient windmills and extending to contemporary modern wind turbines is included in Chapter 2.03, with a scientific trip dating back 7000 years that is, to the use of sails to propel reed boats in Mesopotamia, being the basis of this analysis. Subsequently, the most well-known windmills are described, while the basic ideas and concepts used are also mentioned. Moreover, the major milestones in the progress of wind power applications and the history of the main relevant organizations are presented, while finally, the major competing wind turbine designs are briefly investigated, including the horizontal and vertical axis machines, the number of their blades (basically two- vs. three-bladed ones), etc.

Chapter 2.04 is devoted to giving an overview of the methods used to estimate the wind energy potential, starting from resource description and resulting in contemporary methods of forecasting. More precisely, the basic elements of wind potential evaluation theory and the main measurement techniques are demonstrated. Also the most representative analytical and numerical models used to accurately describe the wind potential of an area are presented, while the most widespread software tools used in order to reproduce the wind resource atlas of an area are described. The chapter concludes with a brief description of the most reliable wind potential forecasting methods, including artificial neural network models and Bayesian model averaging. Besides, the main scope of the entire analysis is estimation of the expected wind energy yield of a wind park as well as scheduling of optimum wind energy integration into an electrical network and implementation of the necessary system maintenance.

The scope of Chapter 2.05 is to describe the transition from ancient windmills to modern electricity generating wind turbines, with special emphasis on underlining the significant changes that the wind energy conversion technology has undergone. This is followed by a discussion of the basic principles governing the wind energy conversion process and a classification of wind turbines, with every wind machine being categorized according to its special characteristics (e.g., number of blades, axis orientation, and control type). Finally, the chapter concludes with an overview of the main components of established wind turbines, while additional effort has been placed on giving a brief description of the time evolution of commercial wind turbines.

In Chapter 2.06, a systematic study is carried out in order to present the main directions for the estimation of energy production by contemporary wind turbines. For this purpose, wind potential principles with operational characteristics of contemporary wind turbines are combined in order to calculate the corresponding mean power coefficient and the corresponding capacity factor. In this context, the basic theoretical models used to describe the wind turbine output and the available wind potential are analyzed. Furthermore, specific issues such as the reliability of calculations based on real measurements compared with pure analytical equations, the impact of hub height on the corresponding energy yield, the wake effect, and the air density impact on the corresponding energy yield are all considered, while subsequently, the impact of the technical availability on the wind turbines' energy yield is also examined. Finally, the representative commercial wind turbines for various typical wind potential cases are classified, providing at the same time detailed guidelines on the selection of the most appropriate wind turbine for a given wind site, in order to ensure both maximum energy yield and optimum operation of the machine.

The contents of Chapter 2.07 include an overview of the basic principles applied during the design of a new wind park. In this context, a general description of the issues that should be taken into consideration during the wind park design procedure is given, including site selection, wind potential evaluation, wind turbine micrositing, array losses, infrastructure required, collaboration with the local electrical network, social approval, and wind park output estimation. Selected representative case studies are briefly analyzed, while special attention is given on presenting the basic installation issues of commercial wind turbines. This chapter concludes with a brief presentation of some of the most characteristic wind parks in the world, including one of the biggest onshore (Roscoe, Texas) and offshore (Thanet, UK) installations.

Chapter 2.08 focuses on providing an overview of the basic aerodynamic methods used to analyze contemporary wind turbines, with regard to modeling and prediction of aerodynamic forces on the various parts of the machine, considering at the same time that wind turbine aerodynamics is the main discipline for the design and construction of wind turbine blades. In this context, all concepts, starting from the basic one-dimensional momentum theory up to the contemporary three-dimensional methods using the complete Navier–Stokes equations, are briefly analyzed. Accordingly, the status of the most important research areas within the aerodynamics of wind turbines, rotor wakes, and wind farms is presented, following which the optimization of wind turbine rotors with respect to minimizing the cost of energy produced by wind turbines is described. Finally, an introduction to the prediction of aerodynamic noise from wind turbine rotors is also provided.

Chapter 2.09 provides an introduction to loads for both onshore and offshore wind turbines with a focus on the respective wind- and wave-induced ones, so as to assess the structural integrity and power performance of wind turbines. Taking into consideration the significant activity and the prospects of offshore wind energy, emphasis is placed on offshore applications as well. In this context, the basic types of loads along with their sources are presented, including loads in the operational and survival conditions, fault cases, controller actions, and response-induced forces. Several innovative concepts concerning huge onshore and offshore turbines as well as floating turbines that require dynamic analysis and comprehensive load modeling are also examined, with selected case studies for both fixed and floating wind turbines being provided.

Chapter 2.10 gives an overview of the main electrical parts of contemporary wind turbines along with their basic operational principles. More specifically, power control, generators, power electronics, grid connection, and lightning protection are all discussed in detail. In this context, the analysis is focused on the basic types of electrical generators (synchronous and induction machines, constant-variable speed, etc.), yaw motors, and pitch control motors, while a brief presentation of the wind turbine ancillary electrical equipment is included as well. Note that although the content of this chapter mainly concerns present-day multimegawatt turbines, small machines are also taken into account. On top of that, a list of the most important manufacturers in the field is included and some insight into the future outlook of the sector is provided.

Chapter 2.11 investigates the control systems of contemporary wind turbines, including an overview of basic principles and representative types. Besides, a brief presentation of the dynamic control theory is included, along with an introduction on monitoring and power production control systems. In this context, the power production control comprises the generator torque control and the pitch control subsystems, the power electronics, and the grid connection. On the other hand, yaw control is also discussed, while emphasis is placed on operating states and fault diagnosis, as well as on the fail-safe backup systems analysis. Finally, the main sensor and actuator manufacturers of the field are briefly presented.

Chapter 2.12 mainly describes testing procedures of new wind turbines along with the up-to-now existing standardization processes. Additionally, emphasis is placed on discussing the major safety issues as well as any manufacturing, installation, and operational issues related to the safe operation of wind turbines, designating coherence between these elements. Accordingly, the various international standards (mostly the International Electrotechnical Commission) related to design aspects for large and small wind turbines onshore and offshore and testing of power performance, mechanical loads, acoustic noise, power quality, and safety are described, while the various certification schemes are also examined. Finally, a presentation concerning the organizations involved in the formal testing, standardization, and certification procedures for both existing and new wind turbines and wind parks is included.

Chapter 2.13 gives an overview of the most important issues related with the design and implementation of a wind power project. Actually, in this chapter, all stages of the project development process, in terms of what needs to be done and how to do it, are described in detail. In this context, the main parameters affecting the design of a new wind park along with the basic practical steps of the implementation of such a project are examined, with emphasis on infrastructure considerations as well as on financial issues during the project design and implementation. Subsequently, environmental aspects and social approval of new power stations are analyzed together with the experience from mitigating possible reactions in such projects. Finally, available information concerning the operation and maintenance of wind parks is also provided, including condition and performance monitoring as well as plant decommissioning and site restoration.

Chapter 2.14 presents offshore wind energy activity all over the world, providing a historical review from the very beginning of offshore applications along with an overview and future trends of the technology employed. In addition, the basic concepts of offshore wind farm design as well as issues concerning installation and maintenance activities are discussed. Accordingly, special emphasis is placed on presenting the support structures and towers used in offshore wind parks, while finally the most important economic, environmental, and social considerations during the development and operation of offshore wind farms are examined in detail.

Chapter 2.15 reviews the generation costs concerning onshore and offshore wind parks, determines the relative importance of turbine prices, slight costs, and other factors, and indicates how generation costs are influenced by the major economic parameters (capital cost, inflation rate, etc.) and the depreciation period. Accordingly, additional parameters that should be taken into consideration for a fair comparison between wind energy and fossil fuel electricity generation cost are also examined, for example, external cost, embedded benefits, and extra balancing cost, while methods of valuing wind energy are also considered. Finally, examples of 'total cost estimates' are discussed, taking into account most of the debits and credits associated with wind energy applications. The chapter concludes with a discussion of published forecasts of future price trends.

Chapter 2.16 deals with the main social and environmental benefits from the introduction of wind energy in a given area, such as reduction of carbon dioxide and air pollutants' emissions, decrease in the import of fossil fuels, creation of new job positions, and regional development. In addition, environmental concerns resulting from wind power plants, such as noise, visual impacts, and possible disturbance of the wildlife are described. Accordingly, special attention is paid on offshore wind power plants since they may impose distinct and in many cases quite different environmental impacts from onshore installations. Besides, another very interesting issue investigated is the social acceptance and public attitude of wind energy, while finally methods for the reliable assessment of impacts, mitigation measures, and future trends are also being discussed.

Chapter 2.17 examines the role of renewable energy within the context of global energy markets, investigating at the same time the skepticism toward wind energy. In this context, the link between energy and economic development is considered, while special emphasis is placed on the role of fossil fuels and nuclear energy. Accordingly, the opportunities of renewable energy sources and more specifically of wind energy to largely contribute to the world energy market are discussed, underlining that economic feasibility is the major obstacle for the wider participation of wind energy. Subsequently, the economics of wind energy are investigated in view of the economic structure of electricity grids, while finally the costs that wind energy may impose on the rest of the electricity generation systems are also examined, especially in case of large-scale wind energy integration.

Chapter 2.18 presents an overview of the opportunities and problems associated with the integration of wind energy into electrical networks currently in operation or under development. More precisely, a description of wind energy integration requirements and consequences that the particular characteristics of wind energy, namely its fair predictability (stochastic behavior) and fluctuations of generated power, may induce into an electrical network is provided. Accordingly, distributed systems are presented and the benefits of wind energy integration into common interconnected microgrids and stand-alone microgrids are described. This is followed by a discussion of wind forecasting and economic issues, considering also future trends concerning significant wind energy integration into existing electrical grids.

Chapter 2.19 introduces the reader to the definition and special features of wind-based stand-alone hybrid energy systems. The introduction emphasizes on the basic characteristics of stand-alone and hybrid energy systems including also representative application examples in different sectors. After a short reference to the historic development of wind-based stand-alone systems, the contribution of wind energy in distributed generation is analyzed. The most common commercial system configurations of stand-alone installations are discussed in detail through various case study results in order for the reader to obtain a comprehensive view of the opportunities given by the different combinations. Furthermore, a short description of the energy storage systems available is presented along with a short reference to the most well-known free software tools that are extensively used for the design and optimization of hybrid energy systems.

Chapter 2.20 gives an overview of the wind power industry in the course of time along with the corresponding market development, addressing at the same time key drivers and new trends. In this context, the galloping wind power development noted during the past 15–20 years on a global scale is illustrated, emphasizing on the long-term annual growth rate of almost 25%. Accordingly, the major wind energy markets are analyzed, including China, the United States, Germany, and Spain. Finally, a brief presentation of the major wind power manufacturers along with their market share time evolution is included.

In Chapter 2.21, a systematic study is carried out in order to present the main trends, prospects, and R&D directions of wind turbine technology. For this purpose, investigation of the main technological developments throughout the entire period of wind energy growth is undertaken, while emphasis is placed on recording the most important research efforts that have allowed wind energy establishment. Accordingly, several research efforts remarkably financed during the previous years are acknowledged, while simultaneously, major wind energy technological problems and the most challenging future R&D issues are discussed. The chapter concludes by synopsizing the most important problems to be faced by the wind energy community at all levels in order to ensure that growth trends encountered until today will not be limited in the years to follow.

The volume is integrated in Chapter 2.22 with the examination of representative wind power applications. In this context, one of the most important applications analyzed is the desalination of seawater and/or brackish water, utilized in order to supply the required quantities of freshwater to various areas of the planet facing water shortage. Furthermore, other significant applications of wind energy, like the traditional and well-known application of wind-based water pumping and the more modern application of power generation in remote telecommunication stations, are also briefly discussed. Additionally, emphasis is placed on the sizing procedure of these systems as well as on their financial viability. Finally, selected examples of the most representative special wind power applications along with their main technical characteristics are demonstrated as well.

2.01.4 Conclusions

Considering its status quo at the global scale, wind power can nowadays be perceived as one of the most mature and reliable energy solutions, which is reflected by the constantly growing installed capacity, recently exceeding 200 GW. On the other hand, although now suggesting an established power generation source, research efforts in the field of wind energy are still ongoing, with emphatic targets set at both the national and international level configuring the future prospects of wind power applications. At the same time, we are now arguably facing development of the fourth-generation wind machines, while also noticing multidirectional shifts, for example, from onshore to offshore wind power applications, from large-scale rural wind farms to urban environment small-scale wind machines destined to serve on-site domestic electrical loads, and from centralized wind energy generation to distributed generation patterns involving wind-based stand-alone applications.

Within this constantly evolutionary environment in terms of technological trends, global wind power market facts also produce consecutive changes of scene. In this context, according to the current situation, China is currently the leader in wind energy, operating a total of ~45 GW of wind power within its territory, followed by the United States (~40 GW), Germany (~27 GW), and Spain (~21 GW). Meanwhile, India with galloping rates of development during the recent years has installed a cumulative capacity of more than 13 GW. Acknowledging the above, parallel development of different world regions noted reflects the relatively even distribution of wind resources across the globe, nowadays extended to also capture the offshore wind potential.

In this context, the developing rates of offshore applications are even more encouraging, with regional plans, such as those of the European Wind Energy Association, aiming at 600 TWh$_e$ produced by offshore wind energy by 2030. At the same time, according to the reference scenario of the Global Wind Energy Council, the total installed capacity of wind power applications (both offshore and onshore) by 2030 is expected to exceed 1000 GW, thus allowing for considerable contribution of wind energy to the global electrical energy consumption.

On the other hand, to achieve the ambitious targets concerning further promotion of wind energy into electricity markets, numerous challenges need to be encountered first, involving among others design and material issues, integration of wind energy into electrical grids, adaptation of wind energy into urban environments, development of more efficient and reliable small-scale wind turbines, and exploitation of deeper waters for offshore applications. For this purpose, sufficient financial support in the R&D section of wind energy is thought to be imperative, especially if considering that innovative concepts in the field of wind power applications emerge continuously, introducing wind machines of even 1 GW rated power.

At this point, it must be underlined that support offered to wind energy throughout this period of growth, either in the form of policy tools such as feed-in tariffs or in the form of considerable research funds, was efficiently used and has allowed wind energy technology to establish itself in the competitive environment of energy markets. Furthermore, policy instruments developed to promote further penetration of wind energy were accordingly applied in other renewable energy source technologies, producing similar progressive results. However, earlier development of wind energy in comparison with alternative energy sources has provided wind power technologies with a significant edge that may under certain conditions ensure an even more promising future for wind energy applications. At the same time, constant cost reduction and increase of energy efficiency for modern wind turbines set the basis for further expansion of wind energy applications, now being in a position to favorably compete not only with other alternative energy source installations but also with conventional power generation (e.g., oil based and coal based).

Considering also the efforts undertaken in the field of environmental performance so as to reduce/eliminate the already mild impacts in terms of affecting local ecosystems and ensuring sustainable use of energy resources on a life-cycle basis, environmental benefits deriving from the increase of wind energy contribution will become yet more pronounced, even in the case that externalities attributed to fossil-based power generation are not entirely considered.

In conclusion, emphasis must be placed on the fact that wind energy has long since comprised a mature and reliable power source that has established its role in the world energy scene. On the other hand, it seems that following a long period of continuous development and vast progress concerning mainly the concept of onshore wind farms, the time has arrived for wind energy to take the next step and identify itself as one of the main energy suppliers worldwide. For this to be achieved, however, challenges emerging in each of the new wind energy directions (e.g., offshore wind, small-scale wind, urban environment integration, distributed generation patterns, wind hybrid stand-alone systems, and giant wind turbines) need to be encountered on the basis of persisting research efforts, sufficient financial support, fostering policy initiatives, and public perception of the beneficial attributes of wind energy.

References

[1] Pasqualetti MJ, Righter R, and Gipe P (2004) History of wind energy. In: Cleveland C (ed.) *Encyclopedia of Energy*, pp. 419–433. Amsterdam, The Netherlands: Elsevier.
[2] Baker TL (1985) *A Field Guide to American Windmills*, 1st edn. Norman, OK: University of Oklahoma Press.
[3] Lynch M (1999) Oil scarcity, oil crises, and alternative energies – Don't be fooled again. *Applied Energy* 64: 31–53.
[4] European Wind Energy Association (2009) Wind energy the facts, technology, wind turbine technology. http://www.wind-energy-the-facts.org/en/factsheets.html (accessed September 2011).
[5] Snyder B and Kaiser MJ (2009) A comparison of offshore wind power development in Europe and the U.S.: Patterns and drivers of development. *Applied Energy* 86: 1845–1856.
[6] Breton SP and Moe G (2009) Status, plans and technologies for offshore wind turbines in Europe and North America. *Renewable Energy* 34: 646–654.
[7] Chen L, Ponta FL, and Lago LI (2011) Perspectives on innovative concepts in wind-power generation, *Energy for Sustainable Development*, Corrected proof. http://www.sciencedirect.com/ (accessed October 2011).
[8] Global Wind Energy Council (2011) Global wind report 2010. http://www.gwec.net (accessed September 2011).
[9] Energy Information Administration (2011) International energy statistics. http://www.eia.gov/ (accessed September 2011).
[10] Global Wind Energy Council (2011) Global wind power outlook 2010. http://www.gwec.net (accessed September 2011).
[11] Hoogwijk M, de Vries B, and Turkenburg W (2004) Assessment of the global and regional geographical, technical and economic potential of onshore wind energy. *Energy Economics* 26: 889–919.
[12] de Castro C, Mediavilla M, Miguel LJ, and Frechoso F (2011) Global wind power potential: Physical and technological limits. *Energy Policy* 39: 6677–6682.
[13] Jacobson MZ and Delucchi MA (2011) Providing all global energy with wind, water, and solar power. Part I: Technologies, energy resources, quantities and areas of infrastructure, and materials. *Energy Policy* 39: 1154–1169.
[14] British Petroleum (2011) BP statistical review of world energy. http://www.bp.com/ (accessed September 2011).
[15] El-Khattam W and Salama MMA (2004) Distributed generation technologies, definitions and benefits. *Electric Power System Research* 71: 119–128.
[16] Bishop JDK and Amaratunga GAJ (2008) Evaluation of small wind turbines in distributed arrangement as sustainable wind energy option for Barbados. *Energy Conversion and Management* 49: 1652–1661.
[17] Kaldellis JK (2002) Optimum autonomous wind–power system sizing for remote consumers, using long-term wind speed data. *Applied Energy* 71: 215–233.
[18] Kaldellis JK (2004) Parametric investigation concerning dimensions of a stand-alone wind-power system. *Applied Energy* 77: 35–50.
[19] Dayan E (2006) Wind energy in buildings: Power generation from wind in the urban environment-where it is needed most. *Refocus* 7: 33–34, 36, 38.
[20] Mithraratne N (2009) Roof-top wind turbines for microgeneration in urban houses in New Zealand. *Energy Buildings* 41: 1013–1018.
[21] Grant A, Johnstone C, and Kelly N (2008) Urban wind energy conversion: The potential of ducted turbines. *Renewable Energy* 33: 1157–1163.
[22] Saidur R, Rahim NA, Islam MR, and Solangi KH (2011) Environmental impact of wind energy. *Renewable and Sustainable Energy Reviews* 15: 2423–2430.
[23] Morrison ML and Sinclair K (2004) Wind energy technology, environmental impacts of. In: Cleveland C (ed.) *Encyclopedia of Energy*, vol. 6, pp. 435–448, St. Louis, MO: Elsevier.
[24] Kemeny LG (1982) A review of the global environmental impact of fossil and nuclear fuels. *Mathematics and Computers in Simulation* 24: 194–203.
[25] Crawford RH (2009) Life cycle energy and greenhouse emissions analysis of wind turbines and the effect of size on energy yield. *Renewable and Sustainable Energy Reviews* 13: 2653–2660.
[26] White SW and Kulcinski GL (2000) Birth to death analysis of the energy payback ratio and CO_2 gas emission rates from coal, fission, wind, and DT-fusion electrical power plants. *Fusion Engineering and Design* 48: 473–481.
[27] Sovacool BK (2009) The intermittency of wind, solar and renewable electricity generators: Technical barrier or rhetorical excuse? *Utilities Policy* 17: 288–296.
[28] Barbounis TG and Theocharis JB (2007) A locally recurrent fuzzy neural network with application to the wind speed prediction using spatial correlation. *Neurocomputing* 70: 1525–1542.
[29] Riahy GH and Abedi M (2008) Short term wind speed forecasting for wind turbine applications using linear prediction method. *Renewable Energy* 33: 35–41.
[30] Kani SAP and Ardehal MM (2011) Very short-term wind speed prediction: A new artificial neural network–Markov chain model. *Energy Conversion and Management* 52: 738–745.
[31] Salcedo-Sanz S, Ortiz-Garcia EG, Pérez-Bellido AM, et al. (2011) Short term wind speed prediction based on evolutionary support vector regression algorithms. *System Applications* 38: 4052–4057.
[32] Chen H, Cong TN, Yang W, et al. (2009) Progress in electrical energy storage system: A critical review. *Progress in Natural Science* 19: 291–312.
[33] Hadjipaschalis I, Poullikkas A, and Efthimiou V (2009) Overview of current and future energy storage technologies for electric power applications. *Renewable and Sustainable Energy Reviews* 13: 1513–1522.
[34] Kaldellis JK, Zafirakis D, and Kavadias K (2009) Techno-economic comparison of energy storage systems for island autonomous electrical networks. *Renewable and Sustainable Energy Reviews* 13: 378–392.
[35] Baker J (2008) New technology and possible advances in energy storage. *Energy Policy* 36: 4368–4373.
[36] Kondoh J, Ishii I, Yamaguchi H, et al. (2000) Electrical energy storage systems for energy networks. *Energy Conversion and Management* 41: 1863–1874.
[37] Kaldellis JK (2010) *Stand-Alone and Hybrid Wind Energy Systems: Technology, Energy Storage and Applications*, 1st edn. Cambridge, UK: Woodhead Publishing.
[38] Nema P, Nema RK, and Rangnekar S (2009) A current and future state of art development of hybrid energy system using wind and PV-solar: A review. *Renewable and Sustainable Energy Reviews* 13: 2096–2103.
[39] Chen HH, Kang HY, and Lee AHI (2010) Strategic selection of suitable projects for hybrid solar-wind power generation systems. *Renewable and Sustainable Energy Reviews* 14: 413–421.
[40] Kaldellis JK and Kavadias KA (2007) Cost–benefit analysis of remote hybrid wind–diesel power stations: Case study Aegean Sea islands. *Energy Policy* 35: 1525–1538.
[41] Albadi MH and El-Saadany EF (2010) Overview of wind power intermittency impacts on power systems. *Electric Power Systems Research* 80: 627–632.
[42] Chinchilla M, Arnalte S, Burgos JC, and Rodríguez JL (2006) Power limits of grid-connected modern wind energy systems. *Renewable Energy* 31: 1455–1470.
[43] Vilar C, Amarís H, and Usaola J (2006) Assessment of flicker limits compliance for wind energy conversion system in the frequency domain. *Renewable Energy* 31: 1089–1106.
[44] Ibrahim H, Ghandour M, Dimitrova M, et al. (2011) Integration of wind energy into electricity systems: Technical challenges and actual solutions. *Energy Procedia* 6: 815–824.
[45] Tsoutsos Th, Tsouchlaraki A, Tsiropoulos M, and Serpetsidakis M (2009) Visual impact evaluation of a wind park in a Greek island. *Applied Energy* 86: 546–553.
[46] Jerpasen GB and Larsen KC (2011) Visual impact of wind farms on cultural heritage: A Norwegian case study. *Environmental Impact Assessment* 31: 206–215.
[47] Kikuchi R (2008) Adverse impacts of wind power generation on collision behaviour of birds and anti-predator behaviour of squirrels. *Nature Conservation* 16: 44–55.
[48] Desholm M (2009) Avian sensitivity to mortality: Prioritising migratory bird species for assessment at proposed wind farms. *Environmental Management* 90: 2672–2679.
[49] Burkhard B, Opitz S, Lenhart H, et al. (2011) Ecosystem based modeling and indication of ecological integrity in the German North Sea-case study offshore wind parks. *Ecological Indicators* 11: 168–174.
[50] Tegou LI, Polatidis H, and Haralambopoulos DA (2010) Environmental management framework for wind farm siting: Methodology and case study. *Environmental Management* 91: 2134–2147.
[51] Aydin NY, Kentel E, and Duzgun S (2010) GIS-based environmental assessment of wind energy systems for spatial planning: A case study from Western Turkey. *Renewable and Sustainable Energy Reviews* 14: 364–373.

Further Reading

Hau E (2006) *Wind Turbines: Fundamentals, Technologies, Application, Economics*, 2nd edn. Berlin; Heidelberg, Germany: Springer.
Mathew S and Philip GS (2011) *Advances in Wind Energy Conversion Technology*, 1st edn. Berlin, Heidelberg, Germany; New York: Springer.
Gipe P (1995) *Wind Energy Comes of Age*, 1st edn. New York: Wiley.
Kaldellis JK (2005) *Wind Energy Management*, 2nd edn. Athens, Greece: Stamoulis.
Burton T, Sharpe D, Jenkins N, and Bossanyi E (2001) *Wind Energy Handbook*, 1st edn. Chichester, UK: Wiley.
Nelson V (2009) *Wind Energy. Renewable Energy and the Environment*, 1st edn. Boca Raton, FL: CRC Press, Taylor & Francis Group.
Ackermann Th (2005) *Wind Power in Power Systems*, 1st edn. Chichester, UK: Wiley.
Mathew S (2006) *Wind Energy: Fundamentals, Resource Analysis and Economics*, 1st edn. Berlin, Heidelberg, Germany; New York: Springer.
Stanković S, Campbell N, and Harries A (2009) *Urban Wind Energy*, 1st edn. London, UK: Earthscan.
Twidell J and Gaudiosi G (2009) *Offshore Wind Power*, 1st edn. Brentwood; Essex, UK: Multi-Science Publications.
Wood D (2011) *Small Wind Turbines. Analysis, Design and Application*, 1st edn. Berlin, Heidelberg, Germany; New York: Springer.
Asmus P (2000) *Reaping the Wind: How Mechanical Wizards, Visionaries, and Profiteers Helped Shape Our Energy Future*, 1st edn. Washington, DC: Island Press.

Relevant Websites

http://www.eia.doe.gov – US Energy Information Administration.
http://www.gwec.net – Global Wind Energy Council.
http://www.ewea.org – European Wind Energy Association.
http://www.wind-energy-the-facts.org – Wind Energy the Facts (European Wind Energy Association and Intelligent Energy).
http://www.ieawind.org – International Energy Agency – Wind Energy Systems.
http://ec.europa.eu/research/energy/eu/research/wind/support/index_en.htm – European Commission – Research and Innovation in Wind Energy.
http://ec.europa.eu/energy/renewables/wind_energy/wind_energy_en.htm – European Commission – Energy–Wind Energy.
http://windpower.sandia.gov – US Sandia National Laboratories – Wind Energy Department.
http://www.nrel.gov/wind – US National Renewable Energy Laboratory.
http://www.dewi.de – German Wind Energy Institute.
http://www.risoe.dk – Danish National Laboratory for Sustainable Energy.

2.02 Wind Energy Contribution in the Planet Energy Balance and Future Prospects

JK Kaldellis and M Kapsali, Technological Education Institute of Piraeus, Athens, Greece

© 2012 Elsevier Ltd. All rights reserved.

2.02.1	Introduction	11
2.02.2	Energy Consumption around the Planet	12
2.02.3	Electrical Power and Electrical Generation	14
2.02.4	Fossil Fuel Status of Our Planet	17
2.02.4.1	Oil Data	17
2.02.4.2	Natural Gas Data	20
2.02.4.3	Coal Data	20
2.02.5	The Role of RES and Fossil Fuels in the Energy Future of Our Planet	21
2.02.5.1	The Energy Balance of Our Planet	21
2.02.5.2	Time Depletion of Fossil Fuels	22
2.02.5.3	Environmental Impacts of Energy: Carbon Dioxide Emissions	22
2.02.5.4	Comparing RES and Fossil Fuels (Pros and Cons) with Emphasis on Wind Energy	25
2.02.6	Wind Power Status in the World Market	25
2.02.7	Time Evolution of the Major Wind Power Markets	27
2.02.8	Forecasting the Wind Power Time Evolution	31
2.02.9	The Future and Prospects of Wind Energy	35
2.02.10	Conclusions	37
References		37
Further Reading		39
Relevant Websites		39

Glossary

Developing country A term generally used to describe a nation with a low level of material well-being.
Energy fuel mix The distribution within a given geographical area, of the consumption of various energy sources (i.e., crude oil, natural gas, coal, nuclear energy, and renewable energy).
Fossil fuel A hydrocarbon deposit, such as petroleum, coal, or natural gas, derived from the accumulated remains of ancient plants and animals and used as fuel.
Renewable-based electricity generation Electricity which comes from natural resources such as sun, wind, tides, and geothermal heat, which are renewable (naturally replenished).
Thermal power station A place where electric energy is produced from thermal energy released by combustion of a fuel or consumption of a fissionable material.

2.02.1 Introduction

Survival of the humankind along with the majority of human activities are directly dependent on the exploitation of energy sources, with the continuous increase of global energy consumption being actually a reflection of the constant evolution of humankind, especially in the days following the industrial revolution. During the time being, a transition may be noted from the early days of biomass (human power, animal power, wood, etc.), solar and wind energy exploitation, to the times of today, where people's welfare much relies on the consumption of fossil fuel reserves (oil, natural gas, and coal) and nuclear energy, with much faith presently given to the solution of nuclear fusion for the energy supply security of future generations [1].

In this context, if considering the huge amounts of energy consumed in the various sectors (i.e., industrial, residential, commercial, agricultural, stock farming, and transportation), one should emphasize on the critical role of energy in contemporary societies, not only as a measure of life quality [2] but also as an important factor of production processes. On top of that, contribution of energy is also critical in the field of global water reserves' management [3], while during the recent years, special attention has been given to issues of association between energy and the natural environment [4].

Energy use by modern people includes electrical energy consumption, mainly for the satisfaction of domestic needs as well as for the coverage of loads during work hours, and direct consumption of liquid fuels or natural gases for transportation and heating

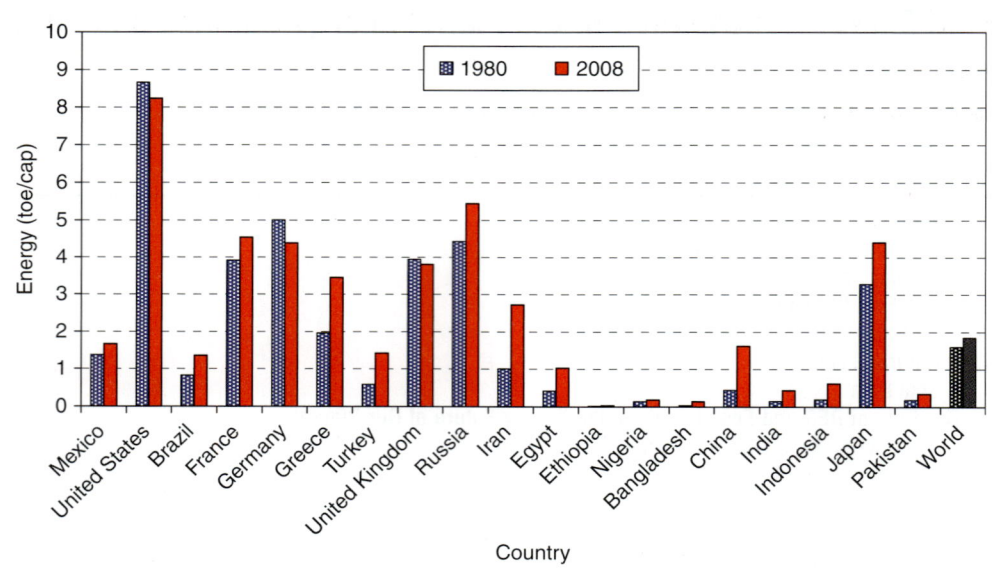

Figure 1 Total primary energy consumption per capita (1980–2008) for selected countries.

needs, while on top of that one should also consider the energy included in nutrition along with the embodied energy of products and services used on a daily basis.

As a result of these activities, the average US resident uses on an annual basis almost 8.5 toe of primary energy (or 60 barrels of oil equivalent), while the corresponding energy consumption per capita in the biggest European countries and Japan is almost 4.5 toe (or 30 barrels of oil equivalent) (see also **Figure 1**). Besides, it is worthwhile mentioning that almost one-third of the above-mentioned energy consumption is attributed to the domestic sector and thus comprises direct energy use by each typical resident of a given country.

On the other hand, primary energy consumption of the less-favored developing countries is by far lower than the one corresponding to the developed world and does not exceed 0.5 toe yr^{-1}, while the global average is kept within the range of 1.9 toe yr^{-1}, presenting an increase of approximately 15% during the last decade. In this context, it is interesting to note that the average annual nutrition requirements of a person does not exceed 0.12 toe yr^{-1}, with implications deriving from the comparison of figures given illustrating the current energy state of our planet.

2.02.2 Energy Consumption around the Planet

In order to describe the energy consumption state of our planet, in **Figure 2** one presents the long-term time evolution of primary energy consumption at a global and regional level during the last 30 years. As it may be concluded from the information provided in the figure,

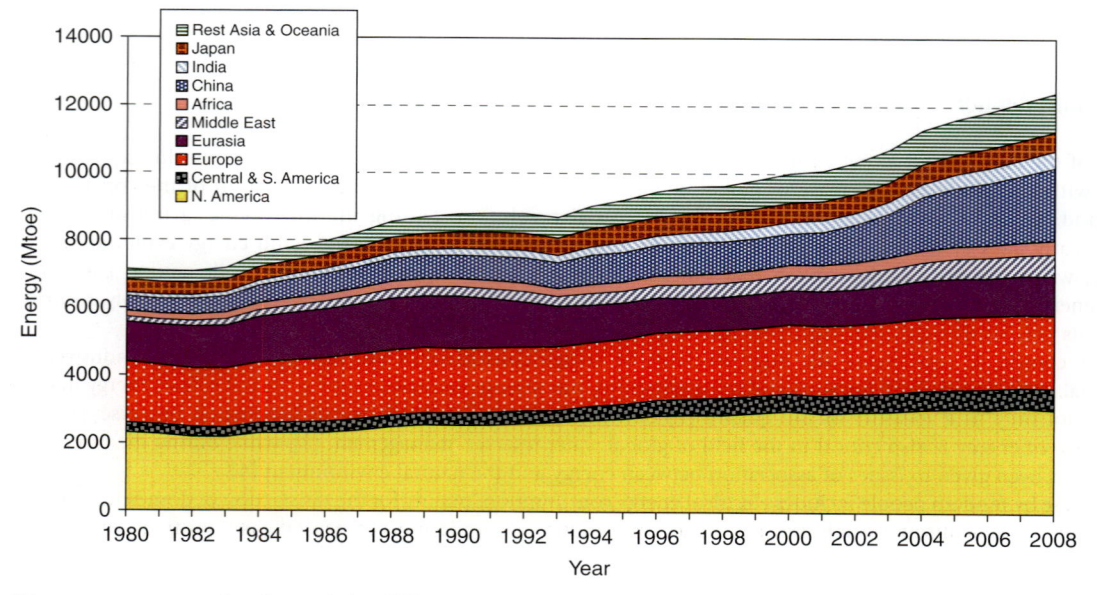

Figure 2 Primary energy consumption time evolution (1980–2008) globally and per region.

there is a remarkable increase of the global primary energy consumption during the specific period that reaches approximately 80%, while at the regional level, one may distinguish the cases of China and India where an impressive increase is recorded [5].

Considering the above, relation between population increase and primary energy consumption is designated [6], especially in cases of developing countries where one should also consider the vast need for the improvement of life quality that also leads to the increase of energy consumption per capita. On the other hand, however, technology advancements, more rational use of energy resources, and efforts toward energy saving comprise the main elements of deceleration for the constant increase of primary energy consumption, especially in the industrially developed countries of our planet [7].

Meanwhile, based on the latest official data (see also **Figure 3**), the world population has increased rapidly since 1950 from 2.5 billion to almost 7 billion people in 2010, while it is expected to exceed 9 billion by 2050. What is even more interesting, however, is the fact that the increase recorded is attributed to the population of developing countries, reaching nowadays a total of 6 billion people. Keep in mind that although in the specific regions primary energy consumption per capita was up to now kept quite low, constant development of local economies shall lead to considerable improvement of life quality standards and thus to an outbreak of primary energy consumption at a global level.

In view of the expected increase of the global primary energy consumption, **Figure 4** presents the long-term time evolution of the energy fuel mix of our planet during the last 30 years. As it may accrue from the data given in the figure, energy demand of our planet is primarily covered by the use of fossil fuel reserves at the dominant percentage of over 90%, while participation of renewable

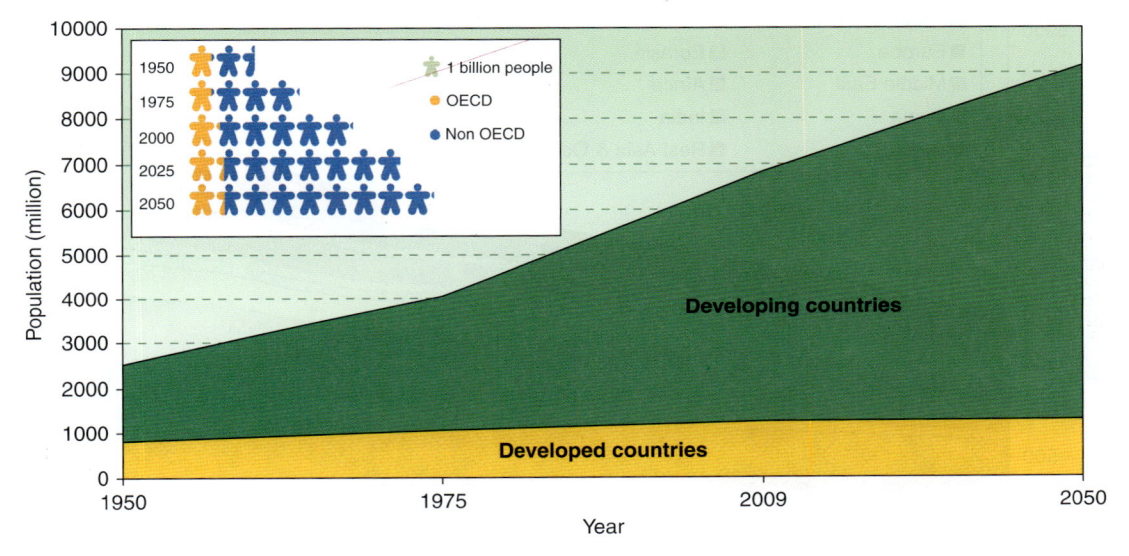

Figure 3 World population growth (1950–2008) [8, 9].

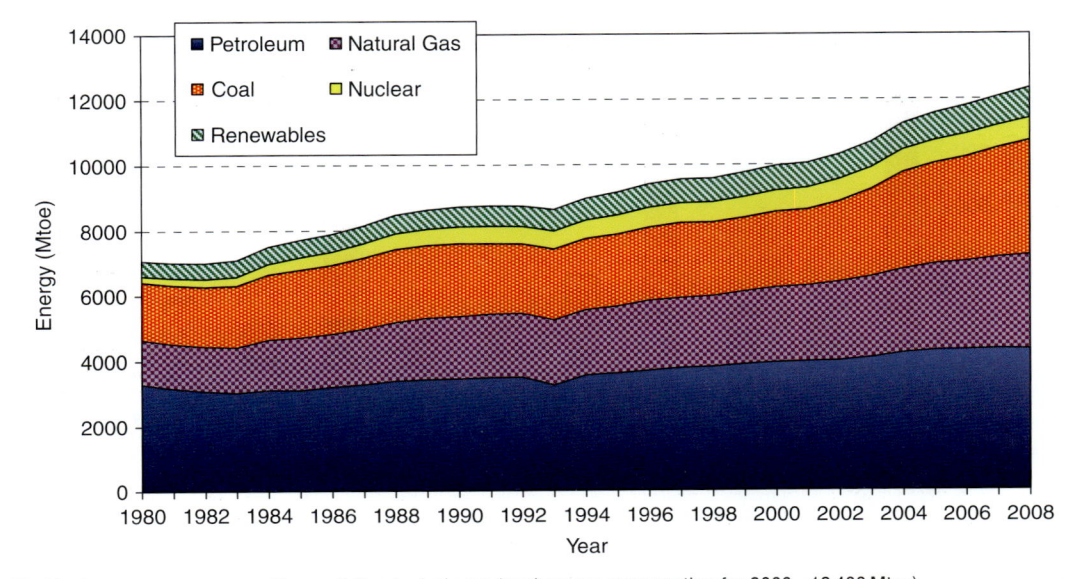

Figure 4 World primary energy consumption evolution by fuel type (total energy consumption for 2008 ≈ 12 400 Mtoe).

energy sources (RES) is restricted to less than 7.5%, mainly owed to the contribution of hydropower in the electricity generation sector [10] and biomass in the coverage of basic energy needs in the less-favored countries of our planet [11].

2.02.3 Electrical Power and Electrical Generation

Among the most user-friendly forms of energy used in the industrialized regions of our planet nowadays is electricity. In fact, according to the most recent data, the installed capacity of electricity power stations globally is now reaching 5000 GW$_e$, with the respective annual electricity production exceeding 20 000 TWh$_e$. This actually corresponds to average electricity consumption per capita in the order of 3000 kWh$_e$ yr^{-1}.

More precisely, according to the data presented in **Figure 5**, during the last 30 years the installed electrical power capacity is more than doubled, that is, from 2000 GW$_e$ in 1980 to almost 5000 GW$_e$ in 2010, mainly owed to the activity encountered in China (especially during the last decade) and the United States. In fact, the installed electrical power capacity at the near end of the previous decade in the United States exceeded 1000 GW$_e$, majority of which corresponds to thermal power stations, with the respective RES share not exceeding 120 GW$_e$ and with the contribution of wind power represented (in 2010) by a total of 40 GW$_e$ (see also **Figure 6**). Second in the list of installed power capacity is Europe with a total of more than 900, 170, and 85 GW$_e$ out of

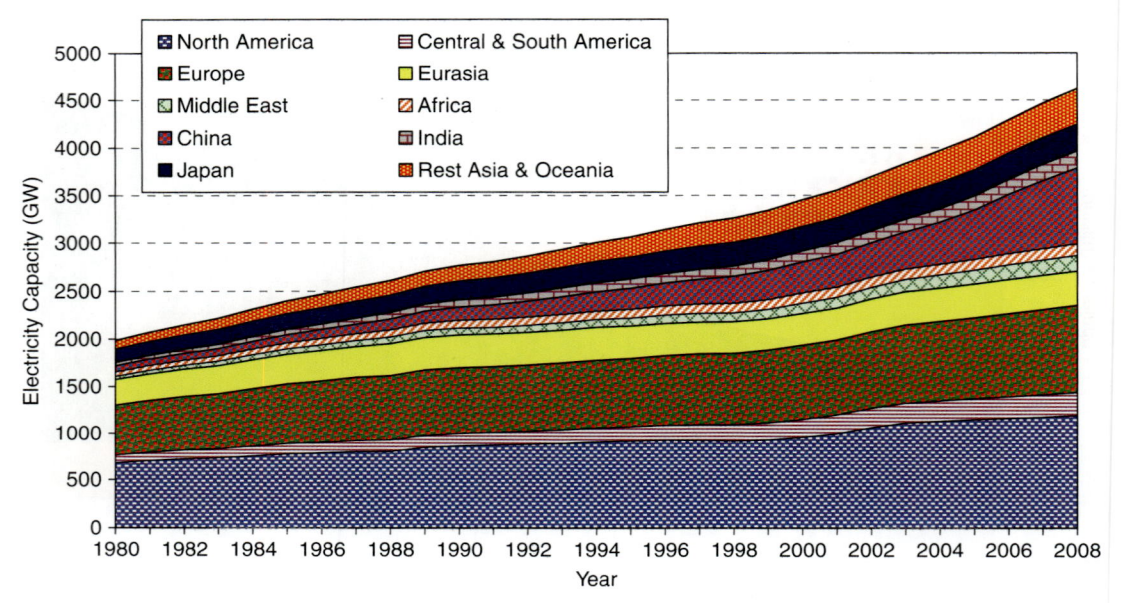

Figure 5 Total installed electricity capacity time evolution (GW$_e$).

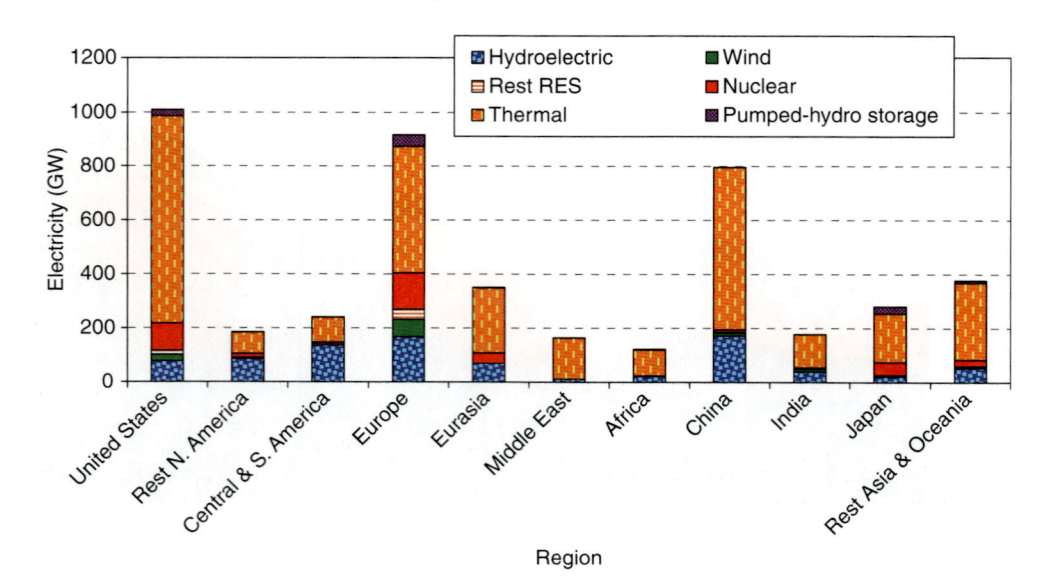

Figure 6 Distribution of the installed electricity capacity per region in 2008.

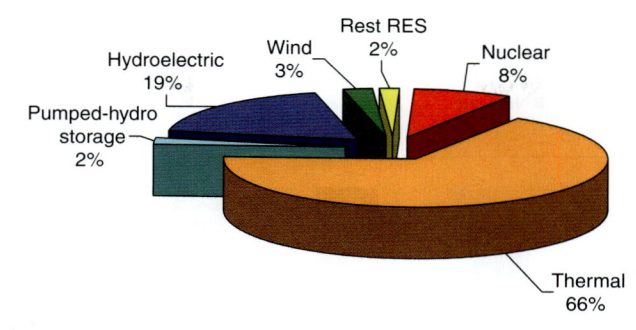

Figure 7 Distribution of the globally installed electric power capacity per source (2008).

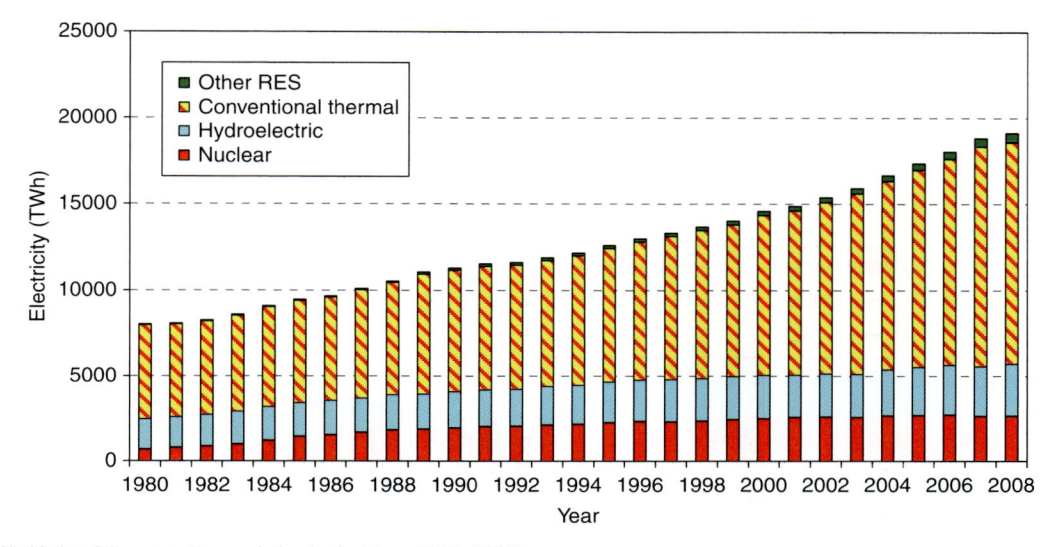

Figure 8 World electricity generation evolution by fuel type (1998–2008).

which (in 2010) hydropower and wind power, respectively. Finally, in the third place of the list, one may encounter China [12, 13] with a total installed capacity of approximately 800 GW$_e$, largely configured by the participation of large-scale hydropower plants (180 GW$_e$) and wind power (exceeding 40 GW$_e$ at the end of 2010).

In total, two-thirds of the planet's installed electrical power capacity regard thermal power stations (coal- natural gas- and oil-fired), 19% concerns hydropower stations, 8% corresponds to nuclear power, and 3% is attributed to wind parks (in 2008) (**Figure 7**) with a total of approximately 200 GW$_e$ by the end of 2010.

Accordingly, **Figure 8** presents the energy production share of the above energy sources during the last 30 years, again at a global level. Among the most interesting conclusions that one may obtain from the analysis of the figure is that there is almost a tripling of electricity generation during the period of study, covered mainly (around 70%) from the operation of thermal power stations. On the other hand, what can also be designated is the consistent role of hydropower throughout the period, as well as the recently emerged wind energy sector achieving an electricity generation contribution of 2% during the last years. In fact, exploitation of wind energy and hydropower for the purpose of electricity production comprises an established practice with fairly good results, expected to dominate among other RES in the forthcoming years.

At this point, it should be noted that although at the moment electrical power mainly derives from thermal power stations, RES-based electricity generation is expected to be the fastest-growing source of energy throughout the world over the next years, followed by coal-fired generation [14]. More precisely, world renewable-based electricity generation is estimated to grow by about 3% annually during the period from 2007 to 2035, with the cumulative RES share increasing from 18% in 2007 to 23% in 2035 (i.e., an increase of 4500 TWh$_e$ over an increase of the total electricity demand from 18 800 to 35 000 TWh$_e$). In this context, hydropower and wind energy are expected to contribute to future RES energy production increase by 54% and 26%, respectively (see also **Figure 9**).

Besides, of great interest is also the investigation of RES penetration in the strongest economies of our planet, given in **Figure 10**. As one may see, the EU presents a steady increase rate in the development of RES applications that has since the end of the previous millennium exceeded the respective electricity generation of the United States kept between 300 and 400 TWh$_e$ for most of the time.

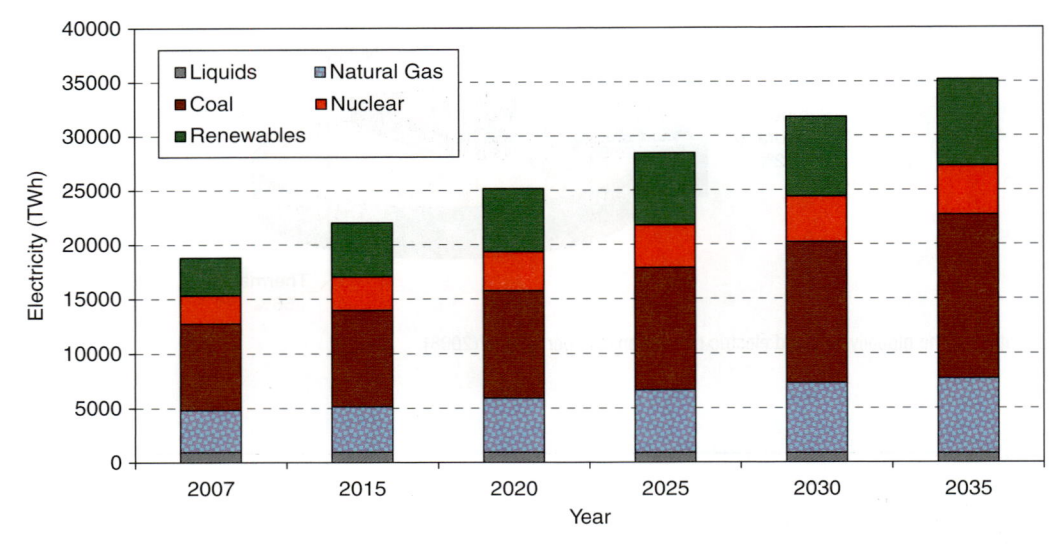

Figure 9 World electricity generation projections by fuel type. Based on data from US Energy Information Administration (EIA) (2010) International Energy Outlook (IEO2010). http://www.worldenergyoutlook.org (accessed February 2011).

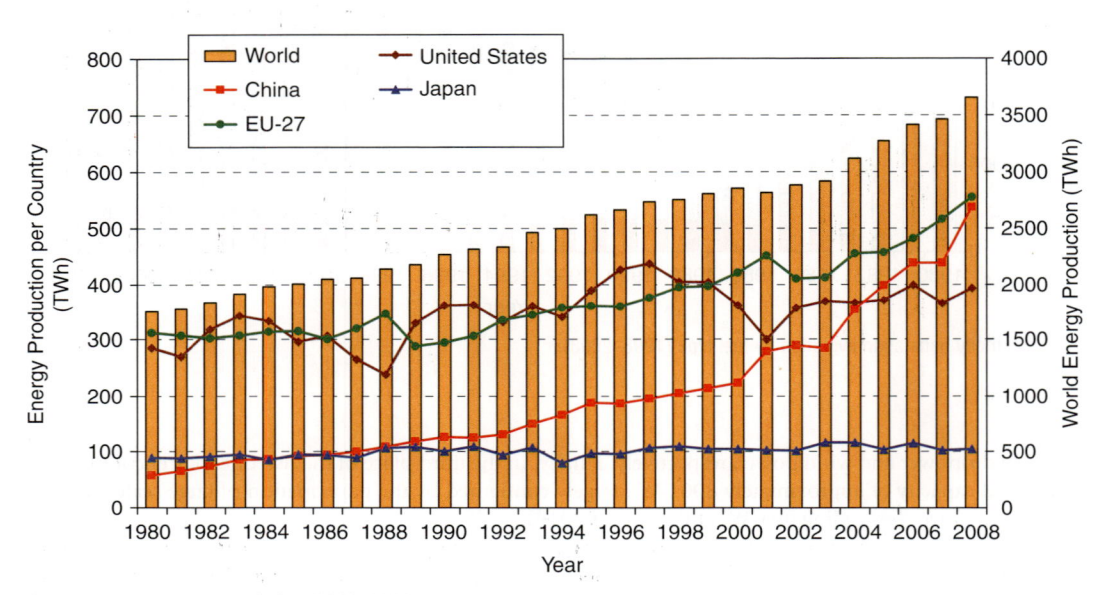

Figure 10 Renewables generation evolution (1980–2008) globally and per region.

In addition, the remarkable activity encountered in China should also be underlined, with the starting generation of 1980 (80 TWh$_e$) now reaching a total of 600 TWh$_e$, threatening the leading position of the EU. Finally, Japan presents a long-term steady state of RES electricity generation at 100 TWh$_e$, while overall, it is fair to say that the significant increase of RES electricity generation recorded during the last years at the global level is mainly attributed to the development of the wind energy sector [16].

To further examine the role of RES, the diachronic evolution of RES mix for the last 30 years, excluding hydropower, is presented in **Figure 11**. As one may see, participation of RES (excluding hydropower) during the 1980s was rather limited, kept at the levels of 50 TWh$_e$ and being mainly attributed to biomass-based and geothermal power plants. Accordingly, in the second half of the 1990s, gradual increase of wind energy recorded is since then comprising the main driver of RES electricity generation increase, exceeding 200 TWh$_e$ on an annual basis.

Moreover, what is also interesting to see is the time evolution of generating capacity of all technologies in the EU during the time from 1995 to 2009 [17]. As one may see in **Figure 12**, during the last 2 years, new wind power capacity exceeds any other technology with more than 10 GW$_e$ of wind power installed in 2009. Additionally, in terms of cumulative installations (see also **Figure 13**), European wind farms exceed oil-based generation by 20 GW and are down by 50 GW when compared to nuclear power. In fact, the developing rate of wind energy capacity is only comparable to the respective of natural gas installations, with

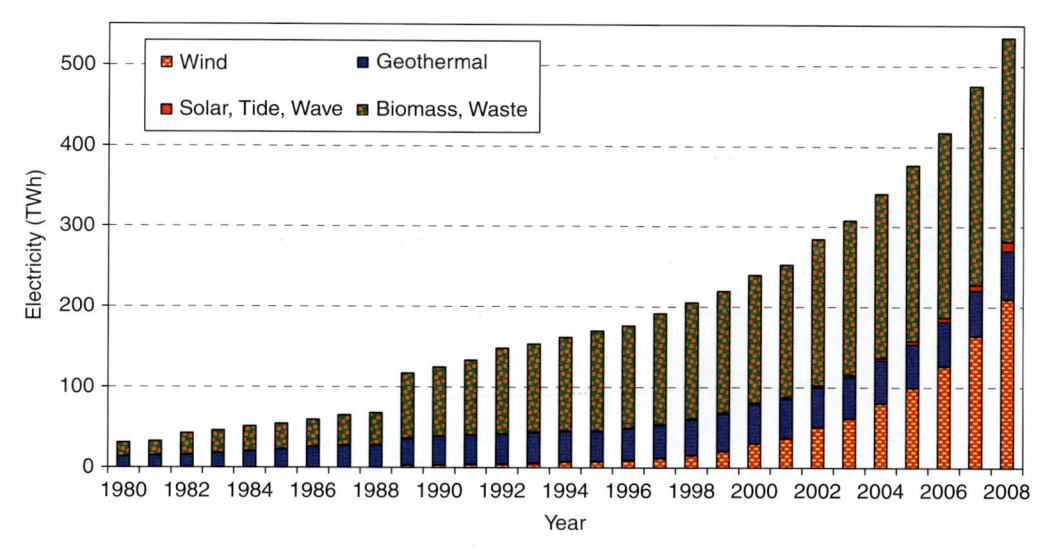

Figure 11 Renewables electricity generation (1980–2008), excluding hydro.

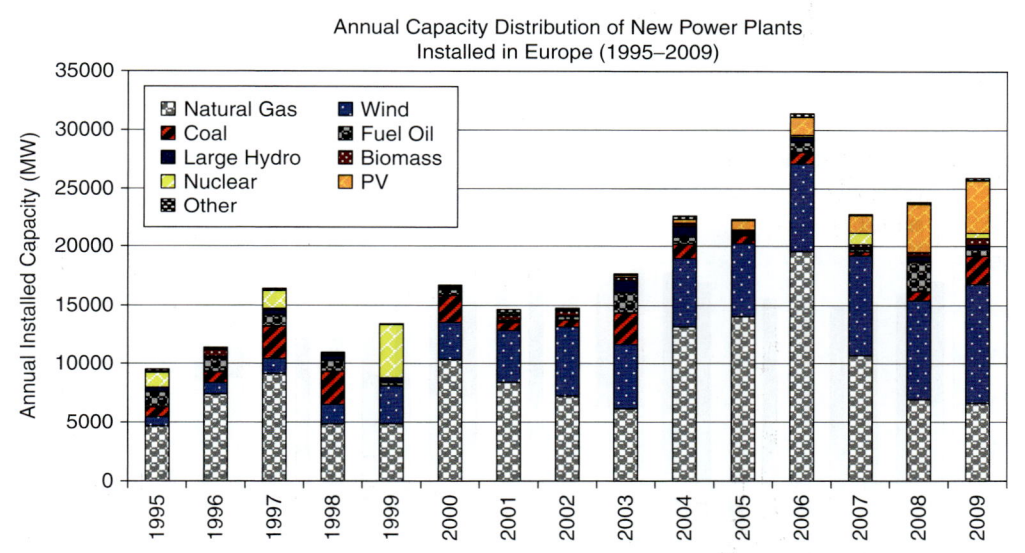

Figure 12 Time evolution of annual power capacity installations in the EU by technology type. Based on data from Eurostat (2010) Energy statistics-infrastructure. http://epp.eurostat.ec. europa.eu/ (accessed December 2010).

the remarkable growth of photovoltaic plants [18] also designating the shift attempted in the EU to clean power generation technologies.

In conclusion, if considering the energy state at a global level, it becomes clear that to encounter the constantly increasing energy demand, considerable contribution of RES is critical. In this context, given the developing stage of each RES technology, it is expected that for the next 20 years wind energy will be the main driver of RES energy generation.

2.02.4 Fossil Fuel Status of Our Planet

2.02.4.1 Oil Data

It is an indisputable fact that oil exploitation has during the last century determined the evolution of the global economy, with today's emphatic numbers describing a situation where the daily oil consumption is almost equal to 90 million barrels (or 4500 Mtoe yr^{-1}) (see also **Figure 14**). Given also the fact that the daily oil requirements of the United States reach 20 million barrels and that the respective number for EU and China is 10 million barrels, what is also indisputable is the dominant role of industrial regions to the consumption of oil reserves. On the other hand, the main oil producers are Saudi Arabia, Russia, and the United States (see also **Figure 15**), with the latter comprising an importer rather than a producer. Furthermore, in **Table 1** one may

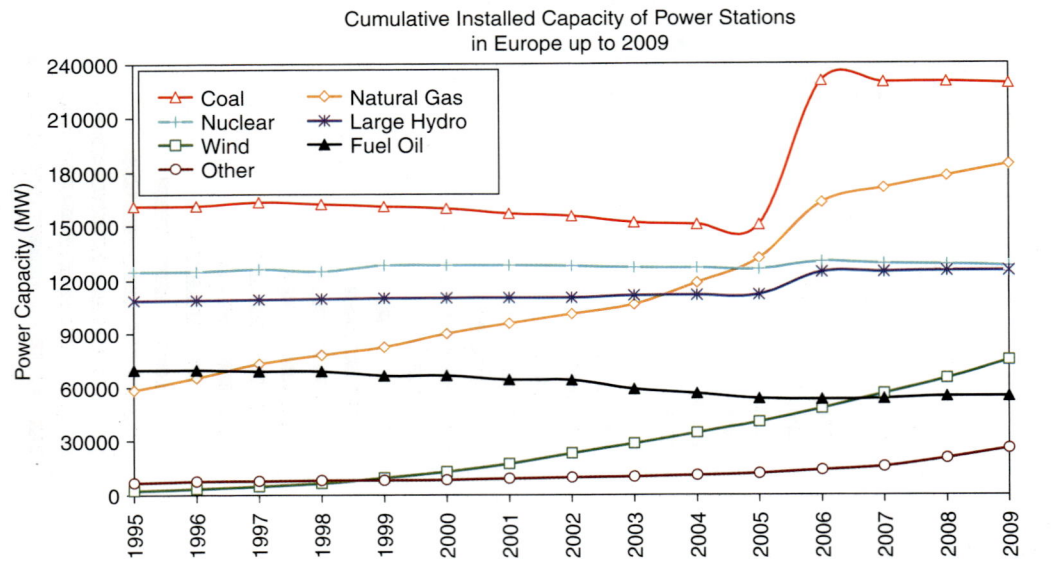

Figure 13 Time evolution of cumulative power capacity installations in the EU by technology type. Based on data from Eurostat (2010) Energy statistics-infrastructure. http://epp.eurostat.ec. europa.eu/ (accessed December 2010).

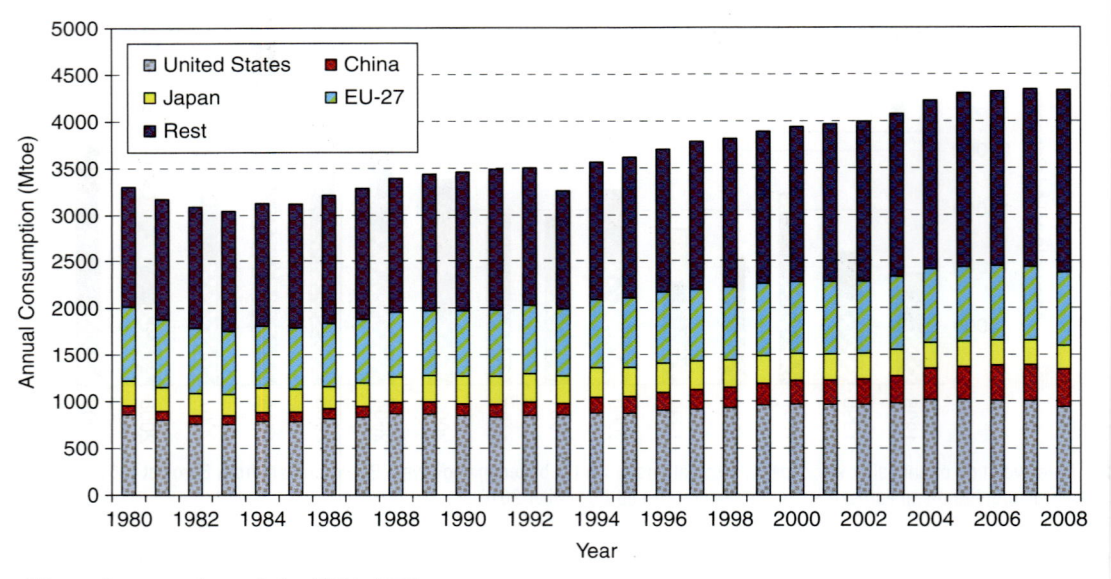

Figure 14 Oil annual consumption evolution (1980–2008).

also find the 15 countries that are responsible for 75% of the global oil production, these including Iran, Iraq, Kuwait, Algeria, UAE, Mexico, Venezuela, Brazil, and Nigeria, as well as China and Norway, with the latter being the only European country exhibiting remarkable oil production.

At the same time, proven global oil reserves are at the moment [20] estimated at the levels of 1350 billion barrels, that is, double the respective reserves of 1980 estimations, underlining the technological developments met in the field of detection and exploitation of oil deposits. Distribution of proven oil reserves is provided by **Figure 16**, with 55% found in the Arabic world. On the other hand, oil reserves of EU and Japan are negligible.

In the meantime, efforts have been recorded during the last years for the exploitation of tar sands (mainly in North America) and slate rocks containing large quantities of oil. Any case given however, the dramatic increase of global energy demand requiring at the moment contribution of oil equal to more than 30 billion barrels per year challenges the finite character of oil reserves and puts depletion sometime in the near future.

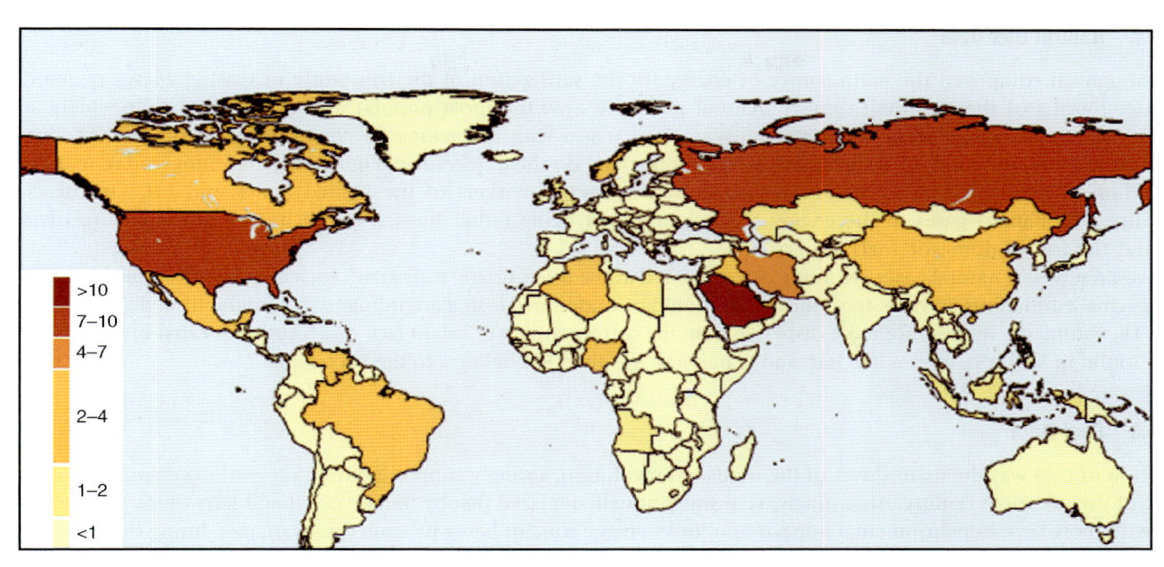

Figure 15 World oil production in 2008 (million barrels per day) [19].

Table 1 Top world oil producers (1000 barrels per day), 2009 [19]

Rank	Country	Production, 2008	Production, 2009
1	Russia	9 790	9934
2	Saudi Arabia	10 782	9760
3	United States	8 514	9141
4	Iran	4 174	4177
5	China	3 973	3996
6	Canada	3 350	3294
7	Mexico	3 186	3001
8	United Arab Emirates	3 046	2795
9	Brazil	2 402	2577
10	Kuwait	2 741	2496
11	Venezuela	2 643	2471
12	Iraq	2 385	2400
13	Norway	2 466	2350
14	Nigeria	2 169	2211
15	Algeria	2 180	2126

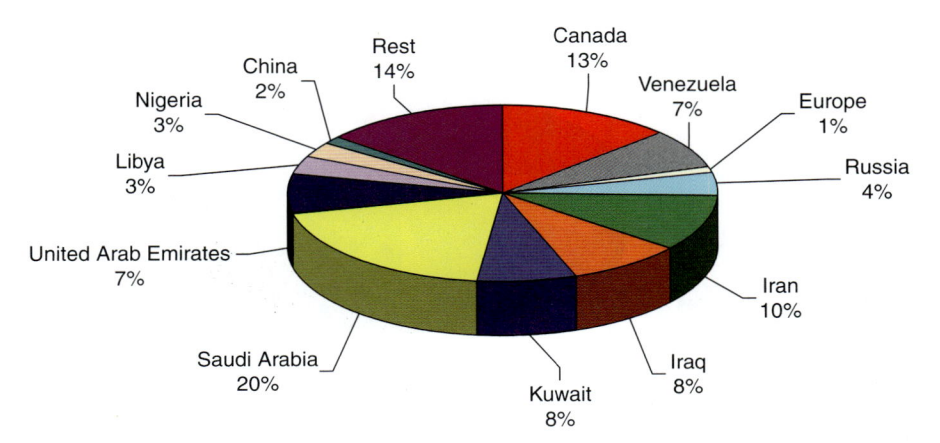

Figure 16 Distribution of crude oil proved reserves in 2010. Based on data from U.S. Energy Information Administration (EIA) International energy statistics. http://tonto.eia.doe.gov (accessed February 2011).

2.02.4.2 Natural Gas Data

Even though oil comprised the main source of energy for the satisfaction of the constantly increasing energy demand in the first three-fourths of the twentieth century, natural gases are now the most popular and at the same time widely accepted (due to their improved environmental attributes in comparison with oil) source of energy [21]. In this context, during the last 30 years, consumption of natural gases has more than doubled (see also **Figure 17**), reaching today a quantity of 3000 billion m^3 per year that is mainly absorbed by the energy markets of the United States and EU. On the contrary, contribution of natural gases in the energy balance of China being rather limited is much attributed to its relatively high price and the use of domestic fuels such as coal.

Proven reserves of natural gases are nowadays estimated at the levels of 200 trillion m^3, increased by 50% when compared with the respective estimations 20 years ago, while what should be underlined is that according to the geographical distribution given in **Figure 18**, natural gas reserves are more dispersed than the corresponding of oil. In fact, one-fourth is located in the Russia region, 40% is found in Arabic countries like Iran and Qatar, and less than 5% belongs to the EU region.

2.02.4.3 Coal Data

Utilization of coal was the main driver of the industrial revolution, strongly supporting technological developments up until the middle of the twentieth century. Accordingly, coal was gradually replaced first by the use of oil and later on by the use of natural gases, with more severe environmental impacts and lower energy content being its main disadvantages during this gradual shift of fossil fuel exploitation for energy generation purposes. Nevertheless, both its low cost and wide dispersion all over the planet have recently revived the interest for coal exploitation [22], leading to a considerable increase of coal-derived energy production mainly

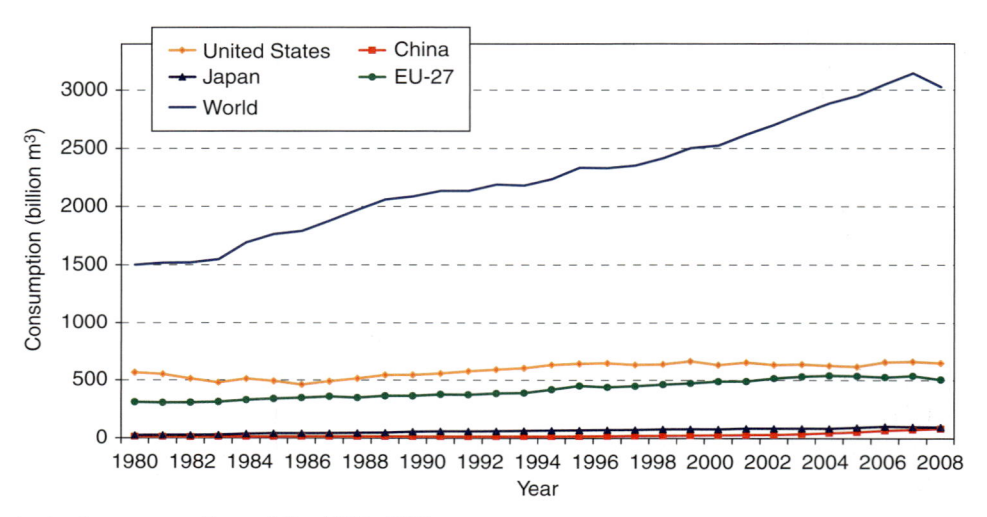

Figure 17 Annual natural gas consumption evolution (1980–2009).

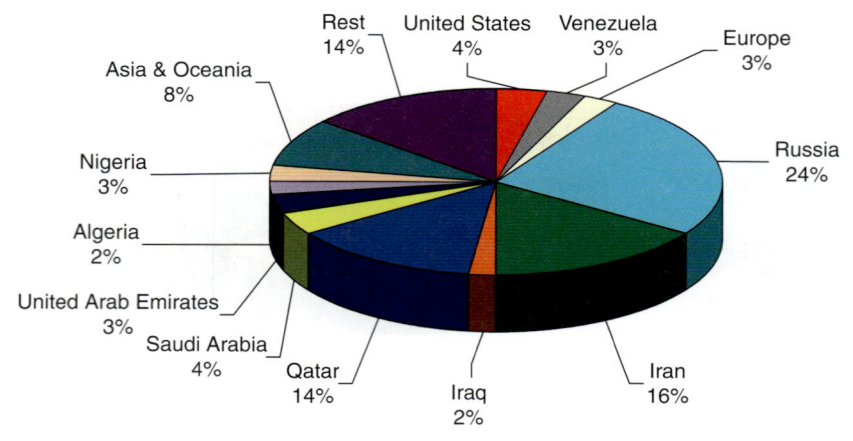

Figure 18 Distribution of natural gas proved reserves in 2010. Based on data from U.S. Energy Information Administration (EIA) International energy statistics. http://tonto.eia.doe.gov (accessed February 2011).

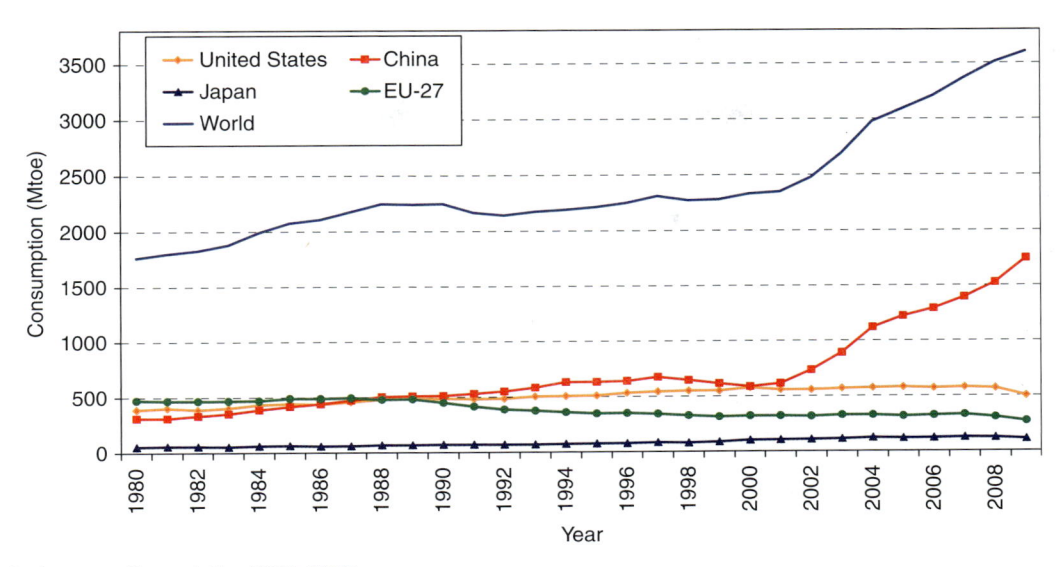

Figure 19 Coal consumption evolution (1980–2009).

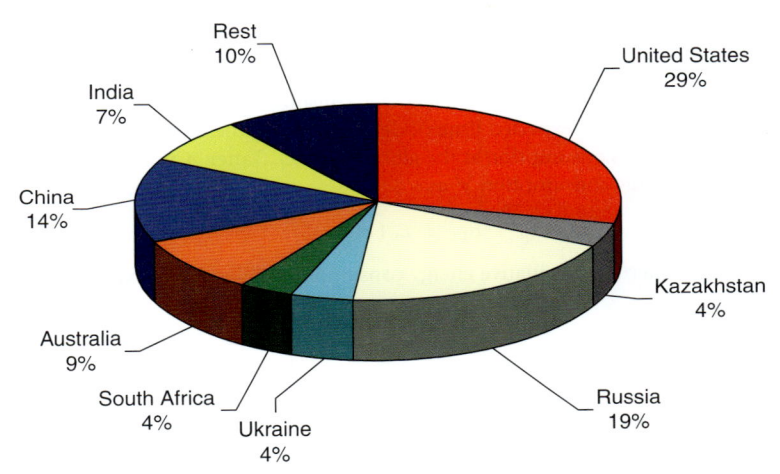

Figure 20 Distribution of proved reserves of recoverable coal in 2009. Based on data from BP (2010) BP statistical review of world energy 2010. http://www.bp.com (accessed February 2011) [24].

in China where 50% of the respective global production is consumed (see also **Figure 19**). Note that today global coal consumption exceeds 3600 Mtoe, with the EU using only 8%.

Furthermore, proven global reserves are at the moment estimated at the levels of 830 billion tons, with the respective energy content however being much dependent on the composition of reserves configuring the respective specific calorific value. On the other hand, it becomes evident that coal reserves present the highest adequacy levels among other fossil fuels [23], while according to the results of **Figure 20**, the greatest reserves are located in the United States, Russia, and China. Considerable are also the reserves located in countries such as India, Australia, and South Africa. Contrariwise, the EU concentrates less than 5% of the planet's reserves, mainly in Poland and Germany, while even the United Kingdom, although comprising one of the main producers during the mid-term of the previous century has much limited its reliance on coal and is now importing most of the quantities required.

2.02.5 The Role of RES and Fossil Fuels in the Energy Future of Our Planet

2.02.5.1 The Energy Balance of Our Planet

According to the information available up to now [25], the main energy flow of our planet derives from the incident solar radiation on the surface of the earth, providing a constant power flux of approximately 173 000 TW. In addition, a comparatively limited power flux comes from the interior of the earth (almost 32 TW) and the tides (3 TW), with the latter being developed from the gravitational forces between the earth and the moon or the earth and the sun.

In this context, it is estimated that 30% of the incident solar energy is reflected back to space, 47% is absorbed by the earth's atmosphere and configures climate conditions, and 23% is used for the process of the hydrological cycle. Furthermore, according to the data available, the kinetic energy of winds and the sea waves produce a constant power flux of approximately 370 TW that accordingly leads to a theoretical annual energy capacity of 3 240 000 TWh$_e$.

At this point, one should keep in mind that the total electricity consumption of our planet does not exceed 20 000 TWh$_e$ on an annual basis, that is, 0.6% of the aforementioned wind and wave energy; however, coverage of the planet's electrical energy demand on the basis of these energy sources is at the moment not thought to be feasible. On the other hand, one should not disregard the fact that according to today's evidence wind energy could provide an actual contribution that would much exceed the current wind energy production of 400 TWh$_e$ (in 2010).

Contrariwise, current primary energy consumption on an annual basis is determined by the use of almost 30 billion barrels of oil, 3 trillion m^3 of natural gases and 3.6 billion toe of coal, with the respective proven reserves being 1350 billion barrels, 190 trillion m^3, and 830 billion toes. Furthermore, the annual consumption of nuclear energy, estimated at the levels of 600 Mtoe, is in the absence of proven reserves of nuclear fuels not providing a clear picture concerning the future of nuclear power.

Considering the situation so far, it seems that humanity was during the last century possessed by an urge to overexploit the valuable energy reserves of our planet, without any sustainable development considerations in practice [26], leaving at the same time the infinite and practically nondepleted RES potential unexploited, with wind energy being the most descriptive example.

2.02.5.2 Time Depletion of Fossil Fuels

According to many, profound reading of the above given numbers reflects the immediate danger of depletion for the fossil fuel reserves of our planet that would at the same time signal the coming of an early era of energy poverty for humankind. On the other hand however, according to the beliefs of others, discovery of new deposits and exploitation of new ones already known but not yet utilized due to techno-economic reasons will maintain adequacy of fossil fuel reserves [27].

In this context, by assuming that 'E_o' is the current annual energy consumption and that the total proven energy reserves of the planet are equal to 'E_t', one may estimate the expected time of depletion using the following set of equations. More precisely, by considering that the future annual energy consumption at the global level '$E_{(n)}$' after 'n' years is estimated on the basis of the mean annual rate of increase/decrease of energy consumption 'e' as:

$$E_{(n)} = E_o(1+e)^n \quad [1]$$

one may accordingly estimate the respective cumulative energy consumption 'E_n' up to the year 'n' using eqn [2]:

$$E_n = \sum_{j=1}^{j=n} E_{(j)} = E_{(1)} + E_{(2)} \ldots + E_{(n)} = E_o \cdot \left[\frac{(1+e)^n - 1}{e}\right] \cdot (1+e) \quad [2]$$

Finally, by comparing the total energy reserves of the planet with the expected cumulative energy consumption, one may estimate the theoretical depletion time 'n^*' using eqn [3].

$$n^* \leq \frac{\ln\left[1 + \frac{e \cdot E_t}{(1+e)E_o}\right]}{\ln(1+e)} \quad [3]$$

Note that in order to apply the above presented model, a series of assumptions and scenarios (taking, for instance, into account the possibility for the substitution of oil and natural gas in their applications by coal and vice-versa) along with the use of the long-term mean annual increase/decrease rate (assumed to be of known value *a priori*) should be first considered [28].

Nevertheless, the aim of the specific analysis is the illustration of results (see also **Figure 21**) showing that if the quantity of reserves is even 10 or 100 times the quantity of current proven reserves the depletion time is only prolonged for 80 and 150 years, respectively. Keep in mind however that in the second case one has to assume that existing reserves are 100 times the ones currently thought as proven, which may be considered as an extreme assumption.

2.02.5.3 Environmental Impacts of Energy: Carbon Dioxide Emissions

The energy sector of production, transmission, distribution and final use is thought to be the one inducing the most severe environmental impacts [29]. Note, however, that environmental impacts vary considerably among different alternatives, especially between conventional fuels such as coal, oil, and natural gas, and RES such as wind energy, solar energy, hydropower, biomass, and geothermal energy. Nevertheless, since the evaluation of energy sources on the basis of environmental criteria is out of the scope of the specific chapter, further analysis is not thought to be required, although some insight concerning the most detrimental environmental issue of our times, that is, climate change, is given in the following.

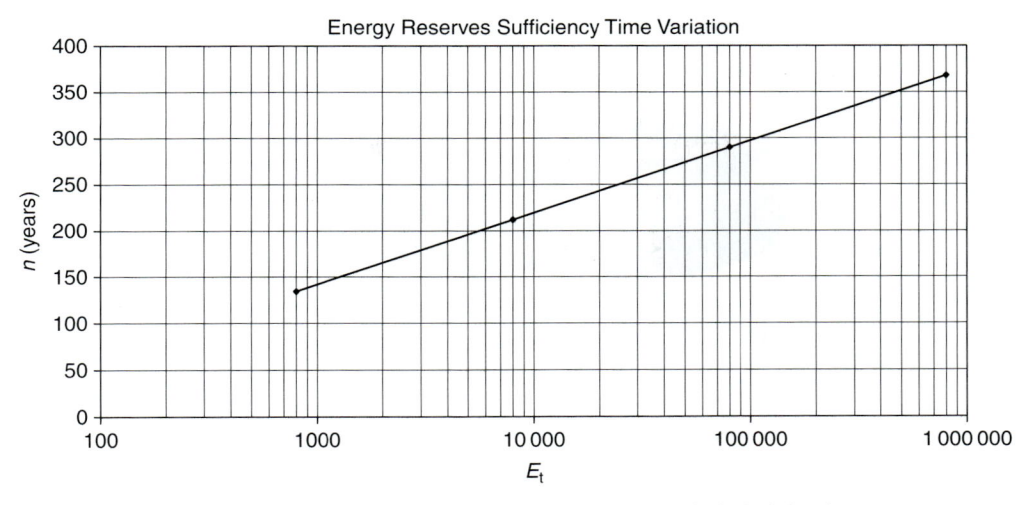

Figure 21 Effect of the base year proven reserves energy content 'E_t' value on the planet fossil fuels depletion time.

In this context and according to the experts of the field, climate change is thought to be directly related with the overproduction of carbon dioxide emissions, due to anthropogenic activities [30]. Carbon dioxide, which is by far the most well known greenhouse gas, is produced from the complete combustion of carbon on the basis of the following chemical equation.

$$C + O_2 \rightarrow CO_2 \quad [4]$$

Based on the stoichiometric relation, if 1 kg of carbon is combusted, then $3.67(\approx 44/12)$ kg of carbon dioxide are released in the atmosphere, on top of the produced heat. As a result, use of conventional fuels containing carbon is directly related with the production of additional amounts of carbon dioxide and thus with the risk of climate change.

In this context, **Figure 22** presents the long-term evolution of the anthropogenic carbon dioxide production for the last 30 years. According to the data presented, there is a tremendous increase of carbon dioxide emissions since 1980, reaching 60%, and exceeding 30 000 Mt in 2008. Among the most heavily aggravated countries, one may encounter the United States and China, with the latter being responsible for the production of more than 25% of the entire planet's carbon dioxide emissions (see also **Figure 23**).

In order to further investigate the magnitude of the problem under examination, which is also much dependent on the extreme consumption of carbon containing fuels, in **Table 2** one presents the time evolution of the carbon dioxide emissions per capita for the most populated countries of our planet. According to the numbers, the United States presents the highest climate aggravation with the average carbon dioxide emission production being equal to 17.7 t per capita, while China has exceeded the respective

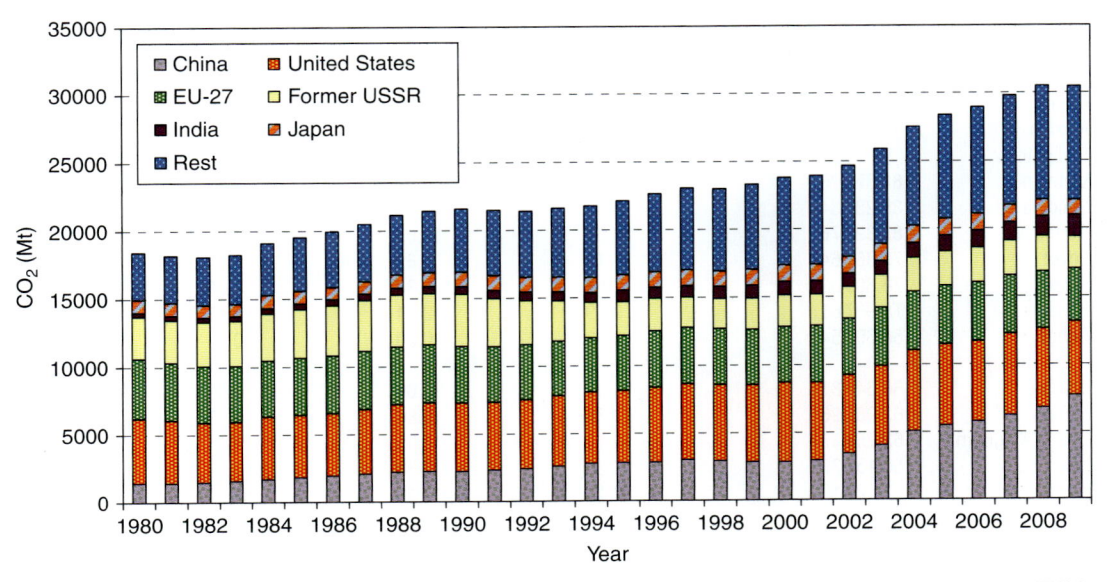

Figure 22 Evolution of CO_2 emissions from energy consumption, 2009. Based on data from U.S. Energy Information Administration (EIA) International energy statistics. http://tonto.eia.doe.gov (accessed February 2011).

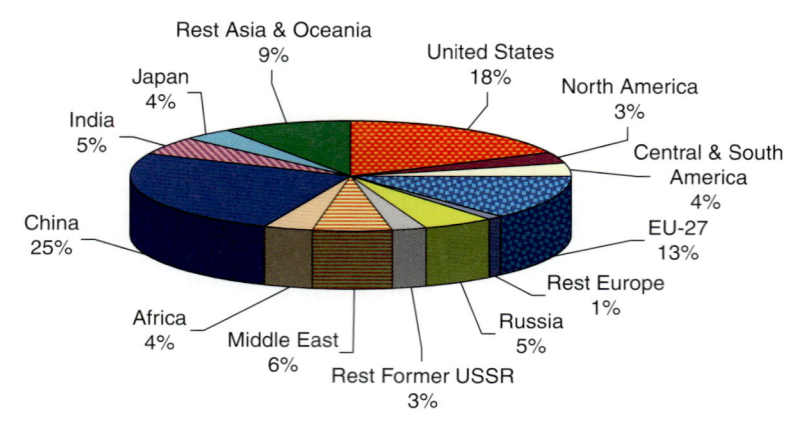

Figure 23 Distribution of CO$_2$ emissions from energy consumption in 2009. Based on data from U.S. Energy Information Administration (EIA) International energy statistics. http://tonto.eia.doe.gov (accessed February 2011).

planet average and is now approaching 6 t per capita, although in the beginning of the 1980s, the respective number was below 1.5 t per capita. Furthermore, EU countries present carbon dioxide emission production in the area of 7–9 t per capita, with the EU's efforts for the reduction of emissions during the last decade illustrated in **Table 2**.

Finally, it should be noted that the planet average kept for a long time at the levels of 4 t per capita is now reaching 4.5 t per capita, presenting an increase that exceeds 10%. Hence, it is expected that unless the current energy production patterns begin to alter in the following years, the problem of carbon dioxide emissions' overproduction will become even more severe, especially if also considering the trends of emission production per capita in the most populated areas of the planet including India (see also **Table 2**). At this point, emphasis must be given on the fact that wind energy –as most of RES – is an environmentally friendly energy source, with wind farms producing minimum carbon dioxide emissions even on a life-cycle basis evaluation [31].

Table 2 Annual CO$_2$ emissions per capita from energy consumption in the largest (on the basis of their population) countries in the world

Rank	Country	Population in 2009 (millions)	1982 (t per capita)	1991 (t per capita)	2000 (t per capita)	2009 (t per capita)
1	China	1323.592	1.49	2.04	2.26	5.83
2	India	1156.898	0.49	0.73	0.99	1.39
3	United States	307.006 6	19.04	19.76	20.77	17.67
4	Indonesia	240.271 5	0.59	0.92	1.24	1.72
5	Brazil	198.739 3	1.34	1.60	1.95	2.11
6	Pakistan	181.457 3	0.45	0.56	0.72	0.77
7	Bangladesh	153.700 3	0.09	0.13	0.22	0.36
8	Nigeria	149.229 1	0.71	0.89	0.66	0.52
9	Russia	140.041 3	11.93	12.15	10.61	11.23
10	Japan	127.078 7	7.59	8.60	9.48	8.64
11	Mexico	111.211 8	3.94	3.58	3.83	3.99
12	Philippines	97.976 6	0.596	0.626	0.873	0.739
13	Vietnam	88.576 76	0.25	0.25	0.58	1.12
14	Ethiopia	85.237 34	0.05	0.05	0.05	0.08
15	Germany	82.329 76	14.61	11.61	10.4	9.3
16	Egypt	78.866 64	1.19	1.69	1.84	2.44
17	Turkey	76.805 52	1.54	2.38	2.99	3.29
18	Iran	75.967 61	3.09	3.74	4.67	6.94
19	Congo (Kinshasa)	68.692 54	0.12	0.09	0.05	0.04
20	Thailand	66.644 81	0.68	1.66	2.60	3.80
21	France	62.982 96	7.76	6.86	6.73	6.29
22	United Kingdom	62.258 57	10.12	10.55	9.44	8.35
23	Italy	58.157 33	6.28	7.34	7.75	7.01
24	Burma (Myanmar)	52.826 12	0.13	0.11	0.19	0.24
25	South Africa	49.052 49	8.47	7.9	8.57	9.18
	World	6776.917	3.92	4.01	3.91	4.49

Based on data from U.S. Energy Information Administration (EIA) International energy statistics. http://tonto.eia.doe.gov (accessed February 2011).

2.02.5.4 Comparing RES and Fossil Fuels (Pros and Cons) with Emphasis on Wind Energy

Having presented the energy state of the planet, presentation of the main advantages of RES – in relation with the use of conventional fossil fuels – and the main reasons that RES are not yet established is thought to be advisable, with emphasis currently given on wind energy.

To begin with, both wind energy and the rest of RES do not run the risk of depletion since they are the result of natural ongoing processes and thus eliminate the security of energy supply risk. In addition, although RES potential may vary considerably from one area to another, RES are available across the entire planet without being concentrated in certain regions of the globe [32], thus also eliminating any attempt of possessive control (such as in the case of fossil fuels). At the same time, wind energy induces negligible environmental impacts [33] that are rather restricted within the area of operation [34–36] and are estimated to be remarkably less considerable than the respective of conventional thermal energy sources [37]. Moreover, wind energy presents a rather low operational cost [38], which is independent from the volatile fuel prices and has considerably reduced in the course of time due to the development of wind energy technologies. Besides, wind energy plants require minimum space, implying also zero effect on human activities in cases of remote or offshore wind farms, while at the same time wind farms do not constrain water resources as in the case of thermal power stations requiring large quantities of water for their operation.

On the other hand, wind energy installations are still capital-intensive [38], with the reduction of initial cost encountered during the last 20 years recently decelerating, despite technology developments noted in the meantime and economies of scale expected to apply. This situation encountered concerning the capital cost of wind energy plants may be at some level justified, especially if considering the considerable reduction of wind turbine manufacturers that has actually led to considerable downgrade of market competition.

Furthermore, one of the inherent characteristics that wind energy is faced with is the stochastic behavior of wind [39] and the inability of energy production control during times of low or extreme wind speeds, requiring the use of back-up power [40, 41] or the application of energy storage systems [42–45] in order to safeguard agreement between energy production and energy demand at all times. In parallel, by taking into account that most windy areas are found in either remote regions or offshore, it becomes obvious that the cost of required infrastructure along with the induced transmission energy losses comprise a serious burden on the unlimited exploitation of wind energy. Moreover, the ability of contemporary wind turbines to capture the kinetic energy of wind per unit of rotor area hardly exceeds 150–200 W m^{-2}, reflecting the need for the installation of large-scale machines in order to obtain an appreciable power output. In this context, efforts to build wind turbines in the scale of 10 MW have up to now raised a series of obstacles related to load design, power control and plant installation [46]. Finally, although direct use of wind energy for the transportation sector is for the moment unrealistic, wind energy may reach transportation means through the indirect production of hydrogen [47] or through the use of electricity for the new generation transportation fleets.

2.02.6 Wind Power Status in the World Market

It was centuries ago when the technology of wind energy made its first actual steps – although simpler wind devices date back thousands of years ago – with the vertical axis windmills found at the Persian–Afghan borders around 200 BC and the horizontal axis windmills of the Netherlands and the Mediterranean following much later (1300–1875 AD) [48–50]. It was after the oil crisis of 1973 that the interest for exploitation of RES and more precisely of wind energy revived. Thus, in the years between 1973 and 1986, the commercial wind turbines' market evolved from domestic and agricultural (1–25 kW) to utility interconnected wind farm applications (50–600 kW). In this context, the first large-scale wind energy penetration outbreak was encountered in California [51], where over 16 000 machines, ranging from 20 to 350 kW (a total of 1.7 GW), were installed between 1981 and 1990, as a result of the incentives (such as the federal investment and energy credits) given by the US government. In northern Europe, on the other hand, wind farm installations increased steadily through the 1980s and the 1990s, with higher cost of electricity and excellent wind resources leading to the creation of a small but stable market. After 1990 most market activity shifted to Europe [52], with the last 20 years bringing wind energy at the front line of the global energy scene with major players from all world regions. Recently, both reheating of the US wind power market and serious involvement of China in the wind energy field configure a new scenery for the global wind power market.

In this context, according to the latest official data [17, 19, 53], the global wind power capacity increased during 2009 by almost 38 GW (**Figure 24**), thus reaching a total of approximately 159 GW on the basis of remarkable development rates exhibited for the past 20 years. In the same direction, the new installed wind power capacity during 2010 approaches 36 GW (mainly in China; 16.5 GW); hence, the total installed wind power is currently (beginning of 2011) estimated to exceed 200 GW. On the other hand, although a 22.5% increase of installed wind power may be noted in comparison with 2009, the annual 2010 new wind power addition (35.8 GW) was for the first time in the last 20 years lower than the one of the previous year (38.6 GW), mainly due to the slowdown met in the United States and Germany.

Concerning the distribution of installed wind power capacity worldwide, Europe has at the moment exceeded 86 GW and is now heading to offshore applications [56]. It is important to note that the countries of EU-27 are represented by a total of 84 GW of installed capacity, adding 9.3 GW during 2010. In fact, it is since the mid-1990s that the EU market corresponds to over 50% of the global installed capacity that is nowadays producing an overall of 400 TWh$_e$ yr^{-1}. In this context, although the EU held only 20% of the word wind energy generation in the early 1990s (**Figure 25**), production of European wind parks managed to even reach 70% in the years after 2000, with a production of approximately 120 TWh$_e$ yr^{-1} already achieved by the end of 2008. However, restart of the

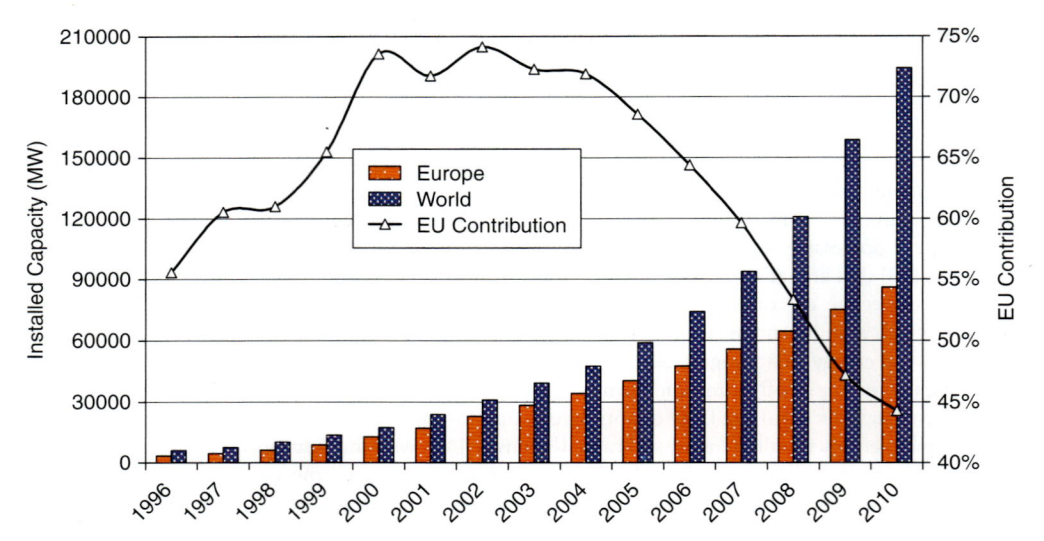

Figure 24 Time evolution of global and European wind power capacity. Based on data from Eurostat (2010) Energy statistics-infrastructure. http://epp.eurostat.ec. europa.eu/ (accessed December 2010); U.S. Energy Information Administration (EIA) International energy statistics. http://tonto.eia.doe.gov (accessed February 2011); European Wind Energy Association (2010) Annual report-2009. http://www.ewea.org (accessed December 2010); Global Wind Energy Council (GWEC) (2010) Global wind energy outlook-2010. http://www.gwec.net/ (accessed December 2010); Global Wind Energy Council (GWEC) (2011) Global wind energy statistics report for 2010.

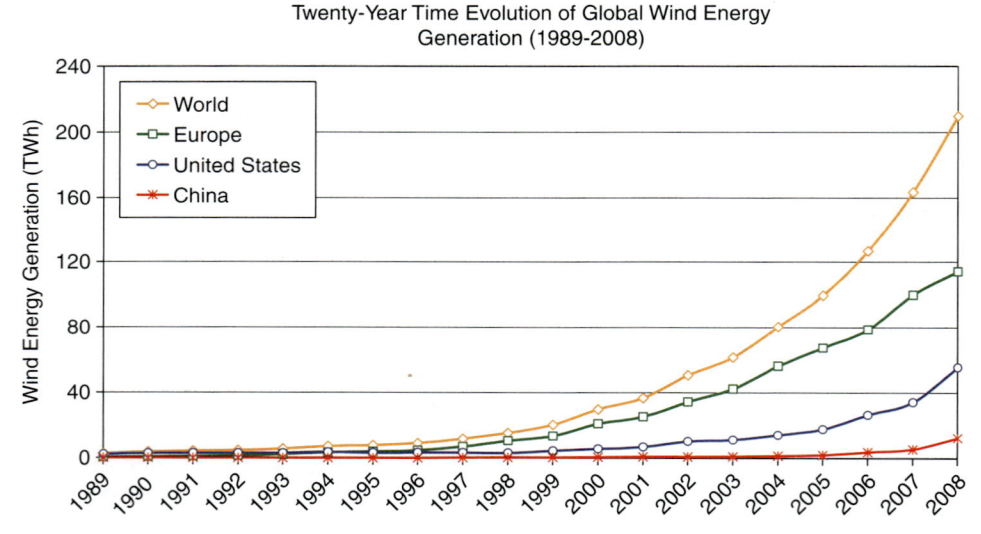

Figure 25 Time evolution of global and European wind energy generation. Based on data from Eurostat (2010) Energy statistics-infrastructure. http://epp.eurostat.ec. europa.eu/ (accessed December 2010); U.S. Energy Information Administration (EIA) International energy statistics. http://tonto.eia.doe.gov (accessed February 2011); European Wind Energy Association (2010) Annual report-2009. http://www.ewea.org (accessed December 2010); Global Wind Energy Council (GWEC) (2010) Global wind energy outlook-2010 [54]. http://www.gwec.net/ (accessed December 2010); Global Wind Energy Council (GWEC) (2011) Global wind energy statistics report for 2010 [55].

US market [57] and development of wind energy industry in China [13] have considerably reduced the aforementioned numbers during the recent years to a current 54%.

With regard to the present status of wind power capacity (**Figure 26**), the United States managed during 2009 to add a new 40% over its cumulative capacity, although during 2010, the US wind industry built approximately 5.1 GW of wind power, which is about half the respective of the 2009 record value. At the same time, the Chinese achieved to install almost 14 GW, that is, 20% and 40% of the EU and the US cumulative capacity during 2009, respectively, while by installing another 16.5 GW in 2010, China has recently claimed the global leadership with 42.3 GW of wind power. As a result, in terms of cumulative wind power at the regional level (**Figure 27**), Asia has managed to clearly surpass North America, while EU is still the world leader with almost 45% of the world's installed capacity.

Finally, at the European level (**Figure 28**), Germany (27.2 GW) and Spain (20.7 GW) are now followed by Italy (5.8 GW), France (5.7 GW), the United Kingdom (5.2 GW), Denmark (3.7 GW), and Portugal (3.7 GW), with Denmark presenting a long-term stagnation

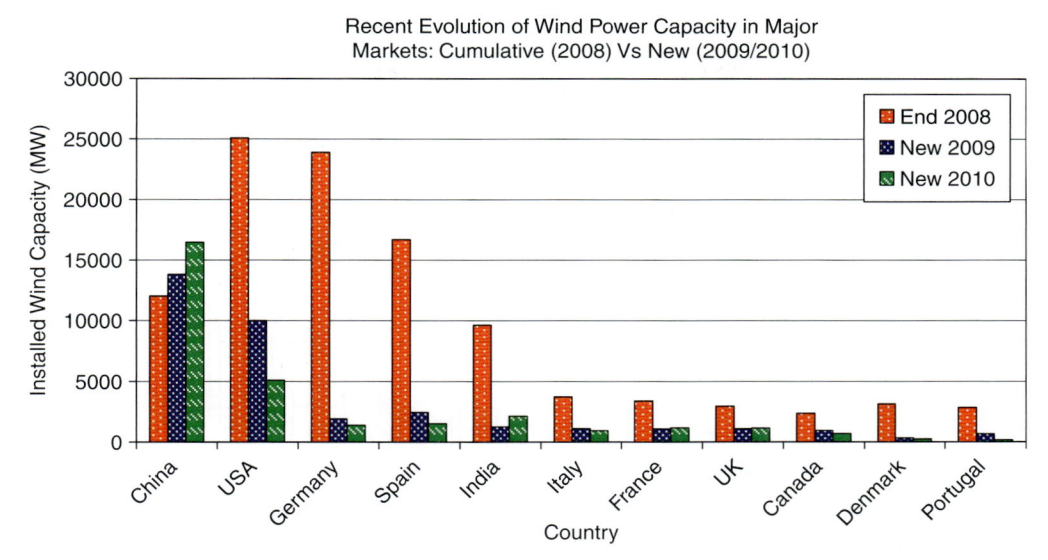

Figure 26 Distribution of wind power capacity by country (cumulative and installed in 2009/2010). Based on data from Global Wind Energy Council (GWEC) (2010) Global wind energy outlook-2010. http://www.gwec.net/ (accessed December 2010); Global Wind Energy Council (GWEC) (2011) Global wind energy statistics report for 2010.

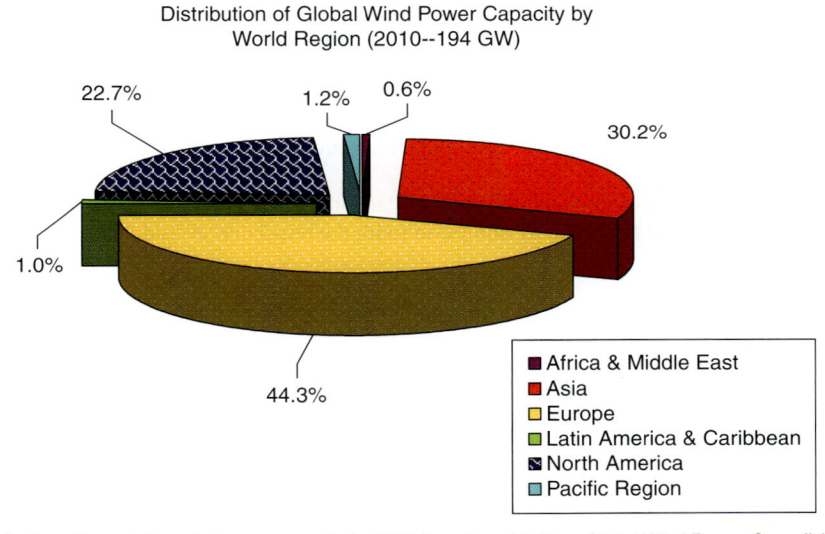

Figure 27 Regional distribution of cumulative wind power capacity in 2010. Based on data from Global Wind Energy Council (GWEC) (2010) Global wind energy outlook-2010. http://www.gwec.net/ (accessed December 2010); Global Wind Energy Council (GWEC) (2011) Global wind energy statistics report for 2010.

that calls for the review of the local legislation [58] although considerable exploitation of the local wind potential has already been achieved. On the other hand, France and Portugal present remarkable developing rates since 2000, while for Italy and Netherlands (2.2 GW) the local wind energy market encountered an earlier start (i.e., since 1990) with analogous results only for the case of Italy.

Recapitulating, one may state that the current installed wind power capacity implies satisfaction of a significant part of the worldwide electricity generation, with expansion of wind energy exploitation in several emerging economies that require considerable energy amounts expected – along with the transition to offshore installations – to be the basic features of the new decade.

2.02.7 Time Evolution of the Major Wind Power Markets

Through the long-term analysis of global energy markets, one may support the existence of two parallel wind energy markets, the first one being environmentally driven (including countries of the industrialized world such as Germany and the United States) and

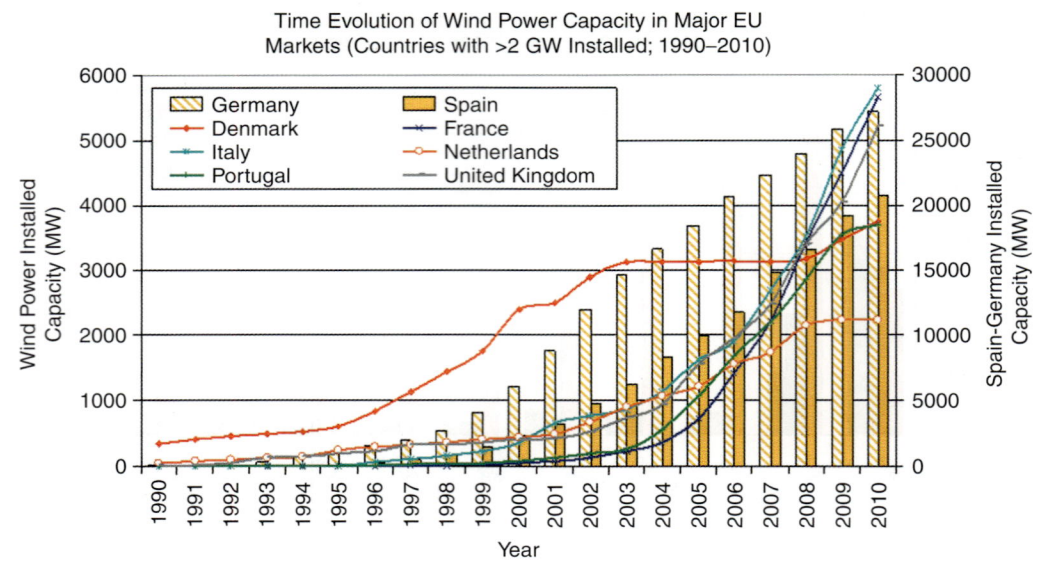

Figure 28 Time evolution of wind power capacity in major EU markets. Based on data from Eurostat (2010) Energy statistics-infrastructure. http://epp.eurostat.ec.europa.eu/ (accessed December 2010); Global Wind Energy Council (GWEC) (2011) Global wind energy statistics report for 2010.

the second one being stimulated by the pressing needs of constantly increased energy consumption (including countries of the developing world such as China and India) [59].

According to the latest official data, the number of countries with installed wind power capacity that is greater than 1000 MW (see also **Table 3**) has now increased to 20, compared with a total of 13 during 2007. Note that 13 out of the 20 countries belong to Europe and four in Asia, while the remaining three correspond to the United States, Canada, and Australia. On top of that, Brazil and Belgium are now close to also exceeding the 1 GW threshold with a cumulative capacity reaching by the end of 2010, 931 and 911 MW, respectively.

In this context, wind energy in Europe is now achieving 4% satisfaction (corresponding to an estimated electricity generation of 142 TWh$_e$ at the end of 2010) of the total electricity consumption (with the respective levels during 2000 kept at 0.9%) and is now

Table 3 Wind power capacity in various countries of the world

Rank	Country	End 2010 (MW)
1	China	42 287
2	United States	40 180
3	Germany	27 214
4	Spain	20 676
5	India	13 065
6	Italy	5 797
7	France	5 660
8	United Kingdom	5 204
9	Canada	4 009
10	Denmark	3 752
11	Portugal	3 702
12	Japan	2 304
13	Netherlands	2 237
14	Sweden	2 163
15	Australia	1 880
16	Ireland	1 428
17	Turkey	1 329
18	Greece	1 208
19	Poland	1 107
20	Austria	1 011
	World	194 390

Based on data from Global Wind Energy Council (GWEC) (2011) Global wind energy statistics report for 2010.

comprising the most attractive energy market with investments exceeding €11 billion annually [53, 55], even overcoming the market of natural gas [53, 60, 61].

At the same time, contribution shares of wind energy production to the gross electricity generation of certain EU countries already exceeds 10% (e.g., Denmark, Portugal, and Spain) [16, 17], while for the Danish approximately 20% should be considered, with the respective EU average kept at 4.1% (**Figure 29**). Nevertheless, shift to offshore attempted by many European countries [63, 64] (1.5 GW already in operation in Denmark and the UK), with short-term plans of 33 GW by 2015 mainly supported by Germany and the United Kingdom (**Figure 30**), shall further increase the contribution shares of EU wind farms. In fact, according to recent studies, the technically exploitable offshore wind potential of the EU in 2030 is estimated to approach 30 000 TWh$_e$ [65], with the United Kingdom and Denmark presenting almost 5000 and 3000 TWh$_e$, respectively.

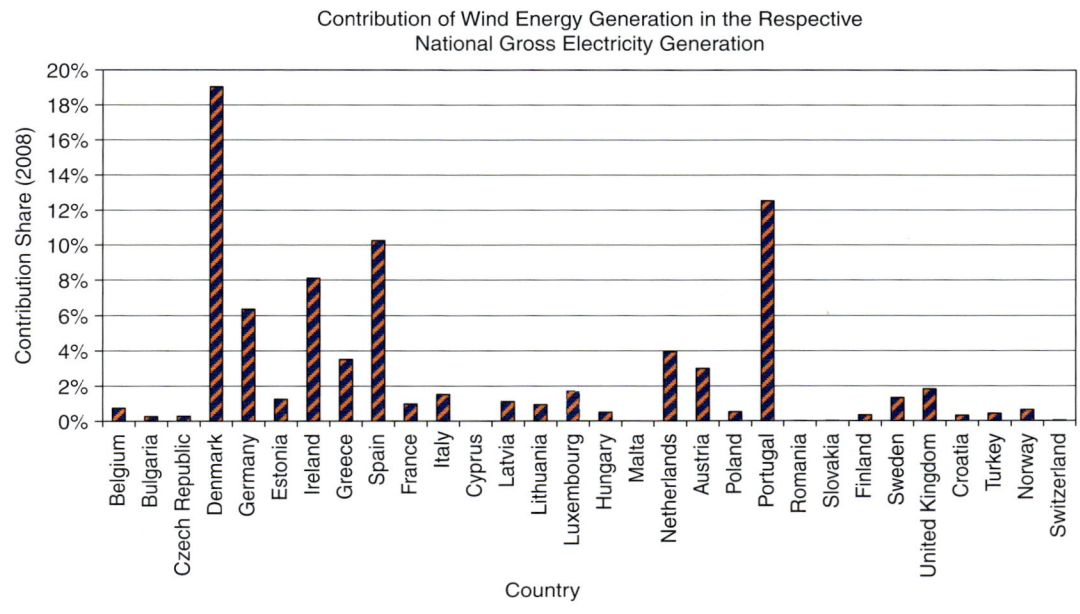

Figure 29 Wind energy contribution to the gross electricity generation of EU countries. Based on data from Eurostat (2010) Energy statistics-supply, transformation, consumption. http://epp.eurostat.ec.europa.eu/ (accessed December 2010) [62].

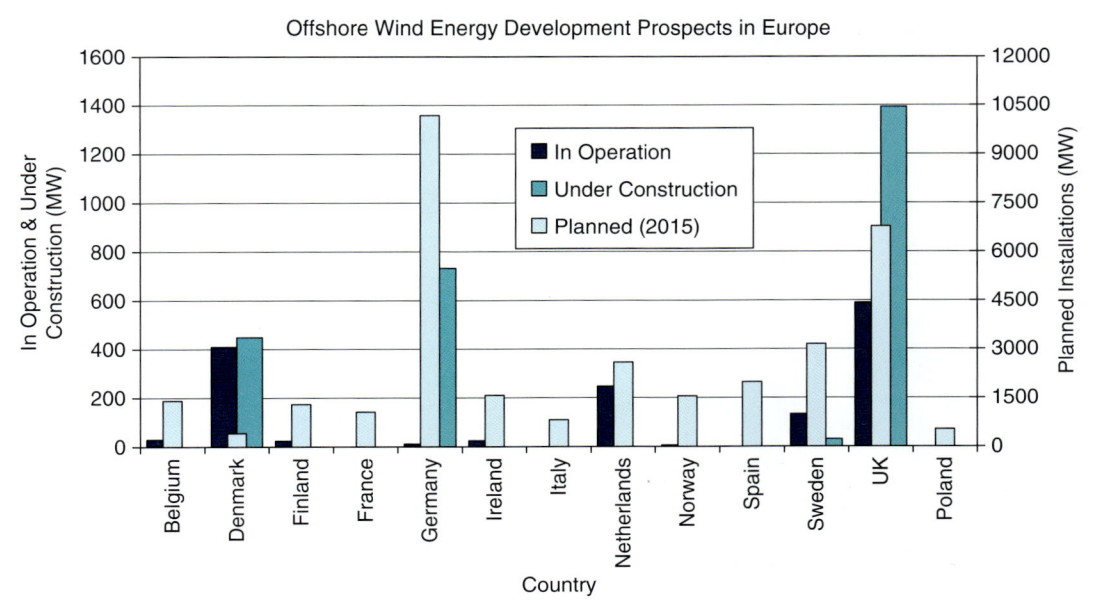

Figure 30 Current status and future plans for the operation of offshore wind energy applications in the EU. Based on data from Wind Energy the Facts (2010) Offshore developments. http://www.wind-energy-the-facts.org/ (accessed December 2010).

Furthermore, as one may obtain from **Figures 26** and **28**, Germany and Spain play the most important role in the European wind energy market, although in the course of time one may encounter more countries entering the field with analogous enthusiasm. Actually, during 2010, if excluding Germany and Spain, the rest of European countries managed to install a total of 6873 MW, with the corresponding number during 2006 and 2002 being 3707 and 716 MW, respectively [59].

Besides, according to predictions, Spain is expected to add almost 2 GW of new wind power on an annual basis for the following 5 years, with Germany keeping up with addition of $1-1.5\,\text{GW}\,\text{yr}^{-1}$, based after 2012 mainly on the installation of offshore wind parks, compensating for the stagnation met in the onshore wind farms of the mainland. On the other hand, although it is expected that the cumulative share of these two countries will by the year 2015 be in the levels of 50% of the total European installed wind power capacity, further reduction is anticipated accordingly, in favor of new European markets emerging in the future. In this context, since 2008, that is, when the second group of Member States adopting wind energy emerged, a more balanced development of wind energy may be noted among the European countries. As a result, during 2010, Italy added new wind power capacity of 962 MW reaching at the same time a total of 5.8 GW, France installed 1086 MW additional wind power leading to an overall of 5.7 GW, and the United Kingdom achieved to reach 5.2 GW through the installation of a new 962 MW, while at the same time, there are 13 Member States of the EU (i.e., almost half) found to already have installed wind power capacity that exceeds 1000 MW (**Table 3**) [55].

In addition, there is a third group of countries that has been recently designated, including Hungary, Bulgaria, and Poland, with all three of them showing considerable development rates although still kept low in terms of installed capacity in absolute figures. Thus, as one may conclude the European wind energy market may be described as a three-speed market, as this is explicitly presented in **Figure 31**, with:

1. Established and mature Western markets (e.g., Spain and Germany) entering a stage of stability (1500–2000 MW added per year).
2. Markets of medium size found in the North and in the South, starting to experience considerable development rates $(200-1000\,\text{MW}\,\text{yr}^{-1})$.
3. Emerging markets of the eastern block, which although presenting a delay, set the foundations for future wind energy development $(50-200\,\text{MW}\,\text{yr}^{-1})$.

Meanwhile, in the Asian continent, development of wind energy market did not always follow a standard pattern (see also **Figure 32**), with the countries of the Asian region found during the last 3 years to actually configure the increase of the respective global wind power capacity. In this context, China is now first in the list of cumulative capacity, having during the recent years added a remarkable 35 GW. Considering the situation encountered lately, it is believed that the eastern Asia region will meet an exponential increase of wind energy in terms of both size of the wind turbines installed and scale of new wind parks.

Apart from China, India is also presenting steady growth rates in the order of $2\,\text{GW}\,\text{yr}^{-1}$, with its cumulative capacity now reaching 13.1 GW (compared with 7.8 GW during 2007), while on top of that it is expected that in the years to follow, promotion of wind energy will be encouraged in other countries of the Asian region as well, entailing designation of new players, as well as widespread diffusion of technical knowledge and realization of investments [66].

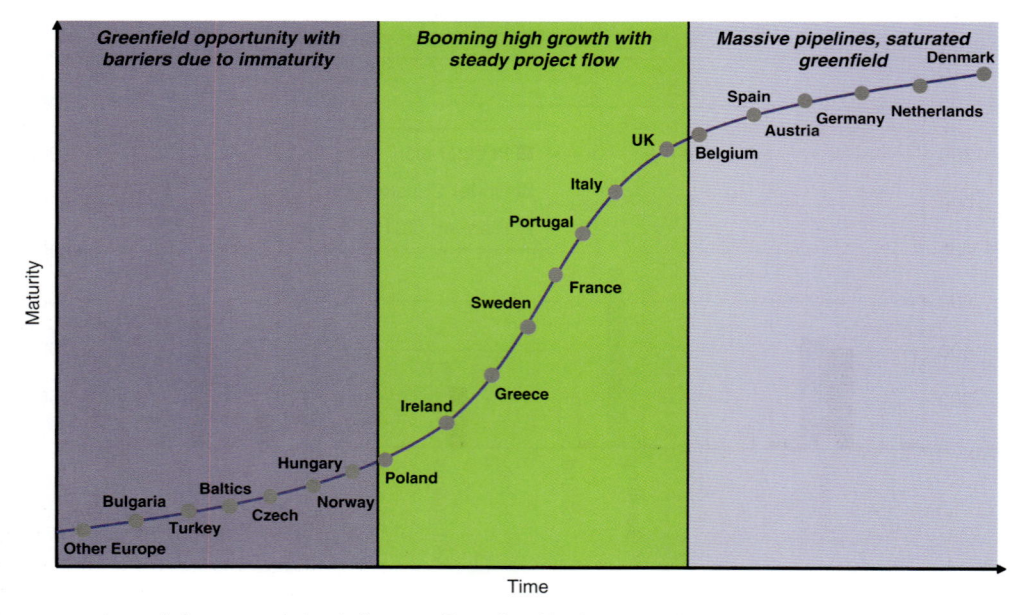

Figure 31 European onshore wind power market maturity curve. Reproduced by the authors based on data from Hays K (2007) Windpower markets surge. *Renewable Energy Focus* 8(5): 42–45 [66].

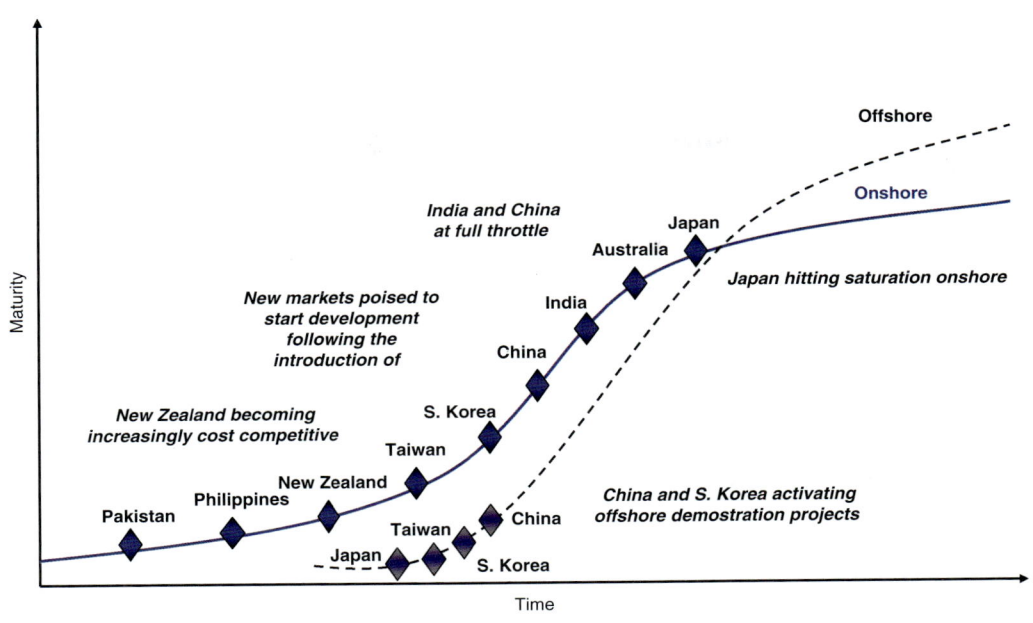

Figure 32 Wind power market maturity in Asia Pacific countries. Reproduced by the authors based on Hays K and Attwood D (2006) *Refocus* 7(6): 24–26.

Furthermore, in the United States, wind energy has during recent years comprised a substantial component of the national fuel mix, offering at the same time considerable environmental and financial benefits as well as alternative solutions in terms of both energy security and reliability of supply [68]. In addition, national targets set concerning wind energy, being analogous with the respective adopted by EU, reflect the future of wind energy in the United States [69]. Moreover, although the market of Western States is not as developed, there is a strong interest lately recorded on deals ensuring the benefits of mergers or joint ventures (e.g., Northern Tier Transmission Group). On the other hand, the situation on the north-west coast is more oriented, since according to the existing plans, 6000 MW are to be installed in the years to follow (Northwest Wind Integration Action Plan), while up until 2015 cumulative wind power capacity is expected to reach 45 GW [66], thus corresponding to investments that exceed US$65 billion. Note also that during 2007, as a result of the federal initiatives concerning tax incentives (i.e., the production tax credit (PTC)), wind energy production was spread to 34 States. On the other hand, one should keep in mind that PTC is actually the only support measure for the promotion of wind energy in the United States, providing a reduction of tax by $1.9 ckWh^{-1} of wind energy produced for the first 10 years of operation, provided of course that the project has been completed and is set to operate under the dictates of the existing time frame [70]. Finally, at this point it is important to also mention the main target set by the American Wind Energy Association, calling for the doubling of wind energy generation in the next 30 years [54].

Summarizing, according to the latest official data, EU still remains the world leader, although the United States made a considerable comeback with over 15 GW installed in 2009 and 2010. Meanwhile, China persists on its outstanding growth rates, each year doubling its cumulative capacity and eventually overtaking the first place in the world ranking table. On top of these, India following a steady growth rate [71] is China's most important ally, adding more than 3 GW for the Asian region during the last 2 years. Besides, after a long stagnating period, Australia managed to install almost 1.2 GW during 2008–10 [72], thus increasing the Pacific capacity at more than 2.3 GW. On the other hand, in Latin America, only the development encountered in Brazil, Chile, Mexico, and Costa Rica is noteworthy, summing up however to a total of only 2 GW [73]. Finally, Egypt, Morocco, and Tunisia [74] are the only active African countries (almost 1 GW), with Iran being the only Middle East country found to considerably exploit its local wind potential (~100 MW) [75].

2.02.8 Forecasting the Wind Power Time Evolution

As already acknowledged, wind energy already comprises an established, and at the same time, aggressively growing electricity generation technology that is nowadays representing 4% of the total world electricity capacity, having for more than a decade presented remarkable growth rates at the levels of 30% on an annual basis. As it may be expected, future evolution of wind power will be subject to numerous factors, including issues of economical competitiveness, environmental impacts, public acceptance, and political decisions. Besides that, technology development issues being of equal importance for the future of wind energy are studied in detail in a separate chapter.

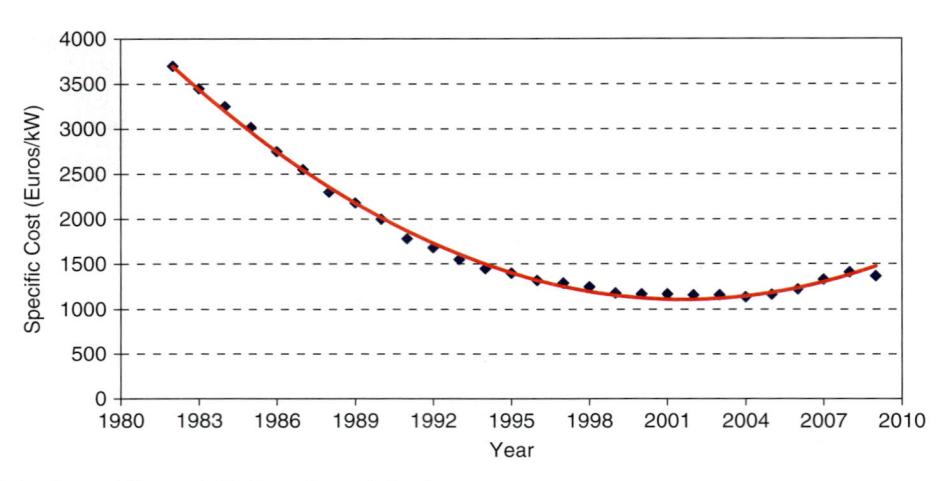

Figure 33 Specific turnkey cost time evolution for onshore wind parks.

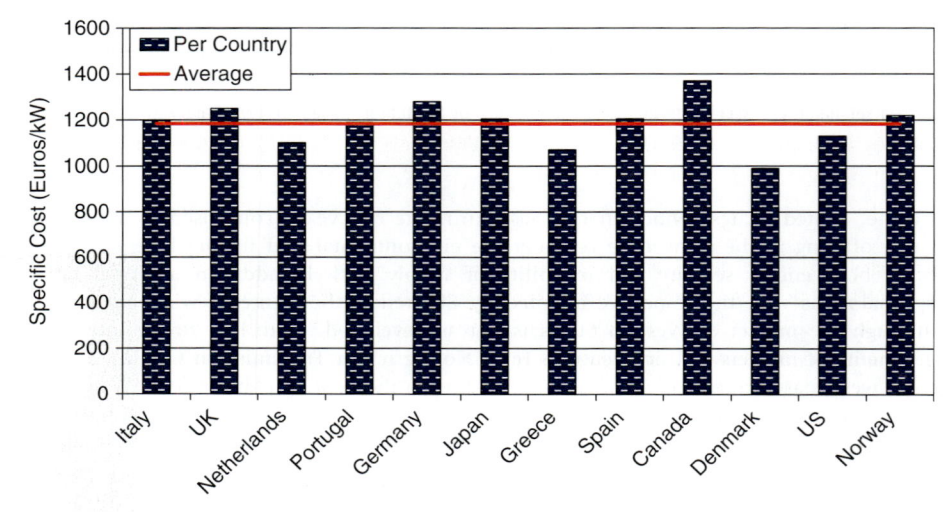

Figure 34 Specific turnkey cost variation by EU country (2006). Based on data from Junginger M, Faaij A, and Turkenburg WC (2005) Global experience curves for wind farms. *Energy Policy* 33: 133–150; Morthorst PE (2009) *Wind Energy the Facts – Part III – The Economics of Wind Power*. Denmark: Risø DTU National Laboratory, Technical University of Denmark.

In this context, among the main trends dominating the market of wind energy during the years, one may note the reduction of the specific investment cost per kW (turnkey cost) of installed wind power capacity [76], which although starting from a remarkable 3500 € kW^{-1} during the mid-1980s, it has during the last years stabilized (**Figure 33**) in the order of 1200 € kW^{-1}, that is, between 1000 and 1400 € kW^{-1} [77], depending also on the area of study (**Figure 34**).

Consequently, some rough numbers may also be given in terms of investment cost breakdown, noting also the difference between onshore and offshore applications. More specifically, the turbine component being critical in the turnkey cost of onshore projects (~75%) drops to a typical 45–50% in offshore plants, while on the other hand, foundation requirements increase by more than four times (from 80 to 350 € kW^{-1}) and grid connection in offshore is increased by more than 150 € kW^{-1}. Overall, the total specific investment cost of offshore applications is found to be higher by more than 40% for most of the plants in operation and may increase to even exceed 3000 € kW^{-1} for installations that are under construction [78, 79]. Besides, based on the experience of in operation offshore parks employment of more turbines implies relatively lower turnkey costs. Any case given, maintenance and operation (M&O) costs for wind power installations, including insurance, regular maintenance, repairs, spare parts, administration, and land rent [38, 80, 81] are nowadays relatively limited (in the order of 1.2–1.5 c€ kWh^{-1}). This is much more evident since the introduction of more efficient machines and the reduction of downtime hours constantly decrease the M&O requirements, while wind power stations are fuel cost free.

As a result of the above, cost of wind energy production is found to be comparable with respect to conventional fossil-fueled generation methods [82], even without internalizing the externalities. More precisely, estimations concerning the near future electricity generation cost of onshore and offshore wind parks support values between 50 and 80 € MWh^{-1} and between 75 and 120 € MWh^{-1}, respectively [14, 83, 84].

On the other hand, as already mentioned in a previous section, State support led to the outbreak of California. In this context, of analogous importance for the remarkable growth of the wind energy market has been the implementation of various support mechanisms [85] including price- and quantity-driven instruments such as feed-in-tariffs, investment and production tax incentives for the first, and quota along with tradable green certificates and tendering systems for the second. At this point, one should underline the effectiveness of most of these measures [86] and especially the feed-in-tariff mechanism [87], which since being adopted by the majority of leading countries worldwide (Germany, the United States, China, Denmark, Spain, India, etc.) [88] led to the remarkable growth of wind energy generation.

Finally, one should also emphasize on the employment opportunities [89] offered by the expansion of the wind energy market at a global level. Somewhat 100 000 plus 50 000 is the number of people employed directly and indirectly in the wind energy field of Europe, while another 85 000 correspond to the 100 manufacturing plants operating in the United States. These include employment posts in manufacturing companies, in promotion, utilities, engineering and R&D (direct employment) or employment in companies providing services or producing components for wind turbines (indirect relation). Note that according to rough estimations [90], among the leader countries on the basis of the people employed per MW installed ratio (**Figure 35**), Denmark, Belgium, and Finland employ more than seven persons, while in terms of absolute numbers Germany currently employs 38 000 people [91].

Although suggesting an *a priori* clean energy source, wind power also comes with certain environmental impacts [33] such as the visual [92] and the noise impact [93], the land use, the bird fatalities [94], the electromagnetic interference, the impacts on fish and marine mammals, the embodied energy, and life-cycle emissions common in every power generation technology. Many of these impacts are nowadays perceived by many as 'myths' [37, 95], while others still lie on the subjectivity of oneself. What is documented however [31, 96–99] is that wind turbines require primary life-cycle embodied energy amounts in the order of only 1–3 MWh kW^{-1} (that usually implies energy payback periods of months), with the stage of manufacturing being the most demanding.

Furthermore, if also considering externalities [100–102], a clear advantage may be recorded for wind power installations in comparison with conventional power plants (see e.g., **Figure 36**). In fact, according to estimations [103], realization of the high expectations set by the EU for 2020 implies avoidance of externalities in the amount of almost 40 billion € yr^{-1}, with the distribution of cost savings per country given in **Figure 37**.

Besides that, environmental performance of wind energy perceived by the majority of people (over 70% in favor) [104, 105] and transformed into widespread social support (only solar energy seems to be more socially accepted) further boosts wind energy developments (**Figure 38**). On the other hand, one of the challenges that wind energy is faced with during recent years is the paradox of increased social support being obscured by real-life NIMBY attitudes [36, 106, 107], especially since availability of good sites is becoming increasingly rare.

Recapitulating, unless out of the box solutions appear, it is anticipated that despite the economic recession encountered at a global level, in the next few years the capital cost of wind energy applications will stabilize at the levels of 1000 € kW^{-1}, with the cost of offshore projects gradually approaching the one of onshore. Furthermore, public attitude toward wind energy applications is expected to remain positive although some minor shocks are also anticipated, owing to the fact that presence of wind parks near densely inhabited areas will inevitably increase. On the other hand, operation of offshore wind parks will alleviate the situation in the industrialized world, while in developing countries of the planet wind energy will continue to be appraised as a 'blessing of nature'. Finally, given the up to now progressive strengthening of competitiveness in the field, it is

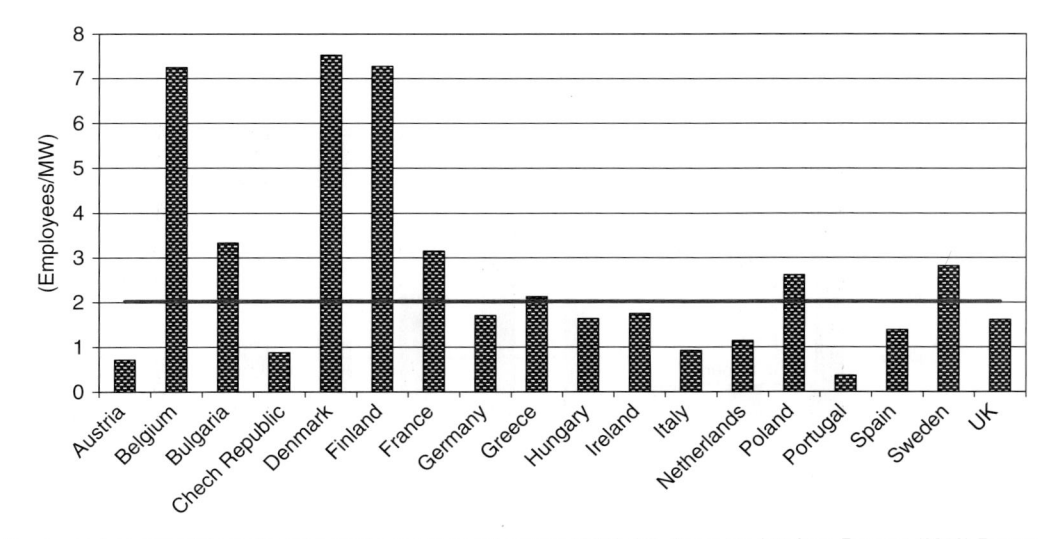

Figure 35 Employment opportunities in the wind energy sector by EU country (2006–07). Based on data from Eurostat (2010) Energy statistics-infrastructure. http://epp.eurostat.ec. europa.eu/ (accessed December 2010); Blanco MI and Rodrigues G (2009) Direct employment in the wind energy sector: An EU study. *Energy Policy* 37: 2847–2857.

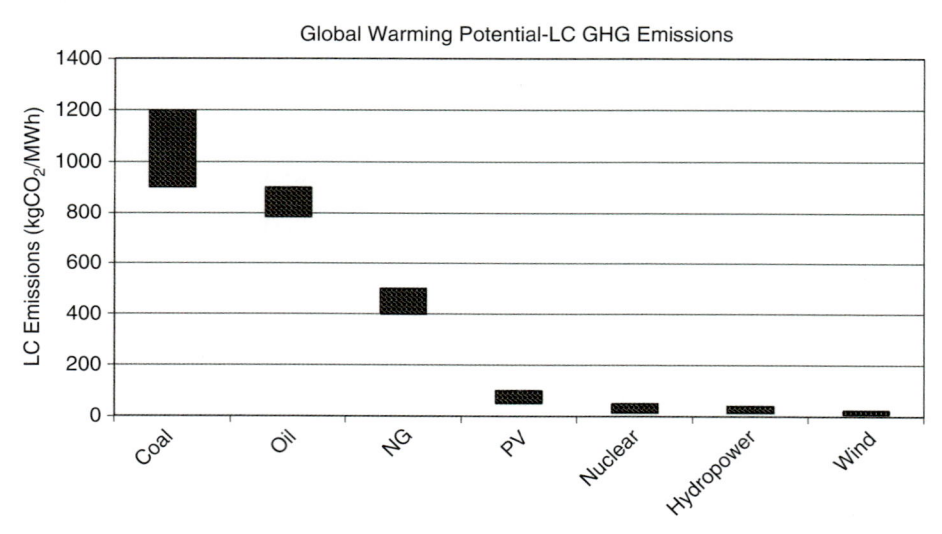

Figure 36 Comparison of life-cycle greenhouse gas emissions between different electricity generation technologies. Based on data from Weisser D (2007) A guide to life-cycle greenhouse gas (GHG) emissions from electric supply technologies. *Energy* 32: 1543–1559.

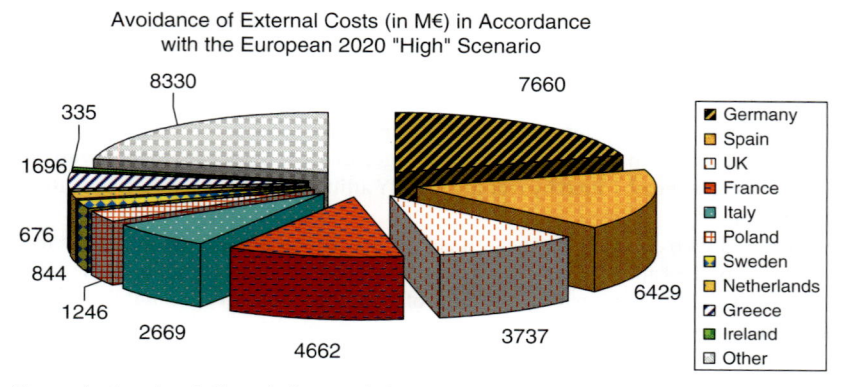

Figure 37 Estimated avoidance of external costs through the use of wind energy in EU in 2020. Based on the data from Wind Energy the Facts (2010) Avoided emissions and external cost for different wind deployment scenarios in the EU27 Member States in 2020. http://www.wind-energy-the-facts.org/ (accessed December 2010).

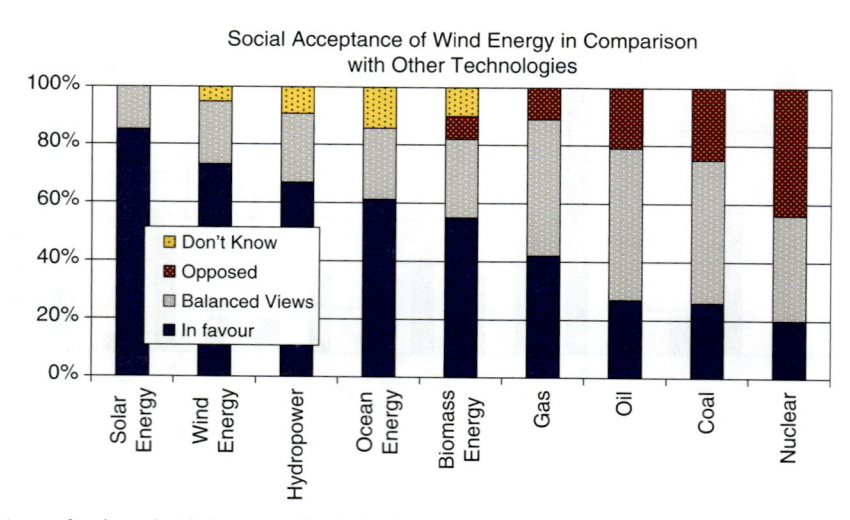

Figure 38 Social acceptance of various electrical power technologies. Based on the data from European Commission (2007) Special Eurobarometer, energy technologies: Knowledge, perception, measures. http://ec.europa.eu/ (accessed December 2010).

anticipated that gradually some of the States' support mechanisms – in force until now – will be gradually abandoned, although wind parks will still entail considerable environmental gains and minimization of external costs of energy through the substitution of thermal power stations.

2.02.9 The Future and Prospects of Wind Energy

Through the study of projections concerning the future of wind energy carried out in the last 15 years, what is impressive to note is the level of underestimation with regard to the evolution of wind power in Europe. More specifically, the initial target of 40 GW set by the White Paper of the European Commission was during 1997 – as one would expect – also adopted by the European Wind Energy Association (EWEA) (**Figure 39**). Nevertheless, 3 years afterwards, due to the remarkable increase rates of wind power growth met in Germany, Spain, and Denmark, EWEA had to review the target set for 2010 and actually increase it by 50%, that is, at 60 GW by 2010 while also setting a target for 2020 at 150 GW. Following, EWEA proceeded to a second review of targets in 2003, this time increasing them by 25%, meaning 75 GW by 2010 and 180 GW by 2020. Eventually, due to the extension of the EU and the inclusion of new Member States, the targets for 2010 and 2020, respectively, were reassessed for the third time to the goal of achieving 80 GW by 2010, maintaining the same 180 GW for 2020, and finally aiming at 300 GW by 2030.

The result of all these projection inadequacies was the emergence of many different points of view and contradictions between experts of the field, with the European cumulative installed capacity of wind power in 2010 however growing, as already mentioned, to 86 GW (i.e., almost 10% of the respective total European electricity power capacity). In this context, by acknowledging the possibility of vitiation for any given claim or prediction, in the following, it is only official data that are recorded concerning future developments in the field of wind energy.

Up till now, the policy framework of the EU was of critical importance for the promotion of RES and wind energy in particular. In this context, new targets set call for 20% coverage of the final energy consumption by RES by 2020, while in terms of electricity consumption, wind energy is expected to contribute by 14–17%. In fact, the two following scenarios have been elaborated on the basis of the 2020 target [108]:

1. The 'baseline' scenario that assumes a total installed wind power capacity of 230 GW (**Figure 40**), producing 580 TWh$_e$ of electricity and increasing the electricity demand coverage by wind from 4.1% in 2008 to 14.2% in 2020.
2. The 'high' scenario where the total installed wind power capacity is assumed to reach 265 GW by 2020, producing 681 TWh$_e$ of electricity and increasing the electricity demand coverage from 4.1% in 2008 to 16.7% in 2020.

In both cases, the EU targets to increase its energy supply security and also reduce the corresponding environmental impacts (including greenhouse gas emissions) replacing imported and heavy polluting fossil fuels with domestic and clean wind-based electricity. In this context, EU forecasts the addition of 250 GW onshore and 150 GW offshore (see also **Figure 41**) by 2030, although it is quite possible that the addition of new offshore installations will be eventually much more significant.

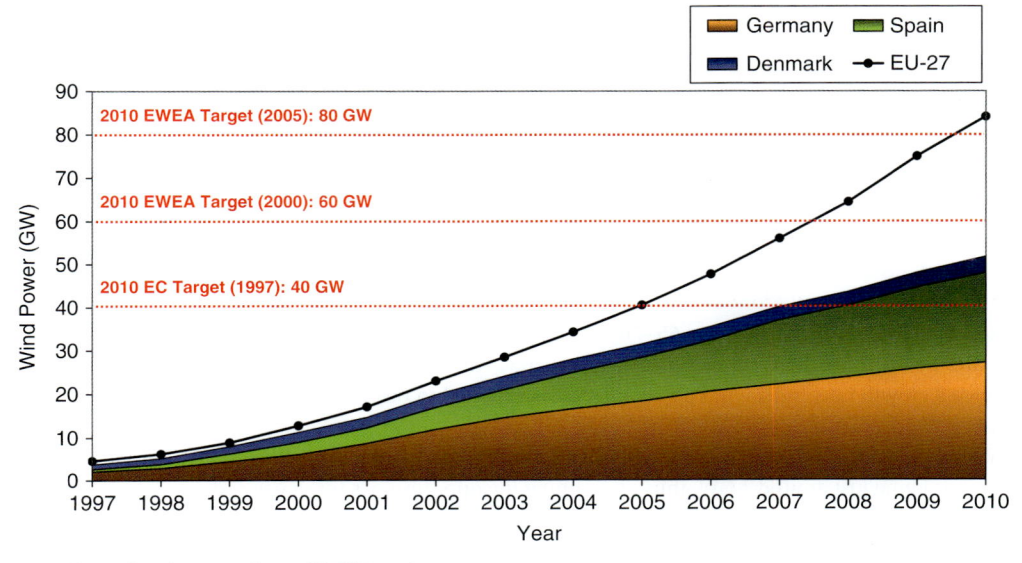

Figure 39 EU Wind Market Development along with EU targets.

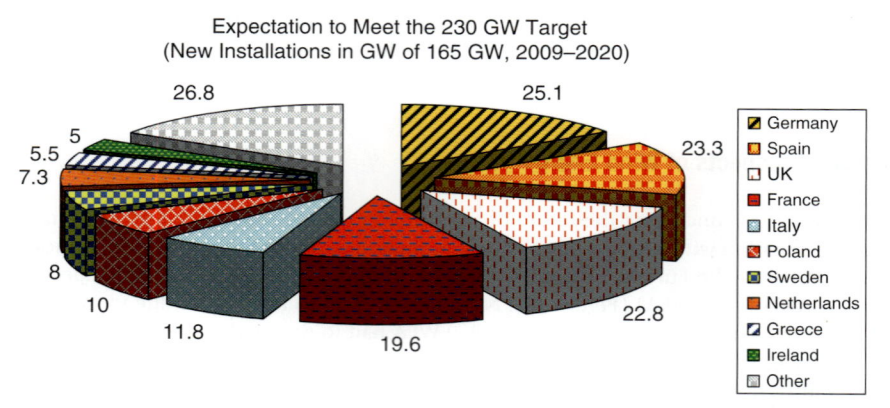

Figure 40 Future targets of wind energy in the EU. Based on the data from Wind Energy the Facts (2010) Scenarios and targets. http://www.wind-energy-the-facts.org/ (accessed December 2010).

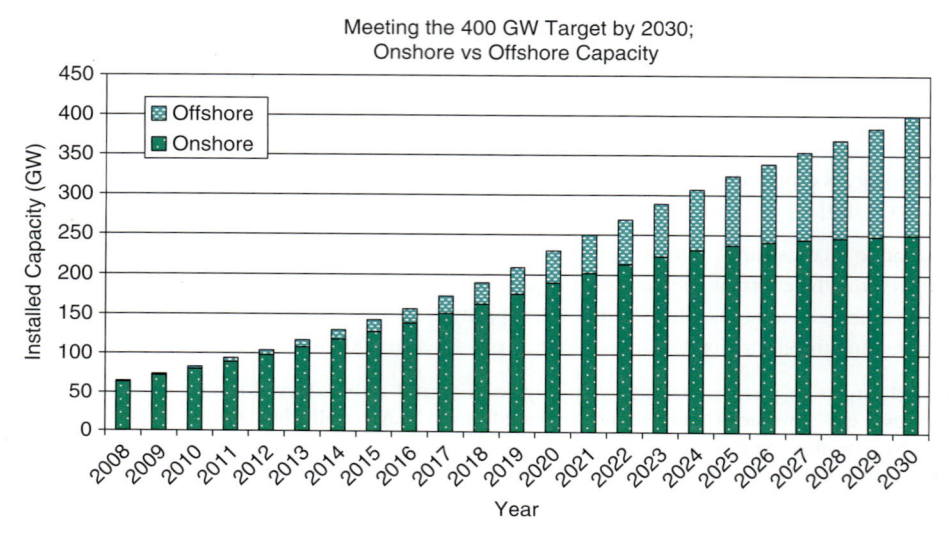

Figure 41 Meeting the EU targets for onshore and offshore wind energy installations. Based on the data from Wind Energy the Facts (2010) Scenarios and targets. http://www.wind-energy-the-facts.org/ (accessed December 2010).

Moreover, according to long-term plans [108], 400 GW of wind power in the EU and 20% of the US electricity demand covered by wind by 2030 [109], along with China requesting 150 GW installed by 2020 [110], set the scenery of wind power prospects and challenge the target of 1000 GW globally by 2030. In this context, one should also note that

- Future of wind energy in the United States is directly related with the time frame dictated by Section 1603 RES grant program of the Congress. Given the already existing capacity of 40.3 GW as well as the planned installation of 10 GW in the early 2011, the target of 150 GW in 2020 seems both achievable and hard to accomplish.
- China has by 2010 installed 42.3 GW, thus the target of 150 GW may be pessimistic in view of the continuous energy consumption increase of the local economy.
- In India, existence of a domestic industry and 65–70 GW of assessed wind potential along with 10% of RES capacity and 4–5% of RES energy shares by 2012 are the main drivers of wind energy, with estimations calling for 2 GW yr^{-1} in the following period. Considering such a growth rate, India wind power increase is expected to push the corresponding installed wind power between 30 and 40 GW by 2020.
- Wind potential for onshore wind energy capacity in Brazil has been assessed at 143 GW (at 50 m high), with the existing wind power installations being just around 1 GW, thus underlining the opportunities for drastical development during the next years.
- At the end of 2008, Australia expanded the country RES target to 20% by 2020; hence, wind energy is expected to strongly contribute to the implementation of the target set.
- South Africans will also turn to wind, since the major part of the 100 TWh produced by RES up to 2025 is to be assigned to wind power.

2.02.10 Conclusions

The continuous increase of energy consumption encountered across the planet along with the techno-economic problems related with the dominance of conventional fuels and the severe environmental impacts entailed by thermal power generation during recent years, illustrate the importance of increased RES contribution in the planet's energy balance. At this point, it should be pointed out that the role of wind energy may be already granted as rather significant, while is expected to be critical during the current decade.

On the basis of the available data, dynamics of wind power at the global energy scene during the last 30 years is illustrated, while according to the targets set, the perspective of exceeding 1 TW of wind power installations by 2030 seems feasible, especially if considering the challenges introduced by the need of each country to safeguard security of supply and promote clean power technologies.

Besides that, although the leading role of the EU throughout the period of wind energy development has been designated, the return of the United States and the tremendous growth of the wind energy industry in China are also reflected. On top of that, of special interest is also the gradual adoption of wind energy by several countries of the developing world, which is clearly demonstrating both the catholic character of wind power and its ability to largely substitute fossil-fueled power generation in the years to come.

References

[1] D'Haeseleer WD (2003) The importance of fusion development towards a future energy source. *Fusion Engineering and Design* 66–68: 3–15.
[2] Martínez DM and Ebenhack BW (2008) Understanding the role of energy consumption in human development through the use of saturation phenomena. *Energy Policy* 36(4): 1430–1435.
[3] Zhelev TK (2005) Water conservation through energy management. *Journal of Cleaner Production* 13(15): 1395–1404.
[4] Dias RA, Mattos CR, and Balestieri JAP (2006) The limits of human development and the use of energy and natural resources. *Energy Policy* 34(9): 1026–1031.
[5] Pachauri S and Jiang L (2008) The household energy transition in India and China. *Energy Policy* 36(11): 4022–4035.
[6] Sheffield J (1998) World population growth and the role of annual energy use per capita. *Technological Forecasting and Social Change* 59(1): 55–87.
[7] Taylor PG, d'Ortigue OL, Francoeur ML, and Trudeau N (2010) Final energy use in IEA countries: The role of energy efficiency. *Energy Policy* 38(11): 6463–6474.
[8] UN Statistics Division, Department of Economic and Social Affairs of the United Nations Secretariat (2009) World population prospects: The 2008 revision. http://www.un.org (accessed December 2010).
[9] Shell International BV (2008) Shell energy scenarios to 2050. http://www-static.shell.com (accessed October 2010).
[10] Sternberg R (2010) Hydropower's future, the environment, and global electricity systems. *Renewable and Sustainable Energy Reviews* 14(2): 713–723.
[11] Hall DO, Rosillo-Calle F, and de Groot P (1992) Biomass energy: Lessons from case studies in developing countries. *Energy Policy* 20(1): 62–73.
[12] Jianzhong X, Dexin H, and Xiaolu Z (2010) Status and prospects of Chinese wind energy. *Energy* 35(11): 4439–4444.
[13] Changliang X and Zhanfeng S (2009) Wind energy in China: Current scenario and future perspectives. *Renewable and Sustainable Energy Reviews* 13(8): 1966–1974.
[14] International Energy Agency (IEA) (2010) *Projected Costs of Generating Electricity*. Paris, France: IEA Publications.
[15] U.S. Energy Information Administration (EIA) (2010) International Energy Outlook (IEO2010). http://www.worldenergyoutlook.org (accessed February 2011).
[16] Kaldellis JK and Zafirakis D (2011) The wind energy (r)evolution: A short review of a long history. *Renewable Energy* 36(7): 1887–1901.
[17] Eurostat (2010) Energy statistics-infrastructure. http://epp.eurostat.ec.europa.eu/ (accessed December 2010).
[18] Razykov TM, Ferekides CS, Morel D, et al. (2011) Solar photovoltaic electricity: Current status and future prospects. *Solar Energy* 85: 1580–1608.
[19] U.S. Energy Information Administration (EIA) International energy statistics. http://tonto.eia.doe.gov (accessed February 2011).
[20] Owen NA, Inderwildi OR, and King DA (2010) The status of conventional world oil reserves: Hype or cause for concern? *Energy Policy* 38(8): 4743–4749.
[21] Economides MJ and Wood DA (2009) The state of natural gas. *Journal of Natural Gas Science Engineering* 1(1–2): 1–13.
[22] Pahle M (2010) Germany's dash for coal: Exploring drivers and factors. *Energy Policy* 38(7): 3431–3442.
[23] Thielemann T, Schmidt S, and Gerling JP (2007) Lignite and hard coal: Energy suppliers for world needs until the year 2100: An outlook. *International Journal of Coal Geology* 72(1): 1–14.
[24] BP (2010) BP statistical review of world energy 2010. http://www.bp.com (accessed February 2011).
[25] Meadows D, Meadows D, and Randers J (1992) *Beyond the Limits*. White River Junction, VT: Chelsea Green Publishing Co.
[26] Lightfoot S and Burchell J (2004) Green hope or greenwash? The actions of the European Union at the world summit on sustainable development. *Global Environmental Change Part A* 14(4): 337–344.
[27] Clarke D (2007) *The Battle for Barrels: Peak Oil Myths and World Oil Futures*. London, UK: Profile Books.
[28] Kaldellis JK, Zafirakis D, and Kondili E (2009) Contribution of lignite in the Greek electricity generation: Review and future prospects. *Fuel* 88(3): 475–489.
[29] Kim SH (2007) Evaluation of negative environmental impacts of electricity generation: Neoclassical and institutional approaches. *Energy Policy* 35(1): 413–423.
[30] Quadrelli R and Peterson S (2007) The energy–climate challenge: Recent trends in CO_2 emissions from fuel combustion. *Energy Policy* 35(11): 5938–5952.
[31] Lenzen M and Munksgaard J (2002) Energy and CO_2 life-cycle analyses of wind turbines: Review and applications. *Renewable Energy* 26: 339–362.
[32] de Vries BJM, van Vuuren DP, and Hoogwijk MM (2007) Renewable energy sources: Their global potential for the first-half of the 21st century at a global level: An integrated approach. *Energy Policy* 35(4): 2590–2610.
[33] Morrison ML and Sinclair K (2004) Wind energy technology, environmental impacts. *Encyclopedia of Energy* 6: 435–448. St. Louis: Elsevier.
[34] Pedersen E, Hallberg LR-M, and Persson WK (2007) Living in the vicinity of wind turbines: A grounded theory study. *Qualitative Research in Psychology* 4: 49–63.
[35] Pedersen E, van den Berg F, Bakker R, and Bouma J (2010) Can road traffic mask sound from wind turbines? Response to wind turbine sound at different levels of road traffic sound. *Energy Policy* 38(5): 2520–2527.
[36] Jones CR and Eiser JR (2010) Understanding 'local' opposition to wind development in the UK: How big is a backyard? *Energy Policy* 38(6): 3106–3117.
[37] Kaldellis JK, Kavadias KA, and Paliatsos AG (2003) Environmental impacts of wind energy applications: Myth or reality? *Fresenius Environmental Bulletin* 12(4): 326–337.
[38] Blanco MI (2009) The economics of wind energy. *Renewable and Sustainable Energy Reviews* 13(6–7): 1372–1382.
[39] Albadi MH and El-Saadany EF (2010) Overview of wind power intermittency impacts on power systems. *Electric Power Systems Research* 80(6): 627–632.
[40] Kabouris J and Perrakis K (2000) Wind electricity in Greece: Recent developments, problems and prospects. *Renewable Energy* 21: 417–432.
[41] Kaldellis JK (2007) Maximum wind energy contribution in autonomous electrical grids based on thermal power stations. *Applied Thermal Engineering* 27: 1565–1573.

[42] Kaldellis JK, Zafirakis D, and Kavadias K (2009) Techno-economic comparison of energy storage systems for island autonomous electrical networks. *Renewable and Sustainable Energy Reviews* 13(2): 378–392.
[43] Kaldellis JK, Kapsali M, and Kavadias KA (2010) Energy balance analysis of wind-based pumped hydro storage systems in remote island electrical networks. *Applied Energy* 87(8): 2427–2437.
[44] Zafirakis D and Kaldellis JK (2010) Autonomous dual-mode CAES systems for maximum wind energy contribution in remote island networks. *Energy Conversion and Management* 51(11): 2150–2161.
[45] Kapsali M and Kaldellis JK (2010) Combining hydro and variable wind power generation by means of pumped-storage under economically viable terms. *Applied Energy* 87(11): 3475–3485.
[46] Kaldellis JK (2002) Estimating the optimum size of wind power applications in Greece. *Proceedings of Global Windpower Conference*, 2–5 April. Paris. Paper No. GWP_077.
[47] Sherif SA, Barbir F, and Veziroglu TN (2005) Wind energy and the hydrogen economy: Review of the technology. *Solar Energy* 78(5): 647–660.
[48] Fleming PD and Probert SD (1984) The evolution of wind-turbines: An historical review. *Applied Energy* 18: 163–177.
[49] Pasqualetti MJ, Righter R, and Gipe P (2004) Wind energy, history. *Encyclopedia of Energy* 6: 419–433. Amsterdam: Elsevier.
[50] Musgrove P (2010) *Wind Power*, 1st edn. Cambridge, UK: Cambridge University Press.
[51] Righter RW (1996) Pioneering in wind energy: The California experience. *Renewable Energy* 9: 781–784.
[52] Ackermann Th and Söder L (2002) An overview of wind energy-status 2002. *Renewable and Sustainable Energy Reviews* 6: 67–127.
[53] European Wind Energy Association (2010) Annual report – 2009. http://www.ewea.org (accessed December 2010).
[54] Global Wind Energy Council (GWEC) (2010) Global wind energy outlook – 2010. http://www.gwec.net/ (accessed December 2010).
[55] Global Wind Energy Council (GWEC) (2011) Global wind energy statistics report for 2010. http://www.gwec.net/.
[56] Breton SPh and Moe G (2009) Status, plans and technologies for offshore wind turbines in Europe and North America. *Renewable Energy* 34: 646–654.
[57] Bird L, Bolinger M, Gagliano T, et al. (2005) Policies and market factors driving wind power development in the United States. *Energy Policy* 33: 1397–1407.
[58] Sperling K, Hvelplund F, and Vad Mathiesen B (2010) Evaluation of wind power planning in Denmark: Towards an integrated perspective. *Energy* 35: 5443–5454.
[59] Kaldellis JK and Zervos A (2002) Wind power: A sustainable energy solution for the world development. *Proceedings of the Energy International Conference* 83: 1384–1403.
[60] Jacob A (2008) Continuing boom in wind-power. *Renewable Energy Focus* 52(2): 42–44.
[61] Blanco MI and Rodrigues G (2008) Can the future EU ETS support wind energy investments? *Energy Policy* 36: 1509–1520.
[62] Eurostat (2010) Energy statistics – Supply, transformation, consumption. http://epp.eurostat.ec.europa.eu/ (accessed December 2010).
[63] Snyder B and Kaiser MJ (2009) Offshore wind power in the US: Regulatory issues and models for regulation. *Energy Policy* 37: 4442–4453.
[64] Wind Energy the Facts (2010) Offshore developments. http://www.wind-energy-the-facts.org/ (accessed December 2010).
[65] European Environment Agency (EEA) (2009) Europe's onshore and offshore wind energy potential. Technical Report No. 6. http://www.eea.europa.eu (accessed December 2010).
[66] Hays K (2007) Windpower markets surge. *Renewable Energy Focus* 8(5): 42–45.
[67] Hays K and Attwood D (2006) Asia: Out of the shadows?: Led by China and India, Asia Pacific wind markets poised for major growth. *Refocus* 7(6): 24–26.
[68] Kirby B and Milligan M (2008) Facilitating wind development: The importance of electric industry structure. *The Electricity Journal* 21(3): 40–54.
[69] Hohler A and Hopwood D (2008) Suzlon feels the need for speed. *Renewable Energy Focus* 9(2): 38–39.
[70] Global Wind Energy Council (GWEC) (2008) Global wind energy outlook 2008. http://www.gwec.net/ (accessed December 2010).
[71] Mabel C and Fernandez E (2008) Growth and future trends of wind energy in India. *Renewable and Sustainable Energy Reviews* 12: 1745–1757.
[72] Zahedi A (2010) Australian renewable energy progress. *Renewable and Sustainable Energy Reviews* 14: 2208–2213.
[73] Bennett C (2010) Latin American wind takes shape. *Renewable Energy Focus* 11: 12–15.
[74] Khalil AK, Mubarak AM, and Kaseb A (2010) Road map for renewable energy research and development in Egypt. *Journal of Advanced Research* 1: 29–38.
[75] Mostafaeipour A and Mostafaeipour N (2009) Renewable energy issues and electricity production in Middle East compared with Iran. *Renewable and Sustainable Energy Reviews* 13: 1641–1645.
[76] Junginger M, Faaij A, and Turkenburg WC (2005) Global experience curves for wind farms. *Energy Policy* 33: 133–150.
[77] Morthorst PE (2009) *Wind Energy the Facts – Part III – The Economics of Wind Power*. Denmark: Risø DTU National Laboratory, Technical University of Denmark.
[78] Department of Trade and Industry (2007) Study of the costs of offshore wind generation. *A Report to the Renewables Advisory Board (RAB) & DTI*. URN Number 07/779. UK.
[79] Garrad Hassan GL (2009) *UK Offshore Wind: Charting the Right Course. Scenarios for Offshore Capital Costs for the Next Five Years*. London, UK: Garrad Hassan on behalf of British Wind Energy Association.
[80] Deutsches Windenergie-Institut (2002) Studie zur aktuellen kostensituation 2002 der Windenergienutzung in Deutschland. http://www.dewi.de (accessed March 2008).
[81] Kaldellis JK (2002) An integrated time-depending feasibility analysis model of wind energy applications in Greece. *Energy Policy* 30: 267–280.
[82] European Commission (2009) Future fossil fuel electricity generation in Europe: Options and consequences. http://ec.europa.eu/ (accessed December 2010).
[83] European Commission. Strategic energy technologies information system, production cost of electricity – 2020 projection. http://setis.ec.europa.eu/ (accessed December 2010).
[84] Royal Academy of Engineering (2004) The cost of generating electricity. http://www.raeng.org.uk/ (accessed December 2010).
[85] Lewis JI and Wiser RH (2007) Fostering a renewable energy technology industry: An international comparison of wind industry policy support mechanisms. *Energy Policy* 35: 1844–1857.
[86] Kaldellis JK (2011) Critical evaluation of financial supporting schemes for wind-based projects: Case study Greece. *Energy Policy* 39: 2490–2500.
[87] Butler L and Neuhoff K (2008) Comparison of feed-in tariff, quota and auction mechanisms to support wind power development. *Renewable Energy* 33: 1854–1867.
[88] Ragwitz M, Held A, Resch G, et al. (2007) Assessment and optimization of renewable energy support schemes in the European electricity market (OPTRES), intelligent energy. http://ec.europa.eu /energy/ (accessed December 2010).
[89] Blanco MI and Rodrigues G (2009) Direct employment in the wind energy sector: An EU study. *Energy Policy* 37: 2847–2857.
[90] Wind Energy the Facts (2010) Employment in the wind energy sector. http://www.wind-energy-the-facts.org/ (accessed December 2010).
[91] Lehr U, Nitsch J, Kratzat M, et al. (2008) Renewable energy and employment in Germany. *Energy Policy* 36: 108–117.
[92] Bishop ID and Miller DR (2007) Visual assessment of off-shore wind turbines: The influence of distance, contrast, movement and social variables. *Renewable Energy* 32: 814–831.
[93] Björkman M (2004) Long time measurements of noise from wind turbines. *Sound and Vibration* 277: 567–572.
[94] Sovacool BK (2009) Contextualizing avian mortality: A preliminary appraisal of bird and bat fatalities from wind, fossil-fuel, and nuclear electricity. *Energy Policy* 37: 2241–2248.
[95] Erickson WP, Johnson GD, and Young DPA, Jr. (2002) Summary and comparison of bird mortality from anthropogenic causes with an emphasis on collisions. http://studentaffairs.case.edu (accessed December 2010).
[96] Crawford RH (2009) Life cycle energy and greenhouse emissions analysis of wind turbines and the effect of size on energy yield. *Renewable and Sustainable Energy Reviews* 13: 2653–2660.
[97] Danish Wind Industry Association (1997) The energy balance of modern wind turbines. http://www.windpower.org/ (accessed March 2009).
[98] Tremeac B and Meunier F (2009) Life cycle analysis of 4.5 MW and 250 W wind turbines. *Renewable and Sustainable Energy Reviews* 13: 2104–2110.
[99] Martínez E, Jiménez E, Blanco J, and Sanz FLC (2010) A sensitivity analysis of a multi-megawatt wind turbine. *Applied Energy* 87: 2293–2303.
[100] El-Kordy MN, Badr MA, Abed KA, and Ibrahim SMA (2002) Economical evaluation of electricity generation considering externalities. *Renewable Energy* 25: 317–328.

[101] Klaassen G and Riahi K (2007) Internalizing externalities of electricity generation: An analysis with MESSAGE-MACRO. *Energy Policy* 35: 815–827.
[102] Weisser D (2007) A guide to life-cycle greenhouse gas (GHG) emissions from electric supply technologies. *Energy* 32: 1543–1559.
[103] Wind Energy the Facts (2010) Avoided emissions and external cost for different wind deployment scenarios in the EU27 Member States in 2020. http://www.wind-energy-the-facts.org/ (accessed December 2010).
[104] European Commission (2006) Special Eurobarometer, attitudes towards energy. http://ec.europa.eu/ (accessed December 2010).
[105] European Commission (2007) Special Eurobarometer, energy technologies: Knowledge, perception, measures. http://ec.europa.eu/ (accessed December 2010).
[106] Kaldellis JK (2005) Social attitude towards wind energy applications in Greece. *Energy Policy* 33: 595–602.
[107] Swofford J and Slattery M (2010) Public attitudes of wind energy in Texas: Local communities in close proximity to wind farms and their effect on decision-making. *Energy Policy* 38: 2508–2519.
[108] Wind Energy the Facts (2010) Scenarios and targets. http://www.wind-energy-the-facts.org/ (accessed December 2010).
[109] American Wind Energy Association (2008) 20% Wind energy by 2030. http://www.awea.org/ (accessed December 2010).
[110] Chinese Renewable Energy Industries Association (2010) China wind energy outlook – 2010. http://www.greenpeace.org/ (accessed December 2010).

Further Reading

[1] Cocks FH (2009) *Energy Demand and Climate Change: Issues and Resolutions*. UK: Wiley.
[2] Diesendorf M (2007) *Greenhouse Solutions with Sustainable Energy*. Sydney: UNSW Press.
[3] Eggleston D and Stoddard F (1987) *Wind Turbine Engineering Design*. USA: Van Nostrand Reinhold.
[4] Giddens A (2009) *Politics of Climate Change*. UK: Wiley.
[5] Gipe P and Canter B (1997) *Glossary of Wind Energy Terms*. Denmark: Forlaget Vistoft.
[6] Goodstein D (2004) *Out of Gas: The End of the Age of Oil*. New York: W. W. Norton & Company.
[7] Johnson G (1985) *Wind Energy Systems*. New York: Prentice Hall.
[8] Kaldellis, JK (ed.) (2010) *Stand-Alone and Hybrid Wind Energy Systems: Technology, Energy Storage and Applications*. UK: Woodhead. Publishing.
[9] Kaldellis JK (2005) *Wind Energy Management*, 2nd edn. Athens, Greece: Stamoulis.
[10] Leggett J (1999) *The Carbon War: Global Warming and the End of the Oil Era*. New York: Penguin.
[11] Le Gourières D (1980) *Énergie Éolienne: Théorie, Conception, et Calcul Pratique des Installations*. Paris, France: Eyrolles.
[12] Molly J-P (1990) *Windenergie*, 2nd edn. Karlsruhe, Germany: C.F. Müller.
[13] Roberts P (2005) *The End of Oil. The Decline of the Petroleum Economy and the Rise of a New Energy Order*. London, UK: Bloomsbury Publishing.

Relevant Websites

http://www.eia.doe.gov – US Energy Information Administration.
http://europa.eu http://europa.eu – Official website of the European Union.
http://www.awea.org – American Wind Energy Association.
http://www.windstats.com – Windstats Newsletter.
http://www.iea.org – International Energy Agency.
http://www.bwea.com – RenewableUK. The voice of wind and marine energy.
http://www.wind-energie.de – Bundesverband WindEnergie e.V.
http://www.canwea.ca – Canadian Wind Energy Association.
http://www.windenergy.org.nz – Wind: New Zealand's Energy.
http://fee.asso.fr/ – France Energie Eolienne.
http://www.wwindea.org – World Wind Energy Association.
http://www.ewea.org – The European Wind Energy Association.
http://www.gwec.net – Global Wind Energy Council
http://www.offshorewindenergy.org – Offshore wind energy.
http://www.sealab.gr – Lab of Soft Energy Applications and Environmental Protection, Technological Education, Institute of Piraeus.
http://www.cres.gr – Center of Renewable Energy Sources and Saving.

2.03 History of Wind Power

DT Swift-Hook, Kingston University, London, UK; World Renewable Energy Network, Brighton, UK

© 2012 Elsevier Ltd. All rights reserved.

2.03.1	Sails	41
2.03.2	Early Wind Devices and Applications	41
2.03.3	Persian Vertical Axis Designs	44
2.03.4	The Introduction of Windmills into Europe	44
2.03.5	Horizontal Axis Machines	45
2.03.6	Post and Tower Mills	46
2.03.7	Technological Developments	48
2.03.8	Theory and Experiment: The Early Science	49
2.03.9	The End of Windmills	51
2.03.10	The American Wind Pump	51
2.03.11	Electrical Power from the Wind	52
2.03.12	Large Machines	54
2.03.13	The Smith-Putnam Machine	56
2.03.14	Postwar Programs	58
2.03.15	The Mother of All Modern Wind Turbines	60
2.03.16	Ulrich Hütter	61
2.03.17	The Battle of the Blades: Two versus Three	61
2.03.18	Large Two-Bladed Wind Turbines	64
2.03.19	The California Wind Rush	66
2.03.20	Other Manufacturers	71
2.03.21	Large Vertical Axis Wind Turbines	71
2.03.22	Organizations: BWEA, EWEA, and IEA	71
Further Reading		72

2.03.1 Sails

The first engineering applications of wind in recorded history were for sailing. There is evidence that ships based in the Tigris/Euphrates Delta traded along the coast as far as Oman and Northwest India and they may have also been used upriver to carry goods between the first Mesopotamian city states of Uruk and Ur (see **Figure 1**).

The earliest known sailing ships, apart from logs and dugout canoes, were built before 5000 BC from reeds, bundled and lashed together to form a 'hull' (see **Figure 2**) and coated with bitumen to make them watertight. Cargo and crew members were carried on top of the bundles.

The pictorial record of such a sailing ship appears on a painted ceramic disc found in 2004 in Kuwait at site H3 from this early period (see **Figure 3**). It shows a bipod (two-footed or inverted V) mast, which is particularly well suited for reed vessel construction when the frame of the boat is not strong enough to support a single socket mast. Before this recent discovery, the earliest record came from the Nile and it is probable that the stones of the great pyramids were moved from Aswan to Giza with the help of the wind.

The explorer Thor Heyerdahl built several reed vessels of this type during the 1970s and sailed them across the Pacific Ocean to Easter Island, proving their long-distance capabilities in ancient times but by the time that Stonehenge was built (ca. 3500 years ago) far more sophisticated vessels with sails were making regular voyages around the Mediterranean Sea, and even venturing into the Atlantic Ocean as far as the British Isles in search of tin, an essential commodity for Bronze Age heroes.

By the Roman era, the Chinese were building large sailing ships that could 'point' well into the wind. So the basic idea of using a sail to capture the wind was well established. The concept of lift was clearly being used practically and effectively, even if the physics of the process was not understood.

2.03.2 Early Wind Devices and Applications

There are many early land-based applications of wind power in the historical record.

Wind was used in ancient times for winnowing – to separate wheat from chaff – as it still is in many parts of the world today, for example, Tibet. The ears of wheat are pounded or beaten – threshed – to detach the husks from the grains of cereal and the mixture is thrown into the air. The denser grains of cereal fall straight to the ground in a heap, while the wind blows away the lighter husks, the chaff. Psalm 1 of the Bible, which is traditionally ascribed to King David (1000–965 BC), refers to 'chaff that the wind blows away', so the practice was going strong at least 3000 years ago.

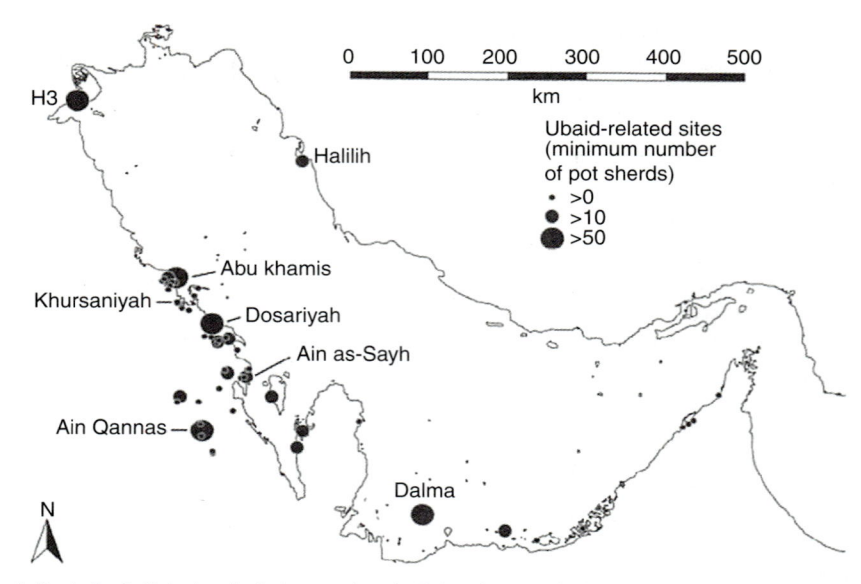

Figure 1 Archaeological sites in the Gulf. Archaeological excavations by Robert Carter and others in Kuwait have revealed the earliest remains anywhere of seagoing boats.

Figure 2 Ceramic model of reed-bundle boat. This 150 mm long model of a reed-bundle boat was found in 2004 by Robert Carter at the H3 site in Kuwait (see **Figure 1**).

Another interesting and ancient application of wind was to power primitive blast furnaces. In Anuradhapura and other parts of ancient Sri Lanka, there is solid evidence that iron smelting furnaces were aligned with the regular Monsoon winds to provide blower power that would enable furnace temperatures of 1200 °C to be achieved.

It is not known when people first built wind machines to do mechanical work. Man-powered and donkey-powered applications (such as the rotary donkey treadmills found in the ashes of Pompeii in AD 79) came first. Water power came next (see **Figures** 4 and 5) but this had to be limited to riverside sites. Wind power followed on, especially where no water power was available.

An important use of mechanical power was for grinding corn. Throughout history, with no refrigerators, it has always been a problem to preserve food and, since the invention of agriculture, cereals have been a major part of staple diets around the world, providing much of the protein for the peasantry, because they can be stored for years. This was true at the time when Joseph was in charge and filled the granaries of Egypt (probably around 1700 BC) and it was still true through to the Middle Ages and beyond. Porridge from oats was a major food in many regions and bread from wheat was the staple food in many others. Cereals could take half of the food budget of a poor family.

Apart from rice, all of these grains needed to be ground or at least crushed. It has been shown that it takes 2 h a day of hard work with a manual quern to grind enough corn to produce enough flour for the bread for a single family for the day. The benefits of automating the grinding process are clear and the technologies of grinding stones and gears were developed well before wind power arrived. The permanent nature of the stones leaves clear archaeological evidence of the processes involved.

The majority of the populations in ancient times were agricultural and grew their own corn. In preference to grinding it themselves by hand, a household would take its corn along to the local mill to be ground and would collect the flour produced

Figure 3 Painted ceramic disc depicting reed-bundle boat with bipod mast. The painting on the ceramic disc shows a boat with a bipod mast, which is suited to the not very rigid structure of a reed-bundle boat.

Figure 4 Waterwheel machinery. Typical waterwheels are horizontal axis with a gear arrangement to turn the torque through a right angle.

Figure 5 An operating water mill. Daniel's Mill at Bridgnorth in Shropshire, UK, has been fully restored to its original form and it operates to produce stone-ground, wholemeal flour as the original mill would have done.

to be taken home and turned into bread. Waterwheels were used to power mills for grinding corn long before the arrival of windmills.

The first instance of wind machines may have been in China more than 2000 years ago, but archaeologists have found no definite record of their use there, either in the form of artifacts or in writing. The machinery would have been made of wood or other less permanent materials. These have sometimes survived for 1000 years or so but rarely longer than that. If such machines did exist in China, they must have fallen out of use again until AD 1219, when next they are heard of in documents by the Chinese statesman Yehlu Chu Tsai.

There are suggestions that wind machines were used in Mesopotamia and/or in ancient Palestine. Hammurabi, king of Babylon somewhere between 1600 and 1700 BC, apparently planned to use wind pumps for his ambitious irrigation schemes, but again no detailed records have survived.

Hero of Alexandria (AD 10–70) described a simple propeller-type wind turbine machine that was used to blow an organ. Hero is more famous for having his name attached to an elementary steam turbine, the aeolipile. This is mentioned in Vitruvius' De Architectura some 100 years earlier than Hero lived but Hero is often mistakenly attributed to a career 200 years earlier than his actual lifetime, which is known from the dates of his publications. However, the earlier invention is often called Hero's engine. As far as can be discovered, these devices were only ever used for amusement and were never put to the engineering applications that we would find so important today.

The prayer wheels that can be seen today in Tibet operate as Savonius rotors, working on the same principle as the rotating advertisements that can be seen outside many garages. The idea is that, with every revolution, they are taken to repeat automatically a Buddhist prayer which is inside the central cylinder. It has been claimed that these may have an ancient heritage, going back to when Buddhism was established in Tibet between AD 755 and 797 but there is no solid evidence for this. Wind chimes may also have an ancient pedigree but we lack historical evidence.

2.03.3 Persian Vertical Axis Designs

We can be sure that wind machines came quite early to the Muslim world. History records that a carpenter 'expert in the construction of windmills' was being taxed two pieces of silver a day when he murdered the second orthodox Caliph, Omar, in AD 644 in Medina. Abu Lulua, the Persian technologist in question, is said to have thought he was being excessively taxed, although the authenticity of this document has been questioned on the grounds that it was dated three centuries after the event.

Certainly by then, several Arabian geographers were writing about windmills in the Persian region of Seistan (a border region of modern Eastern Iran and Southwest Afghanistan). According to Al Masudi in AD 950,

> Segistan is a land of winds and sand. There the wind drives mills and raises water from the streams, whereby gardens are irrigated. There is in the world [and God alone knows it] nowhere where more frequent use is made of the winds.

Gale force winds of $20\,\text{m}\,\text{s}^{-1}$ coming down from the Hindu Kush are not uncommon there during the four windy months of the year, so 'a land of wind and sand' seems a very fair description.

These Persian machines were vertical axis machines with the axle fixed directly to the moving grindstone. It is often claimed that a major advantage of the vertical axis arrangement is that the mechanical drive can reach the ground and be coupled to its output without the need for gearing. This could not be more directly demonstrated than in the early Persian machines.

There were apparently two basic designs, one with the millstones on top of the rotor axle and one with them below. The first type had tapering loopholes in the structure of the surrounding building which funneled the wind onto the sails on one side of the rotor. The other type could be much higher without the need for a large supporting building. It had fixed matting screens to block off the wind from one side of the rotor and to channel the wind to the sails, a panemone design. In each case, the sails themselves were straw matting that formed a rotor up to 5 m in height and 3 m in diameter.

There were no brakes. It is suggested that screens could be moved across the loopholes or to redirect the wind as necessary, although the prospect of moving such large screens around in gale force winds is formidable. It is not surprising to learn that individual mills had to be rebuilt frequently. The Persian panemone design works on drag rather than lift and is inherently far less efficient than modern propeller-type designs, which is why they have prevailed elsewhere. On the other hand, when there are such high wind speeds to cope with, there is a need not to capture the full force of the wind and the Persian designs were evidently in the right place at the right time.

2.03.4 The Introduction of Windmills into Europe

Windmills came later to Europe and were horizontal axis propeller-type designs when they arrived. The winds available were not strong enough to make a practical proposition of the Persian design relying on drag.

It has been suggested that Crusaders in fact introduced these so-called European mills, with sails mounted in a propeller fashion on a horizontal axis, from Eastern Europe or the Middle East but the evidence and the timing strongly suggest that the introductions went the other way.

There is no mention of any windmills in the *Domesday Book*, the survey of England prepared for the king, William the Conqueror, William of Normandy, between AD 1080 and 1086, although it mentions that there were 5624 watermills in around 3000 different places.

That is an average of one mill for every 50 or so households at that time and the watermills were often little more than a kilometer apart. But not every place had streams, and where no water power was available, there was a strong incentive to introduce wind technology, although by the time of Domesday, it clearly had not yet arrived.

It is interesting to note that rights to the wind were free for everyone, in England at least, whereas the water rights belonged to the owner of the river bank on which a watermill was placed. This provided an added incentive for an entrepreneur who was not a landowner to set up a windmill to serve the local community. There was no such advantage in The Netherlands, where the wind belonged to the sovereign, who collected a tax, the 'wind brief', which would not be payable on a mill turned by a horse or a donkey. This may explain why wind-powered mills came first to England, before they came to any other country in Europe.

Half a century or so after the Domesday Book survey, the first definite mention on record of a windmill in England is found in an AD 1155 document, recording that "Hugo de Plaiz gave to the monks of Lewes the windmill in his Manor of Ilford for the health of the soul of his Father." Evidently, this windmill was already up and running and it may well have been operating for some time before then.

It is interesting to note that the monasteries, notably the recently founded Carthusians (AD 1081), were in the forefront of technology at this time. The monks wanted to automate manual labor, not because they were lazy but because they wanted to devote more of their time to their devotions and to contemplation.

After this first historical record, references to other windmills appear thick and fast throughout the length of England as well as in Northern France and Belgium. The technology evidently spread rapidly and by AD 1200 it was well established. The population was increasing and windmills may have helped to populate areas of the country where the rivers and streams were previously insufficient to grind enough corn to support a large population.

Because windmills are known to have been around in the Middle East before the Crusades, and the Crusaders are known to have used windmills, it has been claimed that it was they who introduced windmills into Europe. This claim fails to explain how the complicated horizontal axis design with gears was suddenly developed from the simple vertical axis machines with direct drives that were prevalent in the region. In fact the earliest known report of a Crusader's windmill concerns one the Crusaders carried with them to use during the siege of Acre, which ended in AD 1191. It is not known what design they brought with them but it would most likely have been the horizontal axis design prevalent in England and Northwest France. In that case, the Crusaders were taking technology from Europe to the Middle East, not the other way round.

Evidently wind power arose in England and spread to Northwest Europe in the first half of the twelfth century. It developed rapidly thereafter. For instance, the Bishopric of Ely, which had 22 watermills from AD 1086 throughout its various estates around the country, had added 4 windmills by AD 1222 but that had increased to 32 windmills by AD 1251. This rate of introduction of new wind power technology, doubling in numbers every 10 years, cannot match the rate of increase from 1990 to 2010, when wind power capacity worldwide doubled every 3 years, but it was still quite dramatic for its era.

Wind power spread rapidly across the Great Plains of Northern Europe and into Scandinavia. The date of the first machine in Germany has been given as 1222, Denmark 1259, Sweden 1300, and Spain, Russia, and Latvia 1330. The water flow in rivers and streams would freeze up in the middle of winter but winds would blow all the harder then. In fact windmills could keep going all the year-round whenever the wind blew. This gave wind power a very distinct advantage over water power in many countries.

Unfortunately, the wind was as variable then as it is today, so the applications had to be ones that did not need continuous power. Irrigation is one such application. Large areas of Britain in the fens of East Anglia were drained by the steady operation of wind pumps, whenever the wind blew. The land is 3 m lower today than it was in the Middle Ages.

Grinding corn was another such application. If the wind did not blow today, the miller would grind your corn tomorrow and if not tomorrow, then, as long as it blew sometime before the next harvest, you would not starve.

Fulling was a process of beating woolen cloth with hammers to remove grease, both that which was natural in the original fleece and any that was added to improve the spinning process. The wool would come to no harm if the hammering ceased for a while when the wind dropped.

2.03.5 Horizontal Axis Machines

Although a wind enthusiast will focus on the sails or the rotor as the most important feature of a windmill, from the miller's point of view they are actually peripheral. The central feature was the pair of millstones which had to be level and carefully balanced to run true and not to touch each other. They had to be carefully spaced (or tentered) to control the grade of flour and they were obviously the center of the miller's attention. He had to shut down the mill and reface his millstones every couple of weeks or so. Having established a satisfactory milling arrangement, driven by a waterwheel, it would have been most natural to retain that carefully developed design geometry for the most central feature of the mill when introducing a wind-driven mechanism.

A waterwheel has a horizontal axis, so a 90° gearing arrangement is needed to couple it to the moving millstone. That represented a considerable technical achievement in timber technology. Starting from scratch, a primitive wind machine would not use such a complicated arrangement. The directly coupled vertical axis Persian design is far more natural to start from and that is exactly what happened in Seistan. The millers in England and Northwest Europe were not starting from scratch, however. They had developed water-driven technology in the first place and, when they came to wind technology, they were starting from a well-established milling industry based upon horizontal axis drives from waterwheels. Not surprisingly, when they introduced wind power, they moved on to horizontal axis drives from wind turbines.

To capture the energy in the wind, it was not sufficient to replace the waterwheel with some form of wind wheel. An additional problem had to be overcome. Water flow is always in the same direction determined by the stream or river but, to quote the Christian Gospel according to St. John, "The wind bloweth where it listeth, and thou hearest the sound thereof, but canst not tell whence it cometh, and whither it goeth." It is the exception rather than the rule, certainly throughout Europe, for the wind to have a strongly prevailing direction. A windmill needs to be able to capture the wind coming from any direction. A vertical axis Savonius rotor can do that but a horizontal axis (propeller-type) wind rotor needs to turn to face into the wind.

2.03.6 Post and Tower Mills

The most obvious development was to mount the whole mill on a large post about which it could pivot and this produced the post mill, the type of windmill that is shown in medieval manuscripts. To support the whole of the milling machinery and the cladding which protected it from the weather needed a massive post of timber with an elaborate framework to support it and to provide bearings which would allow it to rotate but would withstand the sideways thrust. It was then the miller's main job to push the whole structure round to face into the wind.

It was not very convenient to have the whole of the space inside the mill rotatable to turn into the wind – or out of the wind when it needed to stop. A subsequent development placed only the essential parts that needed to rotate – the sails and the shaft – in a rotatable cap at the top of the structure, with the rest of the machinery in a fixed tower as the lower part of the structure (**Figure 6**).

Figure 6 Post mill. In a post mill, the whole of the machinery was supported by and turned together with a central post so that the rotor could face the wind. All early windmills in Europe were post mills but this one incorporates advanced technology (after 1600) with the spars nearer the leading edges of the blade.

The iconic tradition of Dutch windmills is for this type of tower mill with a rotatable cap. Around the shores of the Mediterranean, all the heavy timber had been used by the Romans and Greeks for their naval vessels, so post mills could not be built and tower mills were the norm. The characteristic design is circular with vertical sides and a conical cap.

The external appearance of the tower could vary widely according to the local building materials available. Brick and stone were common but a cheaper construction would use a wood frame clad with weatherboard or even thatch to create a so-called 'smock' mill.

The sails would each consist of a light wooden trellis over which canvas cloth could be stretched to catch the wind. Four such sails were almost universal, in the form of a cross, another part of the iconic Dutch tradition. The canvas could be woven and interlaced through the lattice from the central shaft to the outer end of the sail and retracted by ropes. Alternatively, it could be stretched over the frame and tied at the corners and at various points around the edge (**Figure 7**).

In each case, reefing was possible by rolling up some of the canvas and securing the roll to the framework. The miller would have to deal with each sail separately after the whole rotor was 'quartered' or pushed round 90° to be out of the wind. (It was important that he did not push the rotor too far round or the wind coming from behind could lift the entire shaft and rotor out of the mill.)

The prospect of doing this reefing in a strong wind, quite possibly in rain and sleet, handling soaking wet and even freezing canvas, is not attractive. Modern health and safety regulations would make the miller's job extremely difficult today! In parts of Northern Europe, wooden boards could be used instead of canvas, fixed in place with wooden dowels passed through staples (**Figure 8**).

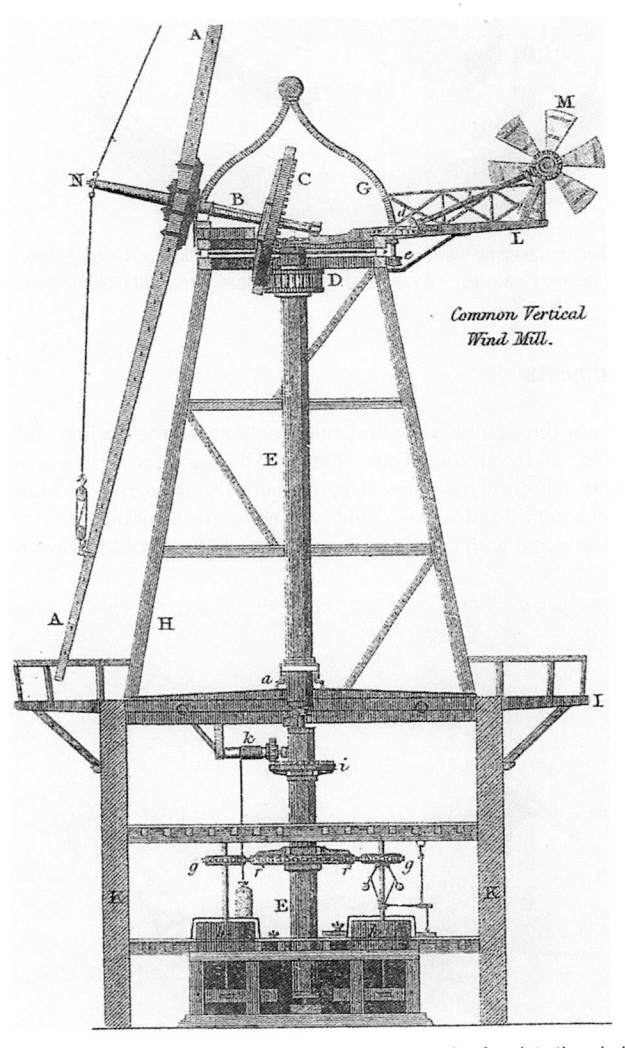

Figure 7 Smock mill. In a smock mill, only the rotor and the top part of the machinery turned to face into the wind. The most important parts that did the milling were inside the fixed structure that formed the lower part of the mill. Many different claddings were used to give protection from the weather and the whole effect resembled someone dressed in a smock, which was what the typical agricultural worker wore.

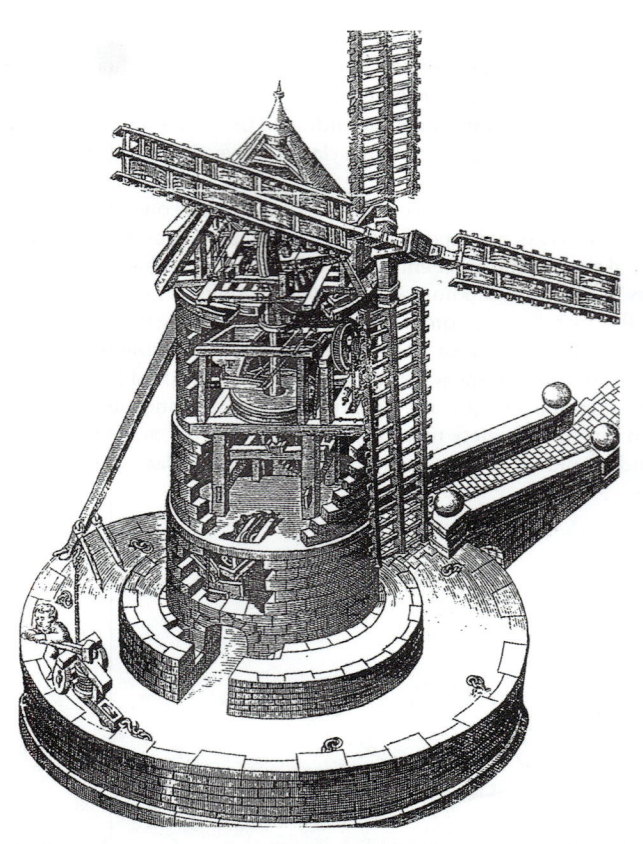

Figure 8 Tower mill. A tower mill worked in the same way as a smock mill but the cladding was more substantial, often brick or stone. This picture by Ramelli published in 1588 shows many detailed features, but note that the blade spars are central along the blades unlike the later design shown in **Figure 6**.

2.03.7 Technological Developments

The center of lift for an aerofoil is not through its centerline, midway between the leading and trailing edges, but further forward, about half-way between the centerline and the leading edge. That is the line along which the spar needs to be fixed if the blade is not to experience a twist force (**Figure 9**). Windmill designers discovered this from experience around 1600 and this made it possible to use longer spars and larger diameter rotors. Fixed boards could be used for the front quarter of the blade (see **Figure 6**) and only the rear part of the blade covered or uncovered with canvas to provide control (compare **Figures 6** and **7**).

Figure 9 Don Quixote's windmills. These tower mills at Campo de Criptana are typical of the ones that were to be found in Central Spain in the early part of the seventeenth century when 'The Ingenious Gentleman Don Quixote of La Mancha' invented by author Miguel Cervantes mistook them for knights-errant and famously proposed to tilt at them.

Figure 10 Brueghel's painting of a landscape with windmills. Oil painting by Jan the Elder Brueghel (1568–1625) of a village entrance with windmill. The windmill blades are tapered and twisted representing the latest technological developments at the time.

Figure 11 Brueghel's painting of a village entrance with a windmill. Oil painting by Jan The Elder Brueghel (1568–1625) of a village entrance with windmill. The miller can be seen turning his windmill into the wind.

Many other technological improvements were introduced from time to time over the next few centuries. Leonardo da Vinci (1452–1519) sketched a windmill with six sails rather than four, but it did not catch on (**Figure 10**).

A brake was a rather vital component which is not mentioned in the literature until 1588 and windmills were still being built without a brake as late as 1756. However, the brake was a rather dangerous contraption. If a windmill accelerated in a gust of wind despite the brake being on, the brake could become red hot and the wooden mechanism could burst into flame. With inflammable powder from the flour, an explosion could occur. Many windmills came to a fiery end and burnt down.

Twisted blades were thought to improve performance and Cornelis Dircksz Muys, an engineer of Delft, took out letters patent on sails with double curvature in 1589, which duly appeared in paintings by Brueghel around 1614 (**Figure 11**).

The fantail, which automatically turns a windmill to face into the wind, was not patented until 1745. A secondary rotor mounted at right angles to the main rotor axis can drive the main rotor round until it is exactly sideways to the wind and the main rotor axis is aligned to the wind. **Figure 17** shows a typical example of a fantail on a more modern machine.

2.03.8 Theory and Experiment: The Early Science

Simon Stevin was able to show in 1607 that the power of one of his mills was about 10 hp by working backward from how fast it pumped water and how high it raised the water. As he had no way of measuring wind speeds, he was not able to develop any theory. Many books of the period show how to build windmills but none is able to give any theory.

Francis Bacon wrote in 1622

> There is nothing very intricate in the motion of windmills but yet it is not generally demonstrated or explained... The wind rushing against the machine is compressed by the four sails and compelled to make a passage through the four openings between them. But this confinement it does not willingly submit to; so that it begins as it were to joy [sic] the sides of the sails and turn them round as children's toys are set in motion and turned by the finger. If the sails were stretched out equally it would be uncertain to which side they would incline. As, however, the side which meets the wind throws off the force of the wind to the lower side and thence through the vacant intervals... But it should be observed that the origin of the motion is not from the first impulse [that which is made in the front] but from the lateral impulse after compression has taken place.

Bacon's best attempt to provide himself with an open-ended wind tunnel used bellows. His models had paper sails of various shapes but he advised, "If these experiments be put into practice in windmills, the whole machine, especially its foundations, should be strengthened."

Antoine Parent published *Recherches de Mathématiques et de Physique* in 1713, 3 years before he died, which included a proof that the wind force on the sails was proportional to the square of its speed and the square of the sine of the angle of incidence, from which he deduced the optimum should be 54°44′.

Those calculations stood for 50 years until in 1754 William Emerson published *The Principles of Mechanics* in which he explained that Parent had ignored the effect of rotation on the angle of incidence, so the calculation was only correct with the rotor at rest, as it is when starting. He said that the optimum

> would always be so, if the wind struck them when moving as when at rest. But by reason of the swift motion of the sails, especially near the end [the tip], the wind strikes them under a far less angle; and not only so, but as the motion of the end is so swift, it may strike them on the backside. Therefore it will be more advantageous to make the angle of incidence greater, and so much more as it is further from [the axis].

These qualitative observations were being developed quantitatively in France by two outstanding mathematicians, Leonhard Euler and Jean-Baptiste le Rond d'Alembert, but John Smeaton, FRS, was ahead of them. He won the Copley Medal of the Royal Society in 1759 for his work on waterwheels and windmills, while at the same time famously working on plans for the Eddystone lighthouse. He was a brilliant mechanical engineer but he is also regarded as the 'father of civil engineering' having invented the forerunner of portland cement.

For his paper 'An experimental enquiry concerning the natural powers of water and wind to turn mills and other machines depending on circular motion', Smeaton had built a hydraulic test rig to compare different types of waterwheels. For a wind test rig, he noted that "the wind itself is too uncertain to answer the purpose, we must therefore have recourse to an artificial wind" and he fixed his test devices on the end of a 1.54 m long arm that could be rotated in a horizontal circle, keeping time with a swinging pendulum.

He found that with fixed pitch blades, the velocity of the sail varied as the wind velocity, V. The force varied as the velocity of the wind times the velocity of the sail, that is, as V^2. Finally, the 'effect' (or power output) was proportional to V^3. "The effects of the sails at a maximum are nearly, but somewhat less than, as the cubes of the velocity of the wind." These findings pretty well summarize the basic science of wind turbines as we know them today and Smeaton's work on many other details was regarded as definitive for the next century or more (Figure 12).

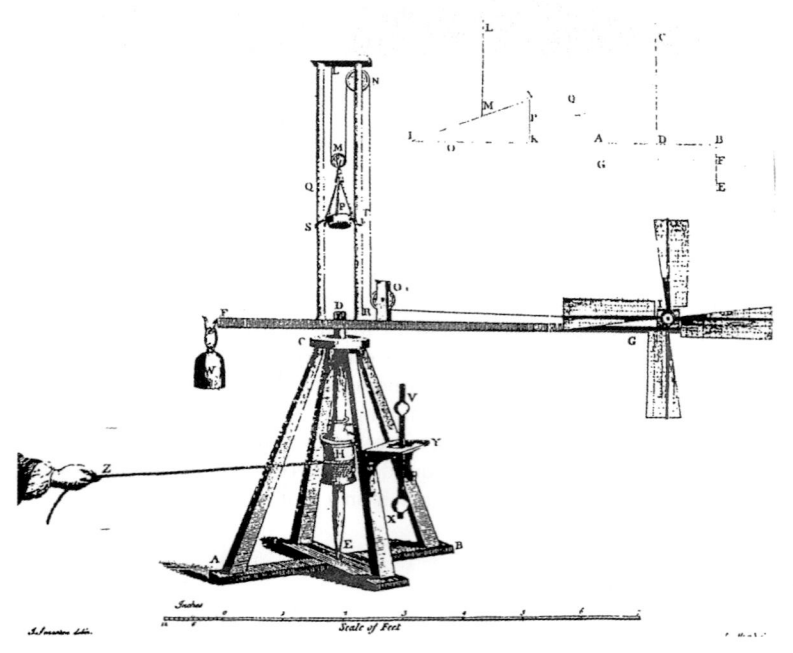

Figure 12 John Smeaton's test apparatus (1759). The apparatus was rotated by hand (Z) pulling on a rope wound round the axle (H). Rotations were timed by synchronizing with the balanced pendulum (V–X). The work done by the rotor on the end of the arm was measured by raising weights in the pan P.

Figure 13 Hammers for pressing oil. These hammers are for pressing oil from rapeseed or olives. Coulomb was able to measure accurately the rate of work done by such a machine as each of the hammers is lifted a fixed distance before being allowed to drop.

Another scientist and engineer who made careful measurements of the performances of working windmills (pressing oil from rapeseed near Lille in 1781) was Charles Coulomb, who is better remembered for his work on electrostatics (**Figure 13**). (The unit of electrical charge is named after him.)

2.03.9 The End of Windmills

Just as understanding was developing of how the large post and tower windmills worked, James Watt was pursuing the development that would eclipse them almost completely.

Hero's engine and other steam devices, such as those described by Taqi al-Din in 1551 and Giovanni Branca in 1629, were turbine devices with little practical use. Thomas Savery and many others worked on steam engines during the 1600s but it was Thomas Newcomen who built, in 1712, the first truly useful steam engine that could pump water out of mine workings from a hitherto impossible depth.

Newcomen's steam engine was not very efficient, probably much less than 1%, but James Watt made many improvements, especially that of building a separate condenser, and by 1776 he was installing steam engines in various commercial enterprises, mainly for pumping water out of mines in Cornwall.

From then on, the days of the windmill were numbered. No longer would the miller be at the mercy of the wind.

2.03.10 The American Wind Pump

When steam took over the role of wind in Europe, wind pumps for water still flourished in the Great Plains of America. Any enthusiast of cowboy movies will be familiar with two very characteristic scenes. The first is the cows, as far as the eye can see, tens of thousands of cows, which gave the cowboys their raison d'être. The next shot is of the desert – as far as the eye can see, dry dusty desert. It is obvious with a little thought that there must be some third shot, just out of these two frames, which explains how these two scenes can come within a hundred miles of each other. In dry, dusty desert, cows will die without water.

Well the water was there all right. Across the Great Plains, the proverbial dust bowl, groundwater is only a few meters below the dry, dusty surface. All the rancher running the herd had to do to find water was to dig down. He then had the problem of raising the water to the surface and for that the American wind pump was ideally suited.

The American wind pump was a multiblade machine of typically less than 1 hp mechanical output and, between 1850 and 1970, over six million of these small wind machines were installed in the United States alone.

The primary use was water pumping and the main applications were stock watering and farm home water needs. Very large wind pumps, with rotors up to 18 m in diameter, were used to pump water for the steam railroad trains that provided the primary source of commercial transportation in areas where there were no navigable rivers.

The most important refinement of the American fan-type windmill was the development of steel blades in 1870 (**Figure 5**). Steel blades could be made lighter and worked into more efficient shapes. They worked so well, in fact, that their high speed required a reduction (slowdown) gear to turn the standard reciprocating pumps at the required speed (**Figure 14**).

Most of these wind pumps had tails to orient them into the wind but some had downwind rotors coned to allow the wind itself to steer them directly. Some designs controlled their speed by hinging sections of blades to fold back like an umbrella in high winds, reducing the rotor capture area.

The simplex 'geared' wind engine.

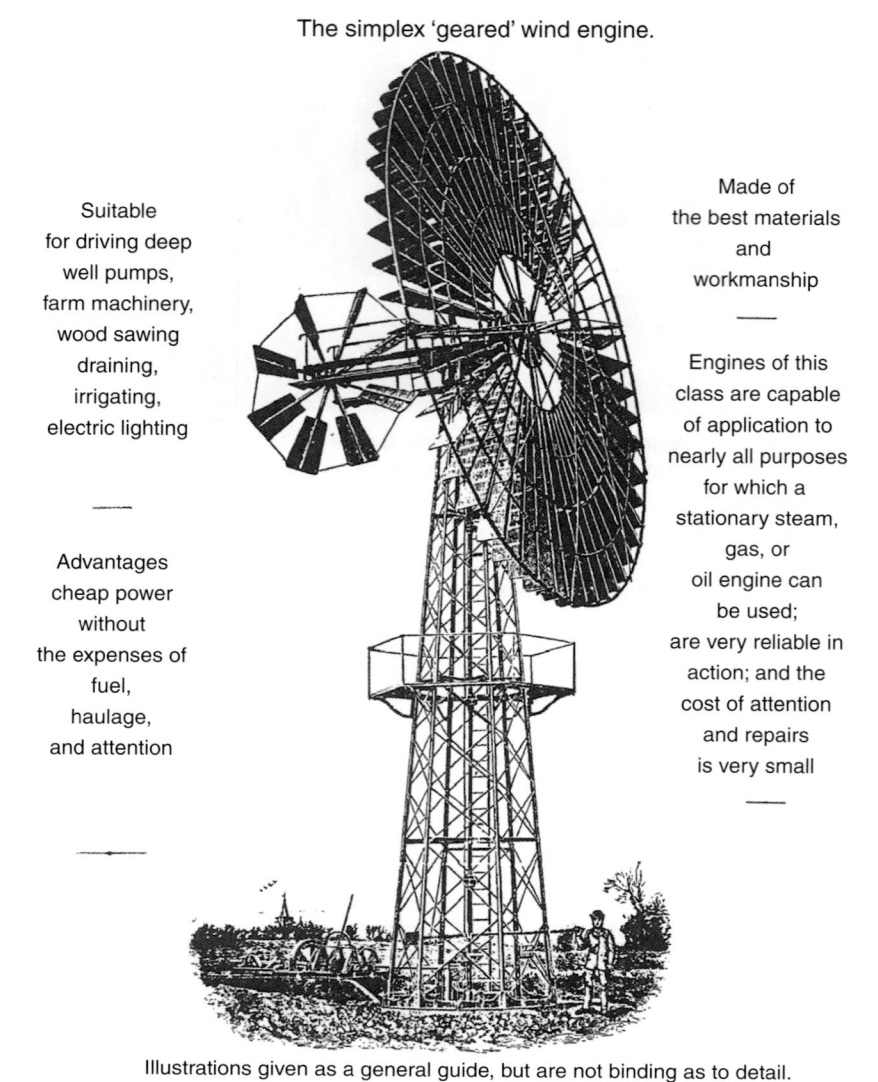

Suitable for driving deep well pumps, farm machinery, wood sawing draining, irrigating, electric lighting

Made of the best materials and workmanship

Engines of this class are capable of application to nearly all purposes for which a stationary steam, gas, or oil engine can be used; are very reliable in action; and the cost of attention and repairs is very small

Advantages cheap power without the expenses of fuel, haulage, and attention

Illustrations given as a general guide, but are not binding as to detail.

Figure 14 American multiblade wind pump. Thousands of American wind pumps like this one advertised in a 1905 catalog were sold to drive reciprocating pumps. The shutters could be feathered and a fantail keeps the main rotor facing into the wind.

It is not too much to claim that it was the American wind pump that opened up the American West, at least as far as the Rockies. A similar situation is found in Australia where the arid central region of semidesert covers water courses and underground aquifers that are fed from the tropical jungles of New Guinea.

American wind pumps disappeared almost overnight in the 1920s. The coming of the great dams and cheap electricity, starting with the Hoover Dam, meant that, when a wind pump broke down, it was cheaper to install a small electric motor than to mend the rotor and its couplings.

2.03.11 Electrical Power from the Wind

In 1821, Michael Faraday at the Royal Institution demonstrated the first electrical motor, a small DC homopolar unit. Ten years later, he had discovered electrical induction (although others, including the American Joseph Henry, could claim to have done so independently). Within 10 more years, he had built a dynamo.

There is no argument that the first public power supply was water-driven to light the streets of Godalming in Surrey, England, in 1881. Steam power followed rapidly in 1882 when Thomas Edison opened a power plant at Holborn Viaduct in London and, later in the year, he opened one at Pearl Street in Manhattan. By 1887, there were 121 Edison power stations in the United States delivering DC electricity to customers. The new electrical technology was advancing at a cracking pace.

It was perhaps natural to think of driving an electrical dynamo from a wind machine to produce wind power generation and several people can claim to have been among the first (**Figure 15**).

Figure 15 Blyth's wind generator. Prof. James Blyth from a forerunner of University of Strathclyde can claim to be the first to have generated electrical power from the wind. His first experiments in 1887 used a smock mill design (horizontal axis) but this 10 m diameter vertical axis machine was built at Marykirk, Scotland, in 1891 and continued to operate until 1914. Each semicylindrical box is 1.8 × 1.8 m and the lady standing at the door of the electrical enclosure gives the scale. A railway embankment and bridge over the North Esk River are in the background.

William Thomson, later to become Lord Kelvin, can probably claim to be the first to propose it seriously in his 1881 address to the British Association 'On the sources of energy in nature available to man for the production of mechanical effect'.

Prof. James Blyth was appointed professor of Natural Philosophy in Anderson's College, Glasgow, and, shortly after the College became Glasgow and West of Scotland Technical College in 1886 (which in due course became University of Strathclyde in 1964), he was experimenting with a wind-to-electricity machine. His first generation was recorded in July 1887 and that seems to be the first electrical power from the wind, although Blyth did not patent his vertical axis wind turbine for generating electricity until 1891.

On a much grander scale, Charles Brush in the United States first generated power from the wind in the winter of 1887 and he is often credited with the leading role. His huge wind turbine generator gave his home the first electricity supply in Cleveland, Ohio, in 1888 and it is claimed that "Over its 20 year life, the turbine never failed to keep the home continuously powered." As an inventor and industrialist he had made a fortune selling arc lighting systems across America from New York to San Francisco and he set up what became Brush Electrical Engineering in Loughborough, England (**Figure 16**). He sold his American company off to General Electric (GE).

Figure 16 Brush's wind generator. American inventor and industrialist Charles Brush was one of the first to generate electrical power from the wind and he built a huge wind turbine generator 17 m in diameter with 144 blades to power his home in Cleveland, Ohio, throughout the 1890s.

Figure 17 Poul La Cour's experimental station. Wind turbine generators built at La Cour's experimental station at Askov, Denmark, in 1891 and 1897. La Cour is regarded in Denmark as the father of wind power.

Poul La Cour was also active in the field and he may also have generated electricity from the wind around the same time in 1887. Certainly by 1891 La Cour was the director of a windmill experimental station established by the Danish government at Askov near Esbjerg and his work provided a lasting foundation for later wind power developments in Denmark.

After the Wright Brothers' successful powered flight in 1903, aeronautical developments proceeded rapidly, for instance with the founding of the Royal Aircraft Establishment at Farnborough, UK, as a center of expertise in 1909. Betz, at Göttingen in Germany, pointed out in 1920 that his theory of propellers to drive aeroplanes, with simple reversal of the flow, established the limit of 16/27ths for the extraction of power from the wind with a propeller type of rotor. Frederick Lanchester in England in fact deserves priority because he had already derived the same expression which is valid for incompressible flow but he published his result in 1915 in the Proceedings of the Institution of Naval Architects because he was interested in ships propellers. Joukowski had also discovered the limit independently in 1920 but he published his result in Russian. For the aerodynamics community, both these contributions were published in unfamiliar places and Betz' name was firmly associated with the 16/27 limit before either of his competitors for priority was properly recognized (Figure 17).

Many small wind turbine generators were developed for sites remote from electrical supplies, which were commonplace in the late 1800s and early 1900s, including ones on sailing ships. The range of machines in widespread use was considerable and around 1930 a team from Oxford University set up a test site near Harpenden, 25 miles north of London, where they operated a range of different types of wind turbine, nine in all. The machines varied from slow-turning multiblade American designs to ones with aerofoil blades. Rotor diameters ranged from 2.4 to 9 m and annual electrical generation was from 83.5 to 199 kWh m^{-2} (from 10 to 25 W year-round average per square meter).

This was the era of small machines and by 1947 the market in America alone was more than 10 000 per year for wind turbines generating less than 1 kW and at the 1954 World Power Conference in Brazil, Russia claimed to have nearly 30 000 wind power plants averaging around 4 kW each.

2.03.12 Large Machines

Interest in large machines to supply electrical power systems was sporadic until the 1980s. The individual machines that were built were designed by different enthusiasts and teams with no connections or access to the details of what had gone before and most of the expertise was from other fields of mechanical and aeronautical engineering.

In 1925, Flettner crossed the Atlantic in a ship powered by two vertical electrically driven rotating rotors using the Magnus effect and the following year he built a four-bladed propeller rotor with each blade consisting of an electrically driven rotating cylinder.

The Magnus effect excites interest because it provides the means to avoid the Betz limit of 16/27 or 59%. A rotor cannot extract all the kinetic energy in the wind. If it did, it would bring the air to rest and the incoming flow would be diverted round the obstruction. The best that can be done is to reduce the wind speed to one-third and therefore the kinetic energy of the air that goes through the rotor to one-ninth, but the slowed air then pushes one-third of the air flow aside from the rotor, so the rotor only captures two-thirds of eight-ninths of the incoming energy or 16/27ths (Figure 18).

Betz's theory was for irrotational and incompressible flow through a rotor such as a propeller. A rotating cylinder creates a vortex which extends to a far greater radius than the central cylinder which constitutes the rotor and it can capture energy from the wind over a much broader area.

Mádaras proposed to take this principle to a grand scale. He proposed to mount rotating cylinders on a train of flat railway trucks on a circular track (which would reverse the direction of thrust twice in each circuit round the track) and in 1933 he built and tested a full-scale single-cylinder demonstration unit, which was 27.5 m in height and 8.5 m in diameter, at Burlington, New Jersey.

Demonstrably the principle works, but, despite these successes, Magnus effect machines have not gained favor.

Figure 18 Flettner rotors' trans-Atlantic crossing. Flettner's ship the *Baden Baden* was fitted with two electrically driven rotating cylinders which used the Magnus effect to sail successfully across the Atlantic in 1925.

In 1929, Darrieus designed a very elegant propeller machine with a two-blade, 20 m diameter rotor, which was built on the French side of the English Channel at Le Bourget. However, he is better known for his vertical axis wind turbines with troposkein blades that took the shape of a skipping rope or 'egg whisk' under centrifugal forces. He patented his design in 1931 but little work was done on it until it was taken up by the Canadians 40 years later.

Balaclava in the Crimea is famous for the heroic (and useless) Charge of the Light Brigade in 1854. Seventy-seven years later, in 1931, at a site overlooking the Black Sea (which is repeatedly and erroneously in the literature referred to as the Caspian Sea), the Central Wind Power Institute of Russia built a 30 m diameter, two-blade propeller-type wind turbine, which reached its rated power of 100 kW at a wind speed of 11 m s^{-1}. An aerodynamically shaped nacelle sat on a 30 m tower and was supported against the force of the wind by an angled strut, the bottom end of which moved around a circular track on the ground (**Figure 19**).

Figure 19 Darrieus' two-blade, 20 m diameter wind turbine. This wind turbine was erected at Le Bourget in France in 1929.

Figure 20 Russian two-blade, 30 m diameter, 100 kW wind turbine. The first machine to feed AC into a local grid was built at Balaclava in 1931. It ran successfully for 10 years.

This was the first wind turbine generator to feed AC into the local electricity network and it was maintained in service for 10 years, until it was damaged by World War II. The reported performance as a generator was somewhat ambiguous. When it had operated for more than 2 years feeding power into the local 6.3 kV power distribution network, it was claimed to have generated 200 000 kWh. That would correspond to an average load factor of less than 12%, although an annual load factor of 32% was optimistically claimed. Nevertheless, it represented a noteworthy achievement (**Figure 20**).

2.03.13 The Smith-Putnam Machine

Palmer Cosslett Putnam served in the British Royal Air Force toward the end of the first world war. He graduated from MIT (Massachusetts Institute of Technology) with a degree in geology in 1924 and was chairman of the Putnam family publishing house from 1930 to 1932. He developed an interest in power from the wind after reading about the Balaclava machine and experiencing high winds at the holiday home he built for himself at Cape Cod in 1934.

Putnam put together proposals to build and operate a large 1.5 MW wind turbine. He had a wide range of contacts in Cambridge (Massachusetts) and by 1937 he had gained the interest and support of the dean of engineering at MIT. The dean introduced him to a vice president of GE, who provided him with office space and agreed to supply the generator. The engineers at GE introduced him to the president and the chief engineer of the New England Public Service Corporation, who arranged that a subsidiary, the Central Vermont Public Service Corporation, would integrate the wind turbine into their local system (**Figure 21**).

In 1939, he found the S. Morgan Smith Company, a prosperous family business, which was prepared to undertake the construction of the 1.5 MW wind turbine and to provide most of the necessary finance entirely from its own private resources, which were substantial. The company appointed Putnam as project manager. By the end of the project, the company had spent more than US$1.25 million on the prototype turbine, US$19 million in today's money. The whole of the project is described in great detail by Putnam in his 1948 book *Power from the Wind*.

The huge Smith-Putnam project brings us full cycle from the introduction of horizontal axis wind turbines into Europe when wind machines were developed from waterwheels. This was what happened inside the S. Morgan Smith Company. The company's main business was to build variable-pitch hydraulic turbines to generate water power. They thought that wind

Figure 21 The first megawatt-sized wind turbine was built in 1941. The Smith-Putnam project on Grandpa's Knob, Vermont, was for a two-bladed, 53 m diameter, 1.25 MW machine. The whole project is set out in detail in Putnam's book *Power from the wind* (van Nostrand, 1948).

would be valuable to use in conjunction with hydroelectricity to save water when it was running low, so they went for a wind turbine project.

Putnam had numerous academics to advise him. John Wilbur who was head of the Department of Civil Engineering at MIT acted as chief engineer. Sverre Petterssen was head of the Department of Meteorology at MIT. Charles Brooks was professor of meteorology at Harvard University. Prof. S. J. Newell of the Aeronautical Engineering Department at MIT did the structural analysis of the turbine blades. Dr. J. P. den Hartog of Harvard University did the vibration analysis of the whole structure. Theodore von Karman of CIT (California Institute of Technology) supervised and advised on aerodynamics (and it would be difficult to find anyone more authoritative). Dr. Elliott Reid of Stanford University did the wind tunnel testing of blades. Dr. Th Troller of CIT did wind tunnel tests of flow over hills. Dr. R. F. Griggs of George Washington University did ecological studies and there were many others. Putnam also retained many engineering consultants and private companies to do different aspects of the design and to manufacture the component parts of the machine.

The site selected was a 610 m high hill in Castleton, Vermont. Putnam explains that, "This peak had not been distinguished on maps by a separate name. It was bought from a Vermont farmer whose family always referred to it as 'Grandpa's.' Because of this and its shape, we christened it Grandpa's Knob."

This wind turbine was far larger than any previous machine, with its rotor diameter of 53 m. It had two 2.4 m wide steel blades each about 20 m long. With no tapering, they looked like the wings of an aeroplane and were mounted on the downwind side of a lattice tower. The blades had steel spars with ribs and skins of stainless steel and the pitch of the whole blade could be varied. Yaw control was from a vane on top of the nacelle, which sent an electrical signal to a hydraulic motor to drive a small gear wheel which would move the whole nacelle round to align it with the wind. Almost every large wind turbine built today uses this type of yaw control.

The Smith-Putnam machine first turned in August 1941 and was tested under no-load conditions to verify mechanical operation of the rotor and the blade control system. The synchronous generator was first synchronized to the local electrical grid on the evening of 19 October 1941, when it was tested under loads varying from zero to 700 kW. Putnam was able to claim, "For the first time anywhere, power from the wind was being fed synchronously to the high-line of a utility system."

Under test, the unit operated in winds up to 70 mph or more generating as much as 1.5 MW. It ran for about 1000 h in all between start-up and February 1943, when a shaft bearing failed. Due to wartime material priorities, the bearing was not replaced until 3 March 1945 and even then it was not practical to complete a full repair and reinforcement of the blade root.

The unit then achieved another 3 weeks of successful operation but on 26 March 1945 at 3.10 a.m. in the middle of the night, "One of the 8-ton blades had let go when in about the 7 o'clock position [as subsequently computed by von Kármán], and had been tossed 750 feet, where it landed on its tip." "Inspection showed that the blade spar had failed along multiple and corroded cracks" and the causes were seen to be due to stress concentrations and "some fatigue due to 1,500,000 revolutions of the turbine, with stress variations [but not complete reversals] in each revolution".

When a wind turbine fails today, the manufacturers and operators tend to keep quiet and to release very little information about what has actually happened. We are fortunate in having a graphic report from an insider who was on the spot. The erection foreman was in the nacelle at the time and showed an amazing presence of mind.

Figure 22 The blade that failed. After operating successfully for only a few weeks altogether, the Smith-Putnam machine shed a blade due to a fatigue failure in 1945.

Putnam records that,

> At 3.10 A.M. Harold Perry, the erection foreman, was aloft, standing on the side of the house away from the control panel and separated from it by the 24-inch rotating main shaft. A shock threw him to his knees against the wall. He started for the controls, but was again thrown to his knees. He tried again, and was again thrown down. Collecting himself, he dove over the rotating shaft, reached the controls, and, overriding the automatic controls which were already functioning, he brought the unit to a full stop in about 10 seconds by bringing the remaining blade to full feather.

The rotor with only one blade remaining had made about three revolutions at full speed and four more as it slowed down and came to a stop (**Figure 22**).

A study completed in 1945 showed that a 9 MW wind farm of six turbines similar to the prototype could be installed in Vermont for around US$1.7 million (US$25 million in today's money). Even if the technical problems that had led to the dramatic failure could be overcome, this was 50% above the commercial value, so further development was not considered profitable and repairs were never carried out after the March 1945 breakdown. The break-even cost of US$25 million in 1945, corresponding to around US$1900 million in 2010 money, is interestingly close to today's break-even figures. The prototype turbine was dismantled in 1946, leaving only concrete footings and a marker plaque on Grandpa's Knob today.

Structural metal fatigue, which destroyed the Smith-Putnam machine, was well enough recognized as a problem in 1948 to be the subject of Nevile Shute's novel *No Highway* based upon his experiences as a research engineer at the Royal Aircraft Establishment, Farnborough. His novel seemed to presage the Comet air disasters in 1954 but it was not until those two crashes that work on metal fatigue was intensified and the problem was promoted to the forefront of technology across the whole field of aerodynamics.

2.03.14 Postwar Programs

The United Kingdom had one of the most serious postwar programs to develop wind turbines. In 1948, E. W. Golding at the Electrical Research Association laboratories in Leatherhead, UK, was put in charge of a national program. Much of the knowledge and expertise that he gained in this position are set out in his text book *The Generation of Electricity by Wind Power* published by Spon in 1955, which remained the most comprehensive and authoritative text on the subject for the next three decades.

In addition to many paper studies (there were no serious computers at that time), the program focused upon three practical designs that were built.

In 1952, Tom Mensforth of Constructors John Brown (the firm that had built the original Queen Mary and Queen Elizabeth liners for Cunard) erected a 100 kW wind turbine on Costa Hill on Orkney Mainland off the northern tip of Scotland, one of the windiest sites in the United Kingdom. Golding claimed, "It has a long-term annual average wind speed of 25 m.p.h. at 10 ft above the ground," that is, 11 m s^{-1} at 3 m height, so the machine's rated wind speed was set remarkably high at 16 m s^{-1}. The cliff-top site he chose, just inland from Costa Head, facing the Atlantic gales, must also be one of the most turbulent sites in the United Kingdom (**Figure 23**).

The rotor was downwind and started out at 18.3 m diameter but, although it was coned downstream away from the hub, one of the fabricated wooden blades managed to hit the lattice tower with a tip speed of 124 m s^{-1}. The original blades were duly replaced with shortened ones to give a 15.2 m diameter rotor. Testing and development to iron out the many problems that arose continued until 1956 when the project was shut down (**Figure 24**).

Tom Mensforth indefatigably came up with another forward-looking idea which he presented at the Future Energy Concepts Conference at the IEE (Institution of Electrical Engineers) in London in 1979 after his retirement. It worked on the same structural principle as the 135 m diameter Eye of London – or, indeed, a bicycle wheel – with a compressed rim supported by spokes or cables

Figure 23 Tom Mensforth's 100 kW wind turbine on Costa Head in 1952. With an 18.3 m diameter rotor turning at 130 rpm, the blades hit the tower at nearly 300 mph despite being mounted downwind. Shorter stubbier blades reduced the diameter to 15.2 m. The project was terminated in 1956.

all in tension. This design has the potential for scaling up to huge sizes. Although the concept was somewhat skeptically received when it was first presented, it was later the subject of a substantial joint study by the Central Electricity Generating Board (CEGB), Howdens of Glasgow, and John Laing Construction, which considered a 20 MW rotor 200 m in diameter.

The second British machine, designed by a Frenchman, J. Andreau, was built by the de Havilland aircraft company for Enfield Cables Ltd. It was a 100 kW two-bladed wind turbine with a 24 m diameter rotor downwind of a 30 m tubular tower. The blades were made of aluminum, which did not bode well for an adequate fatigue performance. It was built on a site at St. Albans, north of London, in 1955. This design attempted to overcome the gearbox problem by using hollow blades so that air was sucked up by centrifugal forces and expelled from the tips of the blades, first passing through a small high-speed air turbine directly coupled to an alternator inside the tower (**Figure 25**).

One of the most serious problems facing wind turbine constructors today is the difficulty of obtaining planning consents from local authorities. The Enfield-Andreau machine has the distinction of being one of the first machines to suffer from this problem. The initial site at St. Albans was to be a temporary one. It had a poor wind regime but it was convenient for the constructors (de Havillands at Hatfield, only 5 km away) and the owners at Enfield (only 15 km). The site with the windiest velocity duration curve shown in Golding's book is Mynydd Anelog in North Wales and that is where it was planned to move the machine to after initial commissioning and testing. Unfortunately and unhappily, planning consent was refused! In 1957, the machine was sold to Électricité et Gaz d'Algérie and was dismantled and reerected on the Grand Vent hilltop near Algiers. It ran for a total of less than 200 h before fatigue cracks developed near the blade roots, a development that is not very surprising to the modern engineer familiar with metal fatigue in aluminum.

The third machine in the British program built in 1959 was a much simpler and lower cost machine sited on the Isle of Man. It was what would be regarded today as a fairly conventional design. It had a 15 m diameter rotor with three fixed blades (made from extruded aluminum but with steel bracing) mounted upwind on a lattice tower and rated at 100 kW. The air brakes at the blade tips caused considerable drag even when not deployed (losing as much as 30 kW of power). In many ways, this machine with stall

Figure 24 Tom Mensforth's design for a giant wind turbine. The 'bicycle wheel' structure is very strong and light aerofoils mounted on the 'spokes' do not need to be structural members as in a conventional propeller design.

control and an induction generator for grid connection was similar in principle to the larger Gedser machine which we shall meet next.

The Isle of Man machine operated experimentally fairly successfully for 6 years until a blade hit the tower. By this time, the British nuclear energy program was well under way with several Magnox nuclear power stations already commissioned. Oil prices had come down as well, so enthusiasm for alternative forms of energy had evaporated and with it the funding for the British program.

2.03.15 The Mother of All Modern Wind Turbines

In 1956, with funding from the American Marshall Plan for postwar reconstruction, Johannes Juul, a former student of Poul La Cour, built a 200 kW, 24 m diameter machine for the electricity company SEAS at Gedser on the southeastern coast of Denmark on the Baltic. This machine featured a three-bladed upwind rotor with fixed pitch blades that used mechanical windmill technology augmented with an airframe support structure and it was a far simpler and more basic design than the Smith-Putnam machine (**Figure 26**).

In fact, the design was not that far removed from Poul La Cour's 1920-era wind turbine and this machine had the distinction of operating for more than a decade without falling apart as most of its predecessors had done. It can be said to have led to all the subsequent developments in Danish wind turbine manufacturing, which have eventually been turned to by all major manufacturers around the world. All the Danish commercial machines were three-bladed upwind designs, which the rest of the world has eventually followed, and the Danes often call the Gedser machine "the mother of all modern wind turbines" (**Figure 27**).

The Gedser machine ceased operating in 1967, a fact usually blamed on falling oil and coal prices, although, with zero energy costs, that explanation needs explaining. In fact the repair and maintenance costs were found to be too large to justify continuing the operation.

The French designed a number of wind turbines around this time. Following the Enfield-Andreau machine built at St. Albans in England, a 31 m diameter wind turbine was built by Électricité de France in 1958, which fed 800 kW of power into the grid at Nogent-le-Roi and continued operating until 1963. An even larger 1.1 MW, 35 m diameter unit was built at St. Rémy des Landes at the end of 1963 and generated successfully for 7 months before the main shaft broke and Électricité de France decided to pull out of wind power and focus on nuclear power instead, which they very successfully proceeded to do.

Figure 25 The Enfield-Andreau machine. Enfield Cables were the owners and Jean Andreau was the designer of this 24 m diameter, 100 kW wind turbine built with two aluminum blades in 1955. This represents an early example of planning consent problems when it could not be sited at Mynydd Anelog in Wales.

These machines were highly rated by today's standards for such small diameters, which meant that they would have very low load factors but Golding's book had shown that the generation costs from a given rotor have a very flat optimum versus the size of the electrical generator.

2.03.16 Ulrich Hütter

Austrian Ulrich Hütter, after a career in the German aircraft industry, became a professor at the University of Stuttgart in Germany in 1959. He developed a series of advanced, horizontal axis designs of intermediate size that utilized modern, airfoil-type fiberglass and plastic blades with variable pitch to provide lightweight and high efficiencies. These were recognized as being high technology but they were all downwind machines (**Figure 28**).

He preferred two high-performance blades to three blades and his design approach sought to reduce the resultant bearing and structural stresses (which had led to so many previous failures in two-bladed designs) by shedding aerodynamic loads, rather than withstanding them as did the Danish approach. One of the most innovative load-shedding design features was the use of a bearing at the rotor hub that allowed the rotor to 'teeter' in response to wind gusts and vertical wind shear. Hütter's advanced designs achieved over 4000 h of operation before the experiments were ended in 1968.

There was little major wind power construction elsewhere for the next few years but 1973 saw the burst of activity that has continued to the present day.

2.03.17 The Battle of the Blades: Two versus Three

The Yom Kippur War in 1973 caused a worldwide oil crisis which spread across the whole energy field (and precipitated a 3-day working week in Britain). In the mistaken belief that the world was running out of oil, there was a burst of interest in all types of renewable energy, because renewable energy can never run out – it is endlessly renewable.

It turned out that the belief in disappearing oil was mistaken. Despite rapidly increasing consumption, oil reserves increased almost every year for the next 30 years but, fortunately for those of us working on renewables, by the time this trend had become apparent, concerns about global warming had emerged to justify our continuing activities.

Figure 26 The Isle of Man machine. This 15 m diameter machine built in 1959 had three fixed blades (aluminum with steel bracing) with stall control and an induction generator rated at 100 kW.

The Americans, looking for immediate results, funded a renewed testing program on the Gedser wind turbine, which was brought back into service. This program confirmed how the machine operated and gave a fresh impetus to the Danish wind industry, which proceeded to develop three-bladed machines. It showed, however, how relatively old the technology was and NASA, fresh from their flights to the moon, were interested in more sophisticated possibilities.

The UK government was slow off the mark with wind. Perhaps there were memories of the substantial postwar wind power program that had come to nothing less than a decade ago. A think tank in the prime minister's office preferred wave power and, for a number of years, that was at the top of the UK agenda, with enthusiasts like Stephen Salter with his 'nodding duck' and Sir Christopher Cockerell of hovercraft fame with his 'Cockerell raft' leading the way. It was left to an English baronet, Sir Henry Lawson-Tancred, to build a 17 m diameter wind turbine on his own estate at Aldborough near Boroughbridge in Yorkshire in 1977 with his own funds. The rotor had three fixed pitch blades mounted upwind of a lattice tower and was reminiscent of the last British-built machine turning on the Isle of Man, which had also been rated at 100 kW just over a decade earlier.

When the British discovered some of the problems – and costs – of wave power and finally turned to take an interest in wind power again, the Lawson-Tancred machine became the focus of a program of measurements by the CEGB, much as the Americans had turned to the Gedser machine. Its initial rating was 30 kW because that seemed quite sufficient to meet the demand for power on his estate but Sir Henry was soon encouraged to install a larger dynamo to give his machine a 100 kW rating. This wind turbine continued as a focus of attention for many years but Sir Henry was overtaken by the major British companies who entered the field after him (**Figure 29**).

In setting up the US research program, NASA pursued Hütter's advanced ideas and technology, which focused strongly on two-blade designs. The Danes, with Gedser in their backyard, pursued three blades and the battle between these designs was fought throughout the 1980s.

Betz had shown that no matter how many blades there are on a rotor, the turbine can capture only a maximum of less than 60% (16/27) of the energy flowing through its cross section. (To capture 100%, the air would have to slow down to zero speed, which would prevent any more air entering the rotor and would push the flow around the edge, so no more energy would be captured.) A single blade swept round fast enough can capture virtually all the available energy and two or three or more blades cannot do appreciably better.

From the cost point of view, one blade is obviously cheaper than two blades and two blades are cheaper than three blades. The period of post and tower windmills was dominated by four blades and the era of the American wind pumps had

Figure 27 The Gedser machine: 'the mother of all modern wind turbines'. This is a 24 m diameter, 200 kW machine with three fixed blades rotating upwind. It operated reliably from 1956 for 10 years, when falling oil and coal prices made its operation and maintenance costs uneconomical. It was shut down for a period but following the 1973 oil crisis, NASA paid for it to be recommissioned.

many more blades. A measure of the cost is the rotor fill factor or solidity, the proportion of the swept area that is covered with solid blades. (A funnel or concentrator that focuses the wind onto a small rotor starts with the major disadvantage of 100% solidity.) With fewer blades, the solidity is usually lower, although the blades must travel faster to sweep up the wind energy across the whole rotor area.

Technically the problem is all a matter of balance. A single blade is clearly not statically balanced and a counterweight must be attached to correct this.

Wortmann at MBB (Messerschmitt-Bölkow-Blohm) developed a series of one-bladed (Monopteros) wind turbines including a 350 kW, 48 m diameter machine and culminating in a 1 MW, 56 m diameter machine. The single blade needs to go round rapidly to sweep up all the wind energy passing through the rotor and that means that these machines tended to be very noisy. At all events, work on single-bladed machines ceased on Wortmann's death in 1986.

Two blades (or a counterweighted single blade) are statically but not dynamically balanced. When the rotation of a body is perturbed (or indeed the state of any physical system), it will tend to sink to a state of minimum energy. This will correspond to rotation about the axis with the lowest moment of inertia. In the two-blade case, this minimum axis is along the line of the blades, an impossible rotation as far as the bearings are concerned. The whole force of any perturbation, for example, due to gusting wind must be corrected by the bearings, calling for heavy and costly installations.

With three (or more) blades spread symmetrically round the rotor, the principal moments of inertia are equal, so the rotor is neutrally balanced dynamically. If the rotation is perturbed, it can continue in its new mode without seeking a different energy state because all states have the same energy. So the bearings have no extra forces to cope with (**Figures 30 and 31**).

Hütter had seen the stability problem with two blades very clearly and proposed a 'teetered' hub to deal with it, an angled bearing on a wishbone-shaped support. Any perturbation tending to push the blade backward or forward in the direction of the wind (rotating it about a 90° axis) will then produce a rotation in the plane of the rotor to counterbalance such a change.

The race developed between the Danish three-blade design and the two-blade designs pursued by the Americans and the British had been spearheaded by the Germans.

Figure 28 Hütter's wind turbines. Prof. Hütter of Stuttgart University developed a range of machines with two high-performance blades on teetered hubs mounted downwind of slender towers. These operated well for more than 4000 h and they formed the basis of the two-bladed designs preferred by NASA and most other countries, with the notable exception of Denmark, in the 1970s and 1980s.

2.03.18 Large Two-Bladed Wind Turbines

By the 1970s, a single power station would typically generate 1000 or 2000 MW and, if wind was to make any serious contribution to the energy scene, it was felt that at least megawatt sizes of wind turbines were called for. Certainly, this view had been held and put into practice a generation earlier by Palmer Cosslett Putnam on Grandpa's Knob. Most major government programs around the world concentrated upon megawatt-sized machines, while the Danish manufacturers continued successfully selling much smaller machines rated at no more than 50 or 100 kW.

The United States led the two-bladed way with the MOD series of wind turbines. The 100 kW MOD-0 was installed at NASA's Plum Brook, Ohio, facility in 1975. This was a downwind machine with a rigid hub and it suffered from severe buffeting of the blades as they entered and left the shadows of the large lattice towers. Hütter had avoided this problem by using the more costly and complex teetered hub and his much smaller towers had not created such severe shadowing. It took several years of engineering studies, responding to outraged congressional inquiries (from none other than Barry Goldwater) and other diversions, to figure out what was going on and for the US program to switch to an upwind, teetered hub configuration (**Figure 32**).

The rigid hub downwind turbines nonetheless served as useful demonstration projects until the larger machines arrived in the early 1980s. Several 200 kW MOD-0A machines were built by Westinghouse and the US program's biggest early success was the operation of four MOD-0A machines by US utility companies.

They led to the GE MOD-1 installation at Boone in North Carolina in 1979, which was with a 2 MW machine. It had a downwind rotor with all the problems of severe tower shadow, not least of generating low-frequency noise. With three states objecting (because Boone was close to Kentucky, Ohio, and North Carolina), this venture was unsuccessful and the company dropped out of wind power for a generation until the Enron debacle in 2003 left a successful wind turbine manufacturing subsidiary in the hands of the administrators. GE stepped in to snap this up and they are now one of the leading manufacturers with an 18% share of the world market.

Figure 29 Lawson-Tancred's machine at Aldborough in 1977. Sir Henry Lawson-Tancred, an English baronet, built this 17 m diameter, 100 kW machine on his own estate at Aldborough in Yorkshire, UK.

The first US wind turbine to avoid most of the tower shadow effect by using an upwind rotor was the 91 m diameter MOD-2 built by Boeing. Three MOD-2 machines with two-bladed steel rotors 91 m in diameter were built in 1980 at a site near Goldendale, Washington, overlooking the Columbia River and connected into the Bonneville Power Administration power system the following year, the first US wind farm. Others were erected at Solano, California, and near Medicine Bow, Wyoming.

The US Department of Energy (DoE) was trying to involve the major aerospace companies in wind power but with limited success. GE dropped out after the problems with MOD-1. Boeing did not involve their aircraft arm but gave the wind turbine project to Boeing Engineering, a subsidiary that undertook a wide range of engineering projects, most of which did not involve flying.

Another major aerospace company that was enlisted was Pratt & Whitney, a leading jet engine (gas turbine) manufacturer. They involved their propeller subsidiary, Hamilton Standard, to design the WTS-4 (WTS, wind turbine system) with a target rating of 4 MW. This used flexible blades made of plastic composite materials (in contrast to the relatively stiff steel blades used by Boeing) and a relatively light and flexible tower to provide a soft-soft design hoping to avoid damaging resonances and vibrations. The first WTS-4 was erected at Medicine Bow in Wyoming and another at Maglarp in Sweden.

Boeing then proceeded to build in 1987 what was (and still was in 2010) the most powerful wind turbine ever built, the MOD-5B. The MOD-2 design represented a huge technological leap from the MOD-1 and, despite its failings (or perhaps because of them), it provided valuable engineering data and helped to pinpoint design weaknesses (**Figure 33**).

Learning from their previous experiences, Boeing designed MOD-5B with a two-bladed rotor mounted upwind. Initially it was 97.5 m in diameter on a 61 m steel tower and rated at 3.2 MW but, following various development problems, it was modified and Boeing claim that it reached 7.2 MW in a wind speed of 13.7 m s^{-1}. This behemoth was still operating (not without problems) on the Island of Oahu, Hawaii, in 1997.

Germany also built a very large two-bladed wind machine (Große Windkraftanlage or GROWIAN) rated at 4 MW with a 100 m diameter rotor in the Kaiser-Wilhelm-Koog where it stood from 1983 to 1987. It suffered from cracks around the blade roots as had so many of the two-bladed designs.

Starting in 1978, the British Wind Energy Group, WEG, with UK Department of Energy funding, designed a two-bladed machine with a 60 m diameter rotor mounted upwind. This group brought together three powerful British companies, British Aerospace, GEC, and Taylor Woodrow, the last one being a major construction company that provided the offices and top management in the person of Dr. David Lindley. He subsequently became chairman of the British Wind Energy Association (BWEA) and then of the European Wind Energy Association (EWEA) and, in due course, managing director of National Wind Power, a leading British wind turbine manufacturer and wind farm operator.

Figure 30 The 38 m diameter, 100 kW MOD-0 installed in 1975. NASA's test bed for a variety of rotor and tower designs.

On a very windy site at Burgar Hill, in the middle of Orkney Mainland (which is, somewhat confusingly, an Island off the northern tip of mainland Scotland), where the annual average wind speed exceeds 12 m s^{-1} (at hub height), this machine was rated at 3 MW. A half-scale version of this machine was initially proved and the full-scale unit finally commissioned in 1987. By this time, the three-bladed design had forged ahead during the California wind rush (**Figure 34**).

2.03.19 The California Wind Rush

The California wind rush was started in New Hampshire by a small Massachusetts company, with the appropriately arrogant name of US Windpower. In 1980, they built the world's first wind farm at Crotched Mountain consisting of 20 machines. At the same time, they noted the generous tax credits and guaranteed purchase prices for electricity that were being offered in the State of California.

In 1978, to save oil and encourage the use of indigenous energy sources, the Carter administration had passed the PURPA legislation, the Public Utility Regulatory Policy Act, requiring public utilities to buy renewable energy. It was left to each state to decide what that price should be and California set a higher price than most other states.

For capital expenditure in any manufacturing sector, there were already 10% tax credits in place throughout the United States and this was increased by another 15% for energy-related investments following the Shah of Iran's overthrow in 1979. Also, in 1978, the State of California decided to give 25% tax credits on the cost of any solar or wind power projects. So by 1980, 50% of tax credits were available.

US Windpower leased large tracts of land in the Altamont Pass through the coastal range of mountains which funnels cool air from the coast and sea region through to where the hot air rises over the central valley. In 1981, 150 wind turbines were installed in the Altamont and the rush was on.

Figure 31 The 61 m diameter, 2 MW MOD-1 installed in 1979. This machine was built by GE with steel blades by Boeing. The two-bladed rotor was mounted downwind, which led to fatigue and noise, both due to tower shadow.

Figure 32 MOD-2 installed in 1982. The MOD-2 machines, built by Boeing, were 90 m in diameter with two blades upwind mounted on a teetered hub and a slender steel tower, all features designed to reduce fatigue loads but the machines were nevertheless bedeviled with fatigue problems.

Most of these first machines were the US Windpower design, which was reminiscent of the Lawson-Tancred machine: a 17 m diameter rotor with three fixed blades was mounted upwind on a lattice tower. There was no connection between the US company and the English Lord; being faced with the same problems, both arrived at the same answers. US Windpower installed a 50 kW generator initially, where Sir Henry chose 30 kW, but both soon uprated their generator to 100 kW. But there the similarity ends. Sir Henry led the way by building one machine on his own land for his own use. US Windpower raced away building literally hundreds of their machines in the next 5 years.

Other companies followed suit, many in the San Gorgonio and Tehachapi Passes. Most built machines with three blades but some were built with two blades and some with four blades, while Flowind built several hundred vertical axis machines of the Darreius 'egg-whisk' design. The rush is recorded in **Table 1**.

Figure 33 GROWIAN: the large wind turbine. GROWIAN (short for Grosse Windkraft Anlage, which is German for large wind turbine) was built in 1982 by MAN. It had a 100 m diameter downwind rotor of two blades rated at 3 MW and mounted on a slender 100 m guyed tower. It ran into fatigue problems and operated for only 500 h altogether until it was shut down in 1987 and dismantled a year later.

Figure 34 Wind Energy Group's LS1. This machine had a long gestation period but was finally commissioned on Burgar Hill, Orkney Mainland, in 1987.

Table 1 The California wind rush

Year	Number of wind turbines built	Total new capacity (MW)
1980	20[a]	1
1981	150	10
1982	1150	65
1983	2500	170
1984	4700	380
1985	4300	400
1986		275
1987		155

[a] In New Hampshire.

It is interesting to note that most of the money came from the US government but not from the DoE, whose program was firmly aimed at megawatt-sized machines with two blades built by major engineering corporations, like Westinghouse, GE, Boeing, and Pratt & Whitney (through their propeller subsidiary Hamilton Standard). The wind rush was mainly funded by the inland revenue.

Politicians in the United States had become impatient with the DoE RD&D program. The 'Development' end was not producing the sort of results and resounding successes that were expected from NASA. Large companies in US industry were receiving large government handouts but there seemed to be little real competition between them and no signs of them taking serious responsibility for commercial developments by putting any substantial amounts of their own money into their projects. The 'American way' was to involve as many companies as possible and to encourage 'commercialization' by competition. Government handouts could be used to overcome initial start-up and expansion problems to enable commercial companies to establish manufacturing capacity and reach profitability, when they could stand on their own feet. That did not seem to be happening.

Evidently subsidizing RD&D was not enough and the political pressure was to subsidize manufacturers directly. The way the revenue service became involved was like this. A group of tax-paying Californians could get together to buy a wind farm and, with 50% tax credits in California, they could get back half or more of their investment straight away from their federal and state taxes. Then they could get back the rest over the next 5 years or less. That meant that the investors could not lose money, even if the machines were not terribly successful – even if they fell over as soon as they had been commissioned! – so reliability was not a primary concern for the owners.

This led to many hopeful manufacturers entering the field with unproven ideas for lightweight, low-cost machines. The proving process led to large numbers of broken-down wind turbines. Major highways run through the Altamont and San Gorgonio Passes, so these failures were very visible and wind farms had a very bad name for reliability in the early 1980s (**Figure 35**).

Those machines that did survive received a very favorable price for their electricity and were commercially successful but, broadly speaking, these were heavy and robust Danish designs and designs by US Windpower, who only built wind turbines for their own wind farms. By 1985, more than half of the machines being installed were Danish imports and a quarter were US Windpower machines.

Figure 35 US Windpower 100 kW wind turbines in the Altamont Pass. The most successful American wind turbine manufacturer and wind farm developer was US Windpower.

It became clear to the authorities that their subsidies were building up Danish industry, not American and the federal tax breaks were not extended beyond the end of 1985. Then in 1986, a string of financial problems hit the wind industry. The oil price dropped and stayed low for nearly two decades; this meant that the value of wind as a fuel saver fell sharply. The Danish kroner strengthened against the US dollar, so Danish wind turbines were suddenly 25% dearer. Investors seemed to have used up all their spare cash and to have lost their appetite for investing in wind farms. And to cap it all, at the end of the year, the tax breaks from the State California came to an end. So the American side of the wind rush faltered.

But all was not well on the Danish side, either. Danish manufacturers had built up a huge market share, which had grown to as much as 65%, but that was 65% of very many fewer wind turbines. If their customers had to pay installments in dollars the Danes got fewer kroner and if they had to pay in kroner, they could not afford the extra dollars and there were nonpayments. Many of the wind farms using Danish machines ran into financial difficulties. On top of this was the fall off in orders calling for much reduced production capacity and all but one of the Danish manufacturers went broke (**Figure 36**).

All of them managed to restructure themselves financially, when they had divested themselves of their liabilities, and they all carried on manufacturing but it was for a very much reduced market and only when the European market started to develop, particularly in Germany, did the Danish wind industry recover their full production capacity and enthusiasm.

Despite all these business problems, a clear outcome of the California wind rush was that it demonstrated the preeminence of the Danish design of machines, with three blades mounted upwind. All successful further developments have followed that pattern, with many refinements in the detailed designs (perhaps the most visible being the preference for tubular rather than lattice towers) but there has been no change in the basic scheme as the designs have been scaled up to larger and larger machines, of 120 m diameter or more (**Figure 37**).

Progress has been incremental. At the height of the wind rush, most Danish wind turbines were rated at 50–100 kW; the 15 m diameter Vestas machine rated at 65 kW was typical. By the end of the 1980s, 200–250 kW was more typical; the standard Vestas machine, the V27, was rated at 225 kW. Twenty years later, ratings had grown steadily to more than 10 times greater, with 2.5 and 3 MW machines as standard and machines rated at 5 MW or more were under test. (The largest machines are usually offered for

Figure 36 Flowind 17 m diameter, 150 kW wind turbines in the Altamont Pass. Flowind built 500 vertical axis wind turbines during the California wind rush but they never caught on.

Figure 37 Danish (Micon) 65 kW wind turbines in the Altamont Pass. Most of the wind turbines in the California wind rush were of Danish manufacture. Their designs were heavier and more expensive but they were correspondingly more reliable.

offshore installations where the capital cost of creating a firm foundation is much greater, so there is considerable pressure to install the largest possible machine on each site and little or no objection to increasing the height of the installation, as there frequently is with land-based machines.)

2.03.20 Other Manufacturers

Apart from WEG, the only other British wind turbine manufacturer in the 1980s was James Howden of Glasgow, who built a 25 MW wind farm in the Altamont Pass in California. They ran into blade problems but seemed to have them solved when the company, clearly able to demonstrate expertise in rotating machinery, gained a contract to build a huge tunnel boring machine. This costly monster was to drive a shaft under the English Channel for the English half of what is now the Channel Tunnel. This took all the development resources the company could command and they abruptly pulled out of wind power altogether.

Following Howdens into the Californian wind rush, WEG built a 5 MW wind farm in the Altamont Pass in 1986 using their smaller 300 kW MS-3 two-bladed machine and this was relatively successful. In 1992, they built three wind farms with two-bladed machines in the United Kingdom: Cemaes in North Wales, Cold Northcott in Cornwall, and Llangwyryfon in Mid-Wales. The two-bladed venture was set back in 1993 when a severe storm wrecked half a dozen wind turbines at Cemaes. The fault was found to be a weakness in the blade pitch control but although this was corrected and the machines returned to service, no further sales were forthcoming. In the course of a few years, WEG sold out to NEG Micon in 1998 and that was the end of two-bladed machines. (It was also the end of British wind turbine manufacture.)

The two-bladed concept had seemed to be much beloved by the large American companies too but, when direct government funding of the R&D disappeared, the major companies did not pursue their designs commercially. In most cases, the demonstration units had failed catastrophically, but even where they did not, the manufacturers were not prepared to take any further commercial risks. The field was left to the Danish three-bladed designs, which had by then already grown substantially in size and would go on to greater things.

2.03.21 Large Vertical Axis Wind Turbines

The British pursued an H-shaped rotor geometry developed first by Peter Musgrove and then by Ian Mays. Sir Robert McAlpine Ltd built a 130 kW machine, 25 m in diameter, their VAWT25 (VAWT, vertical axis wind turbine) on the CEGB's national test site at Carmarthen Bay in 1986 and subsequently a 500 kW machine, 35 m in diameter, the VAWT50 was erected on the same test site in mid-1990. The smaller machine worked reliably for several years but the larger machine lost a blade in February 1991.

A vertical axis machine does not suffer fatigue from gravitational stress reversals as a horizontal axis machine does. However, it does not extract power from the wind when the blades are traveling upwind or downwind, but only when they are traveling across the wind. So each blade suffers two aerodynamic stress variations (from zero to full) in each rotation. With an H-shaped rotor, the horizontal bar of the H couples these forces to the central column where the power is extracted, so it too suffers reversals of the bending moments. All in all, there were plenty of sources of fatigue on the Carmarthen Bay machine and in due course a blade failed.

The CEGB which owned the national test site had been privatized in 1990 and the new owner, National Power, found little interest among the other companies formed from the breakup to support it as a national facility. They could not justify keeping it operational solely on their own account and it was shut down, along with all the machines on the site.

There has been interest in large vertical axis machines in Canada as well as the United Kingdom. In 1988, the National Research Council of Canada in conjunction with Hydro-Québec built Eole, a 4 MW Darrieus-type design with troposkein curved blades, a demonstration unit that achieved 94% availability over a 6 years period at Cap-Chat in Quebec. This represented something of a technical triumph but the economics were less favorable.

2.03.22 Organizations: BWEA, EWEA, and IEA

One outcome of the oil crisis in 1973 was the creation of the International Energy Agency (IEA) in 1974 with 17 member countries. This is an intergovernmental body and the members were those governments in the OECD (Organisation for Economic Co-operation and Development), now 30 in all, that chose to join. The original objective was to provide a counter to the joint actions of the OPEC (Organization of Petroleum Exporting Countries) cartel, which was causing huge rises in the price of oil. This meant that all the information should be restricted to member governments and not freely distributed to the general public or to other countries.

(France chose not to join initially but that did not prevent the headquarters from being sited in Paris. All OECD members except Mexico and Iceland have now joined.) The IEA now also works with countries beyond its present membership including China, India, and Russia, which are designated as 'first priority' countries.

The IEA promotes collaboration and information exchanges between its members, holds workshops and conferences, and organizes joint research and development projects, both on a cost-sharing and a task-sharing basis. Aspects of energy to be studied are made the subject of agreements and there are 42 of these, including one on Wind Energy Systems. In the early 1980s, there was a separate agreement on Large Wind Turbines, attempting, among other things, to share information about major failures in much the same way that the aero industry shares information about accident investigations, but this agreement was terminated and merged with the Wind Energy Systems Agreement when it became clear that no more large machines were being funded.

In the later 1970s and throughout the 1980s, various important and forward-looking international programs of research were coordinated as annexes to the IEA Wind Energy Systems Agreement. For instance, the Wakes and Clusters Annex was looking at how close together wind turbines could be sited in a cluster, what would now be termed a wind farm. This research included wind tunnel measurements on arrays of wind turbine (using propeller anemometers to model the turbines) and field measurements on the pair of wind turbines at Nibe, near Aalborg in Northern Denmark (from anemometers at various positions up a central meteorological mast and other masts in line with the pair of turbines) which were 45 m in diameter each, generating 600 kW and spaced 450 m apart.

This work established, well before any wind farms had been built, how much wind turbines would interfere with each other in a cluster, like a sailing ship taking the wind of another ship downwind of it. The appropriate spacing in a (nondirectional) array was found to be 7–10 diameters to keep the loss of power below 10%.

Several countries collaborated in an Off-Shore Wind Power Annexe to share their research activities. As early as 1980, the United States, United Kingdom, Denmark, Holland, and Sweden were anticipating planning problems for the wind installations they envisaged on land and were considering the possibility of moving offshore to avoid planning objections if siting became too difficult. These countries effectively merged their research in a task-sharing annex to look into the problems of building wind farms offshore, leading to the completion of the Vindeby Wind Farm in 1991, to be followed by many others.

A particularly valuable activity was to standardize a range of procedures, measurements, and specifications, including methods of costing and aerodynamic analysis.

While the IEA focused on government-based programs, which had some measure of confidentiality, not being open to all countries, many professional and trade associations were being formed in the 1970s to bring together academics and industrial engineers. Probably the earliest foundation was the Dutch Society for the preservation of (Dutch) windmills, De Hollandsche Molen, dating back to 1923. The American Wind Energy Association (AWEA) was formed in 1974 as a trade association, while the BWEA (British Wind Energy Association) was founded in 1978 as a learned society of professional engineers and scientists with Peter Musgrove (then of Reading University) as chairman. Denmark had had ready-made wind organizations since the time of Poul La Cour.

When Donald Swift-Hook took over as chairman of the BWEA in 1981, he also represented the United Kingdom on the International Energy Association Agreement on Wind Energy Systems. He was impressed by the way that cooperation between governments of many countries was assured by the IEA (International Energy Association), albeit on a somewhat confidential basis which excluded non-member countries, and he felt that nongovernment organizations and academics should also have a vehicle that would enable them to cooperate freely with each other in exchanging ideas, as professional organizations do. He envisaged a coming together of the various national professional associations to cooperate and coordinate their conferences and publications and general networking.

He discussed the prospects of a worldwide international association but felt that an IWEA (International Wind Energy Association) was too ambitious at that point and he proposed the establishment of an EWEA, a European Wind Energy Association. At a BWEA international conference in Brighton in 1981, he called together representatives of various national associations, Jos Buerskens from Holland, Horst Selzer from Germany, Maribo Pedersen from Denmark, and Giuseppe Selva from Italy, to discuss this proposal and to form the Provisional Council of an EWEA. By the time of the first meeting of the membership at a conference in Stockholm in 1982, many other European countries had fledgling national associations which came into the European fold.

As the wind industry has developed, these associations, particularly the EWEA and BWEA, have changed from being impoverished learned societies for individual professionals, mainly concerned with publications and conferences, to well-funded trade associations like the AWEA has always been, providing services and information for their membership of industrial companies, lobbying governments, and setting standards and guidelines for the wind industry.

The United Kingdom has played a leading part in researching marine sources of renewable energy, notably wave power, tidal barrages, and tidal flow systems. The popularity of the patriotic song 'Rule Britannia, Britannia rules the waves' may predispose any British government to include marine renewables in its portfolio of funding. Certainly the corporate members of the BWEA found they had strong interests in that direction and they decided in 2005 to include marine sources of renewable under the BWEA umbrella and in 2010 to change the name of their association to RenewableUK (although they do not embrace any other renewable).

Further Reading

[1] Musgrove P (2010) *Wind Power*. Cambridge, UK: CUP.
[2] Hills RL (1994) *Power from Wind: A History of Windmill Technology*. Cambridge, UK: CUP.
[3] Golding EW (1955) *The Generation of Electricity by Wind Power*. London, UK: Spon.
[4] Putnam PC (1948) *Power from the Wind*. New York: Van Nostrand Reinhold.
[5] BWEA (1982) Lipman NH, Musgrove P, and Pontin G (eds.) *Wind Energy for the Eighties*. Stevenage, UK: Peter Peregrinus.

2.04 Wind Energy Potential

H Nfaoui, Mohammed V University, Rabat, Morocco

© 2012 Elsevier Ltd. All rights reserved.

2.04.1	Introduction	74
2.04.2	**Wind Characteristics**	74
2.04.2.1	Origin of Wind	74
2.04.2.2	Meteorology of Wind	74
2.04.2.3	Wind Direction and Wind Velocity	74
2.04.2.4	Fundamental Causes of Wind	74
2.04.3	**Wind Measurements**	75
2.04.3.1	Wind Speed	75
2.04.3.2	Cup Anemometers	75
2.04.3.3	Other Anemometers	75
2.04.3.3.1	Pressure plate anemometer	75
2.04.3.3.2	Pressure tube anemometer	75
2.04.3.3.3	Hot-wire anemometer	76
2.04.3.3.4	Laser Doppler anemometer	76
2.04.3.3.5	Sonic anemometer	76
2.04.3.4	Wind Direction	76
2.04.3.5	Wind Rose	76
2.04.3.6	Wind Speed Profiles	77
2.04.3.6.1	Roughness classes and lengths	77
2.04.3.6.2	Wind shear	78
2.04.3.6.3	Turbulence	78
2.04.3.6.4	Landscape without neutral stability	78
2.04.3.6.5	Modified log law	79
2.04.3.6.6	Nature of atmospheric winds	80
2.04.3.6.7	Power spectrum of wind speed: Averaging periods	80
2.04.4	**Analysis of Wind Regimes**	81
2.04.4.1	Wind Speed Variation with Time	81
2.04.4.1.1	Instantaneous phenomenon: Wind gust	81
2.04.4.1.2	Diurnal breezes: Land–sea and valleys breezes	82
2.04.4.1.3	Seasonal phenomenon	82
2.04.4.1.4	Time distribution	82
2.04.4.1.5	Calm wind spells	82
2.04.4.1.6	Frequency distribution	82
2.04.4.2	Mathematic Representation of Wind Speed	83
2.04.4.2.1	Weibull distribution	84
2.04.4.2.2	Weibull hybrid distribution	84
2.04.4.2.3	Cumulative distribution	85
2.04.4.3	Wind Resource Atlas Models	86
2.04.4.3.1	Physical basis	86
2.04.4.3.2	Stability model	86
2.04.4.3.3	Roughness change model	86
2.04.4.3.4	Shelter model	86
2.04.4.3.5	Orographic model	86
2.04.4.4	Wind Resource Atlas	87
2.04.5	**Dynamic Study of Wind Speed**	87
2.04.5.1	Stochastic Models for Simulating and Forecasting Wind Speed Time Series	88
2.04.5.2	Bayesian Adaptive Combination of Wind Speed Forecasts from Neural Network Models	88
2.04.5.2.1	Artificial neural network models	88
2.04.5.2.2	Bayesian model averaging	89
2.04.6	**Wind Energy**	89
2.04.6.1	Wind Energy Production	89

2.04.6.2	Wind Energy Potential	90
2.04.6.2.1	Power output from an ideal turbine: Betz limit	90
2.04.6.2.2	Axial momentum theory	90
2.04.7	**Conclusions**	91
References		91
Further Reading		92

2.04.1 Introduction

The winds, in the macro-meteorological sense, are movements of air masses in the atmosphere. These large scale-movements are generated primarily by temperature differences within the air layer due to differential solar heating. Because the energy per unit surface area received from the sun depends on geographical latitude, temperature differences arise and hence pressure gradients which, together with the centripetal force and the Coriolis force associated with the rotation of the Earth, induce the movements of the air masses known as the gradient wind.

Solar radiation, evaporation of water, cloud cover, and surface roughness all play important roles in determining the conditions of the atmosphere. The study of the interactions between these effects is a complex subject called meteorology, which is covered by many excellent books, for example, *Météorologie Générale* edited by Triplet and Roche [1]. Therefore, only the part of meteorology concerning the flow of wind will be considered in this chapter.

2.04.2 Wind Characteristics

2.04.2.1 Origin of Wind

Wind is caused by differences in pressure. When a difference in pressure exists, the air is accelerated from higher to lower pressure. On a rotating planet the air will be deflected by the Coriolis effects, except exactly on the equator. Globally, the two major driving factors of large-scale winds are the different heating between the equator and the poles and the effect of the Earth's rotation. Outside the tropics and upward from frictional effects of the surface, the large-scale winds tend to approach geostrophic balance. Near the Earth's surface, friction causes the wind to be slower than it would be otherwise. Surface friction also causes winds to blow more inward into low pressure areas.

2.04.2.2 Meteorology of Wind

The basic driving force of air movement is a difference in air pressure between two regions. This air pressure is described by several physical laws. One of these is the ideal gas law:

$$pV = nRT \qquad [1]$$

where p is pressure in Pascal ($N\,m^{-2}$), V is volume (m^3), n is the number of moles, R is the universal gas constant ($8.3144\,J\,K^{-1}\,mol^{-1}$), and T is absolute temperature (°K).

2.04.2.3 Wind Direction and Wind Velocity

As the warm air expands and the cold air condenses, this process creates zones of relative high or low pressure. Afterwards, the wind is fundamentally the movement of air created by these differences in pressure.

Theoretically, at the Earth's surface, the wind blows from high-pressure areas toward low-pressure areas. However, at the medium and higher latitudes, its direction is modified by the earth's rotation. The wind becomes parallel to isobaric lines instead of being perpendicular to them. In the northern hemisphere, the wind rotates counter-clockwise round cyclonic areas and clockwise round anticyclonic areas. In the southern hemisphere, these wind directions are reversed. The wind direction is determined by the direction from which it blows. For example, it is a westerly wind if the air blows from the West.

2.04.2.4 Fundamental Causes of Wind

There are two principal reasons for the movement and direction of motion of the Earth's atmosphere – the unequal amounts of solar radiation received at different latitudes and the rotation of the earth. Superimposed upon the general world wind circulation, due to these two factors, modifications arising from local disturbances, such as the tropical cyclone.

We have on a terrestrial scale regular pressure systems that produce important winds, called dominant winds or general circulation. In practice, atmospheric circulation may be represented as it is shown in **Figure 1** and it is useful in identifying the most important global wind characteristics.

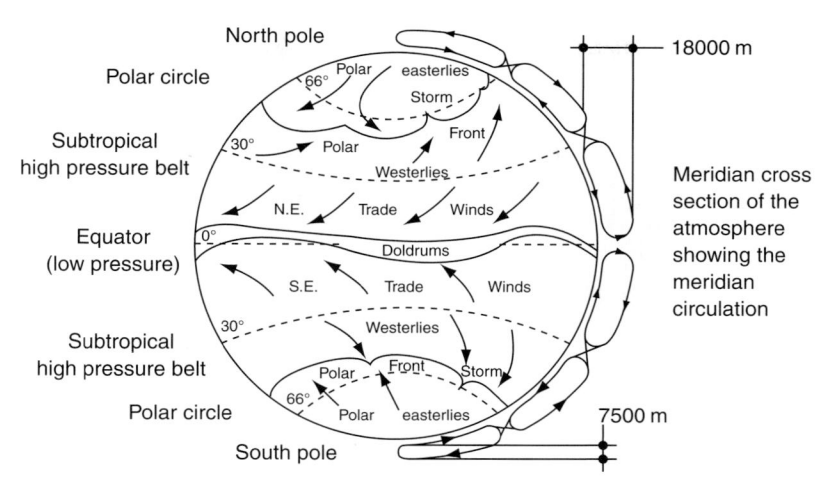

Figure 1 General world wind circulation [2].

In each hemisphere, we can discern three more or less individualized cells: a tropical cell, a temperate cell, and a polar cell, which turn one against the other like cogs in a gear box. The north and south tropical cells are separated from one another by the equatorial calm which is a low-pressure area and from the temperate cells by the subtropical high-pressure zones.

Actually, the sketch is not perfect. The unequal heating of oceans and continents surface, relief, vegetation, and seasonal variations deform and modify the high- and low-pressure zones. There are also atmospheric disturbances created by masses of cold air that move, from time to time, from the poles towards the equator. Thus, the state of the atmosphere is continually evolving. As a result, the most favorable area for wind energy production is situated on the continents near the seashores or in the sea.

2.04.3 Wind Measurements

2.04.3.1 Wind Speed

An anemometer is a device for measuring wind speed and is a common weather station instrument. The term is derived from the Greek word '*anemos*', meaning wind. The oldest anemometer, invented in 1846, is the cup anemometer [3].

2.04.3.2 Cup Anemometers

The cup anemometer consists of three or four hemispherical cups each mounted on one end of four horizontal arms, which in turn are mounted at equal angles to each other on a vertical shaft. The airflow that pass the cups in any horizontal direction turns the cups in a manner that is proportional to the wind speed.

The three-cup anemometer was developed in 1926. It had a more constant torque and responded more quickly to gusts than the four-cup anemometer. It was further modified in 1991 to measure both wind direction and wind speed. **Figure 2** shows a cup-type anemometer used by most national weather service stations and airports [3, 5].

2.04.3.3 Other Anemometers

Anemometer types include the propeller, cup, pressure plate, pressure tube, hot wire, Doppler acoustic radar, sonic, and so on. The propeller and cup anemometers depend on rotation of a small turbine for their output, while the others basically have no moving parts.

2.04.3.3.1 Pressure plate anemometer
Another type of anemometer is known as a pressure plate or normal plate anemometer. This is the oldest anemometer known having been developed in 1667. It uses the principle that the force of moving air on a plate being normal to wind is proportional to the area of the plate and to the square of wind speed. The main application of this type of anemometer has been in gust studies because of its very short response time [3, 5].

2.04.3.3.2 Pressure tube anemometer
Yet another type of anemometer is the pressure tube anemometer. It is not used much in the field because of difficulties with ice, snow, rain, and the sealing of rotating joints. However, it is often used as the standard in a wind tunnel when these difficulties are not present. It has been known for almost two centuries that the wind blowing into the mouth of a tube causes an increase of pressure in the tube, and that an airflow across the mouth causes a suction [3, 5].

Figure 2 Cup anemometer [4].

2.04.3.3.3 Hot-wire anemometer

The hot-wire anemometer uses a very fine wire electrically heated up to some temperature above the ambient. Air flowing via the wire has a cooling effect on the wire. As the electrical resistance of most metals is dependent upon the temperature of the metal, a relationship can be obtained between the resistance of the wire and the flow speed.

The hot-wire anemometer, while extremely delicate, has extremely high-frequency response and fine spatial resolution compared to other measurement methods, and as such is almost universally employed for the detailed study of turbulent flows, or any flow in which rapid velocity fluctuations are of interest [3, 5].

2.04.3.3.4 Laser Doppler anemometer

The laser Doppler anemometer uses a beam of light from a laser that is divided into two beams, with one propagated out of the anemometer. Particulates flowing along with air molecules near where the beam exits reflect, or backscatter, the light back into a detector, where it is compared to the original laser beam. When the particles are in great motion, they produce a Doppler shift for measuring wind speed in the laser light, which is used to calculate the speed of the particles, and therefore the air around the anemometer [3, 5].

2.04.3.3.5 Sonic anemometer

The sonic anemometer was developed in the 1970s. It uses ultrasonic sound waves to determine instantaneous wind speed by measuring how much sound waves traveling between a pair of transducers are sped up or slowed down by the effect of the wind. Sonic anemometers can take measurements with very fine temporal resolution, 20 Hz or better, which makes them well suited for turbulence measurements. The lack of moving parts makes it appropriate for long-term use in exposed automated weather stations and weather buoys where the accuracy and reliability of traditional cup-and-vane anemometers is adversely affected by salty air or large amounts of dust [3, 5].

Two-dimensional (wind speed and wind direction) sonic anemometers are used in applications such as weather stations, ship navigation, wind turbines, aviation, and weather buoys.

2.04.3.4 Wind Direction

The wind vane, used for indicating wind direction, is one of the oldest meteorological instruments. When mounted on an elevated shaft or spire, the vane rotates under the influence of the wind such that its center of pressure rotates to leeward and the vane points into the wind (**Figure 3**). Wind direction is measured in degrees from true north. The word 'vane' comes from the Anglo-Saxon word 'fane' meaning 'flag' [3, 5]. The wind direction is determined by the direction from which it blows. It is a westerly wind if the air current blows from the West.

Modern aerovanes combine the directional vane with anemometer. Colocating both instruments allows them to use the same axis and provides a coordinated read out.

2.04.3.5 Wind Rose

A wind rose is a graphic tool used by meteorologists to give a succinct view of how wind speed and direction are typically distributed at a particular location. It summarizes the occurrence of winds at a location, showing their strength, direction, and frequency (**Figure 4(a)**).

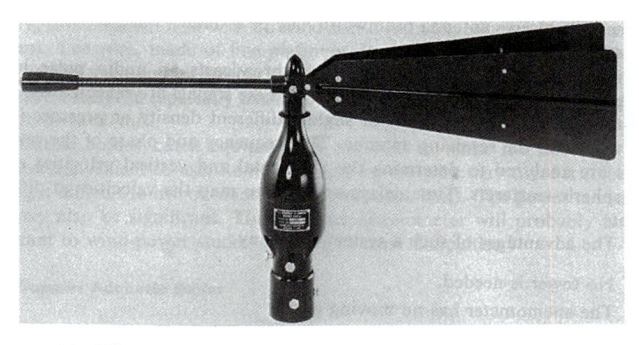

Figure 3 Wind direction: vane and transmitter [5].

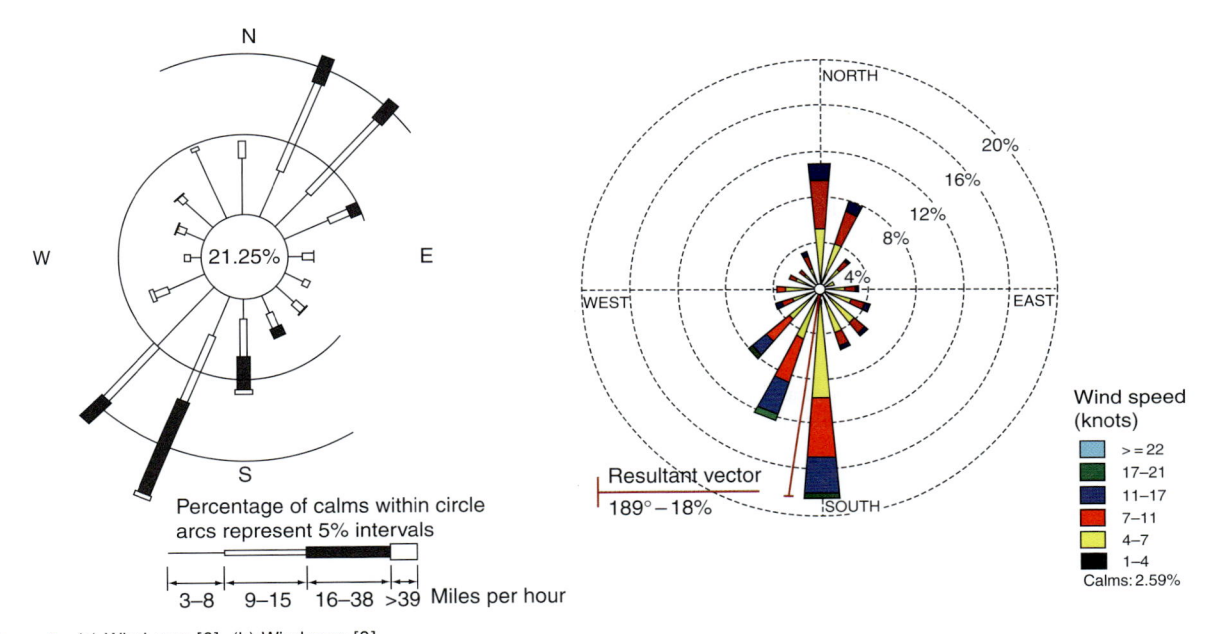

Figure 4 (a) Wind rose [6]. (b) Wind rose [3].

Historically, the wind rose was a predecessor of the compass rose, as there was no differentiation between a cardinal direction and the wind which blew from such a direction. It was included on maps in order to let the reader know the characteristics of the eight major winds. Using a polar coordinate system of gridding, the frequency of winds over a time period could be plotted by wind direction, with color bands showing wind ranges. Presented in a circular format, the wind rose shows the frequency of winds blowing from particular directions. The length of each 'spoke' around the circle is related to the frequency of time that the wind blows from a particular direction. Each concentric circle represents a different frequency, emanating from zero at the center to increasing frequencies at the outer circles. A wind rose plot may contain additional information, in that each spoke is broken down into color-coded bands that show wind speed ranges. The wind rose typically uses 16 cardinal directions, such as North (N), NNE, NE, and so on.

There are a number of different formats that can be used to display wind roses. A particular method for describing wind speed and direction is shown in **Figure 4(b)**.

2.04.3.6 Wind Speed Profiles

2.04.3.6.1 Roughness classes and lengths

The shape of the terrain over which the wind is flowing will have a frictional effect upon the wind speed near the surface. Both the height and the spacing of the roughness elements on the surface will influence the frictional effect on the wind. A single parameter, the surface roughness length, z_0, is used to express this effect.

Roughness classes (RCs) and roughness lengths are characteristics of the landscape used to evaluate wind conditions at a potential wind turbine site. The roughness length is defined as the height above ground z_0 in meters at which the wind speed is theoretically equal to zero [7]. RCs are defined in terms of the roughness length in meters z_0, according to

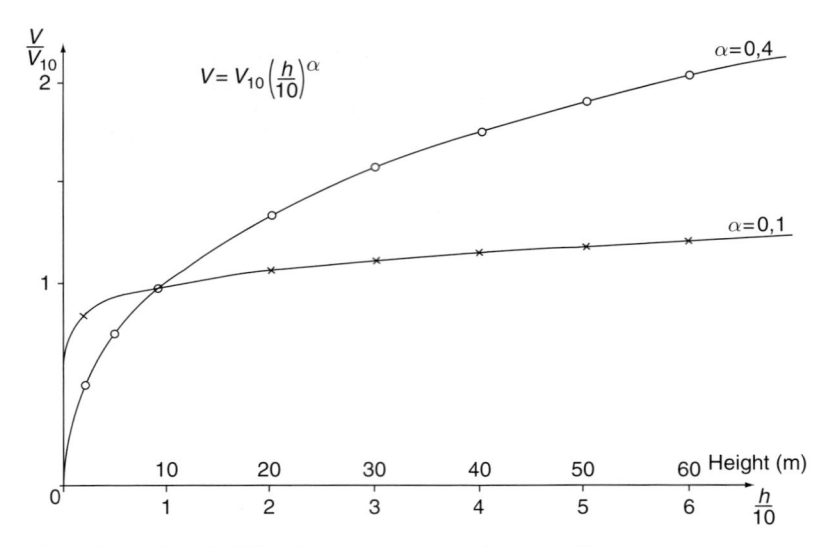

Figure 5 Wind shear related to a reference height of 10 m, for various roughness heights, α [6].

$$RC = 1.699\,823\,015 + \frac{\ln(z_0)}{\ln(150)} \quad \text{for } z_0 \leq 0.03 \qquad [2]$$

$$RC = 3.912\,489\,289 + \frac{\ln(z_0)}{\ln(3.3333)} \quad \text{for } z_0 > 0.03 \qquad [3]$$

2.04.3.6.2 Wind shear

The wind speed profile tends to a lower speed as it moves closer to the ground level. This is designated as wind shear. It is found that wind velocity increases with height above the ground according to formula [4] [2–8]. The rate of change strongly depends upon the roughness of the terrain (**Figure 5**)

$$\frac{V_1}{V_2} = \left(\frac{h_1}{h_2}\right)^{\alpha} \qquad [4]$$

where V_1 is the wind velocity at some reference height h_1 and V_2 is the wind velocity at height h_2.

The constant α, Hellman exponent, depends on the nature of the surface and the stability of the air. Thus, α may be defined as follows [8]:

$$a = 0.096(\ln(z_0)) + 0.016(\ln(z_0))^2 + 0.24 \qquad [5]$$

The variation of wind speed with height depends on the surface roughness and the atmospheric stability, and we could assume that wind speed grows logarithmically with height. The wind speed at a certain height above ground can be also estimated as a function of height above ground z and the roughness length z_0 in the current wind direction from the formula [7]

$$V(z) = V_{\text{ref}} \frac{\ln\left(\dfrac{z}{z_0}\right)}{\ln\left(\dfrac{z_{\text{ref}}}{z_0}\right)} \qquad [6]$$

The reference speed V_{ref} is a known wind speed at a reference height z_{ref}.

2.04.3.6.3 Turbulence

Wind flowing around buildings or over very rough surface locations exhibits rapid changes in speed and/or direction, called turbulence. This turbulence decreases, for example, the power output of the windmill and can also lead to unwanted vibration of the machine (**Figure 6**).

Hills can sometimes be used to give an enhancement of wind velocity over that on the surrounding plain. The best hills are those having smooth sides and fairly steep conical shape (**Figure 7**). The effect of height above the top of the hill is complex and the previously quoted relationship cannot be used and it is necessary to measure wind speed on the considered site.

2.04.3.6.4 Landscape without neutral stability

The previous analysis assumed neutral atmospheric stability conditions meaning that a parcel of air is adiabatically balanced from a thermodynamic perspective. Neutral stability is a reasonable assumption in high wind when shearing forces rather than buoyancy

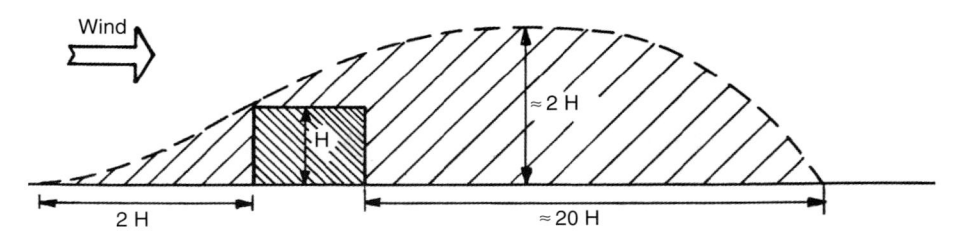

Figure 6 Zone of turbulence over a small building [8].

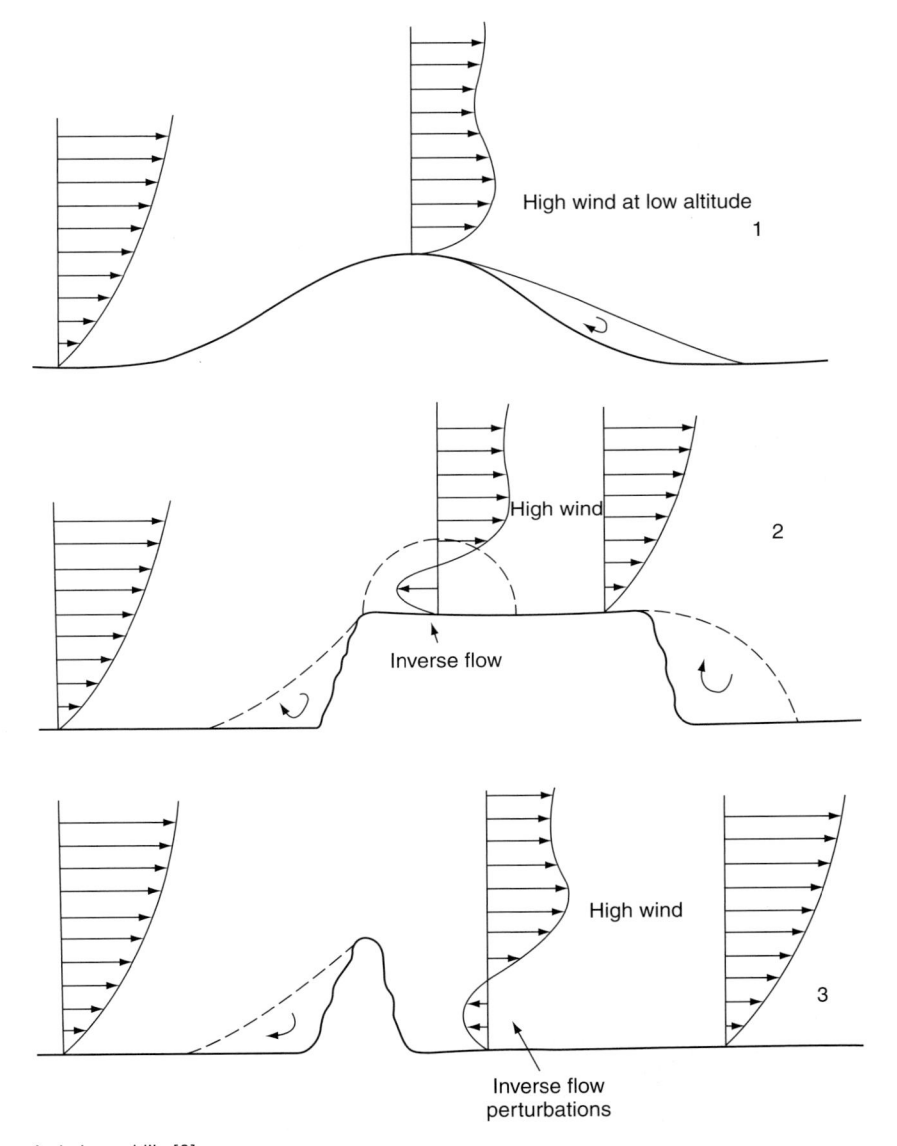

Figure 7 Acceleration of wind over hills [6].

forces are dominant. However, the atmosphere is rarely neutral and the buoyancy forces usually predominate over the shear forces as noticed from the scattering of the measurements at neighboring data collection points.

2.04.3.6.5 Modified log law

The logarithmic wind profile equation in the lowest 100 m may still be used under nonequilibrium conditions with some appropriate modifications [7]:

$$V(z) = \frac{V_{fr}}{k}\left[\ln\left(\frac{z}{z_0}\right) - \Psi\left(\frac{z}{L}\right)\right] \qquad [7]$$

where V_{fr} is friction velocity, k is von Karman constant ($k = 0.4$), L is Monin–Obukhov length, Ψ is correction term, and z_0 is roughness length.

The Monin–Obukhov length L is a scaling parameter that depends upon the heat flux at the ground surface q_0, and is given by [7]

$$L = \frac{T_0 c_p V_{fr}^3}{k g q_0} \qquad [8]$$

where T_0 is ground surface absolute temperature (°K), q_0 is ground surface heat flux, c_p is heat capacity of the air at constant pressure, and g is gravity's acceleration.

2.04.3.6.6 Nature of atmospheric winds

To be able to understand and predict the performance, for example, of wind turbines, it is essential that the designer has knowledge of the behavior and structure of the wind itself that will vary from time to time and from site to site dependent on the climate and topography of the region, the surface condition of the terrain around the site, and various other factors. Since the early 1970s, significant progress has been made in our understanding of the structure of the wind, in our ability to predict the conditions likely to be experienced at a site and to assess the suitability of a site for generating power from wind.

Figure 8 shows typical anemograph records of wind speed monitored at three heights on a tall mast during strong wind conditions. These records demonstrate the main characteristics of the flow in the region near the ground. The turbulent fluctuations are random in character and they are not always governed by deterministic equations, but we will need to use statistical techniques. This short-spanned change in wind speed is primarily due to the local geographic and weather effects.

2.04.3.6.7 Power spectrum of wind speed: Averaging periods

In order to separate the short-period fluctuations of wind speed due to mixing from the long-term changes associated with macroscale meteorological phenomena, we introduce the time average mean wind speed, $\bar{V}$. Thus it is defined by [7]:

$$\bar{V} = \frac{1}{T}\int_{t_0-\frac{T}{2}}^{t_0+\frac{T}{2}} V(t)\,dt \qquad [9]$$

where $V(t)$ is the instantaneous wind speed component along the average wind direction at time, t, and we must define the time interval, T, over which the average is taken.

Figure 9 shows the frequency variation of kinetic energy of the horizontal wind speed near the ground as measured at Brookhaven, New York [9]. This spectrum shows the long-term distribution of energy. An important feature of all long-term spectra is the gap between periods of about 10 min and 2 h where the spectrum contains very little energy. The significance of the spectral gap is that, if the averaging period for the mean wind speed is chosen to lie within this range, the synoptic variations can be separated from those due to turbulence. It has been suggested that a good averaging period for defining mean wind speeds lies between 20 min and 1 h.

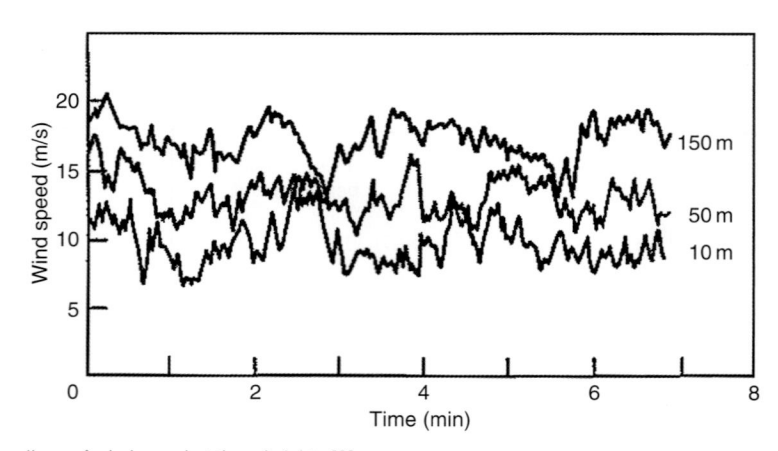

Figure 8 Simultaneous recordings of wind speed at three heights [9].

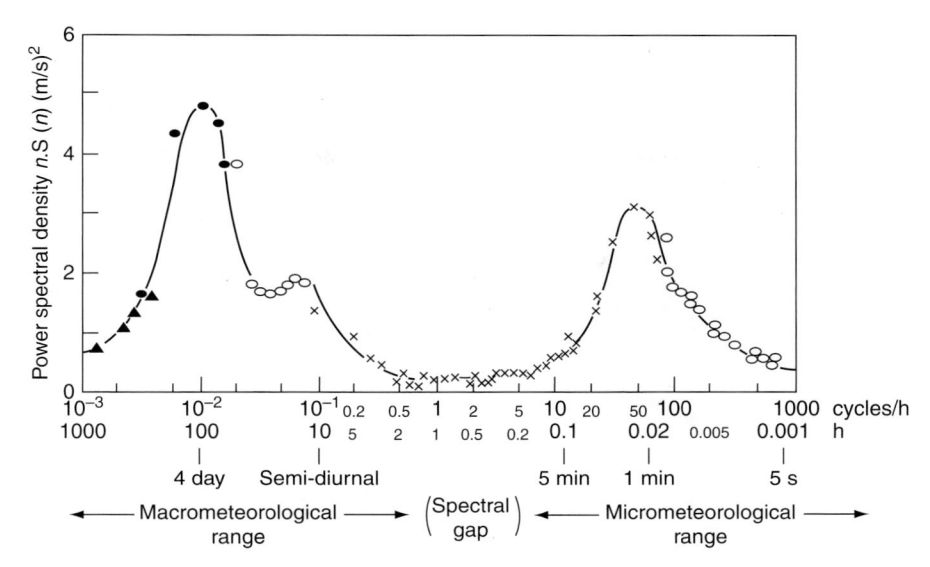

Figure 9 Spectrum of horizontal wind speed at Brookhaven National Laboratory [9].

2.04.4 Analysis of Wind Regimes

Here we will discuss the wind pattern as such and its characterization by numbers and graphs. We assume that a set of short-time measurements from a meteorological station is available. The reliability of the data is not questioned here.

2.04.4.1 Wind Speed Variation with Time

2.04.4.1.1 Instantaneous phenomenon: Wind gust

The lower region of the atmosphere is known as the planetary boundary layer and the movement of the air is retarded by frictional forces and large obstructions on the surface of the Earth, as well as by the Reynolds stresses produced by the vertical exchange of momentum due to turbulence. The turbulence, which may be mechanical and/or thermal in origin, also causes rapid fluctuations in the wind velocity over a wide range of frequencies and amplitudes, commonly known as gusts (**Figure 10**).

It is often useful to know the maximum wind gust that can be expected to occur in any given time interval. This is usually represented by a gust factor G, which is the ratio of a wind gust to the hourly mean wind speed. G is obviously a function of the turbulence intensity, and it also clearly depends on the duration of the gust. Thus, the gust factor for a 1 s gust will be larger than for a 3 s gust, since every 3 s gust has within it a higher 1 s gust [10].

Time-varying wind speeds and, more specifically, the uncertainty over what wind speed will be during the next hour or by hour for the next day is a challenge for wind turbine designers. For example, a wind gust that rapidly changes the wind turbine's output necessitates a control system that adjusts the rotor speed and thus optimizes the turbine's power output for slow wind speed variation and attenuates high-frequency wind gust effects to reduce the resulting fatigue.

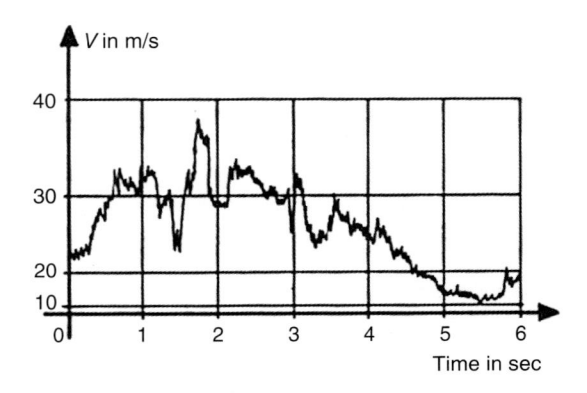

Figure 10 Wind gusts from Orkney (UK) [2].

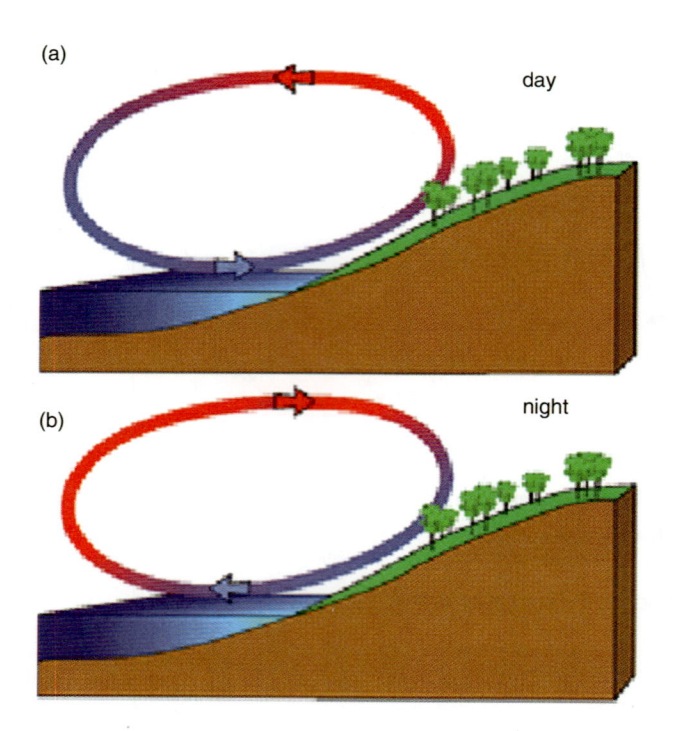

Figure 11 Diurnal wind.

2.04.4.1.2 Diurnal breezes: Land–sea and valleys breezes
At the sea shore the General Circulation Patterns have superimposed on them an airflow from the sea to the land at night, and in the reverse direction during the day (**Figures 11**(a) and **11**(b)).

These sea/land breezes can be quite strong and can dominate the wind pattern. A rather similar situation to the sea breeze can arise between valleys and mountains.

2.04.4.1.3 Seasonal phenomenon
The monthly variation of wind speed depends essentially on geographical location and only meteorological measurements can give information about these variations. But, generally, the yearly variations are repetitive with a good precision.

2.04.4.1.4 Time distribution
Plotting the monthly average of each hour of the day shows the diurnal fluctuations of the wind speed in that particular month (**Figure 12**). The major reason for the velocity variation here is the difference in temperature between the sea and land surface. It should be noted that in this specific case, the diurnal variation can be advantageous for wind energy generation as we may need more power during the daytime hours than at night.

In a similar manner, the monthly average can be plotted to show the monthly fluctuations of the wind speed, compared with the annual average wind speed (**Figure 13**). Knowledge of this variation of velocity at a potential wind site is essential to ensure that the availability of power matches the demand.

2.04.4.1.5 Calm wind spells
According to the Beaufort wind scale at a standard altitude of 10 m above an open, even surface, the action of wind is calm when the wind speed is less than $0.3 \, \text{m s}^{-1}$ and smoke rises vertically [1, 4].

2.04.4.1.6 Frequency distribution
Another type of information that can be extracted from the time distribution of the data is the distribution of periods with low wind speed. In other words, how often did it happen that the wind speed was lower than, for example, $2 \, \text{m s}^{-1}$ during 12 h or during 2 days. This type of information is valuable for the calculation of the size of storage devices.

Apart from the distribution of the wind speeds over a day or a year, it is important to know the number of hours per month or per year during which the given wind speeds occurred, that is, the frequency distribution of the wind speed (**Figure 14**). The maximal value of this histogram corresponds to the most frequent wind speed.

It is often important to know the number of hours that a windmill, for example, will not run or the time fraction that a windmill produces more than a given power. In this case, it is necessary to add the number of hours in all intervals above the given wind

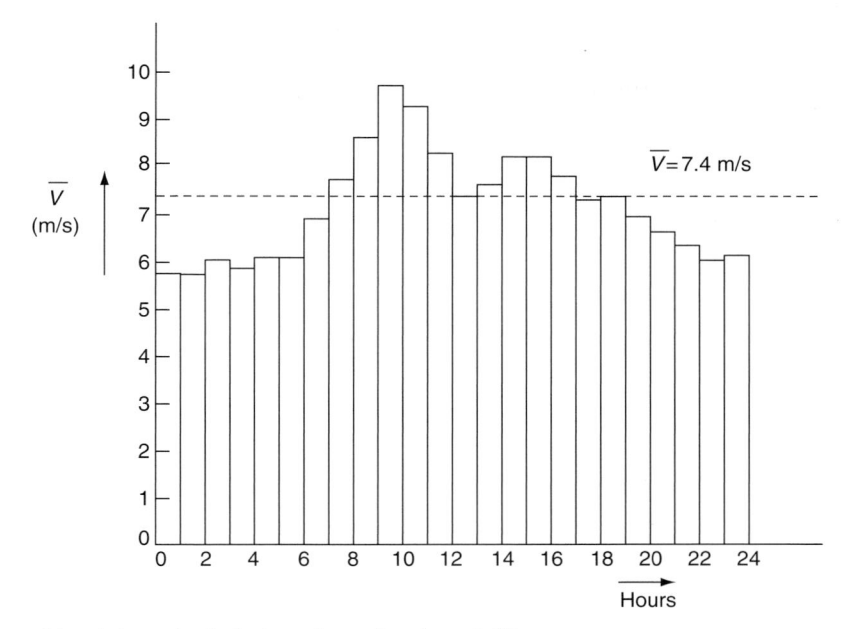

Figure 12 Diurnal pattern of the wind speed at Praia airport for a selected month [8].

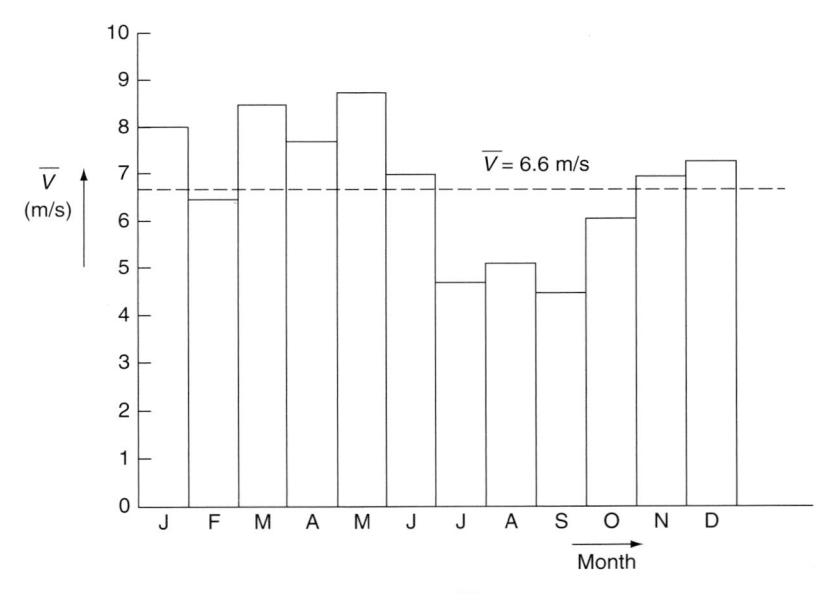

Figure 13 Monthly average wind speeds at Praia airport for a selected month [8].

speed. The result is the duration distribution (**Figure 15(a)**). The flatter the duration curve, that is, the longer one specific wind speed persists, the more constant the wind regime is. The steeper the duration curve, the more irregular the wind regime is.

In some cases it is preferred to plot the time during which the wind speed was smaller than a given wind speed, and when this is plotted versus the wind speed, a cumulative distribution results (**Figure 15(b)**).

2.04.4.2 Mathematic Representation of Wind Speed

In order to predict the output of a wind generator system by using simulation methods, it is necessary to have a large series of measurements for the considered site. The real data are variable. To be usable, this enormous volume of data must be reduced without losing any information. One way to achieve this is the statistical treatment of data. For instance, one may use mathematical functions that approach the velocity frequency data in a histogram as closely as possible. In this respect, much attention has been given to the Weibull function, since it gives a good match with the experimental data. But, in some cases the Rayleigh distribution, a special case of the Weibull distribution, assuming $k = 2$, is preferred.

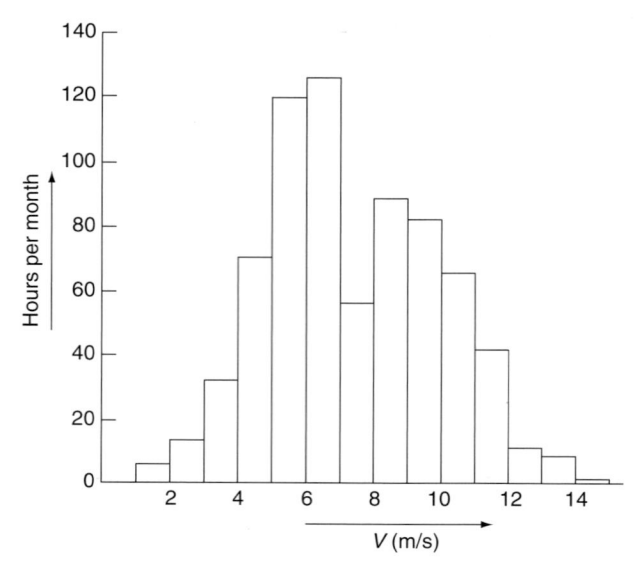

Figure 14 Velocity frequency data for Praia airport for a selected year [8].

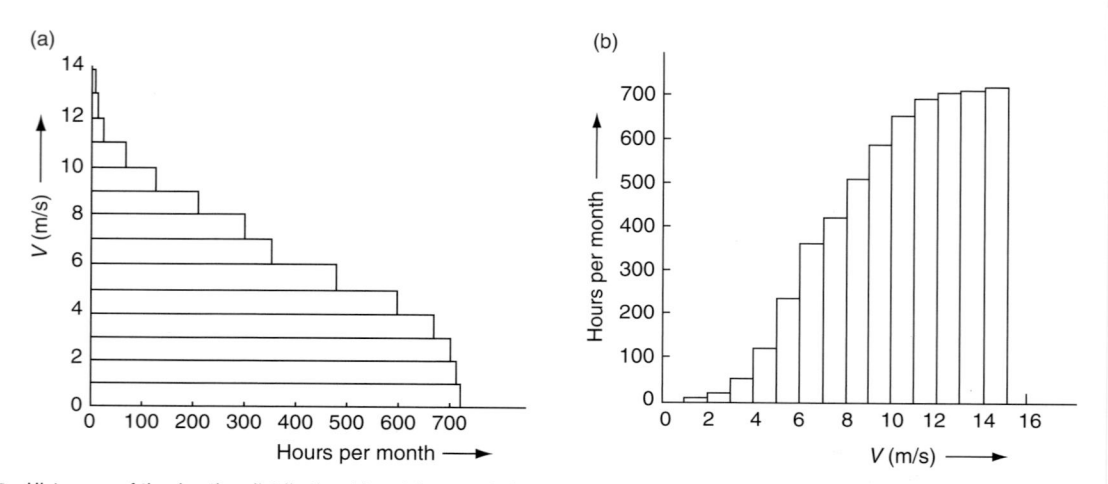

Figure 15 Histogram of the duration distribution (a) and the cumulative distribution (b) for Praia (during a selected month) [8].

2.04.4.2.1 Weibull distribution

In probability theory and statistics, the Weibull distribution is a continuous probability distribution. It is named after Waloddi Weibull who described it in detail in 1951 [11]. It is mostly used to describe wind speed distributions, and it is important in weather forecasting due to its flexibility.

The presentation of wind data makes use of the Weibull distribution as a tool to present the experimental frequency distribution of wind speed in a compact form. The two-parameter Weibull distribution is expressed mathematically as [8, 12]

$$p(V) = \left(\frac{k}{c}\right)\left(\frac{V}{c}\right)^{k-1} \exp\left[-\left(\frac{V}{c}\right)^{k}\right] \qquad [10]$$

where p is the frequency of occurrence of wind speed V. The two Weibull parameters thus defined are usually referred to as the scale parameter c (m s^{-1}) and the shape parameter k (dimensionless) (**Figure 16**).

2.04.4.2.2 Weibull hybrid distribution

This method is used also, if we neglect the frequent calms. It is a little complex to use, but the results are often comparable to those obtained by Weibull distribution and sometimes better. It must be solved by an iterating method. It is given by the following eqn [13]:

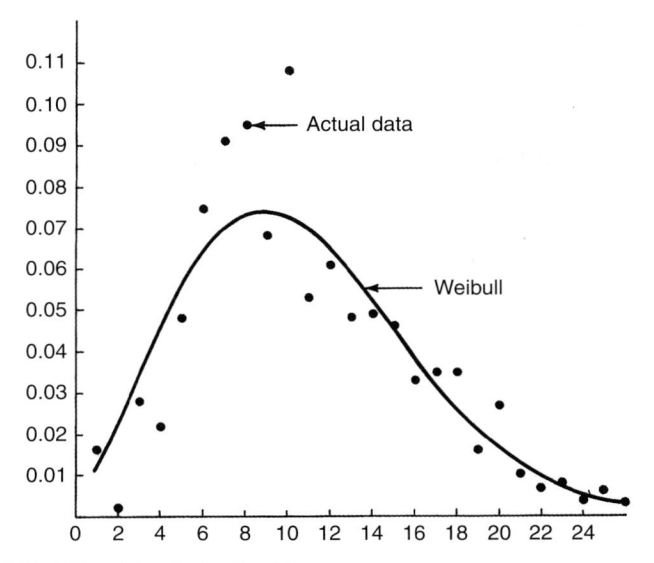

Figure 16 Actual wind data and weighted Weibull density function [5].

$$k = \left[\left(\frac{\sum_{1}^{N} n_i V_i^k \ln(V_i)}{\sum_{1}^{N} n_i V_i^k}\right) - \left(\frac{\sum_{1}^{N} n_i V_i}{N}\right)\right]^{-1} \quad [11]$$

and

$$C = \left[\frac{\sum_{1}^{N} n_i V_i^k}{N}\right]^{\frac{1}{K}} \quad [12]$$

where N is the total number of observations of no zero wind speed.

2.04.4.2.3 Cumulative distribution

The cumulative distribution function $F(V)$ indicates the time fraction or probability that the wind speed V is smaller than or equal to a given wind speed V':

$$F(V) = P(V \leq V') \quad [13]$$

The probability density function, represented in our case by the velocity frequency curve:

$$f(V) = \frac{dF(V')}{dV} \quad [14]$$

or

$$F(V) = \int_{0}^{v} f(V') dV' \quad [15]$$

and the cumulative distribution function (on the basis of Weibull distribution) is given by

$$F(V) = 1 - \exp\left[-\left(\frac{V}{c}\right)^k\right] \quad [16]$$

The velocity duration function $S(V)$, defined as the time fraction or probability that the wind speed V is larger than a given wind speed V', can be written as

$$S(V) = 1 - F(V) = P(V > V') \quad [17]$$

2.04.4.3 Wind Resource Atlas Models

The topography of the site can greatly affect the wind at a specific location. The wind speed will tend to accelerate up hill and decelerate down hill. If the slopes are too steep, however, the wind may 'separate' from the terrain and produce some damaging excess turbulence and lower mean wind speed. Careful siting is therefore essential. Some major progress has been made in computation of the local topographical effects by the Danish National Laboratory, RISO, who have published a very 'user-friendly' topographical wind flow model 'WASP' [13], which allows relatively inexpert users access to a very powerful tool of computational fluid dynamics. Used under the correct conditions this tool can produce reliable results for local flows and has been used extensively by wind energy community.

2.04.4.3.1 Physical basis

The layer closest to the ground is called the atmospheric boundary layer. It extends up to about 100 m on clear nights with low wind speeds and up to more than 2 km on a fine summer day. The lowest part of this layer is called the surface layer, which is sometimes defined as a fixed fraction, say 10% of the boundary layer depth. For the purpose of climatology relevant to wind power utilization, we can neglect the lowest wind speeds, so only situations where the atmospheric boundary layer extends to approximately 1 km and surface-layer physics apply in the lowest 100 m of the layer are of concern [13, 14].

The wind in the atmospheric boundary layer can be considered to arise from pressure differences caused mainly by the passing of high- and low-pressure systems. As the boundary layer structure has a rather rapid response to changes in pressure forcing, an approximate balance is found between the pressure gradient force and the frictional force at the surface of the earth. This balance can be theoretically derived under idealized conditions of stationarity, homogeneity, and barotropy [13, 15].

2.04.4.3.2 Stability model

The stability modifications of the logarithmic wind profile are often neglected in connection with wind energy, the justification being the relative unimportance of the low wind speed range. The model can treat stability modifications as small perturbations to a basic neutral state [13, 15].

2.04.4.3.3 Roughness change model

If the driving force of the wind or the geostrophic wind is the same over the area under consideration, it is possible to still use a modified logarithmic law to describe the profile. The effect of this is to alter the stability of the wind profile and the vertical movement of the air becomes more important.

Note that the logarithmic wind profile applies only if the upwind terrain is reasonably homogeneous. If this is not the case, deviation will be observed and it is not possible to assign a unique roughness length to the terrain. Even though 'effective' roughness lengths can be assigned by different methods, these will depend on the height observation. An exception to this is the effective roughness length implicitly defined by the geostrophic drag law [13]. The relations describing the vertical wind profile in neutral conditions within the boundary layer are [13, 16] the logarithmic wind profile law

$$V = \frac{V_*}{k} \ln\left(\frac{z}{z_0}\right) \quad [18]$$

the geostrophic drag law, $G(\text{m s}^{-1})$:

$$G = \sqrt{\left(\ln\left(\frac{V_*}{|f|z_0}\right) - A\right)^2 + B^2} \quad [19]$$

where V_* is the friction velocity (m s^{-1}), z_0 is surface roughness (m), f is Coliolis' parameter (1 s^{-1}), k is von Karman's constant, A is the empirical constant, $A = 1.8$, and B is the empirical constant, $B = 4.5$.

2.04.4.3.4 Shelter model

The frictional effect of a land surface is caused by drag on surface – mounted obstacles ranging from individual sand grains, grass, leaves, and so on, to large trees and buildings. Their collective effect is modeled through the surface roughness length. Close to an individual obstacle, at distances comparable to the height of the obstacle and at heights likewise comparable to the height of the obstacle, the wind profile is perturbed, particularly in the downstream wake, and the object must be treated separately. In the wake immediately behind a blunt object, such as a row of trees or a house (less than five object heights downstream and at heights less then twice the height of the object), the details of the object exert a critical influence on the effects. The wake behind a building depends, for example, on the detailed geometry of the roof and the incidence angle of the wind, to mention two parameters. Besides, wakes from other nearby objects may interfere, causing the problem to become very complicated [13].

2.04.4.3.5 Orographic model

Like the change-of-roughness and shelter models, the orographic model is used to correct measured wind data for the effect of local terrain inhomogeneities; in the present case, this means differences in terrain height around the meteorological stations [16].

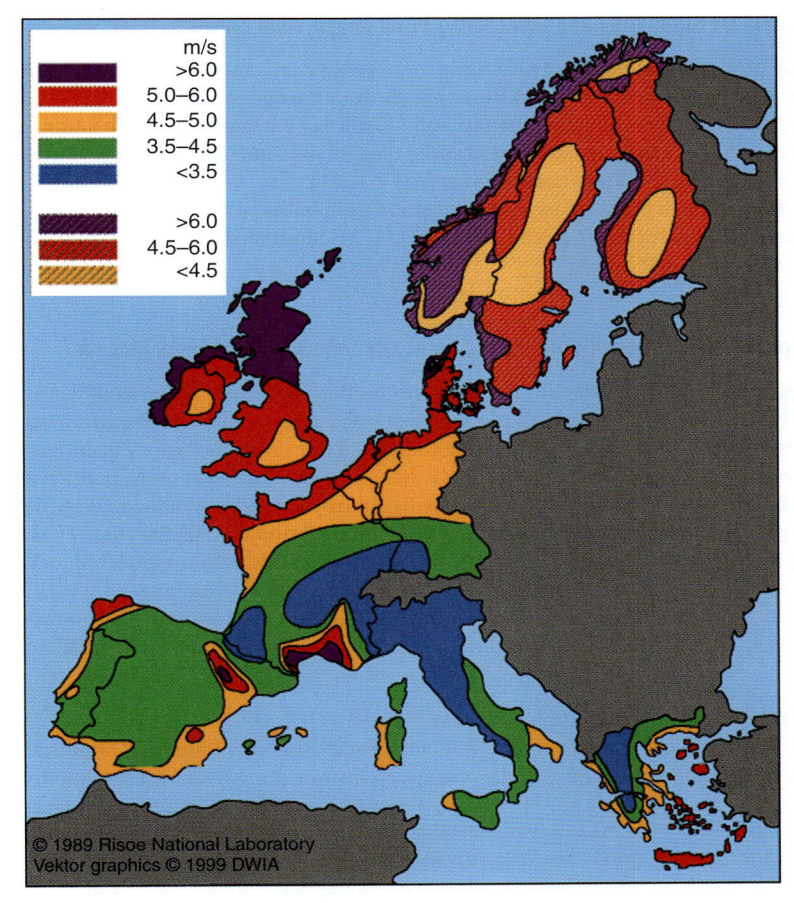

Figure 17 Mean annual wind speed in Western Europe (in m s^{-1} at 10 m height above ground surface).

2.04.4.4 Wind Resource Atlas

The aim of a Wind Atlas is to establish the meteorological basis for the assessment of wind energy resources. The wind energy measured at a meteorological station is determined mainly by two factors: the overall weather systems, which usually have an extent of several hundred kilometers, and the nearby topography out of a few tens of kilometers from the station [17–20].

The application of measured wind speed stations to wind energy resource calculations in a region therefore requires methods for the transformation of a comprehensive set of models for the horizontal and vertical extrapolation of meteorological data and the estimation of wind resources. The models are based on the physical principals of flows in the atmospheric boundary layer and they take into account the effect of different surfaces conditions, sheltering effects due to buildings and obstacles, and the modification of the wind imposed by the specific variation of the height of ground around the meteorological station in question. Meteorological models are used to calculate the regional wind climatologies from the raw data. In the reverse process – the application of the Wind Atlas – the wind climate at any specific site may be calculated from the regional climatology. Consequently, the mean annual wind speed can be used to estimate actual mean power (**Figure 17**).

2.04.5 Dynamic Study of Wind Speed

Due to the stochastic nature of wind speed from time to time and from site to site, short-term wind speed forecasting is of great importance to control the dynamic aspects of a wind system so that it can be quickly adjusted to respond to the predicted change in wind speed. It is also crucial for decision-making on the scheduling maintenance and the integration of wind energy into the traditional electricity systems.

To date, huge research effort has been witnessed on developing effective methods for wind speed forecast. The approaches in the literature to wind speed forecasts include physical methods, such as numerical weather forecast (NWF), conventional statistical methods such as Box–Jenkins ARIMA models, Markov chain models, hybrid physical–statistical models, and others. In recent years, artificial intelligence techniques have been adopted for the purpose of wind speed forecasting, such as neural networks of multilayer perceptrons (MLPs), recurrent neural networks, and so on [17–20].

2.04.5.1 Stochastic Models for Simulating and Forecasting Wind Speed Time Series

A model that describes the probability structure of a sequence of observations is called a stochastic process. Among the model that has been widely used for the description of stationary time series is the autoregressive (AR) model [21]. The model was built using the methodology for time-series analysis developed by Box and Jenkins [17]. It is combined statistical–dynamic model that could simulate the statistical characteristics of the observed wind speed data. It takes into account the past values of the data and random change of the climate represented by the white noise process $w(t)$ [17, 21].

Another model is the Markov chain process based on a transition probability matrix developed from quantitative observed data. It can be also used to generate a synthetic wind speed time series [22–24]. Both models are predictive models and could be used for forecasting times series.

2.04.5.2 Bayesian Adaptive Combination of Wind Speed Forecasts from Neural Network Models

It is possible that no single model can be declared to be superior to other models for all types of wind applications and under all conditions. On the other hand, for wind energy applications, a final single forecast that can take advantage of the available models is often desired. Ideally, this forecast should be better than the individual ones with the best available prediction. Motivated by this idea, Li et al. [25, 26] have proposed a two-step approach to enhance the wind speed forecast performance of NN models.

Multimodel techniques can provide consensus predictions by linearly combining individual model predictions according to different weighting strategies. As one typical multimodel method, Bayesian model averaging (BMA) has recently gained popularity in various fields because it can produce more adaptive and reliable predictions than other techniques. On the top of that, BMA approach demonstrated also its capability of describing long-term wind speed distributions with high reliability and robustness. Therefore, it is appealing to apply this Bayesian method to combine the short-term wind speed forecasts from different NN-based models, aiming to develop an adaptive and robust methodology for short-term wind speed forecasting [25–30].

2.04.5.2.1 Artificial neural network models

Neural network models trained with time series have the ability to model arbitrarily linear and nonlinear functions. The model can learn from past data, recognize hidden patterns or relationships in historical observations, and use the relationships to forecast future values [25, 26].

An artificial neural network (ANN) is a massively parallel distributed processor made up of simple processing units, which have the natural propensity for storing experiential knowledge through a learning process and making it available for use. ANN is a type of artificial intelligence technique that mimics the behavior of the human brain. ANNs have ability to model linear and nonlinear systems without the need to make assumptions implicitly as in most traditional statistical–physical approaches, applied in various aspects of science and engineering.

A neural network usually contains an input layer, one or more hidden layers, and an output layer. Each layer consists of one or more neurons and each neuron functions as an independent computation unit. Knowledge is stored as a set of connection weights. The neuron receives a set of inputs with corresponding adaptable synaptic weights, calculates the weighted average of these inputs, and generates an output via the activation function [25, 26]. The typical topology of feed-forward neural networks, where computations proceed along the forward direction only, is illustrated in **Figure 18**. The term f_{t+k} denotes a forecast value of the wind speed y_{t+k}, which is estimated at time point t, based on n historical measurements $y_t, y_{t-1},...,y_{t-n+1}$. In order to have an accurate wind speed forecast, time horizon k is chosen to be small and this is called short-term wind speed forecast.

As the training process proceeds, the connection weights are modified in certain way by using a suitable learning method. The network uses a learning mode, in which an input is presented to the network along with the desired output and the weights are adjusted so that the network attempts to produce the desired output. Therefore, the weights, after the training process, contain meaningful information.

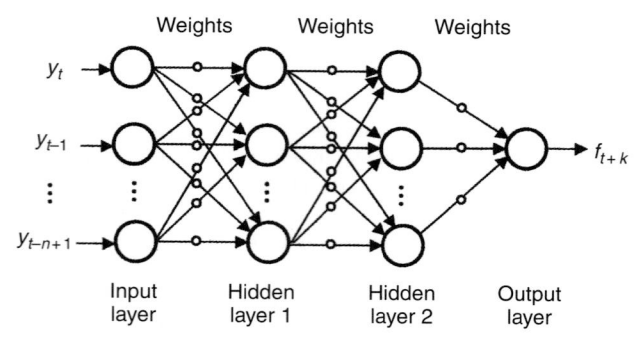

Figure 18 A generic topology of feed-forward neural networks [26].

2.04.5.2.2 Bayesian model averaging

BMA is a statistical procedure that infers consensus predictions weighing individual forecasts based on their posterior model probabilities, and thus generated an averaged model, with the better performing forecasts receiving higher weights than the worse performing ones. A model space M composed of J models M_j ($j = 1, 2, ..., J$) is considered for forecasting y, the wind speed. Let D denote the training data of wind speed observations and f_j the forecast of model j. As shown in eqn [20], the probability density function of the BMA probabilistic forecast of y is an average of the posterior distributions $p(y/M_j, D)$ under each model considered, weighted by their posterior probabilities $w_j = P(M_j/D)$ [25, 26]

$$p(y|D) = \sum_{j=1}^{J} w_j p(y|M_j, D) \quad [20]$$

The posterior mean and variance of the BMA forecast can be calculated as follows:

$$E[y|D] = \sum_{j=1}^{J} p(M_j|D) \cdot E[y|M_j, D] = \sum_{j=1}^{J} w_j f_i \quad [21]$$

$$\text{Var}[y|D] = \sum_{j=1}^{J} w_j \left(f_j - \sum_{i=1}^{J} w_i f_i \right)^2 + \sum_{j=1}^{J} w_j \sigma_j^2 \quad [22]$$

where σ_j^2 is the variance associated with model prediction f_j given observation data D and $w_j = P(f_j/D)$ represents the posterior probability of the jth model forecast being correct. For a particular model space, it always holds that $\sum_{j=1}^{J} w_j = 1$. Equation [21] indicates that the BMA forecast is actually a combination of the forecast with the corresponding posterior model probability. Thus, the algorithm is often called Bayesian combination algorithm as well. It can be seen that the critical issue is how to estimate the posterior model probability.

The posterior probabilities of the component model can be estimated using Markov chain Monte Carlo (MCMC) method and expectation-maximization (EM). MCMC methods are usually of high computational complexity and time-consuming, but it can simulate any complex probability distribution. Compared with MCMC method, EM algorithm is significantly more efficient, although it is mainly limited to normal or approximately normal distributions. However, the Box–Cox transformation could be used to transform wind speed into Gaussian distribution before the EM algorithm can be applied [26, 30].

2.04.6 Wind Energy

2.04.6.1 Wind Energy Production

Air mass flowing with a velocity V through an area A represents a mass flow rate m of (**Figure 19**)

$$m = \rho_{\text{air}} A V \, (\text{kg s}^{-1}) \quad [23]$$

and thus a kinetic energy flow per second or kinetic power P_{kin} of

$$P_{\text{kin}} = \frac{1}{2} (\rho_{\text{air}} A V) V^2 = \frac{1}{2} \rho_{\text{air}} A V^3 \quad [24]$$

where ρ is air density (kg m^{-3}), A is the area swept by the rotor blades (m^2), and V is the undisturbed wind velocity (m s^{-1}).

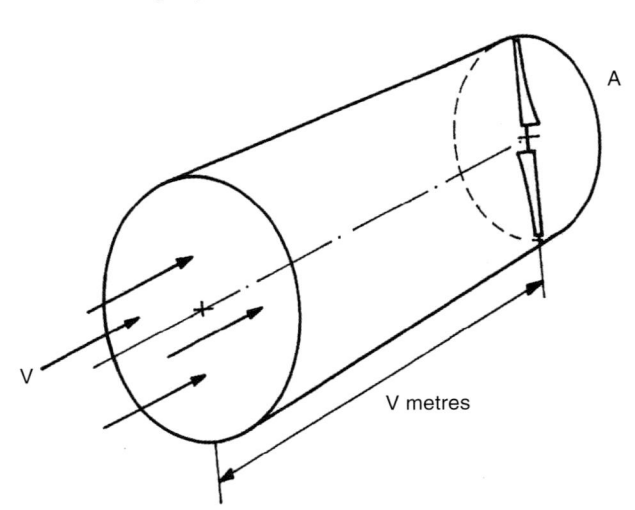

Figure 19 Mass flow per unit area per second [8].

2.04.6.2 Wind Energy Potential

2.04.6.2.1 Power output from an ideal turbine: Betz limit

A wind rotor can only extract power from the wind, because it slows down the wind: the wind speed behind the rotor is lower than in front of the rotor. Too much slowing down causes the air to flow around the wind rotor area instead of through the area and it turns out that the maximum power extraction is reached when the wind velocity in the wake of the rotor is 1/3 of the undisturbed wind velocity V_1. In that case, the rotor itself 'feels' a velocity $2/3V_1$, so the effective mass flow is only $\rho A 2/3 V_1$. Therefore, since the mass flow is slowed down from V_1 to $1/3V_1$, the extracted power is equal to

$$P_{max} = \frac{1}{2}\left(\rho A \frac{2}{3} V_1\right) V_1^2 - \frac{1}{2}\left(\rho A \frac{2}{3} V_1\right)\left(\frac{1}{3} V_1\right)^2 \quad [25]$$

or

$$P_{max} = \frac{16}{27} \times \frac{1}{2}\rho A V_1^3 \quad [26]$$

In other words, the theoretical maximum fraction of extracted power is 16/27 or 59.3%.

This maximum is called the Betz-maximum in honor of the wind pioneer who first derived its value. The fraction of extracted power, which we call power coefficient C_p, in practice, seldom exceeds 40% if measured as the mechanical power of a real wind rotor [8].

2.04.6.2.2 Axial momentum theory

The first description of the axial momentum theory was given by Rankine in 1865 and was improved later by Froude. The theory provides a relation between the forces acting on a rotor and the resulting fluid velocities and predicts the ideal efficiency of the rotor. Later on, Betz included rotational wake effects in the theory. Recently, Wilson, Lissaman, and Walker have further analyzed the aerodynamic performance of wind turbine [4, 5, 8]. For our analysis we shall use the symbols as indicated in **Figure 20**.

The assumptions underlying the axial momentum theory are as follows:

- incompressible medium
- no frictional drag
- infinite number of blades
- homogenous flow
- uniform thrust over the rotor area
- nonrotating wake
- static pressure far before and far behind the rotor is equal to the undisturbed ambient static pressure.

Considering the stream tube, the conservation of mass dictates

$$\rho A_1 V_1 = \rho A V = \rho A_2 V_2 \quad [27]$$

The thrust force T on the rotor is given by the change in momentum of the incoming flow compared to the outgoing flow

$$T = \rho A_1 V_1^2 - \rho A_2 V_2^2 \quad [28]$$

with eqn [27] this becomes

$$T = \rho A V (V_1 - V_2) \quad [29]$$

Also the thrust on the rotor can be expressed as a result of the pressure difference over the rotor area:

$$T = (p^+ - p^-)A \quad [30]$$

The pressure difference can be estimated using Bernoulli's equation [3–5]:

$$p^+ - p^- = \frac{1}{2}\rho(V_1^2 - V_2^2) \quad [31]$$

and the thrust becomes

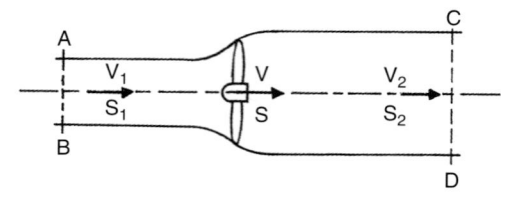

Figure 20 Condition for maximum power extraction, Betz limit [4, 5, 8].

$$T = \frac{1}{2}\rho A(V_1^2 - V_2^2) \qquad [32]$$

Equating [29] with [32] provides the important relation:

$$V = \frac{1}{2}(V_1 + V_2) \qquad [33]$$

Practical wind mills will no achieve the Betz limit; thus, the wind velocity at the disc will be somewhat lower than the value of V_1. The value of the wind velocity at the disc is expressed in terms of an inflow factor, a, such that the wind velocity is given by $V_1(1-a)$ [5].

The power absorbed by the rotor is equal to the change in kinetic power of the mass flowing through the rotor area:

$$\begin{aligned}P &= \frac{1}{2}\rho AV(V_1^2 - V_2^2) \\ &= 4a(1-a)^2 \frac{2}{3}\rho A V_1^3\end{aligned} \qquad [34]$$

The maximum value of P is reached for dP/da = 0 and results in

$$a = \frac{1}{3}$$

and

$$P = \frac{16}{27} \times \frac{1}{2}\rho A V_1^3 \qquad [35]$$

The factor 16/27 is called the Betz coefficient, as we have mentioned before, and represents the maximum fraction that an ideal wind rotor under the given conditions can extract from the flow.

Note that this fraction is related to the power of an disturbed flow arriving at area, where as in reality only the undisturbed flow through area $A1 = A(1-a)$ reaches the rotor. This means that the maximum efficiency related to the real mass flow through the rotor is equal to $16/27 \times 3/2 = 8/9$.

2.04.7 Conclusions

The most critical aspect for the success of investment in the wind energy sector is having an accurate wind resource assessment at the considered site that depends on the wind speed frequency observations and the length of the record period. But, such large quantities of reliable meteorological measurements are not available everywhere. Therefore, a wide variety of statistical analysis techniques like Weibull distribution, topographical models, and computational fluid dynamics tools have been developed for estimating wind characteristics in different conditions of atmospheric stability and on complex terrain sites.

Due to the stochastic nature of wind speed from time to time and from site to site, other methods focusing on wind speed simulating and forecasting would help wind energy integration. These methods are also crucial for decision-making on the scheduling maintenance and the integration of wind energy into the conventional electricity systems.

To date, huge research effort has been witnessed on developing effective methods for wind speed forecast. The approaches in the literature to wind speed forecasts include physical methods, such as numerical weather forecast, conventional statistical methods such as AR processes, Markov chain models, and hybrid physical–statistical models. In recent years, artificial intelligence techniques have been adapted for the purpose of wind speed forecasting, such as adaptive neural network of MLPs, recurrent neural networks, and BMA.

Meteorological models are used to calculate the regional wind climatologies from the raw data. In the reverse process – the application of the Wind Atlas – the wind climate at any specific site may be calculated from the regional climatology. Consequently, the mean annual wind speed, for example, can be used to estimate actual mean power.

References

[1] Triplet TP and Roche G (1977) *Météorologie Générale*. France: Météorologie Nationale.
[2] (1982) *Wind Power Plants: Theory and Design*. Oxford, UK: Pergamon Press, Ltd.
[3] http://en.wikipedia.org/
[4] Dunn PD (1986) *Renewable Energies: Sources, Conversion and Application*. London, UK: Peter Peregrinus, Ltd.
[5] Johnson GL (1985) *Wind Energy Systems*. London, UK: Prentice Hall Ltd.
[6] Cunty G (1979) *Eoliennes et Aérogénérateurs: Guide de l'Énergie Éolienne*. C-Y Chaudoreille, Aix-en-Provence: EDISUD.
[7] Ragheb M *Wind Shear, Roughness Classes and Turbine Energy Production*. https://netfiles.uiuc.edu/
[8] Lysen EH (1983) *Introduction to Wind Energy*. Amersfoort, Netherlands: CWD 82-1.
[9] Freris LL (1990) *Wind Energy Conversion Systems*. London, UK: Prentice Hall, Ltd.
[10] Burton T, Sharpe D, Jenkins N, and Bossany E (2004) *Wind Energy Handbook*. West Sussex, England: Wiley.
[11] Weibull W (1951) A statistical distribution function of wide applicability. *Journal of Applied Mechanics* 18(3): 293–297.

[12] Nfaoui H, Buret B, and Sayigh AAM (1998) Wind characteristics and wind energy potential in Morocco. *Solar Energy* 63(1): 51–60.
[13] Troen I and Petersen EL (1989) *European Wind Atlas*. Denmark: Riso National Laboratory.
[14] Wind energy resource Atlas of the United States, Denver. http://redc.nrel.org, 1999.
[15] Giebel G and Gryning S-E (2004) *Shear and Stability in High Met Masts, and How WAsP Treats It*. Riso National Laboratory. www.wasp.dk
[16] Gryning S-E and Batchvarova E *Modelling of the Wind Profile: Effect of Boundary Layer Height, Baroclinicity, Friction Ross by Number and Brunt-Vaisala Frequency*. Denmark: Wind Energy Division, Riso DTU.
[17] Box GEP and Jenkins GM (1976) *Times Series Analysis: Forecasting and Control*. San Francisco: Holden-Day, Inc.
[18] MacKay DJC (1992) Bayesian Methods for Adaptive Models. PhD Thesis, California Institute of Technology.
[19] Isaacson DL and Madsen RW (1976) *Markov Chains: Theory and Applications*. New York: Wiley.
[20] Bishop CM (1995) *Neural Networks for Pattern Recognition*. Oxford: Oxford University Press.
[21] Nfaoui H, Buret J, and Sayigh AAM (1996) Stochastic simulation of hourly average wind speed sequences in Tangiers (Morocco). *Solar Energy* 56(3): 561–575.
[22] Kirchhoff RH, Kaminsky FC, and Woo JS (1988) A Markov chain analysis of wind speed at Windsor, Massachusetts. *Proceedings of the 7th ASME Symposium on Wind Energy*.
[23] Nfaoui H, Essiarab E, and Sayigh AAM (2004) A stochastic Markov chain model for simulating wind speed times series at Tangiers, Morocco. *Renewable Energy* 29: 1407–1418.
[24] Shamshad A, Bawadi MA, Hussin WMA, *et al.* (2005) First and second order Markov chain models for synthetic generation of wind speed times series. *Solar Energy* 30: 693–708.
[25] Haykin S (2009) *Neural Networks and Learning Machines*. New Jersey, USA: Pearson Education, Inc.
[26] Li G, Shi J, and Zhou J (2011) Bayesian adaptive combination of short-term wind speed forecasts from neural network models. *Renewable Energy* 36(1): 352–359.
[27] Widrow B and Lehr MA (2002) 30 years of adaptive neural networks: Perceptron, Madaline, and backpropagation. *Proceedings of IEEE* 78(9): 1415–1442.
[28] Burnham KP and Anderson DR (2002) *Model Selection and Multimodel Inference*, 2nd edn. New York: Springer.
[29] Hoeting JA, Madigan D, Raftery AE, and Volinsky CT (1999) Bayesian model averaging: A tutorial. *Statistical Science* 14(4): 382–417.
[30] McLachlan GJ and Krishnan T (1997) *The EM Algorithm and Extensions*. New York: Wiley.
[31] Mathew S (2006) *Wind Energy, Fundamentals, Resource Analysis and Economics*. The Netherlands: Springer.

Further Reading

[1] Ackermann Th (2005) *Wind Power in Power Systems*, 1st edn. Chichester, UK: Wiley.
[2] Burton T, Sharpe D, Jenkins N, and Bossanyi E (2001) *Wind Energy Handbook*, 1st edn. Chichester, UK: Wiley.
[3] Hansen MOL (2008) *Aerodynamics of Wind Turbines*, 2nd edn. London, UK: Earthscan.
[4] Hau E (2006) *Wind Turbines: Fundamentals, Technologies, Application, Economics*, 2nd edn. Berlin, Heidelberg, Germany: Springer.
[5] Kaldellis JK (2010) *Stand-Alone and Hybrid Wind Energy Systems: Technology, Energy Storage and Applications*, 1st edn. Cambridge, UK: Woodhead Publishing.
[6] Stiebler M (2008) *Wind Energy Systems for Electric Power Generation*, 1st edn. Berlin, Heidelberg, Germany: Springer.
[7] Walker JF and Jenkins N (1997) *Wind Energy Technology*, 1st edn. Chishester, UK: Wiley.

2.05 Wind Turbines: Evolution, Basic Principles, and Classifications

S Mathew, University of Brunei Darussalam, Gadong, Brunei Darussalam
GS Philip, KCAET, Malapuram, Kerala, India

© 2012 Elsevier Ltd. All rights reserved.

2.05.1	Introduction	93
2.05.2	Evolution of Modern Wind Turbines	93
2.05.2.1	Growth in Installed Capacity	94
2.05.2.2	Increase in Turbine Size	95
2.05.2.3	Improvements in System Performance	96
2.05.2.4	Advances in the Control and Power Transmission Systems	98
2.05.2.5	Economic Evolution	100
2.05.3	Basic Principles	100
2.05.3.1	Power Available in the Wind	100
2.05.3.2	Power Coefficient, Torque Coefficient, and Tip Speed Ratio	102
2.05.3.3	Airfoil Lift and Drag	102
2.05.4	Classifications of Wind Turbines	104
2.05.4.1	Horizontal Axis Wind Turbines	104
2.05.4.2	Vertical Axis Wind Turbines	106
2.05.4.2.1	Darrieus rotor	107
2.05.4.2.2	Savonius rotor	109
2.05.5	Rotor Performance Curves	110
References		111
Further Reading		111

Nomenclature

A wind rotor swept area exposed to the wind stream
C_D drag coefficient
C_L lift coefficient
C_P power coefficient of the rotor
$C_{P\,max}$ maximum power coefficient of the rotor
C_T torque coefficient of the rotor
D airfoil drag force
F thrust force experienced by the rotor
L airfoil lift force
m air mass
N rotational speed of the rotor
P theoretical power of the rotor
P_T power developed by the turbine rotor
R rotor radius
t temperature
T theoretical torque of the rotor
T_T torque developed by the rotor
V wind velocity normal to the rotor plane
V_R resultant velocity
V_T tangential velocity due to the blade's rotation
Z elevation of the site
α angle of attack
λ tip speed ratio
ρ density of air
Ω angular velocity

2.05.1 Introduction

During its transition from ancient 'windmills' to modern electricity generating 'wind turbines', the wind energy conversion technology has undergone significant changes. Turbines of various shapes and sizes, working on different design principles, were introduced by researchers and inventors during the course of this development. In this chapter, we will briefly describe this evolution of the modern wind energy conversion technology. This is followed by discussions on the basic principles governing the wind energy conversion process and classifications of wind turbines.

2.05.2 Evolution of Modern Wind Turbines

While looking back at the history, we can see that the wind energy conversion technology has undergone three distinct stages of development. From the inception of the technology through the invention of grain grinding windmills by the Persians in 200 BC to the popular wind pumps of the eighteenth century, it was the era of ancient windmills. By the 1800s, engines powered by steam and gas started getting popular and the use of wind machines was restricted only for remote applications, where a steady and reliable supply of power is not critical. Several such systems served the power needs of remote areas during the eighteenth century.

The next phase of development began with the introduction of electricity generating wind 'turbines' in the early 1900s. The first wind electric generator was constructed in Denmark in 1890 and a utility-scale system was installed in Russia by 1931. Though efforts in similar direction were made in different parts of the world, the interest in wind energy gradually declined due to the popularity of diesel generators, which were considered to be more convenient and economic in those times. Though the restriction in oil supply during the First and Second World Wars prompted us to reconsider the wind energy option, it sustained only for a short period and the interest in wind energy declined gradually, till the oil shock in the 1970s.

With the oil crisis in 1973, the world recognized the importance of energy independence, and as a result, activities for wind energy development were once again revived on a global scale. A number of research and development programs were instantiated during this period, and several turbine prototypes of different sizes and shapes were built. Research was focused on developing efficient, reliable, and cost-effective systems by modifying all the hardware components – right from the rotor to the control systems. Some of the milestones in this development are the MOD series turbines by the National Aeronautics and Space Administration (NASA) [1] and the Vertical Axis Darrieus turbines developed by Sandia National laboratories [2]. Research and development activities in this area were further accelerated as a result of the increased environmental consciousness. These efforts gave birth to the next phase of wind energy development – the era of modern wind turbines. In this section, we will restrict our discussions to the evolution of modern wind turbines, giving emphasis to

- growth in wind power capacity,
- increase in unit size,
- improvements in system performance,
- technological advances in control and power transmission systems, and
- economical competitiveness.

2.05.2.1 Growth in Installed Capacity

One of the major milestones in the evolution of wind energy conversion technology is the significant increase in the installed wind power capacity. Time series evolution of wind energy capacity from 1996 to 2010, based on studies of the Global Wind Energy Council (GWEC) [3], is shown in **Figure 1**. The cumulative installations have increased from 6100 to 194 390 MW during this period.

The rates of growth of wind power installations for the past 10 years are shown in **Figure 2** [3]. It could be seen that wind energy could register an average growth rate of 27.4% over the last decade. This is an impressive achievement, which makes wind the fastest growing energy source in the world.

A region-wise wind power scenario is displayed in **Figure 3** [3]. Considering the installations by 2010, the major contribution to this impressive status comes from Europe. Germany (27 214 MW) and Spain (20 676 MW) are the leaders in this region. With capacity additions over 19 000 MW during the last three consecutive years, Asia is emerging as one of the significant players in wind power development.

The two emerging economies, China and India, share the credit for this growth. For example, in 2010, China added 16 500 MW to its wind power capacity to reach a total of 42 287 MW. This enabled China to exceed the cumulative installations of the United States (40 200 MW) and become the world leader in wind energy utilization.

The major driving force behind this rapid growth in global wind power deployment is the environmental commitments and emission reduction targets set by different countries. For example, under the Kyoto protocol, China and the United States (responsible for 22.30% and 19.91% of the global emission, respectively) have a CO_2 reduction target of 40% and 17%,

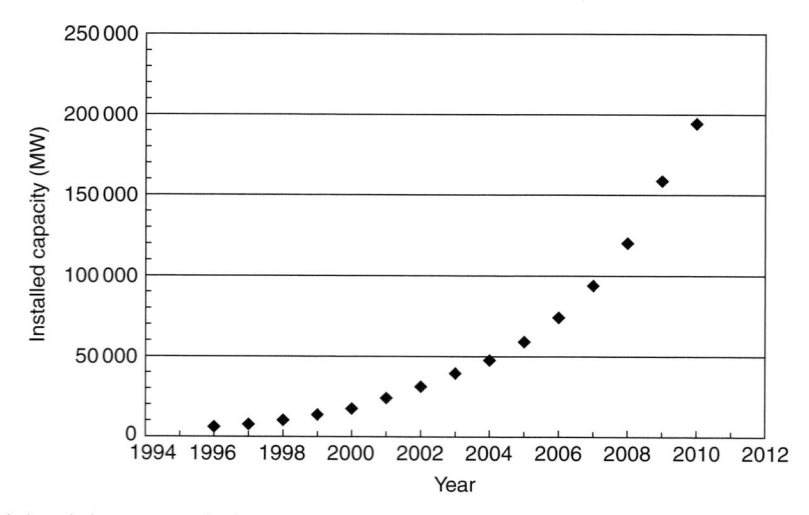

Figure 1 Growth in cumulative wind power capacity from 1996 to 2010.

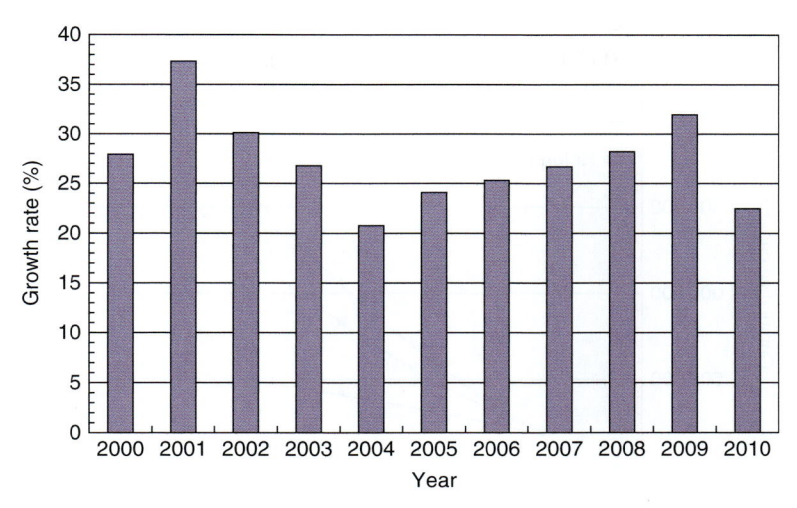

Figure 2 Annual growth rate of wind power over the last decade.

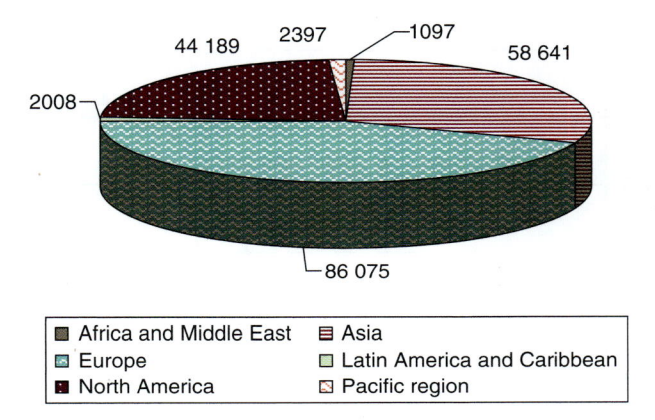

Figure 3 Region-wise distribution of global wind power capacity by the end of 2010.

respectively, by 2020 [4]. Other countries also have similar commitments. Wind energy, with its clean, mature, and economically competitive technology, would be the obvious choice among the renewables for meeting these environmental obligations. As a result, economic incentives of different kinds are being offered for catalyzing wind-based clean energy generation in these countries. Other factors like concern over energy security and creation of the so-called green collar jobs are also in favor of the wind power sector.

The current boom in the wind power sector is expected to continue in the coming years as well. For example, GWEC, in collaboration with Greenpeace International and the German Aerospace Centre (DLR), examined the future growth potential of wind power [4]. Three scenarios, namely, reference, moderate, and advanced, were considered for the projections. The reference scenario took only the existing policies and measures in the energy sector into account whereas the moderate scenario considered the current and planned policy measures to support the renewables. The advanced scenario brings out the highest possible level to which the global wind industry can grow under the most favorable situations.

Results of this analysis are shown in **Figure 4**. In the next 20 years, the global cumulative wind power capacity is expected to reach 572 733 MW under the reference scenario. Corresponding growth expected under the moderate and advanced scenarios are 1 777 550 and 2 341 984 MW, respectively. Under these predictions, share of wind energy in the global power generation is found to vary between 4.9% and 5.6% under the reference, 15.1–17.5 under the moderate, and 18.8–21.8 under the advanced scenarios. Hence, under favorable conditions, wind energy is going to be a major player in the global energy market, meeting a fifth of the world's power demand.

2.05.2.2 Increase in Turbine Size

During the evolution of modern wind turbines, the unit size of the machine has been considerably increased. From small systems limited to a few kW capacity, wind turbines have grown to gigantic machines of MW class. This scaling-up trend is shown in **Figure 5**. Today's largest commercially available wind turbine has a rotor of 127 m diameter and 12 668 m^2 swept area [5]. The rated

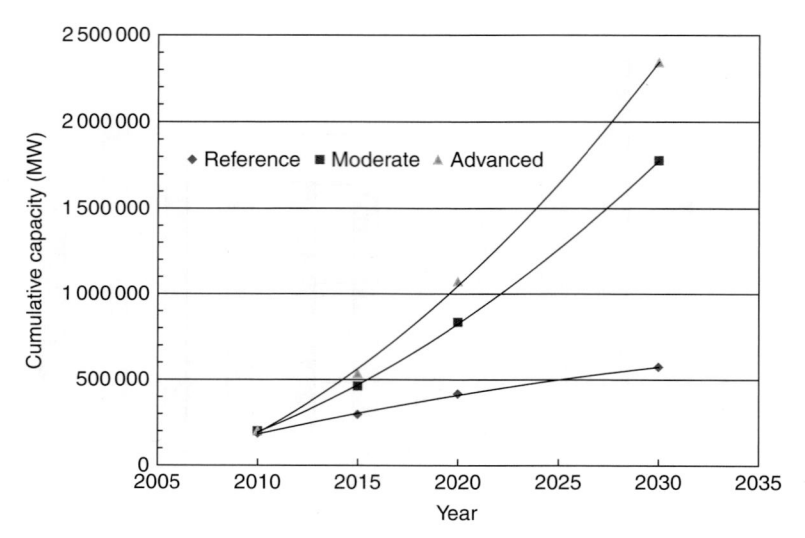

Figure 4 Projected growth of wind power in the next 20 years.

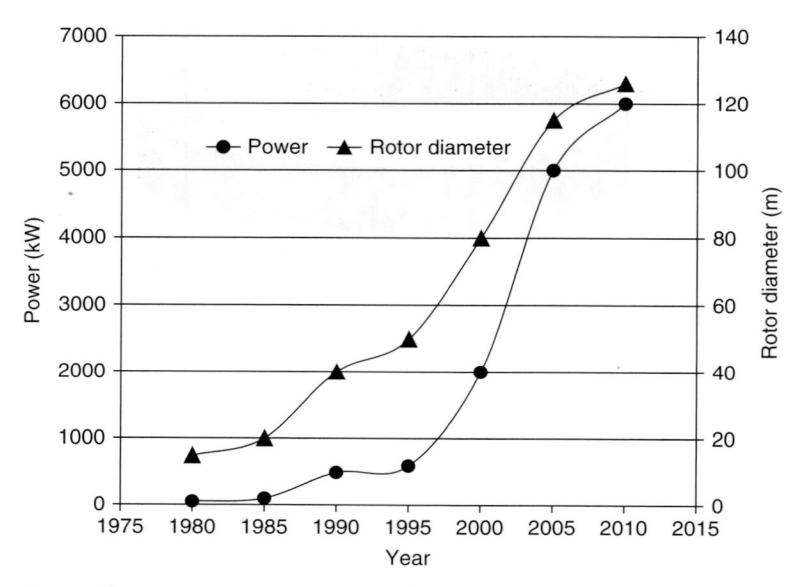

Figure 5 Increase in turbine size over the years.

capacity of the machine is 7.5 MW. Several bigger designs are under planning and development stages. The 10 MW turbine planned by the Norwegian industry is an example [6].

There are many factors favoring the scaling up of the size of wind turbines. The most obvious one is the economic advantages. Cost of the wind turbines, per unit size ($ kW^{-1}), can be considerably reduced by scaling up the system size. It is a fact that the expenditures on many components, systems, and services (e.g., safety features, electronic circuits, investments in R&D, and production manpower) do not scale up at the same rate as that of turbine size. Similarly, a single higher capacity turbine is easier to maintain than a number of smaller turbines contributing to the same capacity. Thus, scaling-up of the system is one of the major factors contributing to the unit cost reduction in wind turbine technology in recent years.

Environmental factors also favor the scaling up of wind turbines. Due to the larger rotor size, bigger turbines are designed to run slower to keep the optimal tip speed ratio. For example, the 7.5 MW turbine mentioned above runs at a speed of 5–12 rpm whereas a 330 kW unit of the same design rotates at 18–45 rpm. Lower rotational speed minimizes the risk of avian mortality, which is one of the major environmental concerns raised against wind farms. Similarly, aerodynamic noise can also be minimized by reducing the operating speed.

2.05.2.3 Improvements in System Performance

The process of converting wind into electrical energy has also become more efficient during the course of time. Improvements in the wind turbine capacity factor over the years are shown in **Figure 6**. The trend is derived from a compilation of capacity factor data

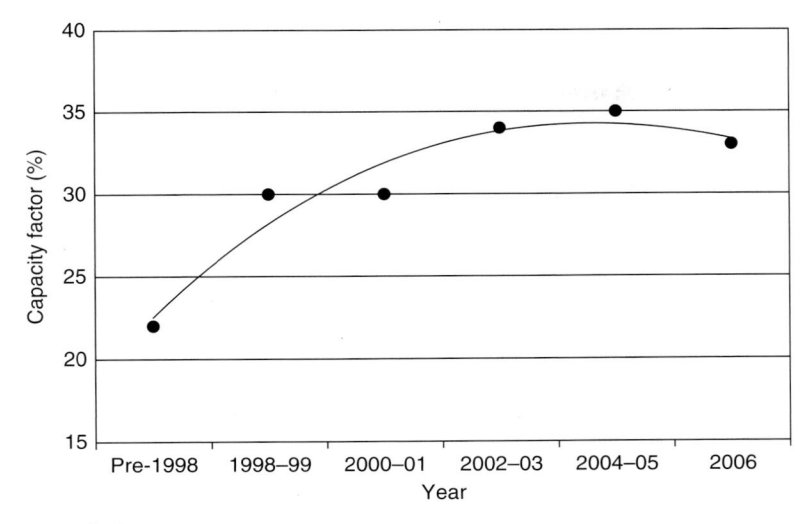

Figure 6 Improvement in the capacity factor.

from 170 US wind farms between 1983 and 2006 [7]. An impressive improvement in the capacity factor can be observed from the figure. For example, comparing the weighted average capacity factor during 2004–06, the study indicated an improvement of 33–35% by 2007. In general, projects at high wind resource areas could attain a capacity factor above 40% during 2007. The Hawaii 2 project which showed a capacity factor of 45% is a good example. The major reasons for this impressive improvement in wind farm performance are (1) higher hub heights, (2) improvements in siting, and (3) technological advances in the control and power transmission systems.

With the increase in wind turbine size, the diameter of the rotor also has increased considerably in recent years. For example, today's most popular 2 MW class turbines have diameters around 90 m, with slight variations depending upon the design. Taller towers are required to accommodate rotors of this size. A general trend in the variations in hub height with the rotor diameter, brought out in a study by Garrad Hassan [8], is shown in **Figure 7**. The relationship between the rotor diameter (D) and hub height (h) can be expressed as $h = 2.7936 D^{0.7663}$.

Apart from meeting the technical requirements, taller towers enable the turbine to capture the stronger wind spectra available at higher elevations. Wind velocity increases with height due to wind shear reduction. For example, the increase in wind velocity with height under three terrain conditions is shown in **Figure 8**. It should be noted that, even a small increase in the velocity could result in significant change in energy capture due to the cubic velocity–power relationship. Hence, contemporary wind turbines are capable of extracting more power from a given site due to the higher hub height.

Recent advances in computer modeling made it possible to have a better understanding on the wind resource available at the wind farm sites. These computer models could not only identify potential locations for wind farm activities but also describe the variations in wind power availability within the site by incorporating the effects of elevation, topography, and ground cover

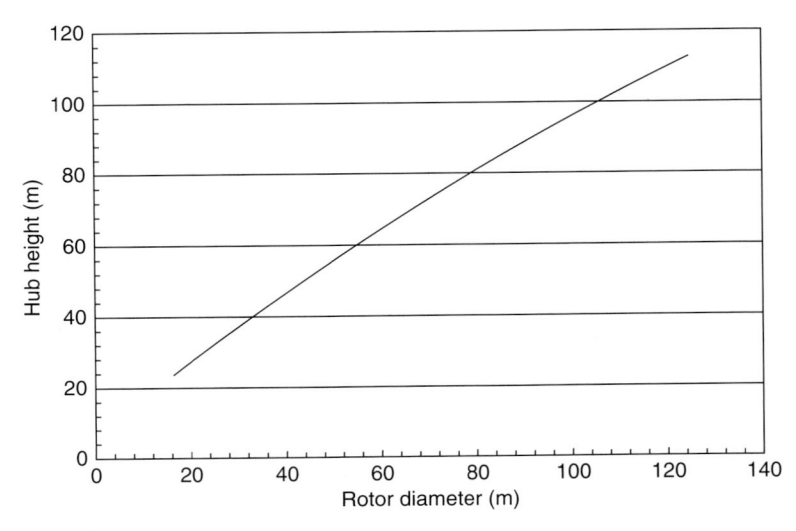

Figure 7 Variations in hub height with rotor diameter.

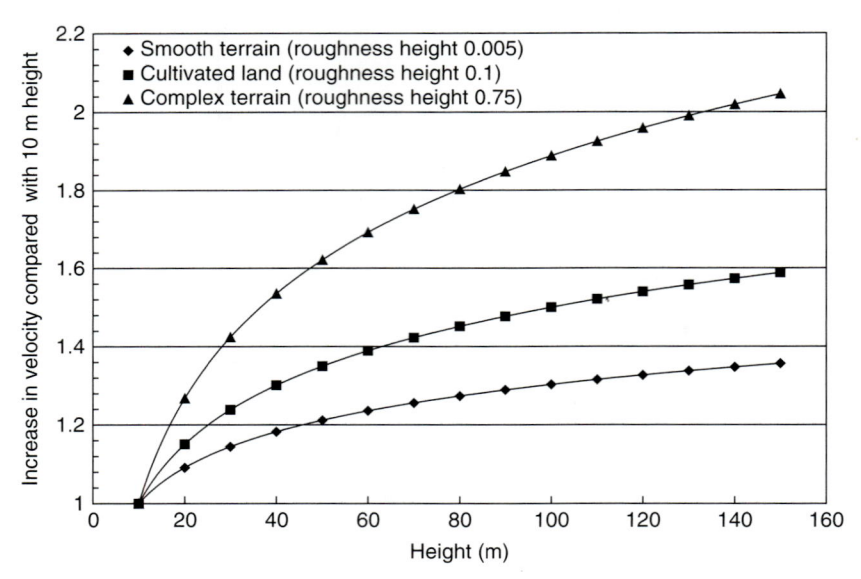

Figure 8 Increase in wind velocity with height.

conditions. Further, the effect of wake and other losses experienced by a turbine due to the presence of other turbines in the farm also could be modeled with some level of accuracy. These models, when used in conjunction with the available ground measurements and geographic information, could yield optimal options for micrositing the turbines.

Other major factors that contributed to the improvement in capacity factor are the recent technological advances in the control and power transmission system designs. These are discussed as a separate section below.

2.05.2.4 Advances in the Control and Power Transmission Systems

Power developed by modern wind turbines is regulated either by pitch or by stall control mechanisms. In pitch control, the angles of individual blades are changed to adjust the angle of attack, thereby controlling the driving lift force and thus the power. Stall-controlled blades are aerodynamically profiled in such a way that, when the wind speed exceeds a certain limit, the angle of attack increases. This changes the flow pattern over the top side of the blade from laminar to turbulent. Thus the lift force is spoiled at the desired level and power is regulated. Stall control can be either active or passive. Even a combination of pitch and stall control concepts is employed in some of the designs.

Though the stall-controlled designs were preferred by the industry in the earlier days, pitch-controlled turbines dominate the market today. **Figure 9** illustrates this shift in the control options. The number of pitch-controlled turbines available in the market is

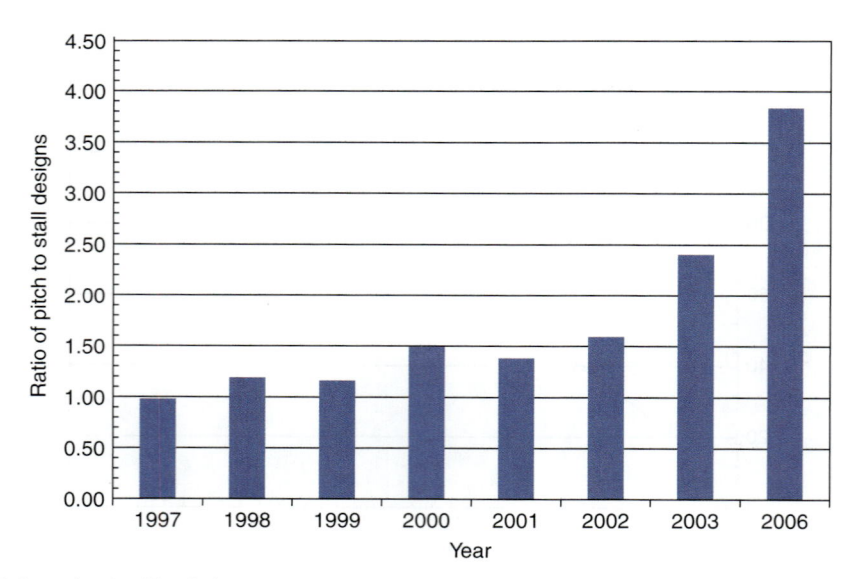

Figure 9 Increase in pitch-regulated turbine designs.

almost 4 times that of the stall-controlled machines. The major reason is that the pitch-controlled machines offer better output power quality. This is a definite advantage, especially when the grid presence of wind-generated electricity becomes significant. On the other hand, concerns about the stall-induced vibrations, vibrations at the edge of the rotor blades, and aerodynamic losses make the option of stall regulation less attractive, especially for today's multimegawatt machines.

Today's commercial wind turbines can operate either at fixed or at variable speed modes. The variable speed option can be continuously variable or two-staged variable types. The share of these three designs among the large wind turbine market (1 MW and above) is shown in **Figure 10**. It can be seen that most of the large turbines adopt the variable speed design today.

The industry adopts several methods to achieve variable speed operation. The 'traditional method' allows the rotor to rotate at varying speeds in tune with the fluctuations in the wind velocity, and the rotor power is transmitted to the generator through suitable gear drives. Electrical energy is thus produced at variable frequency depending upon the speed of the rotor. Before feeding the electricity to the grid, it is further conditioned by power electronic controllers, which modify the frequency as per the grid requirement. Another approach is to use direct drive systems, which have the capability to operate at a wide range of speeds. Variable speed systems, which are becoming popular these days, employ doubly-fed induction generators (DFIG). In turbines with DFIG, the stator winding is directly connected to the grid, whereas the rotor winding is fed through a converter, which can vary the electrical frequency as desired by the grid. Thus the electrical frequency is differentiated from the mechanical frequency, which allows the variable speed operation possible. The advantage of this approach is that, as only a fraction of the power passes through the converter, its size can be reduced approximately by a third. Thus, the costs and losses can be reduced considerably.

The major advantage of the variable speed option is its ability for better power capture. In contrast with fixed speed turbines which can operate at peak efficiency point at only one wind speed, the variable speed turbines can be designed to have peak performance at a wide range of wind speeds. Thus, considering the frequent fluctuations in wind velocity at a site, the variable speed turbines produce more energy and yield better capacity factor. Further, with well-designed electronic controllers, the variable speed option can give better power quality, thus improving the 'grid friendliness' of wind-generated electricity. If the rotational speed is kept constant, while transmitting a large amount of power at higher wind speeds, the torque and load levels experienced by the transmission system would be significantly high. Hence, another factor favoring the choice of variable speed drive is the reduction in drive train loads.

In recent years, there has been a significant trend in the industry toward the direct drive machines. The major attractions in avoiding gears in the power train are as follows:

- Gearboxes are considered as the most failure-prone component of a wind turbine. It requires constant care and maintenance. Several instances of premature failures of the gearboxes have been reported.
- Gears are expensive and add significantly to the system cost.
- Gears contribute to energy losses during transmission.
- Drive trains with heavy gears demand stronger towers to support their weight.

Enercon, with its time-proven direct drive technology, has the major market share in the direct drive sector. The current design trend is to develop direct drive turbines with permanent magnet generators (PMG), resulting in higher efficiency and reliability. Reduction in cost and weight are the major challenges. Some innovative concepts like superconducting drive trains and continuously variable transmissions with fluid drive systems are also being proposed to improve reliability and performance of wind turbine drive trains [9].

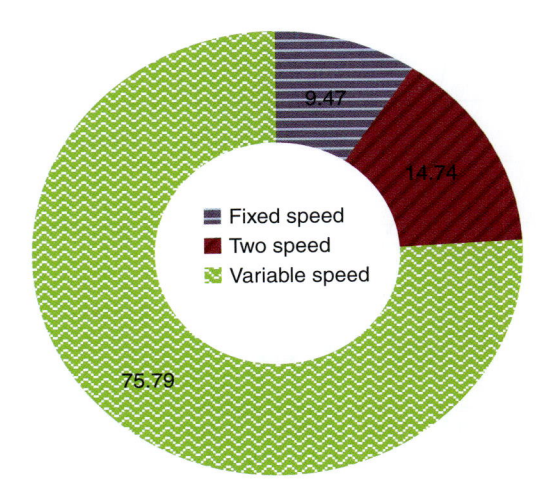

Figure 10 Market shares of fixed, two speed, and variable speed turbines.

2.05.2.5 Economic Evolution

One of the reasons behind the wide acceptance of wind energy as a clean energy alternative is its economic competitiveness. With the technological evolution, wind energy is much cheaper than other renewable options like solar PV and small hydroelectric power plants [10]. At sites with good wind resource potential, the cost of wind-generated electricity is even comparable with the energy generated from traditional sources like nuclear, coal, and natural gas. Hence, wind energy is no more a technology for demonstration that survives on subsidies and incentives. Today, it is an economically viable energy option.

Historical and projected capital investments for wind energy projects are shown in **Figure 11**. The historic data are based on the average cost estimates from 36 US wind farms, with a total capacity of 4079 MW [7]. The projections are based on a study by the GWEC [4].

During the period 1980–2000, a steady decline in the unit cost of the projects can be observed. For example, the cost kW^{-1} dropped by USD 2700 kW^{-1} during this period, to reach its lowest level in 2000. The major reason for this decline is the scaling up of the turbine size, as we discussed earlier. Better engineering approaches in the production and installation of turbines also contributed to this cost reduction.

However, the average project costs have shown an increasing trend in recent years. This is mainly due to the increase in turbine prices (which covers almost 50% of the total project cost [10]) during this period. Recently, turbine prices have gone up mainly due to the increase in the prices of the raw materials, requirements for highly sophisticated turbine designs, and the shortage in the supply of sensitive components. Future projections indicate that this trend will continue for some more years, after which a slight decline in the project cost can be expected. For example, the cost kW^{-1} may drop to USD 1775 by 2030, from 2010's level of USD 1937 kW^{-1}. In a more optimistic scenario, this drop can even be up to USD 1600 kW^{-1} by 2030 [4].

Interestingly, in spite of the recent increase in the capital cost of wind energy projects, cost of wind-generated electricity keeps on showing a declining trend as in **Figure 12**. As the generation cost is influenced by a number of site-specific factors (e.g., the wind resource available at the site), the cost of generation cannot be simply generalized for all the wind farms. However, a general trend can be derived from the figure. It can be seen that the unit generation cost has declined by almost half during the last 10 years. This trend is expected to be continued in the coming years as well. The major contributing factor toward this is the steady improvement in the performance of wind farms as we have seen in the earlier sections.

2.05.3 Basic Principles

Wind results from the movement of large quantities of air mass over the Earth's surface. Hence, the basic form of energy contained in a wind stream is the kinetic energy. A wind turbine interferes with the free wind flow, allowing its blades to extract kinetic energy from wind, which is then transformed to mechanical or electrical forms depending on our end use. In this section, we will introduce the basic principles governing this energy transfer.

2.05.3.1 Power Available in the Wind

Consider a wind rotor with a swept area A exposed to the wind stream of velocity V normal to the rotor plane (**Figure 13**). The kinetic energy in the stream is given by

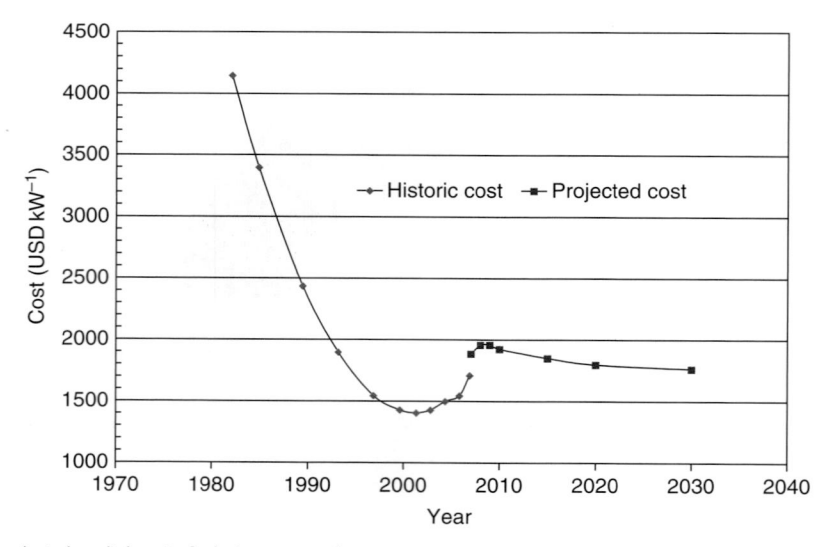

Figure 11 Historic and projected capital cost of wind energy projects.

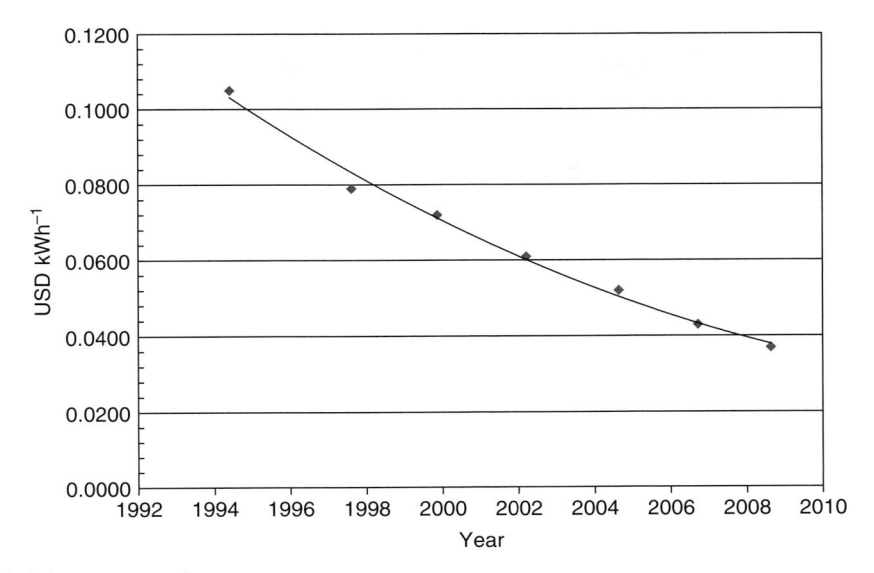

Figure 12 Unit cost of wind energy generation.

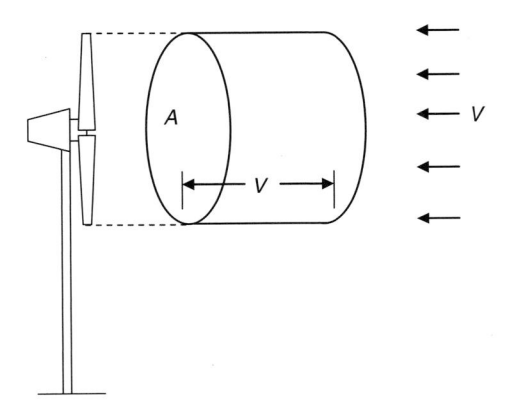

Figure 13 A wind turbine interacting with wind stream.

$$E = \frac{1}{2}mV^2 \quad [1]$$

where m is the mass of air interacting with the turbine, which is basically volume times the density of air. The volume of air interacting with the turbine per unit time is given by AV. Hence, the energy contained in the air stream per unit time – i.e., the power – is expressed as

$$P = \frac{1}{2}\rho AV^3 \quad [2]$$

where ρ is the density of air.

From the above expression, we can see that the power is proportional to the cube of the wind velocity. As a result, even a slight variation in the wind velocity can result in significant changes in the power available.

Another factor influencing the power available is the density of air. Density of air is influenced by the temperature and elevation of the location. For any given site at an elevation Z and temperature t, air density can be approximated as [11]

$$\rho = \frac{353.049}{t} e^{\left(-0.034\frac{Z}{t}\right)} \quad [3]$$

According to the International Standard Atmosphere (ISA), density of air at sea level and at 15 °C can be taken as 1.225 21 kg m^{-3}. Hence, the air density may be taken as 1.225 for most of the practical calculations. This low density of air (e.g., 1/816th of water) makes wind a rather diffused form of energy. Hence, large-sized systems are required for wind energy generation.

Equation [2] shows that the power is directly proportional to the rotor area. This indicates that, by doubling the rotor diameter, the power could be enhanced by 4 times. Along with this, the unit cost of generation can be reduced significantly by increasing the size of the wind turbine. This justifies the current trend in the wind power industry to develop huge turbines of several MW capacity.

2.05.3.2 Power Coefficient, Torque Coefficient, and Tip Speed Ratio

Equation [2] gives us the theoretical power contained in a wind stream. Rotor of a wind turbine can receive only a fraction of this power. The efficiency with which a rotor can extract the kinetic energy of the passing wind stream depends on many factors like the profile of the rotor blades, blade arrangement and setting, and variations in the velocity. This efficiency is commonly known as the power coefficient of the rotor. Thus, the power coefficient (C_P) can be defined as the ratio of actual power developed by the rotor to the theoretical power available in the wind stream. So,

$$C_P = \frac{2P_T}{\rho A V^3} \quad [4]$$

where P_T is the power output of the turbine rotor.

Similarly, the theoretical thrust force experienced by the rotor (F) can be expressed as

$$F = \frac{1}{2}\rho A V^2 \quad [5]$$

If R is the rotor radius, then the corresponding torque T is given by

$$T = \frac{1}{2}\rho A V^2 R \quad [6]$$

The above expression represents the maximum theoretical torque. The ratio between the actual torque developed by the rotor (T_T) and this theoretical torque is known as the torque coefficient (C_T). Thus,

$$C_T = \frac{2T_T}{\rho A V^2 R} \quad [7]$$

The velocity of the tip of the rotor relative to the wind velocity is a critical factor deciding the power coefficient and thereby the power output of a wind turbine. If the rotor blades move too slowly and wind velocity is high, a considerable portion of the incoming wind stream may pass through the blade gaps, without interacting with the blades. On the other hand, if the rotor is rotating too fast and the wind velocity is low, the wind stream may get deflected from the rotor and thus the energy may be lost due to turbulence and vortex shedding. Hence, for maximum energy extraction, a dynamic matching between the rotor and wind velocities is essential.

The ratio between the velocity of the rotor tip and the wind velocity is termed as the tip speed ratio (λ). Thus,

$$\lambda = \frac{R\Omega}{V} = \frac{2\pi N R}{V} \quad [8]$$

where Ω is the angular velocity and N is the rotational speed of the rotor in rad s^{-1}. The power and torque coefficients of a rotor vary significantly with λ. For every rotor, there is an optimum λ at which the energy transfer is most efficient and thus the power coefficient is the maximum ($C_{P\,max}$).

As we have seen in eqn [4], the power coefficient is given by

$$C_P = \frac{2P_T}{\rho A V^3} = \frac{2T_T \Omega}{\rho A V^3} \quad [9]$$

Dividing the above equation by eqn [7], we get

$$\frac{C_P}{C_T} = \frac{R\Omega}{V} = \lambda \quad [10]$$

Thus, the tip speed ratio is given by the ratio between the power coefficient and torque coefficient of the rotor.

2.05.3.3 Airfoil Lift and Drag

For the efficient transfer of energy from the wind stream to the turbine, modern wind turbines have rotors made up of airfoil-shaped blades. At the earlier stages of the technology development, airfoils from the aviation industry were adopted for wind turbine applications. However, currently, custom-made airfoils capable of working under a wide range of Reynolds' number and having better stall characteristics are being used in the turbines. The DU airfoil series developed by the Delft University of Technology [12] is a good example. A sectional view of a typical airfoil, indicating its major features, is shown in **Figure 14**.

Figure 15 illustrates such an airfoil placed in a flow stream. Near the leading edge of the airfoil, the flow will get separated with streamlines above and below the airfoil. Obviously, due to the typical curvature of the airfoil, particles following the upper streamlines would experience a higher velocity as they have to travel a longer distance and join back with the particles moving through the lower streamline at the same time. As per Bernoulli's theorem, to keep the total head above and below the airfoil the same, the increase in velocity should be compensated for with a reduction in pressure. Hence, a pressure drop is experienced at the upper surface of the airfoil, casing a lift force L as shown in the figure. Similarly, the fluid would also exert a drag force D on the airfoil. The net force experienced by the airfoil F would be the resultant of these lift and drag forces.

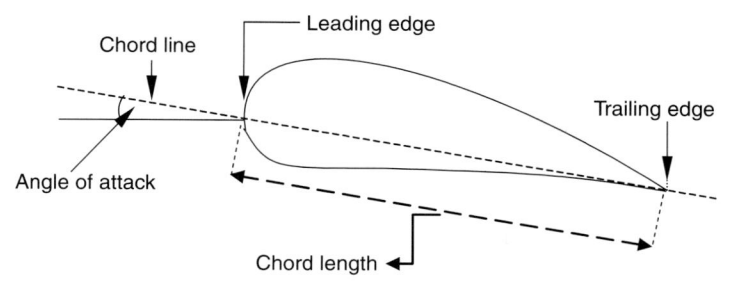

Figure 14 Sectional view of an airfoil.

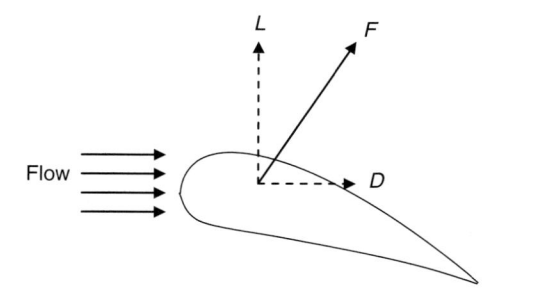

Figure 15 Flow around an airfoil.

If C_L and C_D are the lift and drag coefficients, then the lift force L is given by

$$L = C_L \frac{1}{2} \rho A V^2 \qquad [11]$$

and the drag force D can be expressed as

$$D = C_D \frac{1}{2} \rho A V^2 \qquad [12]$$

For a given airfoil, the lift and drag forces are influenced by the angle at which the airfoil is oriented toward the wind flow. This angle, which is the angle between the undisturbed wind direction and the chord of the airfoil, is known as the angle of attack (**Figure 14**). The effect of angle of attack on airfoil lift is shown in **Figure 16**. As we can see, lift increases with the angle of attack and reaches its maximum at a certain angle. With any further increase in angle of attack, the lift is drastically reduced. This is because, if the angle of attack is increased beyond a certain limit, the flow enters an excessively turbulent region and the boundary layers get separated from the airfoil. At this region, lift force decreases and drag force is rapidly built up, resulting in the stall of the blade.

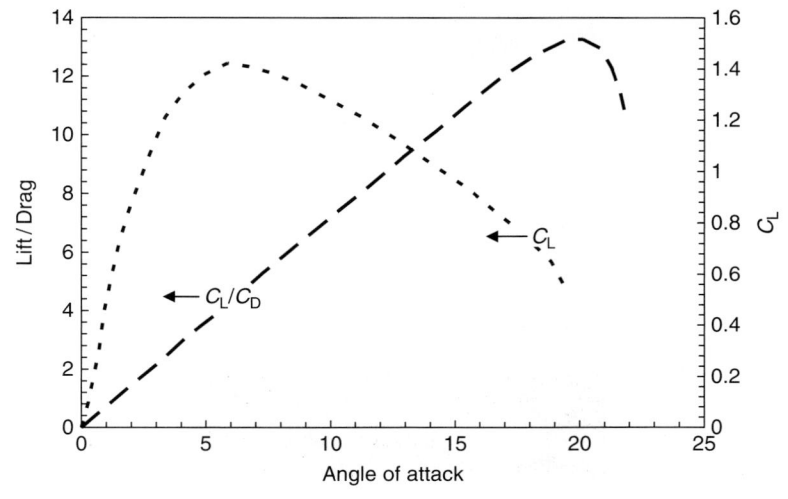

Figure 16 Lift–drag characteristics of an airfoil.

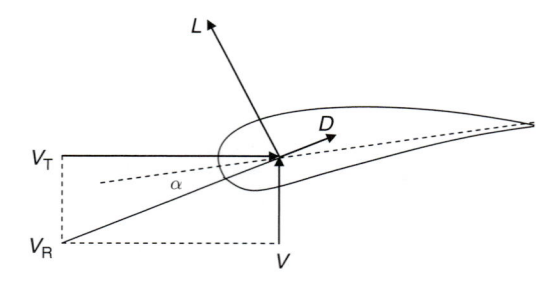

Figure 17 Forces on a rotating blade.

In case of a wind turbine operating on lift principle, the lift force contributes to the energy conversion whereas the drag is a parasitic component. Hence, in a given flow, we would like to place the blades at an angle for which the C_L/C_D ratio is the maximum. C_L–C_D characteristic of an airfoil is shown in **Figure 16**. In this case the lift–drag ratio reaches its maximum for an angle of attack of 5°.

Now consider the blades of a wind turbine under rotating condition (**Figure 17**). In addition to the free wind stream velocity V, the blade section is subjected to the tangential velocity V_T due to the blade's rotation. Hence, the velocity experienced by a point at the section would be the resultant of V and V_T. This is represented by V_R in the figure, which has drag force D in line with and lift component L perpendicular to V_R. Under this condition, the angle of attack α is the angle between 'V_R' and the chord line of the airfoil.

For a given rotational speed, the tangential velocity V_T at different sections of the blade varies with the distance of the section from the rotor hub. Hence, the angle at which the resultant velocity approaches the rotor would also be different along the blade section, being steeper at the root of the blade. As we have seen, the C_L/C_D ratio for an airfoil is the maximum at a particular angle of attack. To maintain this optimum attack angle throughout the blade sections, the blade may be twisted along its length.

2.05.4 Classifications of Wind Turbines

Based on the axis of rotation, wind turbines are classified as horizontal axis wind turbines (HAWTs) and vertical axis wind turbines (VAWTs).

2.05.4.1 Horizontal Axis Wind Turbines

HAWTs have their axis of rotation horizontal to the ground and almost parallel to the wind stream. Most of today's commercial wind turbines fall under the HAWT category (**Figure 18**).

Figure 18 An offshore wind farm with three bladed horizontal axis wind turbines. Retrieved 1 November 2011, from http://en.wikipedia.org/wiki/Wind_turbine, © Hans Hillewaert, http://creativecommons.org/licenses/by-sa/3.0/

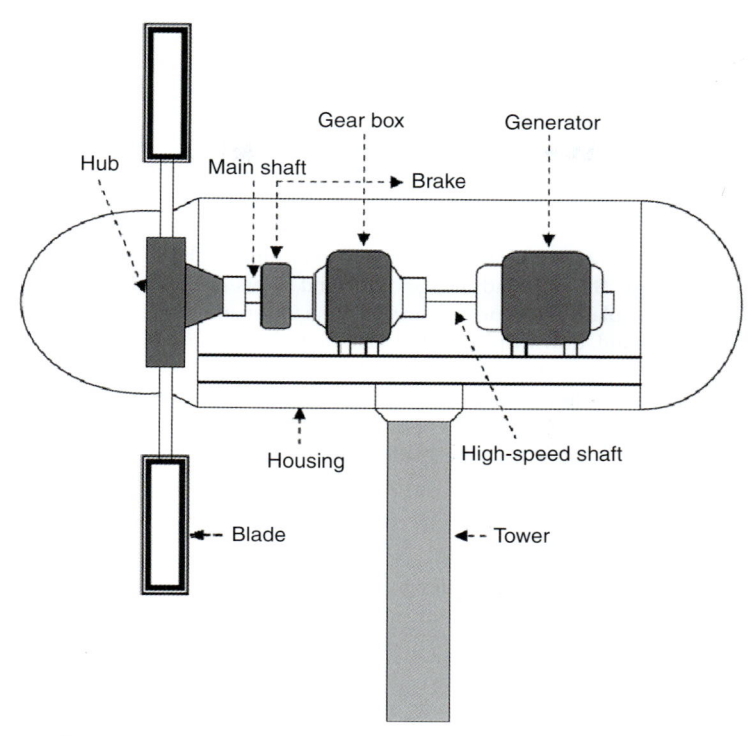

Figure 19 Sectional view of a HAWT.

Constructional features of a typical HAWT are shown in **Figure 19**. HAWTs work predominantly on lift principle. As the wind stream interacts with the rotor blades, lift force is generated as explained in the previous section, causing the rotor to rotate. The rotational speed varies with the design features and the size of the rotor. For a typical MW-sized turbine, this could be as low as 16 rpm [5]. The low-speed main shaft transmits this rotation to the high-speed shaft through the gearbox (there are direct drive turbines also, which do not have a gearbox in the transmission line). The speed is enhanced by the gear trains to match with the higher speed requirement of the generator. The generator then converts the mechanical energy to electrical energy. There are a series of control systems in between for yaw alignment, power regulation, and safety. A detailed description of these systems and their working principles are included in later chapters.

The number of rotor blades in a HAWT varies depending on the application for which they are used and wind regimes in which they are expected to work. Based on the number of blades, HAWT rotors can be classified as single bladed, two bladed, three bladed, and multibladed. Some of these classifications are shown in **Figure 20**.

The major advantage of a single-bladed rotor is the saving in blade materials, making them comparatively cheaper. It should be noted that the rotor accounts for 20–30% of the cost of a modern wind turbine. Moreover, as the blade area exposed to the flow would be minimum for the single-bladed designs, the drag losses on the blade surface also would be lower. Single-bladed designs are not very popular due to problems in balancing and visual acceptability. Two-bladed rotors also have these drawbacks, but to a lesser extent. Most of the modern wind turbines employed for electricity generation have three-bladed rotors. The loading pattern for these rotors is relatively uniform and they are visually more acceptable.

Figure 20 Single bladed (a), two bladed (b), and multibladed (c) turbines. Retrieved 1 November 2011, from http://en.wikipedia.org/wiki/Wind_turbines_design. Source: (a) Viterna, (b) NASA, and (c) Thomas Conlon, Iron Man Windmill Co. Ltd., http://creativecommons.org/licenses/by-sa/3.0/.

Wind turbines with more rotor blades (say 6, 8, 12, 18, or even more) are also available, which are usually used for specific applications like water pumping. For example, wind-powered water pumping system with piston pumps requires high starting torque to overcome the initial load imposed by the water column on the piston. For such systems, starting torque demand goes up to 3–4 times that of the running torque demand [13]. As the starting torque increases with solidity (the ratio between the actual area of the blades and the swept area of a rotor), rotors with more number of blades (high solidity) are preferred for such applications. However, high-solidity rotors work at low tip speed ratios and hence are not recommended for wind electric generators. Similarly, their efficiency would also be lower as aerodynamic losses increase with solidity.

Further, a HAWT can have upwind- or downwind-type rotors. An upwind turbine has its rotor fixed in front of the unit, directly facing the incoming wind stream (**Figure 21**). In contrast, the downwind turbines have their rotors positioned at the back side, leaving the nacelle to face the wind first. The major advantage of upwind rotors is that they do not suffer from the tower shadow effect. However, upwind rotors are to be placed at some distance from the tower and a yaw mechanism is essential to keep the rotor always facing the wind. On the other hand, downwind machines are more flexible and may not require the yaw mechanism. This makes these designs relatively cheaper. But, as the rotors are placed at the leeward side of the tower (see **Figure 21**), there may be uneven loading on the blades as they pass through the shadow of the tower.

There are several aerodynamic theories put forth for defining the performance of HAWTs. Some of the basic theories are the axial momentum theory, blade element theory, and the blade element momentum (BEM) theory. The most widely applied aerodynamic analysis for HAWT is based on the BEM theory. Detailed discussions on these theories are presented in the corresponding Chapter of this Volume.

HAWTs have the following distinct advantages:

- They are the most stable and commercially accepted design. Today, most of the large – grid-integrated – commercial wind turbines work on three-bladed horizontal axis designs.
- They have a relatively lower cut-in wind velocity and higher power coefficient resulting in higher system efficiency and energy yield.
- There are possibilities of using taller towers to tap the better wind potential available at higher elevations. This would be a distinct advantage at sites with strong wind shear where the velocity at higher levels could be significantly higher.
- There is greater control over the angle of attack, which can be optimized through variable blade pitching. This results in better system output under fluctuating wind regimes.
- There is easy furling by turning the rotor away from the wind direction.

However, HAWTs have some inherent drawbacks as well:

- HAWTs require yaw drives (or tail mechanism in case of small turbines) to orient the turbine toward wind.
- The heavy units of generator and gearbox are to be placed over the tall tower, which requires stronger structural support. This makes the HAWTs more complex and expensive.
- Taller towers make installation and maintenance more difficult and expensive.
- Again, the taller mast height can make HAWT visible even from longer distances, which may aggravate problems related to the visual impact of wind farms.

2.05.4.2 Vertical Axis Wind Turbines

Wind turbines, which have their axis of rotation vertical to the ground and almost perpendicular to the wind direction, are called VAWTs (**Figure 22**). VAWTs have some distinct advantages over the HAWTs.

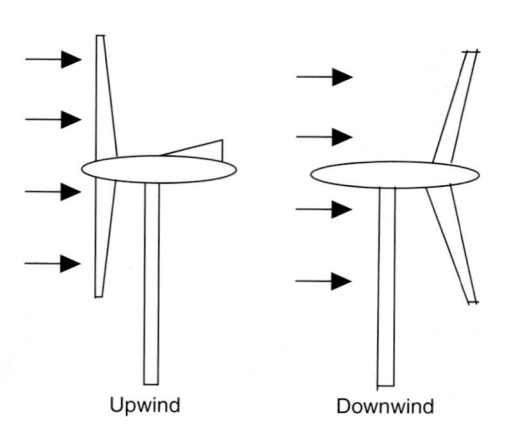

Figure 21 Upwind and downwind turbines.

Figure 22 A vertical axis Darrieus wind turbine. Retrieved 1 November 2011, from http://en.wikipedia.org/wiki/File:Darrieus-windmill.jpg. Source: Aarchiba/http://creativecommons.org/licenses/by-sa/3.0/.

- VAWTs can receive wind from any direction. They do not require yaw drives to get oriented toward the wind.
- The gearbox and generator can be positioned near ground level, simplifying the structural requirement of the tower.
- Maintenance is easier as it can be done at ground level.
- VAWTs do not require pitch control for synchronous applications.

The major disadvantages of VAWTs are the following:

- In general, VAWTs are not self-starting (except for drag-driven designs like the Savonius rotor) and hence not suitable for stand-alone applications. This may not be a serious issue for grid-integrated systems as the generator can be used as a motor to push-start the system.
- As the tower height is low and the rotor is close to the ground, these turbines may not be able to utilize better wind at higher elevations.
- As the rotor completes its rotation, the blades have to pass through aerodynamically dead zones. Hence the overall system efficiency may not be very impressive.
- The support structure may require guy wires which may cause inconveniences during installation and maintenance.

Though there are several types of VAWTs having different shape variations, we will limit our discussions to two major designs: Darrieus and Savonius turbines.

2.05.4.2.1 Darrieus rotor

Darrieus turbine concept was proposed by Georges Jean Marie Darrieus in 1931. In the original design, the blades were shaped like egg beaters or *troposkein* (turning rope) to minimize the bending stress experienced by the blades.

A typical Darrieus rotor is shown in **Figure 22** and its operating principle is illustrated in **Figure 23**. The rotor has airfoils vertically mounted on a central shaft. These symmetrically arranged airfoils are set to be aligned (at zero angle) with the mounting structure. When the rotor starts its rotation, along with the incoming wind velocity, the blades would experience airflow due to the spinning of the rotor. Hence, the velocity experienced by a blade would be the resultant of these two velocities as shown in the figure. Thus, between the resultant wind flow and the chord of the blade, a positive angle of attack is experienced. A net lift force is created as shown in the figure and the rotor is forced to rotate in a forward direction.

From the above discussion, it is evident that the angle of attack changes with the blade's rotation. With the changes in angle of attack, the lift force also would change. Hence, the power developed by the blades would vary in a sinusoidal pattern with peaks at two opposite points (at the front and back of the turbine). This cyclic power pattern makes the design more complicated.

Further, it should be noted that for deriving the driving force, the rotor must already be spinning, and under stationary conditions, rational forces could not be developed. This is the reason why Darrieus rotors are generally not self-starting. Sometimes, high-solidity drag devices like Savonius rotors are used in combination with Darrieus rotors to make them self-starting (**Figure 24**).

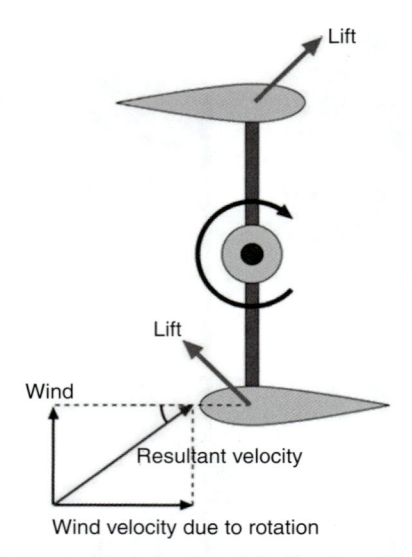

Figure 23 Working principle of Darrieus rotors. Retrieved 1 November 2011, from http://en.wikipedia.org/wiki/File:Darrieus-windmill.jpg. Source: GRAHAMUK, http://creativecommons.org/licenses/by-sa/3.0/.

Figure 24 A Darrieus rotor coupled with Savonius rotor, Retrieved 1 November 2011, from http://en.wikipedia.org/wiki/File: Taiwan_2009_JinGuaShi_Historic_Gold_Mine_Combined_Darrieus_Savonius_Wind_Turbines_FRD_8638.jpg. Source: Hsu, http://creativecommons. org/licenses/by-sa/3.0/.

Another challenge is protection against high wind speeds. As is evident, the rotor cannot be turned away from wind as it could be in the case of a HAWT. Due to the typical shape of the blades, pitch control is also not possible. Mechanical braking is the only option, though it is not a completely safe solution.

A variation of the Darrieus rotor with straight blades is shown in **Figure 25**. These straight-bladed Darrieus designs are often called Giromill or H turbines. One advantage of this design is that as blade pitching is possible, overspeed protection is easier. However, due to the intensive centrifugal forces, the loads acting on the blade would be very high. Further, the H rotors require long spokes to connect the blades with the hub and these spokes have to be aerodynamically shaped to avoid excessive drag forces. Cycloturbines, helically bladed VAWTs, and Musgrove rotors are some variations of the Darrieus concept.

Figure 25 Straight-bladed Darrieus rotor. Retrieved 1 November 2011, from http://en.wikipedia.org/wiki/File:H-Darrieus-Rotor.png.jpg. Source: Stahlkocher, http://creativecommons.org/licenses/by-sa/3.0/.

In spite of all its inherent technical limitations, it should be noted that the Darrieus turbines are the only VAWT which are being commercially manufactured. The Darrieus concept still fascinates many wind turbine inventors and different versions of this technology are being proposed.

2.05.4.2.2 Savonius rotor

The Savonius wind turbine is a simple vertical axis wind machine invented by Sigurd J. Savonius in 1922. In its original design, it was made with two half-cylindrical blades arranged in an 'S' shape. The convex side of one half-cylinder and the concave side of the other face the wind at the same time as shown in **Figure 26**. As the drag coefficient of the concave surface is more than that of the convex side, in a given wind stream, the drag force experienced by the concave half would be higher than that of the other half (refer eqn [12]). It is this difference in drag force that spins the rotor to develop mechanical power.

Several variations of Savonius rotors are available. For example, the Savonius rotor shown in **Figure 27** has two sets of rotors placed at 90° offset to smoothen out torque fluctuations during the operation. Similarly, instead of cylindrical rotors, blades with elliptical bases are also tried to improve aerodynamic efficiency. Another attempt to improve performance was to attach deflector augmenters with Savonius rotors [11]. The augmenter shades the convex half facing the wind and directs the flow to the concave half, thereby enhancing rotor performance.

The major advantage of the Savonius rotor is its simplicity. As no sophisticated methods or technical skills are required for its fabrication, it can even be made in small local workshops. This makes it attractive for applications in less developed countries. Savonius rotors have high solidity and run at low speeds. As high-solidity rotors can develop high starting torque, they are suitable for applications like water pumping.

The major disadvantage of these rotors is low efficiency. Being a drag machine working at low tip speed ratios, these rotors have a relatively lower power coefficient (however, efficiency up to 35% has been reported for some experimental rotors [11]). Further, due

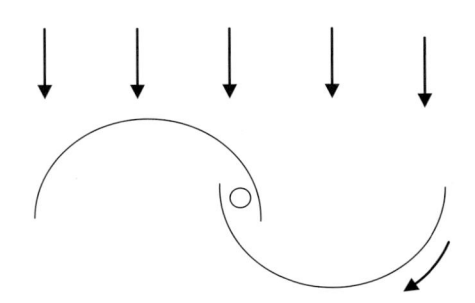

Figure 26 Operational principle of a Savonius rotor.

Figure 27 A modified Savonius rotor with elliptical blades.

to their structural features, these rotors are installed on shorter towers and hence stronger wind speeds at higher heights cannot be utilized. Similarly, compared with the HAWT option, Savonius rotors consume more materials per unit power rating.

2.05.5 Rotor Performance Curves

For a given design, the efficiency of a wind rotor depends on the relative speed between the rotor and the incoming wind. Hence, the performance of the rotor is generally expressed in terms of the variations in the power coefficient (C_P) with the tip speed ratio (λ). As we can see from eqns [4] and [8], both C_P and λ are dimensionless parameters. Hence, the C_P–λ relationship deduced for a particular rotor will be valid for dimensionally similar rotors of any size.

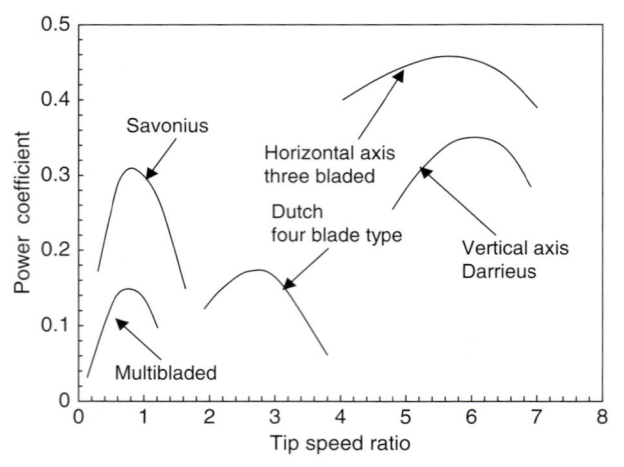

Figure 28 Performance characteristics of wind rotors.

Based on the axial momentum theory, it can be shown that the maximum theoretical efficiency of a wind turbine operating on lift principle is 16/27 (Betz limit). On the other hand, the maximum level of efficiency that a drag turbine can attain is only 8/27 [11]. This is why rotors operating on lift principles are always preferred over drag devices.

Typical C_P–λ curves for various wind rotors are shown in **Figure 28**. In general, the power coefficient increases with the tip speed ratio, reaches a maximum, and then decreases with further increase in the tip speed ratio. In general, high-solidity multibladed rotors, operating at lower tip speed ratios, show poor power coefficients. For example, a typical value for the peak power coefficient of such rotors could be 14% at tip speed ratios less than unity. Efficiency of Savonius rotors is also not very impressive.

Two- and three-bladed horizontal axis rotors show the highest efficiency (C_P between 0.4 and 0.5). Darrieus rotors, though running at higher tip speed ratios, show a lower power coefficient compared with low-solidity propeller turbines. The reasons are explained in the previous sections [14].

References

[1] NASA (1982) Mod-2 wind turbine system development final report. *DOE/NASA/0002-2, NASACR.-168007.* National Aeronautics and Space Administration, Lewis Research Center, Cleveland, Ohio, USA.
[2] http://windpower.sandia.gov/other/VAWThist.pdf. Sandia National Laboratories, CA. Retrieved 1 November 2011.
[3] GWEC (2011) Global wind report: Annual market update 2010. Global Wind Energy Council, Brussels, Belgium.
[4] GWEC (2011) Global wind energy outlook 2010. Global Wind Energy Council, Brussels, Belgium.
[5] ENERCON (2010) *Wind Energy Convertors Product Review.* Aurich, Germany: ENERCON GmbH.
[6] John V (2010) Engineers race to design world's biggest offshore wind turbines. *The Guardian*, 26th July 2010, p. 19.
[7] Wiser R and Bolinger M (2008) Annual report on U.S. wind power installation, cost, and performance trends: 2007. DOE/GO-102008-2590/May 2008, U.S. Department of Energy, Springfield, USA.
[8] http://www.wind-energy-the-facts.org/en/part-i-technology/chapter-3-wind-turbine-technology/technology-trends/hub-height.html. European Wind Energy Association, Brussels, Belgium. Retrieved 1 November 2011.
[9] DOE (2010) Advanced wind turbine drive train concept: Workshop report. Wind and Water Power Programme. DOE/GO-102010-3198/December 2010, U.S. Department of Energy, Springfield, USA.
[10] Kaldellis JK and Zafirakis D (2011) The wind energy (r)evolution: A short review of a long history. *Renewable Energy* 36(7): 1887–1901.
[11] Mathew S (2006) *Wind Energy: Fundamentals, Resource Analysis and Economics*, 1st edn. Berlin, Heidelberg, Germany: Springer.
[12] Timmer WA and vanRooy RPJOM (1993) Wind tunnel results for 25% thick wind turbine blade airfoil. In: *Proceedings of EWEC'93*. Lubeck, Travemunde, Germany, European Wind Energy Association, Brussels, Belgium, pp. 416–419.
[13] Mathew S and Pandey KP (2003) Modelling the integrated output of mechanical wind pumps. *Journal of Solar Energy Engineering, Transactions of the American Society of Mechanical Engineers* 122(4): 203–206.
[14] UNFCCC (2010) Report of the conference of the parties on its fifteenth session, held in Copenhagen from 7 to 19 December 2009 – Addendum – Part Two: Action taken by the conference of the parties at its fifteenth session. United Nations Framework Convention on Climate Change, 30 March 2010, Copenhagen.

Further Reading

[1] Burton T, Jenkins N, Sharpe D, and Bossanyi E (2011) *Wind Energy Handbook*, 2nd edn. Hoboken, NJ: Wiley.
[2] Chiras D (2010) *Wind Power Basics: A Green Energy Guide*, 1st edn. Canada: New Society Publishers.
[3] European Wind Energy Association (2009) *Wind Energy – The Facts: A Guide to the Technology, Economics and Future of Wind Power*, 1st edn. Oxford, UK: EarthScan.
[4] Gipe P (2009) *Wind Energy Basics: A Guide to Home- and Community-Scale Wind-Energy Systems*, 2nd edn. White River Junction, VT: Chelsea Green Publishing.
[5] Manwell JF, McGowan JG, and Rogers AL (2010) *Wind Energy Explained: Theory, Design and Application*, 2nd edn. Hoboken, NJ: Wiley.
[6] Mathew S and Philip GS (2011) *Advances in Wind Energy Conversion Technology*, 1st edn. Berlin, Heidelberg, Germany: Springer.
[7] Musgrove P (2010) *Wind Power*, 1st edn. Cambridge, UK: Cambridge University Press.
[8] Spera DA (2009) *Wind Turbine Technology: Fundamental Concepts in Wind Turbine Engineering*, 2nd edn. American Society of Mechanical Engineers, ASME Press, New York, USA.

2.06 Energy Yield of Contemporary Wind Turbines

DP Zafirakis, AG Paliatsos, and JK Kaldellis, Technological Education Institute of Piraeus, Athens, Greece

© 2012 Elsevier Ltd. All rights reserved.

2.06.1	**From Wind Power to Useful Wind Energy**	114
2.06.1.1	Assessment of Wind Energy Losses	114
2.06.2	**Wind Potential Evaluation for Energy Generation Purposes**	117
2.06.2.1	Wind Speed Distributions	117
2.06.2.1.1	Weibull distribution	117
2.06.2.1.2	Rayleigh distribution	118
2.06.2.1.3	Other distributions	119
2.06.2.2	Determination of Weibull Main Parameters	120
2.06.2.2.1	Graphical method	120
2.06.2.2.2	Standard deviation – Empirical method	120
2.06.2.2.3	Maximum likelihood method	121
2.06.2.2.4	Moment method	122
2.06.2.2.5	Energy pattern factor method	122
2.06.2.3	The Impact of the Scale and Shape Factor Variation	122
2.06.2.4	Performance Assessment for the Weibull Distribution	124
2.06.2.5	Long-Term Study of Wind Energy Potential	124
2.06.2.6	Calm Spell Period Determination	125
2.06.2.7	Wind Gust Determination	126
2.06.3	**Power Curves of Contemporary Wind Turbines**	127
2.06.3.1	Description of a Typical Wind Turbine Power Curve	127
2.06.3.2	Producing a Wind Turbine Power Curve	127
2.06.3.3	Power Curve Modeling	129
2.06.3.3.1	Linear model	130
2.06.3.3.2	Cubic model	130
2.06.3.3.3	Quadratic model	131
2.06.3.4	Power Curve Estimation	131
2.06.4	**Estimating the Energy Production of a Wind Turbine**	132
2.06.4.1	From the Instantaneous Power Output to Energy Production	132
2.06.4.2	Estimating the Annual Wind Energy Production	134
2.06.4.3	Estimating the Mean Power Coefficient	135
2.06.4.4	The Impact of the Scale Factor Variation on the Mean Power Coefficient	136
2.06.4.5	The Impact of the Shape Factor Variation on the Mean Power Coefficient	137
2.06.4.6	The Impact of the Shape and Scale Factor Variation on the Annual Energy Production	138
2.06.4.7	Energy Contribution of the Ascending and Rated Power Curve Segments	138
2.06.4.8	Energy Yield Variation due to the Use of Theoretical Distributions	140
2.06.5	**Parameters Affecting the Power Output of a Wind Turbine**	140
2.06.5.1	The Wind Shear Variation	140
2.06.5.2	Extrapolation of the Shape and Scale Parameters of Weibull at Hub Height	144
2.06.5.3	Estimation of Wind Speed at Hub Height, Upstream of the Machine	144
2.06.5.4	The Impact of Air Density Variation	146
2.06.5.5	The Impact of the Wake Effect	149
2.06.6	**The Impact of Technical Availability on Wind Turbine Energy Output**	151
2.06.6.1	Causes of Technical Unavailability	152
2.06.6.2	Estimating Technical Availability	153
2.06.6.3	Experience Gained from the Monitoring of Technical Availability	155
2.06.7	**Selecting the Most Appropriate Wind Turbine**	158
2.06.7.1	The Role of Wind Turbine Databases	159
2.06.7.2	Selecting the Most Appropriate Wind Turbine	162
2.06.7.3	Determination of General Trends	164
2.06.8	**Conclusions**	164
References		166
Further Reading		168
Relevant Websites		168

Glossary

Aerodynamic coefficient A measure of the wind turbine rotor ability to exploit the available kinetic energy of wind.
Betz limit The maximum theoretical value that the aerodynamic coefficient may get. Its value is equal to 16/27.
Capacity factor The ratio of actual energy production of the machine for a given time period to the respective potential energy production of the same machine if it had operated at its rated power for the entire time period.
Cut-in speed The wind speed at which a given wind turbine starts to operate.
Cut-out speed The wind speed at which a given wind turbine ceases to operate.
Mean power coefficient Provides a measure of how poor or good the adjustment of a given wind turbine is for a given site. Typical values range between 0.2 and 0.6.
Rated power speed The minimum wind speed at which a given wind turbine operates at its rated power.
Scale factor The first critical parameter of Weibull distribution, which is analogous to the average wind speed of the area under investigation.
Shape factor The second critical parameter of Weibull distribution, which is reversibly analogous to the standard deviation of wind speeds in the area of investigation.
Technical availability Configured by the hours of operation of a given wind turbine or a given wind farm, by considering the time period that the machine is kept out of operation due to, for example, scheduled maintenance and unforeseen faults of the machine.

2.06.1 From Wind Power to Useful Wind Energy

Wind turbines are man-made machines developed to exploit wind energy potential in order to produce electricity. More specifically, wind turbines are used to convert the kinetic energy of wind first into mechanical energy and accordingly into electricity, with each of the energy conversion stages existing introducing – as expected – energy losses that need to be considered. Mechanisms of energy losses are described in order to assess the ability of contemporary wind turbines to exploit the kinetic energy of wind and thus provide useful wind energy for covering electricity needs.

2.06.1.1 Assessment of Wind Energy Losses

Power P_A carried by a wind stream of constant speed V and given air density ρ crossing through a surface of area A that is vertical to the wind speed vector is provided by eqn [1]:

$$P_A = \frac{1}{2} \cdot \rho \cdot V^3 \cdot A \qquad [1]$$

The wind power of a wind stream is found to be analogous to the third order of wind speed, thus suggesting remarkable variation of the former with only minor variation of wind speed (e.g., 10% variation in wind speed implies 33% variation in wind power). Nevertheless, even in the ideal case that both electromechanical and turbulence losses [1] are considered to be negligible, it is impossible to entirely capture the available wind power flux. Reasons for that include the following:

1. Based on the mass continuity theory, the air mass crossing the rotor of a wind turbine should maintain sufficient wind speed in order to escape fast enough downstream of the rotor. This results in a loss of appreciable power carried by the wind stream leaving the wind turbine rotor.
2. A small percentage of the air mass that should cross through the rotor area is actually crossing it by, due to the deflection of streamlines imposed by the rotor on the incident wind stream.
3. Finally, a small percentage of the wind kinetic energy is also not exploited due to inability of the rotor to immediately turn itself toward the wind direction (thus, there is a time lag), although with the introduction of new electronic systems, response of the wind rotor to changes of wind direction has considerably improved [2]. On the other hand, in the case of successive sudden changes of wind speed direction, partial loss of available wind energy amounts is inevitable.

Except for the above-mentioned reasons explaining the reduced exploitation of available wind power, mechanical and aerodynamic losses upon the rotor blades along with additional restrictions further reduce the actually exploited wind energy. More specifically, as also reflected in **Figure 1**, potentially and actually exploited wind power is found to be considerably lower than the respective theoretical wind power flux and is thus not actually analogous to the third power of wind speed, as may be easily misinterpreted, due to the following:

1. A part of the wind stream kinetic energy remains unexploited due to the fact that for low wind speeds encountered, the wind turbine is unable to rotate since friction losses in the shafts and the gearbox are higher than the power produced by the machine. As a result, production of exploitable power begins when power production by the wind turbine P_{wt} exceeds these losses of zero load P_{cr} that is, $P_{wt} \geq P_{cr}$ which coincides with the point that available wind speed exceeds the cut-in wind speed V_c of the wind turbine (i.e., the wind speed at which the wind turbine starts to operate). Thus, it becomes clear that for wind speeds that are lower than

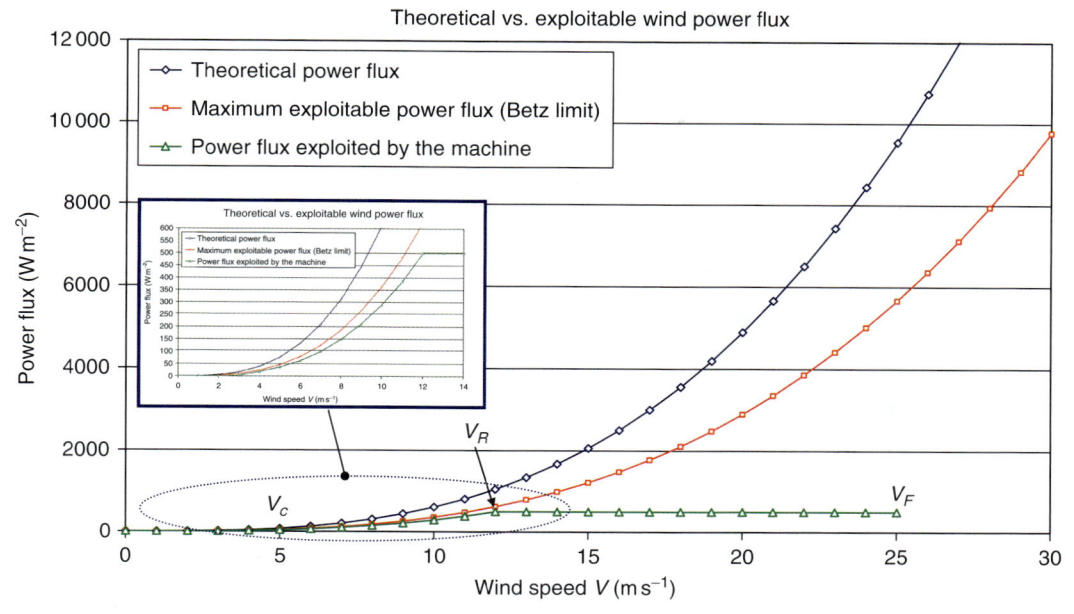

Figure 1 Comparison of power carried by a wind stream with the respective power potentially and actually exploited by a wind turbine.

the respective cut-in speed of the machine, wind power available is not captured by the wind turbine. At this point, it should be underlined that although such wind speeds are not appreciable in terms of magnitude, they are of primary importance when it comes to probability [3], meaning that since it is quite possible for such low wind speeds to appear, considerable amounts of wind energy are eventually lost. Note that even in areas of high-quality wind potential, the possibility of encountering wind speeds below 4 m s^{-1} (which is a normal cut-in wind speed) on an annual basis may reach 40%. On the other hand, cut-in wind speeds usually range from 2.5 to 5 m s^{-1}, with the large-scale machines normally presenting (at least during the past) higher cut-in wind speeds due to the considerably heavier structure. Nevertheless, acknowledging the importance of low wind speed exploitation, considerable efforts have been encountered during recent years for the transition of cut-in speeds to lower values [4].

2. Power output of a wind turbine being lower than the respective available wind power is also due to energy losses upon the rotor blades. Such losses include friction losses between the wind stream and the blades, off-design losses, and turbulence losses, all together known as aerodynamic losses of the rotor. Note that the respective losses correspond to a rather considerable part of the available kinetic energy of wind and are quantified through the introduction of the aerodynamic coefficient C_p of the rotor, usually ranging from 0.35 to 0.45. Also keep in mind that C_p generally depends on the type of the machine and the tip speed ratio λ, while it cannot exceed the respective theoretical upper limit $C_{p\max}$ of 16/27 (known as the Betz limit) [5], see also **Figure 2** [6], based on the actuator disk theory, that is, application of a simple linear momentum theory model. λ is given by eqn [2], where D is the rotor diameter and n_r is the rotor rotational speed in rpm:

$$\lambda = \frac{\pi \cdot D \cdot n_r}{60 \cdot V} \qquad [2]$$

while by considering the above, power extraction by the rotor P_r is finally given by eqn [3]:

$$P_r = \frac{1}{2} \cdot \rho \cdot V^3 \cdot A \cdot C_p \qquad [3]$$

3. After exceeding a certain wind speed threshold, wind power production by the wind turbine is kept almost constant in order to ensure smooth operation of the machine. As a result, a significant part of the available wind energy is also lost due to the inability of the machine to fully exploit high wind speeds (e.g., above 12 m s^{-1}). More precisely, power production of the wind turbine presents an increase up to the point of nominal power P_R, where from constant (or almost constant) power output is maintained through power regulation [7] (via either pitch- or stall-control application). The minimum wind speed at which the rated power of the machine is achieved is called rated speed and is symbolized with V_R. Thus, for wind speeds that exceed the rated speed of the machine, considerable amounts of wind energy cannot be captured by the machine due to power regulation (**Figure 3**). In practice, the rated power speed of wind turbines usually ranges between 10 and 14 m s^{-1}.

4. Safety reasons impose interruption of the machine's operation at very high wind speeds [8] (e.g., above Beaufort 9), with the respective cut-out or furling speed V_F of the machine usually found in the range of 20 m s^{-1} (for smaller scale wind turbines) to 30 m s^{-1} (for quite solid machines). In that case, the entire wind energy carried by wind speeds that are higher than the cut-out

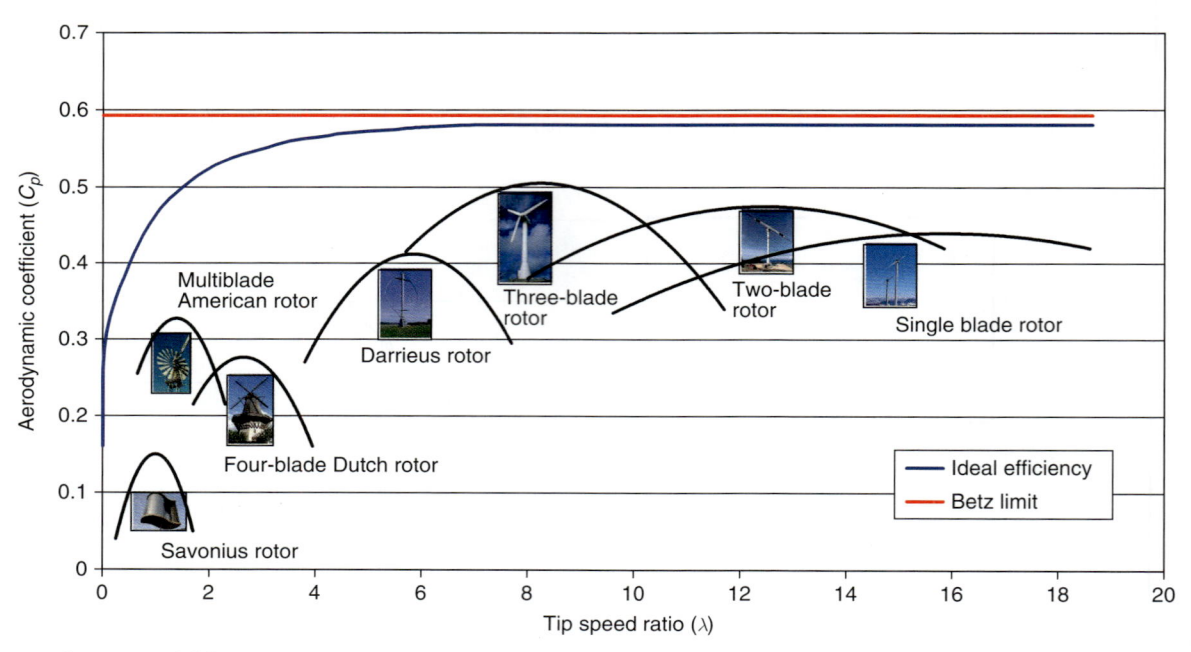

Figure 2 C_p–λ curves of different wind turbine rotors [6].

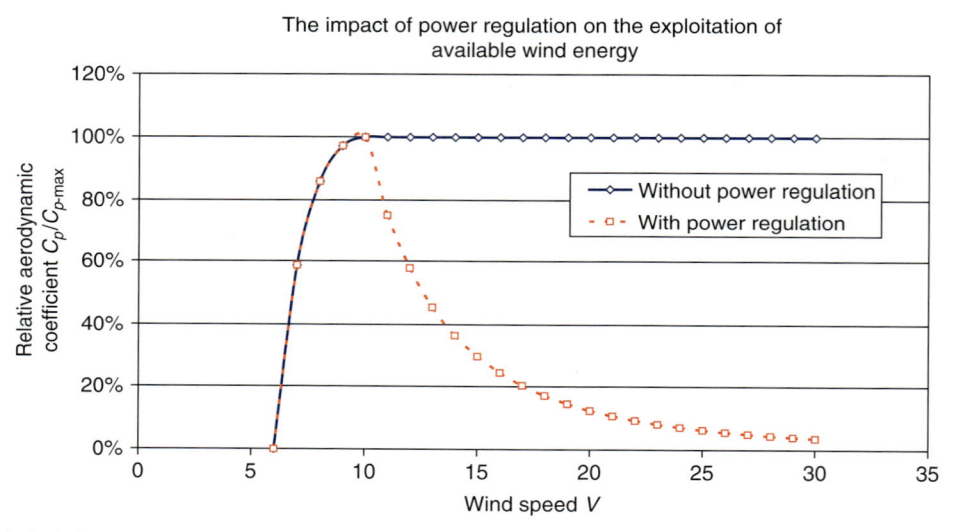

Figure 3 Unexploited wind energy due to power regulation.

wind speed remains unexploited. On the other hand, however, unlike the possibility of low wind speeds appearing, such wind speeds are quite rare (normally below 5% on an annual basis).

5. On top of aerodynamic losses, mechanical losses of the shafts and the gearbox as well as electrical losses of the electrical generator should also be considered. It is estimated that electromechanical losses are relatively limited and correspond to 3–10%, usually considered equivalent to the respective zero load losses. Thus, by introducing an electromechanical efficiency factor $\eta_{e/m}$, the output power of the machine P_{ex} is given by eqn [4]:

$$P_{ex} = \frac{1}{2} \cdot \rho \cdot V^3 \cdot A \cdot C_p \cdot \eta_{e/m} \qquad [4]$$

6. Finally, for the precise estimation of energy output in relation to the available kinetic energy of wind, the technical availability Δ of the installation should also be taken into account. Note that the term of technical availability is actually configured by the hours of operation of a given wind turbine or a given wind farm by considering the time period that the machine is kept out of operation due to, for example, scheduled maintenance, unforeseen faults of the machine, and so on [9].

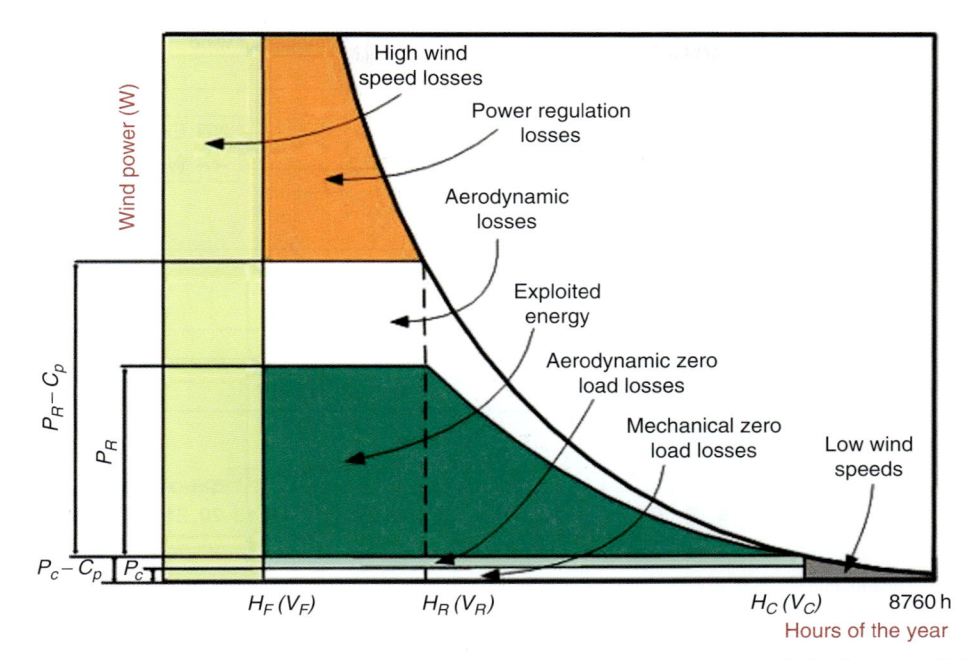

Figure 4 Distribution of energy losses through the process of conversion from available wind power to useful electrical power [10].

Acknowledging the above, in **Figure 4**, one may obtain the distribution of available wind power into exploited power output by the wind turbine and into the various losses during an entire year period [10].

2.06.2 Wind Potential Evaluation for Energy Generation Purposes

As already realized from Section 2.06.1, characteristics of the local wind resource are critical for the energy production of a wind turbine. For the proper evaluation of the available wind energy potential of a given site, knowledge solely of the mean wind speed is not adequate. On the contrary, detailed information concerning the probability distribution of different wind speeds during the entire year period along with the determination of the duration of calm spells and the probability–intensity of wind gusts appearing are all necessary to obtain a clear picture.

For this purpose, prior to the installation of a wind turbine at a given site, it is very important to first collect all available wind resource data and then proceed to statistical processing for the estimation of the probability density of the wind speed. In addition, due to the fact that wind turbines are unable to either operate or produce much below their nominal output, of primary importance is also the determination of probability and duration for both calm spells and low wind speeds, which is directly relevant to the consideration and specifications of back-up systems. On the other hand, determination of wind gusts and extreme wind speeds is related to both loading of the machine and the fact that operation of wind turbines for such high wind speeds is avoided due to safety reasons.

Thus, for safe conclusions to be deduced concerning the wind energy potential of a certain location, long-term detailed wind speed measurements are required. On the other hand, cost issues and the inevitable time delay induced by the need for long-term measurements often lead to either use of generalized functions [11], which have the ability to sufficiently evaluate the wind potential of a site based on a small number of parameters required, or application of more requiring CFD codes. At this point, however, it should be noted that generalized functions do, as expected, imply accuracy issues, while in certain cases may even prove to be unreliable. A short description of the most commonly used wind speed distributions is given in the following paragraphs, aiming to emphasize the role of the main parameters involved in the estimation of energy produced by a wind turbine operating at a given area of specific wind resource characteristics.

2.06.2.1 Wind Speed Distributions

2.06.2.1.1 Weibull distribution

The most commonly used distribution for the description of wind regimes is Weibull [12]. The Weibull distribution is considered appropriate for the evaluation of temperate zone areas and for an altitude of up to 100 m, and uses two main parameters, namely, the scale c and the shape k factors, so as to determine the probability density $f(V)$ of a specific wind speed to appear (that is actually the probability of a wind speed to be found in the range from $V - (dV/2)$ to $V + (dV/2)$) under the function of eqn [5] (**Figure 5**):

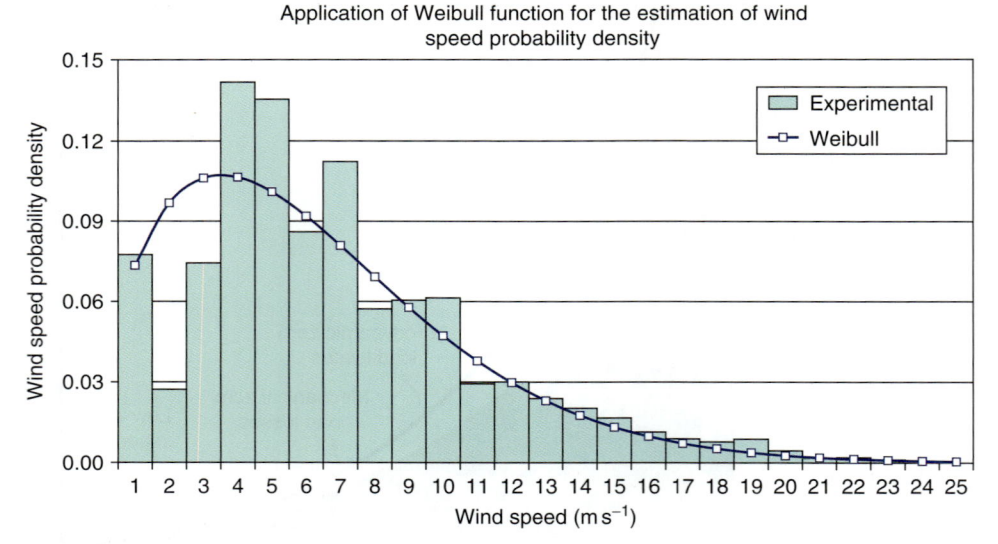

Figure 5 Use of Weibull distribution to describe wind speed probability density.

$$f(V) = \frac{k}{c} \cdot \left(\frac{V}{c}\right)^{k-1} \cdot \exp\left(-\left(\frac{V}{c}\right)^k\right) \qquad [5]$$

with the respective probability $P(V)$ of a certain wind speed to be between two given wind speed values, V_1 and V_2, given as

$$P(V_1 \leq V \leq V_2) = \int_{V_1}^{V_2} f(V)dV \qquad [6]$$

Concerning Weibull, the scale factor c is related to the mean wind speed value $\bar{V}$, on the basis of eqn [7], where Γ represents the Gamma function, while shape factor k is reversibly analogous to the standard deviation σ^2 of wind speeds in relation to the mean wind speed (eqn [8]):

$$\bar{V} = c \cdot \Gamma\left(1 + \frac{1}{k}\right) \qquad [7]$$

$$\sigma^2 = c^2 \cdot \left[\Gamma\left(1 + \frac{2}{k}\right) - \Gamma^2\left(1 + \frac{1}{k}\right)\right] \qquad [8]$$

More precisely, higher values of k correspond to lower dispersion of wind speeds and thus greater concentration of the latter around the mean wind speed. Moreover, it is found that regarding wind speed distributions, k normally takes values above 1 ($k > 1$) [13–16], while if k becomes equal to 1 ($k = 1$) or equal to 2 ($k = 2$), the results of Weibull coincide with the corresponding ones obtained by application of the exponential and the Rayleigh distributions, respectively.

Furthermore, based on the cumulative probability function of the Weibull distribution (eqn [9]), one may also determine the cumulative probability $F(V \leq V_o)$ of wind speeds being lower than a given upper limit V_o. Note also that the cumulative probability function is also complementary to the duration function $G(V \geq V_o)$, that is, $G(V) = 1 - F(V)$, which, as it may result (see also eqn [10]), determines the probability of wind speeds being higher than a given lower limit V_o (**Figure 6**):

$$F(V \leq V_o) = \int_0^{V_o} f(V)dV = 1 - \exp\left(-\left(\frac{V_o}{c}\right)^k\right) \qquad [9]$$

$$G(V \geq V_o) = \int_{V_o}^{\infty} f(V)dV = 1 - F(V \leq V_o) \qquad [10]$$

2.06.2.1.2 Rayleigh distribution

Rayleigh is another distribution – simpler than Weibull – commonly used for the description of wind potential [17], producing results that, as already mentioned, coincide with the results given by Weibull when the shape factor is equal to two. Note that Rayleigh is actually a one-parameter distribution (i.e., the average wind speed $\bar{V}$). Its function given in eqn [11], which may replace the Weibull distribution due to the production of relatively similar results (depending on the wind regime examined; **Figure 7**), on the basis of less calculations carried out:

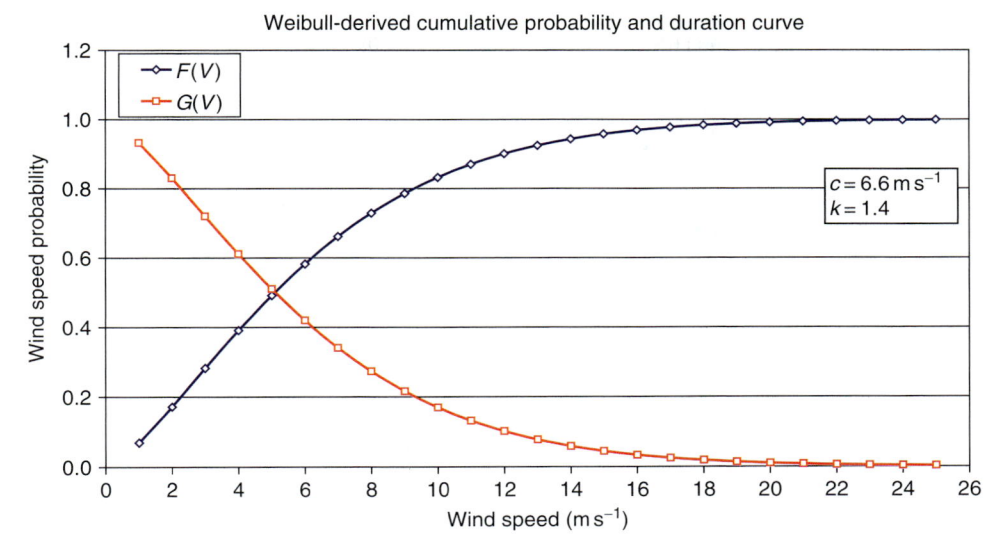

Figure 6 Cumulative probability and duration function curves.

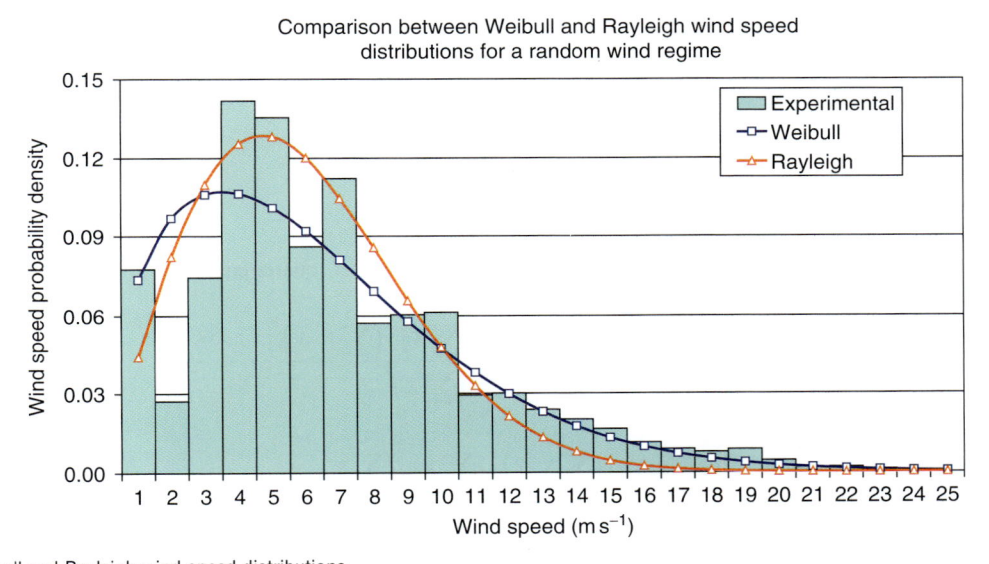

Figure 7 Weibull and Rayleigh wind speed distributions.

$$f(V) = \frac{\pi \cdot V}{2 \cdot \bar{V}^2} \cdot \exp\left(\frac{-\pi \cdot V^2}{4 \cdot \bar{V}^2}\right) \quad [11]$$

Due to the use of data in frequency format, the average wind speed is estimated according to the equation given below:

$$\bar{V} = \sum_{i=1}^{n} V_i \cdot f(V_i) \quad [12]$$

with n being the number of bins used and V_i being the average value of each bin.

2.06.2.1.3 Other distributions

Although Weibull is the most commonly used probability distribution and Rayleigh comprises an established alternative, the inability of the former to represent all types of wind regimes satisfactorily (especially those where null speeds are critical or where a bimodal distribution appears) introduces the need to also consider additional distributions that may produce better results in the case of more unusual wind regimes. Some examples of such distributions examined by various authors [18–24] include the two- and three-parameter Gamma distribution, the two-parameter lognormal distribution, the two-parameter inverse Gaussian distribution, the two-parameter normal truncated distribution, the two-parameter square-root normal distribution, the three-parameter beta distribution, the Pearson type V distribution, the maximum entropy principle distribution, the Kappa distribution, and the Burr distribution, as well as distribution mixtures such as the singly truncated normal Weibull mixture and the Gamma Weibull mixture distribution.

Thus, in cases of relatively abnormal wind speed regimes, evaluation of additional probability distributions, other than Weibull, is thought to be essential in order to adequately assess the local wind potential. However, since analysis of the above-mentioned probability distributions is out of the scope of this chapter, indication on the performance of each probability distribution for various wind regimes may be obtained from some excellent reviews [13, 25, 26]. On the other hand, emphasis is given here to the methods used for the estimation of the main parameters of the most established probability distribution, that is, Weibull, provided in the following paragraphs [27, 28].

2.06.2.2 Determination of Weibull Main Parameters

2.06.2.2.1 Graphical method

For the determination of the c and k parameters, the most commonly used method is the least squares or graphical method [29]. More precisely, based on eqn [9], one may get that

$$\ln(-\ln(1-F(V \le V_o))) = -k \cdot \ln c + k \cdot \ln V_o \quad [13]$$

which actually corresponds to a linear function of the form:

$$Y = A + BX \quad [14]$$

where

$$Y = \ln(-\ln(1 - F(V \le V_o))) \quad [15]$$

and

$$X = \ln V_o \quad [16]$$

Accordingly, having calculated A and B, determination of the scale and shape factors may be performed as follows (**Figure 8**):

$$c = \exp\left(\frac{-A}{B}\right) \quad [17]$$

$$k = B \quad [18]$$

whereas for the initial calculation of A and B (**Figure 8**), one should use the least squares equations given below:

$$A = \frac{\left(\sum Y\right) \cdot \left(\sum X^2\right) - \left(\sum X\right) \cdot \left(\sum X \cdot Y\right)}{n \cdot \sum X^2 - \left(\sum X\right)^2} \quad [19]$$

$$B = \frac{n \cdot \left(\sum X \cdot Y\right) - \left(\sum X\right) \cdot \left(\sum Y\right)}{n \cdot \sum X^2 - \left(\sum X\right)^2} \quad [20]$$

with n being the number of wind speed bins considered.

2.06.2.2.2 Standard deviation – Empirical method

Using the expressions of average and standard deviation given in eqns [7] and [8], it is possible to calculate the shape factor first, through the numerical solution of the following equation:

$$\left(\frac{\sigma}{\bar{V}}\right)^2 = \frac{\Gamma\left(1+\frac{2}{k}\right)}{\Gamma^2\left(1+\frac{1}{k}\right)} - 1 \quad [21]$$

while accordingly, one may also calculate the respective scale factor by using eqn [7], provided that both the average and the standard deviation are of known value. Alternatively, the two empirical approximation expressions [30] given below may be used equally well:

$$k = \left(\frac{\sigma}{\bar{V}}\right)^{-1.086} \quad [22]$$

$$c = \frac{\bar{V} \cdot k^{2.6674}}{0.184 + 0.816 \cdot k^{2.73855}} \quad [23]$$

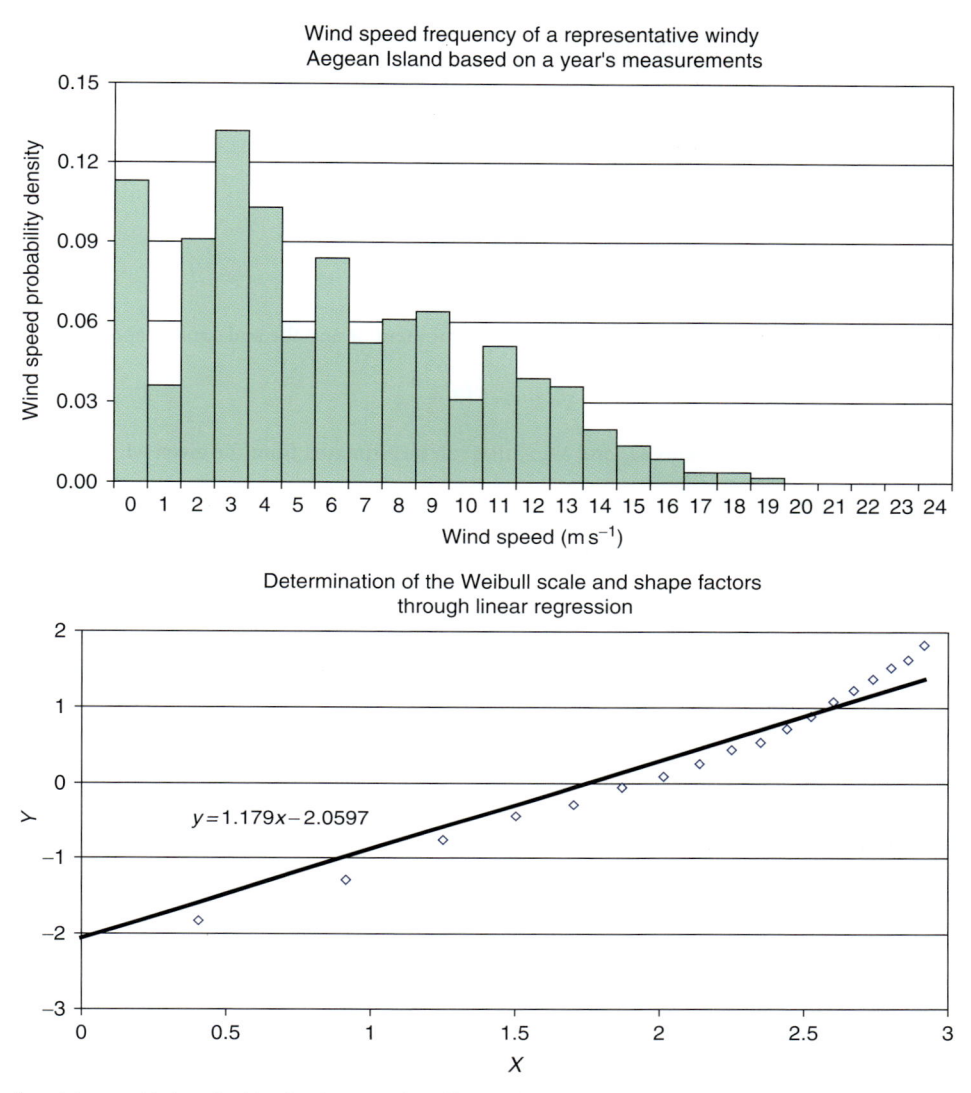

Figure 8 Application of the graphical method for the determination of Weibull parameters.

2.06.2.2.3 Maximum likelihood method

In the method of maximum likelihood [15, 31], through the application of the iteration method, one first determines the shape factor and accordingly the scale factor, based on eqns [24] and [25]:

$$k = \left[\frac{\sum_{i=1}^{n} V_i^k \cdot \ln(V_i)}{\sum_{i=1}^{n} V_i^k} - \frac{\sum_{i=1}^{n} \ln(V_i)}{n} \right]^{-1} \qquad [24]$$

$$c = \left(\frac{1}{n} \sum_{i=1}^{n} V_i^k \right)^{1/k} \qquad [25]$$

Instead, if the data available are given in a frequency distribution format, modification of the above two equations is performed in accordance with the following two expressions, with V_i being, as already mentioned, the average value of the bin n used; $f(V)$ being the respective frequency; and $P(V \geq 0)$ being the probability for wind speed equal to or exceeding zero:

$$k = \left[\frac{\sum_{i=1}^{n} V_i^k \cdot \ln(V_i) \cdot f(V_i)}{\sum_{i=1}^{n} V_i^k \cdot f(V_i)} - \frac{\sum_{i=1}^{n} \ln(V_i) \cdot f(V_i)}{P(V \geq 0)}\right]^{-1} \quad [26]$$

$$c = \left(\frac{1}{P(V \geq 0)} \sum_{i=1}^{n} V_i^k \cdot f(V_i)\right)^{1/k} \quad [27]$$

2.06.2.2.4 Moment method

The moment method is based on the relation between the Weibull moment M and the scale and shape factors [28], that is,

$$M_n = c_n \cdot \Gamma\left(1 + \frac{n}{k}\right) \quad [28]$$

Thus, by using two consecutive order moments M_n and M_{n+1} that can be estimated from the given wind data, one gets that

$$c = \frac{M_{n+1}}{M_n} \cdot \frac{\Gamma\left(1 + \frac{n}{k}\right)}{\Gamma\left(1 + \frac{n+1}{k}\right)} \quad [29]$$

while it is also valid that

$$\frac{M_{n+1}}{M_n^2} = \frac{\Gamma\left(1 + \frac{n}{k}\right)}{\Gamma^2\left(1 + \frac{n+1}{k}\right)} \quad [30]$$

with k and c being finally obtained from the solution of eqns [29] and [30].

2.06.2.2.5 Energy pattern factor method

In the specific method, one uses the energy pattern factor E_{pf}, defined as the ratio of the average cube wind speeds to the cube of the average wind speed [32], that is,

$$E_{pf} = \frac{\frac{1}{n} \cdot \sum_{i=1}^{n} V_i^3}{\left(\frac{1}{n} \cdot \sum_{i=1}^{n} V_i\right)^3} \quad [31]$$

After estimating the energy pattern factor, the shape factor may be approximated using eqn [32] or [33]:

$$k = 1 + \frac{3.69}{E_{pf}^2} \quad [32]$$

$$k = 3.957 \cdot E_{pf}^{0.898} \quad [33]$$

while the scale factor may be given by the use of eqn [7].

The application for some of the above-described calculation methods is given in **Figure 9**, where two random wind regimes are examined in order to emphasize the potential variation between results obtained. Thus, as it may be concluded, for the selection of the most appropriate method of calculation for the Weibull parameters, one should use accuracy judgment criteria on the basis of indices such as the root mean square error (RMSE) and the Chi-square error or the results of the Kolmogorov–Smirnov test.

2.06.2.3 The Impact of the Scale and Shape Factor Variation

In **Figures 10** and **11**, one may obtain the impact of the scale and shape factor variation on both the wind speed frequency $f(V)$ and the cumulative probability $F(V \leq V_o)$ estimation on the basis of applying eqns [5] and [9]. Based on the results of **Figure 10**, the lower the value of the scale factor c, the greater is the maximum wind speed frequency appearing, with the exact opposite being concluded from **Figure 11** concerning the impact of the shape factor k. In the same figures, one may also note that for the lower values of the c factor, the asymptotic of the cumulative probability curve is achieved for lower wind speed values, while again the opposite appears in the case of the k factor variation.

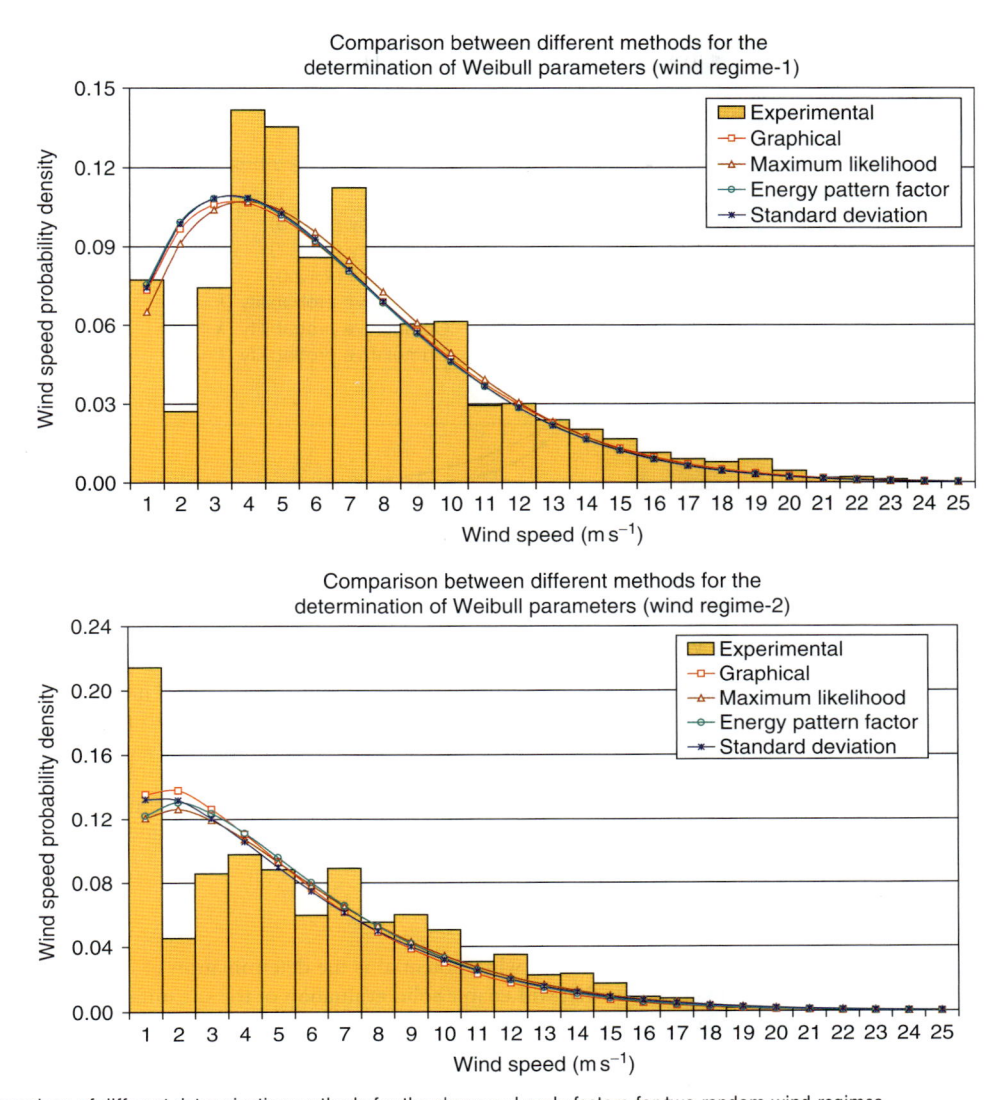

Figure 9 Comparison of different determination methods for the shape and scale factors for two random wind regimes.

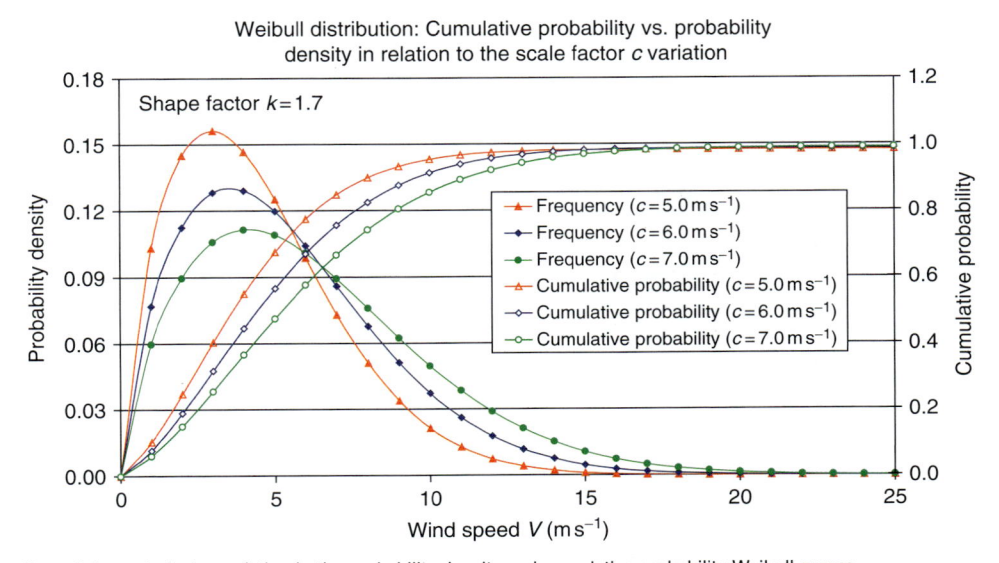

Figure 10 The effect of the scale factor variation in the probability density and cumulative probability Weibull curves.

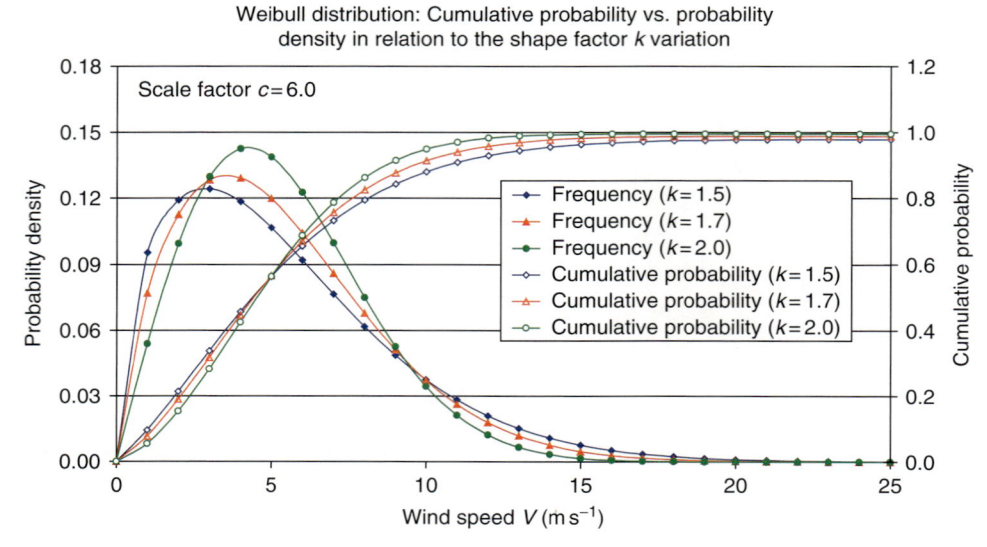

Figure 11 The effect of the shape factor variation in the probability density and cumulative probability Weibull curves.

2.06.2.4 Performance Assessment for the Weibull Distribution

By applying Weibull for some given sites, performance of the distribution in relation to experimental measurements is reflected in **Figure 12**, where, as one may see, Weibull performance is site-dependent, with strong variations appearing in wind regimes 1 and 2. However, according to the up-to-now gained experience, the Weibull distribution produces rather satisfactory results while, in general, overestimation of the low wind speed frequency (apart from zero values not captured by the Weibull function) and underestimation of the high wind speed frequency should be expected. On the other hand, by subtracting wind speed values lower than $1\,\mathrm{m\,s^{-1}}$ (i.e., the area where the Weibull function imposes zero frequency of wind speed), considerable improvement of the Weibull curve fit may be achieved (**Figure 13**).

2.06.2.5 Long-Term Study of Wind Energy Potential

One of the most important issues regarding the evaluation of wind potential is the determination of the minimum time period required for the conduction of detailed measurements that will enable solid evaluation of the site under investigation. Costs and delays induced by the need to obtain a satisfactory data sample and variability of the wind potential characteristics during the useful lifetime of a wind power project need to be balanced.

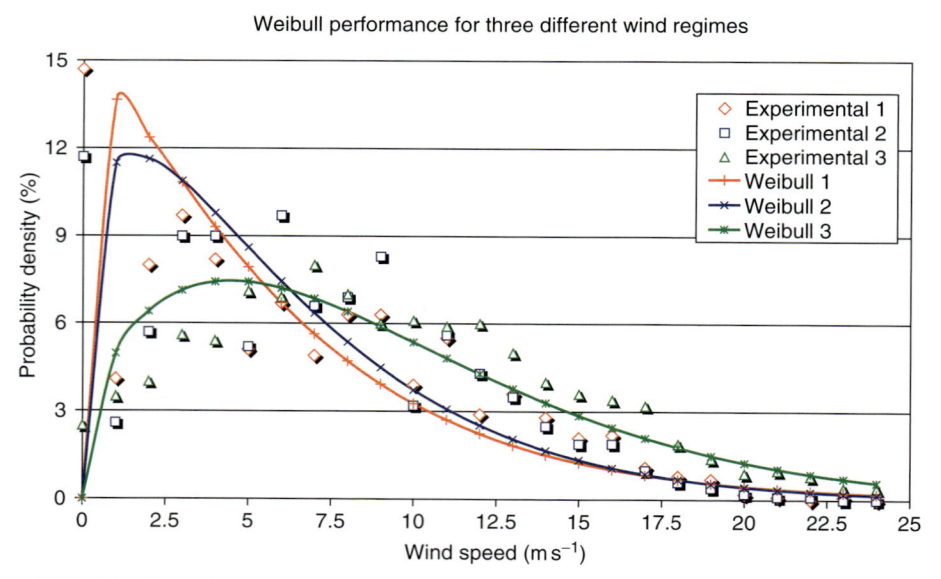

Figure 12 Accuracy of Weibull for three different wind regimes.

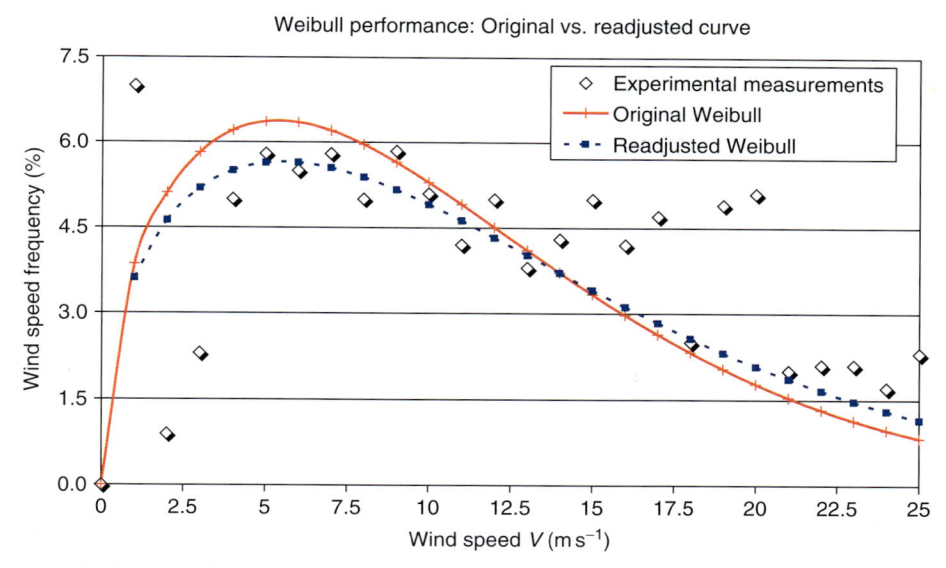

Figure 13 Improvement of Weibull fit performance through reassessment [10].

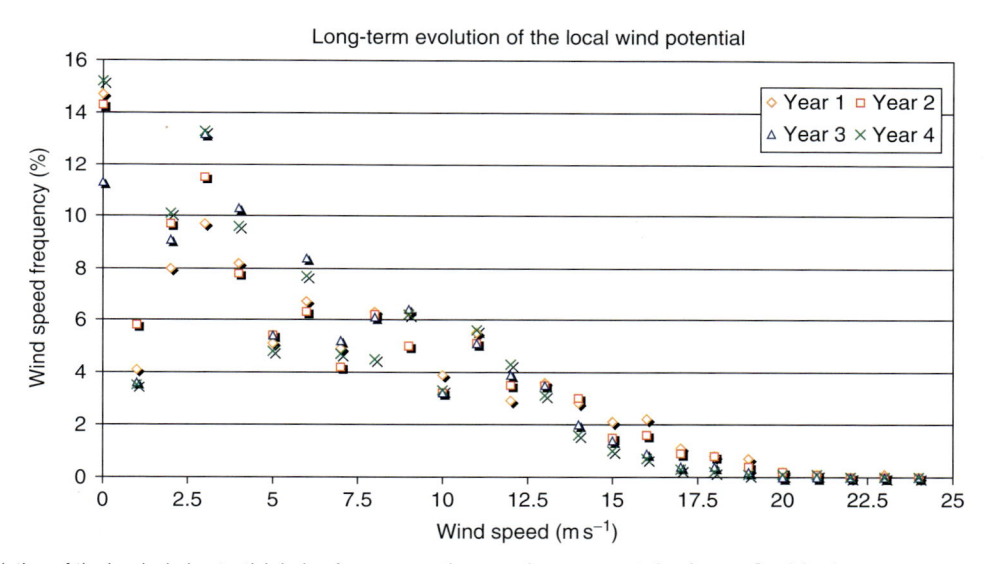

Figure 14 Evolution of the local wind potential during four consecutive years in a representative Aegean Sea island.

Special attention should be given to the possibility of also obtaining the data of a nontypical wind year that will lead to inaccurate estimation of the machine's energy yield. In general, it is expected that the characteristics of wind potential for a given site shall remain relatively stable from one year to another (**Figure 14**), although over longer periods one may even encounter variation in the order of ± 20% [33]. Thus, to minimize uncertainty, measurements of at least 1 year's time are thought to be necessary, with the extension of the monitoring period further increasing reliability.

2.06.2.6 Calm Spell Period Determination

Of major importance for the evaluation of a given site wind potential for the purpose of energy production is the determination of calm spell periods. More specifically, by determining different classes of calm spell periods (i.e., from the minimum, e.g., 1 h calm spell to the respective maximum, e.g., 50 consecutive hours of calm spells), one may proceed to the estimation of frequency for each of the bins selected. As a result, one may accordingly produce calm spell period curves, such as those appearing in **Figure 15**, for different upper limits of wind speed that correspond to the cut-in wind speed V_c of the wind machine under consideration each time. Besides, determination of such non-energy production curves is critical in the case of stand-alone wind energy-based systems [34, 35], where detailed sizing of the storage system requires good knowledge of the characteristics of calm spells.

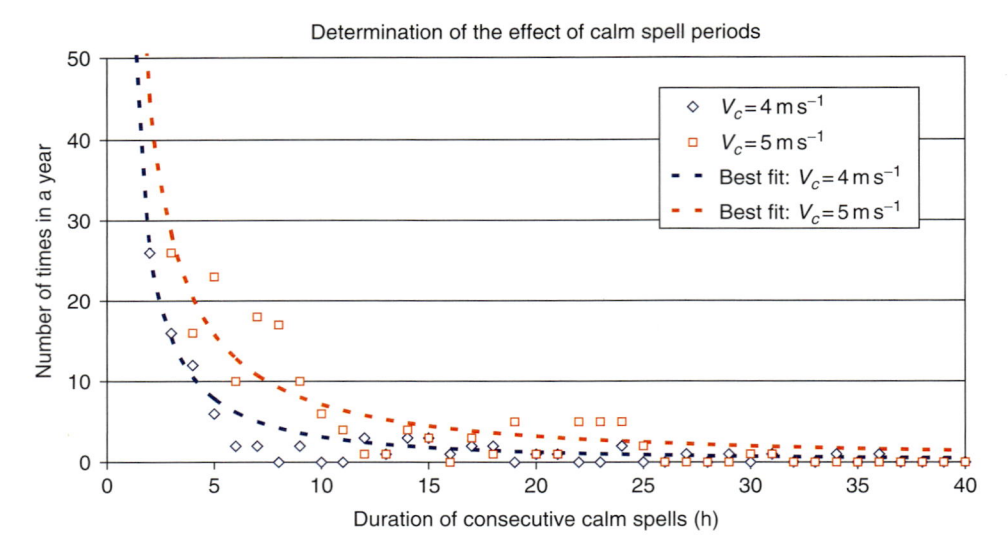

Figure 15 Probability curves for the appearance of different calm spell duration bins in relation to the cut-in speed of the wind generator.

2.06.2.7 Wind Gust Determination

The frequency and intensity of wind gusts, that is, wind speeds exceeding Beaufort 9 for time durations of a few seconds, is also of major concern for the evaluation of a site, with determination of gust probability being achievable on the basis of processing the available wind speed data [36]. In this way, the structure of the wind turbine to be installed in a given area of interest may be configured, with more solid and heavier structures used to ensure operation under extreme wind speed conditions. Such wind turbines are determined by both higher cut-out wind speeds and survival speeds that even reach 80 m s^{-1}, entailing, of course, a higher purchase cost as well.

The probability of extreme wind speeds V_{ext} appearing may be determined through the use of the Fisher–Tippett distribution I, using the following expression:

$$P(\leq V_{ext}) = e^{-e^{[-\alpha \cdot (V_{ext} - V_m)]}} \qquad [34]$$

where parameters α and V_m result from the statistical process of wind speed measurements concerning maximum mean hourly wind speeds and annual maximum gusts on an annual basis (**Figure 16**).

Equation [34] may be accordingly transformed in order to directly relate the V_{ext} and V_m:

$$V_{ext} = V_m + \frac{\zeta}{\alpha} \qquad [35]$$

with ζ given as

$$\zeta = -\ln[-\ln(P \leq V_{ext})] \qquad [36]$$

As a result, through the application of the least squares method (see also eqns [13]–[20]) to the data of ζ and V_{ext}, one may determine the values of constants α and V_m, while the maximum wind speed V_{max} (gust or mean hourly wind speed) with a recurrence period R may be estimated using eqn [37]:

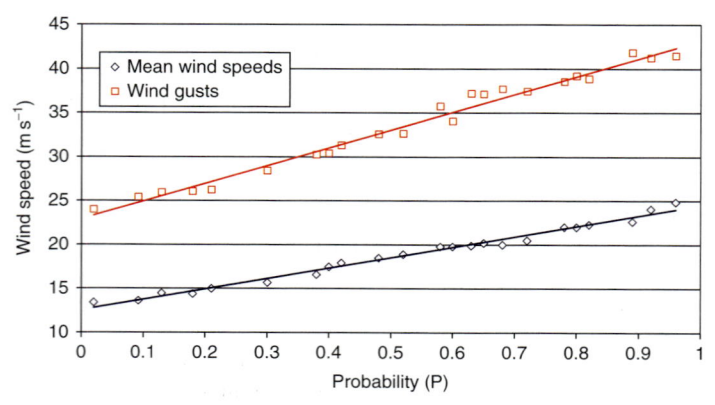

Figure 16 Example of statistical estimation of extreme wind speeds.

$$V_{\max} = V_m + \frac{1}{\alpha} \ln R \qquad [37]$$

where recurrence period R is based on the service period of the installation τ and an acceptable risk value r (probability) to exceed the value of $V_{\max}$ during the period of τ years, that is,

$$R = \frac{1}{1-(1-r)^{1/\tau}} \approx \frac{\tau}{r} \qquad [38]$$

2.06.3 Power Curves of Contemporary Wind Turbines

After providing the main directions for the evaluation of wind potential characteristics for energy generation purposes, determination of the most critical parameters related to the energy performance of a given wind turbine is presented, with emphasis given to the presentation of contemporary wind turbine power curves. Through detailed examination of typical wind power curves, interaction between the local wind potential and the wind turbine investigated may afterward lead to the estimation of energy production.

2.06.3.1 Description of a Typical Wind Turbine Power Curve

A simplified, though representative, wind turbine power curve, that is, the curve of the machine's power output P_{ex} as a function of wind speed at hub height, is given in **Figure 17(a)**. As already made clear, no power production is encountered up until sufficient wind speed is exploited, that is, wind speed that exceeds the minimum speed of operation for the wind turbine and ensures coverage of zero load losses P_c, also known as the cut-in wind speed V_c of the wind turbine. As the wind speed increases above the respective cut-in speed of the machine, a constant increase of the output power is noted up to the point of rated speed V_R, that is, the minimum wind speed corresponding to the nominal power of the machine P_R. Note that the increase rate noted in this ascending segment of the wind power curve varies and does not necessarily follow a linear pattern such as the one illustrated in **Figure 17(a)**, with exponential or parabolic patterns also encountered (**Figure 17(b)**). Finally, in the nominal power segment, where the power curve flattens, an attempt is carried out in order for the power output to remain constant and wind speed-independent through power regulation. Power regulation is used so as to avoid extreme loading of the machine and may be achieved with the application of several techniques [7] such as implementation of appropriate aerodynamic designs, pitch control, change of rotor direction, or even variable-speed operation. Constant power output is maintained up to the point of the cut-out wind speed V_F, where power production of the machine is eliminated so as to protect the machine from heavy loading. On the other hand, storm control features [37] recently adopted by certain wind turbine manufactures allow for the gradual reduction of power production in the event of extremely high wind speeds, preventing instant shutdown of the machine and thus allowing for greater wind energy exploitation (the red curve in **Figure 17(a)**). The respective survival speed V_s is normally found in the area of 50–80 m s^{-1} (i.e., from 180 km h^{-1} to almost 290 km h^{-1}), depending on the class of the machine. To synopsize, mathematical expression of the typical power curve (without storm control) illustrated in **Figure 17(a)** may be summarized as

$$\begin{array}{ll} P_{ex} = 0 \ (V \leq V_c) & P_{ex} = P_{ex}(V)(V_c \leq V \leq V_R) \\ P_{ex} = P_R(V_R \leq V \leq V_F) & P_{ex} = 0 \ (V \geq V_F) \end{array} \qquad [39]$$

As already discussed, exploited wind energy is much limited by both the operational range of the wind turbine and the need for power regulation after a certain wind speed (**Figures 1** and **3**). To demonstrate the impact of the wind generator operational range, an attempt is undertaken in **Figure 18** to present the energy production results (details of the estimation of a wind turbine's energy production are given in the following section) deriving from the variation of critical wind speeds, that is, cut-in, cut-out, and rated power speed for a reference scenario of $V_c = 5$ m s^{-1}, $V_R = 11$ m s^{-1}, and $V_F = 23$ m s^{-1}, under a given wind potential of $\bar{V} = 6.93$ m s^{-1}. As expected, reduction of both cut-in and rated power speeds implies considerable increase of energy yield (even 25%), explained by the high probability density values of lower wind speeds (in the case of the cut-in speed reduction) as well as from the extension of the nominal power segment (in the case of the rated power speed reduction).

On the other hand, increase of these two characteristic speeds leads to an analogous reduction of energy yield, opposite to the behavior exhibited by the cut-out wind speed, which if increased leads to a minimum increase in wind energy exploitation. Similarly, reduction of the cut-out speed leads to reduction of energy yield, which is, however, not as influencing as in the case of the cut-in and rated power speeds, reflecting the relatively lower importance of very high wind speeds. Results obtained are directly dependent on the wind potential examined each time; nevertheless, only in extreme cases would increase of the cut-out wind speed allow greater wind energy exploitation than the one accruing from an analogous reduction of the cut-in speed.

2.06.3.2 Producing a Wind Turbine Power Curve

Configuration of a wind turbine power curve is directly dependent on the selected power regulation strategy and the operational features of the machine. More precisely, depending on the characteristics of the electrical generator selected, rotational speed of the rotor may be either constant or variable, with the second option, although inducing a more expensive solution, also allowing for optimization of the power output over a large range of wind speeds [38]. On the other hand, in the case that a constant speed machine is used, operation of the rotor is restricted to a standard rotational speed that is wind speed-independent and thus cannot

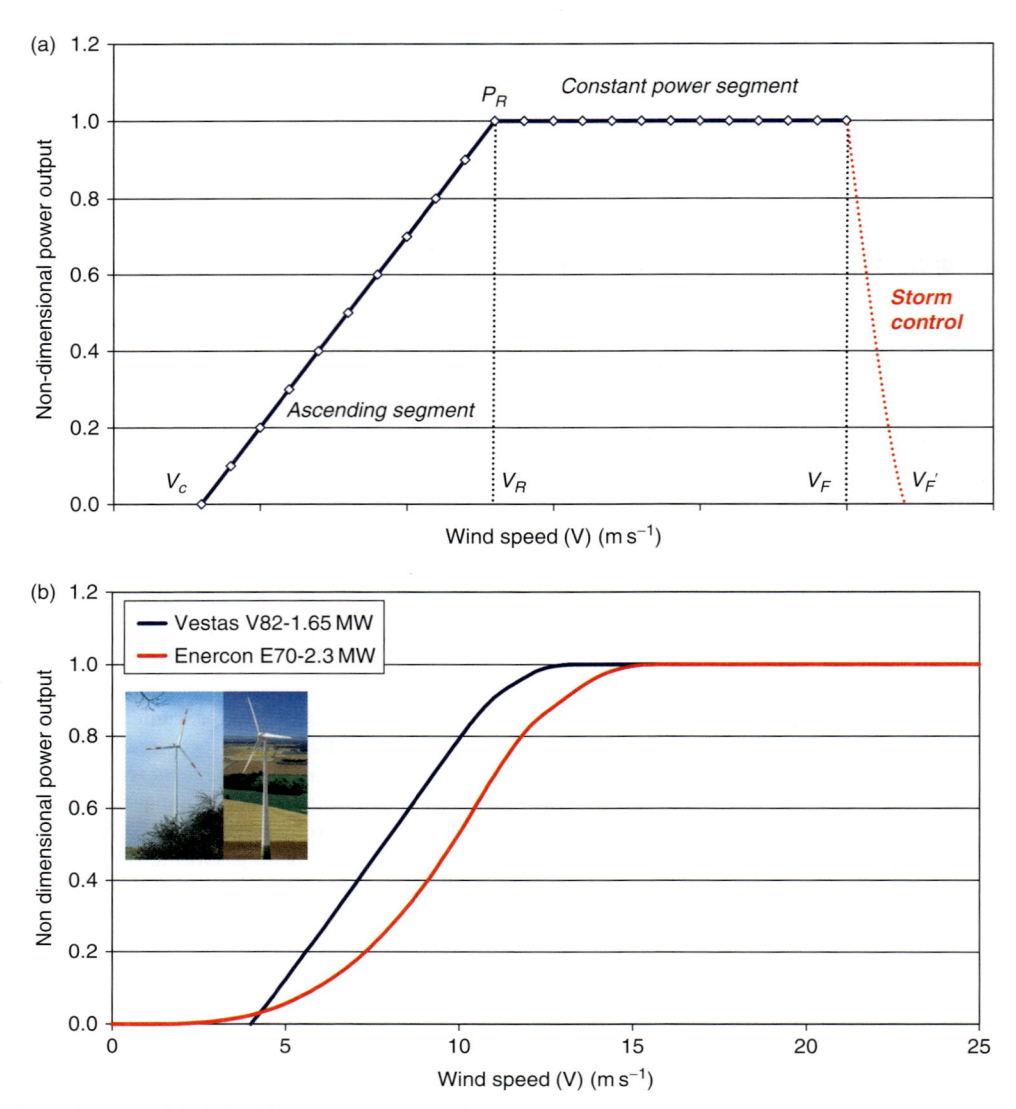

128   Energy Yield of Contemporary Wind Turbines

Figure 17 Typical and commercial wind turbine power curve examples.

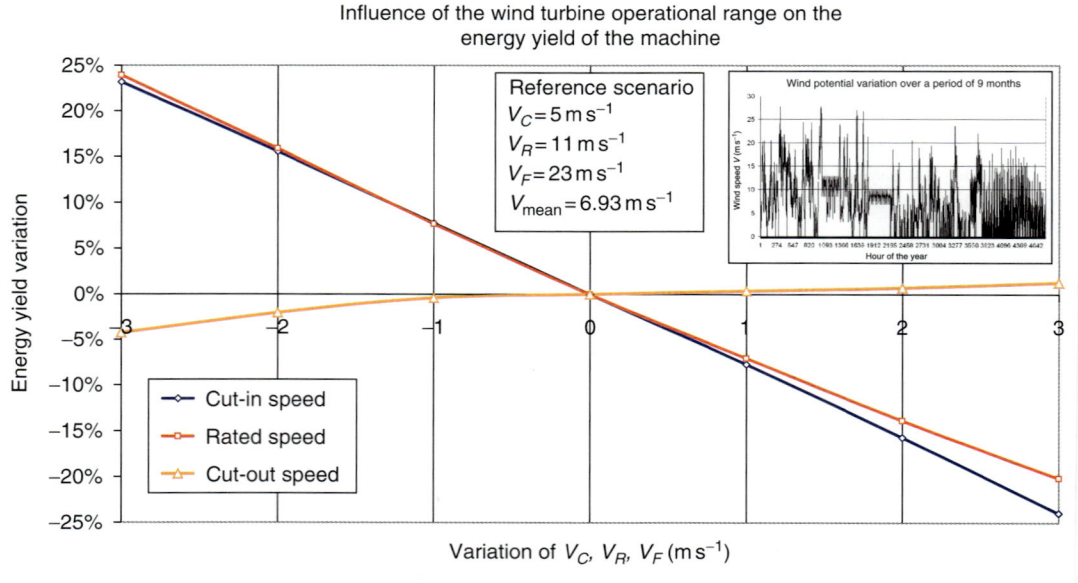

Figure 18 The impact of cut-in, rated power, and cut-out wind speed variation on wind turbine energy output.

obtain maximum power output. Furthermore, depending on whether rotor blades are pitchable or fixed, either regulation of power (normally in the nominal power segment of the power curve) is achievable through variation of the pitch angle (pitch regulation or active stall regulation) or a standard angle is selected that takes advantage of the aerodynamic stall phenomenon.

As a result, there are three common options used in power regulation, that is, constant speed of the rotor and fixed blades using stall regulation (e.g., NM 1000/60), constant speed of the rotor and pitchable blades using pitch/active stall regulation (e.g., WindMaster 750/48 and Vestas V82) and, finally, variable speed of the rotor and pitchable blades using pitch regulation (e.g., Enercon E126), with activation of power regulation not necessarily restricted in the nominal power segment area of the power curve. The influence of the rotor speed regulation is demonstrated in **Figure 19**, where comparison of constant and variable-speed strategies designates different wind power curve configurations and clearly reflects energy exploitation benefits accruing from the selection of a variable-speed generator.

The adoption of fixed or pitchable rotor blades normally influences the nominal power segment of the power curve (**Figure 20**), where in an effort to both maintain constant power output and limit extreme loading of the machine, either stall (passive control) or pitch regulation (active control) is performed. Up until the mid-1990s, the majority of in-operation wind generators used the stall-control concept; nevertheless, since the introduction of large-scale machines and the imposition of power quality requirements, pitch regulation dominated in the years to come [39], with the pitch-regulated variable-speed concept being gradually established during the time being (**Figure 21**).

2.06.3.3 Power Curve Modeling

Description of a wind turbine power curve may be approached by some generic models that are common in the literature [40–44] and are used to describe the ascending segment of a wind turbine power curve, using only the cut-in and the rated power speed of

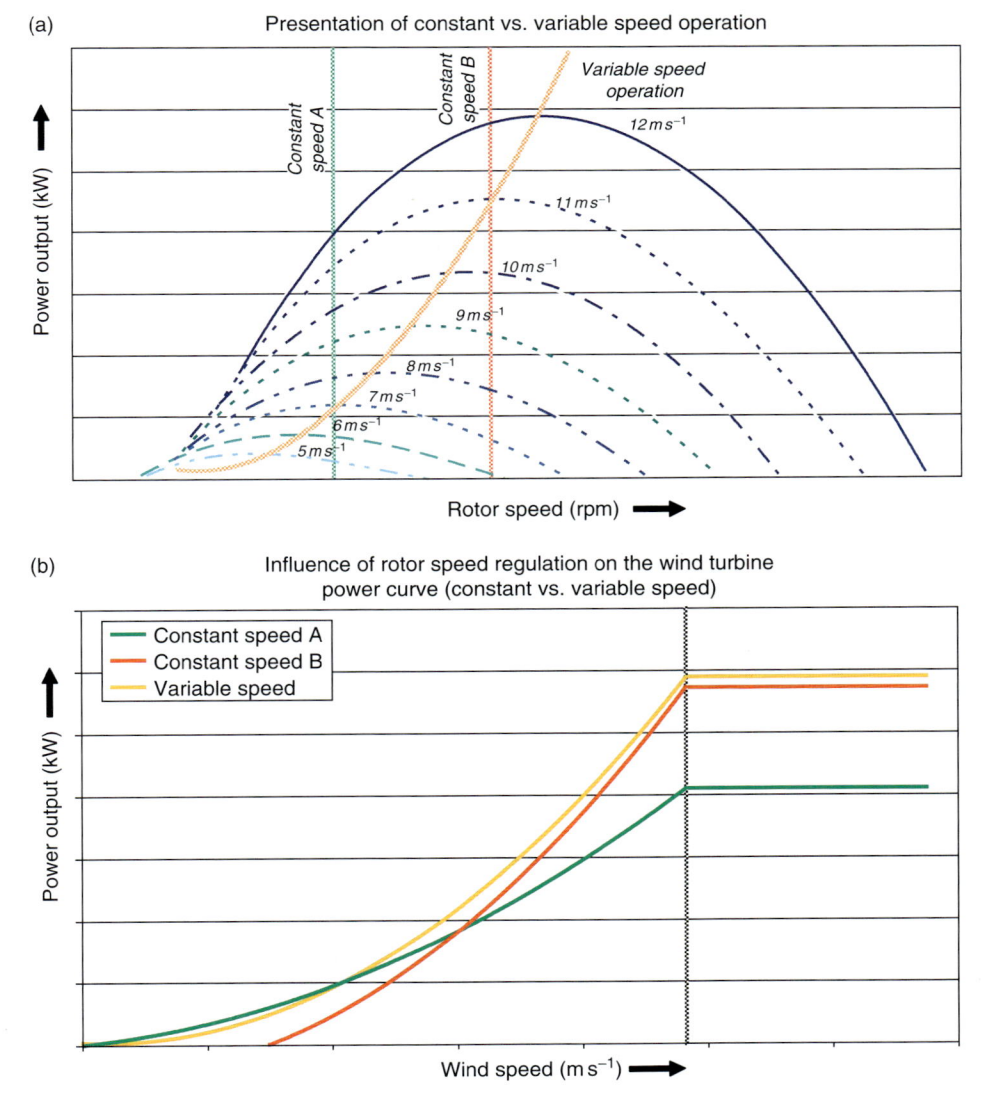

Figure 19 Power curve configuration for constant- and variable-speed machines.

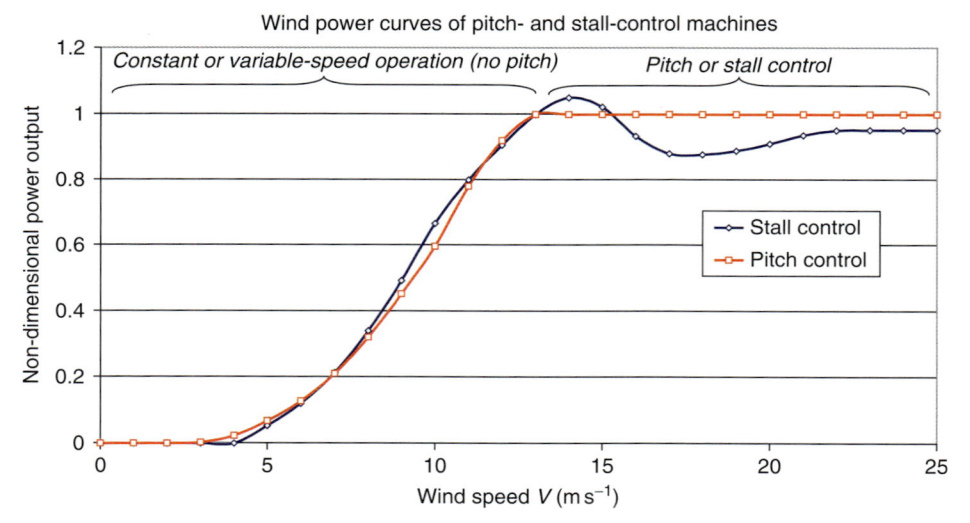

Figure 20 Power curves of pitch- and stall-control wind turbines.

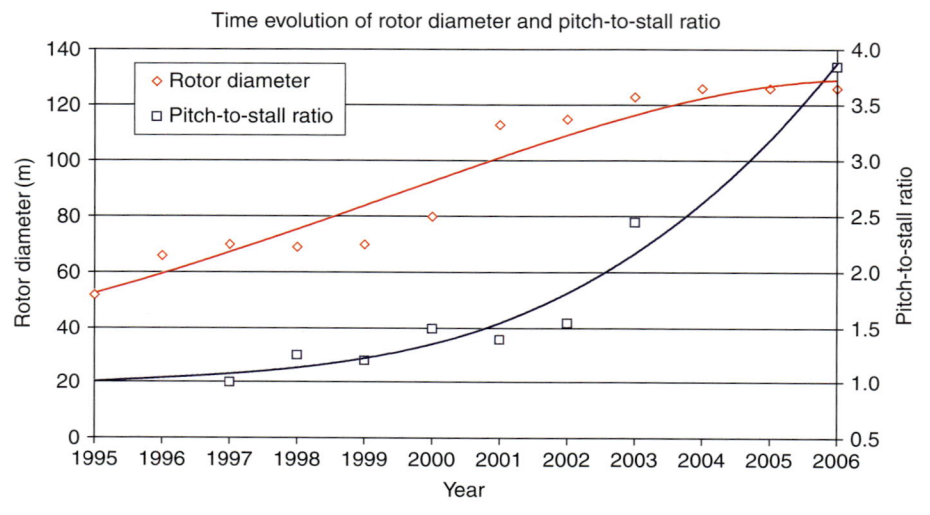

Figure 21 Time evolution of rotor diameter and pitch-to-stall ratio for contemporary wind turbines.

the machine. These include linear, quadratic, and cubic models, with adjustment of each one clearly depending on the form of the original power curve configured by the manufacturer data.

2.06.3.3.1 Linear model
In the case that a linear model is used, a linear relation is assumed between the non-dimensional power output of the machine $P_{ex}(V)/P_R$ and the wind speed at hub height V on the basis of the following relation:

$$\frac{P_{ex}(V)}{P_R} = \frac{V-V_c}{V_R-V_c} \qquad [40]$$

2.06.3.3.2 Cubic model
Based on the assumption of constant efficiency over the entire ascending segment, the cubic model is expressed on the basis of eqn [41] or by using the more simplified version of eqn [42]:

$$\frac{P_{ex}(V)}{P_R} = \frac{(V-V_c)^3}{(V_R-V_c)^3} \qquad [41]$$

$$\frac{P_{ex}(V)}{P_R} = \frac{V^3}{V_R^3} \qquad [42]$$

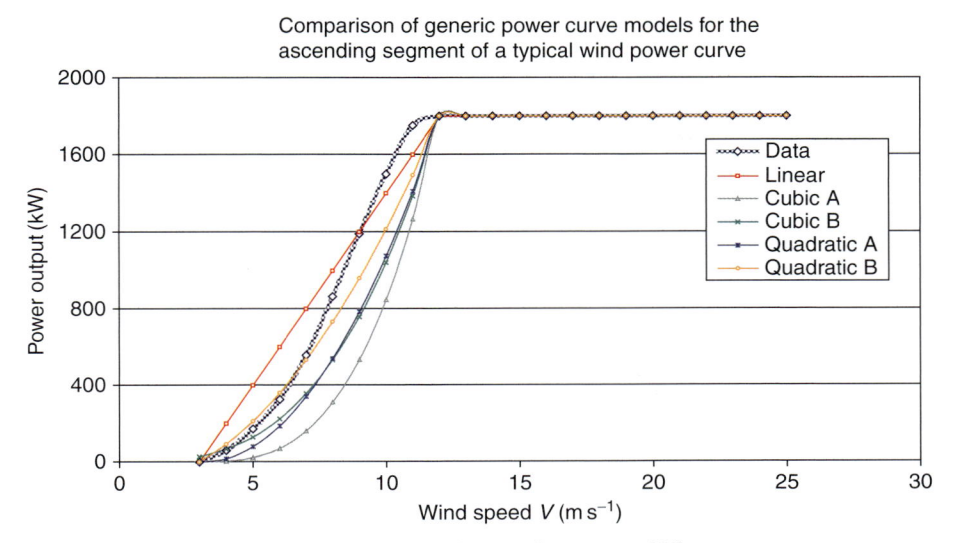

Figure 22 Application results of generic models for the description of the ascending segment [44].

2.06.3.3.3 Quadratic model

In the quadratic model, power output is assumed to vary parabolically from the cut-in V_c to the rated power wind speed V_R in accordance with the following equation:

$$\frac{P_{ex}(V)}{P_R} = a + bV + cV^2 \qquad [43]$$

considering also, however, that from the midpoint between the cut-in and the rated power speed $(V_c + V_R)/2$ up to the rated speed V_R, power output follows the cubic model of eqn [42]. Alternatively, eqn [44] may also be used for the application of the quadratic model on the basis of a second expression, that is,

$$\frac{P_{ex}(V)}{P_R} = \frac{V^2 - V_C^2}{V_R^2 - V_C^2} \qquad [44]$$

while polynomial functions of higher order may also be used to describe the ascending segment of a wind turbine power curve. In order to demonstrate the application of the above-mentioned models, a typical example is given in **Figure 22**, with results obtained reflecting the difference between the outcome of the various models. Hence, selection of the most appropriate model for the wind turbine power curve investigated should also take into account evaluation of adjustment to the manufacturer data through the use of common best-fit criteria.

2.06.3.4 Power Curve Estimation

For the estimation of a wind turbine power curve, detailed measured data of wind speed and wind turbine electrical output are required for an appreciable time period in order to assess actual performance of the machine. Wind speed measurements may be obtained either from a meteorological mast in the area of the wind turbine or wind park installation, or from the nacelle anemometer downstream of the rotor. For any given case, what should be considered is that in order to obtain the actual wind speed at hub height, upstream of the rotor, correction of the original measurements is required. Power output measurements, however, may be obtained from the SCADA monitoring system of the machine (**Figure 23(a)**).

Acknowledging the above, the current standard method for the determination of a wind turbine power curve corresponds to the use of IEC 61400-12-1, introduced by the International Electrotechnical Commission [45]. According to the standard procedure, collected data of wind speed and power output are transformed into 10-min averages and are accordingly averaged into 0.5 m s^{-1} wind speed bins. Although the method is considered as applicable, especially in the case that sufficient data are available, the inability of capturing short-term wind speed fluctuations designates important limitations that need to be considered, with alternative approaches existing suggesting dynamical and maximum principle methods of power curve determination. To proceed to further analysis, division of available wind speed data into direction sectors per wind speed bin is also desirable (**Figure 23(b)**), while depending on the terrain and exact point of wind speed measurements, determination of the power curve may also require the use of numerical simulation methods that will also capture any terrain effects [46].

It is common for power curves of all commercial wind turbines to be measured and certified (**Figure 24**) by independent institutions such as the Deutsches Windenergie-Institut in Germany, included among others in the International Network for Harmonised and Recognised Measurements in Wind Energy (MEASNET), which is responsible for the development of standardization methods [47] (**Table 1**).

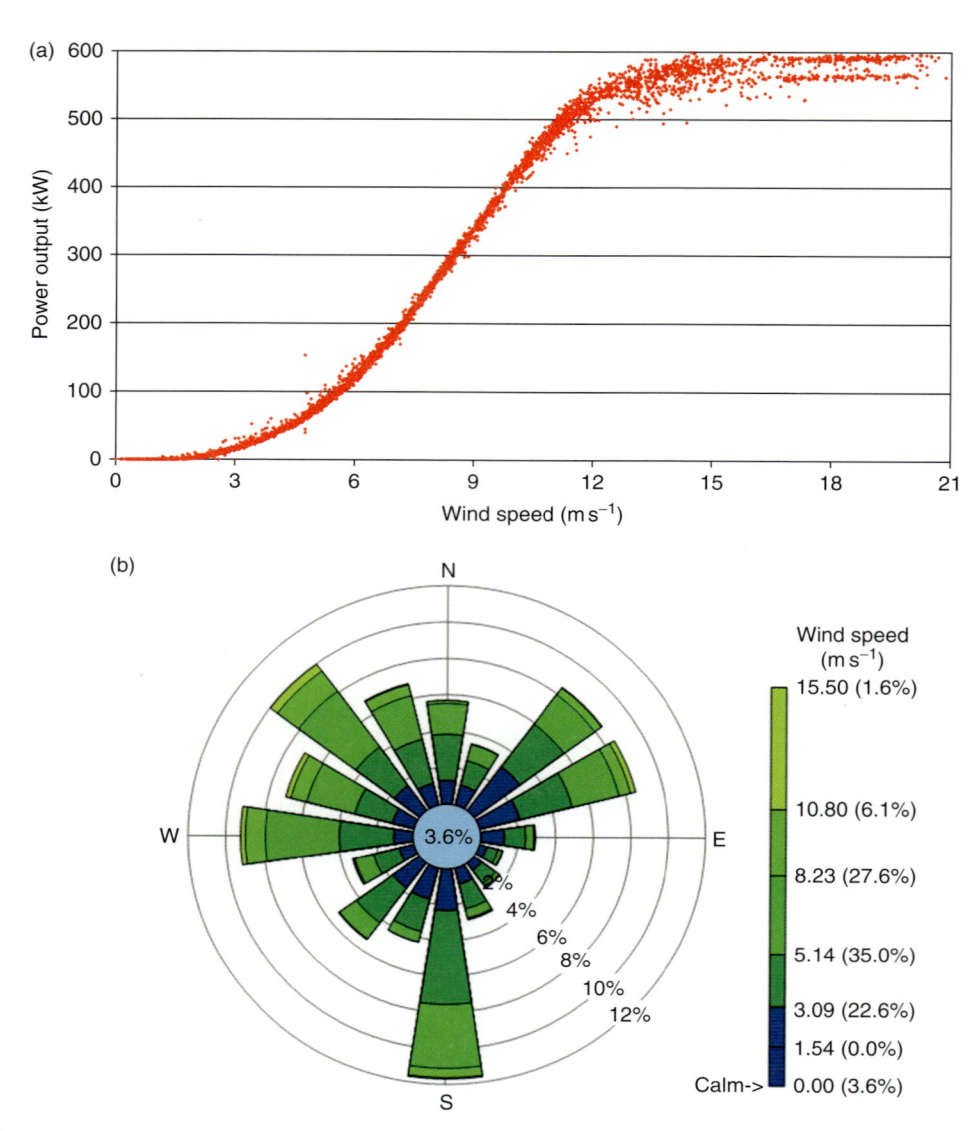

Figure 23 (a) Power output measurements and (b) wind speed sector division.

2.06.4 Estimating the Energy Production of a Wind Turbine

After the investigation of typical wind turbine power curves and the assessment of wind resource main characteristics, synthesis of the respective data may lead to estimation of the energy production output of a given wind turbine. We provide here an analysis of energy production calculations, with emphasis accordingly given to the impact of wind potential characteristics on the wind energy output of a given wind machine.

2.06.4.1 From the Instantaneous Power Output to Energy Production

As already seen, the purpose of a wind turbine is the exploitation of the kinetic energy of wind and the production of useful energy at the outlet of the machine. For the estimation of the instantaneous useful power output at a given moment t, knowledge of wind speed at hub height upstream of the rotor turbine V, technical availability of the machine δ, and wind turbine standard power curve $P_{ex}(V)$ are all necessary, with the resulting power production given by eqn [45]:

$$P_{ex}(t) = P_{ex}(V(t)) \cdot \delta(t) \qquad [45]$$

where the technical availability (or Kronecker) function $\delta(t)$ becomes either equal to 1 (the machine is in operation) or equal to 0 (the machine is out of operation (downtime)) (**Figure 25**).

Considering eqn [45], energy production of a wind turbine during a time period Δt is estimated as

Figure 24 Example of wind turbine certification.

Table 1   MEASNET participating institutes and approved measurements per institute [47]

Institute	Anemometer calibration	Power performance	Noise emission	Power quality
CENER	No	Yes	Yes	Yes
CRES	Yes	Yes	Yes	Yes
Deutsche WindGuard wind tunnel services	Yes	Yes	No	No
DEWI GmbH	Yes	Yes	Yes	Yes
ECN	No	Yes	Yes	No
RISØ	No	Yes	No	No
TRIPOD wind energy ApS	No	Yes	No	No
WINDTEST Kaiser-Wilhelm-Koog GmbH	No	Yes	Yes	Yes
WINDTEST Grevenbroich GmbH	No	Yes	Yes	No
Barlovento Recursos Naturales S. L.	No	Yes	No	No
NREL	No	No	Yes	Yes
WIND-consult GmbH	Yes	Yes	Yes	No
IDR/UPM	Yes	No	No	No
Svend Ole Hansen ApS, wind engineering	Yes	No	No	No
Ingenieurbüro Dr.-Ing. Dieter Frey	Yes	No	No	No
Energy to quality S. L.	No	No	No	Yes
Deutsche WindGuard Consulting GmbH	No	Yes	No	No
WINDTEST Ibérica S. L.	No	Yes	No	No

NREL, National Renewable Energy Laboratory.

$$E(\Delta t) = \int_{t_o}^{t_o + \Delta t} P_{\text{ex}}(t) \mathrm{d}t \quad [46]$$

with the integral of eqn [46] being normally solved with the use of numerical methods.

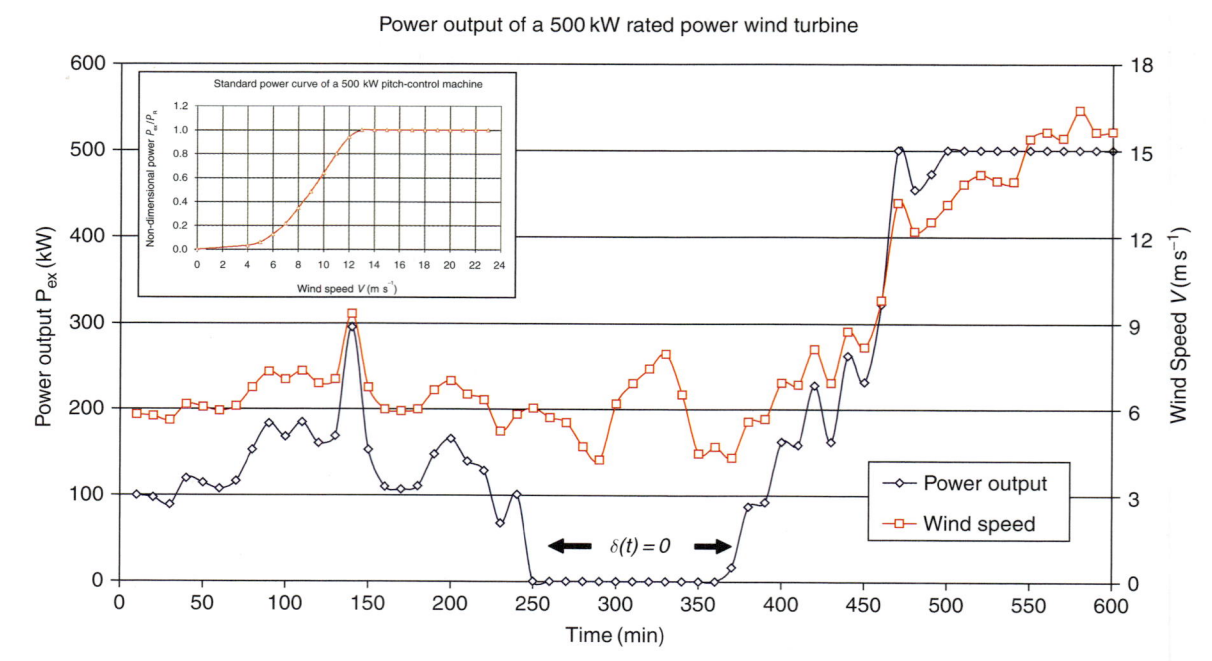

Figure 25 Instantaneous power output of a wind turbine on the basis of available wind speed measurements, manufacturer's power curve, and technical availability time series.

In order to facilitate any techno-economic calculations required for the evaluation of a wind energy project, it is also convenient to equate the operation of a wind turbine with that of a hypothetical constant power machine that produces – during a certain time period Δt of mean technical availability Δ – the exact energy amount that the respective wind turbine does.

For that reason, one introduces the parameter of the mean power coefficient ω [48], estimated on the basis of eqn [47]:

$$\omega(\Delta t) = \frac{E(\Delta t)}{P_R \cdot \Delta t \cdot \Delta} \qquad [47]$$

Using the mean power coefficient, it is assumed that the variable power output wind turbine of rated power P_R operates as a constant power machine with rated power equal to $P_R \cdot \omega$ for a time period of $\Delta \cdot \Delta t$.

2.06.4.2 Estimating the Annual Wind Energy Production

The process for determining the annual energy production of a certain wind turbine may be applied either to *ex post*, for example, at the end of the year under investigation (so as to evaluate its operation), or in advance, in order to obtain an indication of the energy production to be expected on an annual basis.

In the first case, by using the recorded time series of wind speed, meteorological conditions and technical availability of the machine, along with the characteristics of the wind turbine manufacturer power curve, estimation of the expected wind energy production for a time period (t_o, $t_o + \Delta t$, e.g., 1 year) is possible on the basis of the following equation, modifying eqn [46] in order to also consider for any variation in standard day conditions:

$$E(\Delta t) = \int_{t_o}^{t_o + \Delta t} P_{ex}(V(t)) \cdot \frac{\rho(t)}{1.2215} \delta(t) dt \qquad [48]$$

with 1.2215 being the air density ρ (kg m^{-3}) at standard day conditions (i.e., air temperature $T = 15\,°C$ and barometric pressure $P_{atm} = 1.035$ bar, satisfying the manufacturer wind turbine power curve $P_{ex}(V)$). Furthermore, as already mentioned, the Kronecker function $\delta(t)$ is used to determine whether the wind turbine is in operation ($\delta(t) = 1$) or is down due to 'technical' problems ($\delta(t) = 0$). The energy output of eqn [48] is accordingly compared with the respective measured wind energy production during the same time period of 1 year in order for useful conclusions to be made regarding the operation of the machine.

In the case that estimation of energy production is attempted in advance, the probability density $f(V)$ curve of the local wind potential is used, in combination with the manufacturer power curve, while estimation of a realistic value for the technical availability during the entire year is also required. In that case, the energy production of a wind turbine during this certain time period Δt of 1 year (i.e., 8760 h) is estimated on the basis of eqn [47], where the mean power coefficient ω of the wind turbine may be calculated using eqn [49], considering also that the energy production of a wind turbine is limited within the range of wind speeds from the cut-in to the cut-out wind speed.

$$\omega = \int_0^\infty \frac{P_{ex}(V)}{P_R} \cdot f(V) dV = \int_{V_c}^{V_F} \frac{P_{ex}(V)}{P_R} \cdot f(V) dV \qquad [49]$$

Note that normally ω takes values between 0.2 and 0.6, without, however, excluding the possibility of a lower or a higher value. Besides that, it should also be mentioned that one often uses the product of mean technical availability Δ and mean power coefficient ω, known as the capacity factor (CF) [49] of the wind turbine of the installation or alternatively as the utilization factor of the local wind potential:

$$\text{CF} = \Delta \cdot \omega \qquad [50]$$

In conclusion, as one may obtain from eqn [49], the value of the mean power coefficient depends on both the local wind energy resource characteristics and the operational curve of the wind turbine examined. In addition, by using eqn [49], it is possible to estimate the contribution of wind speeds up to a certain level, for example, $V \leq V_o$, to the respective energy production of a wind machine:

$$\omega(V_o) = \int_{V_c}^{V_o} \frac{P_{ex}(V)}{P_R} \cdot f(V) dV \qquad [51]$$

2.06.4.3 Estimating the Mean Power Coefficient

The precise value of the mean power coefficient derives from the detailed knowledge of the available wind energy potential and the operational features of the wind turbine under examination. If one wishes to estimate the energy contribution of the transitional (ascending) segment of a typical power curve (i.e., from V_c to V_R), eqn [52] may be used:

$$\omega_1 = \int_{V_c}^{V_R} \frac{P_{ex}(V)}{P_R} \cdot f(V) dV \qquad [52]$$

Similarly, for speeds exceeding the rated power speed V_R of the wind generator (i.e., in the rated power segment), we get that

$$\omega_2 = \int_{V_R}^{V_F} \frac{P_{ex}(V)}{P_R} \cdot f(V) dV \qquad [53]$$

with the total mean power coefficient ω being

$$\omega = \omega_1 + \omega_2 \qquad [54]$$

In addition, in the case that the wind power curve follows the typical form of **Figure 26**, the power coefficient of the rated power segment may be directly estimated from the simplified form of eqn [53], as follows:

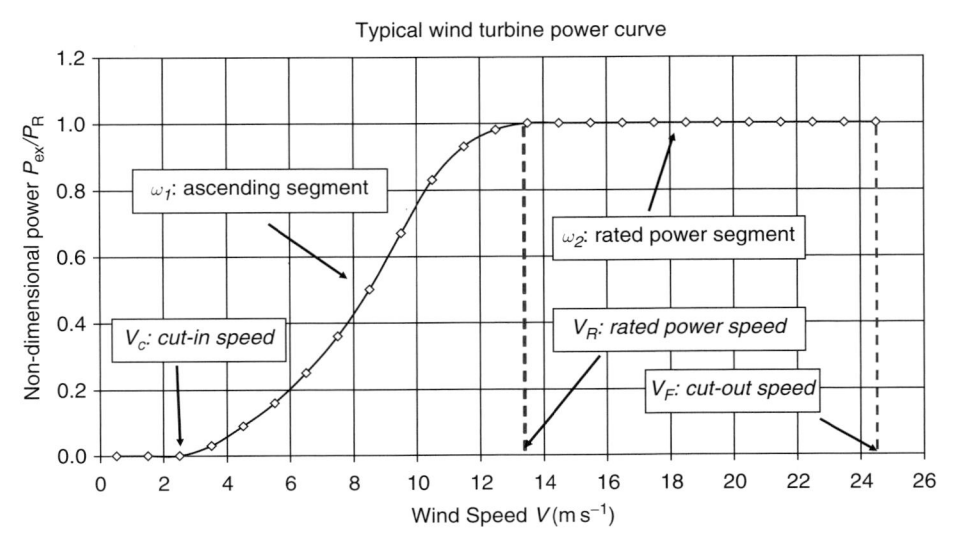

Figure 26 Typical pitch-control wind turbine power curve.

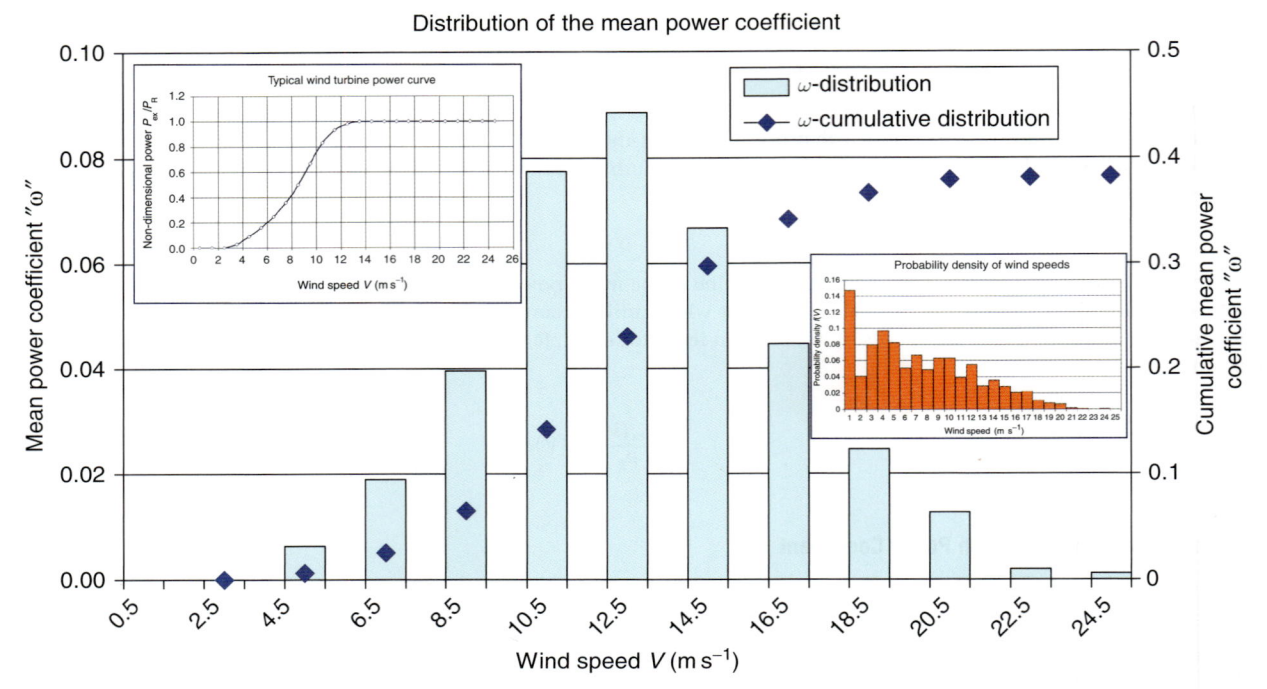

Figure 27 Calculation of the power coefficient distribution based on the numerical method of Simpson.

$$\omega_2 = \int_{V_R}^{V_F} f(V)dV = F(V_F) - F(V_R) \quad [55]$$

while, in the case that the Weibull distribution is used for the description of the wind potential under examination, eqn [55] is rewritten on the basis of the respective cumulative probability density function $F(V \leq V_o)$ in the form given below:

$$\omega_2 = \exp\left[-\left(\frac{V_R}{c}\right)^k\right] - \exp\left[-\left(\frac{V_F}{c}\right)^k\right] \quad [56]$$

Using eqn [56], one may estimate the contribution of the rated power segment corresponding to ω_2, using only the values of parameters V_R, V_F, k, and c. At the same time, dependence of ω_2 on the relation between the rated wind speed of the wind turbine and the average wind speed of the area studied is designated, while as it accrues from the equation, the impact of V_F variation is not as considerable because the probability for such high wind speeds to appear is rather low (**Figure 18**).

For a more detailed estimation of ω and the production of the respective distribution, numerical methods are required [50]. Some of the most common numerical integration methods include Simpson's rule, the trapezoidal rule, and Lagrange interpolation. The results obtained from the application of Simpson's rule are given in **Figure 27**, expressed on the basis of eqn [57], applying for equally distant points, that is, equally distant bins of wind speed:

$$\int_{V_0}^{V_2} \frac{P_{ex}(V)}{P_R} \cdot f(V)d(V) = \frac{(V_2-V_0)}{6} \cdot \left[\frac{P_{ex}(V_0)}{P_R} \cdot f(V_0) + 4 \cdot \frac{P_{ex}(V_1)}{P_R} \cdot f(V_1) + \frac{P_{ex}(V_2)}{P_R} \cdot f(V_2)\right] \quad [57]$$

2.06.4.4 The Impact of the Scale Factor Variation on the Mean Power Coefficient

As already mentioned, the scale factor c of the Weibull distribution is directly related to the mean annual wind speed $\bar{V}$ of the area under examination. More precisely, when c takes high values, the area of examination is determined by high wind speeds, while the opposite is valid in the case that c takes low values. Using five different realistic values for the scale parameter of Weibull (e.g., from $c = 4.0$ m s^{-1} to $c = 8.0$ m s^{-1}) and a constant shape parameter value $k = 1.7$, the influence of the scale factor variation on the mean power coefficient distribution for a typical pitch-control wind turbine is obtained from **Figure 28**.

As one may see, differences accruing due to the variation of the scale factor are rather significant, with the ω value obtained for $c = 7.0$ m s^{-1} being almost double the ω value for $c = 5.0$ m s^{-1}, which practically implies that the specific wind turbine shall produce double the energy amount if installed in an area of $c = 7.0$ m s^{-1}, in comparison with its operation at an area of $c = 5.0$ m s^{-1}. As one may easily understand, this also influences the economic performance of the machine, thus designating the importance of the local

[Figure 28: Graph titled "The impact of the scale parameter c variation on the mean power coefficient ω distribution" showing cumulative ω distribution vs wind speed V (m s⁻¹) for c = 4.0, 5.0, 6.0, 7.0, 8.0 m s⁻¹]

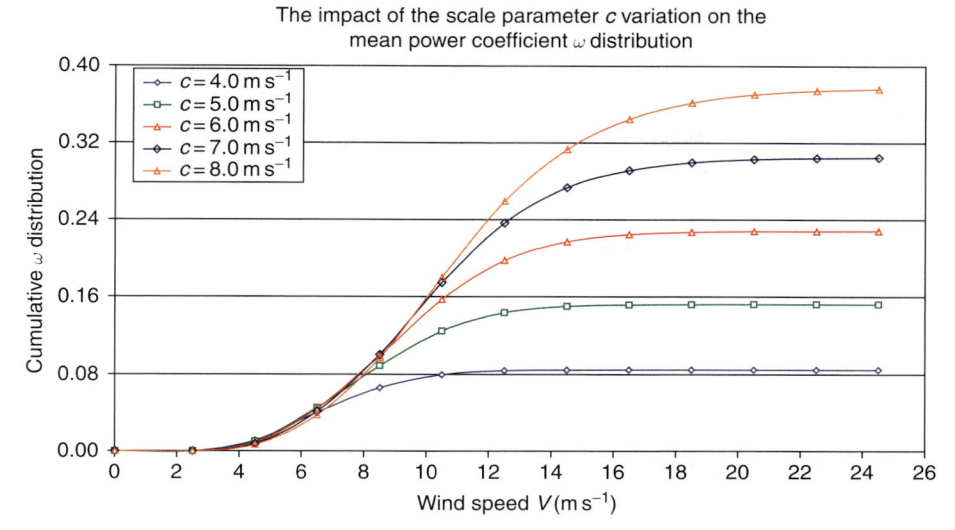

Figure 28 Presentation of the power coefficient cumulative distribution in relation to the Weibull scale parameter variation.

wind potential scale factor, especially in the case of such great variation entailed in the respective power coefficient. The magnitude of discrepancy between results obtained is even more characteristic for the extreme scale factors currently studied, with the respective power coefficients differing by a factor of almost 4.5 (i.e., $\omega_{c=8.0} = 0.376$ and $\omega_{c=4.0} = 0.085$), directly related to the ability of annual energy production of the specific wind generator.

2.06.4.5 The Impact of the Shape Factor Variation on the Mean Power Coefficient

The shape factor of the Weibull distribution is, as previously mentioned, inversely analogous to the standard deviation of wind speed. As a result, low values of the k parameter lead to the production of more 'flat' and dispersed probability distributions, while, on the contrary, high values of the shape factor suggest relatively sharper distributions, with the probability distribution being rather concentrated around the average wind speed value. Besides, as already seen, variation of the k parameter also has a slight impact on the average wind speed.

In **Figure 29**, we investigate the effect of the shape parameter variation on the resulting power coefficient, with values selected ranging from $k = 1.3$ to $k = 2.2$ and with the scale parameter held constant at $c = 6.0$ m s^{-1}. As one may see, the impact of the shape parameter may be thought as inconsiderable, especially if taking into account the effect that is induced by the variation of the scale

[Figure 29: Graph titled "The impact of the shape parameter k variation on the mean power coefficient ω distribution" showing cumulative ω distribution vs wind speed V (m s⁻¹) for k = 1.3, 1.5, 1.7, 2.0, 2.2]

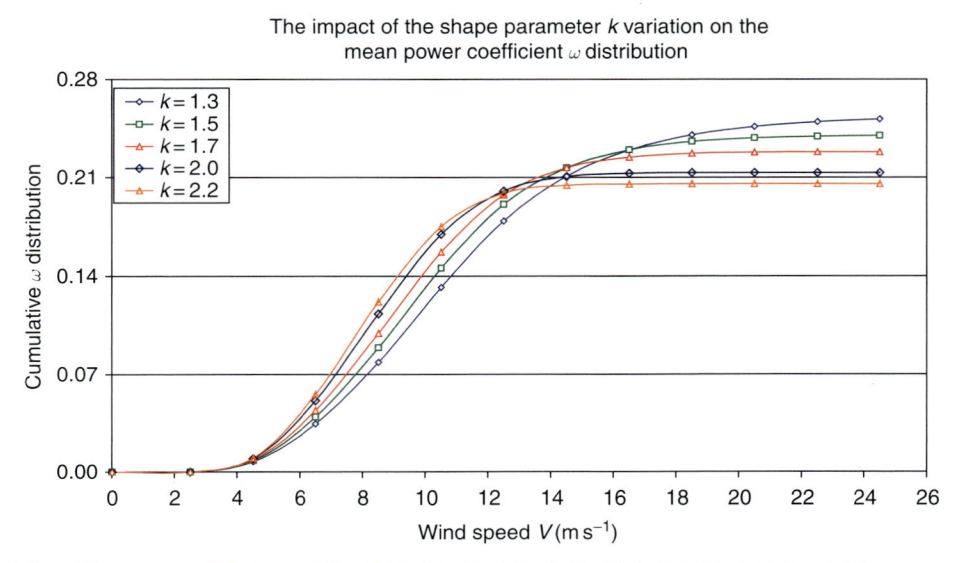

Figure 29 Presentation of the power coefficient cumulative distribution in relation to the Weibull shape parameter variation.

factor, with the highest variation currently calculated between $k = 1.3$ and $k = 2.2$, not exceeding 22%. Finally, it is interesting to also note that inverse behavior of k curves as the wind speed increases leads to the decrease of the ω coefficient as the k value increases.

2.06.4.6 The Impact of the Shape and Scale Factor Variation on the Annual Energy Production

In order to better demonstrate the influence of the Weibull parameter variation on the actual energy production of a wind generator, in **Figure 30** one may obtain the results concerning the annual energy production of a 600 kW pitch-control machine, assumed to be determined by a mean annual technical availability value of $\Delta = 0.95$ (see also eqn [47]), a rated wind speed $V_R = 10 \text{ m s}^{-1}$, a cut-in wind speed $V_c = 4.0 \text{ m s}^{-1}$, and, finally, a cut-out speed $V_F = 25 \text{ m s}^{-1}$. As expected, there is a strong influence of the scale parameter on the annual energy production achieved by the machine, which is almost linear, whereas on the other hand, the shape parameter variation effect is only considerable for either very high or very low values of c. Furthermore, as one may obtain from the figure, although for low values of c, it is the lower values of k that seem to achieve a greater energy production, the opposite is valid in the case of a high average wind speed (for $c \sim 8 \text{ m s}^{-1}$), where the higher k values imply strict concentration of wind speed values around the relatively high mean wind speed of the area.

This may be easily justified if considering the fact that the scale parameter is actually a reflection of the average wind speed of the area, whereas the shape parameter is inversely analogous to the standard deviation of wind speeds around the respective average wind speed. Thus, in the case of a low average wind speed, that is, low values of the c parameter, low values of k introduce wide dispersion of values around the average wind speed, which is in the specific case desirable, exactly due to the fact that wider dispersion also increases the possibility of higher wind speeds appearing. Lower values of wind speed appearing are, of course, of analogous probability; nevertheless, their effect minimizes as the c factor approaches the cut-in wind speed V_c. On the contrary, when the scale parameter takes high values, a decrease in the value of the shape parameter implies that it is quite possible for lower wind speeds to appear, that is, something that implies reduction of the energy production, especially in cases that the average wind speed (or c) is close to the machine's rated wind speed V_R (since higher values in that case would produce the same energy production, especially in the case of a pitch-control machine).

2.06.4.7 Energy Contribution of the Ascending and Rated Power Curve Segments

Investigation of energy contribution by each of the two main segments of the wind turbine power curve (**Figure 31**) is of great interest. For this purpose, in **Figure 31**, one may obtain the energy contribution of both segments, expressed on the basis of the ω_1/ω and ω_2/ω ratios (see also eqns [51]–[53]) in relation to the random increase of both the k and c parameters, for a wind turbine of $V_c = 5 \text{ m s}^{-1}$, $V_R = 10 \text{ m s}^{-1}$, and $V_F = 25 \text{ m s}^{-1}$. As one may see, increase of the Weibull parameters is, as expected, inducing an increase of ω_2, which for the highest of the values studied allows for a contribution of the rated power segment that even approaches 80%. The opposite is encountered in the case of the low value scenario, where the contribution of the rated power segment minimizes and the greatest share of energy production derives from the exploitation of wind speeds much below the rated wind speed V_R.

The effect of the Weibull parameters on the energy contribution of ω_1 and ω_2 is further investigated in **Figures 32** and **33**. More precisely, in **Figure 32**, the influence of the k variation for three different values of the scale parameter is studied, for the same wind turbine producing the results of **Figure 33**. As one may see, the impact of k variation depends on the exact value of the scale parameter. In fact, for c values found below the area of rated power wind speed (i.e., $c = 6.5$ and $c = 8.0$), an increase of the k value suggests an increase of the ω_1 contribution, justified on the basis of a narrower dispersion around the average wind speed, which in these two cases is inferior to the rated power wind speed of the machine ($V_R = 10 \text{ m s}^{-1}$). In the case that the scale parameter becomes

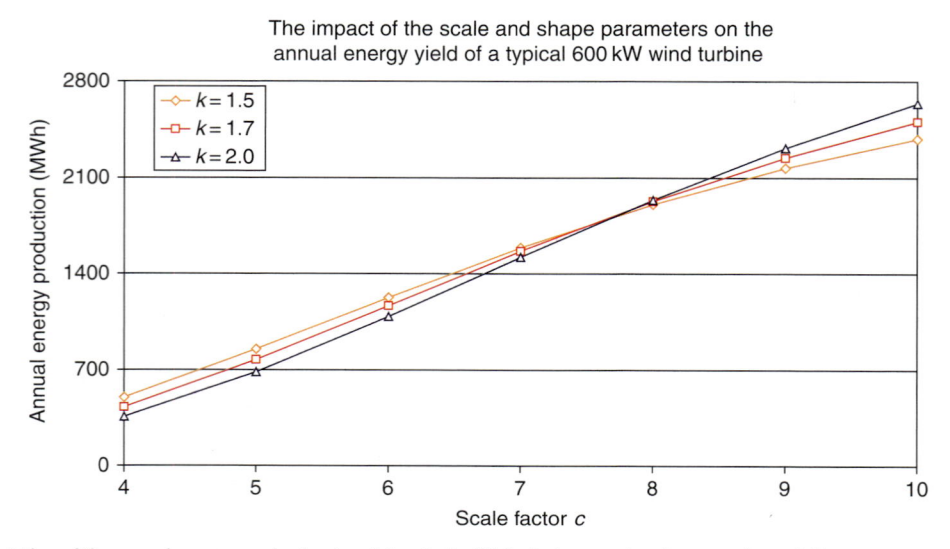

Figure 30 Presentation of the annual energy production in relation to the Weibull shape and scale parameter variation.

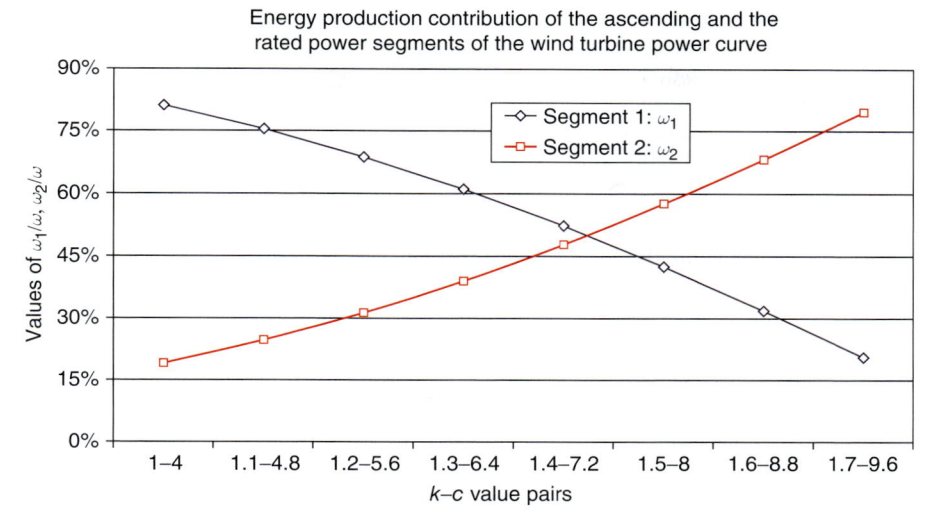

Figure 31 The effect of parallel increase of Weibull parameters on the energy production contribution of the ω_1 and ω_2 power coefficients.

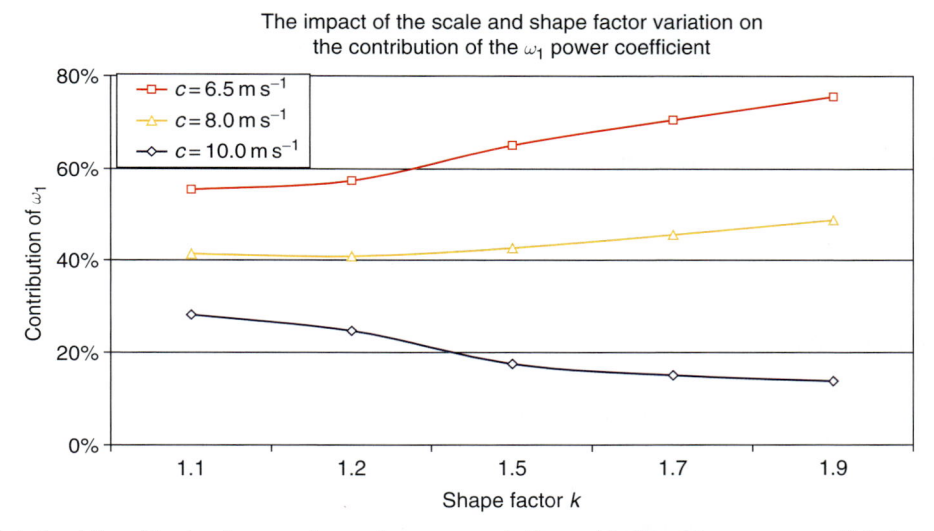

Figure 32 The effect of variation of the k and c parameters on the energy production contribution of the ω_1 power coefficient.

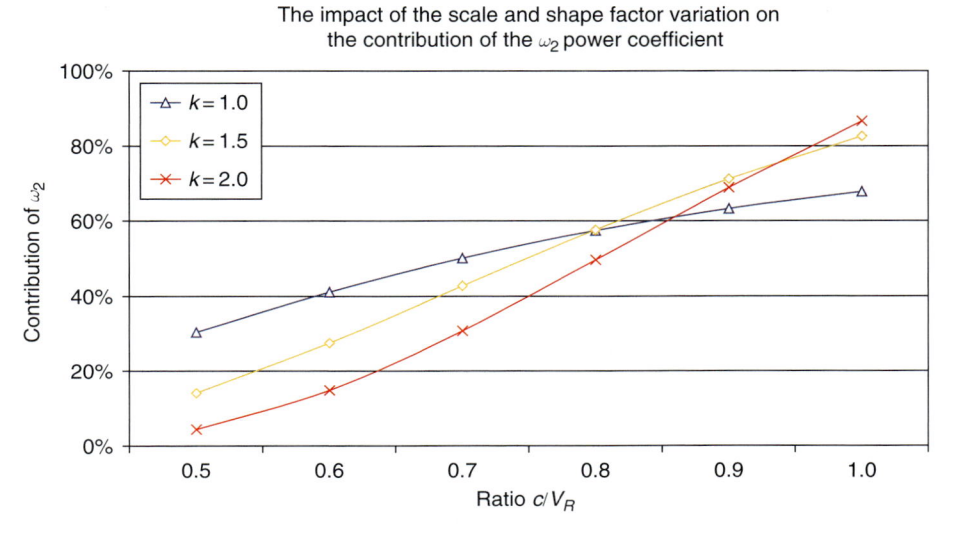

Figure 33 The effect of variation of the k and c parameters on the energy production contribution of the ω_2 power coefficient.

equal to the rated power wind speed of the machine, an increase of the k factor yields the opposite results, since wind speeds are now gathered in the area of the rated power segment, that is, where ω_2 starts to contribute.

The above conclusion is further validated by the results of **Figure 33**, where the ratio of c/V_R is plotted against ω_2. Based on the results obtained, as the scale parameter approximates the rated wind power speed V_R, narrow dispersion of wind speeds achieved for higher values of k brings about an increase in the contribution of the rated power curve segment. On the contrary, low values of k for the cases that the c/V_R ratio reduces considerably allow for the exploitation of higher wind speeds (due to the wider dispersion of wind speed values) that also fall into the rated power segment of the wind turbine power curve.

2.06.4.8 Energy Yield Variation due to the Use of Theoretical Distributions

Estimation of the energy production of a certain wind turbine depends on the set of data used, meaning that this could comprise either a set of actual wind speed measurements or a set of results produced with the application of a certain wind speed distribution. In the second case, as expected, the estimated energy output is directly related to the accuracy of the distribution used; thus selection of the appropriate distribution is, as already seen, of major importance for a reliable estimation of the energy yield. In **Figures 34** and **35**, a good and a poor adjustment scenario of the Weibull distribution on the given wind regimes is studied, in order to demonstrate the importance of either using the appropriate wind speed distribution or acknowledging the difficult task of describing some more complex wind regimes.

More precisely, in **Figure 34**, results of good Weibull adjustment at a wind regime that appears to be relatively mild are also reflected in the calculation of the ω-distribution, with minor variations noted in the area of low and medium wind speeds, that is, the area where Weibull fails to describe the given wind regime satisfactorily. In the case that Weibull presents poor adjustment over the given wind regime, such as in the case of **Figure 35**, where the given wind regime is rather abrupt, the coincidence of the two ω-distributions, with the difference noted between the two final ω values exceeding 30% ($\omega_{experimental} = 0.318$ and $\omega_{weibull} = 0.238$) is also analogous. As a result, there is a rather considerable underestimation of the energy output of the wind turbine under examination, due to the fact that Weibull fails to capture the increased probability density of high wind speeds.

2.06.5 Parameters Affecting the Power Output of a Wind Turbine

Because the power output of a wind generator is dependent on constantly varying parameters such as wind speed and air density, this variation needs to be considered when attempting a reliable estimation of the actual energy yield. In the following paragraphs, some insight is provided regarding the variation of wind shear, the impact of air density fluctuations, and, finally, the influence of the wake effect.

2.06.5.1 The Wind Shear Variation

Acknowledging the lack of existing measurements at the required height, in order to properly predict the energy production output of contemporary wind turbines, extrapolation is necessary in order to assess wind speeds at hub heights that may well exceed 50 m and even reach 100 m, starting from available wind speed measurements, usually at a height of 10 m above ground level. The flow of

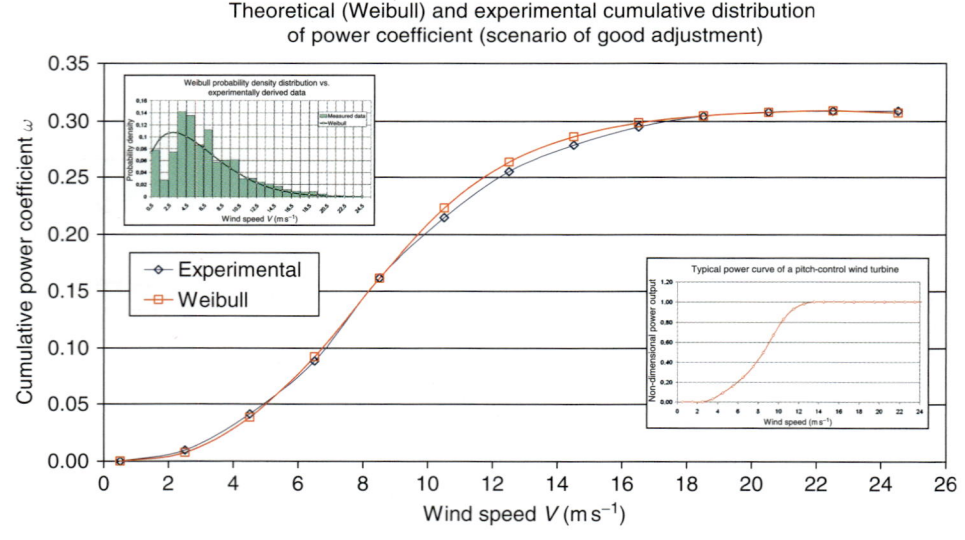

Figure 34 Comparison of power coefficient distributions produced from experimental and Weibull data sets in the case of satisfactory Weibull performance.

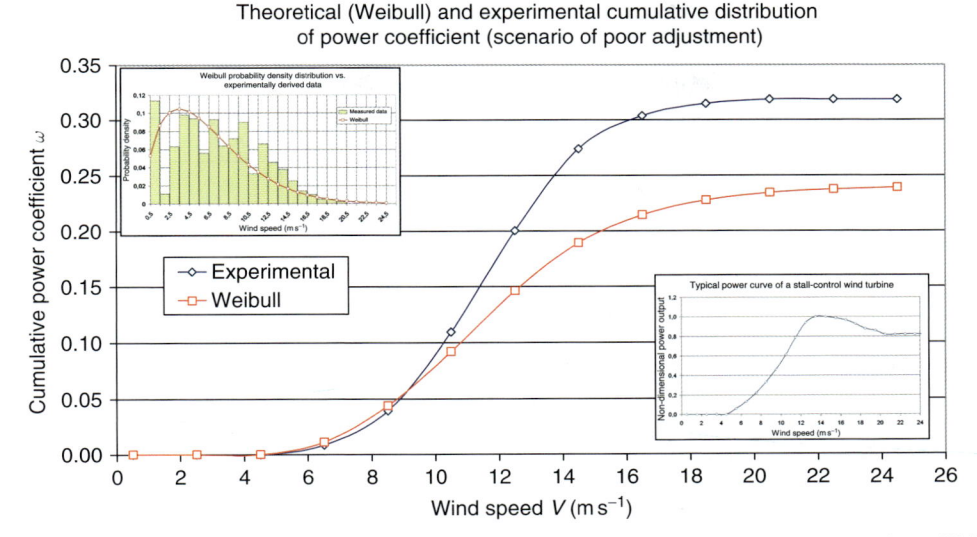

Figure 35 Comparison of power coefficient distributions produced from experimental and Weibull data sets in the case of poor Weibull performance.

air upon the earth surface is, as well known, subject to the laws of fluid mechanics. As a result, application of both analytical and numerical methods used in fluid mechanics and aerodynamics in order to study the vertical profile of wind speed is possible. More specifically, wind shear is supposed to follow the norms of a turbulent boundary layer, much depending on the characteristics of the site under examination. In fact, configuration of the wind shear depends on wind speed, features of the terrain (meaning surface roughness), the atmospheric stability, and, finally, the height interval to be studied. For the assessment of the wind shear, there are several analytical relations that have been proposed, based on the boundary layer theory. As a general remark, however, one should bear in mind that wind speed is found to considerably increase with the increase of height above ground level. It should be noted that this increase may be quite noteworthy within the first 100 m, with the number given actually coinciding with the normal thickness of the atmospheric boundary layer.

The main distributions (laws) proposed for the accurate description of wind shear [51–53] include the following:

1. 'The log-linear law' is expressed as

$$V_{h_2} = V_{h_1} \frac{\ln\left(\frac{h_2}{z_o}\right) - \Psi\left(\frac{h_2}{L}\right)}{\ln\left(\frac{h_1}{z_o}\right) - \Psi\left(\frac{h_1}{L}\right)} \qquad [58]$$

and may be used to predict wind speed V_{h_2} at a height h_2, through the use of roughness length z_o and wind speed V_{h_1} at a base height h_1, and the estimation of the stability function Ψ, depending on the Monin–Obukhov length L and height under study h [54]. More precisely, the stability function Ψ can be calculated on the basis of the following three conditions through the use of the non-dimensional stability measure h/L.

- $\Psi = -4.7 \cdot \frac{h}{L}$ for stable conditions, that is, $h/L > 0$
- $\Psi = 0$ for neutral conditions, that is, $h/L \sim 0$
- $\Psi = 2 \cdot \ln(1+x) + \ln(1+x^2) - 2\tan^{-1}(x)$ for unstable conditions, that is, $h/L < 0$

with $x = (1 - 19.3 \cdot (h/L))^{1/4}$

Results of extrapolation based on the application of different atmospheric stability conditions are given in **Figure 36**, where one obtains an aspect of the effect of unstable conditions on the increase of wind speed with the parallel increase of height for an area of $z_o = 0.2$ m (i.e., an area of small, low height building density). As one may see, wind speed prediction on the basis of stable conditions leads to an almost linear increase of wind speed V_{h_2} with the increase of height h_2, while in the case of either unstable or neutral conditions, an exponential curve is expected, with unstable conditions yielding a minor increase of wind speed even at the upper levels of the boundary layer. Note, however, that a more sophisticated extrapolation of wind speed is a rather complex task, since variation of the Monin–Obukhov length L is constant, deriving mainly from the thermal stratification of the atmosphere (**Table 2**).

2. 'The logarithmic (log)' law is expressed as

$$V_{h_2} = V_{h_1} \cdot \frac{\ln\left(\frac{h_2}{z_o}\right)}{\ln\left(\frac{h_1}{z_o}\right)} \qquad [59]$$

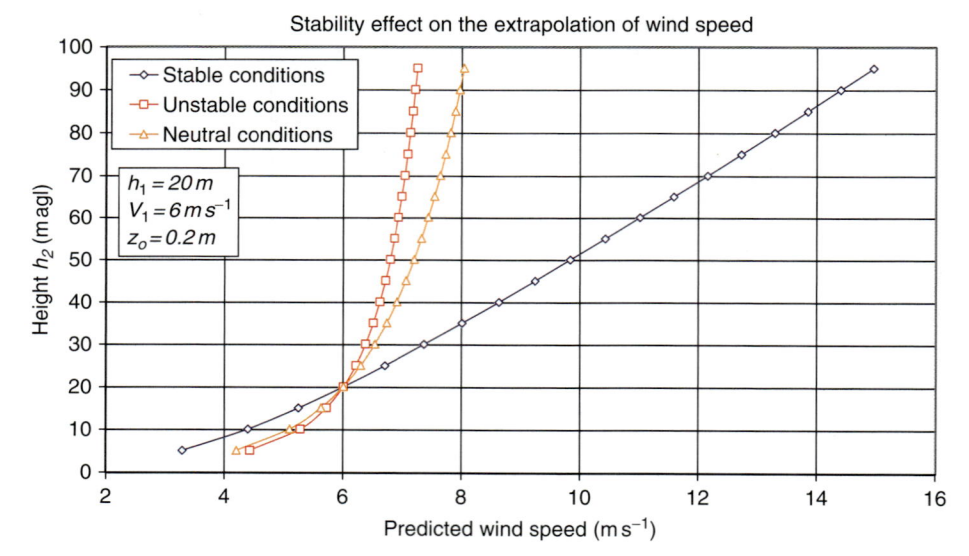

Figure 36 The influence of atmospheric conditions on the extrapolation of wind speeds at a given height.

Table 2 Variation of the Monin–Obukhov length L

Atmospheric conditions	L
Strongly convective days	−10
Windy days with some solar heating	−100
Windy days with little sunshine	−150
No vertical turbulence	0
Purely mechanical turbulence	∞
Nights where temperature stratification slightly dampens mechanical turbulence generation	>0
Nights where temperature stratification severely suppresses mechanical turbulence generation	≫0

and actually corresponds to the rearranged expression of the original log-linear law for neutral atmospheric conditions, that is, $\Psi = 0$. Thus, the log law only depends on the roughness length parameter z_o and is easier to apply, although it presents certain limitations that are synopsized on its application restriction to relatively low heights near the ground and flat terrains to be considered.

3. 'The power law' is expressed as

$$V_{h_2} = V_{h_1} \left(\frac{h_2}{h_1}\right)^a \qquad [60]$$

where a is the friction exponent – or better known as the wind shear coefficient – expected to vary within a range from 0.45 for urban areas to 0.05 for smooth terrains, calculated either on the basis of empirical expressions [55] such as

$$a = \frac{0.37 - 0.088 \cdot \ln(V_{h_1})}{1 - 0.088 \cdot \ln\left(\frac{h_1}{10}\right)} \qquad [61]$$

$$a = \left(\frac{z_o}{h_1}\right)^{0.2} \cdot (1 - 0.55 \log(V_{h1})) \qquad [62]$$

and

$$z_o = 15.25 \cdot \exp\left(\frac{-1}{a}\right) \qquad [63]$$

or by using typical values such as
- $a = 1/7$ over the sea or flat fields
- $a = 1/5$ over flat areas with trees and low buildings
- $a = 1/3$ over city centers with high building structures

Prediction of wind speeds using the power law (see eqn [60]; with the curves of exponents α_1-α_2-α_3 based on eqns [61]–[63], respectively) and the log law (see eqn [59]) are given in **Figure 37**, where one may also obtain the impact of the site roughness length z_o, with values selected corresponding to a flat agricultural area ($z_o = 0.001$ m), a low-density populated area with low

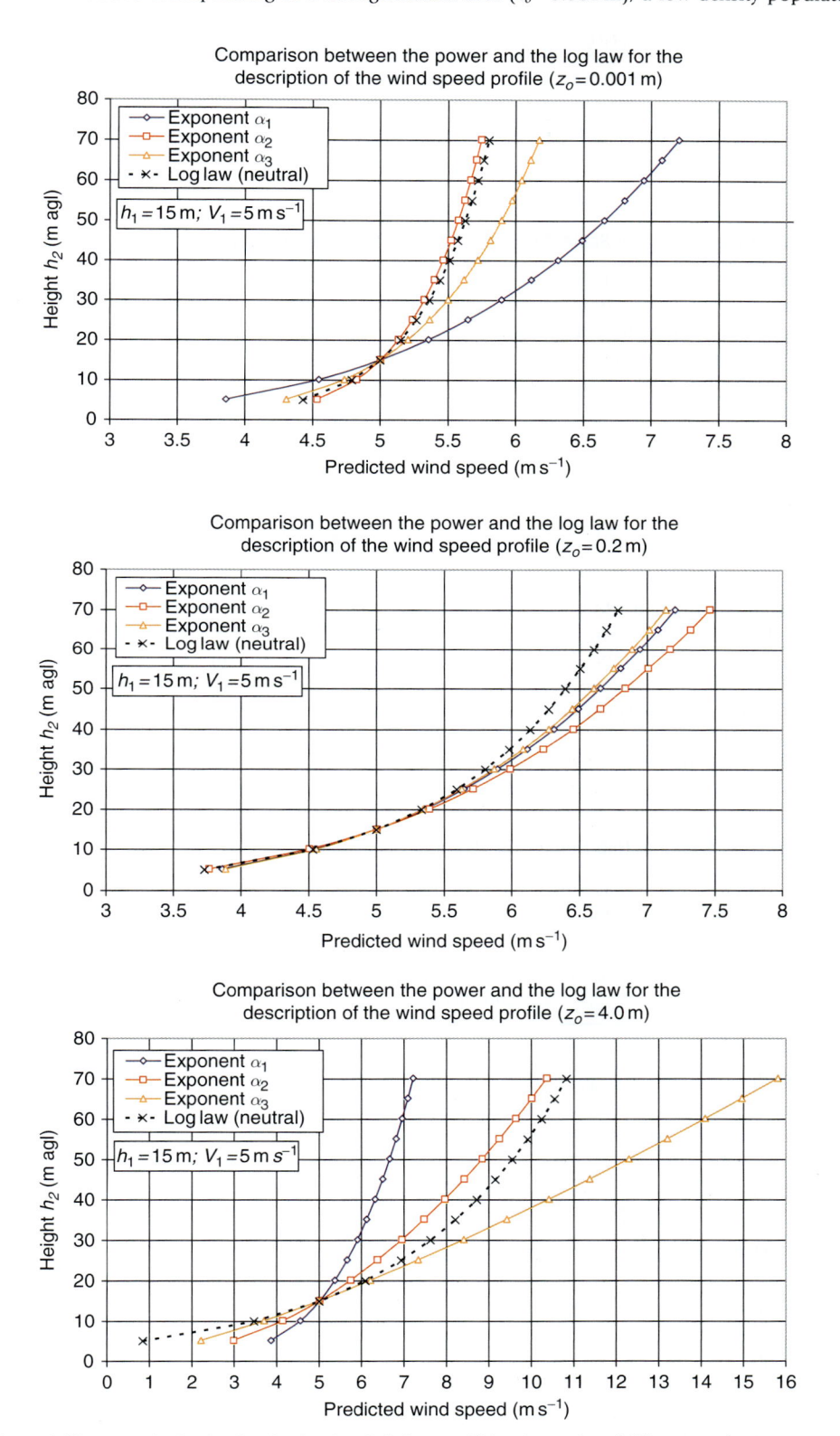

Figure 37 Comparison of different methods of estimation for the wind shear coefficient in terrains of different roughness.

height building structures and trees ($z_o = 0.2$ m), and, finally, a city center with building structures exceeding 10 m height ($z_o = 4.0$ m).

Based on the results obtained, it becomes clear that there is a strong variation of the predicted wind speed among the different expressions of the exponent a, which seems to maximize in the case of a rough terrain (e.g., $z_o = 4.0$ m). On the other hand, results seem more alike in the case of medium z_o values, while what should also be noted is that the respective log law appears to produce lower wind speeds apart from the case of considerable surface roughness. Overall, consideration of the z_o parameter is of primary importance when estimating the wind shear coefficient of the power law in detail (see, e.g., the curve of exponent a_1 where z_o is not taken into account), although for rough calculations to be undertaken, typical values given above are recommended.

2.06.5.2 Extrapolation of the Shape and Scale Parameters of Weibull at Hub Height

In the absence of wind speed measurements from a wind mast installed in the area of interest, the scale and shape parameters of Weibull may also be extrapolated at the required hub height in order to provide the respective power coefficient distribution and thus an estimation of the energy production of a given wind turbine. In this regard, one uses the following two empirical relations [56], where k_1 and c_1 refer to the initial values of parameters at base height h_1 and $k_2 - c_2$ refer to the values obtained for the new height h_2, normally being the hub height of the machine.

$$c_2 = c_1 \cdot \left(\frac{h_2}{h_1}\right)^a \quad [64]$$

$$k_2 = k_1 \cdot \left(\frac{1 - 0.088 \ln\left(\frac{h_1}{10}\right)}{1 - 0.088 \ln\left(\frac{h_2}{10}\right)}\right) \quad [65]$$

By applying eqns [64] and [65], in **Figure 38** the Weibull probability density $f(V)$ is plotted against height variation, considering a case of $k_1 = 1.7$ m s^{-1} and $c_1 = 8.0$ m s^{-1}. As one may see, there is considerable variation among the different curves, with an inverse behavior noted in the low and high wind speed areas. More precisely, height increase implies, as expected, reduction of probability density for lower wind speed values but yields an increase in the respective high wind speed region.

Reflection of the probability density variation on the estimation of the mean power coefficient is given in **Figure 39**, where the impact of height increase becomes clear. In fact, due to the remarkable increase of the ω_2 values and the relatively negligible reduction of the ω_1 component, the total mean power coefficient presents a significant increase, which, in the case of hub height exceeding 50 m, yields values of ω that are greater than 0.45.

2.06.5.3 Estimation of Wind Speed at Hub Height, Upstream of the Machine

Although approximation of wind speed at hub height is usually based on the laws previously analyzed, either by using the measurements recorded at a given mast height or by extrapolating the scale and shape parameters of Weibull, it is normally quite

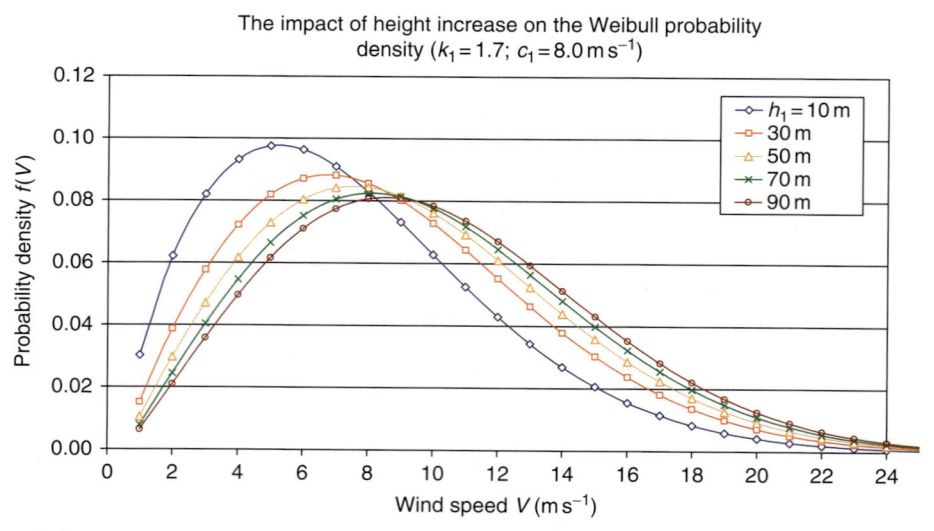

Figure 38 The effect of shape and scale factor variation on the wind speed probability density distribution due to the increase of height.

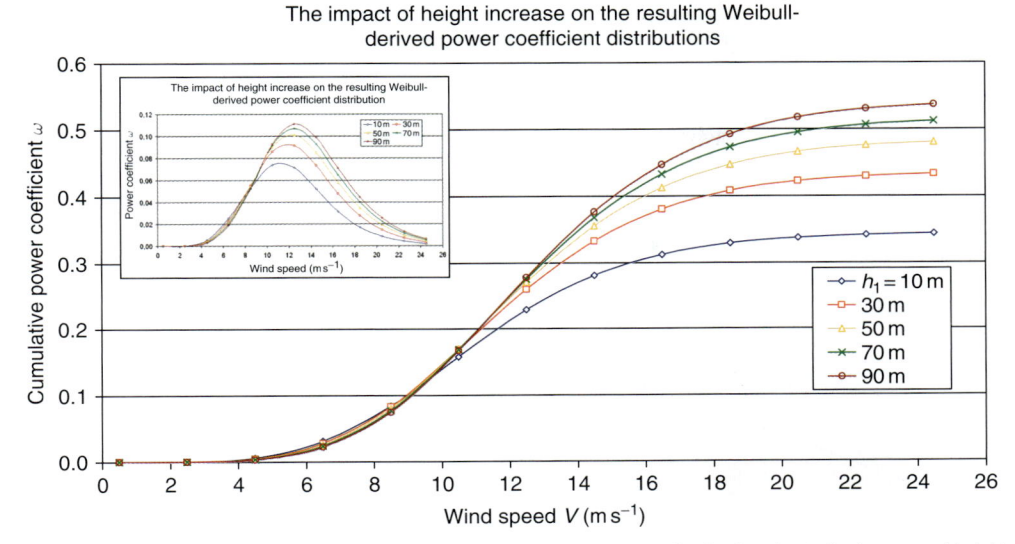

Figure 39 The effect of shape and scale factor variation on the cumulative power coefficient distribution due to the increase of height.

difficult to reliably estimate the wind speed values upstream of the rotor of the wind turbine, that is, the wind speed to be actually exploited by the rotor of the machine.

One should also mention that, normally, anemometers placed upon the nacelle of large-scale contemporary wind turbines measure the downstream flow of wind (apart from exceptional cases where a special structure is added to the side of the rotor) and thus provide an insufficient aspect of the incident – on the rotor – wind flow.

As a result, in order for measurements recorded from wind masts to produce accurate wind speeds upstream of the wind turbine rotor, application of numerical simulation methods is required. More precisely, using commercial CFD software, one may capture both height and terrain effects (due to the different location between the mast and the wind turbine) [46] and model wind speed for each of the different sectors considered.

Using the actual wind speed measurements at the mast level along with the initial results of the model, one may accordingly apply sector-wise correction factors and proceed to the correction of the model in order for more accurate measurements to be produced (**Figure 40**). Using the measurements of nacelle anemometers (downstream of the rotor), model wind speeds at hub height (upstream) may be compared with the respective actual measurements (downstream) and thus through correlation lead to the assessment of the relation between the two [57] (**Figure 41**).

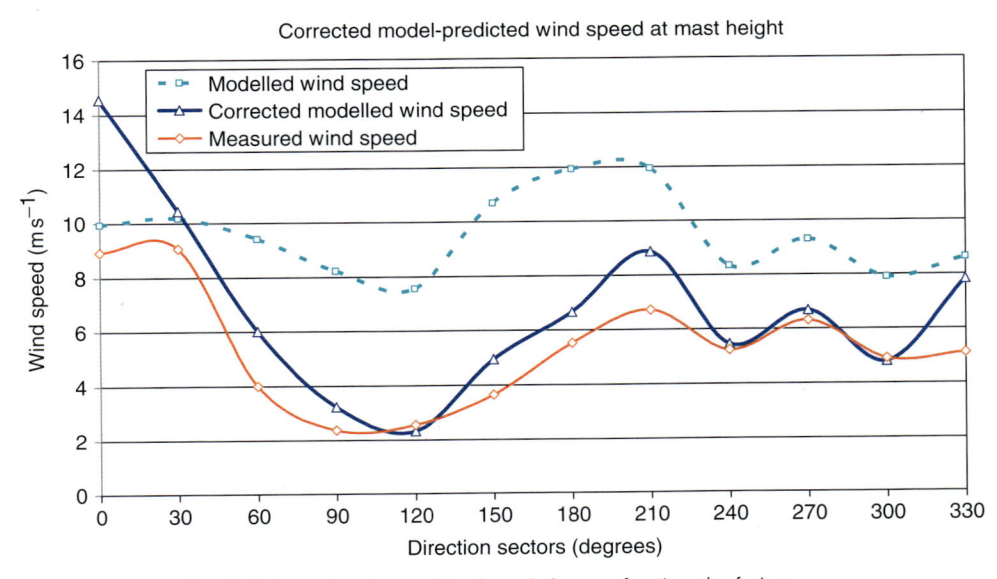

Figure 40 Production of model-predicted wind speeds and correction through the use of sector-wise factors.

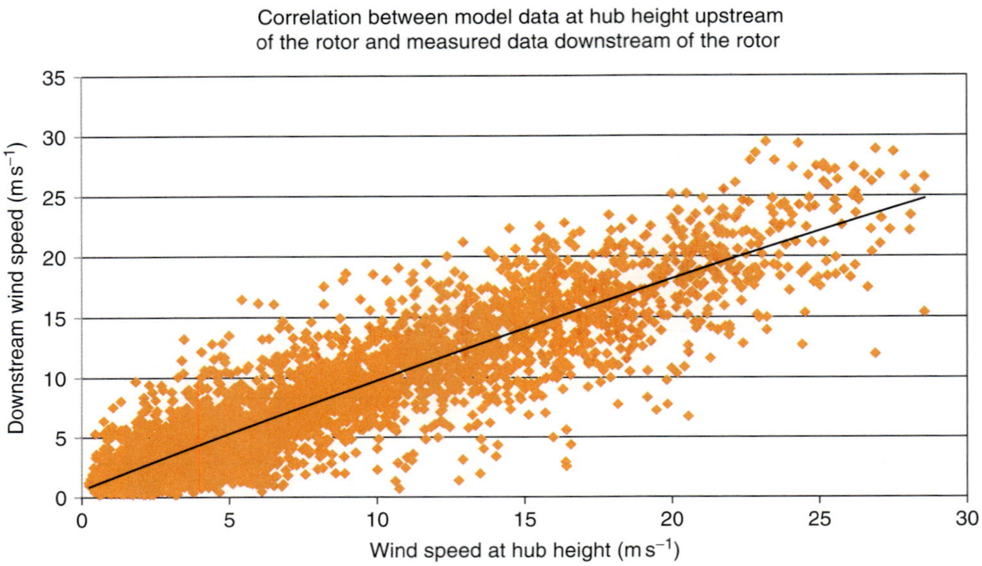

Figure 41 Correlation between wind speed measurements downstream of the rotor and model-predicted wind speed values upstream of the rotor.

2.06.5.4 The Impact of Air Density Variation

Up to now, emphasis has been given to the correct prediction of wind speed values. However, according to long-term measurements, one may state that local environment conditions also have a serious effect on the wind energy production [58–60] since the power output of a wind turbine depends on the air density at the wind park location (see also eqn [4]). For example, an increase of either the air temperature or the height of installation will cause, as a result, a decrease of the air density and vice versa. In fact, by changing the air temperature from 10 °C to 40 °C, one may expect a power decrease that may even reach 20% for stall-control wind turbines [61]. Similarly, in the case of pitch-control machines, there is a remarkable increase of the nominal wind speed value ($\sim$1.5–2.0 m s^{-1}), which accordingly decreases [48] the corresponding energy yield (**Figure 42** concerning height variation).

One may estimate the air density variation impact at the wind park level, first taking into account that the total wind power produced by a wind park of y wind turbines in the course of time t is the sum of the electricity generation of all wind turbines, that is,

$$P_{wp}(t) = \sum_{i=1}^{i=y} P_{ex-i}(t) \qquad [66]$$

with the common method used to simulate the output of a wind park being the use of the central anemometer of the installation [62]. Hence, one may write that

$$P_{wp}(t) = {}^sP_{wp}(t) \cdot \delta(t) \qquad [67]$$

where ${}^sP_{wp}(t)$ is the analytical function describing the power curve of the entire wind park for standard day conditions, expressed as a function of the wind speed at hub height, that is,

$${}^sP_{wp}(t) = {}^sP_{wp}(V(t)) \qquad [68]$$

and $\delta(t)$ is, as already seen, corresponding to the Kronecker's delta function, taking values either equal to unity or zero.

Furthermore, for the calculation of the analytical simulation function ${}^sP_{wp}(t)$, one may use the available large number of measurements concerning the wind power output of the wind park (see, e.g., **Figure 43**), concerning a 10 MW wind park located in East Crete (Greece). Note that, as already mentioned in the previous paragraphs, since wind speed values normally correspond to measurements from the central mast of a wind park, one cannot use these velocity values and the power curve provided by the manufacturer of each wind turbine to reproduce the simulation function ${}^sP_{wp}(t)$. In fact, there is an almost 15% discrepancy between the results given by the direct application of the manufacturers' power curves [48] using the existing wind speed data and the real power output of the wind park.

The above calculations of the wind energy production are based on the mean value of the air density during the investigating period, while the resulting power curve is finally normalized for standard day conditions, that is, air density equal to 1.2215 kg m^{-3}. As a result, in order to investigate the effect of the local air conditions, the calculations should be repeated with a correction factor $f(t)$, which takes into account the time fluctuations ρ' of the air density in comparison with the time average value $\bar{\rho}$ during the operation of the wind park, thus

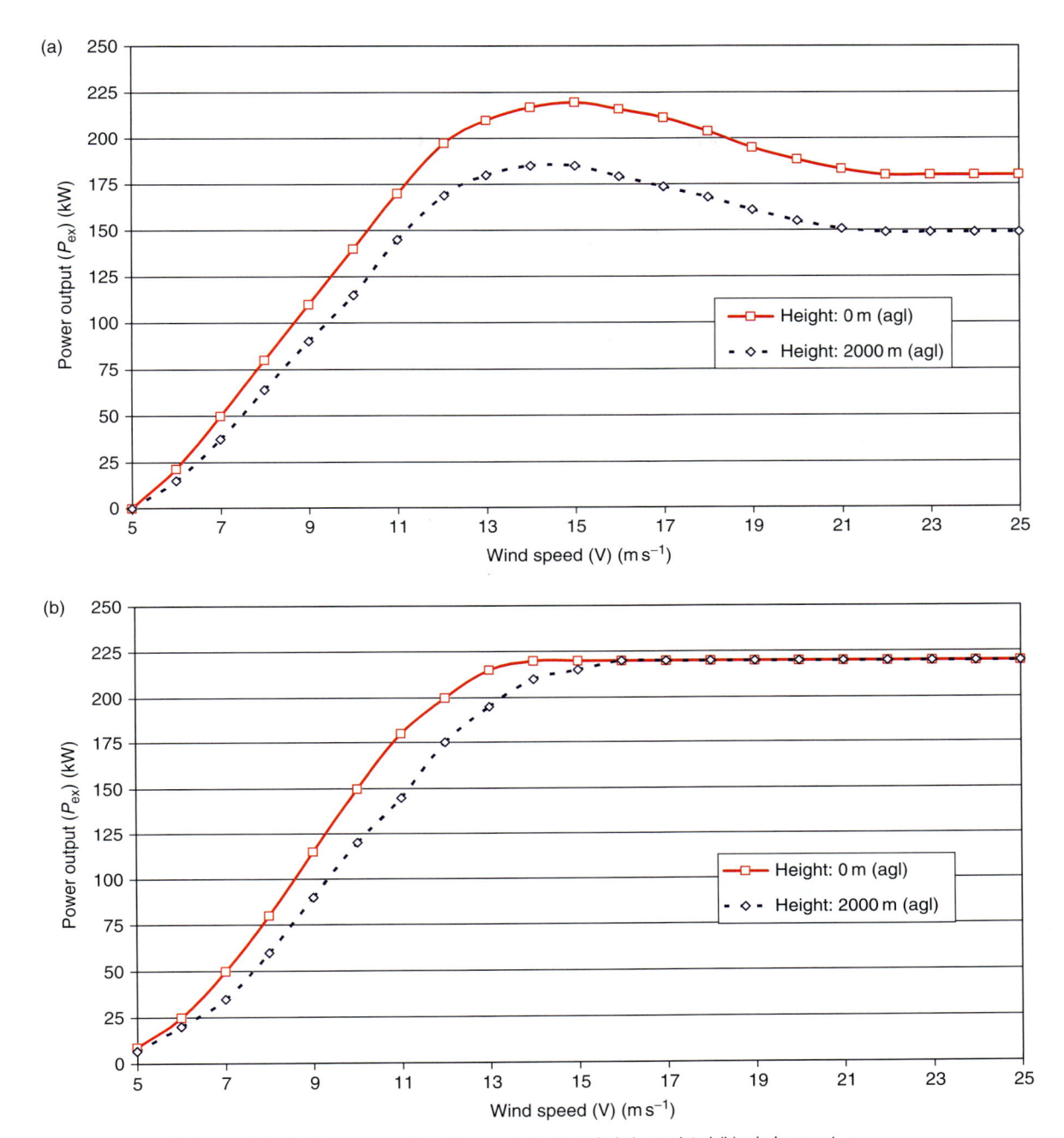

Figure 42 Influence of height variation in the power output of typical stall- (a) and pitch-regulated (b) wind generators.

$$f(t) = \frac{\rho(t)}{\bar{\rho}} = 1 + \frac{\rho'}{\bar{\rho}} \quad [69]$$

where $\rho(t)$ is the instantaneous air density at the wind park's location. The corresponding air density values $\rho(t)$ result from measurements of local temperature θ (in degrees Celsius), ambient pressure P_{atm} (in pascals), and air relative humidity w (**Figure 44**). Thus, one may write

$$\rho(t) = \frac{P_{atm}(t)}{287 \cdot (273 + \theta(t))}(1 + w(t)) \quad [70]$$

with the estimation of the wind energy production using the correction factor $f(t)$ given by eqn [71] as

$$P_{wp}(t) = {}^s P_{wp}(t) \cdot f(t) \cdot \delta(t) \quad [71]$$

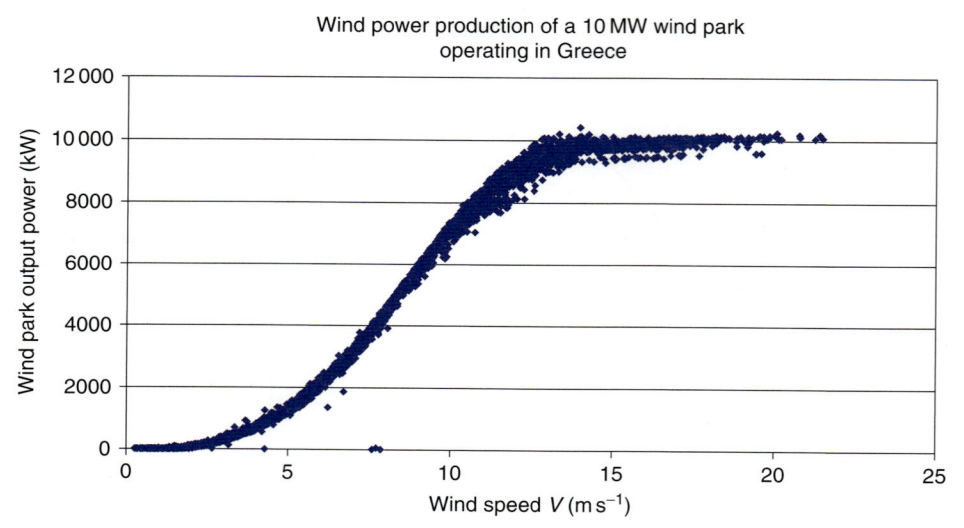

148 Energy Yield of Contemporary Wind Turbines

Figure 43 Wind power output of a 10 MW wind park located in Central Greece.

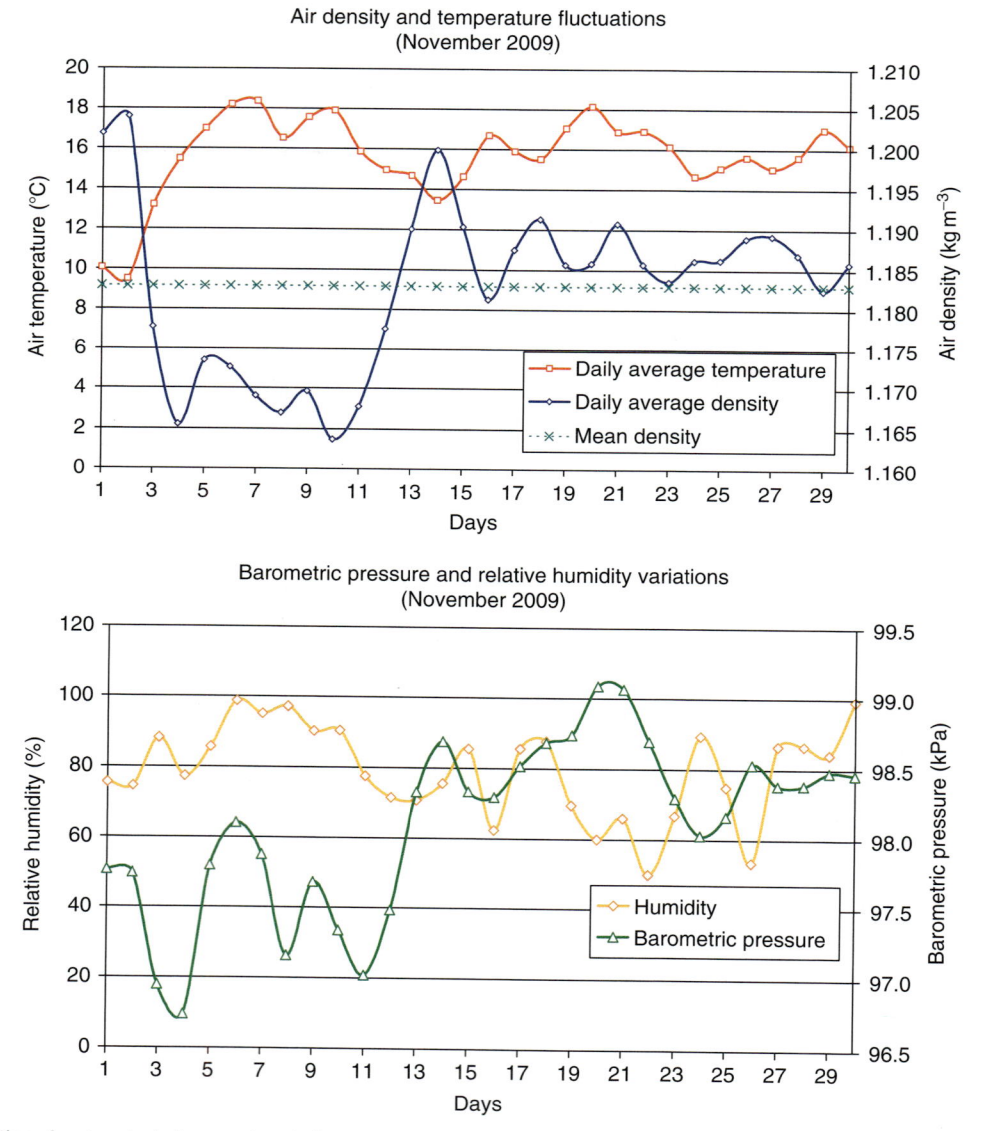

Figure 44 Variation of meteorological parameters during a month period (data extracted from a wind park operating in Central Greece).

Using the set of equations following (eqns [72]–[75]), one may also proceed to the estimation of the instantaneous wind power output, based on the use of the manufacturer wind turbine power curve for standard day conditions, and thus allow for the estimation of the corrected energy yield for a given time period. The instantaneous power output $P_{ex\text{-}cor}$ is given by eqn [72],

$$P_{ex-cor} = \frac{\rho}{1.2215} \cdot P_{ex}(V) \qquad [72]$$

where $P_{ex}(V)$ is the manufacturer standard day power output.

Furthermore, if letting ε be the total error regarding the air density prediction and C_ρ be the corresponding relative density error, then we get that

$$C_\rho = \frac{\sqrt{\varepsilon^2}}{\bar{\rho}} \qquad [73]$$

As a result, the corresponding wind turbine power relative error C_P [63] is given as

$$C_P = C_\rho \qquad [74]$$

while by applying the error transfer analysis on eqn [71] we have that

$$C_\rho^2 = C_{P_{atm}}^2 + C_{(1+w)}^2 + \left[\frac{[\text{aver}(P_{atm} \cdot (1+w))]^2}{[\text{aver}(P_{atm})]^2 \cdot [\text{aver}(1+w)]^2} \right] \cdot C_{(273+\theta)}^2 \qquad [75]$$

Using the above-described theoretical model, one may clearly state that the relative error on the wind turbine output power prediction is practically the sum of the corresponding relative error on ambient pressure, ambient temperature, and relative air humidity values. Bear in mind that even in the case that these errors take relatively small numerical values, the energy production of an installation over a given time period is influenced by the numerical integral of the instantaneous values. Hence, the larger the time interval where the average density value is taken, the bigger the numerical error induced.

2.06.5.5 The Impact of the Wake Effect

The term 'wake effect' is used to describe the phenomenon according to which the reduction of wind speed downstream of a wind turbine (along with high turbulence levels caused) leads to the reduction of the energy yield ideally captured by second or $-n$ row wind turbines downstream of the corresponding first-row (upstream) machines. Depending on the distance between wind turbines, as well as on the arrangement (siting) of machines within the area of the wind park, energy losses from the wake effect may even exceed 20% [64–66], with the first downstream machines shouldering the greatest burden of energy production reduction, since the wake effect is considered to gradually fade out. For the wake effect to be avoided, the minimum distance condition, that is, the minimum distance between wind turbines, in order for the air flow to recover its free stream characteristics should not be violated. Engineering models used for the study of the wake effect are, according to Reference [67], divided into surface roughness models, semi-empirical models, eddy viscosity models, and full Navier–Stokes solutions. More precisely, surface roughness models are based on data obtained from wind tunnel tests, considering a change in surface roughness that results in a modified velocity profile, and are usually applied in areas of flat terrain [68]. Furthermore, semi-empirical models based on the use of empirical constants and on the conservation of momentum have proved rather practical in the estimation of energy losses deriving from the wake effect [69, 70]. Eddy viscosity models [71] use simplified Navier–Stokes equations and are thought to provide accurate wind speed profiles in the wake region, while, finally, for the solution of complete Navier–Stokes, one may also use $k-\varepsilon$ models [72].

To demonstrate the results of the wake effect in the energy production of downstream wind turbines, application of a semi-empirical model [69, 73] is undertaken [67]. More precisely, quantification of the wake effect may be accomplished via the application of the following equation:

$$V_{down} = V_{up} \cdot \left[1 - \left(1 - \sqrt{1 - C_T}\right) \cdot \left(\frac{D}{D + 2k_w \cdot \Delta x}\right)^2 \right] \qquad [76]$$

where V_{down} is the wind speed downstream of the wind turbine, V_{up} is the respective speed upstream of the rotor, D is the rotor diameter, k_w is the wake decay constant used to describe the wake diameter rate of increase [69], and C_T is the coefficient of thrust given as

$$C_T = \frac{8T}{\pi \cdot \rho \cdot D^2 \cdot V_{up}^2} \qquad [77]$$

By applying the above-described semi-empirical model, the magnitude of wake effect as a function of distance Δx – from the initial upstream wind speed profile – for three different values of the upstream wind speed V_{up}, is given in **Figure 45**. As expected, by increasing the ratio of $\Delta x/D$, the initial state of wind velocity gradually recovers, with full recovery of initial conditions achieved after Δx exceeds $10D$.

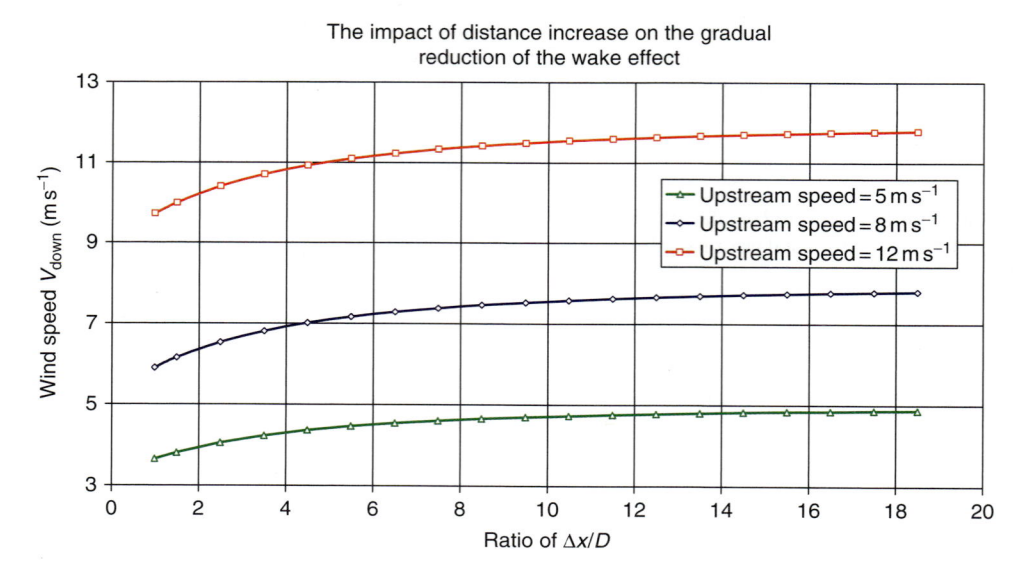

Figure 45 Recovery of wind speed of a first-row wind turbine in relation to the downstream distance ratio $\Delta x/D$.

Furthermore, in **Figure 46**, one may obtain the impact of the upstream wind speed on the magnitude of the wake effect for four different distance ratios, that is, $\Delta x/D = 1, 3, 5$, and 10, as these apply to a first-row pitch-control wind turbine. As one may see, there is a severe reduction of wind speed in the transitional ascending segment of the wind power curve, maximizing in the region of rated power speed (a reduction of over $2.0\,\mathrm{m\,s^{-1}}$ is recorded), which gradually reduces the rated power segment and minimizes for the highest of the wind velocities. Note that minimization of the wake effect for wind speeds that are higher than the rated power wind speed V_R is attributed to the considerable reduction of C_p as the wind speed increases, in order for the wind turbine to maintain a steady power output in the nominal power region (**Figure 3**).

Turbine type, meaning the wind power curve to be considered, is also of importance when estimating the wake effect, with results of comparison between two wind turbines (i.e., a pitch-controlled and a stall-regulated one) of equivalent rotor diameters D and identical C_{pmax} given in **Figure 47**. Based on the results obtained, influence of the C_p distribution previously designated is validated, with the stall concept entailing a less considerable reduction of downstream wind speeds, which becomes apparent in the area above $16\,\mathrm{m\,s^{-1}}$.

Finally, the impact of the wake effect for a given turbine operating downstream of an identical first-row machine is given in **Figure 48**. More specifically, by calculating the wind velocity downstream of the turbine, the probability distribution of the local wind potential is modified accordingly, and thus so does the distribution of the mean power coefficient. As a result, the undisturbed

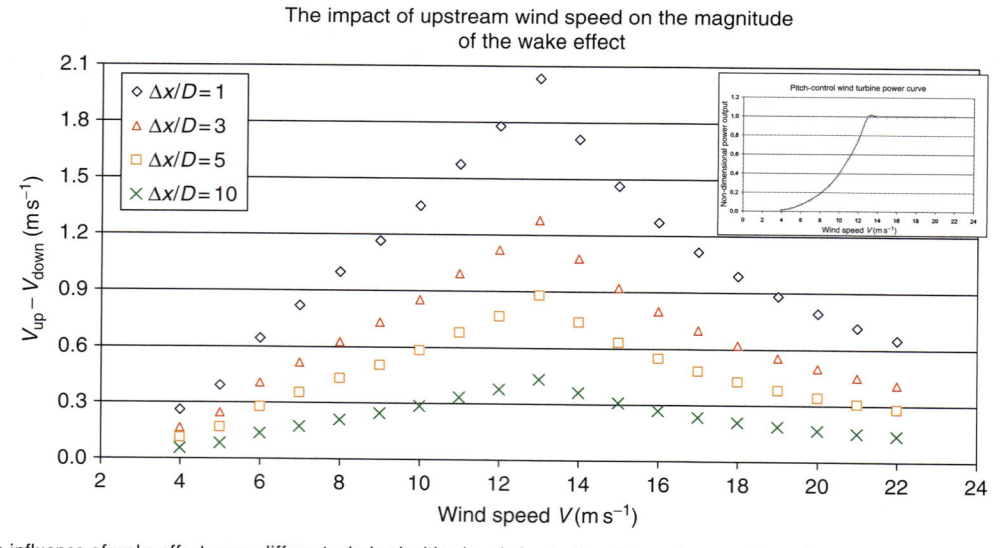

Figure 46 The influence of wake effect upon different wind velocities in relation to the distance increase from the upstream wind speed profile.

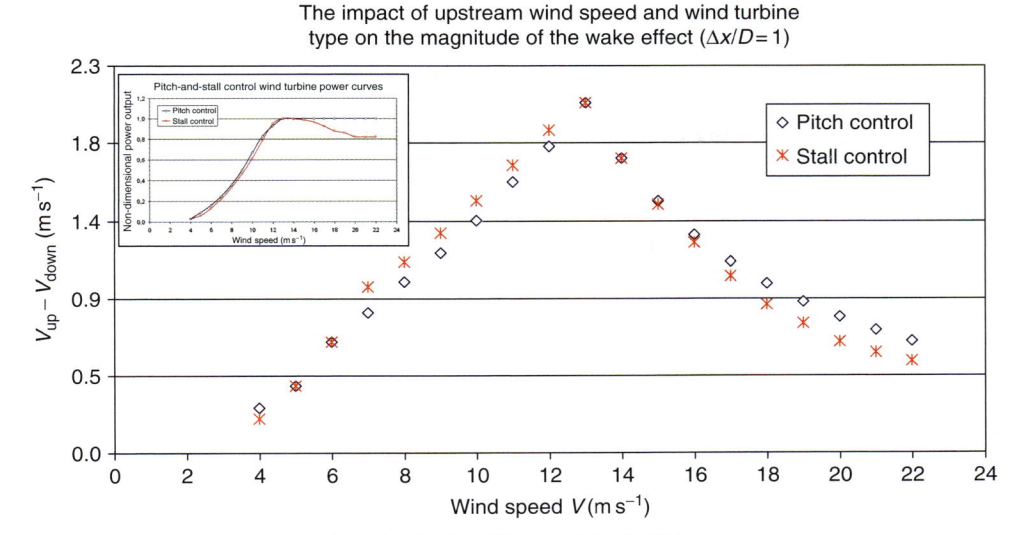

Figure 47 The influence of wind power curve upon the wake effect for different wind velocities.

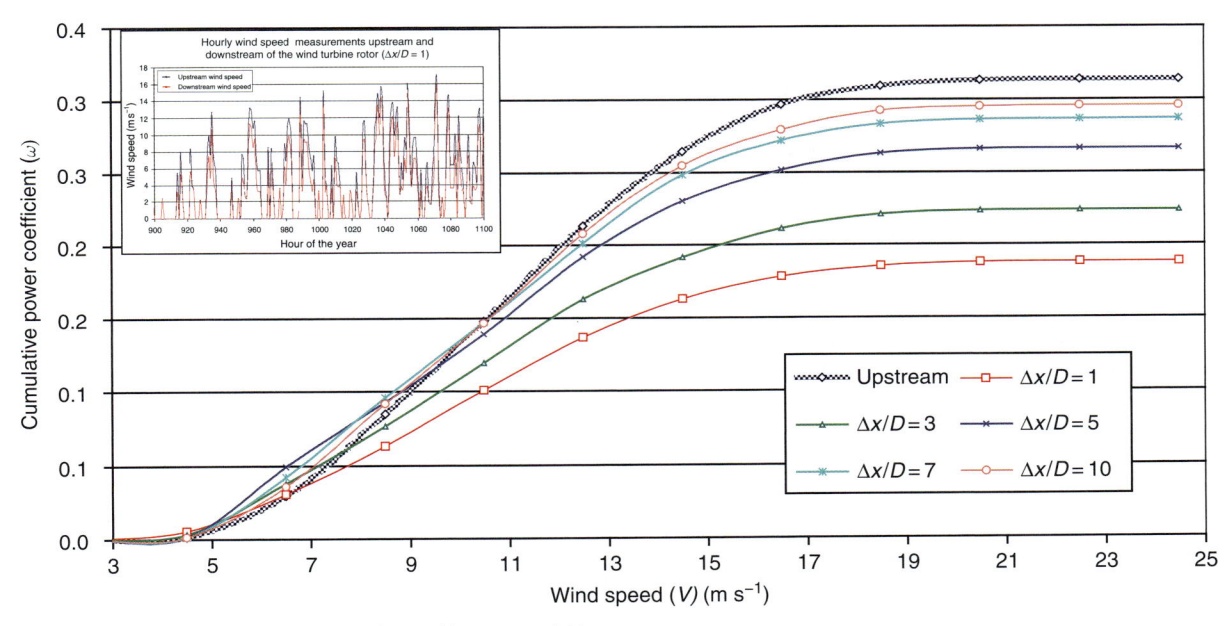

Figure 48 The impact of the wake effect on the resulting energy yield.

upstream wind velocity profile produces an annual power coefficient $\omega_{up} = 0.31$, which reduces to a respective $\omega_{down(\Delta x/D=1)} = 0.19$ for the downstream energy production at a distance of $\Delta x = D$. However, as expected, by gradually increasing the distance between the downstream and the first-row wind turbine, recovery of the original wind speed profile allows for the approximation of ω_{up} when the $\Delta x/D$ ratio becomes equal to 10. What is interesting to note is that due to the wake effect, the probability density of low wind speeds increases and, thus, in the case of $\Delta x/D$ exceeding 3, one may record an increase of the power coefficient against that of the upstream flow in the low wind speed region.

2.06.6 The Impact of Technical Availability on Wind Turbine Energy Output

Among the most influential factors configuring energy production of wind turbines is reliability or technical availability of the machine in general and of the various subcomponents in particular. A description of the main causes of operation interruption or failure is undertaken, and the impact of unavailability on a wind turbine's energy yield is discussed. Finally, statistical data concerning technical availability of contemporary wind turbines are also provided.

2.06.6.1 Causes of Technical Unavailability

The term 'technical availability' or 'reliability' is used to express the ability of a given wind turbine or a wind park to operate safely (reliably) from a technical point of view. Note also that although technical availability is not directly relevant to the local wind potential of the installation area, strong winds appearing increase the possibility of faults and malfunctions and also hinder immediate repair (Section 2.06.2.7). On the other hand, one should acknowledge the fact that wind turbines are machines operating constantly (sometimes for several days without interruption) often in very unfavorable weather and site conditions [74, 75], while their operation is hard to regulate since it is strongly dependent on uncontrolled parameters such as wind speed, ambient conditions, and grid status.

At this point, it is important to note that a wind turbine's reliability greatly depends on the design and construction of the model under consideration, as well as on its material quality and class. The turbine's reliability also varies with the operating environment, stressing the need for careful selection of the appropriate turbine model for each specific location. A wind turbine is not considered to be technically available [76–78] (i.e., downtime periods) in the case of the following:

o Scheduled/regular maintenance
o Electrical grid problems
o Service problems
o Wrong/false failure announcement
o Component–material failure
o Extreme weather conditions
o Corrosion problems
o *Force majeure* problems
o Various other problems.

Facing the specific problems (e.g., grid problems, normal service activities, false failure announcements), although not requiring additional expenses, does – in most cases – imply an increase of the maintenance and operation cost [79]. On top of that, during the time that the wind turbine is out of operation, analogous wind energy production losses may be encountered – mainly dependent on the available wind potential during the specific time period – that, as expected, imply income losses to be considered [80].

Scheduled/regular maintenance of a wind park, including normal service activities, depending on the schedule provided by the manufacturer, is executed between 2 and 4 times per year. Moreover, scheduled/regular maintenance is normally combined with the repair of any appearing damage, lasts for a given time period (5–20 h) depending on the severity of the scheduled maintenance task, and is executed by a service crew of at least two engineers. To moderate wind energy production losses of the installation, it is preferable for the maintenance tasks to be executed during calm spell periods, while the opposite is valid for the windy periods of the year, that is, when any maintenance tasks should be avoided in order to protect the maintenance crew from the risk of accident.

Furthermore, problems met in local electricity grids are also one of the main downtime causes, especially for isolated island networks [81–84]. The most common problems include considerable voltage variation (voltage sags and swells), phase asymmetry due to faults appearing either in the operation of network transformers or in the operation of wind turbines' compensation capacitors, phase discrepancy (normally following the network restoration), frequency deviations, as well as complete collapse of the local system (blackout). In the majority of the above-mentioned cases, the arising malfunctions are automatically repaired within a few minutes' time (10 min up to 1 h), while, during certain times, intervention of the machine operator through the use of a remote control system is necessary. To avoid similar problems during the past, the increase of wind turbine tolerance limits to analogous fluctuations was attempted, involving, however, increased risk of seriously damaging the machine equipment. As already mentioned, the specific problems become more severe in small island networks where the fluctuations of operational parameters are by far greater than those encountered in strong mainland networks, due to both the limited inertia of the thermal power units' operation and the small capacity of the electrical grid.

Another severe problem that is responsible for the restriction of wind turbines' technical availability in island networks, not, however, comprising a fault of either the equipment or the local electrical grid, is the curtailment/rejection of wind energy production due to either low electricity demand encountered [80] or the need to ensure grid stability [81]. More specifically, possible instability of the existing electrical grids and requirement for complete control over the quality of electrical energy provision set some serious obstacles in the dynamic exploitation of wind energy in autonomous electrical networks. For this reason, an upper limit for the instantaneous wind power contribution to the local electricity demand is normally imposed by the operators of such electricity grids (e.g., 30%), which may both lead to insufficient exploitation of the local wind potential by the already existing machines and limit any prospects of further wind energy penetration. Note that it is these curtailments that stand as the main reason for the confined activity concerning the installation of new wind parks in several island areas, with annual wind energy participation in the Aegean area, for example, limited to a maximum of only 10% for only a few islands [85].

Moreover, as far as service problems are concerned, damage or unscheduled interruptions of operation caused by the deficient maintenance of equipment should also be considered. In this category, one may encounter the activation of aerodynamic brakes (due to the marginal adjustment of the respective mechanism) although there is no evidence showing an actual increase of the rotor's speed, the activation of overheating protection sensors, and the overheating of moving shafts/bearings due to deficient lubrication (yaw mechanism, gear box bearings, etc.). The specific problems may be gradually constrained as the maintenance personnel become more experienced and as the technology of the corresponding sensors is improved.

Concerning wrong/false failure announcement faults, representing in many cases the majority of recorded problems for wind turbines during the past, they are usually dealt with through the use of remote control systems, not requiring any considerable cost and not implying a significant reduction of the turbine's energy production time. The cause of these problems may be ascribed to momentary fluctuations of the network parameters, to interruptions among different signals, and to deficient coordination of the turbine's operational parameters, as well as to deficient setup of the controller algorithm (meaning that unforeseen states of operation may appear for the wind turbine). To counter the respective problems, the development of know-how regarding wind turbines, as well as the use of the appropriate components that inhibit the appearance of these mock faults (e.g., cable shields, diode placement, varistors, etc.), is thought to be critical.

Failure of materials and components comprises the most severe factor of unreliability for a wind turbine, while repair of such damage requires considerable time and additional expenses. Equipment failures may include the failure of small parts, and the turbine stops due to certain problems detected in the main components, that is, blades, electrical generator, pitch mechanism, gearbox, yaw system, hydraulics, and so on. In some cases, it is almost certain that one of the pre-mentioned main parts of the turbine should be replaced at least once within the service period of the latter. This considerable cost of replacement is separated from the corresponding fixed maintenance and operation cost and is described [86] by the term of variable maintenance and operation cost. It may in certain cases lead to the abandonment of the turbine, especially if appearing close to the time of the expected service period of the installation. As it is definitely expected, less time is required for repairing the damage in the case that regular personnel are employed, as well as in the case that a stock of the appropriate spare parts is available (in respect of large-scale wind parks) and the area of repair is easily accessed [79].

Such problems become more difficult to solve in isolated areas (e.g., remote islands) or offshore wind parks, due to the fact that arrival of an experienced and trained crew for the damage repair is much affected by the existing weather conditions [75]. For instance, in the area of the Aegean Sea (Greece), appearance of strong winds along with insufficient transport networks between the islands may postpone the repair of any damage, even for a few weeks, hence constraining the energy production ability of the turbine as well. Replacement cost is also affected by weather conditions and size of the wind park. In many cases, mobilization–transition and accommodation expenses for the maintenance crew may even correspond to 50% of the total maintenance cost. Finally, the availability or not of spare parts and the time efficiency of the respective supply chain are also critical for the financial evaluation of each instance of damage.

Extreme weather conditions can affect the reliability of wind turbines in many ways. Some of the common problems encountered include increased levels of moisture due to fog (with the former affecting the electrical and electronic parts of turbines) as well as ice loading [87] and the standstill state for anemometers and wind direction systems, eventually leading to operation disruption. Additionally, both moisture and frost aggravate the operation of blades and other mechanical parts of a wind turbine, often causing increased loads (mainly fatigue) and leading to the acceleration of the equipment's wear. Extreme wind speed phenomena and lightning strikes [88], since classified in the category of 'force majeure' problems, are not currently examined. On the contrary, in the specific type of problems, one may also encounter damage of the electrical and electronic equipment due to the very high temperatures recorded in certain areas of the planet.

Moreover, despite the careful design and the special manufacturing of the equipment, there are always some parts or sections that appear to be more sensitive in the corrosion caused by the marine atmosphere in island environments or in coastal areas and offshore parks [89]. In several cases, minor problems due to corrosion or rust may lead to more accountable problems, like the blockade of the brake system and the electrical revolution reducer, as well as the complete destruction of the corresponding motor.

Reliability problems attributed to 'force majeure' reasons mainly include destruction of equipment due to lightning strikes and extremely strong winds, while one should also consider destruction caused by fires, floods, and considerable disturbances of the local electricity network. Note, for example, that in the Greek territory, lightning is recorded as one of the most severe problems, limiting the technical availability of the existing wind turbines. More specifically, lightning strikes may – according to the best-case scenario – lead to the temporary interruption of the wind turbine operation. In more severe cases, destruction of certain electrical and electronic system parts (mainly the controller's parts) as well as complete destruction of the rotor or even of the entire wind turbine have also been encountered. Although contemporary systems of lightning protection ensure the equipment's protection with high levels of reliability, they cannot ensure absolute protection from the most intense of natural phenomena. Similarly, the extremely strong winds considerably aggravate the strength of a wind turbine's various sections, while, in cases of gusty winds, destruction of both single turbines and entire wind parks has also been reported in several areas.

Finally, in the 'various unclassified problems' one may include damages and problems caused by wrong handling and operation of machinery and control systems by the personnel, as well as by destruction of cables and equipment parts caused by animals or third parties.

Recapitulating, it becomes clear that a series of problems may appear in a wind park operating in an isolated, mountainous, or coastal area, thus leading to both the inhibition of fair wind energy generation and the imposition of a high replacement and reestablishment of safe operation cost.

2.06.6.2 Estimating Technical Availability

The annual (8760 h) energy yield of a wind park of z wind turbines of rated power P_R is usually expressed as

$$E_{wp} = \text{CF} \cdot (z \cdot P_R) \cdot 8760 \quad [78]$$

where CF is the installation annual capacity factor given as the product of the mean power coefficient ω and the technical availability Δ of the installation (see also eqn [50]). As a result, the critical role of mean technical availability over a period of time for the energy production of a given wind turbine or an entire wind park is noted. The technical availability of a wind turbine depends, among other things, on the technological status, the age, and the location of the machine [79, 90]. Thus, one may use the following expression:

$$\Delta(t) = \Delta_o(t_o) \cdot \frac{\Delta_n}{\Delta_o}(\tau) \cdot \Delta_w \cdot \Delta_G \qquad [79]$$

where Δ_o describes the technological status of a newly installed wind turbine at the time t_o that the machine is installed. One should note that in the early 1980s, the technical availability of the first wind parks was approximately 60%, while at the beginning of the next decade, the value of Δ was greater than 90%. Improvement of technical availability in the course of time may be clearly demonstrated in **Figure 49** [91], where reduction of the failure rate of wind turbines in the course of time may be seen (in the order of 10 failures per year at the end of the 1980s to approximately 0.2 failures per year in 2004). As a result, wind energy technology has nowadays achieved such a level of quality that contemporary wind turbines may even be determined by a technical availability of 99%.

The next term Δ_w takes into consideration the accessibility difficulties of the wind park under investigation. This parameter is of special interest for remote areas and offshore wind parks, especially during winter, due to bad weather conditions (high winds and huge waves suspend the uses of ships, thus preventing maintenance and repair of the existing wind turbines). For this purpose, an adapted form of the analysis by Van Bussel [92] may be used in order to simulate the Δ_w parameter of eqn [79] (**Figure 50**).

Subsequently, in small autonomous grids, one should take into account the actual upper limit for wind power penetration, in order to maintain the stability of these weak electrical grids. In similar cases, the period of time Δ_G that wind energy is absorbed by the local grid is strongly decreased [93] as the wind power penetration in the local grids is increased. In **Figure 51**, one may find the maximum annual wind energy contribution in small island electrical systems as a function of the existing wind power penetration. However, detailed cost–benefit analyses and more recent calculations based on stochastic methods state that the actual wind energy contribution without any energy storage devices is quite low and rarely exceeds 10% [82].

Finally, of most relevance to the current analysis is the term $\Delta_n(\tau)/\Delta_o$, which expresses the technical availability changes during a wind turbine's operational life τ. At this point, it is important to mention that there are several 'failure pattern distributions', that is, from the well-known 'bathtub curve' (**Figure 52**) and the 'slow aging' one, up to the 'traditional view'.

Based on real data evaluations [94], it can be assumed that most wind turbine's reliability is characterized by early failures until the third operational year. This phase is generally followed by a longer period (~10 years) of 'random failures' before the failure rate through wear and damage accumulation, 'wear-out failures', increases with operational age. In order to simulate the $\Delta_n(\tau)/\Delta_o$ distribution, the function $d = d(\tau,z)$ is introduced. Thus, eqn [79] may be equally well written as:

$$\Delta(t) = \Delta_o(t_o) \cdot \Delta_w \cdot \Delta_G \cdot [1 - d(\tau,z)] \qquad [80]$$

where $d = d(\tau,z)$ is related to /the wind turbine failure rate FR (**Figures 49** and **52**) via the following relation:

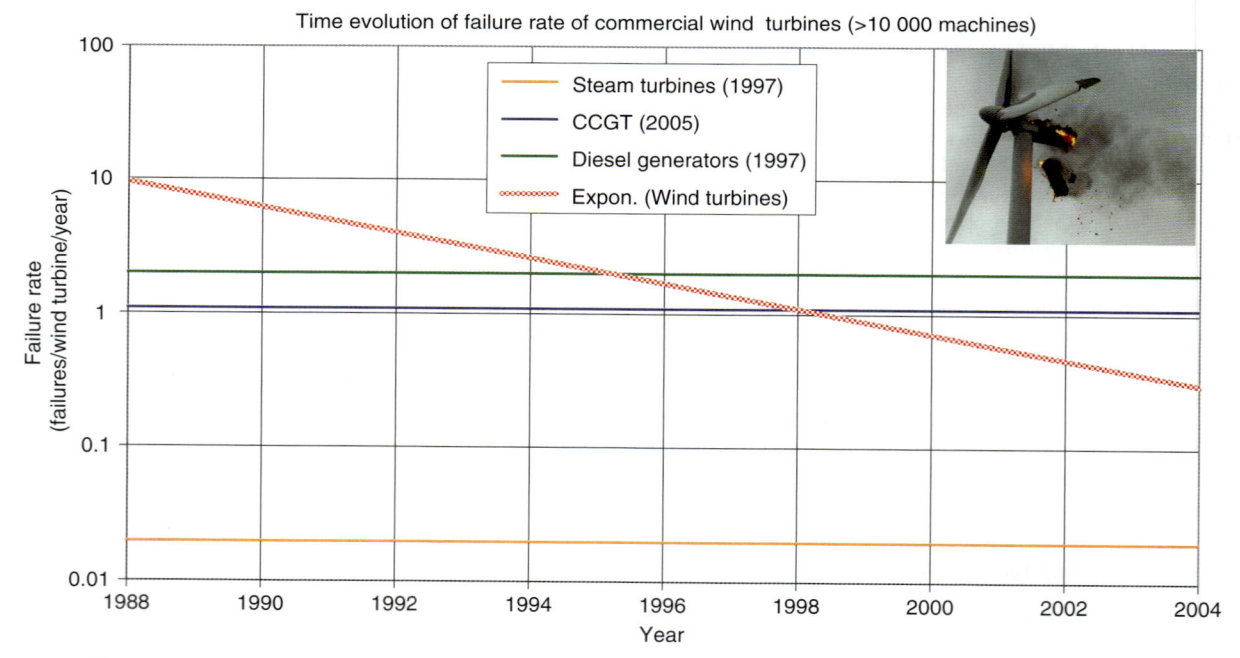

Figure 49 Time evolution of wind turbine failure rate.

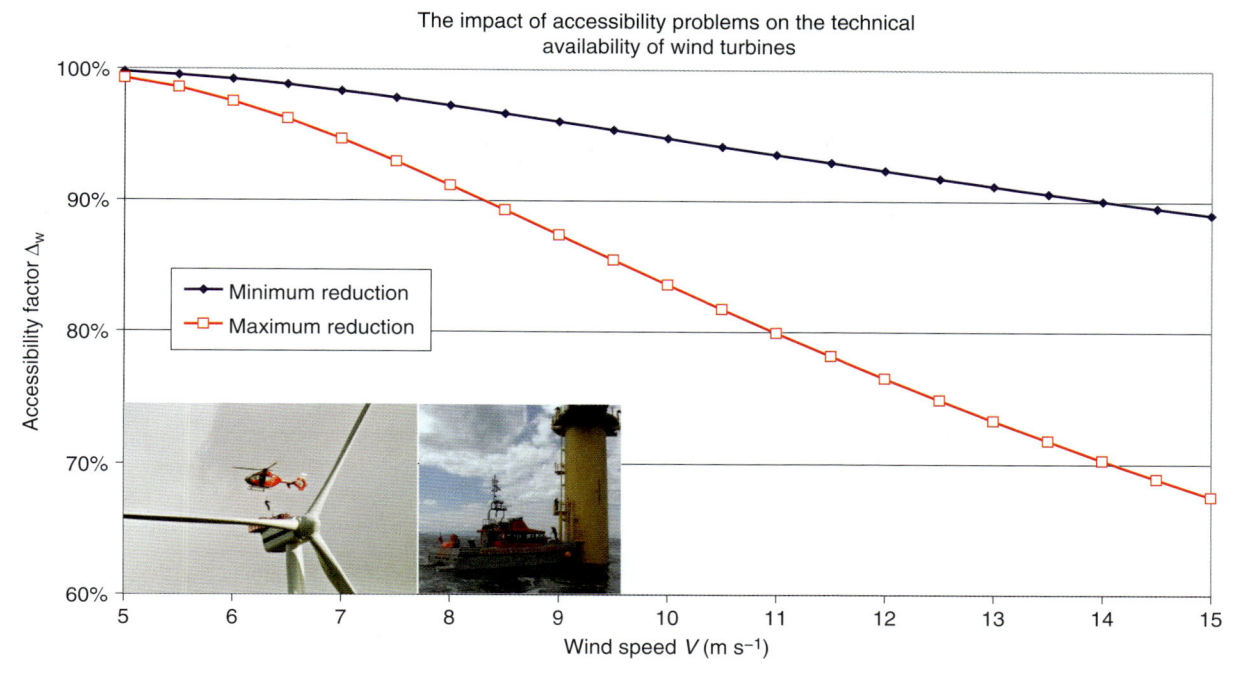

Figure 50 The impact of weather conditions on wind farm accessibility.

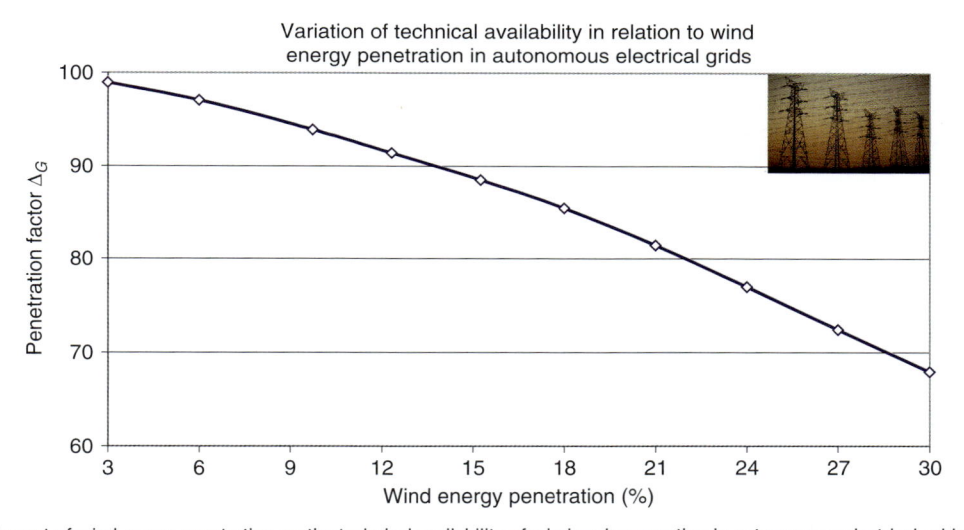

Figure 51 The impact of wind power penetration on the technical availability of wind parks operating in autonomous electrical grids.

$$d(\tau, z) = e^{-FR \cdot \tau} \quad [81]$$

As to be expected, in the case of large numbers of wind turbines, it is more likely for permanent service staff and for a stock of spare parts to exist. For this reason, the operational time-dependent technical availability diminution $d(\tau,z)$ is lower for large wind parks ($z \approx 100$) than for individual wind converters [94–96] (**Figure 53**).

2.06.6.3 Experience Gained from the Monitoring of Technical Availability

Due to the importance of reliable operation, considerable efforts have been devoted during recent years in respect of operation monitoring and dissemination of the data obtained by wind park operators [97–101]. Based on these databases, evaluation of the various causes of technical unavailability may be better approached using information from the numerous wind farms around the entire globe. Some representative results are presented here in order to provide some indication on the current status of reliability of contemporary wind turbines and also designate the detailed monitoring carried out in certain cases.

156 Energy Yield of Contemporary Wind Turbines

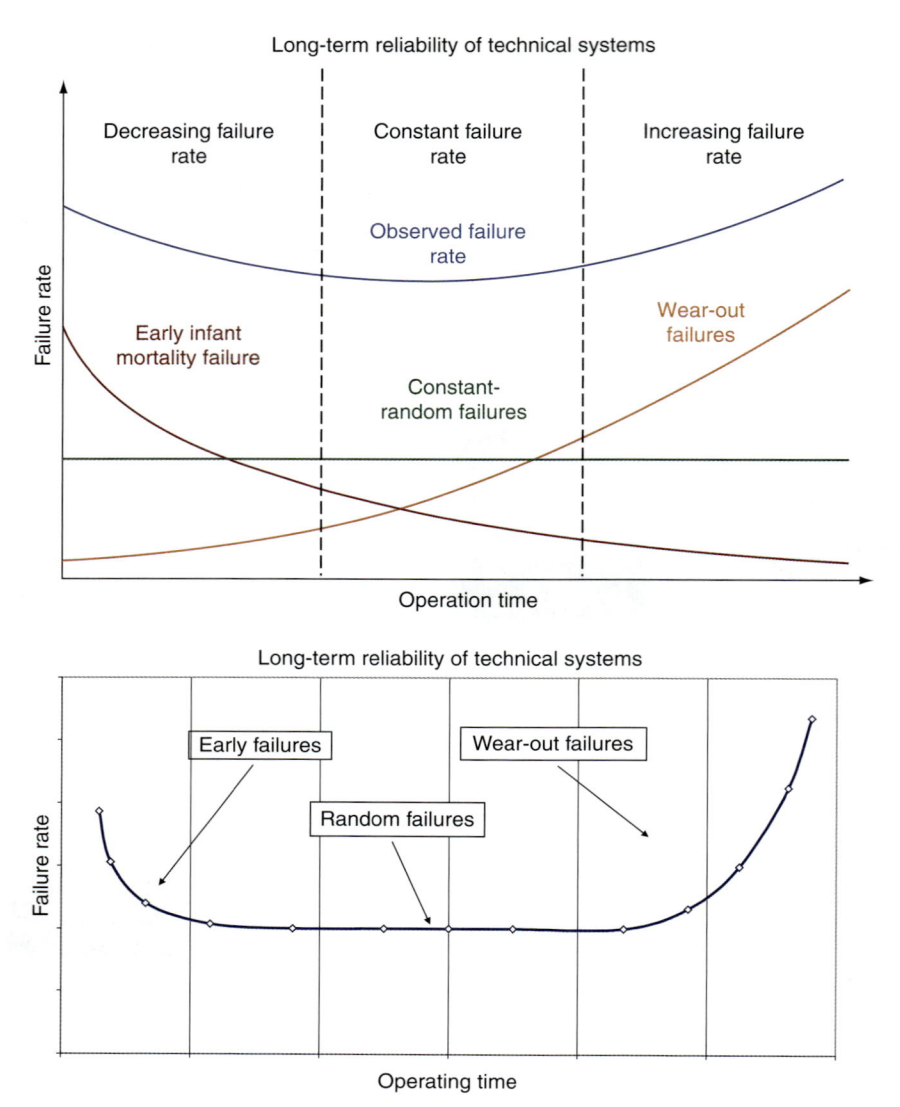

Figure 52 Time evolution of technical systems' reliability under the bathtub curve.

In **Figure 54**, long-term monitoring of 14 GW of wind power, leading to an aggregate of almost 750 wind farm years for approximately 250 wind farms under study, gives a representative distribution of annual technical availability [98]. In fact, based on the results obtained, 50% of the aggregate 750 wind farm years present technical availability values that are higher than 97.5%, while it is only for 6% of the wind farm years that technical availability drops below 90%.

The results obtained from the Finnish and Swedish databases of national wind power monitoring [100, 101] are also similar. More specifically, in **Figure 55(a)**, one may obtain the monthly downtime curves of wind turbines currently in operation in the country of Finland. As one may see, there is a strong decrease in the percentage of operating wind turbines as the downtime hours per month increase, which clearly reflects the ability of local wind machines to operate under minimum interruptions. In fact, it is only 10% of the operating wind turbines that are set out of operation for a considerable time period on a monthly basis (more than 200 h per month or approximately 75% of technical availability), while it is almost 60% that operate at technical availability rates in the order of 98.5%–99%. Furthermore, monitoring of downtime periods for Swedish wind turbines yields similar results with the majority of in-operation machines demonstrating technical availability well above 95% (**Figure 55(b)**).

What is also interesting to present is the scaling impact on the technical availability of both wind turbines and wind farms. Based on the same data of **Figure 49** [91], division of data is attempted in large-scale (MW plus) and small-scale (sub-MW) wind turbines, as well as in large number (more than 40 machines) and small number (less than 40 machines) wind parks, for the first 3 years of operation (**Figure 56**). As one may see from the figure, large-scale machines seem to appear more demanding in terms of maintenance, while, although smaller scale parks appear to present greater reliability in the very early stages of operation, employment of a maintenance crew, normally encountered in the case of large-scale wind parks, considerably increases technical availability in the following years of operation (**Figure 53**).

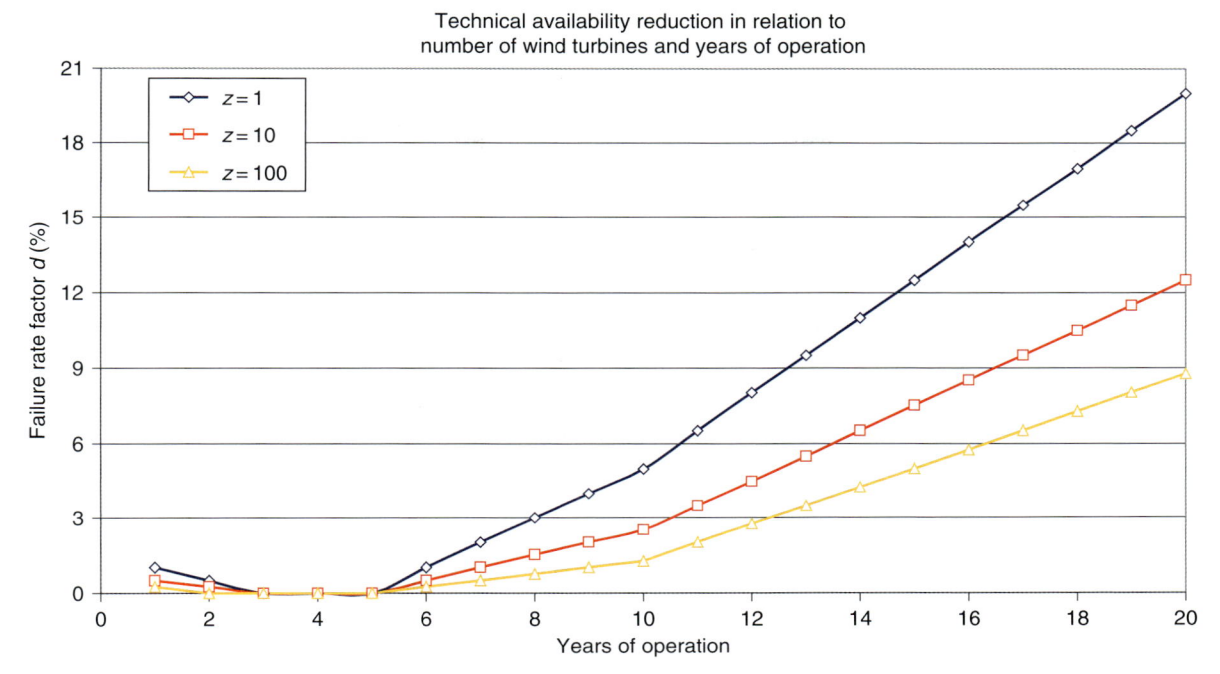

Energy Yield of Contemporary Wind Turbines 157

Figure 53 Variation of failure rate in relation to operation time and number of machines.

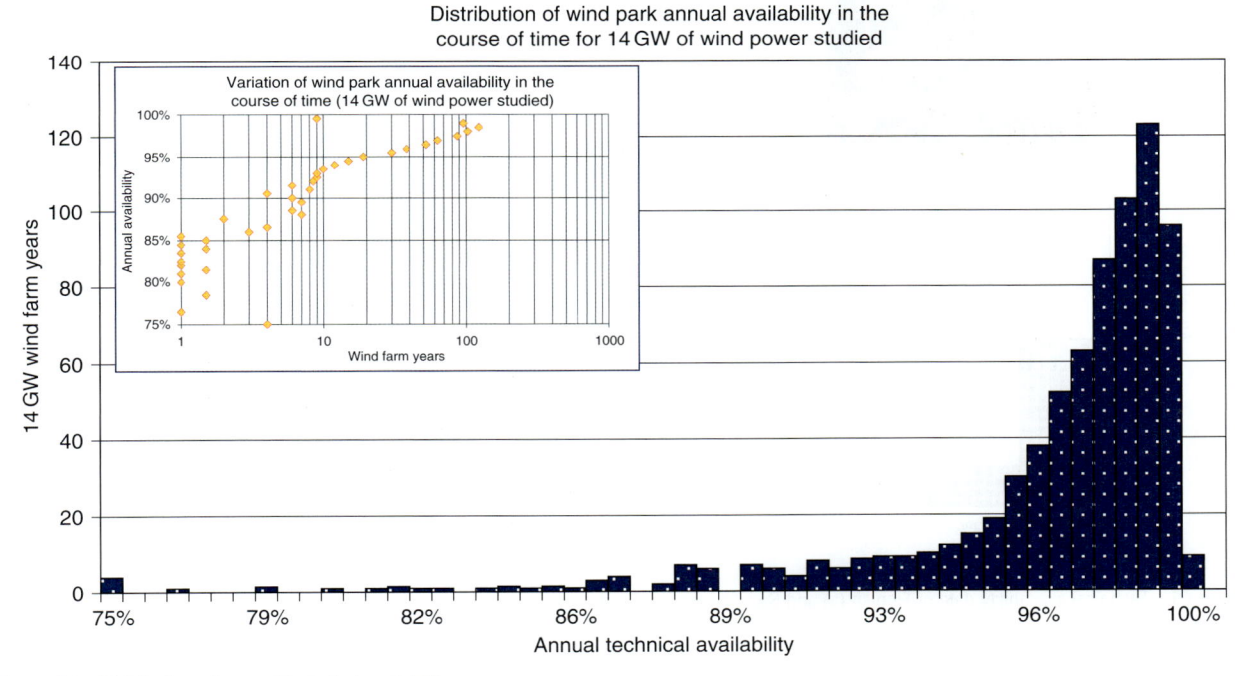

Figure 54 Distribution of annual technical availability.

Finally, one should also note the level of detailed monitoring currently achieved, allowing for the association of technical unavailability causes and effects in considerable depth. For example, in **Figure 57**, one may obtain the downtime hours per machine component and per type of fault for approximately 21 000 wind turbines operating in Germany over the third quarter of 2009. In **Figure 58**, the association of causes and effects is also presented [102, 103]. As one may see, rotor and air brakes, on the one hand, and wear along with failures, on the other hand, comprise the most sensitive components and most frequent causes, respectively, for the given sample (**Figure 57**), while as can be seen from **Figure 58**, service of the rotor component presents the highest downtime hours.

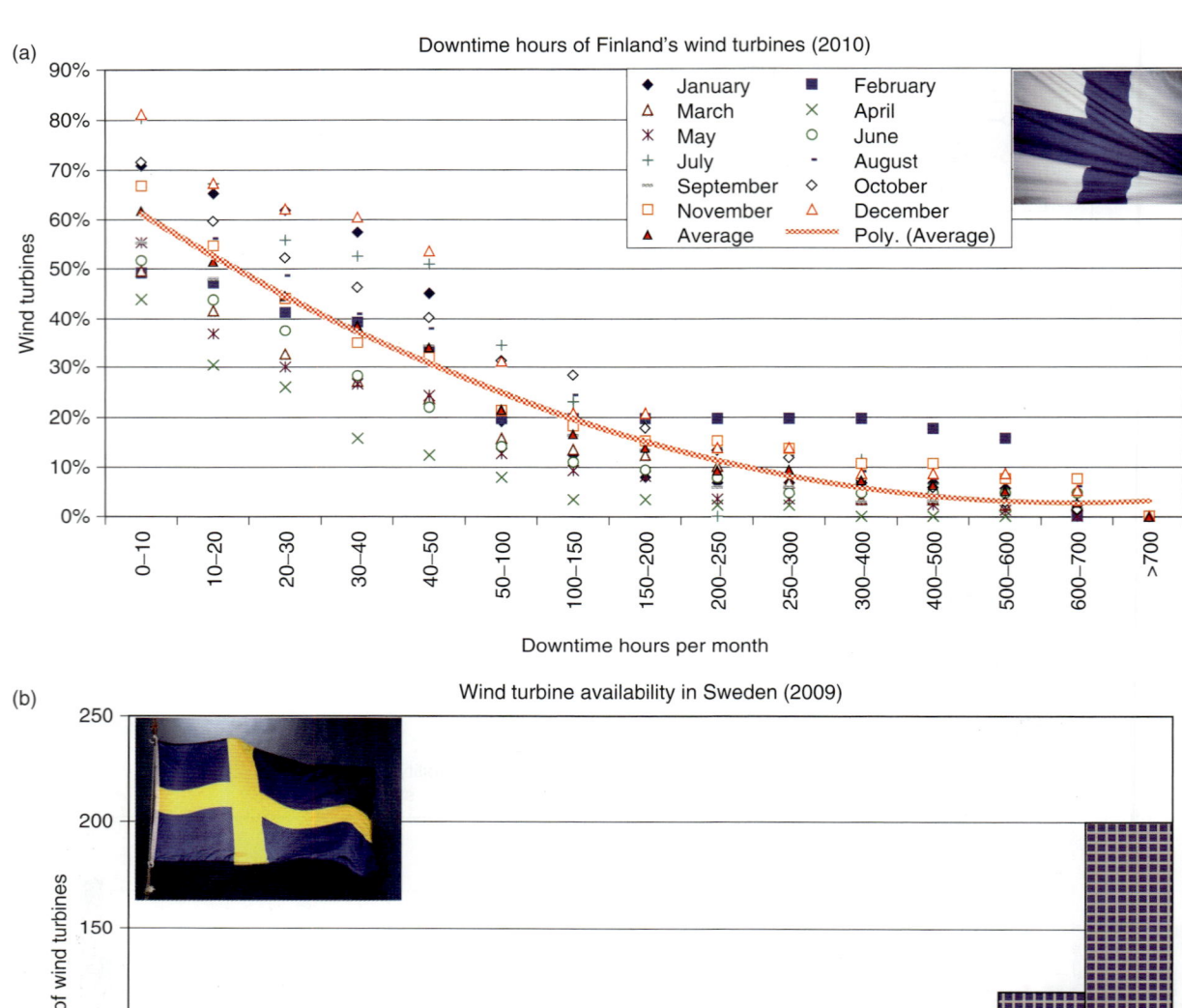

Figure 55 Technical availability data of Finnish (a) and Swedish (b) wind turbines.

Acknowledging the progress encountered in the area of monitoring, detection of the most sensitive components and the most frequent causes of failure, in association with the characteristics of the installation area and the features of the machine investigated, is believed to further evolve the efforts toward the maximization of technical availability and the increase of wind energy production reliability.

2.06.7 Selecting the Most Appropriate Wind Turbine

After analyzing in detail the critical components of wind energy production, a short presentation of directions to be used when called to select the most appropriate wind machine for a given installation site is provided in the final section of the current chapter.

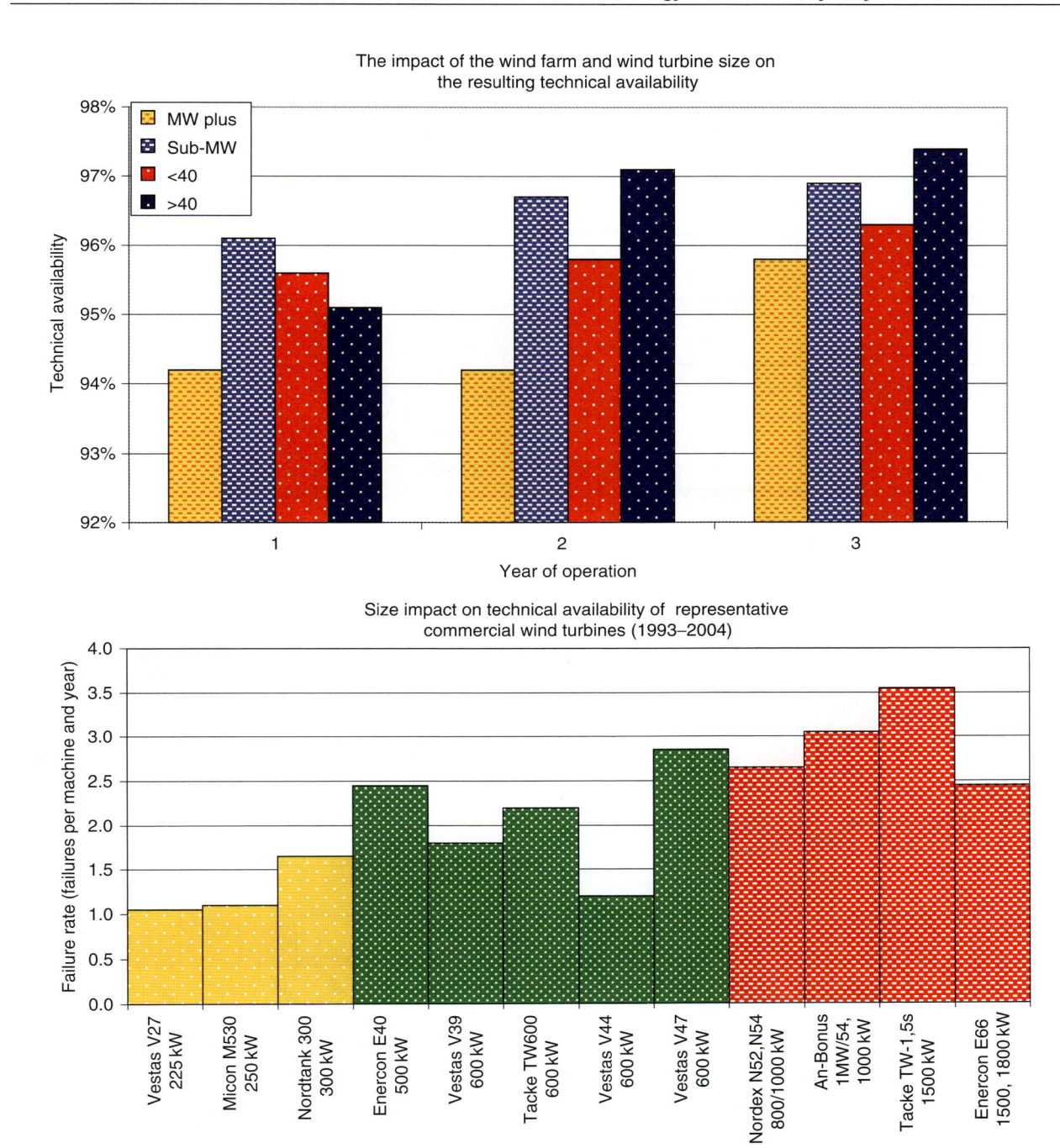

Figure 56 The impact of scaling on the technical availability of wind turbines and wind farms [91].

2.06.7.1 The Role of Wind Turbine Databases

Since the wind power industry counts more than 30 years of activity, various models of wind turbines incorporating different – and sometimes unique – features have become commercial throughout this period of wind energy development. As a result, classification of the constantly evolving body of commercially available wind turbines under a database environment that may enable direct multilevel comparison of wind turbine models is of primary importance. More specifically, by gathering, analyzing, and classifying the main characteristics of available wind turbines, a first comparative market study may be accordingly extended to the evaluation of the most appropriate models for power generation purposes [48]. Similar efforts, although having an *ex post* evaluation character, date back years ago, for example, 1985, when considerable attempts were carried out under the EUROWIN project [104] (Databank on Existing Wind Turbines and Wind Climates in the Community) in order to record the operational status of installed wind farms in the European Community during the time, in relation to the local wind potential attributes of each installation area.

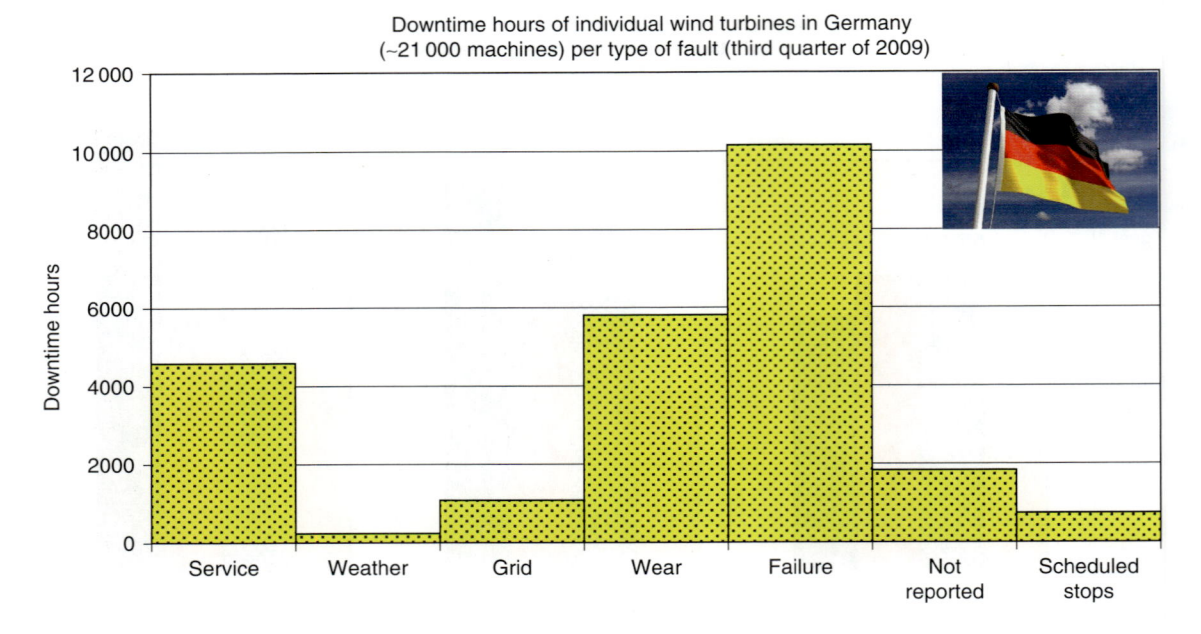

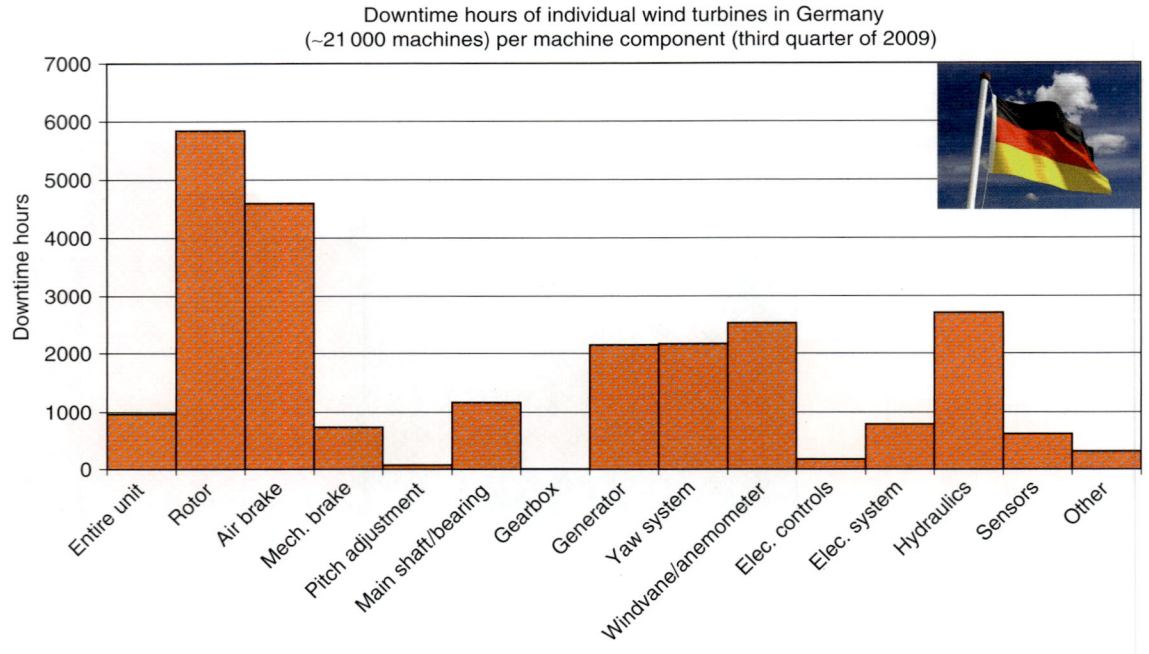

Figure 57 Recorded faults per source and type for German wind turbines.

On the other hand, *a priori* evaluation of a wind energy project is even more critical, with exploitation of organized information sets facilitating the task of using the most appropriate machine for the area investigated. Essential attributes of such a database [48, 105] may include the following (see, e.g., **Figure 59**):

- A description of the wind turbine's general characteristics
- A picture of the machine
- A detailed description of the wind turbine's parts
- The power curve of the wind turbine at standard conditions
- The C_p–V or C_p–λ performance curve of the wind turbine
- Additional data (e.g., price, noise level) of the wind turbine.

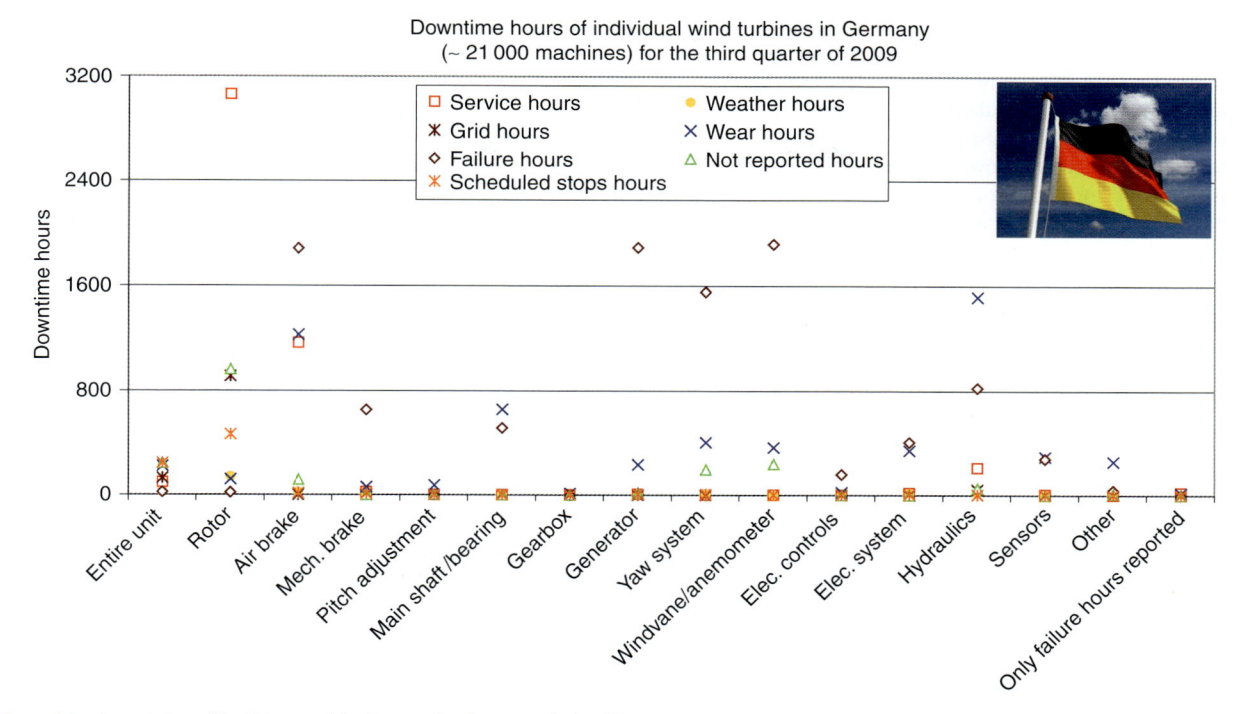

Energy Yield of Contemporary Wind Turbines 161

Figure 58 Association of fault type and fault cause for German wind turbines.

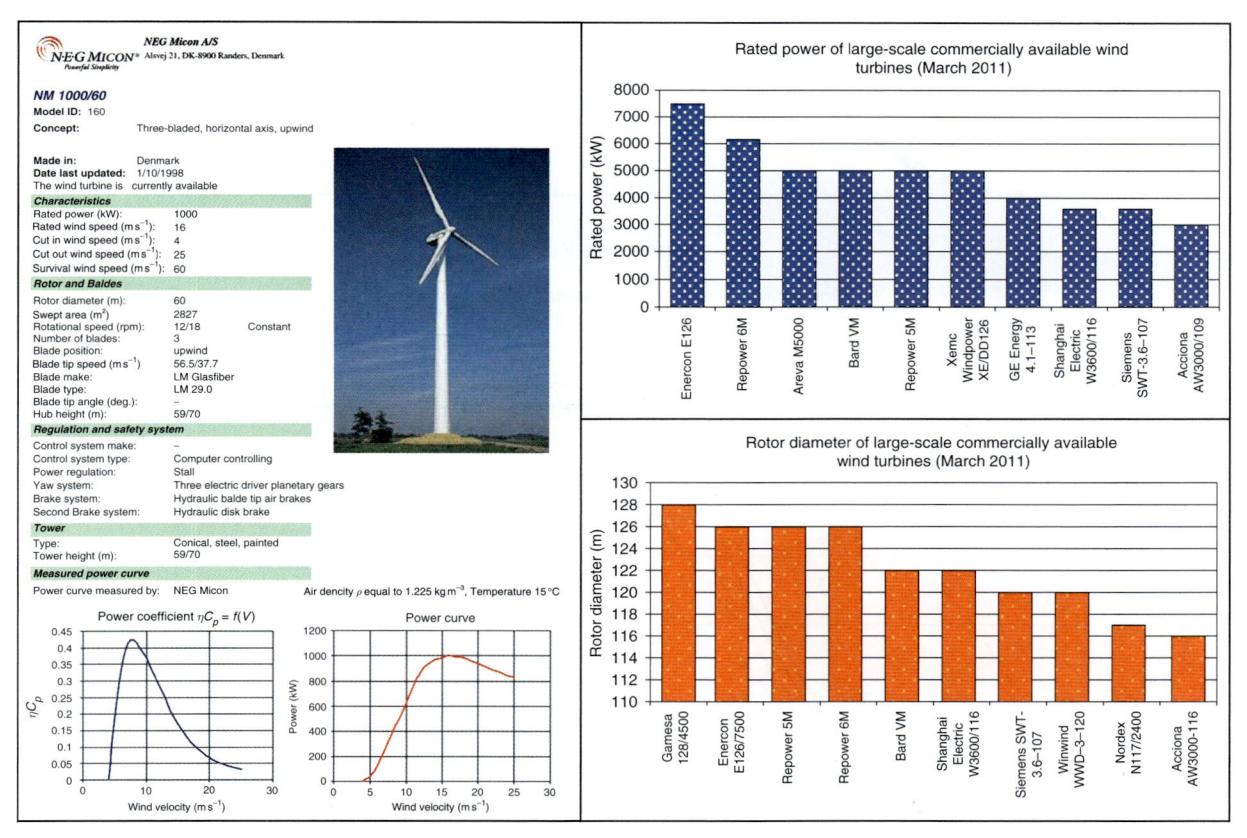

Figure 59 Typical wind turbine brochure extracted from Windbase II [48] and rated power-rotor diameter data obtained from the updated Windpower database [105].

162 Energy Yield of Contemporary Wind Turbines

Using the information included in such a database, it is possible to directly compare wind turbines belonging in the same and different ranges of power and thus proceed to a first evaluation of the machines under consideration. Moreover, it is possible for any expert to find out the complete set of data of the wind energy sector concerning, for example, the available hub height, the blade diameter or weight, the blade tip velocity, the approximate market (ex-works) prices, and so on. Extension of such a database may also include a first rough estimation of the energy production yield of all machines available for a large variety of typical wind potential regimes, that is, low–medium–high wind potential. In this way, it is possible to compare various models of commercially available wind turbines for a given wind potential area and thus select the most energy efficient. More specifically, description of wind regimes may be approached through the use of the Weibull distribution main parameters, while preliminary assessment of the energy yield to expect from a given wind turbine may be achieved with the help of the analysis found in Section 2.06.4.

2.06.7.2 Selecting the Most Appropriate Wind Turbine

By selecting a certain rated power class of commercially available wind turbines (e.g., in the order of 3 MW) and some representative wind regimes (**Figure 60**), one may demonstrate suitability of each machine for each wind potential first through the estimation of the mean power coefficient.

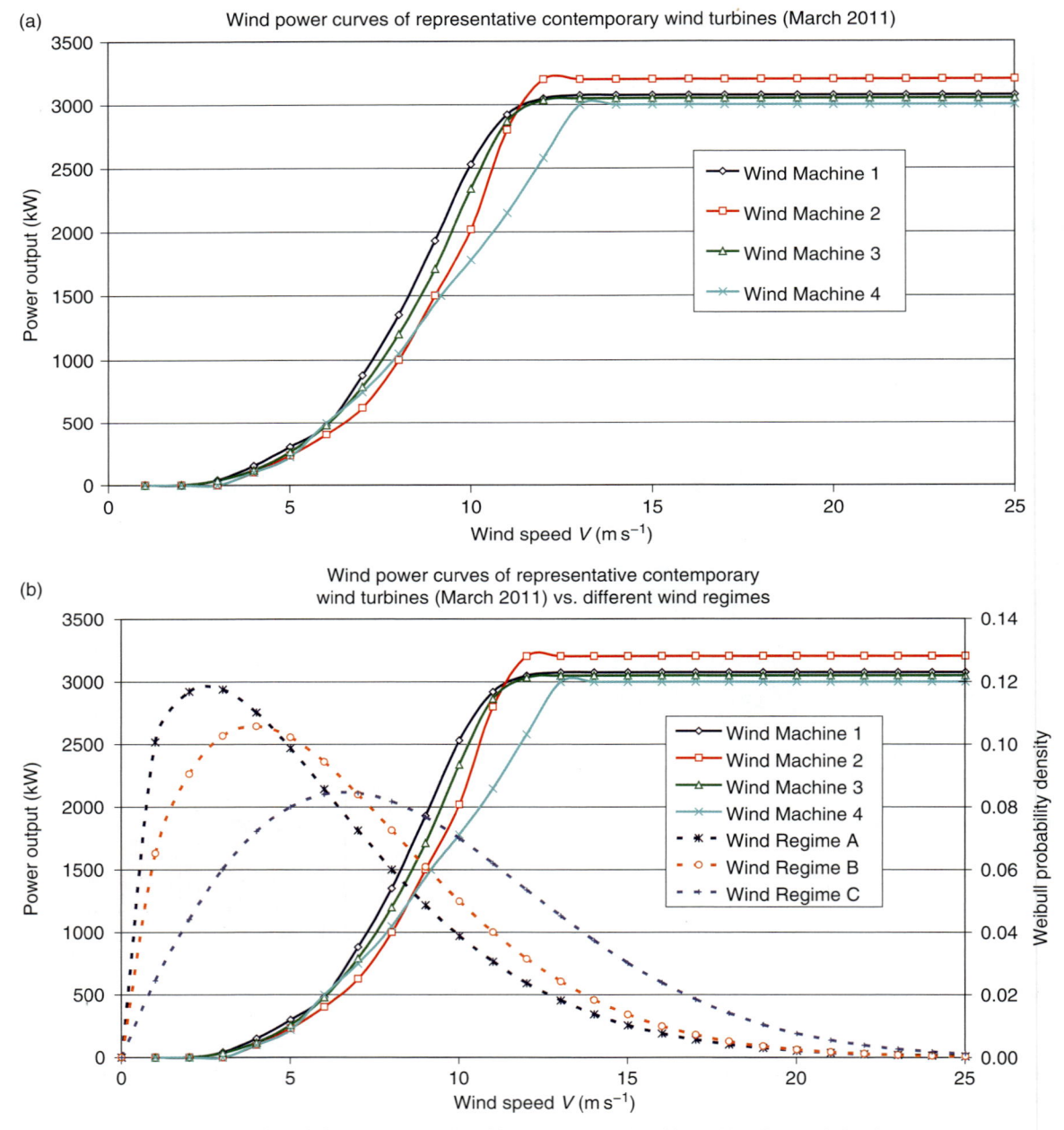

Figure 60 Presentation of representative wind power curves (a) and interaction of wind turbines with different wind regimes (b).

By using four representative wind turbine models, that is, Wind Machines 1–4, corresponding to Vestas V112 (rated power 3075 kW), REpower 3.2M114 (rated power 3200 kW), Enercon E101 (rated power 3050 kW), and WinWinD 3/100 (rated power 3000 kW), respectively, and three representative wind regimes A–C determined by the k and c parameters of Weibull (A: $c = 6.2$, $k = 1.4$; B: $c = 7.2$, $k = 1.6$; and C: $c = 9.8$, $k = 1.9$, respectively), the suitability of each machine for each of the wind regimes may be configured on the basis of estimating the respective mean annual power coefficient (**Figure 61(a)**). As one may obtain from the figure, Wind Machines 1 and 3 seem to better adjust to the given wind regimes. Concerning Wind Machines 2 and 4, the latter seems to be more appropriate for wind regimes A and B, although for wind regime C, Wind Machine 2 presents a higher mean annual power coefficient. Results obtained are accordingly used for the estimation of the annual energy production of each wind turbine, under the assumption that the same value of technical availability, that is, 95%, is considered for all cases examined (**Figure 61(b)**). As one may see, although Wind Machine 2 has the greatest rated power among the group of wind turbines examined (3.2 MW), its

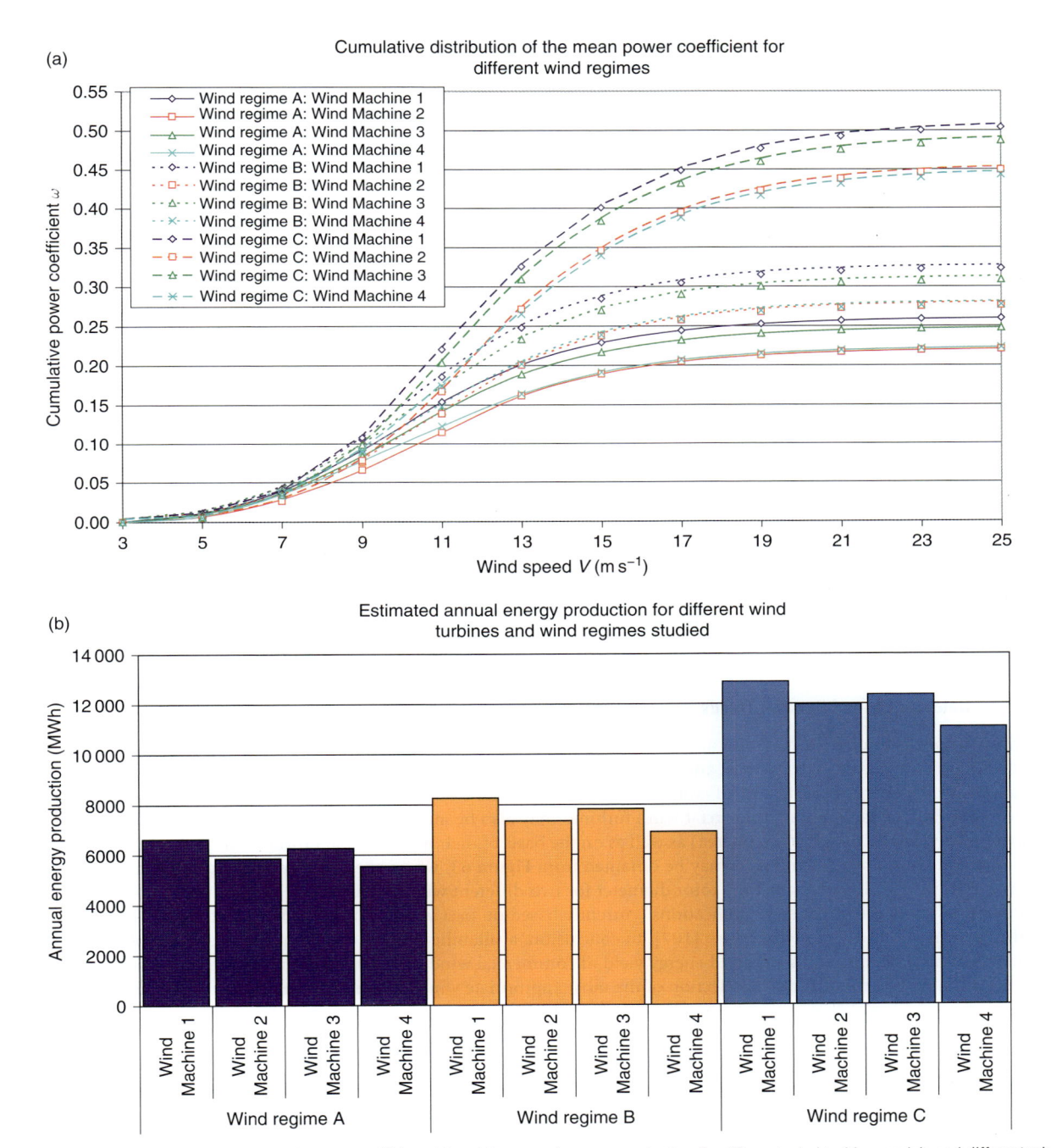

Figure 61 Estimation of the mean annual power coefficient (a) and the annual energy production for different wind turbine models and different wind regimes (b).

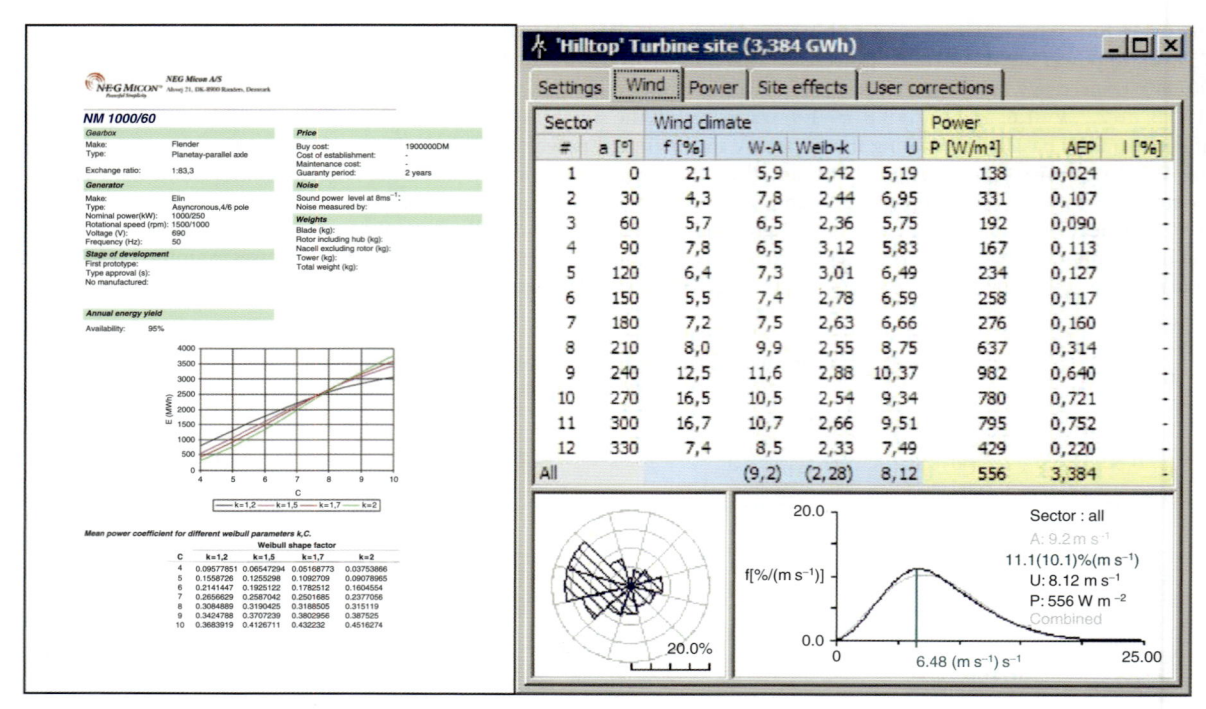

Figure 62 Presentation of energy-related results by Windbase II [48] and WAsP [106].

energy production is found in the case of wind regime A to be only marginally higher than the respective of Wind Machine 4, which has a lower rated power (3 MW). On the other hand, both Wind Machines 1 and 3, presenting a lower rated power than Wind Machine 2, appear to produce higher energy amounts due to better interaction with the local wind potential.

The results obtained for wind regimes B and C are also analogous, while what may be underlined is that for a more appreciable available wind potential to be considered, for example, wind regime C, examination of different machines leads to considerable variation in the annual energy yield estimation (**Figure 61(b)**) and thus selection of the most appropriate wind turbine becomes even more imperative.

Note that similar calculations may equally well be directly presented by databases [48] and software [106] (**Figure 62**) that are updated on a regular basis in order to include both commercially available machines and a satisfactory sample of representative wind potential regimes. In certain cases of such calculation tools, introduction of the local wind potential characteristics and other affecting parameters (Section 2.06.5) may allow for a more detailed estimation of the energy output.

2.06.7.3 Determination of General Trends

As already implied, through elaboration and statistical processing of the available – past and updated – information found in such databases, one may also define past and current trends of wind energy technology in many levels. To proceed even further, indications on the energy productivity of commercial wind machines over time are also useful in terms of both statistical and practical interest. The ranking of commercial wind turbines may also be attempted on the basis of their specific annual energy production (divided by the rotor swept area) as well as on the basis of their mean annual power coefficient achieved under given wind potential conditions. Such results may be obtained from **Figure 63**, where specific annual energy yield and mean annual power coefficient are plotted against the rotor diameter for two different wind potential cases (i.e., a medium–high and a high wind potential case) providing some indications (currently based on past wind turbine models) on the upscaling of machines and their energy productivity performance [107]. In conclusion, availability of data in an organized environment may provide useful general indications on the expected energy yield of commercial wind turbines, allowing at the same time, however, for a quite detailed analysis concerning the selection of the most appropriate wind machine for a given site of specific wind potential characteristics.

2.06.8 Conclusions

Technological developments in the field of wind energy during the past 30 years have gradually led to the establishment of machines determined by constantly higher efficiency and remarkable reliability, able to obtain maximum exploitation of the available wind energy potential. From the initial stall-control concept to the adoption of pitchable blades, and from the

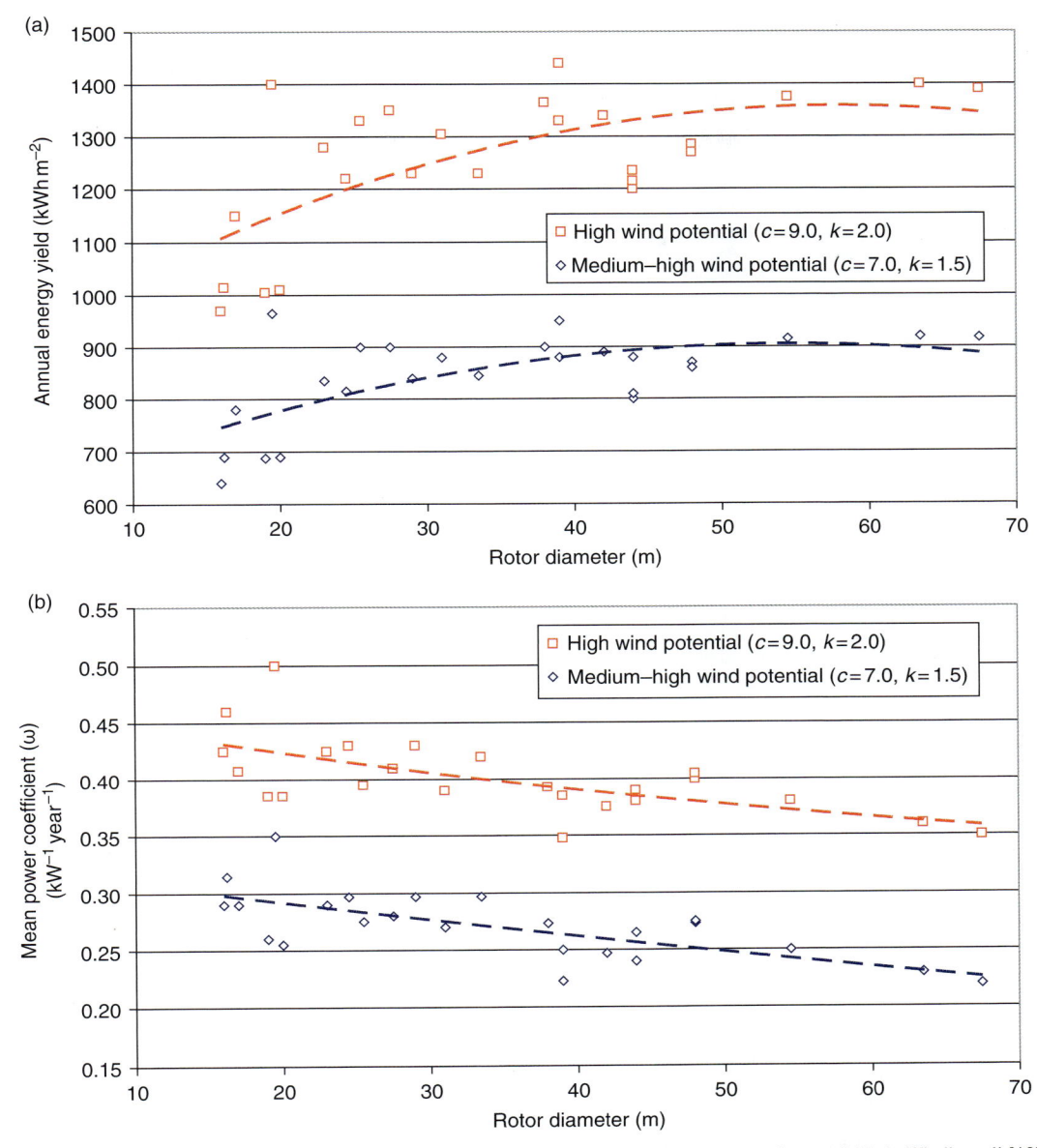

Figure 63 Specific annual energy production (a) and mean power coefficient trends (b) as derived from data available in Windbase II [107].

introduction of variable-speed machines to the development of innovative attributes such as storm control, contemporary wind turbines constantly evolve. On the other hand, inherent characteristics of the primary wind energy resource set barriers that keep challenging both design and operation patterns of wind machines. As a result, sufficient knowledge of a given site wind resources, along with detailed assessment of parameters affecting the energy output of wind turbines, is required in order to obtain optimum performance of the wind turbine selected.

Analytical investigation of the main factors that determine the energy output of commercial wind turbines were examined in this chapter, with special emphasis given to the presentation and elaboration of the numerous variables involved. More specifically, through the analysis and study of wind resource main features, comprehension of limits to the actual exploitation of wind's kinetic energy in order to produce electricity was designated. Accordingly, by presenting in detail the operational characteristics of contemporary wind turbines, the ability of current wind energy technological developments to convert available wind power to useful electricity was reflected. Following this, elaboration of the main parameters affecting the energy output of a wind turbine provided further insight on the multilateral problem of useful wind energy production estimation with guidelines for the selection of the most appropriate wind machine for a given site of certain wind resource characteristics being also given at the end of the chapter.

References

[1] Rohatgi J and Barbezier G (1999) Wind turbulence and atmospheric stability – Their effect on wind turbine output. *Renewable Energy* 16: 908–911.
[2] Choi HS, Kim JG, Cho JH, and Nam Y (2010) Active yaw control of MW class wind turbine. In: *Proceedings of International Conference on Control, Automation and Systems*. KINTEX, Gyeonggi-do, Korea, 27–30 October.
[3] Akpinar EK and Akpinar S (2005) A statistical analysis of wind speed data used in installation of wind energy conversion systems. *Energy Conversion and Management* 46: 515–532.
[4] Wichser C and Klink K (2008) Low wind speed turbines and wind power potential in Minnesota, USA. *Renewable Energy* 33: 1749–1758.
[5] Rauh A and Seelert W (1984) The Betz optimum efficiency for windmills. *Applied Energy* 17: 15–23.
[6] Wilson RE and Lissaman PBS (1974) *Applied Aerodynamics of Wind Power Machines*. Oregon State University.
[7] Dasey MN (2010) *Mechanisms and Strategies of Power Regulation in Wind Turbines*. Universitat Politècnica de Catalunya, Barcelona, Spain.
[8] Xiao YQ, Li QS, Li ZN, *et al.* (2006) Probability distributions of extreme wind speed and its occurrence interval. *Engineering Structures* 28: 1173–1181.
[9] Herbert GMJ, Iniyan S, and Goic R (2010) Performance, reliability and failure analysis of wind farm in a developing country. *Renewable Energy* 35: 2739–2751.
[10] Kaldellis JK (1999) *Wind Energy Management*, 1st edn. Athens, Greece: Stamoulis.
[11] Safari B and Gasore J (2010) A statistical investigation of wind characteristics and wind energy potential based on the Weibull and Rayleigh models in Rwanda. *Renewable Energy* 35: 2874–2880.
[12] Lun IYF and Lam JC (2000) A study of Weibull parameters using long-term wind observations. *Renewable Energy* 20: 145–153.
[13] Chang TP (2011) Estimation of wind energy potential using different probability density functions. *Applied Energy* 88: 1848–1856.
[14] Zhou W, Yang HX, and Fang ZH (2006) Wind power potential and characteristic analysis of the Pearl river delta region, China. *Renewable Energy* 31: 739–753.
[15] Chang TJ, Wu YT, Hsu HY, *et al.* (2003) Assessment of wind characteristics and wind turbine characteristics in Taiwan. *Renewable Energy* 28: 851–871.
[16] Seguro JV and Lambert TW (2000) Modern estimation of the parameters of the Weibull wind speed distribution for wind energy analysis. *Journal of Wind Engineering and Industrial Aerodynamics* 85: 75–84.
[17] Corotis RB, Sigl AB, and Klein J (1978) Probability models for wind energy magnitude and persistence. *Solar Energy* 20: 483–493.
[18] Safari B (2011) Modeling wind speed and wind power distributions in Rwanda. *Renewable & Sustainable Energy Reviews* 15: 925–935.
[19] Lo Brano V, Orioli A, Ciulla G, and Culotta S (2011) Quality of wind speed fitting distributions for the urban area of Palermo, Italy. *Renewable Energy* 36: 1026–1039.
[20] Carta JA and Ramírez P (2007) Analysis of two-component mixture Weibull statistics for estimation of wind speed distributions. *Renewable Energy* 32: 518–531.
[21] Liu FJ and Chang TP (2011) Validity analysis of maximum entropy distribution based on different moment constraints for wind energy assessment. *Energy* 36: 1820–1826.
[22] Villanueva D and Feijóo A (2010) Wind power distributions: A review of their applications. *Renewable & Sustainable Energy Reviews* 14: 1490–1495.
[23] Akpinar S and Akpinar EK (2009) Estimation of wind energy potential using finite mixture distribution models. *Energy Conversion and Management* 50: 877–884.
[24] Carta JA and Ramírez P (2007) Use of finite mixture distribution models in the analysis of wind energy in the Canarian Archipelago. *Energy Conversion and Management* 48: 281–291.
[25] Carta JA, Ramírez P, and Velázquez S (2009) A review of wind speed probability distributions used in wind energy analysis: Case studies in the Canary Islands. *Renewable & Sustainable Energy Reviews* 13: 933–955.
[26] Morgan EC, Lackner M, Vogel RM, and Baise LG (2011) Probability distributions for offshore wind speeds. *Energy Conversion and Management* 52: 15–26.
[27] Chang TP (2011) Performance comparison of six numerical methods in estimating Weibull parameters for wind energy application. *Applied Energy* 80: 272–282.
[28] Sathyajith M (2006) *Wind Energy Fundamentals, Resource Analysis and Economics*, 1st edn. Berlin, Germany: Springer.
[29] Cran GW (1976) Graphical estimation methods for Weibull distributions. *Microelectronics Reliability* 15: 47–52.
[30] Balouktsis A, Chassapis D, and Karapantsios ThD (2002) A nomogram method for estimating the energy produced by wind turbine generators. *Solar Energy* 72: 251–259.
[31] Stevens MJM and Smulders PT (1979) The estimation of parameters of the Weibull wind speed distribution for wind energy utilization purposes. *Wind Energy* 3: 132–145.
[32] Mengelkamp HT (1988) On the energy output estimation of wind turbines. *Energy Resources* 12: 113–123.
[33] Troen I and Petersen EL (1989) *European Wind Atlas*. Roskilde, Denmark: Risø National Laboratory.
[34] Kaldellis JK (2002) Optimum autonomous wind–power system sizing for remote consumers, using long-term wind speed data. *Applied Energy* 71: 215–233.
[35] Kaldellis JK, Kondili E, and Filios A (2006) Sizing a hybrid wind-diesel stand-alone system on the basis of minimum long-term electricity production cost. *Applied Energy* 83: 1384–1403.
[36] Cheng E and Yeung C (2002) Generalized extreme gust wind speeds distributions. *Journal of Wind Engineering and Industrial Aerodynamics* 90: 1657–1669.
[37] Anlas S (2005) *Technical Description of Enercon E-82*. Enercon, Aurich, Germany.
[38] Thresher RW and Dodge DM (1998) Trends in the evolution of wind turbine generator configurations and systems. *Wind Engineering* 1: 70–85.
[39] Gardner P, Garrad A, Hansen LF, *et al.* (2009) *Wind Energy the Facts: Part I: Technology*. Garrad Hassan and Partners, CIEMAT, European Wind Energy Association, Bristol-UK, Madrid-Spain, Brussels-Belgium.
[40] Salameh ZM and Safari I (1992) Optimum windmill-site matching. *IEEE Transactions on Energy Conversion* 7: 669–676.
[41] Jangamshetti SH and Rau VG (1999) Site matching of wind turbine generators: A case study. *IEEE Transactions on Energy Conversion* 14: 1537–1543.
[42] Justus CG, Hargraves WR, and Yalcin A (1976) Nationwide assessment of potential output from wind-powered generators. *Journal of Applied Meteorology* 15: 673–678.
[43] Giorsetto P and Utsurogi KF (1983) Development of a new procedure for reliability modeling of wind turbine generators. *IEEE Transaction of Power Application System* 102: 134–143.
[44] Albadi MH and El-Saadany EF (2010) New method for estimating CF of pitch-regulated wind turbines. *Electric Power Systems Research* 80: 1182–1188.
[45] International Electrotechnical Commission Standard IEC 61400-12-1 (2005) *Wind Turbines – Part 12-1: Power Performance Measurements of Electricity Producing Wind Turbines*, International Electrochemical Commission, Geneva, Switzerland.
[46] Uchida T and Ohya Y (2003) Large-eddy simulation of turbulent airflow over complex terrain. *Journal of Wind Engineering & Industrial Aerodynamics* 91: 219–229.
[47] International Network for Harmonised and Recognised Measurements in Wind Energy (MEASNET) Allowed measurements per institute. http://www.measnet.org/ (accessed March 2011).
[48] Vlachou D, Messaritakis G, and Kaldellis J (1999) Presentation and energy production analysis of commercial wind turbines. *European Wind Energy Conference and Exhibition*. pp. 476–480. Nice, France: European Wind Energy Association, 1–5 March.
[49] Freris LL (1990) *Wind Energy Conversion Systems*, 1st edn. London, UK: Prentice Hall.
[50] Burden RL and Fairs JD (2001) *Numerical Analysis*, 7th edn. New York: Brooks/Cole.
[51] Elkinton MR, Rogers AL, and McGowan JG (2006) An investigation of wind-shear models and experimental data trends for different terrains. *Wind Engineering* 30: 341–350.
[52] Gualtieri G and Secci S (2011) Comparing methods to calculate atmospheric stability-dependent wind speed profiles: A case study on coastal location. *Renewable Energy* 36: 2189–2204.
[53] Le Gourières D (1982) *Energie éolienne: Théorie, conception et calcul pratique des installations*, 1st edn. Paris, France: Eyrolles.
[54] Monin AS and Obukhov AM (1954) Basic laws of turbulent mixing in the surface layer of the atmosphere. *Trudy Geofizicheskogo Instituta, Akademiya Nauk SSSR* 24: 163–187.
[55] Justus CG and Mikhail A (1976) Height variation of wind speed and wind distribution statistics. *Geophysical Research Letters* 3: 261–264.
[56] Eggleston DM and Stoddard FS (1987) *Wind Turbine Engineering Design*, 1st edn. New York: Van Nostrand Reinhold Company.

[57] Katsirou V, Zafirakis D, Kavadias KA, and Kaldellis JK (2011) An integrated methodology for the experimental validation of a wind turbine's power curve. *European Wind Energy Conference and Exhibition.* Brussels, Belgium: European Wind Energy Association, 14–17 March.
[58] Kaldellis JK, Kavadias KA, Korbakis G, and Vlachou DS (2004) The impact of local ambient conditions on the energy production of contemporary wind power stations. In: *7th Hellenic Conference in Meteorology, Climatology and Atmospheric Physics.* Hellenic Meteorological Society, Cyprus Meteorological Association, Cyprus Meteorological Service, and University of Cyprus, Nicosia, Cyprus, 28–30 September.
[59] Carta JA and Mentado D (2007) A continuous bivariate model for wind power density and wind turbine energy output estimations. *Energy Conversion and Management* 48: 420–432.
[60] Soler-Bientz R, Watson S, and Infield D (2010) Wind characteristics on the Yucatán Peninsula based on short term data from meteorological stations. *Energy Conversion and Management* 51: 754–764.
[61] Kaldellis JK, Arianas L, and Konstantinou P (1996) Validation of the aerodynamic behavior of commercial wind turbines. In: *5th National Conference on Soft Energy Resources.* Athens, Greece, 6–8 November.
[62] Kaldellis JK, Kavadias KA, Filios AE, and Garofallakis S (2004) Income loss due to wind energy rejected by the Crete island electrical network-the present situation. *Applied Energy* 79: 127–144.
[63] Kaldellis JK and Kavadias KA (2000) *Laboratory Applications of Renewable Energy Sources*, 1st edn. Athens, Greece: Stamoulis.
[64] Barthelmie RJ, Hansen K, Frandsen ST, et al. (2009) Modelling and measuring flow and wind turbine wakes in large wind farms offshore. *Wind Energy* 12: 431–444.
[65] Dahlberg JA and Thor SE (2009) Power performance and wake effects in the closely spaced Lillgrund offshore wind farm. In: *Proceedings of the European Offshore Wind 2009 Conference and Exhibition.* European Wind Energy Association, Stockholm, Sweden, 14–16 September.
[66] Beyer HG, Pahkle T, Schmidt W, et al. (1994) Wake effects in a linear wind farm. *Journal of Wind Engineering and Industrial Aerodynamics* 51: 303–318.
[67] Manwell JF, McGowan JG, and Rogers AL (2002) *Wind Energy Explained: Theory, Design and Application*, 1st edn. New York: Wiley.
[68] Bossanyi EA, Maclean C, Whittle GE, et al. (1980) The efficiency of wind turbine clusters. In: *Proceedings of the 3rd International Symposium on Wind Energy Systems*, pp. 401–416. British Hydromechanics Research Association Fluid Engineering and the Technical University of Denmark, Lyngby, 26–29 August.
[69] Katic I, Hojstrup J, and Jensen NO (1986) A simple model for cluster efficiency. In: *Proceedings of the European Wind Energy Conference.* Rome, Italy, 7–9 October.
[70] Lissaman PBS and Bates ER (1977) Energy effectiveness of arrays of wind energy conversion systems. AeroVironment Report AV FR 7050, AeroVironment, Pasadena, CA, USA.
[71] Smith D and Taylor GJ (1991) Further analysis of turbine wake development and interaction data. In: *Proceedings of the 13th BWEA Wind Energy Conference.* Swansea, UK, 10–12 April.
[72] Sorensen JN and Shen WZ (1999) Computation of wind turbine wakes using combined Navier-Stokes actuator-line methodology. In: *Proceedings of the 1999 European Wind Energy Conference and Exhibition*, pp. 156–159. Nice, France, 1–5 March.
[73] Pinilla A, Rodriguez L, and Trujillo R (2009) Performance evaluation of Jepirachi wind park. *Renewable Energy* 34: 48–52.
[74] Larsen K (2010) Offshore wind – Do we have what it takes? *Renewable Energy Focus* 11(24–26): 28–29.
[75] Christensen P and Giebel G (2001) Availability of wind turbines in remote places. A statistical and a real-time view. In: *Proceedings of the 2001 European Wind Energy Conference and Exhibition.* Copenhagen, Denmark, 2–6 July.
[76] Abderrazzaq MA and Hahn B (2006) Analysis of the turbine standstill for a grid connected wind farm (case study). *Renewable Energy* 31: 89–104.
[77] Kalafatis EI, Skittides Ph, and Kaldellis JK (2008) Investigating the relation between the reliability and the technical availability of wind energy applications. In: *International Conference of Medpower 2008.* National Technical University of Athens and Aristotle University of Thessalonica, Greece, 2–5 November.
[78] Kaldellis JK, Vlachou DS, and Paliatsos AG (2003) Twelve years energy production assessment of Greek state wind parks. *Wind Engineering* 27(34): 215–226.
[79] Kaldellis JK (2002) An integrated time-depending feasibility analysis model of wind energy applications in Greece. *Energy Policy* 30: 267–280.
[80] Kaldellis JK, Kavadias KA, Filios AE, and Garofallakis S (2004) Income loss due to wind energy rejected by the Crete island electrical network – The present situation. *Applied Energy* 79: 127–144.
[81] Papathanassiou SA and Boulaxis NG (2005) Power limitations and energy yield evaluation for wind farms operating in island systems. *Renewable Energy* 31: 457–479.
[82] Kaldellis JK (2008) Maximum wind potential exploitation in autonomous electrical networks on the basis of stochastic analysis. *Journal of Wind Engineering & Industrial Aerodynamics* 96: 1412–1424.
[83] Weisser D and Garcia RS (2005) Instantaneous wind energy penetration in isolated electricity grids: Concepts and review. *Renewable Energy* 30: 1299–1308.
[84] Tande JOG (2000) Exploitation of wind-energy resources in proximity to weak electric grids. *Applied Energy* 65: 395–401.
[85] Kaldellis JK and Zafirakis D (2007) Present situation and future prospects of electricity generation in Aegean Archipelago islands. *Energy Policy* 35: 4623–4639.
[86] Kaldellis JK and Gavras TJ (2000) The economic viability of commercial wind plants in Greece. A complete sensitivity analysis. *Energy Policy* 28: 509–517.
[87] Parent O and Ilinca A (2011) Anti-icing and de-icing techniques for wind turbines: Critical review. *Cold Regions Science and Technology* 65: 88–96.
[88] Peesapati V (2010) Lightning protection of wind turbines. In: *Proceedings of the 2010 European Wind Energy Conference and Exhibition.* Warsaw, Poland: European Wind Energy Association.
[89] Thick J (2004) Offshore corrosion protection of wind farms. In: *Proceedings of the 2004 European Wind Energy Conference and Exhibition.* London, UK, 20–23 April.
[90] Kaldellis JK (2003) Feasibility evaluation of Greek state 1990–2001 wind energy program. *Energy* 28: 1375–1394.
[91] Tavner PJ, Xiang J, and Spinato F (2007) Reliability analysis for wind turbines. *Wind Energy* 10: 1–18.
[92] Van Bussel GJW (1999) The development of an expert system for the determination of availability and O&M costs for offshore wind farms. In: *Proceedings of the 1999 European Wind Energy Conference and Exhibition.* Nice, France, 1–5 March.
[93] Kaldellis JK, Skulatos D, and Kladuchos A (1993) Wind energy penetration in electrical grids of small and medium size islands. In: *Proceedings of 3rd International Conference on Environmental Science and Technology.* Global Network for Environmental Science and Technology, Lesvos, Greece, 6–9 September.
[94] Hahn B (1999) Reliability assessment of wind turbines in Germany. Results of the national 250MW wind programme. In: *Proceedings of the 1999 European Wind Energy Conference and Exhibition.* Nice, France, 1–5 March.
[95] Lemming J, Morthorst PE, Hansen LH, et al. (1999) O&M costs and economical life-time of wind turbines. In: *Proceedings of the 1999 European Wind Energy Conference and Exhibition.* Nice, France, 1–5 March.
[96] Kaldellis JK and Kodossakis D (1999) The present and the future of the Greek wind energy market. In: *Proceedings of the 1999 European Wind Energy Conference and Exhibition.* Nice, France, 1–5 March.
[97] Hill RR, Stinebaugh JA, Briand D, et al. (2008) Wind turbine reliability: A database and analysis approach, SANDIA REPORT SAND2008-0983, Sandia National Laboratories, New Mexico–California.
[98] Harman K, Walker R, and Wilkinson M (2008) Availability trends observed at operational wind farms. In: *Proceedings of the 2008 European Wind Energy Conference and Exhibition.* Brussels, Belgium, 31 March–3 April.
[99] EMD International A/S Vindstat – Wind energy index. Available at: http://www.vindstat.dk/ (accessed March 2011).
[100] Vattenfall Power Consultant AB Vindstat – Swedish database. Available at: http://www.vindstat.nu (accessed March 2011).
[101] VTT Technical Research Centre of Finland Wind energy statistics in Finland. Available at: http://www.vtt.fi/proj/windenergystatistics/ (accessed March 2011).
[102] WindStats Newsletter 22, No. 4, Autumn 2009, ISSN 0903-5648.
[103] Carlsson F, Eriksson E, and Dahlberg M (2010) Damage preventing measures for wind turbines Phase 1 – Reliability data. *Elforks Report* 10:68, Vindforsk III project V-316, Stockholm, Sweden.
[104] Schmid J and Klein HP (1991) *Performance of European Wind Turbines*, 1st edn. New York: Elsevier Science Publishers Ltd.

[105] The Windpower, Wind Turbines and Wind Farms Database Turbines list. Available at: http://www.thewindpower.net/index_en.php (accessed March 2011).
[106] WAsP – the Wind Atlas Analysis and Application Program. Available at: http://www.wasp.dk/ (accessed March 2011).
[107] Kaldellis JK and Vlachou DS (2002) Analyzing the historical evolution of contemporary wind turbines. *Global Windpower Conference*. Paris, France.

Further Reading

Burton T, Sharpe D, Jenkins N, and Bossanyi E (2001) *Wind Energy Handbook*, 1st edn. Chichester, UK: Wiley.
Nelson V (2009) *Wind Energy. Renewable Energy and the Environment*, 1st edn. Florida, USA: CRC Press, Taylor & Francis Group.
Ackermann Th (2005) *Wind Power in Power Systems*, 1st edn. Chichester, UK: Wiley.
Hau E (2006) *Wind Turbines: Fundamentals, Technologies, Application, Economics*, 2nd edn. Berlin, Heidelberg, Germany: Springer.
Stiebler M (2008) *Wind Energy Systems for Electric Power Generation*, 1st edn. Berlin, Heidelberg, Germany: Springer.
Hansen MOL (2008) *Aerodynamics of Wind Turbines*, 2nd edn. London, UK: Earthscan.
Walker JF and Jenkins N (1997) *Wind Energy Technology*, 1st edn. Chichester, UK: Wiley.
Kaldellis JK (2005) *Wind Energy Management*, 2nd edn. Athens, Greece: Stamoulis.
Kaldellis JK (2010) *Stand-Alone and Hybrid Wind Energy Systems: Technology, Energy Storage and Applications*, 1st edn. Cambridge, UK: Woodhead Publishing.

Relevant Websites

http://www.windenergy.org – Alternative Energy Institute.
http://www.centrodeinformacao.ren.pt – Centro De Informação.
http://www.dewi.de – DEWI GmbH.
http://www.vindstat.nu – Driftuppföljning vindkraft.
http://www.ecn.nl – ECN: Energy Research Centre of the Netherlands.
http://www.eirgrid.com – EirGrid.
http://www.emd.dk – EMD International A/S.
http://www.ewea.org – EWEA (The European Wind Energy Association).
http://www.measnet.org – measnet.
http://www.bmreports.com – neta (The New Electricity Trading Arrangements)
http://www.nrel.gov – NREL (National Renewable Energy Laboratory).
http://www.ree.es/ – Red Eléctrica de España.
http://www.risoe.dk – Risø DTU: National Laboratory for Sustainable Energy.
http://www.thewindpower.net – The Wind Power: Wind turbines and windfarms database
http://www.vtt.fi – VTT.
http://www.wind-energy-the-facts.org – Wind Energy: The Facts.
https://www.cres.gk – Greek Centre for Renewable Energy Sources.
https://www.sealab.gr/ – Soft Energy Applications and Environmental Protection Laboratory of Greece.

2.07 Wind Parks Design, Including Representative Case Studies

D Al Katsaprakakis and DG Christakis, Wind Energy Laboratory, Technological Educational Institute of Crete, Crete, Greece

© 2012 Elsevier Ltd. All rights reserved.

2.07.1	Introduction	169
2.07.2	The Selection of the Wind Park's Installation Site	171
2.07.2.1	Aiming at the Maximization of the Electricity Produced	171
2.07.2.2	The Effect of Land Morphology on the Site Selection	174
2.07.2.3	Aiming at the Minimization of the Set-Up Cost	177
2.07.2.4	Installation Issues of the Wind Turbines	177
2.07.2.4.1	The equipment transportation	177
2.07.2.4.2	The wind turbines' service area	178
2.07.2.4.3	The wind turbines' foundation	178
2.07.2.4.4	The wind turbines' erection	180
2.07.2.5	Aiming at the Minimization of the Time Required for the Wind Park Project Implementation	181
2.07.3	The Wind Potential Evaluation	183
2.07.4	The Selection of the Wind Turbine Model	186
2.07.5	The Micro-Siting of a Wind Park	190
2.07.6	The Calculation of the Annual Electricity Production	196
2.07.7	Social Approval of the Wind Park	202
2.07.8	The Wind Park Integration in Local Networks	206
2.07.8.1	The Power Quality Disturbances Caused by the Wind Turbines	206
2.07.8.1.1	Steady-state voltage level fluctuations	207
2.07.8.1.2	Voltage fluctuations	207
2.07.8.1.3	Transients	207
2.07.8.1.4	Harmonics	207
2.07.8.1.5	Frequency fluctuations	207
2.07.8.2	Wind Power Penetration in Weak Networks and Dynamic Security	208
2.07.8.3	The Connection of Wind Parks in Electricity Networks	209
2.07.9	Economic Analysis	210
2.07.9.1	The Project's Set-Up Cost Calculation and the Funding Scheme	210
2.07.9.2	The Calculation of the Investment's Annual Revenues	210
2.07.9.3	Annual Expenses	211
2.07.9.4	Investment's Annual Net Profits	211
2.07.9.5	Economic Indexes	211
2.07.10	Presentation of Characteristic Case Studies	211
2.07.10.1	The Design of a Wind Park in a Small Noninterconnected Power System	212
2.07.10.2	The Design of a Wind Park in a Large Noninterconnected Power System	216
2.07.10.3	The Roscoe Wind Park in Texas – Largest Onshore Wind Park	218
2.07.10.4	The Thanet Wind Park in the United Kingdom – Largest Offshore Wind Park	220
2.07.11	Epilog	221
References		222
Further Reading		223

2.07.1 Introduction

The fundamental principles regarding the design of a wind park are presented in this chapter. The design of a wind park is a multiparameter process that aims at the following three goals:

- the maximization of the electricity produced from the wind park
- the minimization of the set-up cost per installed kilowatt of wind power
- the minimization of the time required for the implementation of the wind park project.

The maximization of the electricity produced from the wind park depends on two parameters:

- the selection of an appropriate site for the installation of the wind park, taking into account the available wind potential and the total available area for the installation of the wind turbines
- the optimum micro-siting of the wind turbines in order to avoid or to minimize the wind turbines' shading losses between them.

Higher electricity production from a wind park is expected in sites with remarkable wind potential. The higher the wind blows, the higher the electricity produced will be and vice versa. On the other hand, the micro-siting of the wind turbines aims at the optimum exploitation of the available wind potential, by minimizing any potential energy production losses, arising mainly from the shading effect between the wind turbines or other physical or technical obstacles existing in the vicinity of the installation site.

The set-up cost for a wind park's installation consists of the following basic components:

- the wind turbines' and secondary electromechanical equipment purchase cost
- the wind turbines' and secondary electromechanical equipment transportation cost
- the required infrastructure works' cost
- the new electricity network construction for the connection to the existing one.

The equipment purchase cost is mainly configured by the cost of the wind turbine model selected. This cost varies slightly for different wind turbine models. In most cases, the wind turbines purchase cost constitutes the main cost component of the wind park's total set-up cost. The selection of the wind turbine model, described thoroughly in a following section, is performed taking into account the total wind parks' nominal power, the land available for installation, the electromechanical specifications of the generator, and other special environmental issues. The abovementioned parameters constitute the basic criteria for the selection of a wind turbine model. The purchase cost consists of a secondary parameter regarding the selection of the turbine's model.

The transportation of the wind turbines and the remaining electromechanical equipment, the required infrastructure works, and the construction of the new network are cost components strongly affected by the site selected for the wind park's installation. Hence, the selection of the wind park's installation site, except the expected electricity production, affects the total set-up cost as well. Any efforts toward the reduction of the total wind park's cost should focus on the reduction of these components' cost.

The time required for a wind park's installation is analyzed in the following implementation stages:

- the wind park's licensing procedure
- the wind park's erection procedure.

Former surveys on implemented wind park projects in Europe and worldwide indicate that the most time-consuming procedure regarding the implementation of a wind park project is the licensing procedure [1–3]. Depending on possible peculiarities in the neighborhood of the installation site, such as proximity to archeological sites, places of tourist interest, and special protected areas for birds, the required time period for the licensing procedure can be considerably extended and, in the worst case, the wind park project can even be canceled. Consequently, the minimization of the time required for the implementation of a wind park project is strongly affected by the selected installation site as well.

Summarizing the conclusions from the above brief presentation of the parameters that are taken into account for the design of a wind park, it is revealed that the most crucial one is the selection of an appropriate installation site. The optimum selection of a wind park installation site is determined by the maximization of the electricity produced, the minimization of the set-up cost, and the time required for the implementation of the licensing and erection project's stages.

The basic steps toward the implementation of a wind park project are presented in Figure 1. As seen in this figure, once a site for the wind park's installation is selected, a feasibility study must be fulfilled in order to indicate whether the project is feasible. The feasibility study should examine the following crucial issues:

- a first approximate (in case there is no time for wind potential measurements) or accurate wind potential estimation based on empirical methods or available wind potential measurements in a neighboring position
- the possibility to gain the land's ownership either by renting or by buying it
- the wind turbines' micro-siting, aiming at the annual electricity production maximization and the minimization of the possible impacts on the environment and on human activities
- the investment's evaluation, namely the economic analysis of the wind park project aiming at the calculation of representative economic indexes.

The abovementioned tasks will be thoroughly analyzed in the following sections of this chapter.

If the conclusions of the feasibility study are positive regarding the designed wind park project, the process is continued with the accomplishment of the wind park's final technical and financial studies. A meteorological mast must be installed in the installation site for the measurement of the available wind potential. In order to gain valid information on the wind park's expected power output, the wind potential measurement period must be at least annual.

The wind park's licensing procedure is defined in the national legislation of each country. The scope of this task is the examination from the state authorities of any possible legal violations arising from the implementation of the proposed project. The approval of the project's licensing application allows the developers to proceed with the wind park's erection. If the application is not approved, the wind park's developers have two alternatives:

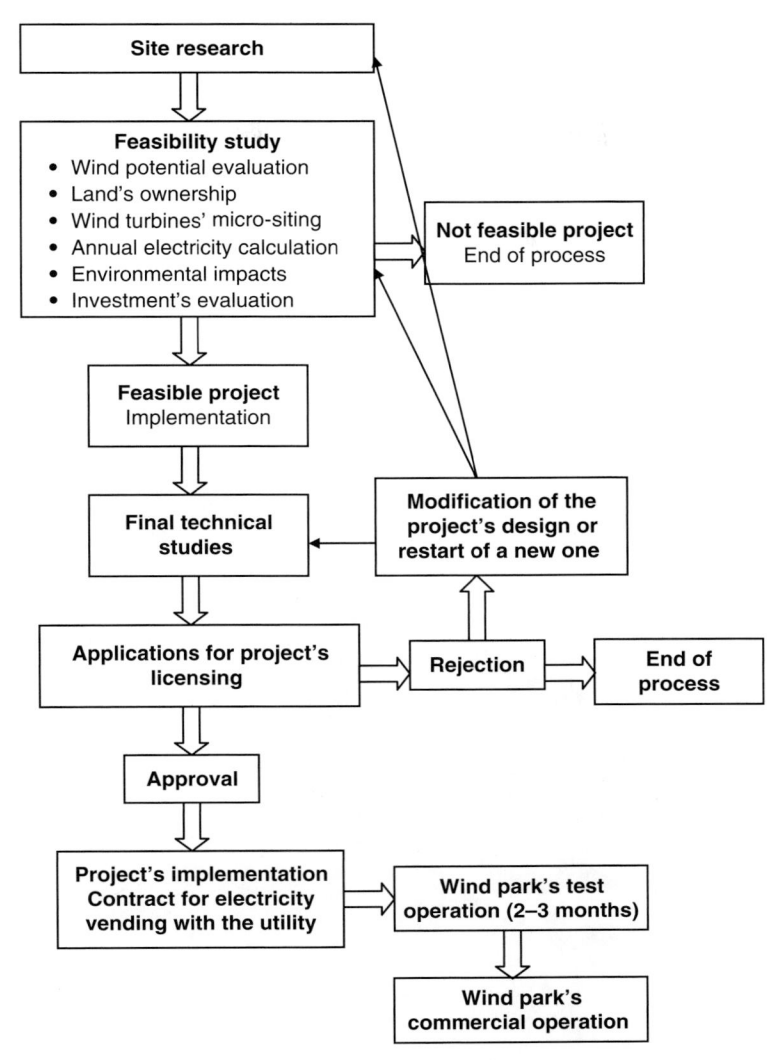

Figure 1 The implementation procedure of a wind park.

- to submit a new licensing application for the same project, following any modifications indicated by the authorities in the rejection decision
- to proceed with the development of a new project.

Once the set-up procedure is completed, the wind park is set under test operation for a period of 2–3 months. The electricity vending contract is then signed between the wind park's owner and the utility and the normal operation of the wind park begins.

2.07.2 The Selection of the Wind Park's Installation Site

2.07.2.1 Aiming at the Maximization of the Electricity Produced

The electricity produced from a wind park depends on the available wind potential in the installation site. The selection of a site with high wind potential is the first crucial issue one should face toward the implementation of a wind park project. At a first stage, information regarding the available wind potential in a geographical territory can be gathered from several sources, such as:

- wind potential maps (or atlases) developed from specialized and reliable institutes or academic laboratories
- the distortion of the vegetation (trees, brushes) at the installation site due to the wind
- the opinion of inhabitants with frequent presence at the area of interest (shepherds, fishermen, etc.).

Reliable wind potential maps are published in relevant scientific articles, handbooks, books, and web-pages [4, 5]. The most common information depicted in wind potential maps is the mean annual wind velocity at a specific height above ground (e.g., 10, 20, 40 m, etc.) or the wind power density (in $W m^{-2}$). In **Figure 2** a comprehensive European Wind Atlas developed by Risø National Laboratory of Denmark is presented [6], while in **Figure 3** a more thorough wind map for the eastern part of the island of Crete in Greece, developed by the Wind Energy Laboratory of the Technological Educational Institute of Crete, is presented [7].

Reliable wind maps can be developed on the basis of several wind potential measurements gathered from a network of meteorological stations dispersed properly in the examined geographical territory. The selection of the installation positions of the meteorological stations depends on the territory morphology. Generally, the meteorological stations must by evenly allocated in characteristic positions, such as top of hills or mountains. The wind potential measurements should be expanded at least in annual time periods.

Once the wind potential measurements have been gathered, the wind potential map is developed with the use of relevant software tools, using as input the gathered wind potential measurements and the land digitized morphology. The wind map is

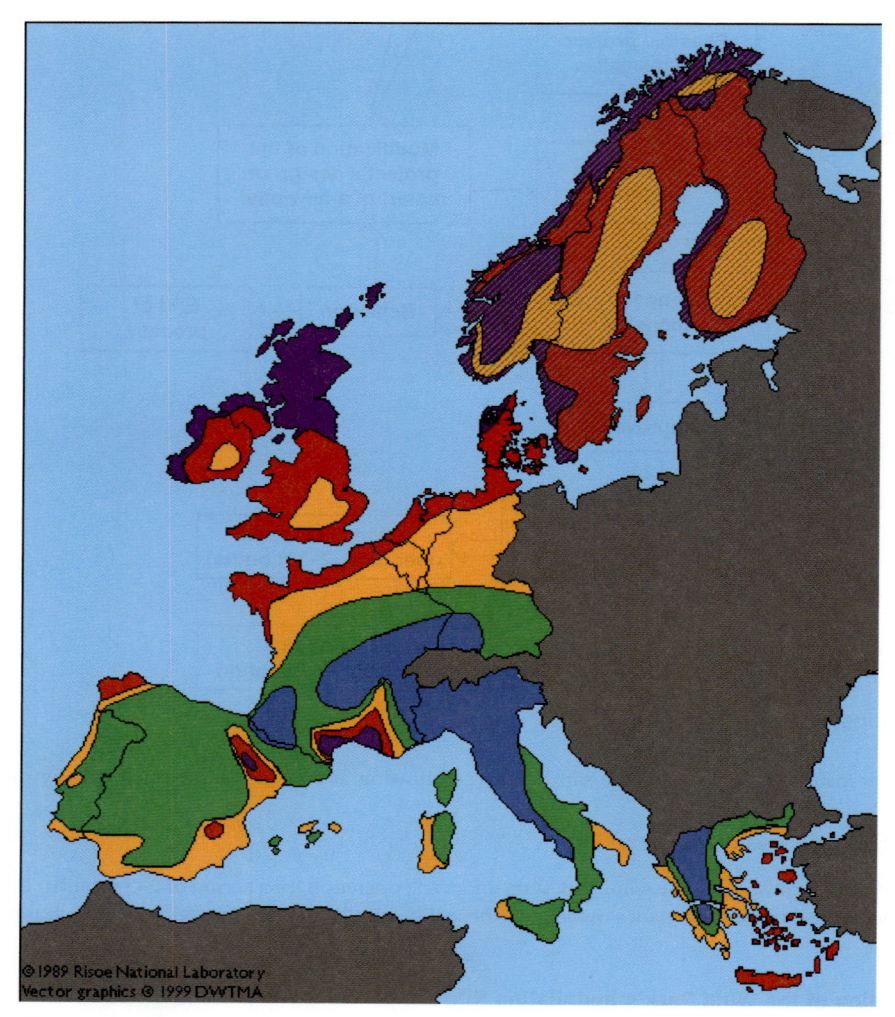

Figure 2 European wind map developed by Risø National Laboratory of Denmark [4, 6].

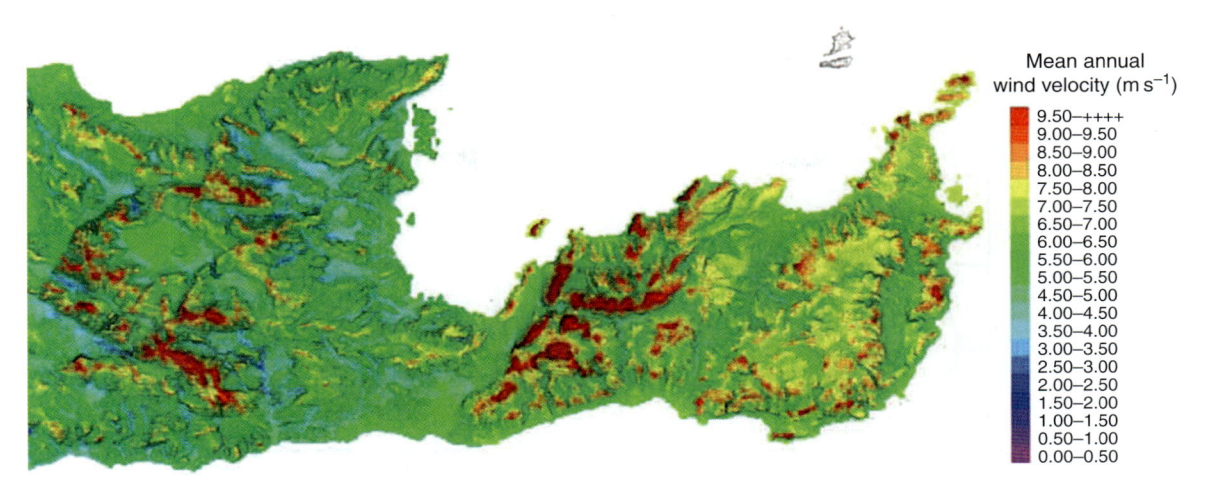

Figure 3 Wind map of the eastern Crete, developed by Wind Energy Laboratory of Technological Educational Institute of Crete [7].

developed with iterative software running. Each running is performed by using meteorological measurements data from different stations. With this method the results from each running are tested and the reliability of the developed wind map is maximized.

Depending on the reliability of the available wind map, the selection of a site with remarkable wind potential can be quite accurate.

A first approach to the estimation of the available wind potential in a site can be performed by observing the distortion of the existing vegetation due to the wind. For example, the existence of trees bent closely to the ground by the wind can be an indubitable evidence for the existence of high wind potential. The distortion degree of the vegetation in an area represents the existing wind potential with specific indexes (see **Table 1**) that have been defined exactly for this purpose. In **Figure 4** the distortion degrees are presented according to Griggs-Putnam, regarding trees of conical shape. In **Figure 5**, the distortion degrees according to Barsch are presented, regarding trees of oval shape [8].

Given the distortion degree of the trees in the examined area, the available wind potential can be estimated using **Table 1** [8]. As seen in this table, the mean annual wind velocity in an area can be preestimated quite satisfactorily, with an error of ± 20–30%, on the basis of the existing vegetation distortion degree. This can be a first piece of information in the site selection procedure.

Except the above, the opinion of people living close to the examined area can always provide important information toward the first estimation of the existing wind potential. Shepherds, farmers, and fishermen with frequent presence at the vicinity of the examined site can be approached tactfully and asked generally about the existing weather conditions. Invaluable information can be gathered from local inhabitants, although special approach skills may be required.

Table 1 Mean annual wind velocity estimation based on the Griggs-Putnam and Barsch indexes

		Mean annual wind velocity (m s^{-1}) and possible estimation error (±m s^{-1})							
		Index value							
Type of tree	Index	0	1	2	3	4	5	6	7
Fir	Griggs-Putnam	6.0 ± 2.0	6.7 ± 1.9	7.4 ± 1.8	8.1 ± 1.8	8.8 ± 1.8	9.5 ± 1.8	10.2 ± 1.9	10.9 ± 2.0
Juniper	Griggs-Putnam	4.4 ± 2.1	5.0 ± 2.0	5.6 ± 1.9	6.2 ± 1.9	6.8 ± 2.0	7.4 ± 2.1	8.0 ± 2.2	8.6 ± 2.5
Fir	Griggs-Putnam	3.0 ± 2.8	4.2 ± 2.6	5.4 ± 2.5	6.6 ± 2.4	7.8 ± 2.5	9.0 ± 2.6	10.2 ± 2.8	11.4 ± 3.0
Pine	Griggs-Putnam	3.3 ± 1.9	4.0 ± 1.8	4.7 ± 1.7	5.4 ± 1.8	6.1 ± 1.8	6.8 ± 2.0	7.5 ± 2.1	8.2 ± 2.3
Pseudotsuga (Douglas Fir)	Griggs-Putnam	3.3 ± 1.7	4.1 ± 1.6	4.9 ± 1.5	5.7 ± 1.5	6.5 ± 1.5	7.3 ± 1.6	8.1 ± 1.8	8.9 ± 1.9
Acer	Barsch	3.4 ± 1.5	4.3 ± 1.0	5.2 ± 1.4	6.1 ± 2.2	7.0 ± 3.1	7.9 ± 4.1	8.8 ± 5.1	9.7 ± 6.1
Acorn tree	Barsch	3.0 ± 1.8	4.1 ± 1.7	5.2 ± 1.7	6.3 ± 1.8	7.4 ± 1.9	8.5 ± 2.1	9.6 ± 2.3	10.7 ± 2.5
Acacia	Barsch	3.7 ± 1.2	4.4 ± 1.0	5.1 ± 1.0	5.8 ± 1.3	6.5 ± 1.7	7.2 ± 2.1	7.9 ± 2.5	8.6 ± 3.0
Elm	Barsch	3.3 ± 1.5	4.4 ± 1.4	5.5 ± 1.4	6.6 ± 1.6	7.7 ± 2.0	8.8 ± 2.4	9.9 ± 2.9	11.0 ± 3.4

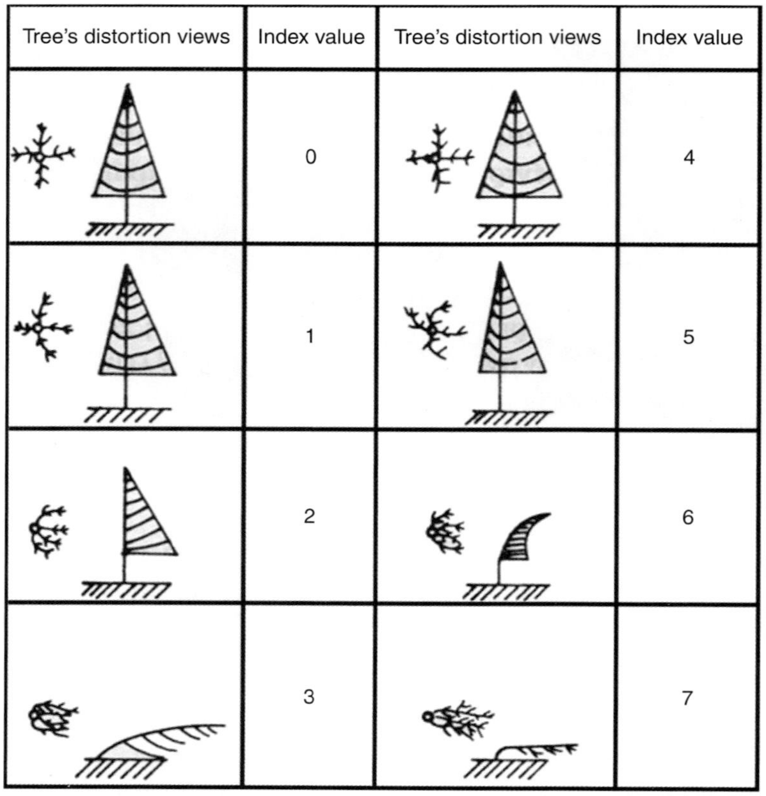

Tree's distortion views	Index value	Tree's distortion views	Index value
	0		4
	1		5
	2		6
	3		7

Figure 4 Distortion degree of trees according to Griggs-Putnam [8].

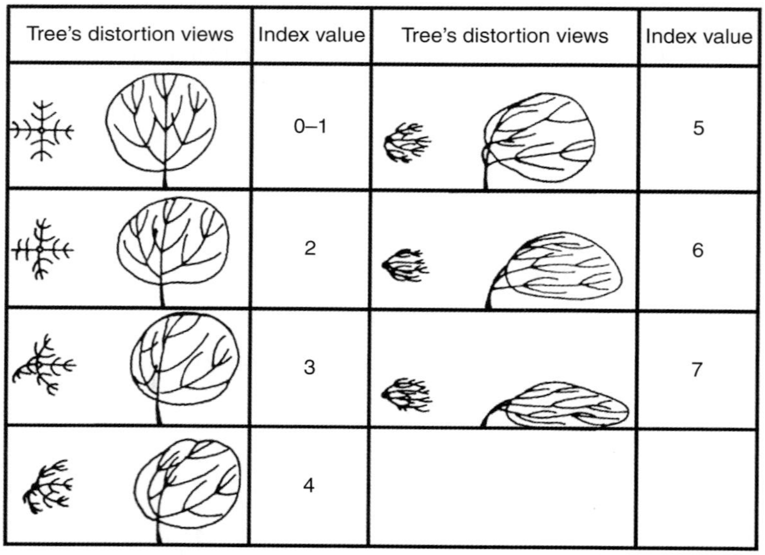

Tree's distortion views	Index value	Tree's distortion views	Index value
	0–1		5
	2		6
	3		7
	4		

Figure 5 Distortion degree of trees according to Barsch [8].

2.07.2.2 The Effect of Land Morphology on the Site Selection

The wind velocity increases with the height above ground. This is because the effect of the ground's roughness on the wind velocity reduces as the height above ground increases. This in turn means that the wind flow aerodynamic and friction losses reduce; hence, the wind kinetic energy becomes higher.

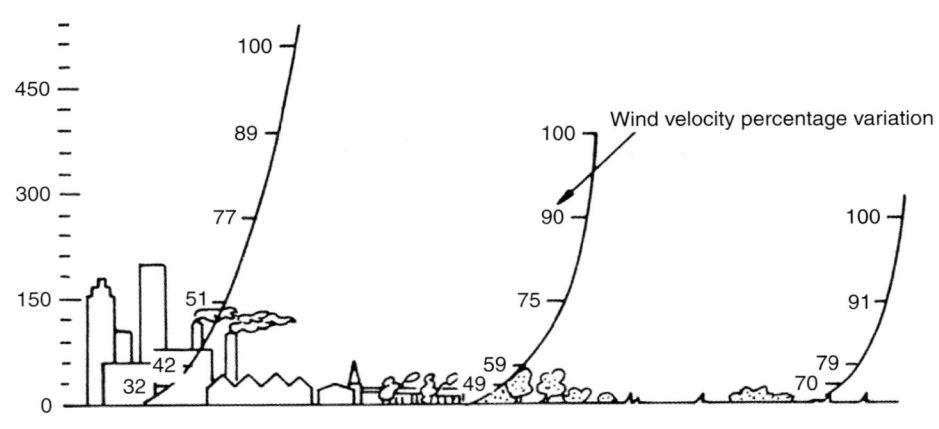

Figure 6 The effect of ground roughness on the atmospheric boundary layer development [8].

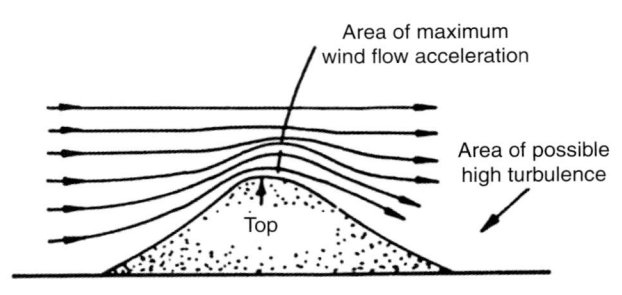

Figure 7 Maximization of the wind velocity above the top of a hill [8].

The wind velocity variation in terms of the height above ground is presented in **Figure 6**. As shown in this figure, a terrain with high roughness (e.g., cities with high buildings, and forests with high trees) causes considerable reduction in the wind's kinetic energy. In these cases, the atmospheric boundary layer is fully developed in higher levels above ground than in a flat area with low ground roughness. The wind velocity variation versus the height above ground exhibits a parabolic shape, reaching maximum value at 100–1000 m above ground, depending on the ground roughness.

Following the abovementioned observations, it is obvious that the wind turbines should be installed in places with a fully developed wind velocity profile, namely in high altitudes above ground or in places with low ground roughness. On the other hand, one must take into account that the wind's kinetic energy is analogous to the wind mass, namely to the wind density, that reduces with the height above sea level (absolute altitude). In absolute altitudes higher than 1000 m, the atmosphere air density reduces considerably and the wind kinetic energy reduces as well.

On top of hills or mountains, the wind velocity increases due to Venturi phenomenon (**Figure 7**) [8]. When the wind blows above the top of hills or mountains, the air pressure decreases and the wind velocity increases. The wind velocity on top of hills or mountains exhibits higher values compared to those in lower altitudes [8].

According to the above remarks, it is concluded that an appropriate site for a wind park's installation should satisfy the following prerequisites:

- the site should be located at the top of hills or mountains, where the wind velocity is maximized
- the absolute altitude of the site should not exceed 1000 m above sea level, in order to preserve the atmospheric air density in high values
- no physical or technical obstacles should exist in the vicinity of the installation area (e.g., other high mountains) that could prevent the wind boundary layer from being fully developed.

The ideal land morphology for wind parks' installation is presented in **Figure 8**. The hill or mountain height should not exceed an upper limit (in **Figure 8** this is set indicatively at 600 m). This upper limit aims to eliminate the possibilities of extreme weather conditions, although this depends on the geographical location of the installation site. On the other hand, a site with lower altitude is usually more easily accessed and, consequently, the required infrastructure works are restricted.

Moreover, the top of the hills or mountains should be rounded and not flat. This is because when wind blows above flat tops a shear effect can be caused [8]. The shear effect is caused by the wind flow detachment above the abrupt change of the land incline. The detached wind flow is characterized with high turbulence close to the flat top (**Figure 9**). The shear effect can be the reason for important malfunctions and even damage to the wind turbines. The most common consequence of the shear effect is the reduction

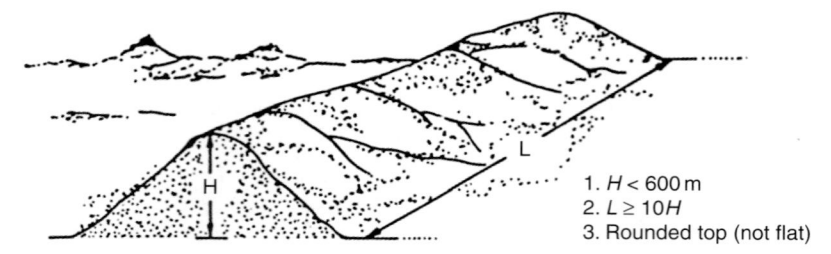

Figure 8 Ideal land morphology for wind park installation [8].

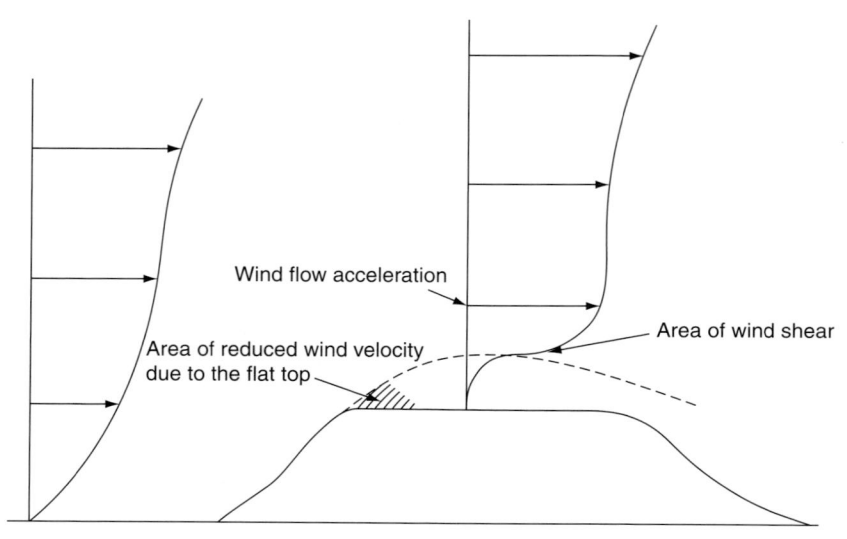

1. $H < 600\,m$
2. $L \geq 10H$
3. Rounded top (not flat)

Figure 9 The shear effect [8].

of wind power production due to wind flow aerodynamic losses. A more serious consequence regarding the normal operation and the security of the wind turbine is the mechanical fatigue of the turbine blades that face wind gusts from opposite direction from the wind flow main one.

For the above presented analysis, it is revealed that it is rather difficult to find ideal sites for wind parks' installations, namely sites that satisfy all the above conditions. Some examples of mountains or hills morphology, compared to the wind main direction, are presented in **Figure 10**. A short description concerning the suitability of the land morphology for wind parks' installations is also provided. As seen in this figure, the optimum land morphology for wind parks' installation is mountain crests with their direction vertical to the prevailing wind. In the case of mountain crests parallel to the wind, the wind turbines' shading losses increase. To avoid this, longer distances must be kept between wind turbines' installation positions. Hence, a larger area for the installation of the wind park is required.

A special category of wind parks are the offshore ones, namely wind parks installed in the sea. In these cases, the lack of physical or technical obstacles enables the full development of the atmospheric boundary layer at lower altitudes than in land. The wind flow turbulence over sea is lower than in land. In cases of highly wavy seas these advantages are eliminated. The selection of an offshore area for the installation of a wind park is performed by taking into account the existing wind potential and the availability of turbines' installation positions normally at depths lower than 30 m.

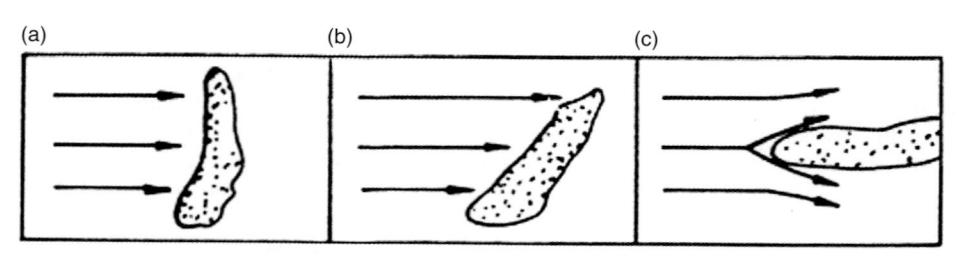

Figure 10 The suitability of different land morphologies for wind parks' installations [8].

2.07.2.3 Aiming at the Minimization of the Set-Up Cost

As already mentioned in the introductory section, the main component of the set-up cost of a wind park is the wind turbines' purchase cost [9, 10]. This cost is configured, via the manufacturer, by several market parameters that are beyond the investors' control. Such parameters can be the original energy sources prices (fossil fuels, electricity), the construction material cost, the turbines manufacturers' policies, and so on. On the other hand, the selection of an appropriate wind turbine model is usually performed by taking into account several other parameters of major importance, such as the nominal power of the wind turbine, the dimensions, the transportation possibilities at the site of installation, the total wind park power and the available land, the generator's specifications, and so on. The cost of the wind turbine is usually a parameter of minor importance, as far as the wind turbine model selection procedure is concerned. The conclusion revealed from this analysis is that the wind park's total set-up cost cannot be reduced with the wind turbine model's purchase cost, although it comprises the main set-up cost component. This cost is defined in the manufacturer's financial and technical quotation, and it usually does not constitute a major parameter affecting the selection of the appropriate wind turbine model.

On the contrary, the set-up cost of a wind park can be reduced mainly by reducing the rest of the cost components of the total set-up cost, such as the required infrastructure works, equipment transportation, and new connection network costs. All these costs depend mainly on the location of the selected site. The technical infrastructure in the vicinity of the selected site, such as the existing roads, the electricity and communication networks, and so on, can eliminate the required infrastructure works of the wind park, reducing, thus, the corresponding costs. Other parameters, strongly connected to the installation site, that affect the total set-up cost can be as follows:

- the geological features of the installation site, affecting directly the required grounding of the wind turbines' towers
- the distance of the site from the connection point of the existing utility network
- the demand for construction of the underground connection network
- special transportation means (e.g., helicopters) in case of sites without possible access by land.

The above listed parameters can affect the total wind park set-up cost positively or negatively, in terms of the special conditions in the selected installation site. Nevertheless, it must be underlined that the expected total cost reduction cannot exceed 20–30%, taking into account that the wind turbines' purchase cost corresponds to 70–80% of the total wind park's cost [9, 10]. A more detailed analysis concerning installation issues of the wind turbines is provided in the next section.

Finally, a special case is offshore wind parks. In this case it is obvious that equipment transportation, the towers' grounding, and the new network construction exhibit much higher costs than those of a wind park on land [10]. Their percentage contribution to the total set-up cost configuration exhibits higher values. The wind turbine tower grounding costs increase with the depth of the sea at the installation site. As mentioned above, it is desirable to install offshore wind parks at depths lower than 30 m, while depths higher than 50 m are avoided for offshore wind parks' installations, since special expensive grounding methods are required [11]. The network connection cost in offshore wind parks increases with the depth of installation and the distance from the network connection point. The transportation cost of the equipment for offshore wind parks' installations increases with the distance from the nearest harbor as well. Consequently, in order to reduce the total set-up cost in offshore wind parks, sea areas with depths lower than 30 m close to the coast must be investigated.

2.07.2.4 Installation Issues of the Wind Turbines

A wind park's installation consists of the following stages:

- the construction of the several infrastructure works, such as roads, wind turbine service areas, and so on
- the equipment's transportation
- the wind turbines' foundation
- the wind turbines' erection
- the secondary electromechanical equipment installation
- the connection of the wind park to the electricity network
- a test operation period of some months.

The first four of the above stages are described analytically in the following sections.

2.07.2.4.1 The equipment transportation

The difficulties in a wind park's equipment transportation mainly arise from the necessity to transfer the long turbine blades. The wind turbines' transportation can include the following phases:

- Transportation from the manufacturer's factories to a harbor. Usually this part of transportation is accomplished without problems, due to the existence of adequate road networks connecting the wind turbine production sites (usually in Western Europe and the United States) to nearby harbors.

Figure 11 Transportation of 44 m long wind turbine's blades, found in relevant manufacturers brochures.

- Transportation overseas from one harbor to another or to the installation site of an offshore wind park. This part of transportation is also accomplished without problems.
- Transportation from a harbor or the manufacturer's factories directly to the installation area. This stage usually includes any difficulties met in the wind turbines' transportation, especially in cases of installation sites located on top of mountains or remote areas with a lack of road networks. The length of a 1 MW wind turbine may exceed 25 m, while in the case of a 3 MW wind turbine the blades' length reaches 45 m. These parts cannot be separated, so it is mandatory to transfer them whole on very long platforms (see **Figure 11**).

The transportation of such long parts can be performed by means of roads with special features concerning their width, especially in bends, and their ability to bear heavy loads. For example, a 44 m long blade exhibits a weight of 7 t; consequently, the transportation of three blades on a platform exhibit a total weight of 21 t. Generally, manufacturers provide certain specifications concerning features of the roads used for the wind turbines' transportation. These features can be the maximum permissible load that can be transferred, the minimum bend radius and road width, and so on.

Apart from the dimensions of the access road, special requirements are also set regarding the quality of the road construction. If the subsoil is soft (boggy soil, etc.), it may be necessary to use more backfill, install a geogrid, and make use of gravel.

The above presented specifications, except the access road, are also applied to the wind park's internal road.

In the case of offshore wind parks, the transportation of the wind turbines is undertaken by companies with relevant expertise and performed with special vessels.

2.07.2.4.2 The wind turbines' service area

For the wind turbines' assembly and erection, a specific area around the installation position is required to be clear and flat. This area is called the turbine's service area. The dimensions of the service area and the specifications concerning the construction materials are provided by the turbine's manufacturer.

2.07.2.4.3 The wind turbines' foundation

The wind turbines' foundation in land is a common task, however, performed under strict specifications set by each manufacturer. Special requirements are set concerning the depth and the diameter of the foundation, the quality of the concrete, and so on. Normally, a geological study of the installation ground preludes the foundation one in order to indicate special issues or peculiarities that should be taken into account. Drilling is also used to collect samples of the subsoil from depths greater than 20 m at a number of positions around the foundation. The results from the subsoil sampling and the geological study configure the requirements of the foundation construction.

However, things are not so simple in the case of offshore wind turbines' foundations. In such cases, the possible foundation solutions vary, depending mainly on the water depths at the installation position. The available alternatives are presented in **Figure 12**.

The common foundations used for offshore wind projects in shallow water are listed below and presented in **Figure 13**:

- *Monopile.* Consists of a steel pile that is driven approximately 10–20 m into the seabed.
- *Gravity foundation.* Currently used for most offshore wind energy projects; the gravity foundation consists of a large base constructed from either concrete or steel that rests on the seabed. The turbine is dependent on gravity to remain erect.

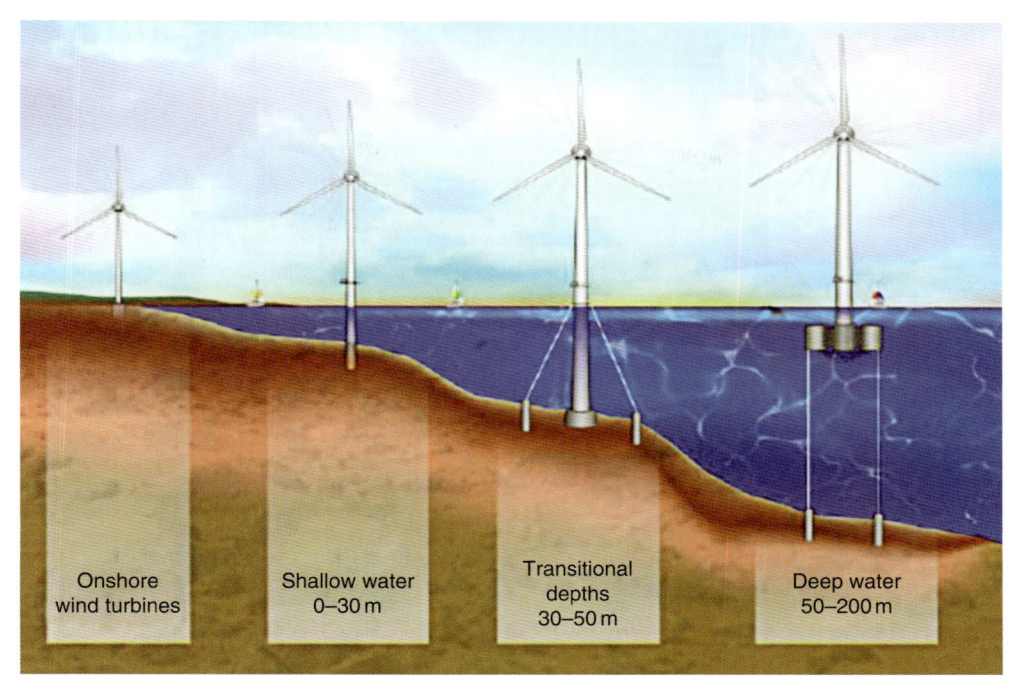

Figure 12 Available alternative solutions for wind turbine installations offshore [12].

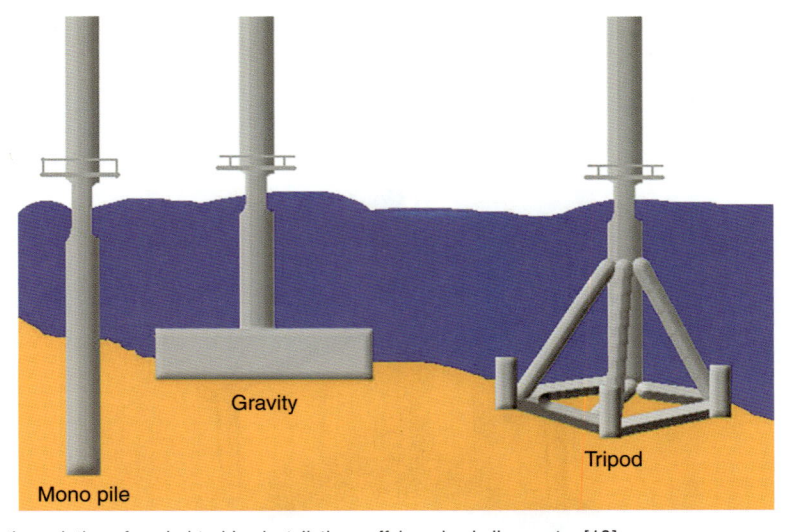

Figure 13 Available alternative solutions for wind turbine installations offshore in shallow water [12].

- *Tripod foundation.* Designs tend to rely on technology used by the oil and gas industry. The piles on each end are typically driven 10–20 m into the seabed, depending on soil conditions. This technology is generally used at deeper depths and has not been used in many projects to date.

As far as the offshore wind turbines' foundation in deep water is concerned, many of the proposed concepts utilize designs borrowed from the oil and gas industry. The advantages of deep water offshore wind energy projects is that winds are stronger far from the shore and projects can be invisible from the shoreline, minimizing opposition of the public. Cost may be one of the biggest challenges facing deep water offshore technology. The following examples may be mentioned.

- The jacket foundation technology has been borrowed from gas and oil platforms and has been deployed at the Beatrice offshore wind energy project in Scotland (**Figures 14(a)** and **14(b)**).
- The Mobile Self-Installing Platform (MSIP), a three-legged platform able to be towed out to sea and lowered into place (**Figure 15**).
- Several floating foundations, such as the examples presented in **Figure 16**.

Figure 14 (a) The jacket foundation [12]. (b) The jacket foundation at Beatrice offshore wind park in Scotland [12].

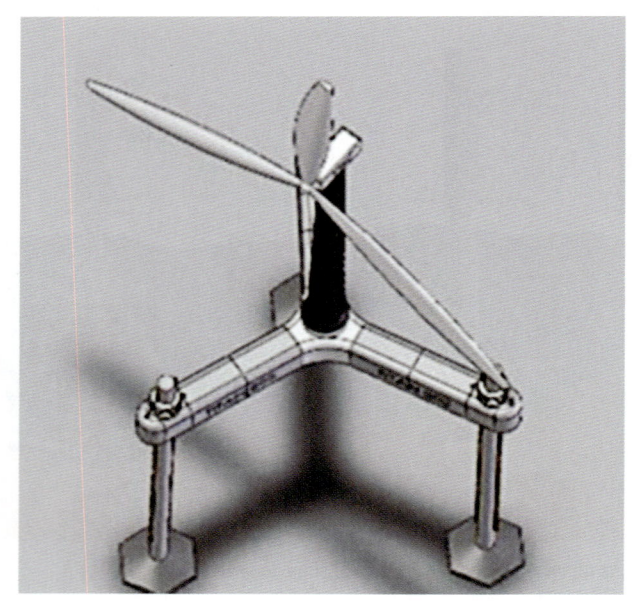

Figure 15 The mobile self-installing platform [13].

2.07.2.4.4 The wind turbines' erection

The wind turbines' erection requires the use of heavy machinery and cranes with high capacity, regarding both the raising height and weight. The erection of the wind turbines is usually accomplished by the manufacturer.

In general, once the transportation of the equipment (tower, nacelle, blades) to the wind turbine's service area is completed, the blades are assembled to the hub. In the case of an offshore wind park, the blades are assembled to the hub on land and the rotor is transferred to the installation position on a vessel (**Figure 17**). Then the two or three parts of the turbine tower are installed, connecting simultaneously the one over the other (**Figure 18**). Once the tower has been installed, the nacelle is lifted to the top of it (**Figure 19**). The last stage includes the raising of the hub with the blades and the installation at the nacelle (**Figure 20**). The procedure is integrated with the wind turbine's converter installation and the electrical connections.

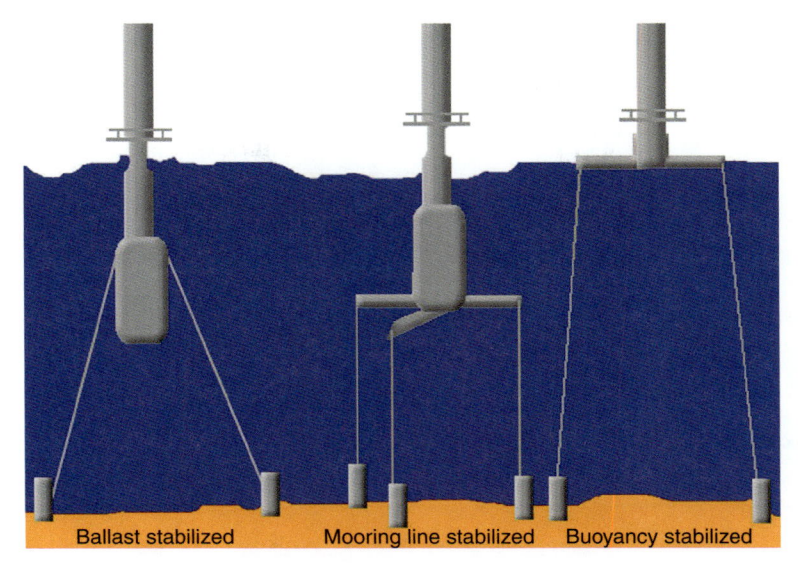

Figure 16 Several floating foundations for wind turbine installations offshore in deep water [12].

Figure 17 Jack-up barge loaded with nacelle, rotor, and blades and transferred to the installation site of an offshore wind park [12].

Figure 18 The assembly of the tower [12].

2.07.2.5 Aiming at the Minimization of the Time Required for the Wind Park Project Implementation

The time required for a wind park project implementation is mainly configured by the time required for the licensing procedure. Although this fact is common in most European countries, it can exhibit slight variations between them, depending on the existing national legislation frameworks. On the other hand, the time required for a wind park's erection depends on the size of the wind

Figure 19 The lift of the nacelle to the top of the tower [12].

Figure 20 The lift of the turbine rotor [12].

park, the existing technical infrastructure in the installation area, and so on. In any case it consists of only a small percentage of the time required for the integration of the licensing procedure and can be extended only in very special and unpredicted cases, such as the existence of extreme weather conditions for long time periods during the erection works. Consequently, any effort toward the reduction of the required time for the implementation of a wind park project should be focused on the minimization of the licensing procedure time period.

The licensing procedure aims at the investigation of the predefined prerequisites in the existing legislation that should be fulfilled by the wind park, in order to avoid any kind of impacts in the natural environment, human activities, and the existing electricity network. Consequently, minimization of the licensing procedure time can be achieved with an investigation in advance of the possible impacts that the wind park could cause and the examination of possible ways to avoid them.

The following wind parks' impacts are usually investigated within the frames of a wind park project development [14]:

- the impact on the esthetic of the landscape
- the noise emissions
- the impact on birds and wildlife
- the shadow flicker from wind turbines
- the occupation of land
- the wind turbines' electromagnetic interference.

The introduced restrictions on the installations in the relevant legislation aim at limitation of the abovementioned wind parks' impacts. Beyond the defined restrictions in the legislation framework, during the selection of the installation site one should take into account experience regarding the impacts, as presented below, in order to avoid any possible reactions from local communities and special environmental organizations (e.g., ornithologists). More information about the importance of the abovementioned impacts on human activities and wildlife can be found in relevant references [15–23] and in the corresponding Chapter of this Volume.

Restrictions are also included in the relevant legislation concerning the effect of a wind park on the existing electricity networks, especially noninterconnected and weak ones. In such cases, the total installed wind power in isolated systems is not allowed to exceed an upper limit, usually set as a portion of the maximum annual power demand [24–26]. This limit is established in order to restrict the possible dynamic security and power quality problems caused by the wind turbines. This would occur in cases of high wind power installations in weak and small-sized systems. The permissible wind power installation in a weak system is estimated on the basis of the maximum wind power that can penetrate into the system without affecting its secure operation. Consequently, this upper limit aims both at the conservation of the system's secure operation and at the protection of the wind park's investors.

More information about the wind power penetration in isolated networks and the potential problems to the system's normal operation is presented in a following section. As far as the selection of an installation site is concerned, in order to eliminate any possible incompatibilities with the relevant legislation and shorten the required licensing time period, one should avoid installations in weak and noninterconnected networks, as well as in areas with already high installed wind power density (wind power installed per hectare or km^2).

Finally, a crucial issue connected to the site selection is the possibility of the wind park's developer gaining the rights to proceed in the implementation of the project on the specific site. Generally, a candidate's land for a wind park's implementation can belong either to the state or to individuals. In cases where the land is under the state's ownership, a special license must be provided from the state to the park's developer, permitting the wind park's set-up at the specific site. In cases where the land belongs to individuals, then the wind park's developer should manage to persuade the owners either to rent or sell the land for the wind park implementation. The possession of the land's ownership is usually a time-consuming procedure, especially in cases where total land of the wind park installation site belongs to more than one owner. This procedure is usually not only a matter of cost but also requires special communication and people-approaching skills. It is very important for the normal and quick integration of the wind park and can even lead to a project's failure if not handled properly on time.

2.07.3 The Wind Potential Evaluation

Once the site for the installation of the wind park is selected, the accurate evaluation of the wind potential is the first task to be fulfilled. The evaluation of the available wind potential is required in order to calculate the expected annual electricity production from the wind park accurately.

The evaluation of the wind potential at the installation site begins with the installation of a meteorological (or wind) mast for the collection of wind potential measurements. Such measurements include the wind velocity magnitude and direction, the wind gusts, and so on. Wind potential measurements are received for very short time intervals (e.g., for every second) and mean measurements are recorded for certain predefined time periods (e.g., for every 10 min). The total measurement period should be at least 1 year, in order to permit secure evaluation of the wind potential. The expansion of the measurement period to more than 1 year will certainly lead to more reliable conclusions concerning the examined wind potential. However, secure information concerning the variability of the wind versus the years can also be gathered from long-term meteorological data, recorded from satellites for specific points on Earth [27, 28]. The long-term data, compared to the short-term wind potential measurements, can also provide reliable information concerning the variability of the wind potential for a time period of 2–3 decades. The wind potential evaluation based on long-term wind potential data is distinguished in the following steps:

- The long-term meteorological data, recorded from satellites, are provided for specific points on Earth and for certain altitudes (~100 m above sea level). Two points nearest to the wind mast installation position with available long-term data are selected.
- By applying interpolation techniques, the long-term data are transferred to the wind mast installation position, taking into account the distances between the long-term data points and the wind mast position.
- The long-term data usually cover a time interval of 30 years with mean values of wind velocity magnitude and direction for every 6 h. The short-term wind potential data measured by the wind mast are considered more accurate and reliable than the long-term one. The mean annual wind velocity of the short-term data is compared to the corresponding long-term, for the measurements' time period. If significant difference between these two values is exhibited, then the long-term time-series is corrected analogically by multiplying its values with the ratio of the short-term over the long-term annual mean wind velocity.

The long-term meteorological data are provided by reliable institutes (e.g., NASA, NREL, etc.) and can be found on specific electronic sites [27, 28]. The possession of annual wind potential measurements and long-term meteorological data can provide accurate information about the existing wind potential at the of Kasos in the installation site, on the condition of a proper statistical correlation of the available time-series, as presented previously. In **Figure 21**, the mean annual wind velocity variation is presented at the installation site of a meteorological mast in the Greek island of Kasos in the southeast Aegean Sea, based on satellite wind potential data, calculated following the above described methodology.

The fundamental feature of a wind mast is its height. The height of the wind mast is mainly implied by the expected wind potential. As explained in an earlier section, the height above ground where the wind boundary layer is fully developed depends

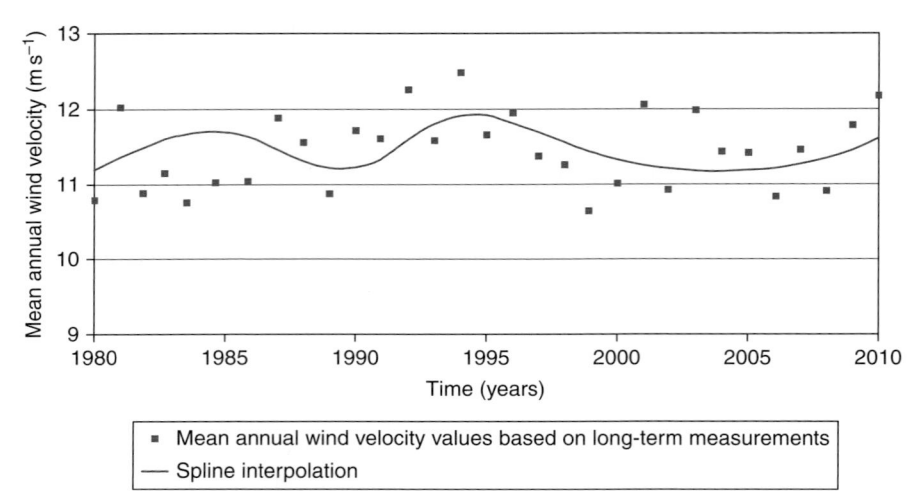

Figure 21 Mean annual wind velocity variation at the installation site of a meteorological mast, based on satellite wind potential data.

on the ground roughness. Generally, the wind velocity increases with the height above ground. Consequently, the higher a meteorological mast is, the higher the measured wind velocity is expected to be. The optimum installation is a meteorological mast with height equal to the hub height of the wind turbine that will be installed. In this case, the measured wind velocity will be exactly that which the wind turbines' rotors will face. However, the cost of the meteorological mast increases almost linearly with its height. For example, the cost of a 10 m high meteorological mast in Greece varies between €10 000 and 15 000, depending on the specific installation site of the mast. This means that the cost for a 40 m high wind mast will exceed €40 000, while the cost of a 60 m high wind mast will exceed €60 000. In sites where the wind potential is estimated to be high beforehand, the height of the wind mast can be restricted. Namely, if the measured wind velocity 10 m above ground exceeds a lower desirable limit set by the developer (e.g., 7.5 m s^{-1}), it is sure that at the wind turbine's hub height the wind velocity will be higher, hence it will meet the expectations of the developer. In this case, the installation of a 10 m high wind mast can be enough. On the other hand, if the wind velocity met at low heights is low, then a higher wind mast should be installed, in order to collect more accurate information about the available wind potential closer to the wind turbine's hub height.

A 40 m high meteorological mast is presented in **Figure 22** with three levels of measurements at 10, 25, and 40 m.

Once measurement of the wind potential is completed, a statistical analysis of the recorded time-series is fulfilled using special software tools. Among the results of this analysis are the wind-rose diagrams or the Weibull probability density distributions of the wind velocity, for monthly time periods and for the total measurements time period. Several characteristic statistical features are also calculated, such as the wind velocity, standard deviation, the mean monthly and annual values, the duration curve of the wind velocity, and so on. In **Figures 23** and **24**, the annual wind-rose and Weibull probability density calculated from annual wind potential measurement time-series are presented.

The gathered measurements are finally imported in specific software tools to evaluate the wind potential on the total installation site. The wind map is developed and several features are calculated, such as the Weibull C and k parameters and the wind-rose graphs in selected positions. Apart from the gathered time-series, other required data for the wind map development are the coordinates of the wind mast installation position, the height of the wind mast, the height above ground at which the wind flow field will be calculated (usually this is set equal to the turbine's hub height), the ground roughness, the area boundaries of the wind flow field development, and so on. The wind potential is calculated in specific points of the total territory (land discrimination). The density of the calculation grid is also defined by the software's user. By importing a specific wind turbine model at the turbine installation site, these tools can further calculate the expected annual electricity production from the wind turbines, including the energy shading losses from one wind turbine to another. More information about the calculation of the annual electricity production from a wind park is provided in a next section.

An example from a wind map developed for a specific site in southern Crete is presented in **Figure 25**. The position of the wind mast installation is presented in this figure, as well as a wind-rose presenting the main wind direction (north). The wind measurements were gathered from 2 July 2008 to 1 July 2009. The wind potential measurements time period is 1 year, giving a mean annual wind velocity of 8.67 m s^{-1}. The Weibull distribution parameters are calculated equal to $C = 9.7$ m s^{-1} and $k = 1.77$.

Another wind map example is presented in **Figure 26**, for a site on the island of Kasos, in the Dodecanese complex (southeast Aegean Sea). The wind mast installation position is also depicted in this figure. The duration of the wind potential measurements is 9 months, from 14 May 2010 to 13 February 2011. The mean wind velocity over the measurements time period is 11.61 m s^{-1}. The Weibull distribution parameters are calculated equal to $C = 13.2$ m s^{-1} and $k = 2.85$.

Finally, a wind map developed for an offshore area in the south west of the Greek island of Rhodes is presented in **Figure 27**, based on wind potential measurements for a 6-month time period. The 10 m high meteorological mast is installed on a small rocky

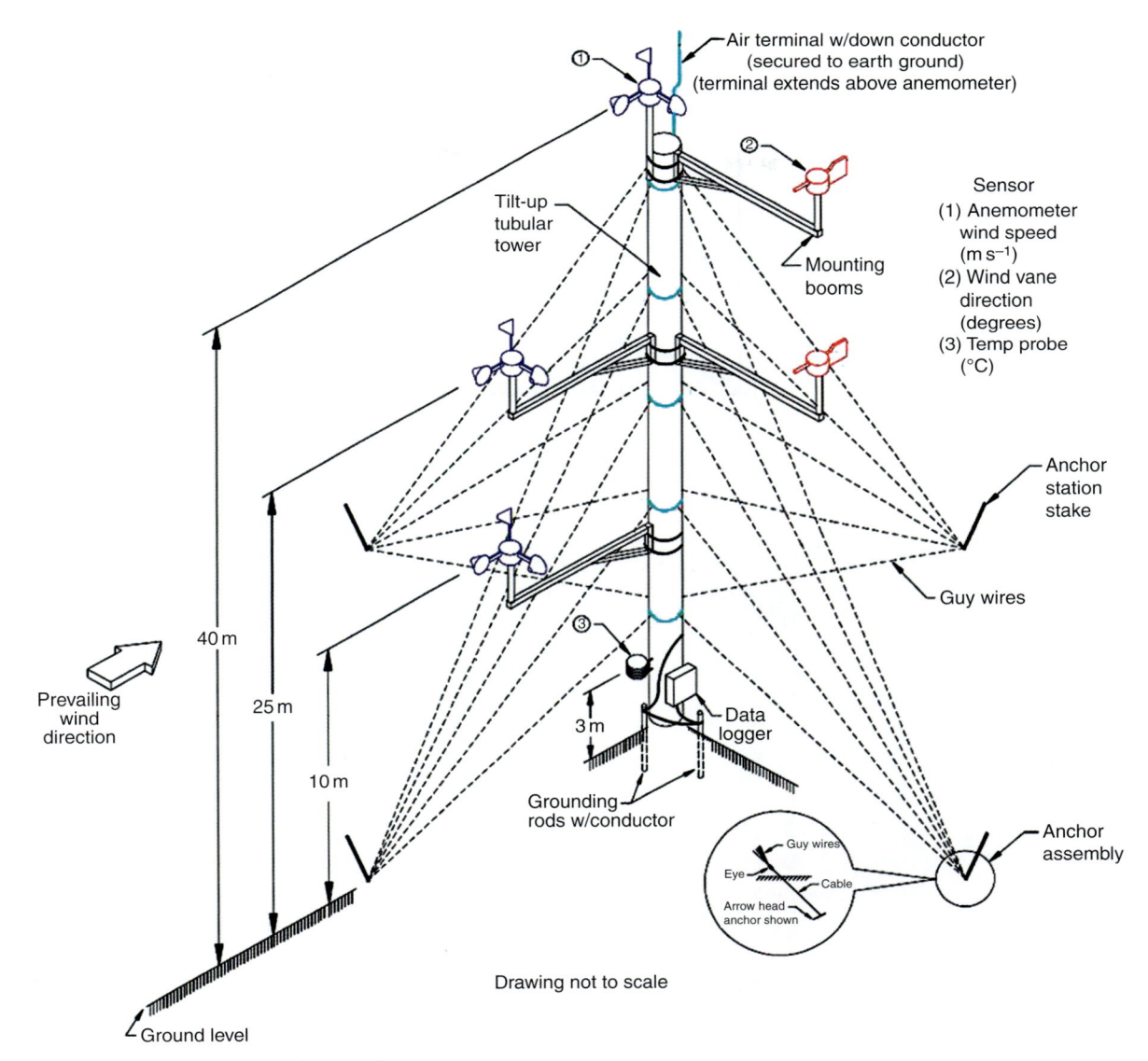

Figure 22 A 40 m high meteorological mast [29].

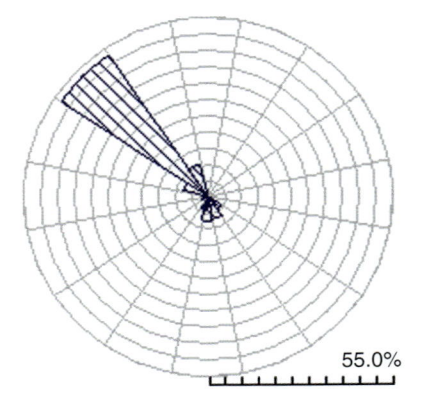

Figure 23 Wind-rose based on annual wind potential measurements on a site on the island of Kasos.

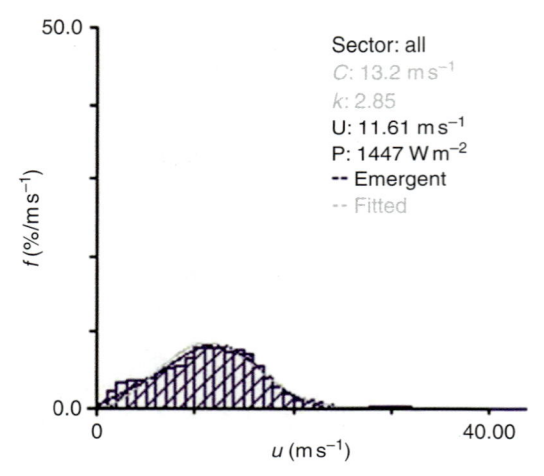

Figure 24 Weibull distribution based on annual wind potential measurements on a site on the island of Kasos.

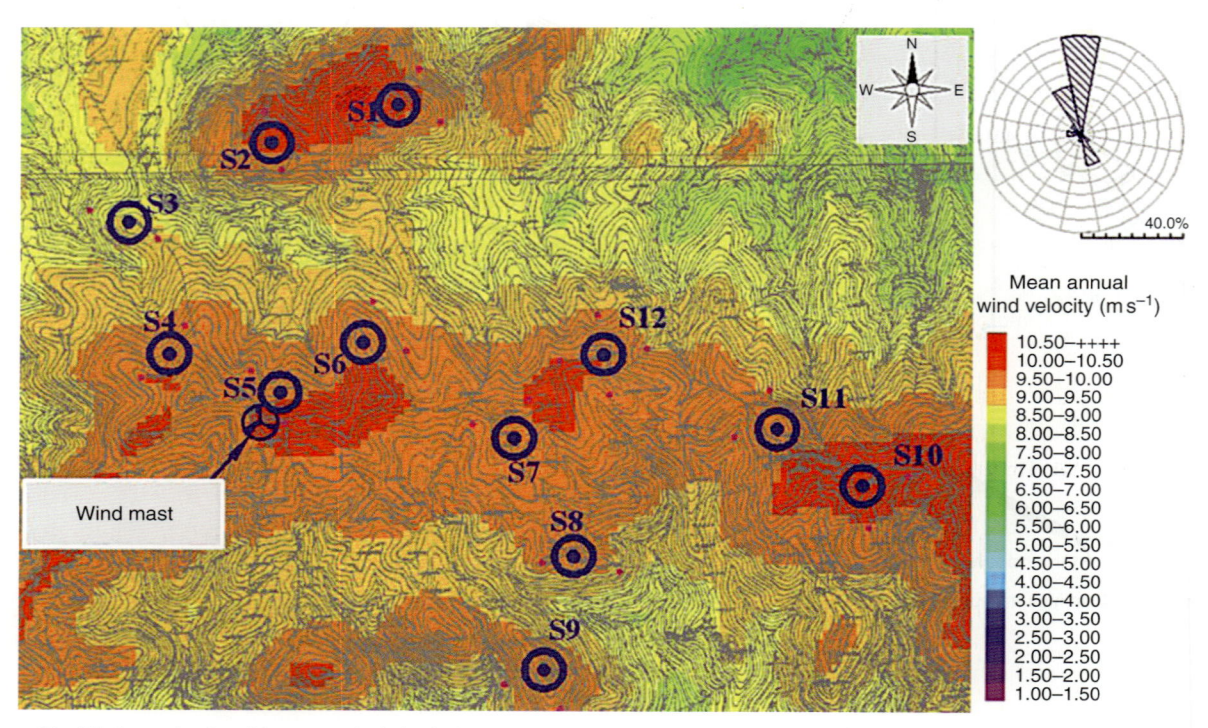

Figure 25 Wind map developed from annual wind velocity measurements for a site in southern Crete. The abbreviation S1, S2, and so on, stands for wind turbines' installation sites.

island. The mean wind velocity is measured as $9.1\ m\ s^{-1}$. The Weibull distribution parameters for the annual time period are calculated equal to $C = 10.3\ m\ s^{-1}$ and $k = 2.2$.

By comparing the wind maps presented in the above figures, the intensive effect of the land morphology on the examined wind potential is revealed. In offshore areas, the wind potential is uniform, without variations for different positions. The wind boundary layer is fully developed at lower altitudes and higher wind velocity values are recorded.

2.07.4 The Selection of the Wind Turbine Model

The wind turbine is the fundamental component of a wind park's equipment. Consequently, the selection of the appropriate wind turbine model constitutes one of the most important stages of a wind park project's development. The selection of a wind turbine model is performed on the basis of several parameters, the most important of which are mentioned below:

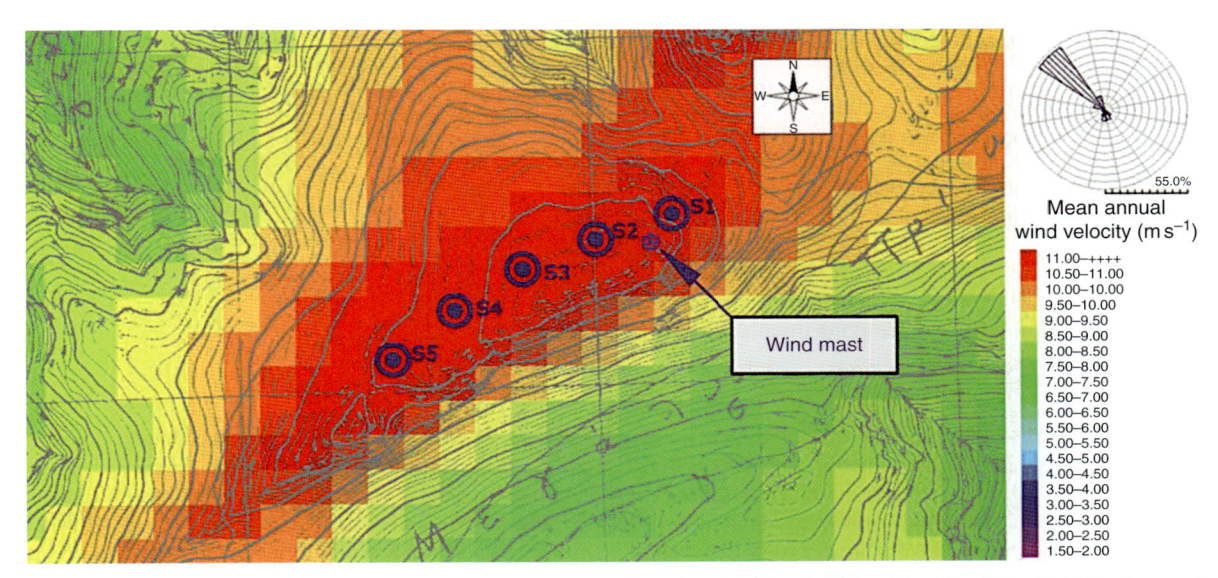

Figure 26 Wind map developed from 9-months wind velocity measurements for a site on the island of Kasos. The abbreviation S1, S2, and so on, stands for wind turbines' installation sites.

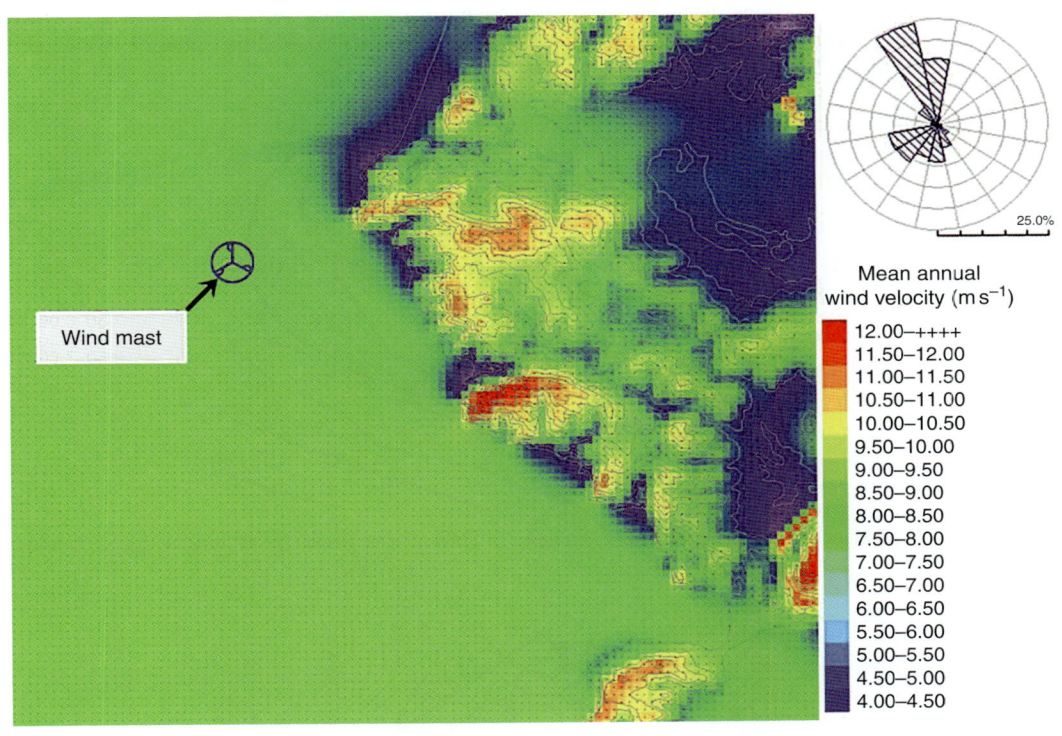

Figure 27 Wind map developed from annual wind velocity measurements for an offshore site in the south west of Rhodes.

- the wind turbine's nominal power
- the wind turbine's physical dimensions
- the available area on the wind park installation site in relation to the wind turbine's nominal power
- the available wind potential
- several peculiarities seen in the general geographical territory of the installation site
- restrictions caused by environmental impacts and human activities
- the demand of the utility for certain specifications regarding the quality of the electricity produced from the wind turbine

Table 2 The evolution of wind turbines during the last 30 years

Year	1980	1985	1990	1995	2000	2005	2010
Nominal power (kW)	50	100	250	600	1000	3000	5000
Diameter (m)	15	20	30	40	55	90	105
Rotor's swept area (m^2)	177	314	706	1256	2375	6361	8659
Hub height (m)	25	35	50	55	60	80	100

- the existing technical infrastructure at the installation site (site accessibility)
- the wind turbines' purchase cost
- the delivery time of the manufacturer.

The nominal power of a wind turbine determines the size of the machine. It is obvious that as the swept area of the turbine's rotor increases, the wind kinetic energy captured by the turbine increases as well. Consequently, the construction of wind turbines with higher nominal power implies the construction of bigger machines. In **Table 2** the evolution of the wind turbines during the last 30 years is presented.

As seen in the table, a wind turbine with nominal power 1 MW exhibits a rotor diameter of approximately 55 m, while a wind turbine with nominal power 3 MW exhibits a rotor diameter of 90 m. The distances of a wind turbine pylon from the wind park's installation site boundaries must be at least $1.0-1.5 \cdot R$, where R is the rotor's radius, depending on the relevant national legislation of each country. Additionally, in order to avoid the wind turbines' shade effect, the minimum distance between two wind turbines installed in a line vertical to the wind's main direction must be at least $2.5-3.0 \cdot D$, where D is the rotor's diameter. A thorough description of the main rules of the wind turbines' micro-siting will be presented in the following section.

Following the abovementioned restrictions, in **Figures 28** and **29** the siting of a wind park with nominal power of 3 MW is presented. In **Figure 28**, wind turbines of 1 MW nominal power and rotor diameter of 55 m are installed, while in **Figure 29** a wind turbine of 3 MW

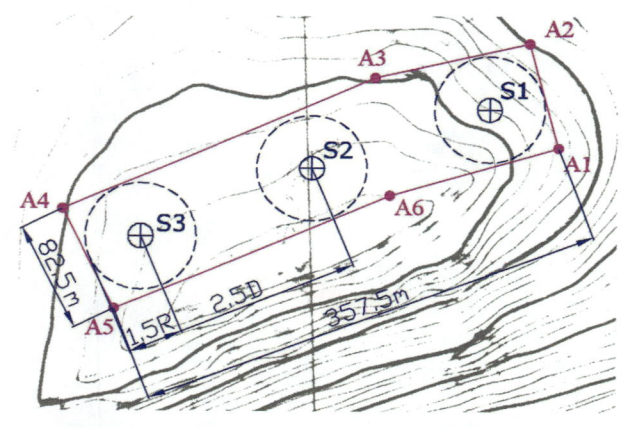

Figure 28 A wind park micro-siting for a 3 MW wind park with wind turbines of 1 MW nominal power. The abbreviation S1, S2, and so on, stands for wind turbines' installation sites.

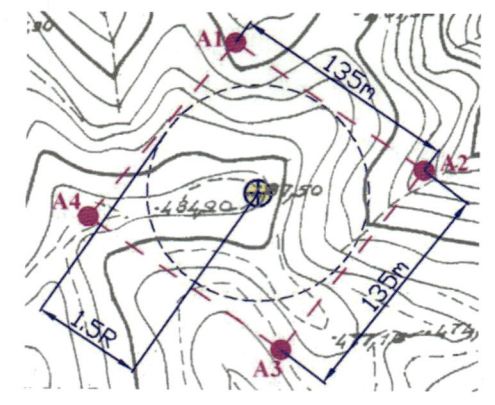

Figure 29 A wind park micro-siting for a 3 MW wind park with one wind turbine of 3 MW nominal power.

nominal power and rotor diameter of 90 m is installed. In the case of **Figure 28**, a total orthogonal area of 357.5 m × 82.5 m = 29 493.75 m² is required for the wind park's installation. In the case of **Figure 29**, a total square area of 135 m × 135 m = 18 225 m² is required. With this simple example it is shown that in case of limited area availability for a wind park's installation, the selection of a wind turbine model with higher nominal power permits the installation of a wind park with higher total nominal power.

As seen in **Table 2**, the hub height and the total maximum height of the wind turbine increase with the wind turbine's nominal power too. For example, a wind turbine with nominal power of 1 MW exhibits a hub height of 60 m and a maximum total height of 87.5 m, while a wind turbine with nominal power of 3 MW exhibits a hub height of 80 m and a maximum total height of 125 m. The increased height of a wind turbine means that the possible impacts of the turbine become more intensive, such as the visibility of the turbine from places of special interest, like archeological sites, tourist destinations, and so on. Another crucial issue is the vicinity of the wind park to airports. The normal operation of special communication instruments installed in the airports' control towers is affected by the maximum height a wind turbine's blade tip can reach. In both of the abovementioned cases, it is most probable that the authorities in charge will demand that the wind park's owner will select a wind turbine model of lower nominal power and physical dimensions. The character of the general geographical area to which the site belongs can also affect the selection of the wind turbine model. For instance, the installation of a 3 MW wind turbine model on the top of a mountain in a small Aegean Sea island will cause higher visual impact and can raise serious negative reactions from the local community than in an industrial area in central Europe. Generally, in sites with natural beauty and special esthetic, the installation of smaller wind turbines can be characterized as a secure selection, capable to protect the wind park project's implementation from several problems.

On the other hand, the installation of a large number of wind turbines of lower nominal power instead of few wind turbines of higher nominal power increases the probability of birds' collisions with the wind turbines' spinning blades. The first bird fatalities observed worldwide was in Altamont wind park in California, where the huge number of installed small wind turbines led to the creation of the 'fence effect', causing the death of thousands of birds. Ornithologists suggest the installation of few wind turbines of higher nominal power in large distances between them, in order to approach the total wind park's nominal power, instead of more wind turbines of smaller size and shorter distances that increase the risk of collision of birds with the spinning blades.

Accessibility to the installation site is another important parameter that must be taken into account while selecting the wind turbine model. Sites at the top of mountains are not easily accessible. The transportation of wind turbines of very large size may require extended infrastructure works, such as existing road modifications or new road construction, or even transportation with helicopters. These tasks increase the project's set-up cost. The above equipment transportation difficulties are more intensive in rural areas (e.g., islands). In the worst cases, the installation of large wind turbines in inaccessible sites can even be impossible. In these cases the selection of a smaller wind turbine model is the only feasible choice.

Special requirements for the specifications of the wind turbine generator are usually introduced by the utilities in cases of wind park installations in weak isolated power systems. These requirements are related to the tolerances of the turbines' generators to the systems' voltage and frequency variations. Special generator characteristics, such as the well-known 'fault ride through' technology, may also be required by the utilities. These requirements can restrict the alternative selections concerning the available wind turbine models.

The available wind potential of the installation site defines the class of the wind turbine. In **Table 3** the wind turbines' classes are presented by IEC 61400-1 [30]. Each wind turbine is constructed for installation in sites with specific wind potential, according to the wind turbines' classes defined in the abovementioned standard. For example, wind turbines of class I can be installed in sites with mean annual wind velocity over 8.5 m s^{-1}, while wind turbines of class II can be installed in sites with mean annual wind velocity between 7.5 and 8.5 m s^{-1}. The installation of a wind turbine of class II in a site of high wind potential can cause the destruction of the machine. On the other hand, the installation of a wind turbine of class I in sites with low wind potential will lead to reduced electricity production from the turbine. Finally, some manufacturers have constructed special wind turbines for sites with very high wind potential (mean annual wind velocity higher than 11 m s^{-1}). These turbines are classified in a special class, named by the turbine's manufacturer. Their fundamental difference with the class I turbines is their slightly smaller dimensions (lower hub height and rotor diameter).

Finally, the cost of the wind turbines and perhaps the delivery time of the manufacturer should also be taken into account in the turbine model selection procedure.

All the abovementioned parameters can contribute toward the selection of the wind turbine model. The significance of each one of them can be different for different wind park projects. They must be carefully inspected in order to make the optimum selection.

In the case of an offshore wind park, the main parameters for the selection of the wind turbine model are the higher foundation cost, compared to the foundation cost on land, and the technical–economic restriction of wind turbines' installation normally in

Table 3 Wind speed parameters and turbulence intensity for wind turbines classes, according to IEC 61400-1

Class	I			II			III			S
Wind speed parameters										
Reference wind speed average U_{ref} over 10 min (m s^{-1})	50.0			42.5			37.5			Values specified by the designer
Turbulence intensity classes	A	B	C	A	B	C	A	B	C	
Turbulence intensity at 15 m s^{-1} I_{15} (%)	16	14	12	16	14	12	16	14	12	

Ten-minute averages, hub height wind velocity, air density 1.225 kg m^{-3}.

depths greater than 30 m. At greater depths, the wind turbines' foundation cost increases considerably. Usually, the use of wind turbines of high nominal power (higher than 3 MW) is preferred in offshore locations due to the following two reasons:

- The high foundation cost per pylon implies that the project's total set-up cost is reduced as the number of the wind turbines decreases. In this case the total wind park nominal power can be maximized with the use of wind turbines of high nominal power.
- In case of deep seas, the possible installation positions with depths greater than 30 m are limited; consequently, the number of wind turbines that can be installed is reduced as well. Thus, in order to ensure the feasibility of the project, the use of wind turbines of high nominal power is usually required.

Consequently, in offshore wind parks, the installation of wind turbines of high nominal power is the only sensible choice, aiming at the feasibility of the offshore project and the minimization of the total set-up cost.

Once the available wind potential has been evaluated for the total area of the installation site and the wind turbine model has been selected, the micro-siting of the wind turbines in the installation site must be designed.

2.07.5 The Micro-Siting of a Wind Park

Wind power is reduced from physical or technical obstacles such as trees, buildings, and so on. The effect of an obstacle on wind power can be extended 2 times the obstacle's height in a vertical direction and 20 times the obstacle's height toward the wind direction (see **Figure 30**). If a wind turbine is located inside the affected area from an obstacle, the available wind power on the wind turbine's rotor will be lower than that available before the obstacle. This phenomenon is called wind turbine shading. The affected area behind an obstacle is called a wake.

Inside the wake of an obstacle, the wind flow exhibits high turbulence and reduced kinetic energy (see **Figure 31**). Apart from reduced available wind power inside this area, the turbulent flow may cause significant fatigue on the turbine's blades that may even lead to the rotor's destruction. The micro-siting of the wind turbines, namely the exact determination of the turbines' installation positions inside the wind park's site, should take into account all the existing obstacles in the vicinity of the wind park, in order to avoid the shading effect.

A wind turbine's shading can be caused from other wind turbines in the wind park as well. The rotor of a wind turbine captures part of the available wind kinetic energy and converts it to electricity. Behind the wind turbine's rotor the wind kinetic energy is reduced approximately to one-third of that available in front of the rotor. The area behind the wind turbine's rotor, where the wind kinetic energy is lower, is called the turbine's shading area. The width of the shading area increases with the distance from the turbine's rotor. The wind velocity inside the shading area increases gradually with the distance from the turbine's rotor as well. The wind kinetic energy is fully restored after a distance of approximately 20 times the rotor's diameter toward the wind direction (see **Figure 32**).

The percentage of the wind energy reduction over the available wind energy in the front of the rotor is called shading loss. A total annual shading loss of 5% in a wind park means that the total annual electricity production from all the wind turbines of the wind

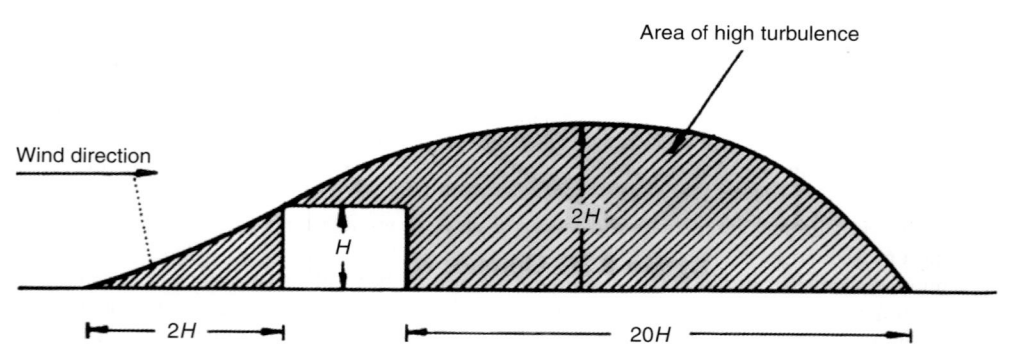

Figure 30 The effect of an obstacle on the wind power [8].

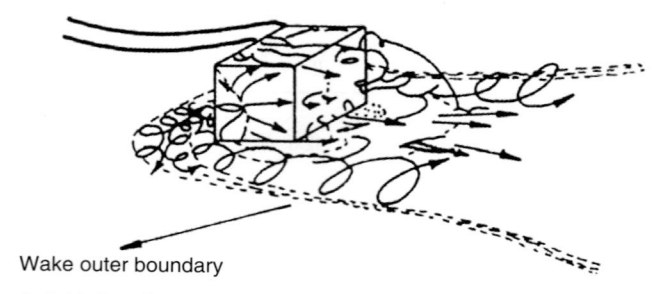

Figure 31 The development of the wake behind an obstacle [8].

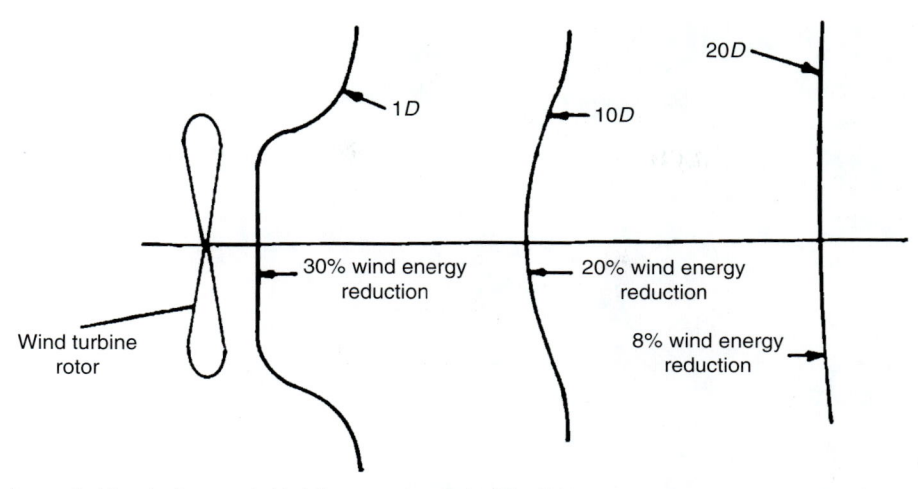

Figure 32 The development of the shading area behind the rotor of a wind turbine [8].

park will be equal to the 95% of the potential maximum annual electricity production from the wind turbines. The shading losses in a wind park depend on

- the distances between the wind turbines
- the wind turbines' installation positions
- the prevailing wind directions.

The proper micro-siting of the wind turbines takes into account the above three parameters and aims at the minimization of the turbines' shading losses. Before the micro-siting procedure, the areas presenting high enough wind potential inside the total site must be selected. It is obvious that regardless of the total available land, the wind turbines should be installed in specific positions that exhibit high enough wind potential, in order to maximize the annual electricity production. The lower limit regarding the available wind potential of the installation positions is set according to the investor's expectations. Once the acceptable areas, regarding the available wind potential, inside the total site are selected, the wind turbines' micro-siting begins. The minimum distance between two wind turbines sited perpendicular to the wind direction should be at least $2.5–3.0 \cdot D$, where D is the rotor's diameter. The minimum distance between two wind turbines sited parallel with the wind direction should be at least $7 \cdot D$, in case the available space in the installation site is limited (**Figure 33**). In **Figure 33**, the micro-siting in an offshore wind park is presented. In this case, the distance between two wind turbines in the same line is kept as $5 \cdot D$.

Some examples of wind turbines' micro-siting are provided below.

In **Figure 34** the final micro-siting of seven wind turbines with nominal power of 3000 kW and rotor diameter of 90 m is presented, for a site in southern Crete. In the same figure the wind-rose calculated from the 9-month wind potential measurements is presented. The wind turbines are installed in positions exhibiting mean annual wind velocity higher than 8 m s^{-1}. The morphology of the mountain's top enables the micro-siting of the wind turbines in a direction perpendicular to the wind blowing main direction. The abovementioned favorable conditions and the small number of wind turbines lead to the minimization of the calculated shading losses.

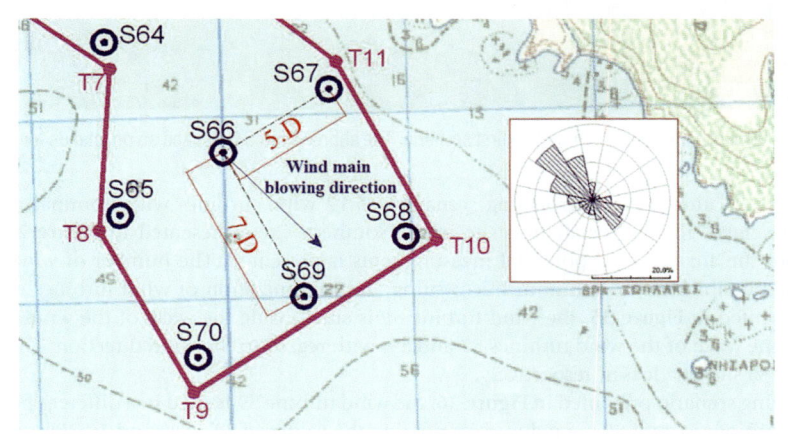

Figure 33 The micro-siting of wind turbines in lines vertical and parallel to the prevalent wind direction. The abbreviation S1, S2, and so on, stands for wind turbines' installation sites.

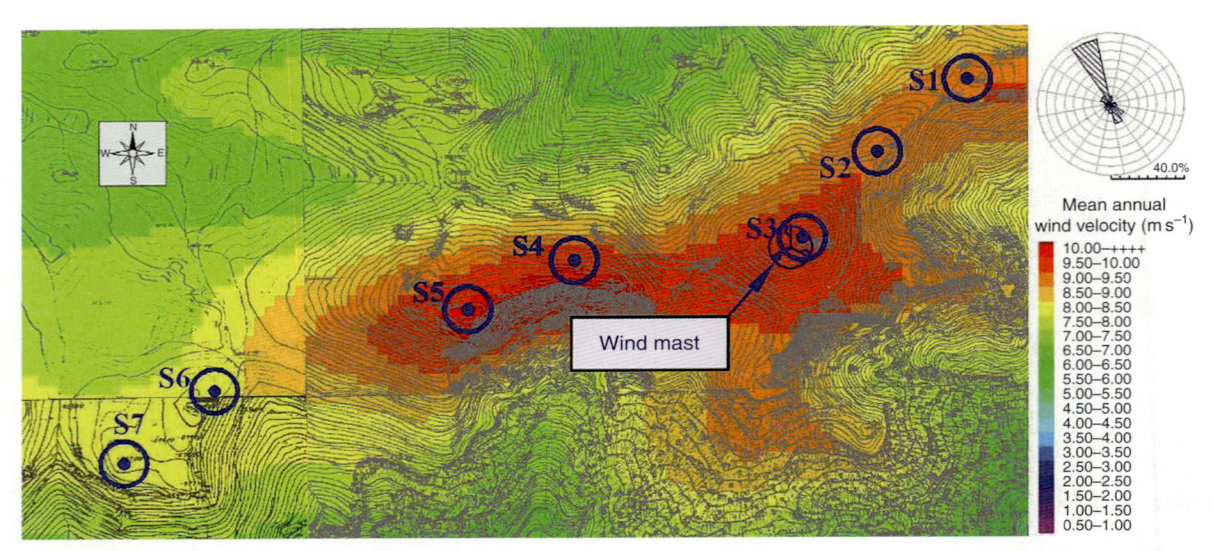

192 Wind Parks Design, Including Representative Case Studies

Figure 34 The micro-siting of a 21 MW wind park on the island of Crete. The abbreviation S1, S2, and so on, stands for wind turbines' installation sites.

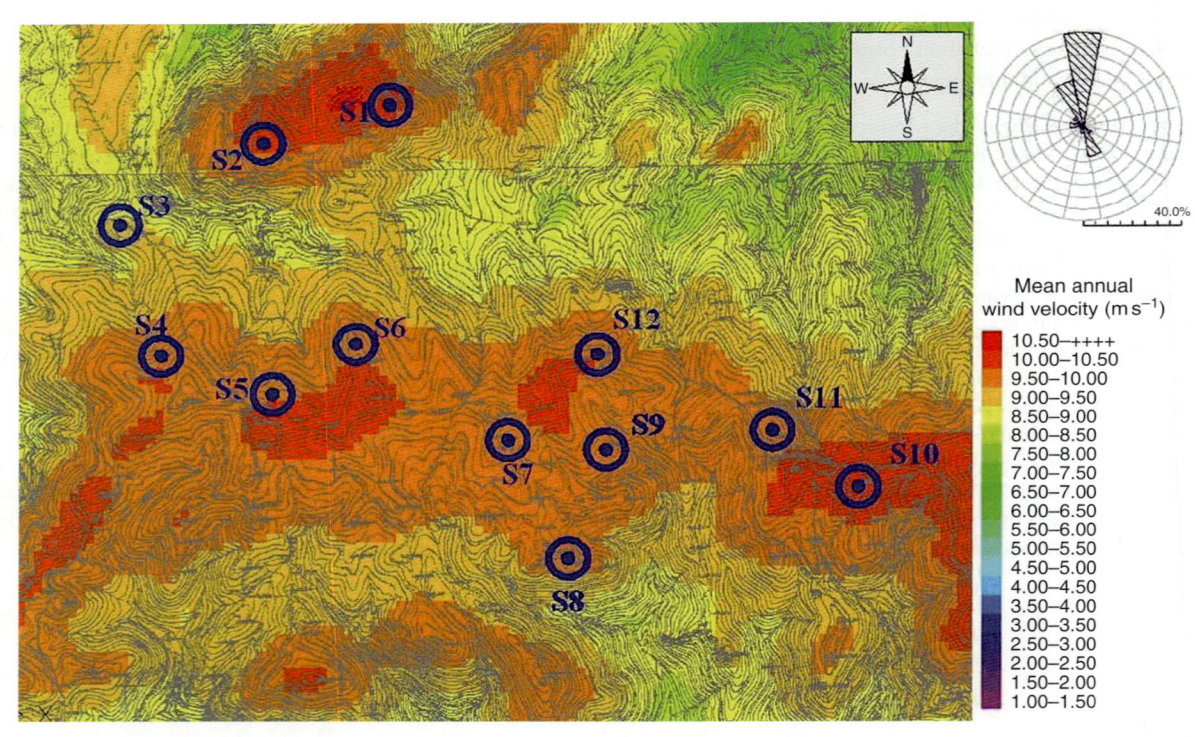

Figure 35 The micro-siting of a wind park in southern Crete – first scenario. The abbreviation S1, S2, and so on, stands for wind turbines' installation sites.

In **Figures 35** and **36**, two alternative micro-siting scenarios of 12 wind turbines with nominal power of 3 MW and rotor diameter of 90 m are presented, for the installation site in the southern Crete presented in **Figure 25**. In the same figure the wind-rose calculated from the annual wind potential measurements is presented. The number of wind turbines and the lack of available land restrict the possibilities for optimum micro-siting and minimization of wind turbines' shading losses. In the first micro-siting scenario presented in **Figure 35**, the wind turbine S9 is sited inside the wake of the wind turbine S12 and the wind turbine S8 is sited inside the wake of the wind turbines S7 and S9, with regard to the wind direction. The wind turbines S8 and S9 exhibit 12.32% and 13.97% shading losses, respectively.

In the second micro-siting scenario presented in **Figure 36**, the wind turbine S9 is sited in a different position. The shading losses percentages of the wind turbines S8 and S9 are reduced, presenting the values of 11.18% and 10.30%, respectively.

In both scenarios, all the wind turbines are installed in positions exhibiting mean annual wind velocity higher than 9 m s^{-1}.

Finally, in **Figure 37** the micro-siting of a large number of 5 MW nominal power wind turbines with a diameter of 105 m in an offshore wind park in the southwest of the Greek island of Karpathos (southeast Aegean Sea) is presented. The wind turbines are

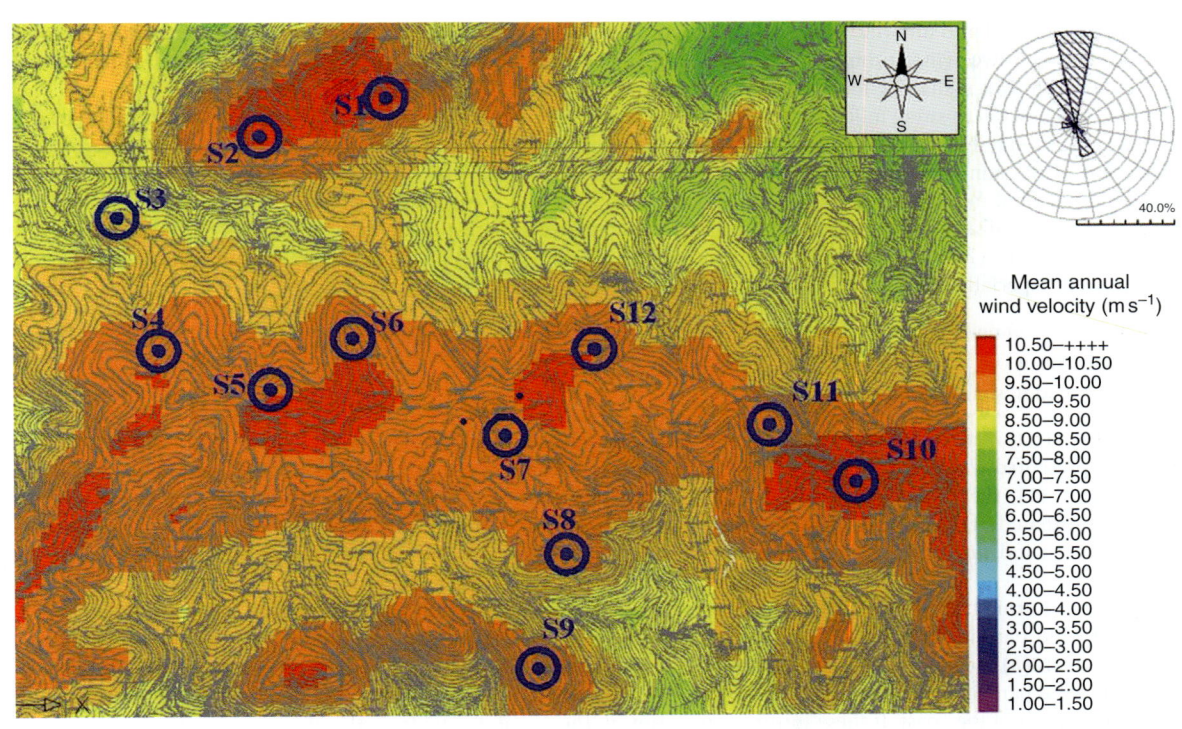

Wind Parks Design, Including Representative Case Studies 193

Figure 36 The micro-siting of a wind park in southern Crete – second scenario. The abbreviation S1, S2, and so on, stands for wind turbines' installation sites.

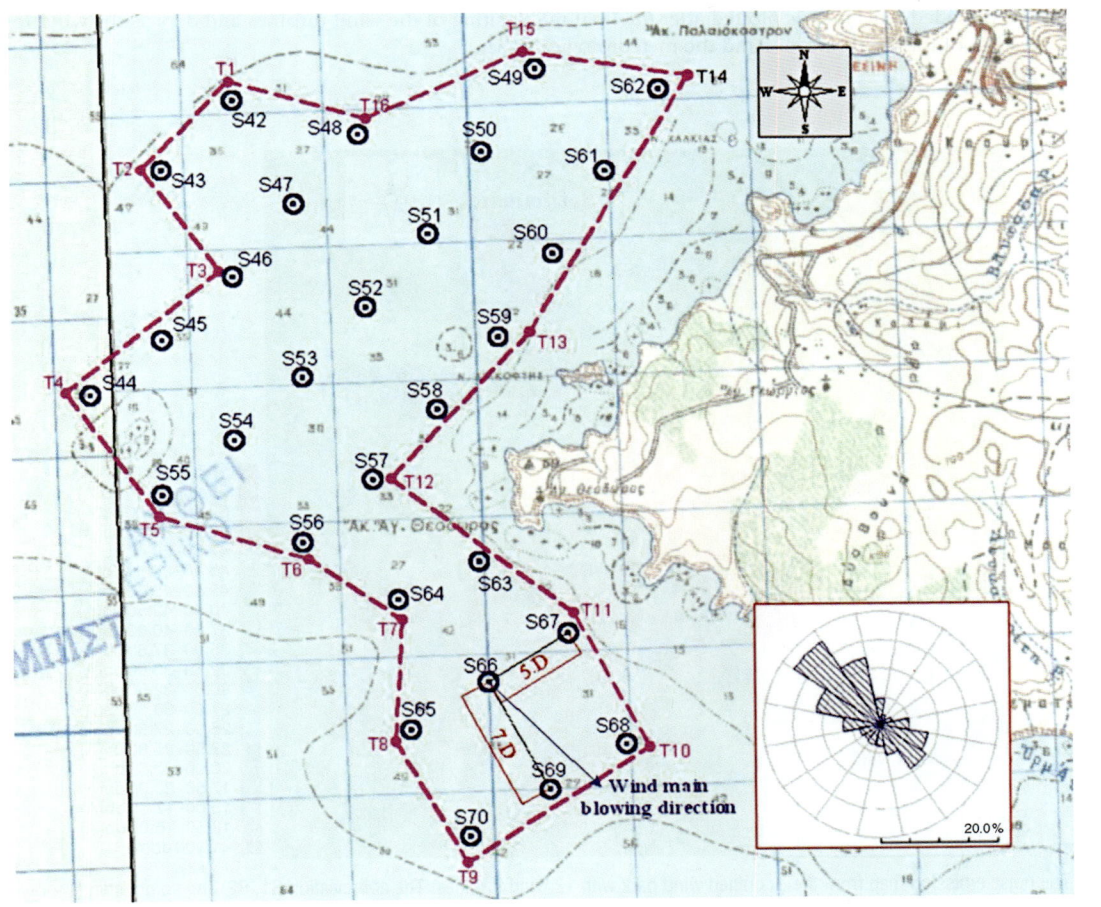

Figure 37 The micro-siting of an offshore wind park in the south west of the island of Karpathos (southeast Aegean Sea). The abbreviation S1, S2, and so on, stands for wind turbines' installation sites.

sited in lines perpendicular to the wind directions. Each wind turbine is sited in the gap of the two wind turbines sited in front of it. The distance between two wind turbines of the same line is $5 \cdot D$. The distance between two lines is $7 \cdot D$. In this micro-siting scenario, the wind turbines' shading losses percentages vary between 2.33% and 8.50%.

The wind turbines' micro-siting following the previously presented methodology is based only on the minimization of shading losses. This is the fundamental scope of the wind turbines' micro-siting. The calculation of the shading losses is performed during the calculation of the annual electricity production from the wind turbines. This calculation is carried out on the basis of the captured wind potential measurements and the developed wind map on the installation site.

However, the maximization of the electricity production from the wind park and the minimization of the shading losses are not the only parameters taken into account during micro-siting. The possible impacts on the environment and human activities must be examined as well, especially the following:

- the visual impact on neighboring places of special importance
- the noise emissions
- the spinning blades' shading effect.

In **Figures 38–41**, the noise emission maps and sectional views from a small wind park's operation in the nearby settlement is presented for two different scenarios concerning the micro-siting of the wind turbines. In the first scenario (**Figures 38** and **39**), the nearest wind turbine (S1) to the neighboring settlement is 792 m away. The noise level in the settlement is estimated at 43.5 dB. In the second scenario (**Figures 40** and **41**), the abovementioned wind turbine does not exist. The nearest wind turbine (S2) to the settlement is now 1045 m away. The noise emission in the settlement is reduced at 41.8 dB.

An example concerning the visual impact of a wind park in a nearby tourist destination is presented in **Figures 42(a)** and **42(b)**. The examined wind park is the one presented in **Figure 34**, consisting of seven wind turbines, giving a total nominal power of 21 MW. In **Figure 42(a)** the photorealistic representation of the wind park from the southern coast of Crete, approximately 4000 m away from the wind park, is presented. As seen in **Figure 42(a)**, there is a slight visual contact between the wind turbines S2 and S3 (see also **Figure 34**) and the coast. If these turbines are removed, the visual impact from the wind park to the coast is eliminated (**Figure 42(b)**).

Depending on the software tool employed for the wind potential evaluation and the wind map development, maps like that in **Figure 43** can be provided. This map is plotted after the final micro-siting of the wind turbines and depicts the wind roses at each installation position of the wind turbines and the meteorological mast.

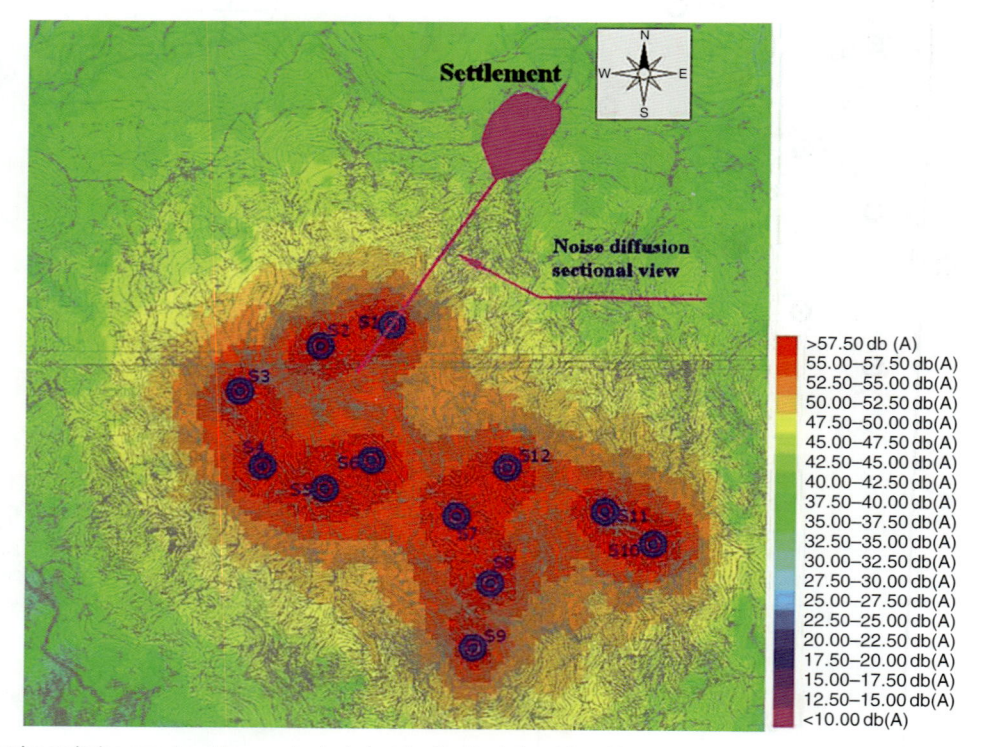

Figure 38 The noise emission map from the examined wind park with 12 wind turbines. The abbreviation S1, S2, and so on, stands for wind turbines' installation sites.

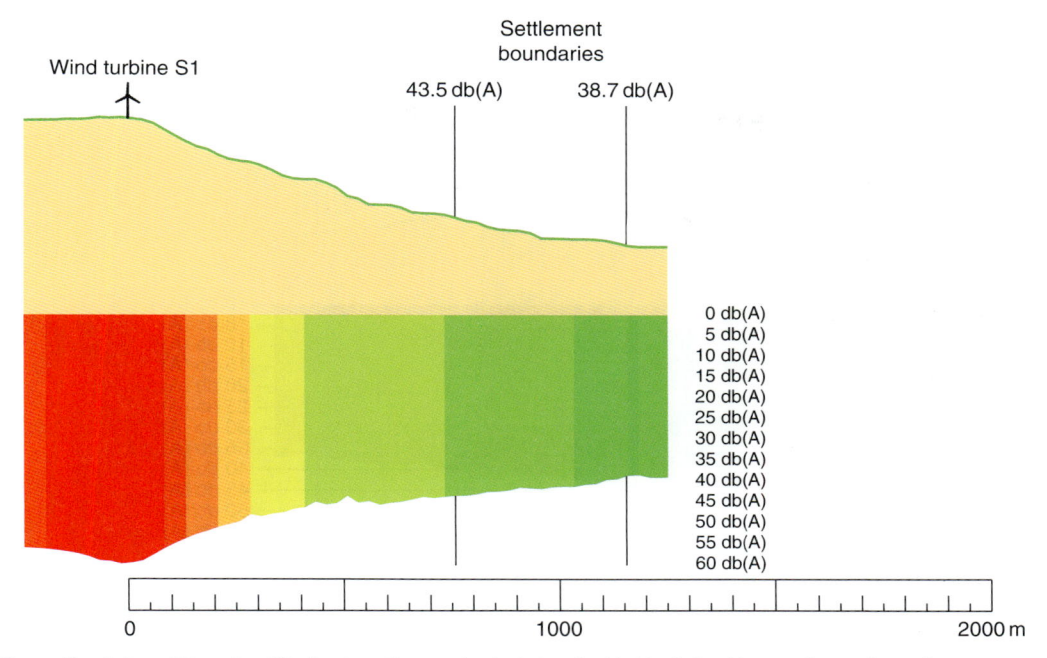

Figure 39 The sectional view of the noise diffusion from the examined wind park with 12 wind turbines to the nearby settlement.

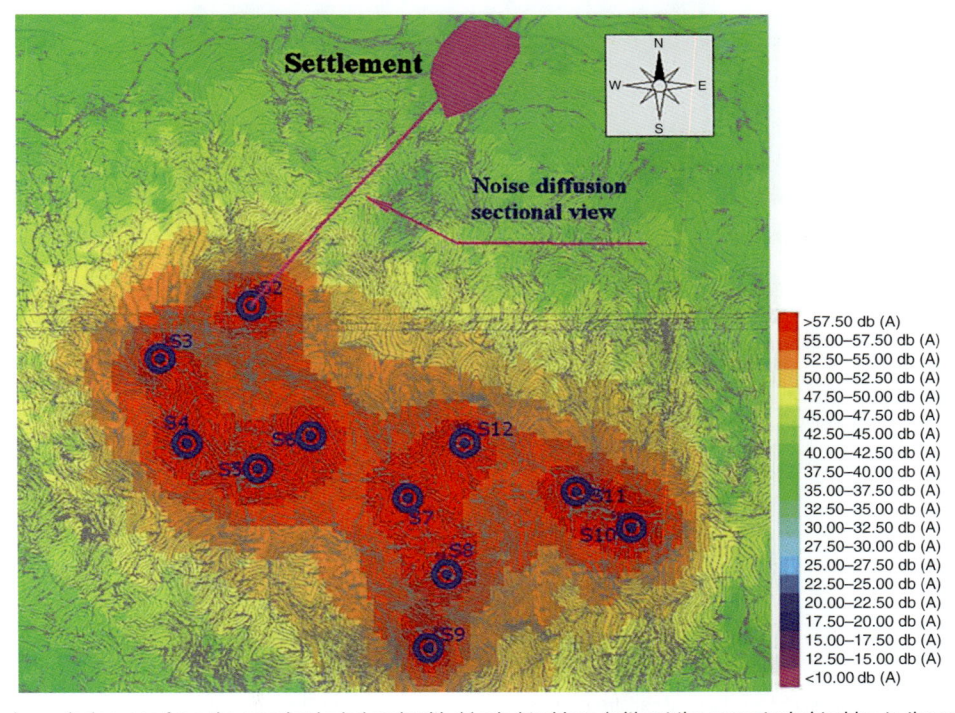

Figure 40 The noise emission map from the examined wind park with 11 wind turbines (without the nearest wind turbine to the settlement). The abbreviation S1, S2, and so on, stands for wind turbines' installation sites.

Apart from the possible impacts from the operation of a wind park, several other special issues, such as the minimum distances from the site boundaries, the elimination of the shear effect, the foundation of the wind turbines in ground with geological peculiarities, and so on, can affect the micro-siting of the wind turbines.

With the above presented examples it is shown that the micro-siting of the wind turbines in a wind park is a multiparameter procedure, although the minimization of the shading losses and the maximization of the electricity produced is the main goal.

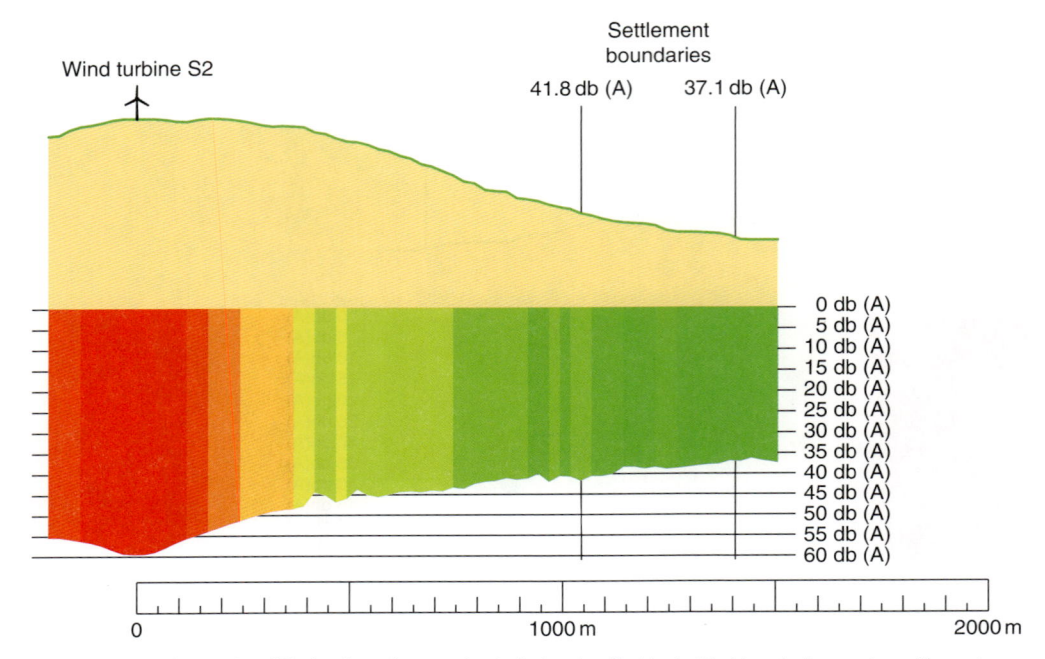

Figure 41 The sectional view of the noise diffusion from the examined wind park with 11 wind turbines to the nearby settlement.

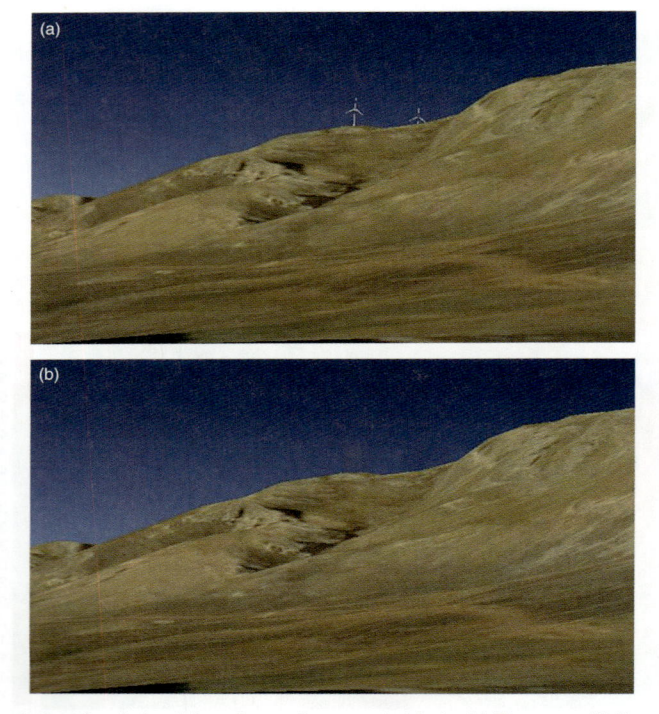

Figure 42 (a) Photorealistic representation of a wind park from the southern coast of Crete. (b) The same with the previous figure view, after the removal of wind turbines S2 and S3.

2.07.6 The Calculation of the Annual Electricity Production

The calculation of the annual electricity production from the wind park is performed after the wind potential evaluation and the wind map development on the installation site and the final micro-siting of the wind turbines. The calculation of the annual electricity production from the wind park will enable the estimation of the annual electricity vending to the utility and the expected annual revenues from the investment.

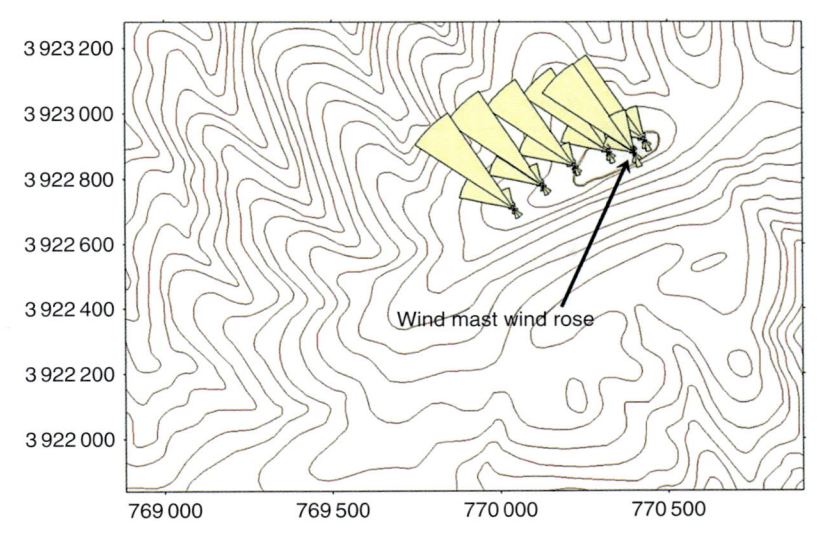

Figure 43 Wind roses map for each wind turbine installation position.

The annual electricity production from the wind park is calculated by specialized software tools. The development of the wind map provides information about the available wind potential at the specific installation positions of the wind turbines. This information may be provided with the Weibull distribution parameters C and k or with annual wind velocities time-series at each installation position, and so on. Giving this information, the annual electricity production from each wind turbine is calculated by introducing the power curve of the selected wind turbine model.

In **Figure 44** a typical power curve of a 850 kW nominal power wind turbine is presented, while in **Figure 45** a wind velocity Weibull probability density annual distribution is presented.

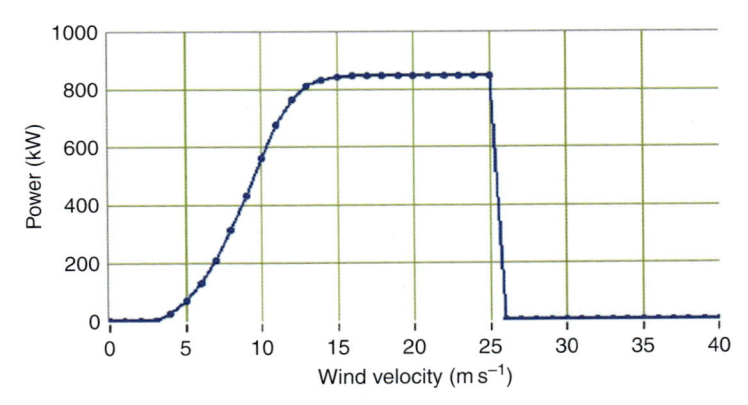

Figure 44 The power curve of a 850 kW nominal power wind turbine.

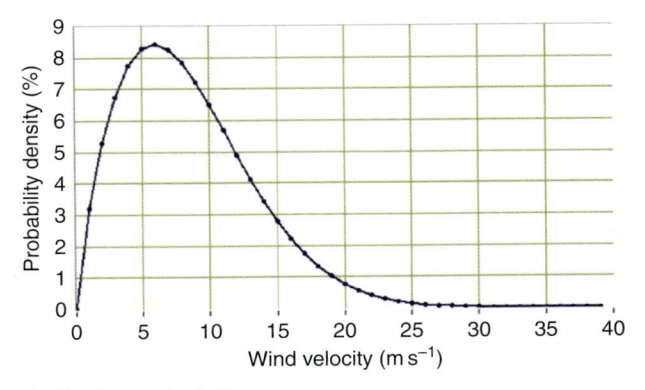

Figure 45 A wind velocity Weibull probability density distribution.

Table 4 The calculation of the annual electricity production from a wind turbine based on the Weibull probability distribution

Wind velocity ($m\,s^{-1}$)	Weibull distribution (%)	Number of hours per year	Wind turbine power curve (kW)	Electricity production (kWh)
0	0.00	0	0.0	0
1	3.20	280	0.0	0
2	5.30	464	0.0	0
3	6.80	596	0.0	0
4	7.70	675	27.0	18 212
5	8.30	727	70.4	51 186
6	8.40	736	130.0	95 659
7	8.30	727	211.0	153 414
8	7.80	683	314.0	214 550
9	7.20	631	435.0	274 363
10	6.50	569	562.0	320 003
11	5.70	499	678.0	338 539
12	4.90	429	764.0	327 939
13	4.10	359	814.0	292 356
14	3.40	298	837.0	249 292
15	2.80	245	846.0	207 507
16	2.20	193	849.0	163 619
17	1.70	149	850.0	126 582
18	1.30	114	850.0	96 798
19	1.00	88	850.0	74 460
20	0.80	70	850.0	59 568
21	0.60	53	850.0	44 676
22	0.40	35	850.0	29 784
23	0.30	26	850.0	22 338
24	0.20	18	850.0	14 892
25	0.10	9	850.0	7 446
26	0.10	9	0.0	0
27	0.10	9	0.0	0
28	0.00	0	0.0	0
Total	100.00	8760		3 183 184

In Table 4 the calculation of the annual electricity production from a wind turbine, based on the wind turbine power curve and the wind velocity Weibull probability density distribution, is presented. The calculation procedure presented in Table 4 is simple. For each wind velocity interval there is one corresponding Weibull probability value and one wind power output from the wind turbine's power curve. The Weibull probability density value corresponds to a total number of hours per year that the wind blows taking values inside the specific wind velocity range. The wind turbine's power curve implies a specific power output during these hours. The product of the total hours per year with the power output from the wind turbine gives the total annual electricity production for each wind velocity interval. The sum of the electricity production from all the wind velocity intervals estimates the expected total annual electricity production from the wind turbine.

In the example presented in Table 4, the annual electricity production from the 850 kW wind turbine installed in a site with the specific wind speed Weibull density distribution is calculated equal to 3 183 184 kWh.

The annual capacity factor of the wind turbine is defined as the ratio of the turbine's annual electricity production over the maximum theoretical one. The annual maximum theoretical production is based on the condition that the power output of the wind turbine remains constant and equal to its nominal power for the whole year. In this case, the expected electricity production is calculated equal to 850 kW × 8760 h = 7 446 000 kWh. The annual capacity factor is then calculated equal to CF = 3 183 184 kWh/ 7 446 000 kWh = 42.75%.

From the above presented analysis it is obvious that the capacity factor depends on the following:

- the selected wind turbine model
- the available wind potential, consequently, the selected installation site
- the time period over which it is calculated.

Above all, the capacity factor depends on the available wind potential and comprises a characteristic index of the wind potential quality of a site. Different sites exhibit different capacity factors. The capacity factor of 42.75% calculated previously is considered high. Such values are obtained in sites with high wind potential, such as those in some of the Greek islands or on the Scottish coast. In central Europe, common values for capacity factor are between 25% and 30%.

Table 5   Wind potential results for each wind turbine in a 21 MW wind park in southern Crete

W/T	Wind velocity ($m\,s^{-1}$)	Wind power density ($W\,m^{-2}$)	Parameter C of Weibull distribution ($m\,s^{-1}$)	Parameter k of Weibull distribution	Annual energy production after shading losses (GWh)
S1	9.32	1050	10.5	1.82	11.675
S2	9.58	1113	10.8	1.86	12.114
S3	10.11	1266	11.4	1.91	12.986
S4	9.84	1259	11.1	1.79	12.280
S5	9.98	1263	11.2	1.85	12.636
S6	8.57	795	9.6	1.86	10.439
S7	8.30	704	9.3	1.90	9.985
Total					82.115

The first results regarding the annual electricity calculation are provided for each wind turbine in the example given in **Table 5**. The wind potential evaluation and the annual electricity production are the first set of results. The results in **Table 5** refer to a 21 MW wind park installed in southern Crete. As shown in this table, the annual energy production calculation, done using the relevant software, has taken into account the shading losses. In order to conclude to the final electricity sold to the utility, the following further losses, except the wind turbine shading losses, must be calculated:

- wind turbines' hysteresis losses
- electricity transportation losses
- losses due to wind turbines' technical unavailability
- losses due to wind power rejection from the utility (mainly in noninterconnected systems).

Each wind turbine cuts out its operation over a wind velocity value, set by the manufacturer usually at 25 m s^{-1}, in order to protect itself. If the wind velocity exceeds this upper operation limit, the wind turbine does not start operation immediately. The wind turbine will start operating again after a certain time interval, configured by the manufacturers, during which the wind velocity must remain under the upper operation limit. During this time interval, the available wind energy is not exploited and the electricity that could be produced corresponds to the energy hysteresis losses. The hysteresis losses depend on the variation of the wind velocity in the turbines' installation positions. Hence the calculation of the hysteresis losses is based on the available wind potential information (wind velocity time-series or Weibull probability density distribution) for every turbine's installation position.

The electricity transportation losses are caused by the network ohmic, inductive, and capacitive resistance. These resistances depend on the existing network's distance from the wind park to the connection point, the connection line voltage, the conductors' cross-section, and so on, and can be calculated accurately. Usually the electricity transportation losses vary between 3% and 5%, for most usual cases, although in wind parks with very long connection networks (higher than 100 km) these losses can exceed 5%.

The wind turbines are not always technically available, due to either unpredicted operational damage or scheduled maintenance. The technical availability of a wind park is usually guaranteed by the turbines' manufacturer, within the purchase and maintenance contract that is signed between the manufacturer and the wind park's owner. The technical availability of a wind park is expressed as the operational time percentage during a year over the total annual time period. This feature can exceed 98% in the case of easily accessed wind parks. In the case of offshore wind parks this feature usually reduces below 95%.

Finally, in the case of wind parks installed in isolated power systems, there is always an upper limit of wind power penetration in the electricity production system. This upper limit is set in order to ensure the isolated system's dynamic security and stability. The maximum instant wind power penetration over the power demand percentage is usually set equal to 30%, following the results of relevant simulations [24–26]. Apart from the upper limit of wind power penetration, wind power rejection is also caused from the restrictions introduced in the system's operation by the on-duty thermal generators' technical minima. More information about the integration of wind power in electricity systems is presented in a following section. Depending on the power demand size and the total wind power installed in an isolated system, wind power rejection due to violation of the upper wind power penetration limit or due to technical minima restrictions can occur. The wind power rejection from the utility network is not easily calculated. It requires the accurate simulation of the system's annual operation, based on annual time-series of power demand and wind power production mean hourly values.

In **Table 6**, an analysis of the calculation of the final electricity production from the 21 MW wind park installed in the southern Crete is provided. The calculation starts from the energy production after wind turbines' shading losses and following all the energy losses calculations presented above, concludes to the final electricity production that is purchased by the utility. The capacity factors in **Table 6** are calculated for the final electricity productions. The wind turbines' availability is set equal to 95%, following the relevant warranty of the manufacturers. The electricity transportation losses, through a 20 kV underground cable that is 20 km long are estimated as approximately 3%. The hysteresis losses are calculated accurately on the basis of wind potential measurements gathered by a 10 m meteorological mast installed at the specific site. The wind power rejection losses are also calculated accurately with the simulation of the system's annual operation, based on annual time-series of the power demand and the wind power production. Finally, the turbines' shading losses are calculated directly by the specialized commercial software tool through which the wind potential evaluation and the wind map analysis of the installation site are also accomplished.

Table 6 Analysis of the electricity production from a 21 MW wind park in southern Crete

W/T	Annual energy production before shading losses (GWh)	Shading losses (%)	Shading losses (GWh)	Annual energy production after shading losses (GWh)	Hysteresis losses (GWh)	Hysteresis losses (%)	Annual energy production after shading and hysteresis losses (GWh)	Energy transportation losses (GWh)	Network rejection losses (%)	Network rejection losses (GWh)	Wind turbines' availability losses (GWh)	Final produced energy (GWh)	Final capacity factor (%)
S1	11.848	1.46	0.173	11.675	0.413	3.54	11.262	0.338	10.00	1.126	0.563	9.235	35.14
S2	12.316	1.64	0.202	12.114	0.449	3.71	11.665	0.350	10.00	1.167	0.583	9.565	36.40
S3	13.173	1.42	0.187	12.986	0.558	4.30	12.428	0.373	10.00	1.243	0.621	10.191	38.78
S4	12.528	1.98	0.248	12.280	0.578	4.71	11.702	0.351	10.00	1.170	0.585	9.596	36.51
S5	12.791	1.21	0.155	12.636	0.557	4.41	12.080	0.362	10.00	1.208	0.604	9.905	37.69
S6	10.573	1.27	0.134	10.439	0.352	3.37	10.087	0.303	10.00	1.009	0.504	8.271	31.47
S7	10.098	1.12	0.113	9.985	0.144	1.44	9.841	0.295	10.00	0.984	0.492	8.070	30.71
Total/averaged values	83.327	1.45	1.212	82.115	3.051	3.72	79.064	2.372	10.00	7.906	3.953	64.833	35.24

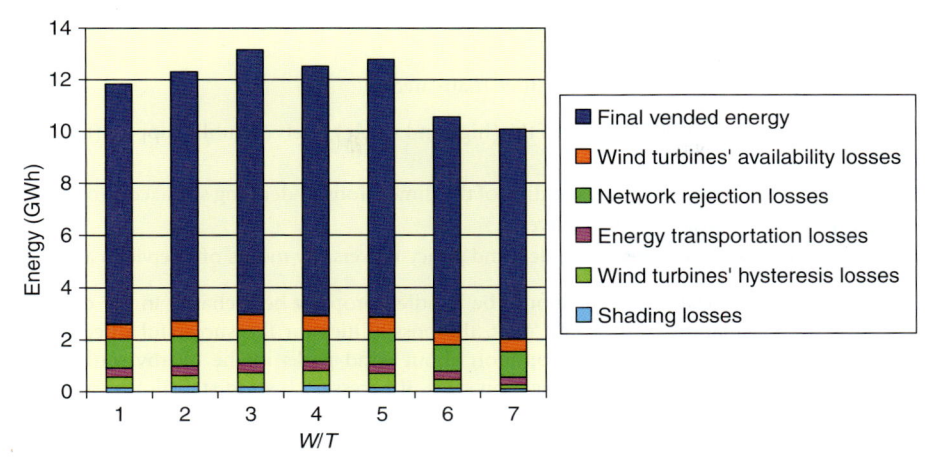

Figure 46 Energy production analysis from a 21 MW nominal power wind park.

The results presented in **Table 6** are also provided graphically in **Figure 46**.

The energy production calculation can be integrated with an uncertainty analysis regarding the probability the wind park's annual energy production will exceed several values. The uncertainty analysis is accomplished on the basis of the short-term wind potential data measured by the installed meteorological mast and long-term wind potential data gathered by satellites from specific points on earth and heights above ground. As mentioned above, the long-term wind potential data are transferred to the installation position of the meteorological mast using simple linear interpolation methods. **Figure 21**, provided in a previous section, presents the mean annual wind velocity values at the specific meteorological mast position in Kasos for the last 30 years, based on long-term satellite data. In **Figure 21** the wind velocity variability versus the years is observed.

The uncertainty analysis takes into account several parameters that increase the uncertainty of the energy production calculation. Such parameters are the accuracy of the anemometers on the meteorological mast, the accuracy of the wind map development, the accuracy of the several losses calculation, the accuracy of the wind turbine's power curve, and so on. The final result of the uncertainty analysis is the uncertainty curve presenting the probability of the wind velocity to exceed a specific value. Such a curve is provided in **Figure 47**, regarding the above described wind park in Kasos.

The calculation of the annual energy production from a wind park, based on short-term wind potential annual measurements, accompanied by the uncertainty analysis based on long-term data, provides secure information about the expected annual energy production and the investment's financial efficiency.

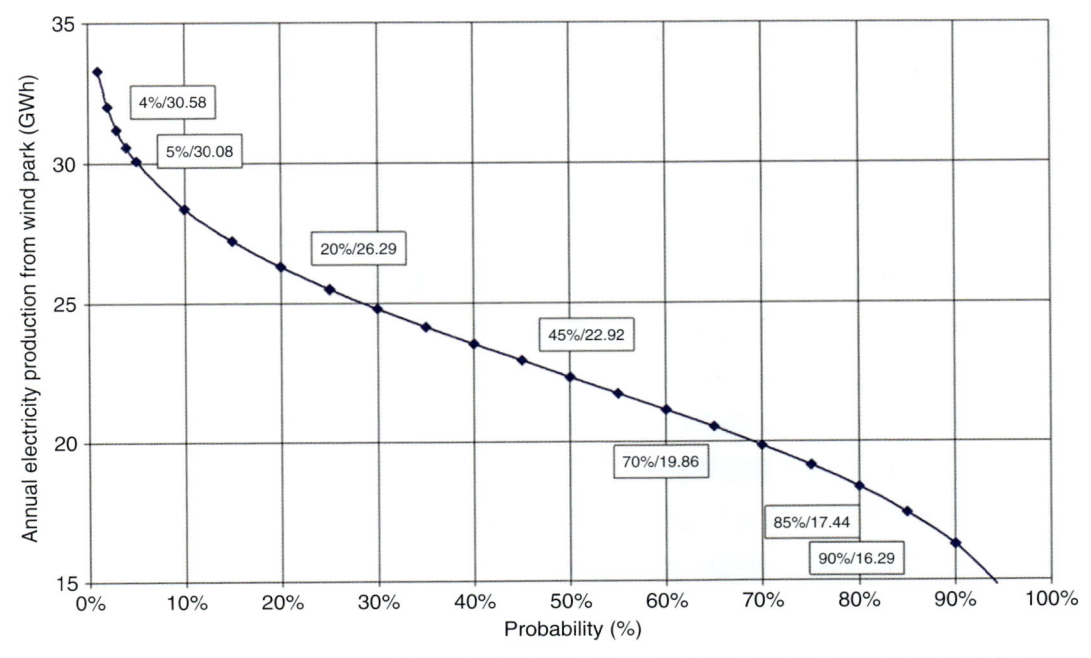

Figure 47 Probability variation for the annual net electricity production from the wind park, based on long-term wind potential data.

2.07.7 Social Approval of the Wind Park

Social research on wind energy has primarily focused on three main areas:

- *Public acceptance.* The assessment (and corroboration) of the (high and stable) levels of public support (by means of opinion polls and attitude surveys).
- *Community acceptance.* The identification and understanding of the dimensions underlying social controversy at the local level (by means of single or multiple case studies, including surveys).
- *Stakeholder acceptance.* Social acceptance by key stakeholders and policy-makers (by means of interviews and multiple case studies).

Social approval of a wind park is a crucial issue that should be handled properly beforehand. In the case of social reactions or negative opinion regarding the installation of the wind park, the possibilities for the successful integration of the project are considerably reduced. An examination of the existing opinion about wind parks in the nearby settlements of the candidate installation site must be performed during the site investigation stage. If necessary, a short statistical survey should be completed.

Over the last 30 years several statistical surveys have been conducted, which proved to be a helpful source of information for EU policy-makers on a broad range of economic, social, environmental, and other issues of importance to EU citizens. Recent Eurobarometer Standard Survey (EB) data on public opinion confirm the strongly positive overall picture for renewable energies in general, and for wind energy in particular, at the EU level, and not only for the present but also for the future. Generally, when EU citizens are asked about their preferences in terms of the use of different energy sources, renewable energies in general, and wind energy in particular, are rated highly positively (especially when compared with nuclear or fossil fuels). The highest support is for solar energy (80%), closely followed by wind energy, with 71% of EU citizens firmly in favor of the use of wind power in their countries, 21% expressing a balanced view, and only 5% are opposed to it (**Figure 48**) [31].

Focusing on the use of wind energy, on a scale from 1 (strongly opposed) to 7 (strongly in favor), the EU average is 6.3. Even higher rates of support arose in some countries, for example, Denmark (6.7), Greece (6.5), and Poland, Hungary, and Malta (6.4). The United Kingdom shows the lowest support figure of the EU (5.7), closely followed by Finland and Germany (5.8) (**Figure 49**) [31].

EU citizens also demonstrated a very positive view of renewable energy in general and of wind energy in particular when asked about their expectations regarding three energy sources that would be the most used 30 years from now. Results showed that wind energy is expected to be a key energy source in the future – just after solar (**Figure 50**) [31]. Furthermore, for EU citizens, the development of the use of wind energy was the third preferred option to reduce our energy dependence on foreign, expensive, and highly polluting sources (31%), after the increase in the use of solar energy (48%) and the promotion of advance research on new energy technologies (41%).

Beyond the above overall statistics regarding the social attitude toward wind energy and wind parks, in **Figure 51**, an example with the most characteristic results from an extended survey concerning the acceptability of wind parks is presented. The survey was completed by the Wind Energy Laboratory of the Technological Educational Institute of Crete in 2007. The sample of 1000 adults was carefully gathered from all over the island of Crete and from different categories of citizens, regarding their age, their educational level, their place of living (towns or countryside), their occupation, and so on.

According to the results presented in **Figure 51**, the following conclusions can be stated:

- The statistical survey in Crete revealed a positive public opinion toward wind parks and wind energy, despite the fact that a high percentage of the local population (40%) has direct experience of a wind park's visual impacts and noise emissions. This is mainly

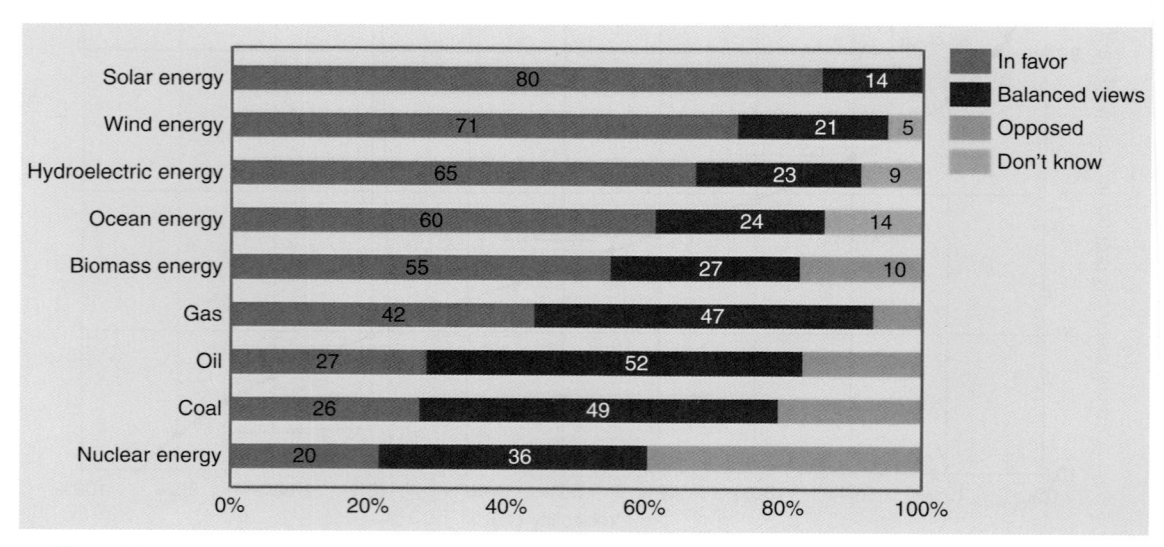

Figure 48 The social attitude in EU toward several energy sources [31].

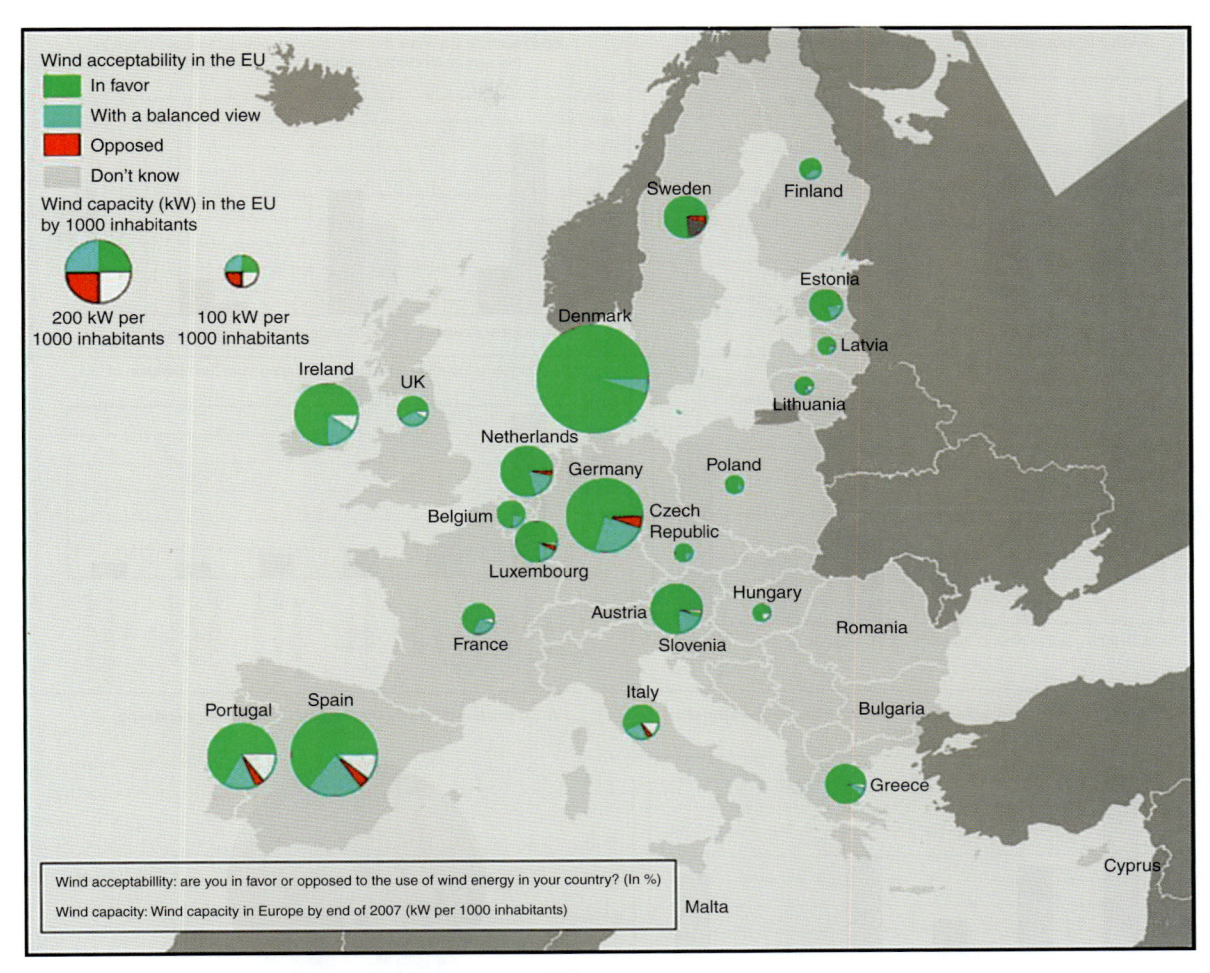

Figure 49 The social attitude in EU countries toward wind energy [31].

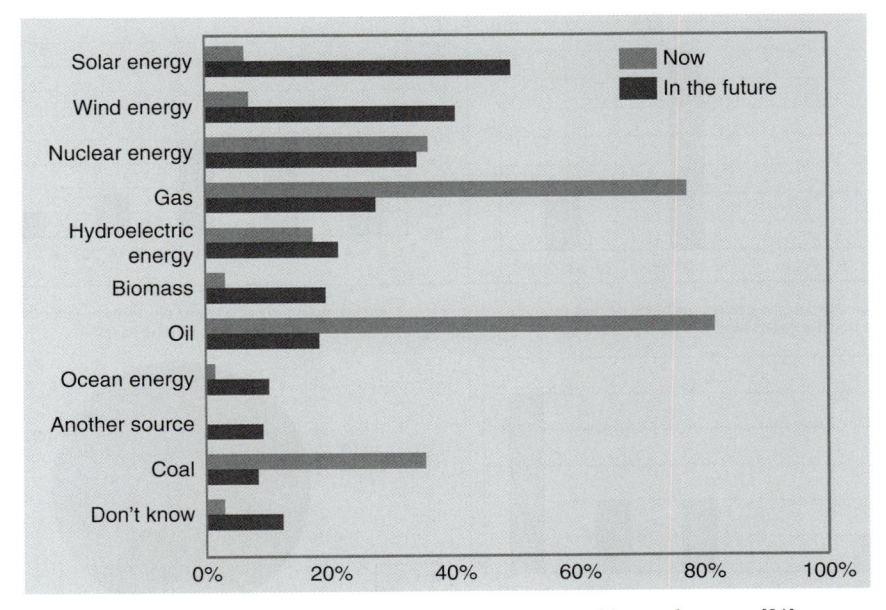

Figure 50 The expectations of the EU citizens concerning the most used energy sources in 30 years from now [31].

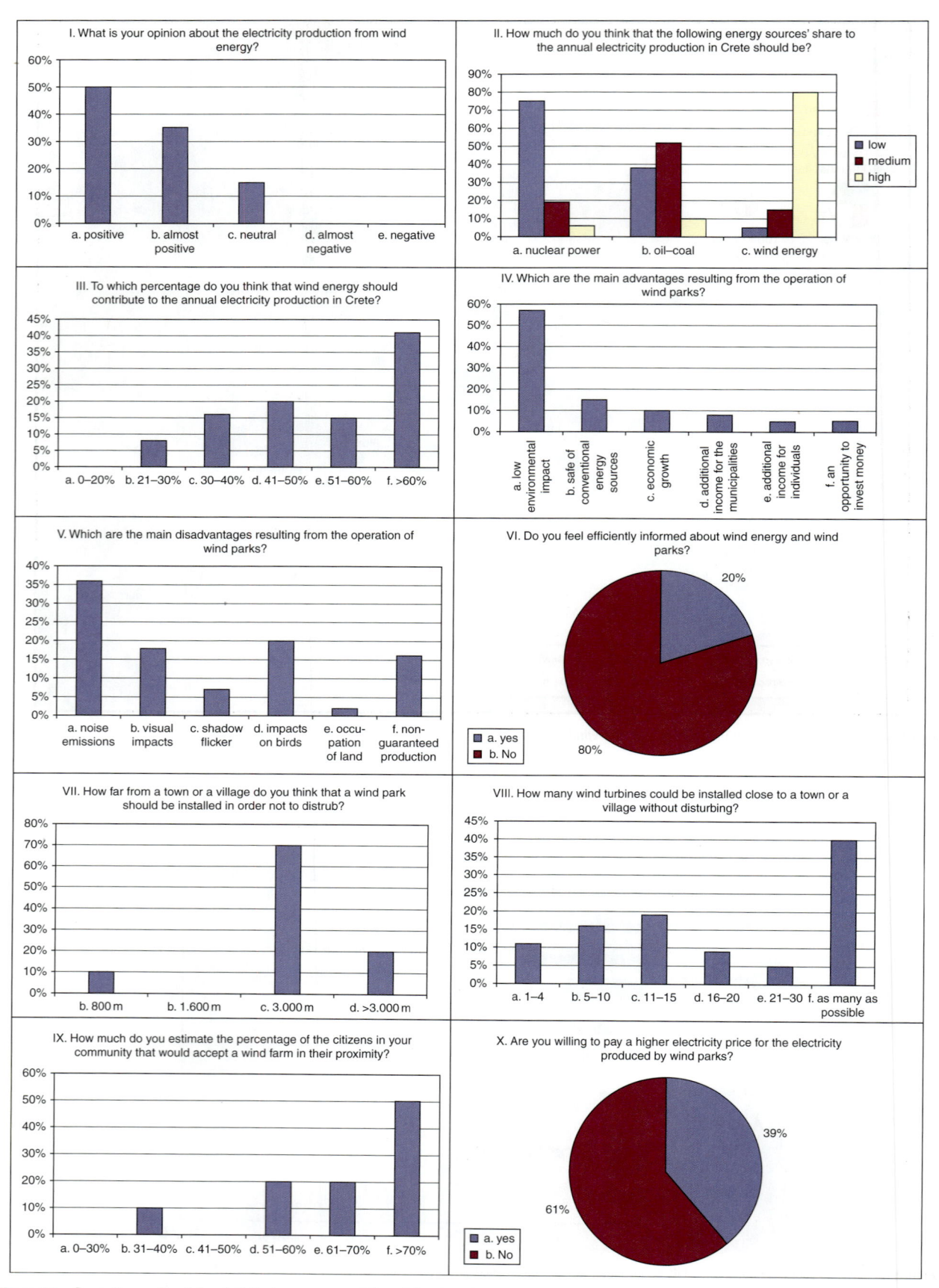

Figure 51 Synoptic results of the statistical survey on public opinion for wind energy and wind parks in Crete fulfilled in 2007.

based on the environmental benefits arising from the wind parks' operation, concerning the limitation of gas emissions and the treatment of the greenhouse effect, as well as the limitation of imported fossil fuel for electricity production in Crete.
- According to the survey's results, in order to ensure the acceptability of a new wind park, the following prerequisites must be fulfilled:

  the noise emissions in the nearby settlements should not exceed the predefined upper limits

  no impact should be caused on birds or wildlife

  the visual impact on landscape with special esthetics or sites with historical, cultural, or tourist value should be limited

  the wind park should operate continuously and efficiently, namely the owners should guarantee its availability with its proper maintenance.
- Although the survey proved that people in Crete have clear knowledge about wind energy and wind parks, they do not feel well informed about this issue. This feeling is presented despite the promotion policies on Renewable Energy Sources, adopted and applied in the European Union during the last decade.
- Despite the positive public opinion concerning wind parks and wind power in Crete, most residents are not willing to pay a higher price for the electricity produced by the wind parks. This result is partially influenced by the economic conditions of the average Cretan household and not only by the residents' willingness to support wind energy.

The abovementioned statistical survey was run in 2007. At that time the total nominal power of the installed wind parks in Crete was approximately 140 MW. Unfortunately, during the last 2 years this positive attitude on wind parks in Crete has changed. The main reason is the attempt of a few big investors to install more than 2000 MW on the island. Since Crete is an isolated power production system with maximum annual power demand in 2010 at 650 MW, the investors suggested the connection of the Cretan system to the Greek mainland one. The required applications for the project's license were submitted without informing the local communities whether they approve the installation of such huge projects in their areas or not. Furthermore, the landowners were not asked if they were willing to sell or rent their possessions for the wind parks' implementation. Serious negative reactions from the Cretan community were raised on the announcement from the state of the submitted applications. The Cretans seem not willing to accept such huge investments on their territory, mainly for the following reasons:

- they cannot tolerate that they were totally neglected by the investors, who are identified more likely as intruders in their lands rather than carriers of important developing projects
- they are not willing to sacrifice the unique Cretan landscape in the economic benefit of the investors
- they are not willing to accept the installation of wind power higher than the power demand in Crete, in favor of the Greek mainland power system.

The ultimate result is that these investments are not likely to be integrated successfully, without the approval of the local communities. With the above presented example it is shown that without a carefully planned dissemination strategy, a wind park project may face serious problems. A wind park's developer owes the proper respect to the culture, the nature, and the history of the selected area, as well as to the inhabitants and the owners of the land at the installation sites.

More data regarding the public opinion of wind parks are obtained from a series of statistical surveys run in United Kingdom by several organizations and published by the British Wind Energy Association [32]. The most interesting of them concern the public attitude toward wind power before and after the implementation of a wind power project. Specifically, a statistical survey was implemented in 1992/1993 to establish attitudes of local residents to the wind farm at Cemmaes immediately after construction (phase one), and 1 year after (phase two) the wind farm became operational, giving the following main results:

- At both phase one and phase two, 86% of respondents were in favor of Cemmaes wind farm. At stage one, safety, lack of pollution, prestige, and economic gain were the main benefits cited.
- At phase two, the number of perceived benefits had increased and included environmentally friendly, renewable energy, natural and a way forward, pollution free, clean, healthier, safe energy, and better than nuclear.
- Most of the minority who were not positive at phase one were neutral at phase two.

Another example comes from a statistical survey run in 2003 in Scotland regarding the local Scottish residents' opinion on wind energy, after having experienced the construction and the operation of a wind park in their vicinity. The results are summarized below:

- Before the construction, people thought problems may arise from wind farm impact on the landscape (27%), traffic during construction (19%), and noise during construction (15%).
- Since the development, only 12% say the landscape has been spoiled, 6% commented on problems with additional traffic, while 4% say there was noise or disturbance from construction traffic.
- 82% support a general increase of wind energy.
- 54% of people living within 20 km of a wind farm would support a 50% expansion of the farm, while support is higher (65%) among those living within 5 km of a wind farm.

What is evident in the United Kingdom is that it is the minority 10% or so who do not like wind energy who too often lead the debate over wind's future.

In any case, a very efficient strategy is the organization of presentations and conferences open to the public of the nearby settlements to provide information about the wind park's implementation plans. It is a safer approach if the local communities are directly informed by the developers instead of the media or the state authorities. The wind park's developer must present to the local communities all the implementation aspects, the total nominal power, the number of the wind turbines and their installation positions, the expected annual electricity production, the expected environmental benefits, and the possible impacts to the local communities. Figures and video clips of photorealistic representations, noise emissions graphs, and animation clips presenting the spinning blades shading effect should be included among the presentation means in order to enable clear and thorough information provision regarding the details of the wind park project. The local communities must fully and validly be informed by the developers about all the aspects concerning the proposed wind park in order to avoid any negative common reactions arising from misinformation coming from invalid sources. The provision of compensative benefits from the wind park's owners to the local communities, such as free electricity to the local settlements or a specific annual amount of money for the construction of common benefit works (e.g., infrastructure works, such as roads, water supply, and irrigation dams and networks, traditional settlements restoration, construction of educational and sports infrastructure, such as schools, libraries, gyms, pools, innovations toward the enforcement of the local economy primary sectors, such as tourist, agriculture and livestock, etc.) can increase the acceptability of the wind park from the local communities.

2.07.8 The Wind Park Integration in Local Networks

The main problems arising from wind parks' integration in existing electricity networks usually refer to weak, noninterconnected power systems. In this section the peculiarities met in such systems regarding the wind power integration will be presented.

The introduction of wind parks in weak, noninterconnected power systems is usually favored from the following parameters:

- The commonly existing high electricity production cost, especially in cases where power is produced by small autonomous thermal power plants. This high electricity production cost is usually configured by the following reasons:
  - the thermal generators' power production being lower than their nominal one for long time periods, mainly due to intensive seasonal power demand variations in such small networks (e.g., between summer and winter periods) lead to operation under lower efficiency
  - the fossil fuel cost increase mainly because of the increased transportation cost
  - the requirement to preserve spinning reserve from the thermal generators frequently, in order to improve the system's dynamic security.
- The available wind potential that frequently exhibits quite attractive characteristics in isolated insular systems [33].
- The global necessity to reduce the use of conventional energy sources and substitute them with renewable ones, for environmental, economic, and national reasons.

On the other hand, the wind parks' development in existing weak networks usually has to face the following barriers:

- The set-up cost increase, mainly due to the increase of the equipment's transportation cost and the extended required infrastructure works in remote geographical areas.
- The difficulties for the installation of wind turbines with nominal power higher than 1 MW in areas with intensive land morphology and shortage of the required heavy machinery for the transportation and the erection of huge wind turbines.
- In many cases the necessity for the introduction of large wind turbines in sensitive ecosystems or in areas with historical and cultural value, usually met in rural areas.
- The wind power penetration restrictions in order to ensure the dynamic security and the stability of the weak networks, as will be analyzed below.
- Any possible investing problems that can occur due to the wind power limited penetration. For example, in the isolated system of Karpathos–Kasos, the total installed wind power in 2010 was 1.25 MW, while the mean annual power demand was 4.29 MW and the maximum annual power demand was 10.21 MW. The annual wind parks' electricity rejection percentage is estimated 4.61%, according to the simulation of the system. If the total installed wind parks' power was doubled (2.50 MW), the annual wind parks' electricity rejection percentage would have been calculated 26.99%. This high rejection percentage means that more than one-quarter of the produced electricity from the wind park is not purchased by the utility, leading to a considerable reduction of the project's revenues.

In the following paragraphs the main effects of the wind turbines operation in the power quality and the dynamic security of weak systems are presented.

2.07.8.1 The Power Quality Disturbances Caused by the Wind Turbines

The power produced by the wind turbines can usually exhibit the following power quality problems [34–37]:

- steady-state voltage level fluctuations
- voltage variations or fluctuations

- transients
- harmonics
- power frequency variations.

The abovementioned power quality disturbances are analyzed below as far as the reasons for their appearance, their intensity, and the possible consequences to the systems' normal operation are concerned.

2.07.8.1.1 Steady-state voltage level fluctuations

The electricity production from wind turbines can affect the networks' steady-state voltage level. This effect depends on the size of the network and the wind power penetration percentage. In weak networks, high wind power penetration can cause fluctuations in steady-state voltage level over the permissible operational limits. This automatically restricts the upper wind power penetration.

The reason that causes the steady-state voltage level fluctuations is the wind averaged wind velocity variations during time intervals of some minutes.

Wind turbines with voltage transformers and power electronics provide automatic reactive power control. Theoretically, they can control the power output in terms of several parameters, such as the conservation of the power factor close to unity or the voltage magnitude regulation.

2.07.8.1.2 Voltage fluctuations

The power production from a wind turbine varies in terms of the available wind velocity. This varied power production causes voltage fluctuations with a frequency of 0.01–10 Hz [37]. The active power variations are less intensive in pitch control, variable-speed wind turbines [37].

The effect of the voltage fluctuations in an electrical network is measured on the basis of the caused lighting flicker. The use of voltage transformers and power electronics in variable-speed wind turbines leads to voltage fluctuation reduction. In these cases the resulting lighting flicker is not detectable and cannot constitute a reason for wind power rejection.

2.07.8.1.3 Transients

Two kinds of transients are caused by the operation of the wind turbines. The first one refers to the voltage sag caused during a wind turbine's operation start [37]. The voltage sag is caused by the high currents required during the starting procedure of the wind turbines. The second kind of transient refers to the turbine capacitors' charging–discharging procedures. These procedures are accompanied with high-frequency currents that cause voltage transients disturbances in the utility network.

The operation of a variable-speed wind turbine does not cause serious transients in the network. The transients caused by wind turbines can be considered as serious power quality problem, only in case that sensitive electrical or electronic equipment is connected at the same low-voltage network as the wind turbines [35–37].

2.07.8.1.4 Harmonics

Wind turbines with voltage transformers and power electronics introduce harmonics in power networks. The produced voltage sinusoidal distortion is more intensive in small and weak systems. In small and weak systems the produced harmonics by the wind turbines should be measured and controlled. The use of harmonics filters can guarantee the compatibility of the produced power with the predefined system's operational specifications. A common conclusion of relevant articles [35–37] is that the harmonics caused by wind turbines do not produce distortion of the produced sinusoidal signal over the permissible limits and, consequently, they do not constitute a reason for wind power rejection.

2.07.8.1.5 Frequency fluctuations

The penetration of a relatively low wind power penetration in a power system does not affect the system's frequency since the introduced disturbances from the wind turbines, due to the wind's variability, are of small size and they are compensated by the system's thermal generators. Nevertheless, as the wind power penetration percentage over the power demand increases, serious problems concerning conservation of the system's fundamental frequency can be introduced, especially if the wind turbine is of steady-speed [37–40]. The system's fundamental frequency is regulated by the thermal generators. The modern variable-speed wind turbines exhibit considerably improved characteristic features regarding the frequency fluctuations. More about the effect of wind turbines on the system's frequency fluctuations are mentioned in the next section.

From the above presentation it is shown that modern wind turbines exhibit quite improved features concerning their induced power quality problems to the utility network. Usually, the induced power quality problems from variable-speed wind turbines do not constitute reasons for the restriction of wind power penetration. Nevertheless, one should investigate the wind turbine's generator features, while selecting the wind turbine model. In any case, pitch control, variable-speed wind turbines must be selected. Any possible further particular improved features concerning the power quality of the produced electricity by the wind turbine must be evaluated, respectively, especially in wind parks' installations in isolated networks.

Another major factor is the concentration of wind parks in a limited geographical area and their connection to the same part of the electricity network (e.g., at the same substation). This phenomenon is very common, since the wind parks are usually concentrated in areas with good wind potential. If the geographically concentrated wind parks are connected at the same part of the electricity network, the effect of the produced power quality disturbances from the wind turbines on this particular part of the network will be more intensive, even in cases of interconnected networks.

The effect of the high wind power penetration in weak networks is more important as far as the dynamic security of the network is concerned. This effect is analyzed in the next section.

2.07.8.2 Wind Power Penetration in Weak Networks and Dynamic Security

The term 'dynamic security' of a power system refers to the conservation of the dynamic balance between the power production and the power demand, namely the possibility of the power production system to cover the power demand successfully following its variations and maintaining the produced electricity characteristic features (voltage, frequency) within the predefined values.

The frequency of the power system varies with the active power demand, while the voltage magnitude varies with the reactive power demand. The dynamic security conservation in a power production system practically implies the production of active and reactive power, following the corresponding demand variations, so that the arisen frequency and voltage fluctuations are always maintained within predefined limits, imposed by the normal operation of the power system.

In the large interconnected power systems, where large power production and distribution systems co-exist and support each other, the dynamic security is easier to be conserved than in small isolated systems. This stands because of the following facts:

- The relevant power demand variations in large interconnected systems are not as intensive as in small isolated ones, or, at least, they are not detectable. The power demand reduction in one area, for example, can be compensated with the simultaneous power demand increase somewhere else. Consequently, the thermal generators do not often need to follow intensive power demand variations.
- In case of extreme emergency situations, the interconnected systems support each other; hence the contingency for serious power production problems (e.g., black-outs) is reduced.

The abovementioned advantages of large interconnected systems are not met in isolated ones. In the case of small, weak systems, the power demand may be covered only by one thermal generator. The angular velocity of this generator defines the frequency of the produced alternating current. The system's security depends on the specific generator's characteristic features, such as its droop, its response ability to abrupt power demand changes, and so on. In most weak systems, the only way to improve their dynamic security is the conservation of spinning reserve from thermal generators, with direct consequence the increase of the electricity production cost.

As the size of an isolated power system increases, the dynamic security depends on a group of generators. Usually in large isolated systems some generators are used for frequency regulation (base production generators) and some others follow the power demand variation (peak production generators).

Practically, in electricity production systems the most common disturbances capable to cause serious dynamic security problems are the voltage and frequency sags. Voltage and frequency sags can be caused by an abrupt power demand increase or by the abrupt loss of the power output (generators tripping). The power system's response in such events depends on the network's protection devices and topology, the on-duty thermal generators specifications, and the thermal generator spinning reserve that may be kept.

The wind turbines' effect on the dynamic security of an electricity network is imposed by the reduced tolerances that they exhibit to the system's nominal voltage magnitude and fundamental frequency variations. Because of these reduced tolerances the wind turbines are characterized as sensitive generators, tripping before any other thermal generator in case of a voltage or frequency contingency in the electricity network.

Typical wind turbines' tolerances in systems' nominal voltage magnitude and fundamental frequency variations are presented in **Table 7**. The data presented in **Table 7** are indicative and can vary for different wind turbine models. New wind turbine models can

Table 7 Typical values of wind turbine generator tolerances in voltage and frequency variations, found in commercial wind turbine model technical handbooks

Contingency	Variation (%)	Time tolerance (s)
Voltage sag	−10.00	60.0
Voltage sag	−15.00	11.00
Overvoltage	+10.00	60.0
Overvoltage	+15.00	2.0
Overvoltage	+20.00	0.08
Overvoltage	+25.00	0.005
Frequency drop	−6.00%	0.2
Frequency	+6.00%	0.2

also exhibit improved tolerances; however, the majority of the already installed wind turbines worldwide are characterized, more or less, by the values presented in **Table 7**.

Dynamic security conservation is a difficult task in weak systems with high wind power penetration. The wind turbine effect on the normal operation of a power system depends on the following parameters:

- the wind power instant penetration percentage over the power demand
- the on-duty thermal generator specifications, especially their exhibiting response to power demand variations
- the spinning reserve conservation from thermal generators
- the wind turbines' tolerances to voltage magnitude and frequency fluctuations.

The maximum instant wind power penetration in order to guarantee the system's secure operation is not constant and depends on certain operational parameters, such as:

- the type of the on-duty thermal generators and their specifications
- the electricity network topology
- the spinning reserve conservation
- the weather conditions.

The above listed parameters imply different upper limits for the wind power instant penetration percentage, under different operational conditions, even of the same electricity system. Practically, the maximum secure wind power penetration percentage can reach 10–15% of the power demand, for small and weak power systems and under unfavorable operational conditions (low power demand, bad weather conditions, low thermal generators spinning reserve, etc.). On the other hand, in larger isolated systems and under favorable operational conditions, the secure wind power penetration percentage can reach 30–35%.

In **Figure 52** the results from a contingency examined in the frames of a general study regarding the dynamic security evaluation of the existing electricity system in Crete is presented. In this figure the reaction of a system after the same contingency (25 MW power production loss from a steam turbine) is examined. The power demand in both scenarios is equal to 250 MW, while the wind power production is also common and equals 80 MW, exhibiting a wind power penetration percentage of 32%. The only difference between the two scenarios is the type and the percentage of the conserved spinning reserve from thermal generators. In the first scenario no spinning reserve is conserved; consequently, the system is not able to recover after the contingency. In the first scenario the dynamic security collapses and the system is led to black-out. In the second scenario it is assumed that spinning reserve from diesel generators with total nominal power of 50 MW is available. The system is able to recover after the contingency, maintaining the network's fundamental frequency close to its nominal value. The above presented simulation shows that the maximum wind power penetration percentage for a secure system's operation cannot be defined uniquely.

2.07.8.3 The Connection of Wind Parks in Electricity Networks

The wind parks are relatively small decentralized electricity production plants. Their installation sites are usually located at the top of hills or mountains or in the sea, where remarkable wind potential is met. Consequently, wind parks are usually connected in rural and weak network's parts.

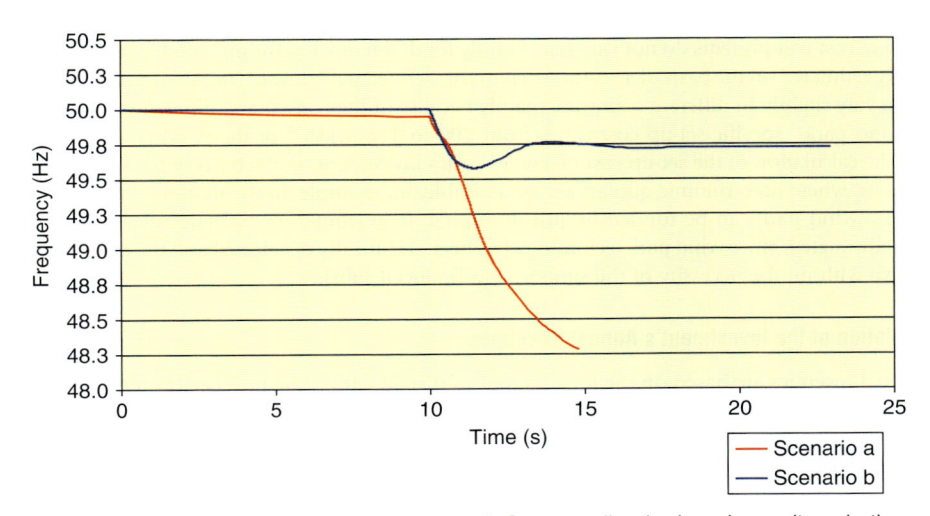

Figure 52 The results from the simulation of the existing electricity system in Crete regarding the dynamic security evaluation.

Table 8 Maximum power transportation ability in terms of the nominal voltage of the electricity network

Connection network nominal voltage (kV)	Wind park's nominal power (MW)
10	1–2
20	5–8
40	13–18
130	30–60

The wind turbines produce low-voltage alternating current (400 V, 690 V, depending on the specific wind turbine model). The electricity produced from all the wind turbines is gathered in the wind park's substation where it is transformed to medium-voltage current, usually at 20 kV. This current must be provided to the network.

The wind parks can be connected in medium-voltage networks (15–60 kV) if their nominal power does not exceed 5 MW and the available network in the wind park's vicinity is not overloaded from other wind parks connections or from the power demand. Where this is not possible, the wind parks must be connected to the nearest high-voltage utility network (over 150 kV). In this case, the construction of a high-voltage substation is required for the connection to the wind park. An empirical criterion for the selection of a wind park's proper connection is that the total power transportation capability of the connection network must be at least 20 times higher than the wind park's nominal power.

The wind power transportation ability of electricity networks with different nominal voltage is presented in Table 8. The values presented in Table 8 are indicative, calculated following the basic electricity transportation theory [41], aiming at the minimization of electricity transportation losses.

2.07.9 Economic Analysis

The design of a wind park is integrated with the accomplishment of the investment's economic analysis. The economic analysis of a wind park's investment aims at the calculation of characteristic economic indexes that constitute the fundamental criteria regarding the implementation of the project. The economic analysis of a wind park's investment consists of the following stages:

2.07.9.1 The Project's Set-Up Cost Calculation and the Funding Scheme

The set-up cost of a wind park consists of the following components:

- the wind turbines' purchase, transportation, and erection cost
- the secondary electromechanical equipment purchase and installation cost
- the new connection network construction cost
- the land purchase cost
- the infrastructure works cost (roads, wind turbines' service areas, etc.)
- consultants fees.

As mentioned in previous sections, the wind park's set-up cost is configured mainly by the wind turbine purchase, transportation, and erection cost. Since these cost components do not vary significantly for different wind turbine models, the wind parks' set-up cost can be quite approximately estimated on the basis of a set-up specific cost, defined per kilowatt (or MW) of installed wind power. The wind park's specific cost can vary slightly in different countries, mainly because of the consequent differences of wind turbines' transportation cost. Onshore wind parks' specific set-up cost varies from 900 to 1200€ kW^{-1} of the wind park's nominal power, regarding European countries. The calculation of the set-up cost of a wind park's investment on the basis of the specific set-up cost can provide relatively accurate results, where no economic quotations are available, for example, in the frames of a preliminary feasibility study.

The set-up cost of a wind park can be funded by private capital, loan capital, or by state subsidies. The availability of state subsidies tends to be eliminated, since wind park technology has been technically developed and the corresponding investments are considered competitive without the necessity of the support of a financial subsidy.

2.07.9.2 The Calculation of the Investment's Annual Revenues

The investment's annual revenues are based on the total annual sold energy from the producer to the local utility. The wind park's annual revenues are calculated by the product of the annual sold energy with the price of the electricity produced by the wind parks. The selling price for the electricity produced by the wind parks depends on the national legislation concerning electricity production from wind parks. In most cases the feed-in-tariff system has been introduced (a steady price for electricity produced by the wind parks). In free markets status regarding the electricity production, the electricity price is not steady and, commonly, depends on the electricity production availability and demand.

```
         ┌─────────────────────────────┐
         │  Wind park's set-up cost    │
         │  calculation and funding    │
         │  scheme determination       │
         └──────────────┬──────────────┘
                        ↓
         ┌─────────────────────────────┐
         │ Annual revenues calculation │
         │     from electricity sales  │
         └──────────────┬──────────────┘
                        ↓
         ┌─────────────────────────────┐
         │    Annual operational and   │
         │     maintenance expenses    │
         └──────────────┬──────────────┘
                        ↓
         ┌─────────────────────────────┐
         │  Annual net profits         │
         │        calculation          │
         └──────────────┬──────────────┘
                        ↓
         ┌─────────────────────────────┐
         │ Investment's economic       │
         │     indexes calculation     │
         └─────────────────────────────┘
```

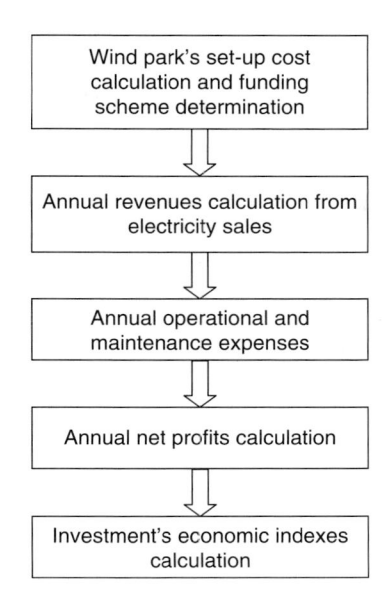

Figure 53 Wind park's economic analysis stages.

2.07.9.3 Annual Expenses

The annual expenses of a wind park strongly depend on the national legislation frameworks. Indicatively, the following can be stated:

- municipal taxes, usually defined as a small percentage over the annual revenues, as a compensation for the installation and the operation of the wind park in the geographical territory of the Municipality
- wind turbines' maintenance, usually taken over by the turbines' manufacturers, with a total annual cost per wind turbine or a total annual cost per produced kWh by the wind park
- equipment insurance
- annual loan payment
- staff salaries
- land rent
- state taxes, defined in the relevant national legislation.

The sum of the abovementioned expenses provide the total annual expenses of the wind park.

2.07.9.4 Investment's Annual Net Profits

The investment's annual net profits are calculated by subtracting the total annual expenses from the annual revenues.

2.07.9.5 Economic Indexes

The wind park investments' economic indexes, such as the payback period, the internal rate of return, and so on, are calculated on the basis of the annual net profits time-series. The economic indexes can be calculated either for the total set-up cost or for the private capitals of the funding scheme.

The above described procedure is presented in **Figure 53**.

2.07.10 Presentation of Characteristic Case Studies

In this section two characteristic wind park development studies will be presented, namely:

- the design of a wind park in a small-sized noninterconnected power system
- the design of a wind park in a large-sized noninterconnected power system.

Finally, a brief description of the largest onshore and offshore wind parks in the world is presented.

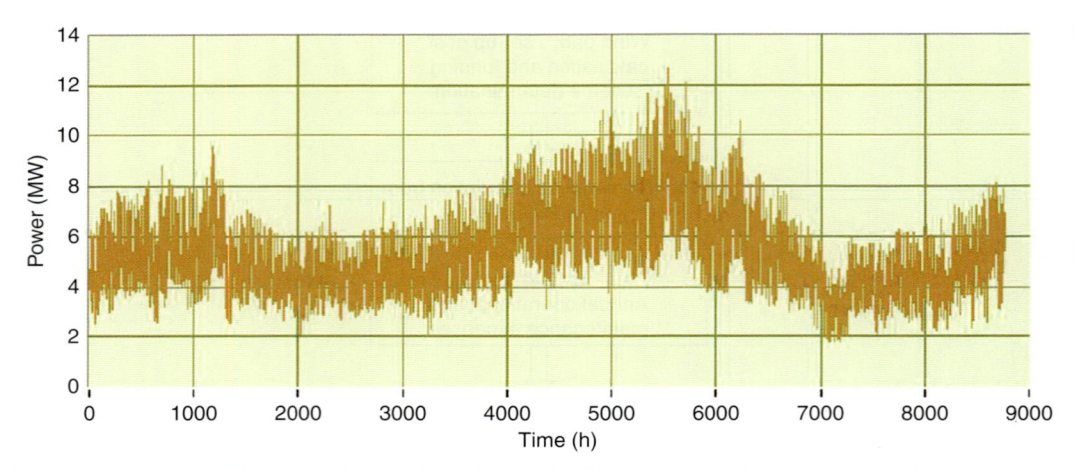

Figure 54 The annual power demand in the noninterconnected system of Karpathos and Kasos islands for the year 2015.

2.07.10.1 The Design of a Wind Park in a Small Noninterconnected Power System

The first case study refers to a small wind park designed for installation in the noninterconnected system of the islands of Karpathos and Kasos. Karpathos and Kasos are two small islands located in the southeast Aegean Sea (Dodecanese complex) in Greece. These islands are electrically connected to each other. In total, they constitute a noninterconnected electricity system. The electricity production in these islands is based on a small thermal power plant and a small wind park of 1.2 MW nominal power, both of them installed on the island of Karpathos. In **Figure 54** the annual power demand variation is presented, as it is predicted for the year 2015. The minimum and maximum annual power demand is expected to equal 1.81 and 12.65 MW, respectively. The annual electricity consumption is calculated as 46 512.37 MWh.

From the power demand characteristic features presented above the restricted possibility of the examined system to accept further installation of wind parks is revealed. Taking into account the wind power penetration maximum percentage, which in small systems cannot exceed 30% of power demand, considerable wind power rejection is expected.

For the abovementioned reasons, a small wind park will be proposed on the island of Kasos, since no power production unit has been so far installed in this island.

The design of the wind park on the island of Kasos begins with an overall observation of the island's land morphology and orientation. A map of the island is presented in **Figure 55**. Since the wind potential is expected to be higher at the top of hills and mountains and the wind boundary layer is also expected to be fully developed at these geographical positions, the available mountains in the island are inspected. The highest mountain in the island is the mountain of Prionas, found in the north east part (see **Figure 56**).

Focusing on the specific mountain, a ridge with a total length of almost 600 m and direction from west to east is located. The most usual wind direction met in the Aegean Sea islands is north–northwest; hence, the specific ridge direction is perpendicular to the expected prevailing wind direction. Moreover, the specific ridge is free of technical or natural obstacles from any direction. The wind potential at the specific geographical point is expected to be maximized due to the abovementioned parameters, namely:

- the high altitude at the selected position
- the lack of any technical or natural obstacles around the selected ridge
- the orientation of the ridge in regard to the expected wind direction.

The wind park's development team visited the island of Kasos several times to inspect the selected area and investigate its ownership. The results were as predicted from the implemented map research. The selected ridge is an area at the highest place of the island, vertically positioned to the north, free of obstacles from any direction. Moreover, the visit to the ridge confirmed the high wind potential that is expected at the specific site. The strong wind that blows in the area and the difficult access discouraged the inhabitants from developing any kind of activities at the selected site. Consequently, the information provided from the inhabitants was that the selected site was not a private possession; hence, it belonged to the state. The favorable conditions met in the investigated site led the development team to make the decision to install a wind mast in the candidate site.

A 22.5 m meteorological mast was installed at the selected site and the collection of the wind potential measurements began in May 2010. The installation of the wind mast was rather a difficult and expensive task, due to the equipment's transportation cost from Crete to the remote island and the lack of road access to the installation point. The wind-rose graph and the Weibull probability density calculated from the annual wind potential measurements have been already presented in **Figures 23** and **24**.

Wind Parks Design, Including Representative Case Studies 213

Figure 55 The island of Kasos and the selected area for investigation.

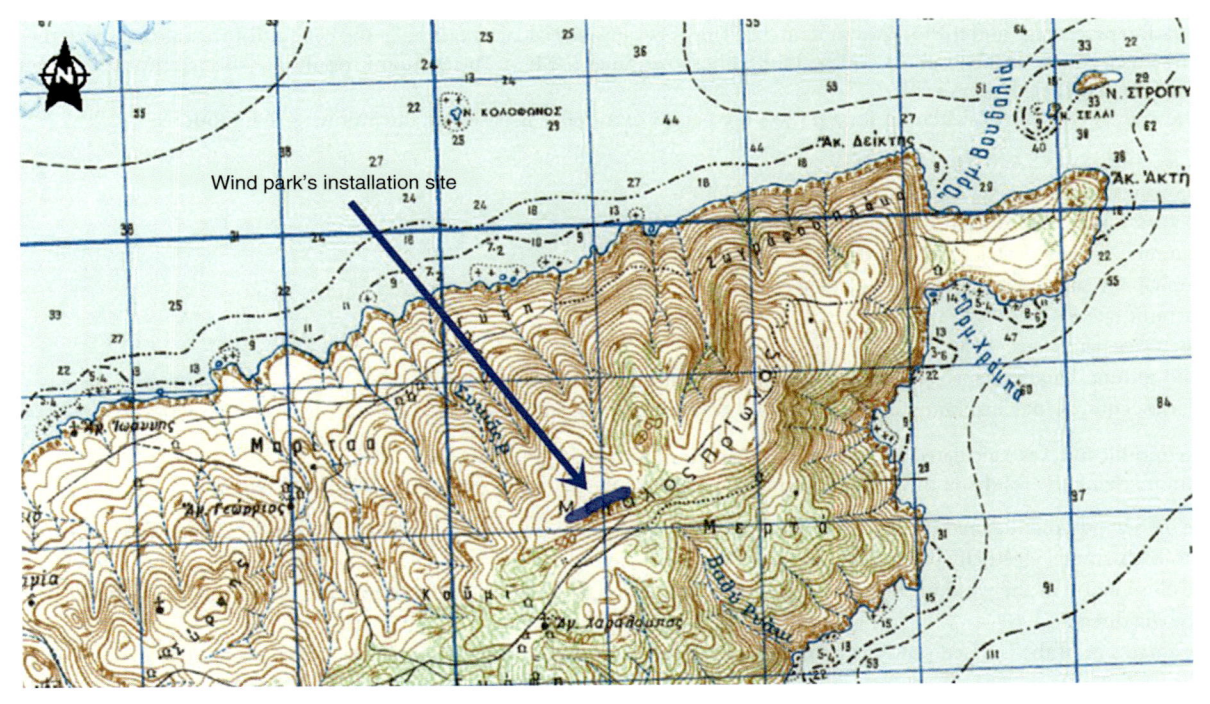

Figure 56 The specific installation site at the mountain of Prionas.

The captured wind potential measurements exceeded the development team's anticipations. The high available wind potential is depicted on the wind velocity mean value over the measurements time period (equal to 11.61 m s^{-1}) and the Weibull distribution parameters, calculated equal to $C = 13.2$ m s^{-1} and $k = 2.85$. The calculated wind potential features of the selected site are excellent. It is considered quite rare to meet such high wind potential in an area. Moreover, the right to proceed to the wind park's installation at the selected site can be obtained by the state, since there were no individuals claiming the ownership of the land. Summarizing these first evaluation results, the selected site for wind park's installation was an excellent choice.

The installation of the wind park at the selected site does not affect any human activities and does not have any direct visual contact with places of tourist and historical interest. The nearest settlement is 3300 m away and does not have a visual contact with the wind park. It must be noted that the whole island of Kasos belongs to Natura 2000 network. However, the selected area is not a zone A one; hence, the installation of wind parks is not prohibited.

Taking into account the low power demand in the Karpathos and Kasos system, the available place in the selected site and the peculiarities met in small islands, a number of medium-sized wind turbines of 900 kW nominal power are selected for installation. The reasons for selecting a medium-sized wind turbine model are listed below:

- The low power demand of the isolated system and the existence of a 1.2 MW wind park will restrict the power penetration of the proposed wind park. Hence, the nominal power of the new wind park cannot be high. So, there is no need to install a large wind turbine model to maximize the nominal power of the wind park.
- There is enough available land in the selected area. So there is no need to install a large wind turbine model to reach the desirable wind park's power, due to the low availability of land.
- The installation of large wind turbines in remote and small islands affect the landscape significantly and is not suggested.
- The transportation possibilities of large wind turbines may not be possible in such places with a lack of technical infrastructure.

Following the abovementioned decision criteria, five wind turbines were selected to be installed in the total available area, giving a wind park of 4.5 MW nominal power. The micro-siting of the wind turbines is rather an easy task. The five wind turbines are sited in a line perpendicular to the wind direction, following the orientation of the ridge. The small number of wind turbines and the ridge direction do not cause problems concerning possible shade losses between the wind turbines. The wind turbines' micro-siting is presented on the developed wind map (**Figure 26**) based on the captured wind potential measurements. As seen in this figure, the available wind potential is equivalent in all the selected installation positions.

The annual electricity production from the five wind turbines, including the wind turbines' shading losses, is calculated directly from the specialized software exploited for the wind map development. The final electricity production is calculated taking into account the electricity transportation losses (3%), the wind turbines' availability (95%), the wind turbines' hysteresis, and the wind power rejection from the isolated network (based on the analysis carried out in a previous section). The results are presented in **Table 9**.

As seen in **Table 9**, the purchased electricity from the wind park is considerably restricted due to the maximum wind power penetration percentage and the low power demand. This is because the capacity factors of the wind turbines, calculated for the final penetrated electricity to the local network, exhibit rather low values (~24%). The economic results are affected negatively from this high wind energy rejection as well.

The annual cash flow calculation for a project life period of 20 years is based on the following assumptions:

- total set-up cost €5 400 000 (1200€ kW^{-1})
- financial scheme: private capital 60%, loan capital 40%
- electricity price 0.099€ kWh^{-1} (feed-in tariff status)
- loan rate 7% and payback period 10 years
- municipality taxes 3% over the annual revenues
- discount rate 8%
- state taxes percentage 25%
- wind turbines' maintenance cost according to the manufacturer's quotation
- salaries, equipment's insurance, and several costs according to statistical and empirical data from similar wind parks [42–44].

The economic indexes, calculated over the investment equities, are presented in **Table 10**.

Summarizing the results of the above presented case study, one should point out the following remarks:

- the high wind potential and the land morphology of the selected site provide the prerequisites for the installation of a wind park with high annual electricity production
- the elimination of the wind turbines' shading losses, due to the micro-siting of the turbines in an vertical line to the wind main blowing direction
- the small size of the isolated power system does not enable the penetration of the total electricity produced from the wind park.

In general, the latter fact may restrict the economic indexes of such investments. This case study was presented to indicate that in very small systems the exploitation of the high wind potential is not always feasible, because of the restrictions concerning the wind power penetration. In such cases, two alternatives are possible aiming at the wind energy rejection minimization:

- to reduce the total nominal power of the wind park
- to combine the wind park with a small pumped-storage system to store the rejected electricity [45–50].

Table 9 Electricity production analysis from the wind park on the island of Kasos

W/T	Electricity production before shading losses (GWh)	Shading losses (%)	Shading losses (GWh)	Electricity production after shading losses (GWh)	Wind turbines' hysteresis losses (GWh)	Wind turbines' hysteresis losses (%)	Electricity production after shading and hysteresis losses (GWh)	Electricity transportation losses (GWh)	Network rejection losses (%)	Network rejection losses (GWh)	Wind turbines' availability losses (GWh)	Final electricity production (GWh)	Capacity factor (%)
S1	4.829	1.01	0.049	4.780	0.166	3.47	4.614	0.138	50.69	2.339	0.231	1.906	24.18
S2	4.832	0.99	0.048	4.784	0.162	3.39	4.622	0.139	50.69	2.343	0.231	1.909	24.21
S3	4.922	0.91	0.045	4.877	0.179	3.67	4.698	0.141	50.69	2.381	0.235	1.941	24.61
S4	4.981	0.74	0.037	4.944	0.200	4.05	4.744	0.142	50.69	2.405	0.237	1.960	24.86
S5	5.013	0.02	0.001	5.012	0.193	3.85	4.819	0.145	50.69	2.443	0.241	1.990	25.24
Total/averaged values	24.577	0.73	0.180	24.397	0.900	3.69	23.497	0.705	50.69	11.911	1.175	9.706	24.35

Table 10 Economic indexes for the wind park investment in the island of Kasos, corresponding to the project's life period (i.e., 20 years)

Net present value (€)	1 087 088.17
Internal rate of return (%)	12.03
Payback period (years)	8.47
Discounted payback period (years)	12.81
Return on investment (%)	80.13
Return on equities (%)	133.55

2.07.10.2 The Design of a Wind Park in a Large Noninterconnected Power System

The second case study refers to a larger wind park designed for installation in the noninterconnected system of the island of Crete. In 2010 the thermal generator installed power exceeded 750 MW. The wind park installed power was 168 MW. In **Figure 57** the annual power demand variation is presented, as it is predicted for the year 2015. The minimum and maximum annual power demand is expected to equal 193.21 and 722.95 MW, respectively. The annual electricity consumption is calculated as 3 383 201.00 MWh.

The site selection for the island of Crete is a more complicated procedure compared to the one applied on the island of Kasos. On the one hand, the available candidate areas with acceptable wind potential are more and the large size of the system enables higher wind power penetration, compared to the previously presented example. On the other hand, a major parameter from which the selection procedure must start is the possibility to gain the land ownership. In **Figure 58**, the Crete wind map [7] is presented. Plenty of sites with high potential are available on Crete, as seen in this figure. For the purposes of the current case study, the wind park was selected to be installed in the Asterousia Mountains at the southern part of Crete. According to the information provided by the wind map of Crete, the selected mountains exhibit a large number of sites with high wind potential.

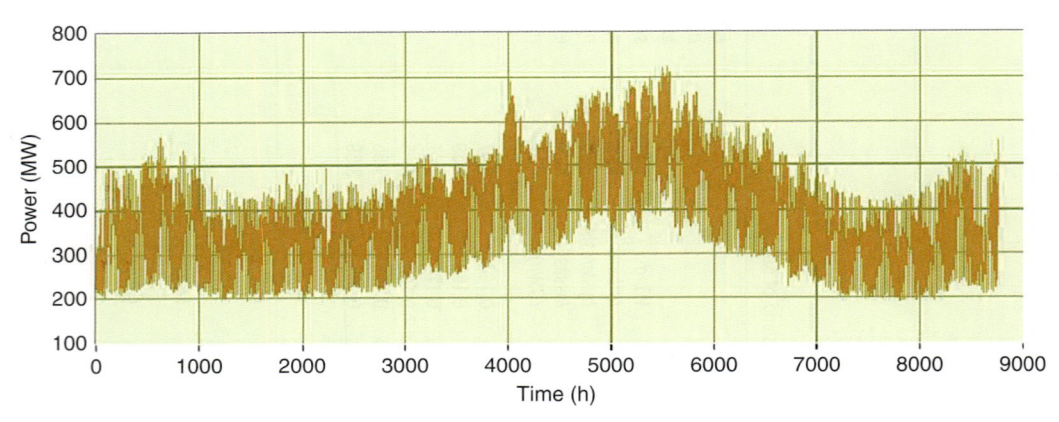

Figure 57 The annual power demand in the noninterconnected system of Crete island for the year 2015.

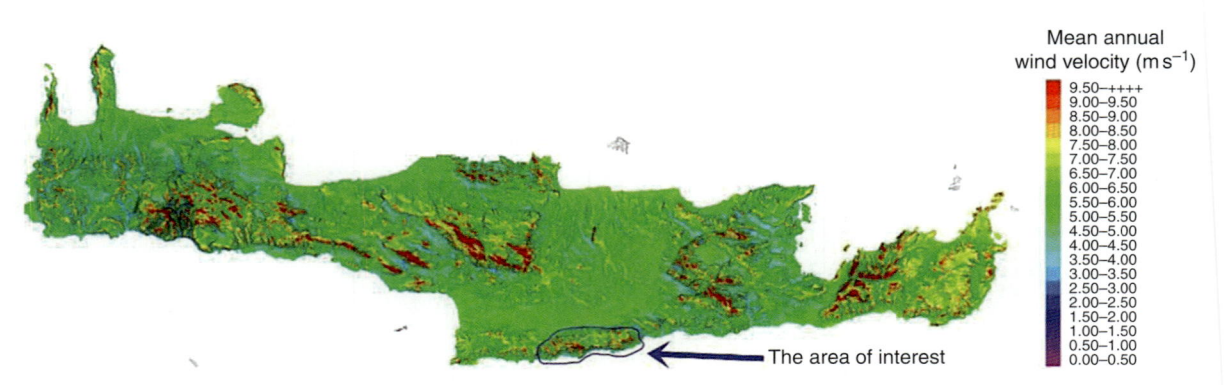

Figure 58 The wind map of Crete and the area of interest [7].

The wind potential map was thoroughly examined at the selected area. The site's selection procedure was implemented taking into account other parameters too, such as:

- the accessibility to the candidate site
- the land ownership and the possibility to gain its possession
- the proximity to special places of natural, cultural, historical, tourist, and military interest.

A number of sites exhibiting high wind potential were chosen and their proximity to the abovementioned areas of special interest was examined. Some of them were excluded through this first evaluation stage. The crucial issue was the investigation of the land's ownership. All belonged to individuals; consequently, the possibility to gain the right to install the wind park in a site was a matter of bargaining, policy, and diplomacy rather than a technical one. Finally, after a time-consuming procedure of meetings and negotiations with the landowners, an ultimate site selection was possible. The choice is presented in **Figure 25**.

The selected site was free of any limitations concerning the wind park installation. There was no direct visual impact with places of special interest, its shorter distance from the nearby settlement was almost 800 m (the minimum one is defined as 500 m in Greek legislation), it did not belong to the Natura 2000, Special Protected Areas (SPA), or Site of Community Interest (SCI) networks, and so on. Moreover, the accessibility to the area was good, since the existing provincial and agricultural roads led directly to the installation site.

Once the abovementioned crucial parameters had been examined, a 10 m high wind mast was installed. The installation of the wind mast was an easy task, mainly due to the existing accessibility to the site. The wind measurements captured period lasted for a whole year and provided the results presented in **Figures 59 and 60**.

The wind velocity mean value over the measurements annual time period (equal to $8.67\ m\ s^{-1}$) and the Weibull distribution parameters, calculated equal to $C = 9.7\ m\ s^{-1}$ and $k = 1.77$ indicate the availability of remarkable wind potential.

A careful investigation of the presented parameters and the properly planned site selection created the prerequisites for the installation of a wind park without problems and time delays, especially during the licensing procedure.

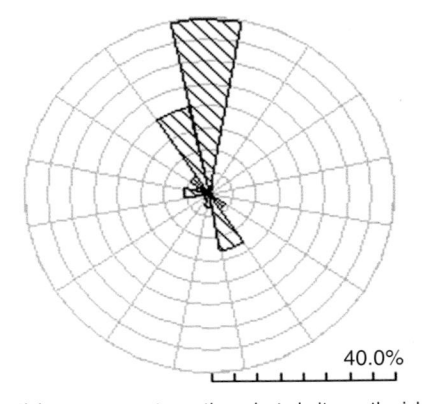

Figure 59 Wind-rose based on annual wind potential measurements on the selected site on the island of Crete.

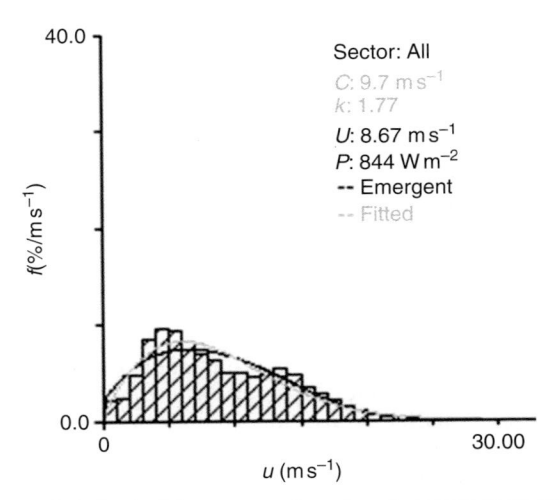

Figure 60 Weibull distribution based on annual wind potential measurements on the selected site on the island of Crete.

The large size of the isolated system on Crete and the land morphology of the selected area enabled the installation of a large-sized wind turbine model of 3 MW nominal power. The reasons for selecting a large-sized wind turbine model are listed below:

- The large size of the isolated system will restrict the power rejection from the proposed wind park. Hence, a main target of the wind park's design is the maximization of its nominal power. This is achieved with a large wind turbine model.
- There is limited land available with high wind potential in the selected area. So a large wind turbine model must be selected to maximize the wind park's nominal power, due to the low availability of land.
- The good accessibility to the selected area and the available infrastructure and machinery on the island of Crete enables the transportation of large wind turbines to the installation site.

The micro-siting of the wind turbines aimed at the maximization of the installed wind power and the minimization of the wind turbine shading losses. Wind turbines were installed only in positions with mean annual wind velocity higher than $8\,\mathrm{m\,s^{-1}}$ (**Figure 25**).

The wind turbines micro-siting is presented on the developed wind map (**Figure 25**) based on the captured wind potential measurements. As seen in this figure, 12 wind turbines were sited in the selected area, giving a wind park with nominal power of 36 MW. The micro-siting of the wind turbines was performed taking into account:

- the ownership of the area (this is why the wind turbines' installation positions do not always coincide with the position of maximum wind velocity)
- the wind potential of the installation positions
- the minimization of the shading losses.

The annual electricity production from the 12 wind turbines, including the wind turbines' shading losses, was calculated directly using the specialized software applied for the wind parks' development. The final electricity production was calculated taking into account the electricity transportation losses (3%), the wind turbines' availability (95%), the wind turbines' hysteresis, and the wind power rejection from the isolated network (based on the analysis carried out in a previous section). The results are presented in **Table 11**.

As seen in **Table 11**, the electricity purchased from the wind park is restricted mainly due to the increased wind turbines' shading and network rejection losses. Nevertheless, the wind energy rejection is considerably reduced in this case, compared to that of the previously presented case study, because the wind park is introduced in a large isolated system. The capacity factors of the wind turbines, calculated for the final penetrated electricity to the local network, vary from 38% (in the case of a wind turbine with 11% shading losses) to 45%.

The annual cash flows calculation for a project's life period of 20 years is based on the following assumptions:

- total set-up cost €36 000 000 ($1000€\,\mathrm{kW^{-1}}$)
- financial scheme: private capital 60%, loan capital 40%
- electricity price $0.099€\,\mathrm{kWh^{-1}}$ (feed-in tariff status)
- loan rate 7% and payback period 10 years
- municipality taxes 3% over the annual revenues
- discount rate 8%
- state taxes percentage 25%
- wind turbines' maintenance cost according to the manufacturer's quotation
- salaries, equipment's insurance, and several costs according to statistical and empirical data from similar wind parks [42–44].

The economic indexes, calculated over the investment equities, are presented in **Table 12**.

Summarizing the results of the above presented case studies (Section 2.07.10.1 and 2.07.10.2), one should point out the following:

- the high wind potential and the land morphology of the selected site provide the prerequisites for the installation of a wind park with high capacity factor
- the small size of the isolated power system does not enable the penetration of the total electricity produced from the wind park, hence restricting the economic indexes of such investments.

2.07.10.3 The Roscoe Wind Park in Texas – Largest Onshore Wind Park

The Roscoe wind park in Roscoe, Texas, is the world's largest wind farm (as of October 2009) with 627 wind turbines and a total installed capacity of 781.5 MW [51]. The project cost more than $1 billion. It is located about 320 km west of Fort Worth, and spans parts of four Texas counties and covers nearly 400 km², several times the size of Manhattan (see **Figure 61**).

Construction on the wind park began in May 2007, and it has been operational since October 2009. The Roscoe wind park project was built in four phases. Of its total installed capacity of 781.5 MW, about 209 and 126.5 MW are generated in the phase I and phase II units, respectively. Phase III and phase IV together generate 446 MW.

Table 11 Electricity production analysis from the wind park on the island of Crete

W/T	Electricity production after shading losses (GWh)	Shading losses (GWh)	Shading losses (%)	Wind turbines' hysteresis losses (GWh)	Wind turbines' hysteresis losses (%)	Electricity production after shading and hysterisis losses (GWh)	Electricity transportation losses (GWh)	Network rejection losses (%)	Network rejection losses (GWh)	Wind turbines' availability losses (GWh)	Final electricity production (GWh)	Capacity factor (%)
S1	15.386	0.394	2.56	0.401	2.67	14.591	0.438	11.00	1.605	0.730	11.819	44.97
S2	15.238	0.355	2.33	0.383	2.58	14.499	0.435	11.00	1.595	0.725	11.744	44.69
S3	13.697	0.389	2.84	0.159	1.20	13.149	0.394	11.00	1.446	0.657	10.651	40.53
S4	14.959	1.108	7.41	0.343	2.48	13.508	0.405	11.00	1.486	0.675	10.941	41.63
S5	14.937	0.917	6.14	0.350	2.50	13.670	0.410	11.00	1.504	0.683	11.072	42.13
S6	14.982	1.263	8.43	0.336	2.45	13.383	0.401	11.00	1.472	0.669	10.840	41.25
S7	14.914	0.916	6.14	0.357	2.55	13.641	0.409	11.00	1.501	0.682	11.049	42.05
S8	14.515	1.623	11.18	0.291	2.25	12.602	0.378	11.00	1.386	0.630	10.207	38.84
S9	15.004	1.545	10.30	0.329	2.45	13.129	0.394	11.00	1.444	0.656	10.635	40.47
S10	15.037	0.391	2.60	0.443	3.02	14.204	0.426	11.00	1.562	0.710	11.505	43.78
S11	14.844	0.395	2.66	0.379	2.62	14.070	0.422	11.00	1.548	0.704	11.397	43.37
S12	14.937	0.532	3.56	0.350	2.43	14.055	0.422	11.00	1.546	0.703	11.385	43.32
Total	178.450	9.828	5.22	4.121	2.39	164.501	4.934	11.00	11.000	8.224	133.245	42.25

Table 12 Economic indexes for the wind park investment on the island of Crete, corresponding to the project's life period (i.e., 20 years)

Net present value (€)	46 531 353.87
Internal rate of return (%)	31.87
Payback period (years)	3.02
Discounted payback period (years)	3.66
Return on investment (%)	189.25
Return on equities (%)	315.42

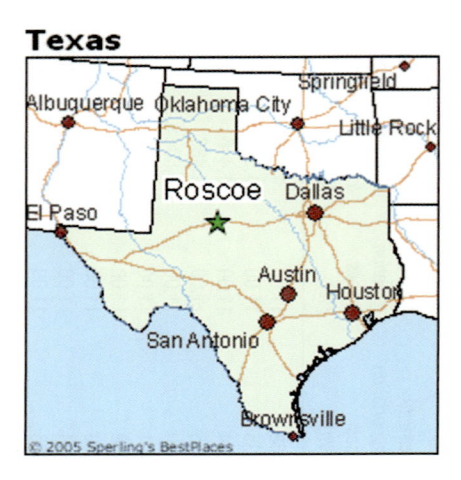

Figure 61 The location of Roscoe in Texas.

Figure 62 The location of Roscoe wind park in Texas [52].

The wind park employs 627 turbines, supplied by three different manufacturers. From the start of the wind farm's construction, a turbine was installed at the farm every day until completion. The turbines installed at the park range in height between 105 and 125 m, and stand 300 m apart (**Figure 62**).

The Roscoe wind complex provides the community with 70 fulltime working positions. In addition to its large size, the wind park is also notable for the large number of individual landowners (as many as 400) who are expected to share in royalties from the project.

2.07.10.4 The Thanet Wind Park in the United Kingdom – Largest Offshore Wind Park

The Thanet wind park is an offshore wind park 11 km off the coast of the Thanet district in Kent, England (**Figure 63**). Since September 2010, it has been the world's largest offshore wind park [53]. It has a nominal power of 300 MW, given by 100 wind turbines of 3 MW nominal power each. It cost £780–900 million (US$1.2–1.4 billion). It was officially opened on 23 September 2010, when it overtook Horns Rev 2 (209 MW) as the biggest offshore wind park in the world.

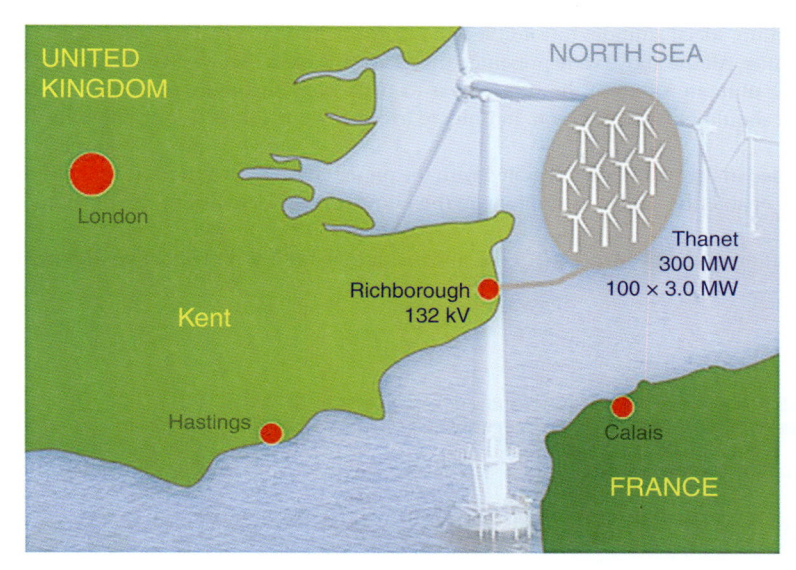

Figure 63 The location of Thanet wind park in United Kingdom.

Figure 64 The location of Thanet wind park in United Kingdom [54].

The project covers an area of 35 km², with 500 m (5.5 D, D the wind turbine's diameter) between wind turbines and 800 m (8.8 D) between the rows (**Figure 64**). The average sea depth at the turbines' installation positions is 20–25 m. Two submarine power cables run from an offshore substation within the wind park connecting to an existing onshore substation in Richborough, Kent, connecting to a world-first two transformers. The offshore substation steps up the turbine voltage of 33–132 kV for the grid. Maintenance of the turbines is carried out by the wind turbines' manufacturer, while a separate maintenance agreement with the erection company covers the turbine foundations.

The development was due to be in place by 2008. The wind turbine model was chosen in July 2006, and the foundation company was chosen as the preferred supplier for the foundations in September 2006. The project was delayed by a number of issues including problems with wind turbines' manufacturer who temporarily withdrew their offshore model from the market in 2007 following gearbox problems. The final model was re-released for sales starting from May 2008.

The erection company acquired the project in November 2008. On 28 June 2010, it was reported that all turbines had been installed for commissioning due by the end of 2010. The wind park was completed in September 2010.

The total capacity factor of the wind park is estimated as 25% [53].

2.07.11 Epilog

The procedure followed for the design of a wind park was presented in this chapter. It was attempted to outline the most crucial issues that could be faced within the design of a wind park. Subjects such as the selection of the appropriate site and the wind turbine model, the wind potential evaluation, the optimum micro-siting of the wind turbines, the calculation of the annual expected electricity production, social attitudes toward the wind park, and fundamental economic concepts were covered within the sections of the current chapter. All the above were presented on a scientific basis that was adapted for understanding by the average, and not expert reader. The ultimate scope of the subject was to make clear the entire procedure for designing a wind park and important parameters that should be paid attention, in order to avoid any difficulties during either the licensing or the installation of the wind park.

The information provided in this chapter is integrated with the presentation of two characteristic wind parks' design case studies. The provided case studies enable the reader to summarize the knowledge gathered from the previous sections and see how it is applied in real situations.

Finally, a brief presentation of the two largest (for the time being) onshore and offshore wind parks is provided.

References

[1] Shafiqur R (2005) Prospects of wind farm development in Saudi Arabia. *Renewable Energy* 30: 447–463.
[2] Kissel Johannes M and Krauter Stefan CW (2006) Adaptations of renewable energy policies to unstable macroeconomic situations – case study: Wind power in Brazil. *Energy Policy* 34: 3591–3598.
[3] Kaldellis JK and Zafirakis D (2011) The wind energy (r)evolution: A short review of a long history. *Renewable Energy* 36: 1887–1901.
[4] http://www.windatlas.dk/
[5] Troen IB and Petersen EL (1989) *European Wind Atlas*, 1st edn. Roskilde, Denmark: Risø National Laboratory.
[6] Official site of Risø National Laboratory. http://www.risoe.dk/
[7] Official site of Wind Energy Laboratory of Technological Educational Institute of Crete. http://www.wel.gr/
[8] Bergeles G (2005) *Wind Converters*. Athens, Greece: Simeon.
[9] Kaldellis JK and Gavras ThJ (2000) The economic viability of commercial wind plants in Greece: A complete sensitivity analysis. *Energy Policy* 28: 509–517.
[10] Dicorato M, Forte G, Pisani M, and Trovato M (2011) Guidelines for assessment of investment cost for offshore wind generation. *Renewable Energy* 36: 2043–2051.
[11] Tong KC (1998) Technical and economic aspects of a floating offshore wind farm. *Journal of Wind Engineering and Industrial Aerodynamics* 74–76: 399–410.
[12] http://offshorewind.net/
[13] http://www.offshorewindpowersystemsoftexas.com/
[14] (2009) *Environmental Impacts Analysis from Installation and Operation of Wind Parks*. Athens, Greece: Hellenic Wind Energy Association.
[15] Álvarez-Farizo B and Nick H (2002) Using conjoint analysis to quantify public preferences over the environmental impacts of wind farms: An example from Spain. *Energy Policy* 107–116.
[16] Pablo HJ, Joaquín F, Parrondo JL, and Eduardo B (2004) Spanish method of visual impact evaluation in wind farms. *Renewable and Sustainable Energy Reviews* 8: 483–491.
[17] Bishop ID and Miller DR (2007) Visual assessment of off-shore wind turbines: The influence of distance, contrast, movement and social variables. *Renewable Energy* 32: 814–831.
[18] Oerlemans S, Sijtsma P, and Méndez LB (2007) Location and quantification of noise sources on a wind turbine. *Journal of Sound and Vibration* 299: 869–883.
[19] Drewitt AL and Langston RHW (2006) Assessing the impacts of wind farms on birds. *Ibis* 148: 29–42.
[20] Ommo H, Jochen D, Klaus-Michael E, *et al.* (2006) Bird migration studies and potential collision risk with offshore wind turbines. *Ibis* 148: 90–109.
[21] Luis B and Alejandro R (2004) Behavioural and environmental correlates of soaring-bird mortality at on-shore wind turbines. *Journal of Applied Ecology* 41: 72–81.
[22] Manuela de L, Janss GFE, and Miguel F (2004) The effects of a wind farm on birds in a migration point: The Strait of Gibraltar. *Biodiversity and Conservation* 13: 395–407.
[23] Garthe S and Hüppop O (2004) Scaling possible adverse effects of marine wind farms on seabirds: Developing and applying a vulnerability index. *Journal of Applied Ecology* 41: 724–734.
[24] Dialynas EN, Hatziargyriou ND, Koskolos N, and Karapidakis E (1998) Effect of high wind power penetration on the reliability and security of isolated power systems. Paper 38-302, 37th session, *CIGRÉ*, 30 August–5 September.
[25] Hatziargyriou N and Papadopoulos M (1998) Consequences of high wind power penetration in large autonomous power systems. *CIGRÉ Symposium*, Neptum, Romania, 18–19 September.
[26] Poul S, Unnikrishnan AK, and Mathew SA (2001) Wind farms connected to weak grids in India. *Wind Energy* 4: 137–149.
[27] National Center for Environmental Prediction (NCEP). Reanalysis Data Provided by the NOAA/OAR/ESRL PSD. Boulder, CO, USA. http://www.cdc.noaa.gov/
[28] Kalnay E, Kanamltsu M, Kistler R, *et al.* (1996) The NCEP/NCAR 40-year reanalysis project. *Bulletin of the American Meteorological Society* 77: 437–470.
[29] AWS Scientific, Inc. (1997) National Renewable Energy Laboratory. *Wind Resource Assessment Handbook*. Fundamentals for Conducting a Successful Monitoring Program. April 1997.
[30] International Standard IEC 61400-1, 3rd edn. International Electrotechnical Commission, August 2005.
[31] EWEA (2009) Wind energy: The facts. *Environmental Issues*. March 2009. Brussels.
[32] Official site of British Wind Energy Association. www.bwea.org
[33] Lynge JT (2000) *Renewable Energy on Small Islands*, 2nd edn. Forum for Energy and Development (FED), ISBN: 87-90502-03-5.
[34] Gerdes G and Santjer F (1994) Power quality of wind turbines and their interaction with the grid. *Proceedings of the European Wind Energy Conference (EWEC '94)*. pp. 1112–1115. Thessaloniki, Greece, 10–14 October.
[35] Tande JOG (2000) Exploitation of wind-energy resources in proximity to weak electric grids. *Applied Energy* 65: 395–401.
[36] Tande JOG (1998) Impact of wind turbines on voltage quality. *8th International Conference of Harmonics and Quality of Power*. Greece, 14–16 October.
[37] Ake L (2003) *The Power Quality of Wind Turbines*. Göteborg, Sweden: Chalmers University of Technology, ISBN: 91-7197-970-0.
[38] Larsson Å (1996) Voltage and frequency variations on autonomous grids: A comparison of two different wind-diesel systems. *Proceedings of the European Union Wind Energy Conference (EUWEC '96)*. pp. 317–320. Göteborg, Sweden, May.
[39] Scott GW, Wilreker VF, and Shalterns RK (1984) Wind turbine generator interaction with diesel generators in isolated power systems. *IEEE Transactions on Power Apparatus and Systems* 5: 933–938.
[40] Hari S, Trevor P, and Syed I (2001) Effect of pitch control and power conditioning on power quality of variable speed wind turbine generators. *AUPEC 2001*. pp. 95–100. Perth, Australia, 23–26 September.
[41] Papadias VK (1999) *Electricity Transportation Networks*. Athens, Greece: Symmetria, ISBN: 9789602660683.
[42] Kaldellis JK, Zafirakis D, and Kavadias K (2009) Techno-economic comparison of energy storage systems for island autonomous electrical networks. *Renewable and Sustainable Energy Reviews* 13: 378–392.
[43] Bueno C and Carta JA (2005) Technical–economic analysis of wind-powered pumped hydrostorage systems, Part I: Model development. *Solar Energy* 78: 382–395.
[44] Bueno C and Carta JA (2005) Technical–economic analysis of wind-powered pumped hydrostorage systems, Part II: Model application to the island of El Hierro. *Solar Energy* 78: 396–405.

[45] Katsaprakakis DA, Christakis DG, Emmanouel V, *et al.* (2007) The introduction of wind powered pumped storage systems in isolated power systems with high wind potential. *International Journal of Distributed Energy Resources* 3: 83–112.
[46] Katsaprakakis DA, Christakis DG, Arthouros Z, *et al.* (2008) Pumped storage systems introduction in isolated power production systems. *Renewable Energy* 33: 467–490.
[47] Katsaprakakis DA and Christakis DG (2006) Experience from the wind parks operation in Crete and perspectives towards the maximization of the wind power penetration. *5th World Wind Energy Conference and Exhibition WWEC 2006: Energy Independence Powered by Wind.* New Delhi, India, 6–8 November.
[48] Katsaprakakis DA, Christakis DG, Pavlopoulos K, *et al.* (2011) Introduction of a wind powered pumped storage system in the isolated insular power system of Karpathos–Kasos. *ICAE 2011 – International Conference on Applied Energy.* Perugia, Italy, 16–18 May.
[49] Kapsali M and Kaldellis JK (2010) Combining hydro and variable wind power generation by means of pumped-storage under economically viable terms. *Applied Energy* 87: 3475–3485.
[50] Kaldellis JK, Kapsali M, and Kavadias KA (2010) Energy balance analysis of wind-based pumped hydro storage systems in remote island electrical networks. *Applied Energy* 87: 2427–2437.
[51] http://en.wikipedia.org/wiki/Roscoe_Wind_Farm
[52] Image courtesy E.ON Climate and Renewables. http://www.power-technology.com/projects/roscoe-wind-farm/roscoe-wind-farm1.html
[53] http://en.wikipedia.org/wiki/Thanet_Offshore_Wind_Project
[54] Photo by Jim Bennett. http://www.eurotrib.com/story/2010/9/23/101324/764

Further Reading

[1] Tony B, Nick J, and David S (2011) *Wind Energy Handbook.* Wiley, ISBN: 0470699752.
[2] Pramod J (2010) *Wind Energy Engineering.* Europe: McGraw-Hill Education, ISBN: 0071714774.
[3] Vaughn N (2009) *Wind Energy.* Taylor & Francis Inc, ISBN: 1420075683.
[4] Musgrove PJ (2009) *Wind Power.* Cambridge University Press, ISBN: 0521747635.
[5] Mathew S (2006) *Wind Energy: Fundamentals, Resource Analysis and Economics.* Berlin and Heidelberg, Germany: Springer, ISBN: 3540309055.
[6] Bhadra SN, Kastha D, and Banerjee S (2005) *Wind Electrical Systems.* Oxford University Press, ISBN: 0195670930.
[7] Olimpo A-L, Nick J, and Janaka E (2009) *Wind Energy Generation.* Wiley, ISBN: 0470714336.
[8] Pasqualetti MJ, Paul G, and Robert R (2002) *Wind Power in View.* Elsevier Science and Technology, ISBN: 0125463340.
[9] (2009) *Wind Energy – The Facts.* Earthscan Ltd., ISBN: 1844077101.
[10] (2006) *Offshore Wind Energy.* Berlin and Heidelberg, Germany: Springer, ISBN: 3540346767.
[11] (2005) *Wind Power in Power Systems.* Wiley, ISBN: 0470855088.
[12] Siegfried H (2006) *Grid Integration of Wind Energy Conversion Systems.* Wiley, ISBN: 0470868996.
[13] Ken D (2010) *Valuing Wind Generation on Integrated Power Systems.* William Andrew Publishing, ISBN: 0815520476.
[14] Manfred S (2008) *Wind Energy Systems for Electric Power Generation.* Berlin and Heidelberg, Germany: Springer, ISBN: 3540687629.

2.08 Aerodynamic Analysis of Wind Turbines

JN Sørensen, Technical University of Denmark, Lyngby, Denmark

© 2012 Elsevier Ltd. All rights reserved.

2.08.1	Introduction	225
2.08.2	**Momentum Theory**	226
2.08.2.1	One-Dimensional Momentum Theory	226
2.08.2.2	The Optimum Rotor of Glauert	227
2.08.2.3	The Blade-Element Momentum Theory	228
2.08.2.3.1	Tip correction	229
2.08.2.3.2	Correction for heavily loaded rotors	230
2.08.2.3.3	Yaw correction	230
2.08.2.3.4	Dynamic wake	230
2.08.2.3.5	Airfoil data	231
2.08.3	**Advanced Aerodynamic Modeling**	231
2.08.3.1	Vortex Models	231
2.08.3.2	Numerical Actuator Disk Models	232
2.08.3.3	Full Navier–Stokes Modeling	232
2.08.4	**CFD Computations of Wind Turbine Rotors**	233
2.08.5	**CFD in Wake Computations**	234
2.08.6	**Rotor Optimization Using BEM Technique**	236
2.08.7	**Noise from Wind Turbines**	238
References		239
Further Reading		240

2.08.1 Introduction

The aerodynamics of wind turbines concerns, briefly speaking, modeling and prediction of the aerodynamic forces on the solid structures of a wind turbine and in particular on the rotor blades of the turbine. Aerodynamics is the most central discipline for predicting performance and loadings on wind turbines. The aerodynamic model is normally integrated with models for wind conditions and structural dynamics. The integrated aeroelastic model for predicting performance and structural deflections is a prerequisite for design, development, and optimization of wind turbines. Aerodynamic modeling may also concern design of specific parts of wind turbines, such as rotor blade geometry or performance predictions of wind farms.

Using simple axial momentum theory and energy conservation, Lanchester [1] and Betz [2] predicted that even an ideal wind turbine cannot exploit more than 59.3% of the wind power passing through the rotor disk. A major breakthrough in rotor aerodynamics was achieved by Betz [2] and Glauert [3], who formulated the blade-element momentum (BEM) theory. This theory, which later has been extended with many 'engineering rules', is today the basis for all rotor design codes in use by industry.

From an outsider's point of view, aerodynamics of wind turbines may seem simple as compared to aerodynamics of, for example, fixed-wing aircraft or helicopters. However, there are several added complexities. Most prominently, aerodynamic stall is always avoided for aircraft, whereas it is an intrinsic part of the wind turbines operational envelope. Stall occurs when the flow meets the wing at a too high angle of attack. The flow then cannot follow the wing surface and separates from the surface, leading to flow patterns far more complex than that of nonseparated flow. This renders an adequate description very complicated, and even for Navier–Stokes simulations, it becomes necessary to model the turbulent small-scale structures in the flow, using Reynolds-averaging or large eddy simulations (LESs). Indeed, in spite of the wind turbine being one of the oldest devices for exploiting the energy of the wind, some of the most basic aerodynamic mechanisms are not yet fully understood.

Wind turbines are subjected to atmospheric turbulence, wind shear from the ground effect, wind directions that change both in time and in space, and effects from the wake of neighboring wind turbines. These effects together form the ordinary operating conditions experienced by the blades. As a consequence, the forces vary in time and space and a dynamical description is an intrinsic part of the aerodynamic analysis.

At high wind velocities, where a large part of the blade of stall-regulated turbines operates in deep stall, the power output is extremely difficult to determine within an acceptable accuracy. When boundary layer separation occurs, the centrifugal force tends to push the airflow at the blade toward the tip, resulting in the aerodynamic lift being higher than what it would be on a nonrotating blade.

When the wind changes direction, misalignment with the rotational axis occurs, resulting in yaw error. Yaw error causes periodic variation in the angle of attack and invalidates the assumption of axisymmetric inflow conditions. Furthermore, it gives rise to radial flow components in the boundary layer. Thus, both the airfoil characteristics and the wake are subject to complicated three-dimensional (3D) and unsteady flow behavior.

In the following, a brief introduction is given to wind turbine aerodynamics. It is not possible in a short form to introduce to all aspects of rotor aerodynamics and the scope is on conventional aerodynamic modeling, as it is still used by industry in the design of new turbines, and on state-of-the-art methods for analyzing wind turbine rotors and wakes. Specifically, the basics of momentum theory, which still form the backbone in rotor design of wind turbines, are introduced. Next, state-of-the-art advanced aerodynamic models is presented. This includes vortex models, generalized actuator disk/line models, and computational fluid dynamics (CFD). Finally, a short introduction is given to rotor optimization and modeling of aerodynamically generated noise.

2.08.2 Momentum Theory

The basic tool for understanding wind turbine aerodynamics is the momentum theory in which the flow is assumed to be inviscid, incompressible, and axisymmetric. The momentum theory consists basically of control volume integrals for conservation of mass, axial and angular momentum balances, and energy conservation. In the following, we will give a brief introduction to momentum theory for design and analysis of wind turbines, starting by the simple, albeit important, one-dimensional (1D) momentum theory, from which the Betz limit can be derived, and ending with the practical BEM theory, which forms the basis for all rotor design codes in use by industry.

2.08.2.1 One-Dimensional Momentum Theory

We first revisit the simple axial momentum theory as originated by Rankine [4], Froude [5], and Froude [6]. Consider an axial flow of speed U_o passes through an actuator disk of area A with constant axial load (thrust) T. Denoting by u_R the axial velocity in the rotor plane, and let u_1 be the axial velocity in the ultimate wake where the air has regained its undisturbed pressure value, $p_w = p_o$, and let ρ denote the density of air. We now consider a 1D model for the stream tube that encloses the rotor disk (see **Figure 1**), and denote by A_o and A_1 the cross-sectional area of the flow far upstream and far downstream of the rotor, respectively.

The equation of continuity requires that the rate of mass flow, $\dot{m}$, is constant in each cross-section. Thus,

$$\dot{m} = \rho U_o A_o = \rho u_R A = \rho u_1 A_1 \quad [1]$$

Axial momentum balance for the considered stream tube results in the following equation for the thrust

$$T = \dot{m}(U_o - u_1) = \rho u_R A (U_o - u_1) \quad [2]$$

Applying the Bernoulli equation in front of and behind the rotor, we find that the total pressure head of the air in the slipstream has been decreased by

$$\Delta p = \frac{1}{2}\rho (U_o^2 - u_1^2) \quad [3]$$

The pressure drop takes place across the rotor and represents the thrust, $T = A\Delta p$. Combining eqns [2] and [3] shows the well-known result that

$$u_R = \frac{1}{2}(u_1 + U_o) \quad [4]$$

Introducing the axial interference factor as follows:

$$a = \frac{U_o - u_R}{U_o} \quad [5]$$

we obtain $u_R = (1-a)U_o$ and $u_1 = (1-2a)U_o$. From eqn [2], we get the following expressions for thrust and power extraction:

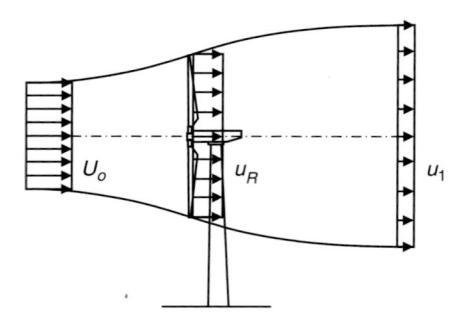

Figure 1 Control volume for 1D actuator disk.

$$T = 2\rho A U_o^2 a(1-a) \qquad [6]$$

$$P = u_R T = 2\rho A U_o^2 a(1-a)^2 \qquad [7]$$

Introducing the dimensionless thrust and power coefficient, respectively,

$$C_T \equiv \frac{T}{\frac{1}{2}\rho A U_o^2}, \quad C_P \equiv \frac{P}{\frac{1}{2}\rho A U_o^3} \qquad [8]$$

we get

$$C_T = 4a(1-a), \quad C_P = 4a(1-a)^2 \qquad [9]$$

Differentiating the power coefficient with respect to the axial interference factor, the maximum obtainable power is obtained as

$$C_{P\max} = \frac{16}{27} = 0.593 \quad \text{for} \quad a = \frac{1}{3} \qquad [10]$$

This result is usually referred to as the Betz limit or the 'Lanchester–Betz–Joukowsky limit', as recently proposed by van Kuik [7], and states the upper maximum for power extraction which is no more than 59.3% of the kinetic energy contained in a stream tube having the same cross-section as the disk area can be converted to useful work by the disk. However, it does not include the losses due to rotation of the wake and therefore it represents a conservative upper maximum.

2.08.2.2 The Optimum Rotor of Glauert

Utilizing general momentum theory, Glauert developed a simple model for the optimum rotor that included rotational velocities. In this approach, Glauert treated the rotor as a rotating axisymmetric actuator disk, corresponding to a rotor with an infinite number of blades. The main approximation in Glauert's analysis was to ignore the influence of the azimuthal velocity and pressure in the axial momentum equation. For a differential element of radial size Δr, eqn [2] then reads,

$$\Delta T = 4\pi \rho U_o^2 (1-a) a r \Delta r \qquad [11]$$

Applying the Bernoulli equation in a rotating frame of reference across the rotor plane, we get the following equation for the pressure drop over the rotor,

$$\Delta p = \rho \Omega r u_\theta + \frac{1}{2}\rho u_\theta^2 \qquad [12]$$

where Ω is the angular velocity.

Combining eqns [11] and [12], we get

$$\Delta T = \Delta p \cdot 2\pi r \Delta r = 2\pi \rho u_\theta \left(\Omega r + \frac{1}{2}u_\theta\right) r \Delta r \qquad [13]$$

where u_θ is the azimuthal velocity behind the rotor. Defining the azimuthal interference factor as,

$$a' = \frac{u_\theta}{2\Omega r} \qquad [14]$$

eqn [13] reads,

$$\Delta T = 4\pi \rho \Omega^2 (1+a') a' r^3 \Delta r \qquad [15]$$

Combining eqns [11] and [15], we get

$$(1-a)a = \lambda^2 x^2 (1+a')a' \qquad [16]$$

where $x = r/R$ and $\lambda = \Omega R / U_o$ is the tip speed ratio. This equation can also be derived by letting the induced velocity be perpendicular to the relative velocity in the rotor plane. Introducing Euler's turbine equation on differential form, we get the following expression for the useful power produced by the wind turbine,

$$P = \Omega \int_0^R 2\pi r^2 \rho u u_\theta dr = 4\pi \rho \Omega^2 U_o \int_0^1 a'(1-a) x^3 dx \qquad [17]$$

or in dimensionless form,

$$C_P = 8\lambda^2 \int_0^1 a'(1-a) x^3 dx \qquad [18]$$

By assuming that the different stream tube elements behave independently of each other, it is possible to optimize the integrand for each x separately (see Glauert [3] or Wilson and Lissamann [8]). This results in the following relation for an optimum rotor,

$$(1-a)\frac{\mathrm{d}a'}{\mathrm{d}a} - a' = 0 \qquad [19]$$

Differentiating eqn [16] with respect to a gives,

$$1 - 2a = \lambda^2 x^2 (1 + 2a') \frac{\mathrm{d}a'}{\mathrm{d}a} \qquad [20]$$

Combining eqns [16], [19], and [20] results in the following relationship

$$a' = \frac{1-3a}{4a-1} \qquad [21]$$

The analysis shows that the optimum axial interference factor is no longer a constant but will depend on the rotation of the wake and that the operating range for an optimum rotor is $1/4 \leq a \leq 1/3$.

The relations between a, a', $a'x^2\lambda^2$, and λx for an optimum rotor are given in **Table 1**. The maximal power coefficient as a function of tip speed ratio is determined by integrating eqn [18] and is shown in **Table 2**. The optimal power coefficient approaches 0.593 at large tip speed ratios only. It shall be mentioned that these results are valid only for a rotor with an infinite number of blades and that the analysis is based on the assumption that the rotor can be optimized by considering each blade element independently of the remaining blade elements.

2.08.2.3 The Blade-Element Momentum Theory

The BEM method was developed by Glauert [3] as a practical way to analyze and design rotor blades. In the BEM theory, the loading is computed using two independent methods, that is, by a local blade-element consideration using tabulated two-dimensional (2D) airfoil data and by use of the 1D momentum theorem. First, employing BEM, axial load and torque are written as, respectively,

Table 1 Flow conditions for the optimum actuator disk

a	a'	$a'x^2\lambda^2$	λx
0.25	∞	0	0
0.26	5.500	0.0296	0.073
0.27	2.375	0.0584	0.157
0.28	1.333	0.0864	0.255
0.29	0.812	0.1136	0.374
0.30	0.500	0.1400	0.529
0.31	0.292	0.1656	0.753
0.32	0.143	0.1904	1.150
0.33	0.031	0.2144	2.630
0.333	0.003 01	0.2216	8.58
1/3	0	0.2222	∞

Table 2 Power coefficient as function of tip speed ratio for optimum actuator disk

λ	$C_{P\mathrm{max}}$
0.5	0.288
1.0	0.416
1.5	0.480
2.0	0.512
2.5	0.532
5.0	0.570
7.5	0.582
10.0	0.593

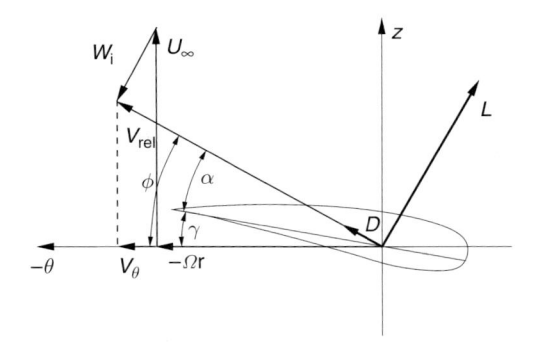

Figure 2 Cross-sectional airfoil element.

$$\frac{dT}{dr} = BF_n = \frac{1}{2}\rho c B V_{rel}^2 \cdot C_n \qquad [22]$$

$$\frac{dM}{dr} = BrF_t = \frac{1}{2}\rho c B r V_{rel}^2 \cdot C_t \qquad [23]$$

where c is the blade chord, B is the number of blades, V_{rel} is the relative velocity, F_n and F_t denote the loading on each blade in axial and tangential direction, respectively, and C_n and C_t denote the corresponding 2D tabulated force coefficients.

From the velocity triangle at the blade element (see **Figure 2**), we deduce that

$$\sin\phi = \frac{U_\infty(1-a)}{V_{rel}}, \quad \cos\phi = \frac{\Omega r(1+a')}{V_{rel}} \qquad [24]$$

where the induced velocity is defined as $W_i = (-aU_0, a'\Omega r)$. Using the above relations, we get

$$V_{rel}^2 = \frac{U_\infty^2(1-a)^2}{\sin^2\phi} = \frac{U_\infty(1-a)\Omega r(1+a')}{\sin\phi \cos\phi} \qquad [25]$$

Inserting these expressions into eqns [22] and [23], we get

$$\frac{dT}{dr} = \frac{\rho B c U_0^2 (1-a)^2}{2\sin^2\phi} C_n \qquad [26]$$

$$\frac{dM}{dr} = \frac{\rho B c U_0(1-a)\Omega r^2(1+a')}{2\sin\phi \cos\phi} C_t \qquad [27]$$

Next, applying axial momentum theory, the axial load is computed as

$$\frac{dT}{dr} = \rho(U_0 - u_{wake})2\pi r u_R = 4\pi\rho U_0^2 a(1-a) \qquad [28]$$

where $u_R = U_0(1-a)$ is the axial velocity in the rotor plane and $u_{wake} = U_0(1-2a)$ is the axial velocity in the ultimate wake.

Applying the moment of momentum theorem, we get

$$\frac{dM}{dr} = \rho r u_\theta 2\pi r u_R = 4\pi\rho r^3 \Omega U_0 a'(1-a) \qquad [29]$$

where $u_\theta = 2\Omega r a'$ is the induced tangential velocity in the far wake. Combining eqns [26] and [27] with eqns [28] and [29], we get after some algebra

$$a = \frac{1}{4\sin^2\phi/(\sigma C_n) + 1} \qquad [30]$$

$$a' = \frac{1}{4\sin\phi \cos\phi/(\sigma C_t) - 1} \qquad [31]$$

2.08.2.3.1 Tip correction

Since the above equations are derived assuming azimuthally independent stream tubes, they are only valid for rotors with infinite many blades. In order to correct for finite number of blades, Glauert [3] introduced Prandtl's tip loss factor. In this method, a correction factor, F, is introduced that corrects the loading. In a recent paper by Shen *et al.* [9], the tip correction is discussed and various alternative formulations are compared. However, here we limit the correction to the original form given by Glauert [3]. In this model, the induced velocities are corrected by the tip loss factor F, modifying eqns [28] and [29] as follows,

$$\frac{dT}{dr} = 4\pi r \rho U_\infty^2 a F(1-a) \qquad [32]$$

$$\frac{dM}{dr} = 4\pi \rho r^3 \Omega U_\infty a' F(1-a) \qquad [33]$$

where $\sigma = Bc/2\pi r$. An approximate formula of the Prandtl tip loss function was introduced as follows,

$$F = \frac{2}{\pi} \cos^{-1}\left[\exp\left(-\frac{B(R-r)}{2r\sin\phi}\right)\right] \qquad [34]$$

where $\phi = \phi(r)$ is the angle between the local relative velocity and the rotor plane.

The coefficients (C_n, C_t) are related to the lift and drag coefficients (C_l, C_d) by $C_n = C_l \cos\phi + C_d \sin\phi$ and $C_t = C_l \sin\phi - C_d \cos\phi$, respectively. (C_l, C_d) depend on local airfoil shape and are obtained using tabulated 2D airfoil data corrected with 3D rotating effects. Equating eqn [26] to eqn [32] and eqn [27] to eqn [33], the final expressions for the interference factors read

$$a = \frac{1}{4F\sin^2\phi/(\sigma C_n) + 1} \qquad [35]$$

$$a' = \frac{1}{4F\sin\phi\cos\phi/(\sigma C_t) - 1} \qquad [36]$$

2.08.2.3.2 Correction for heavily loaded rotors

By putting eqn [32] into dimensionless form, we get the following expression for the local thrust coefficient,

$$C_T = \frac{dT}{\frac{1}{2}\rho U_\infty^2 2\pi r dr} = 4aF(1-a) \qquad [37]$$

For heavily loaded rotors, that is, for a values between 0.3 and 0.5, this expression ceases to be valid as the wake velocity tends to zero with an unrealistic large expansion as a result. It is therefore common to replace it by a simple empirical relation. Following Glauert [3], an appropriate correction is to replace the expression for $a \geq 1/3$ with the following expression:

$$C_T = 4aF\left(1 - \frac{a}{4}(5 - 3a)\right) \qquad [38]$$

As discussed in, for example, Spera [10] or Hansen [11], other expressions can also be used.

2.08.2.3.3 Yaw correction

Yaw refers to the situation where the incoming flow is not aligned with the rotor axis. In this case, the wake flow is not in line with the free wind direction and it is impossible to apply the usual control volume analysis. A way of solving the problem is to maintain the control volume and specify an azimuth-dependent induction. In practice, it works by computing a mean induction and prescribe a function that gives the azimuthal dependency of the induction. The following simple formula has been proposed by Snel and Schepers [12],

$$w_i = w_{i0}\left(1 + \frac{r}{R}\tan\left(\frac{\chi}{2}\right)\cos(\theta_{\text{blade}} - \theta_0)\right) \qquad [39]$$

where w_{i0} is the annulus averaged induced velocity and χ is the wake skew angle, which is not identical to the yaw angle because the induced velocity in yaw alters the mean flow direction in the wake flow. In the notation used here, θ_{blade} denotes the azimuthal position of the blade and θ_0 is the azimuthal position where the blade is deepest in the wake. For more details, the reader is referred to the text book by Hansen [11].

2.08.2.3.4 Dynamic wake

Dynamic wake or dynamic inflow refers to unsteady flow phenomena that affect the loading on the rotor. In a real flow situation, the rotor is subject to unsteadiness from coherent wind gusts, yaw misalignment, and control actions, such as pitching and yawing. When the flow changes in time, the wake is subject to a time delay when going from one equilibrium state to another. An initial change creates a change in the distribution of trailing vorticity which then is convected downstream and first can be felt in the induced velocities after some time. However, the BEM method in its simple form is basically steady; hence, unsteady effects have to be included as an additional 'add-on'. In the European CEC Joule II project 'Dynamic Inflow: Yawed Conditions and Partial Span Pitch' (see Schepers and Snel [13]), various dynamic inflow models were developed and tested. Essentially, a dynamic inflow model predicts the time delay through an exponential decay with a time constant corresponding to the convective time of the flow in the wake. As an example, the following simple model was suggested,

$$Rf\left(\frac{r}{R}\right)\frac{du_i}{dt} + 4u_i(U_0 - u_i) = \frac{\Delta T}{2\pi r \Delta r} \quad [40]$$

where the function $f(r/R)$ is a semiempirical function associated with the induction. The equation can be seen to correspond to the axial momentum equation, eqn [28], except for the time-term that is responsible for the time delay.

2.08.2.3.5 Airfoil data

As a prestep to the BEM computations, 2D airfoil data have to be established from wind tunnel measurements. In order to construct a set of airfoil data to be used for a rotating blade, the airfoil data further need to be corrected for 3D and rotational effects. A simple correction formula for rotational effects was proposed by Snel and van Holten [14] for incidences up to stall. For higher incidences (>40°), 2D lift and drag coefficients of a flat plate can be used. These data, however, are too big because of aspect ratio effects and here the correction formulas of Viterna and Corrigan [15] are usually applied (see also Spera [10]). Furthermore, since the angle of attack is constantly changing due to fluctuations in the wind and control actions, it is needed to include a dynamic stall model to compensate for the time delay associated with the dynamics of the boundary layer and wake of the airfoil. This effect can be simulated by a simple first-order dynamic model, as proposed by Øye [16], or it can be considerably more advanced, taking into account also attached flow, leading edge separation and compressibility effects, as in the model of Leishman and Beddoes [17].

2.08.3 Advanced Aerodynamic Modeling

Although the BEM method is widely used and today constitutes the only design methodology in use by industry, there is a big need for more sophisticated models for understanding the underlying physics. Various numerically based aerodynamic rotor models have in the past years been developed, ranging from simple lifting line wake models to full-blown Navier–Stokes-based CFD models. In the following, the most used models will be introduced.

2.08.3.1 Vortex Models

Vortex wake models denote a class of methods in which the rotor blades and the trailing and shed vortices in the wake are represented by lifting lines or surfaces. At the blades, the vortex strength is determined from the bound circulation which is related to the local inflow field. The global flow field is determined from the induction law of Biot–Savart, where the vortex filaments in the wake are advected by superposition of the undisturbed flow and the induced velocity field. The trailing wake is generated by spanwise variations of the bound vorticity along the blade. The shed wake is generated by the temporal variations as the blade rotate. Assuming that flow in the region outside the trailing and shed vortices is curl-free, the overall flow field can be represented by the Biot–Savart law. Utilizing the Biot–Savart law, simple vortex models can be derived to compute quite general flow fields about wind turbine rotors. The first example of a simple vortex model is the one due to Joukowsky [18], who proposed to model the wake flow by a hub vortex plus tip vortices represented by an array of semi-infinite helical vortices with constant pitch (see also Margoulis [19]). However, this model contains inherent problems due to the singular behavior of the vortices, and as an axisymmetric approximation, one may represent the tip vortices as a series of ring vortices.

To compute flows about actual wind turbines, it becomes necessary to combine the vortex line model with tabulated 2D airfoil data. This can be accomplished by representing the spanwise loading on each blade by a series of straight vortex elements located along the quarter chord line. The strength of the vortex elements are determined by employing the Kutta–Joukowsky theorem on the basis of the local airfoil characteristics. When the loading varies along the span of each blade, the value of the bound circulation will change from one filament to the next. This is compensated for by introducing trailing vortex filaments whose strengths correspond to the differences in bound circulation between adjacent blade elements. Likewise, shed vortex filaments are generated and advected into the wake whenever the loading undergoes a temporal variation. While vortex models generally provide physically realistic simulations of the flow structures in the wake, the quality of the obtained results still depends on the input airfoil data.

In vortex models, the flow structure can either be prescribed or computed as a part of the overall solution procedure. In a prescribed vortex technique, the position of the vortical elements is specified from measurements or semiempirical rules. This makes the technique fast to use on a computer, but limits its range of application to more or less well-known steady flow situations. For unsteady flow situations and complicated flow structures, free wake analysis becomes necessary. A free wake method is more straightforward to understand and use, as the vortex elements are allowed to advect and deform freely under the action of the velocity field. The advantage of the method lies in its ability to calculate general flow cases, such as yawed wake structures and dynamic inflow. The disadvantage, on the other hand, is that the method is far more computing expensive than the prescribed wake method, since the Biot–Savart law has to be evaluated for each time step taken. Furthermore, free-vortex wake methods tend to suffer from stability problems owing to the intrinsic singularity in induced velocities that appears when vortex elements are approaching each other. This can to a certain extent be remedied by introducing a vortex core model in which a cut-off parameter models the inner viscous part of the vortex filament. In recent years, much effort in the development of models for helicopter rotor flow fields have been directed toward free wake modeling using advanced pseudo-implicit relaxation schemes, in order to improve numerical efficiency and accuracy (see Leishman [20]). A special version of the free-vortex wake methods is the method by Voutsinas [21] in which the flow modeling is taken care of by vortex particles or vortex blobs.

A generalization of the vortex method is the so-called Boundary Integral Element Method (BIEM). Where the rotor blade in a simple vortex method is represented by straight vortex filaments, the BIEM takes into account the actual finite thickness geometry of the blade. The theoretical background for BIEMs is potential theory where the flow, except at solid surfaces and wakes, is assumed to be irrotational. In a rotor computation, the blade surface is covered with both sources and doublets, while the wake only is represented by doublets (see, e.g., Katz and Plotkin [22] or Cottet and Koumoutsakos [23]). The circulation of the rotor is obtained as an intrinsic part of the solution by applying the Kutta condition on the trailing edge of the blade. The main advantage of the BIEM is that complex geometries can be treated without any modification of the model. Thus, both the hub and the tower can be modeled as a part of the solution. Furthermore, the method does not depend on airfoil data and viscous effects can, at least in principle, be included by coupling the method to a viscous solver.

2.08.3.2 Numerical Actuator Disk Models

The actuator disk denotes a technique for analyzing rotor performance. In this model, the rotor is represented by a permeable disk that allows the flow to pass through the rotor, at the same time as it is subject to the influence of the surface forces. The 'classical' actuator disk model is based on conservation of mass, momentum, and energy, and constitutes the main ingredient in the 1D momentum theory. Combining it with a blade-element analysis, we end up with the BEM model. In its general form, however, the actuator disk might as well be combined with a numerical solution of the Euler or Navier–Stokes equations.

In a numerical actuator disk model, the Navier–Stokes (or Euler) equations are typically solved by a second-order accurate finite difference/volume scheme, as in a usual CFD computation. However, the geometry of the blades and the viscous flow around the blades are not resolved. Instead, the swept surface of the rotor is replaced by surface forces that act upon the incoming flow. This can either be implemented at a rate corresponding to the period-averaged mechanical work that the rotor extracts from the flow or by using local instantaneous values of tabulated airfoil data. In the simple case of an actuator disk with constant prescribed loading, various fundamental studies can easily be carried out. The generalized actuator disk method resembles the BEM method in the sense that the aerodynamic forces has to be determined from measured airfoil characteristics, corrected for 3D effects, using a blade-element approach. For airfoils subjected to temporal variations of the angle of attack, the dynamic response of the aerodynamic forces changes the static aerofoil data and dynamic stall models have to be included. The first computations of wind turbines employing numerical actuator disk models in combination with a blade-element approach were carried out by Sørensen and Myken [24] and Sørensen and Kock [25]. This was later followed by different research groups who employed the technique to study various flow cases, including coned and yawed rotors, rotors operating in enclosures, and wind farm simulations. For a review on the method, the reader is referred to Vermeer et al. [26], Hansen et al. [27], or the VKI Lecture Series [28].

The main limitation of the axisymmetric assumption is that the forces are distributed evenly along the actuator disk; hence, the influence of the blades is taken as an integrated quantity in the azimuthal direction. To overcome this limitation, an extended 3D actuator disk model has been developed by Sørensen and Shen [29]. The model combines a 3D Navier–Stokes solver with a technique in which body forces are distributed radially along each of the rotor blades. Thus, the kinematics of the wake flow is determined by a full 3D Navier–Stokes simulation, whereas the influence of the rotating blades on the flow field is included using tabulated airfoil data to represent the loading on each blade. As in the axisymmetric model, airfoil data and subsequent loading are determined iteratively by computing local angles of attack from the movement of the blades and the local flow field. The concept enables one to study in detail the dynamics of the wake and the tip vortices and their influence on the induced velocities in the rotor plane. A model following the same idea has been suggested by Leclerc and Masson [30]. A main motivation for developing such types of model is to be able to analyze and verify the validity of the basic assumptions that are employed in the simpler more practical engineering models. Reviews of the basic modeling of actuator disk and actuator line models can be found in the PhD dissertations of Mikkelsen [31], Troldborg [32], and Ivanell [33].

2.08.3.3 Full Navier–Stokes Modeling

During the past four decades, a strong research activity within the aeronautical field has resulted in the development of a series of CFD tools based on the solution of the Navier–Stokes equations. Within aerodynamics, this research has mostly been related to flows around fixed-wing aircraft and helicopters. Looking specifically on the aerodynamics of horizontal-axis wind turbines, we find some striking differences as compared to usual aeronautical applications. First, as tip speeds generally never exceed 100 m s^{-1}, the flow around wind turbines is incompressible. Next, the optimal operating condition for a wind turbine always includes stall, with the upper side of the rotor blades being dominated by large areas of flow separation. This is in contrast to the cruise condition of an aircraft where the flow is largely attached.

Some of the experience gained from the aeronautical research institutions has been exploited directly in the development of CFD algorithms for wind turbines. Notably is the development of basic solution algorithms and numerical schemes for solution of the flow equations, grid generation techniques, and the modeling of boundary layer turbulence. These elements together form the basis of all CFD codes, of which some already have existed for a long time as standard commercial software.

Today, there exist two main paths to follow when conducting CFD computations; either the equations are solved by using Reynolds averaging or by introducing space filtration. The most popular method is based on solving the Reynolds-averaged Navier–Stokes (RANS) equations, closing the system by introducing a suitable one-equation or two-equation turbulence model, such as the Spalart–Allmaras [34] or the $k-\varepsilon$ [35] model. By using this kind of model, only the time-averaged flow field is computed, whereas the unsteady field is modeled through the turbulence model. If the flow is dominated by a broad spectrum of time scales, the low frequencies may be simulated partly by maintaining the time-term in the RANS equations. In this case, it is sometimes referred to as URANS (unsteady RANS). The advantage of RANS or URANS is that a fully resolved computation can be established with some few million mesh points, which makes it possible to reach a full 3D solution even on a portable computer. In the past years, refined one- and two-equation turbulence models have been developed to cope with specific flow features. In particular, the $k-\omega$ SST model developed by Menter [36] has shown its capability to cope with lightly separated airfoil flows, and today this model is widely used for wind turbine computations. The accuracy of the computations, however, is restricted by the turbulence model's lack of ability of representing a full unsteady spectrum. Thus, for attached flow the accuracy is fully adequate, whereas for stalled flows, it may degenerate completely. This is further rendered complicated by the laminar–turbulent transition process that also has to be modeled in order compute the onset of turbulence. An alternative to RANS/URANS is LES. In LES, the Navier–Stokes equations are filtered spatially on the computational mesh and only the subgrid scale (SGS) part of the turbulence is modeled using a so-called SGS model. The advantage of LES is that all the dynamics of the flow field is captured and that accurate solutions can be obtained even under highly separated flow conditions. The computational price, however, is often prohibitive, even when solving parallelized computing algorithms on large cluster systems, because of the large number of mesh points that are needed to resolve practical flows at high Reynolds numbers. As compared to direct numerical simulation (DNS), where the Navier–Stokes equations are solved directly without any modeling of the turbulence, LES is, however, still several orders of magnitude faster.

To give an estimate of computing expenses and the number of mesh points required to resolve a turbulent flow field, one can use the Kolmogorov length scale, ℓ, as the smallest scale and the length of the considered object, L, as the largest length scale. According to Lesieur et al. [37], an estimate of the ratio between the largest and the smallest length scale can be given as $L/\ell \approx \mathrm{Re}_L^{3/4}$, where the Reynolds number $\mathrm{Re}_L = UL/v$, with U denoting a characteristic wind speed and v is the kinematic viscosity. For an airfoil of a wind turbine blade, a typical value is $\mathrm{Re}_C \cong 5\cdot 10^6$ where index C denotes the chord length. Thus, for a DNS computation of an airfoil section, we need in the order of 10^5 mesh points in each direction, resulting in a total of approximately 10^{15} mesh points. For a corresponding LES computation, this may be reduced to about 10^{10} mesh points, if we assume that the SGS covers about 1.5 decades. A main difference between RANS and LES is that RANS computations may be carried out in a pure 2D domain, for example, when studying or designing airfoils, whereas LES is always intrinsically unsteady and 3D. As a compromise between the fast computing time of RANS methods and the accuracy of LES, Spalart et al. [38] developed the detached eddy simulation (DES) technique. This technique is a hybrid approach in which the flow near boundaries is solved using a traditional RANS turbulence model and the outer flow is modeled using a SGS model. However, this technique puts severe bounds on the grid, since very high aspect ratios are needed near the boundaries, whereas the grid is required to be as isotropic as possible in the LES domain. When computing wakes, the number of mesh points need not depend on the Reynolds number, if for example, the influence from the surface is ignored. In this case most of the flow can be simulated by using LES technique to simulate the dynamics of the main vortex structures and model the smaller scales by an SGS model. However, if one wishes to include the surface-bounded boundary layer in the computation the number of mesh points is mainly determined by the Reynolds number, which for a modern wind turbine of a diameter of about 100 m is about $\mathrm{Re}_D \cong 10^7$. An overview of the required number of mesh points for different approaches is given in **Table 3**.

2.08.4 CFD Computations of Wind Turbine Rotors

The research on CFD in wind turbine aerodynamics was initiated through European Union-sponsored collaborate projects, such as VISCWIND [39], VISCEL [40], and KNOW-BLADE in Europe. The first full Navier–Stokes simulation for a complete rotor blade was carried out by Sørensen and Hansen [41] and later followed by Duque et al. [42] and Sørensen et al. [43] in connection with the American NREL experiment at NASA Ames and the accompanying National Renewable Energy Laboratory/National Wind Technology Center (NREL/NWTC) aerodynamics blind comparison test [44]. This experiment has achieved a significant new insight into wind turbine aerodynamics and revealed serious shortcomings in present-day wind turbine aerodynamics prediction tools. First, computations of the performance characteristics of the rotor by methods based on the BEM technique were found to be extremely sensitive to the input blade section aerodynamic data. The predicted values of the distribution of the normal force coefficient deviated from measurements by as much as 50%. Even at low angles of attack, model predictions differed from measured data by 15–20% [44]. Next, the computations based on Navier–Stokes equations convincingly showed that CFD had matured to become an important tool for predicting and understanding the flow physics of

Table 3 Number of required mesh points for various types of computations

	Airfoil	Full rotor	Wake
RANS	10^5	10^7	$10^5 - 10^8$
DES	10^7	10^8	$10^7 - 10^{10}$
LES	10^{10}	10^{12}	$10^7 - 10^{14}$
DNS	10^{15}	10^{17}	$10^7 - 10^{19}$

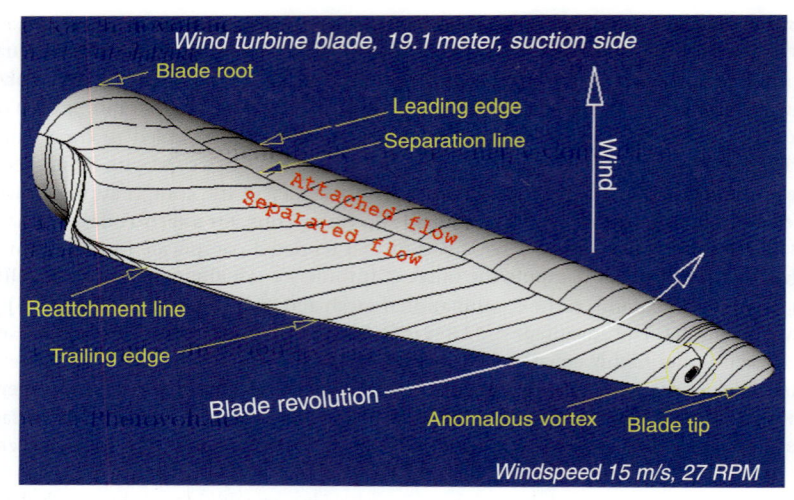

Figure 3 Sketch of flow topology and limiting streamlines on a wind turbine blade.

modern wind turbine rotors. The Navier–Stokes computations by Sørensen et al. [43] generally exhibited good agreement with the measurements up to wind speeds of about $10\,\mathrm{m\,s^{-1}}$. At this wind speed, flow separation sets in and for higher wind speeds it dominates the boundary layer characteristics. Hence, it is likely that the introduction of a more physically consistent turbulence modeling and the inclusion of a laminar/turbulent transition model will improve the quality of the results (Sørensen [45]). A large number of full 3D Navier–Stokes computations have later been carried out by different research groups. The computations include RANS and DES simulations of full rotor systems, the hub, studies of tip flows, blade–tower interaction, and wind turbine blades under parked conditions. Reviews can be found in Hansen et al. [27] and Sørensen [46], and various contributions were published in the proceedings from TWIND2007 [47]. To illustrate the degree of complexity one obtains using a full 3D Navier–Stokes methodology in **Figure 3**, we show a computation of a rotating 19.1 m long wind turbine blade. It is clearly seen here that a complicated flow topology results, including a large separated area, which could not be obtained using the BEM technique or inviscid computations.

2.08.5 CFD in Wake Computations

Modern wind turbines are often clustered in wind parks in order to reduce the overall installation and maintenance expenses. Because of the mutual interference between the wakes of the turbines, the total power production of a park of wind turbines is reduced as compared to an equal number of stand-alone turbines. Thus, the total economic benefit of a wind park is a trade-off between the various expenses to erect and operate the park, the available wind resources at the site, and the reduced power production because of the mutual influence of the turbines. A further unwanted effect is that the turbulence intensity in the wake is increased because of the interaction from the wakes of the surrounding wind turbines. As a consequence, dynamic loadings are increased that may excite the structural parts of the individual wind turbine and enhance fatigue loadings. The turbulence created from wind turbine wakes is mainly due to the dynamics of the vortices originating from the rotor blades. The vortices are formed as a result of the rotor loading. To analyze the genesis of the wake, it is thus necessary to include descriptions of the aerodynamics of both the rotor and the wake. Although many wake studies have been performed over the past two decades, a lot of basic questions still need to be clarified in order to elucidate the dynamic behavior of individual as well as multiple interactive wakes behind wind turbines.

When regarding wakes, a distinct division can be made between the near- and the far-wake region. The near wake is normally taken as the area just behind the rotor, where the properties of the rotor can be discriminated, so approximately up to 1 rotor diameter downstream. Here, the presence of the rotor is apparent by the number of blades, blade aerodynamics, including stalled flow, 3D effects, and the tip vortices. The far wake is the region beyond the near wake, where the focus is put on the influence of wind turbines in park situations; hence, modeling the actual rotor is less important. The near wake research is focused on the performance and the physical process of power extraction, while the far wake research is more focused on the mutual influence when wind turbines are placed in clusters or wind farms.

The far wake has been a subject of extensive research both experimentally and numerically. Semianalytical far wake models have been proposed to describe the wake velocity after the initial expansion (e.g., Ainslie [48]). Detailed numerical studies of the far wake have been carried out by Crespo and Hernández [49] using methods based on the UPMWAKE model in which the wind turbine is supposed to be immersed in an atmospheric boundary layer. This model uses a finite difference approach and a parabolic approximation to solve the RANS equations combined with a $k-\varepsilon$ turbulence model.

As illustrated in **Table 3**, prohibitively many mesh points are needed if one wishes to carry out LES or DNS of the wake in an atmospheric boundary layer. However, employing the actuator line technique and representing the ambient turbulence and shear flow by body forces, the number of mesh points become affordable even for a high Reynolds number LES computation. Using this technique, near-wake computations have been carried out by Sørensen and Shen [29], Ivanell et al. [50, 51], and Troldborg et al. [52, 53]. In a recent survey by Vermeer et al. [26], both near-wake and far-wake aerodynamics are treated, whereas a survey focusing solely on far-wake modeling was earlier given by Crespo et al. [54].

To illustrate the type of results that may be achieved combining LES and the actuator line technique, results obtained from simulations by Troldborg et al. [53] of a stand-alone wind turbine will be presented. The computations were carried out using airfoil data from the Tjæreborg wind turbine. The blade radius of this turbine is 30.56 m and it rotates at 22.1 rpm, corresponding to a tip speed of 70.7 m s^{-1}. The blade sections consist of NACA 44xx airfoils with a chord length of 0.9 m at the tip, increasing linearly to 3.3 m at hub radius 6 m. The blades are linearly twisted 1° per 3 m.

Figure 4 shows instantaneous vortex structures in the near wake of a rotor operating at a wind speed of $W_0 = 6$ m s^{-1}, corresponding to a tip speed ratio of about 12. It is seen here that the wake flow collapses into small-scale turbulence about 1 diameter behind the rotor. The actual position depends on the loading and the ambient turbulence level. In the simulation in **Figure 4** the inflow conditions were pure laminar and the collapse is due to intrinsic instabilities of the flow. **Figure 5** shows the contours of the instantaneous absolute vorticity in the $x/R = 9$ plane for three different cases. Regions of high vorticity appear as light colors. Note that the rotor is located to the left in the plots and that only the downstream development of the wake is shown. The

Figure 4 Vortex structures in the near wake after the Tjæreborg wind turbine (Troldborg et al. [53]).

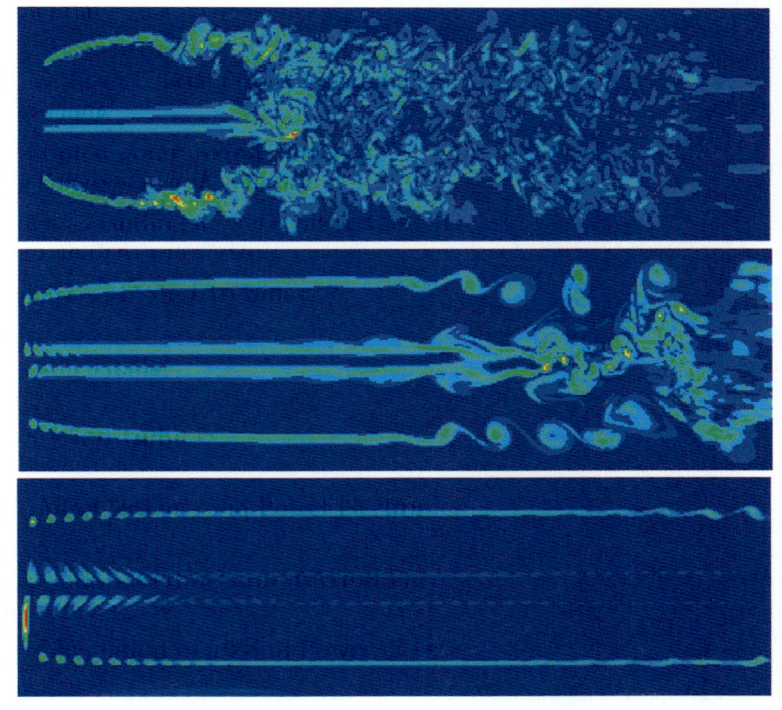

Figure 5 Downstream development of wake behind wind turbine. Upper figure: $W_0 = 6$ m s^{-1}; middle figure: $W_0 = 10$ m s^{-1}; lower figure: $W_0 = 14$ m s^{-1}. In all figures, the rotor is located to the left (Troldborg et al. [53]).

bound vorticity of the blades is seen to be shed downstream from the rotor in individual vortex tubes. A closer inspection of the vorticity contours at $W_0 = 6$ m s^{-1} revealed that the distinct tip-vortex pattern is preserved about 0.5 rotor radii downstream, where after they smear into a continuous vorticity sheet. In the case where the free stream velocity is $W_0 = 10$ and 14 m s^{-1}, distinct tip vortices can be observed about 1.5 and 7 rotor radii downstream, respectively. In all cases, the structures might have been preserved even further if a finer grid had been used. Moreover, it should be noted that using the absolute value of the vorticity as a means of identifying vortices is limited by its strong dependence on the chosen contour levels, and therefore, vortex structures might very well be present even though they are not immediately visible. For the rotor operating at the highest tip speed ratio, instability of the tip vortices are observed only 2 and 5 rotor radii downstream where the entire wake flow completely breaks up. In the case where $W_0 = 10$ m s^{-1}, the tip vortices are observed to undergo a Kelvin–Helmholtz instability approximately 7 rotor radii downstream. The root vortex also becomes unstable at this position. Further downstream the root and tip vortices interact, which causes the flow to become fully turbulent. Instability of the tip vortices is also observed in the last case where $W_0 = 14$ m s^{-1}, but as expected it takes place even further downstream (ca. 10 rotor radii downstream) and is not as strong due to the generally higher stability and persistence of the tip vortices, when the tip speed ratio and thus also the thrust is low.

2.08.6 Rotor Optimization Using BEM Technique

In the past three decades, the size of commercial wind turbines has increased from units of about 50 kW in the early 1980s to the latest multi-MW turbines with rotor diameters over 120 m. In spite of repeated predictions of a leveling off at an optimum mid-range size and periods of stagnation, the size of commercial wind turbines has steadily increased with about a 5-doubling in installed generator power over a period of one decade. The overall goal is to reduce the cost price of the produced energy, and as long as increasing the size results in a reduction of the cost price, it is likely that the wind turbines will increase in size also for many years to come. There are obviously factors that may bring this trend to an end, such as problems related to the handling and manufacturing of the large blades. A more sophisticated way of capturing more energy from the wind, however, is to improve the aerodynamic efficiency of the energy conversion by using optimization techniques in the initial design. In the development of new wind turbines, aerodynamic and structural optimization has become an important issue for optimizing the energy yield and thereby minimizing the cost price of the produced energy. How to reduce the cost of a wind turbine per unit of energy is an important task in modern wind turbine research. Classical models for aerodynamic optimization of rotors can be found in the text books of Glauert [3] and Theodorsen [55] and in revised form by Okulov and Sørensen [56, 57]. However, an aerodynamic optimal rotor may not necessarily be the most cost-effective, as the target is to reduce the price of the produced energy. Since an optimization technique works together with aerodynamic and structural models, results from an optimization procedure will often be influenced a great deal by the models used. Thus, accurate and efficient models for predicting wind turbine performance are essential for obtaining reliable optimum designs of wind turbine rotors. The first multidisciplinary optimization method for designing horizontal-axis wind turbines is due to Fuglsang and Madsen [58]. The objective used in their method was to minimize the cost of energy employing multiple constrains. Generally, multiobjective optimization methods are employed in which the blades are optimized by varying blade structural parameters such as stiffness, stability, and material weight. Site specifics from sites comprising normal flat terrain, offshore, and complex terrain wind farms can also be incorporated in the design process of the wind turbine rotors [59].

To illustrate the basics of design optimization of wind turbine rotors, in the following we show the features of an optimization model developed at Technical University of Denmark and ChongQing University [60] for optimizing the geometry of wind turbines to maximize the energy yield. The method is based on combining an aeroelastic model containing 11 degrees of freedom with the BEM technique. The most important issue when performing optimizations is to locate the main parameters and a suitable object function. In the model, the object function is defined as the minimum cost price of the produced energy, determined by computing the annual energy production (AEP) and the production cost of the turbine. In the following, the cost model and the design variables used in the optimization model are presented. As design variables we choose chord length, twist angle, relative thickness, and tip pitch angle. Estimating the cost of a wind turbine is an important and difficult task, but also crucial for the success of an optimization. The cost model includes the capital costs from foundation, tower, rotor blades, gearbox, and generator plus the costs from operation and maintenance. The total cost of a wind turbine can be expressed as

$$C = \sum_{i=1}^{N} C_i = \sum_{i=1}^{N} R_i(b_i + (1-b_i)w_i) \qquad [41]$$

where C_i is the cost of the i-th component of the wind turbine and N is the number of main components, R_i is the initial cost of the i-th component determined from a reference rotor, b_i is the fixed part of the i-th component that counts for manufacturing and transport, $(1-b_i)$ is the variable part of the i-th component, and w_i is the weight parameter of the i-th component. The weight parameter in Fuglsang and Madsen [58] was dependent on the design loads of extreme forces and moments and lifetime equivalent fatigue forces and moments. To get more information about the cost of a whole wind turbine, the reader is referred to Fuglsang and Madsen [58]. As the costs from operation and maintenance often can be counted as a small percentage of the capital cost, reduction of the capital cost becomes the essential task for the design. Further, a well-designed wind turbine with a low energy cost always has an aerodynamically efficient rotor. Therefore, the rotor design plays an important role for the whole design procedure of a wind turbine. In the current study, we restrict our objective to the cost from the rotor. Thus, the objective function is defined as,

$$f(x) = \text{COE} = \frac{C_{\text{rotor}}}{\text{AEP}} \quad [42]$$

where COE is the cost of energy of a wind turbine rotor and C_{rotor} is the total cost for producing, transporting, and erecting a wind turbine rotor. In the current study, the fixed part of the cost for a wind turbine rotor b_{rotor} is chosen to be 0.1. Therefore, the total cost of a rotor, C_{rotor}, is a relative value defined as

$$C_{\text{rotor}} = b_{\text{rotor}} + (1 - b_{\text{rotor}})w_{\text{rotor}} \quad [43]$$

where w_{rotor} is the weight parameter of the rotor. In the present study, the weight parameter is calculated from the chord and mass distributions of the blades. Dividing a blade into n cross-sections, w_{rotor} is estimated as

$$w_{\text{rotor}} = \sum_{i=1}^{n} \frac{m_i \cdot c_{i,\text{opt}}}{M_{\text{tot}} \cdot c_{i,\text{orig}}} \quad [44]$$

where m_i is the mass of the i-th cross-section of the blade, $c_{i,\text{opt}}$ is the mean chord length of the i-th cross-section of the optimized blade, $c_{i,\text{orig}}$ is the mean chord length of the i-th cross-section of the original blade, and M_{tot} is the total mass of the blade. The power curve is determined from the BEM method. In order to compute the AEP, it is necessary to combine the power curve with the probability density of wind speed (i.e., the Weibull distribution). The function defining the probability density can be written in the following form

$$f(V_i < V < V_{i+1}) = \exp\left(-\left(\frac{V_i}{A}\right)^k\right) - \exp\left(-\left(\frac{V_{i+1}}{A}\right)^k\right) \quad [45]$$

where A is the scale parameter, k is the shape factor, and V is the wind speed. In the current study, the shape factor is chosen to be $k = 2$, corresponding to the Rayleigh distribution. If a wind turbine operates the full 8760 h yr^{-1}, its AEP is computed as

$$\text{AEP} = \sum_{i=1}^{M-1} \frac{1}{2}(P(V_{i+1}) + P(V)_i) \times f(V_i < V < V_{i+1}) \times 8760 \quad [46]$$

where $P(V_i)$ is the power at wind speed V_i and M denotes the number of wind speeds considered.

As an example of the optimization model, we here show how the performance of the Tjæreborg 2 MW rotor may be improved using optimization. The optimization is based on the original rotor; thus, the rotor diameter and the rotational speed are chosen to be the same, whereas chord length, twist angle, relative thickness, and tip pitch angle are chosen as design variables. A cubic polynomial is used to control the chord distribution and a spline function is used to control the distributions of twist angle and relative thickness. Since the cost of a rotor depends on the lifetime of the blades, power output, shaft torque, and thrust are constrained in the optimization process. The values are here constrained not to exceed the values of the original design. As a usual procedure for optimization problems, we have one objective function and multiple constraints. To achieve the optimization, the *fmincon* function in Matlab is used.

The Tjæreborg turbine is equipped with a three-bladed rotor of radius 30.56 m. In the BEM computations, 20 uniformly distributed blade elements are used. The optimization design is performed from a radial position at a radius of 6.46 m to the tip of the blade. In the optimization process, the lower limits for chord, twist angle, and relative thickness are 0 m, 0°, and 12.2%, respectively, and the upper limits are 3.3 m, 8°, and 100%, respectively. To reduce the computational time, four points along the blade are used to control the shape of the blade. The outcome of the optimization is shown in **Figure 6**, in which the chord and twist distributions of the original and the optimized Tjæreborg rotor are compared.

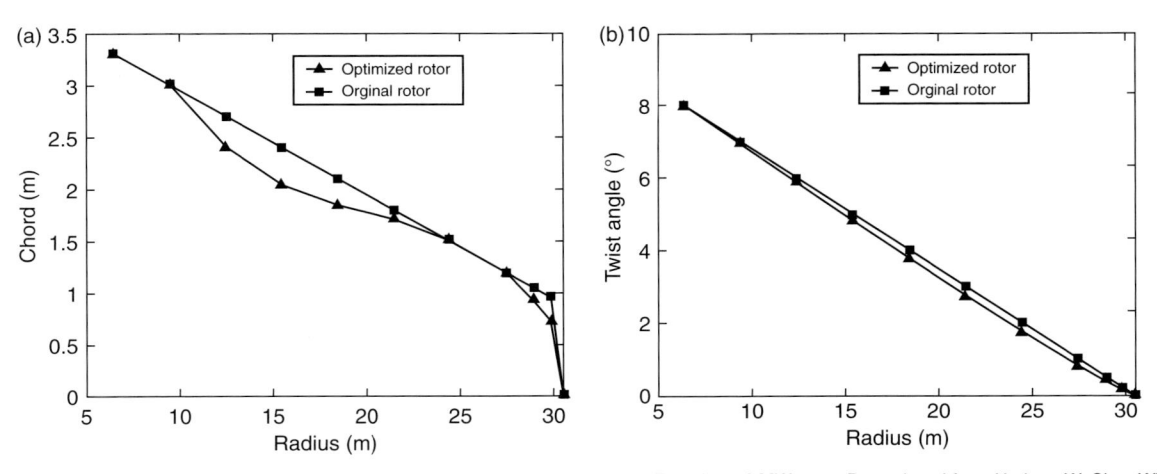

Figure 6 (a) Chord and (b) twist angle distributions of the original and the optimized Tjæreborg 2 MW rotor. Reproduced from Xudong W, Shen WZ, Zhu WJ, *et al.* (2009) Shape optimization of wind turbine blades. *Wind Energy* 12(8): 781–803.

From **Figure 6(a)**, it is seen that the optimized blade attains a remarkable reduction in chord length in the region between 10 and 23 m, as compared to the original rotor. At a radius of 15 m, the chord reduction reaches a maximum value of about 16%. From a position at a radius of 23 m to a position at a radius of 28 m, the optimized chord has almost the same value as the original distribution of the chord, whereas it decreases significantly in the tip region. The twist angle, **Figure 6(b)**, is slightly smaller than the original distribution. The performance of the optimized rotor is computed using the aerodynamic/aeroelastic code and compared to the original rotor. Since the Tjæreborg rotor is a pitch-controlled rotor, the output power of the rotor is set to be the rated power of 2 MW when the wind speed is larger than the rated wind speed of 15 m s^{-1}. The AEP of the optimized rotor is reduced about 4%, whereas the cost of the optimized rotor is reduced by about 7.1%. Thus, the cost of energy of the Tjæreborg rotor is reduced about 3.4%.

2.08.7 Noise from Wind Turbines

Although offshore wind energy is evolving fast, most wind turbines are still placed in rural environments, where wind turbine noise is of great concern since it may be the only major noise source. Machinery noise is generally not as important as aerodynamic noise, as it has been reduced efficiently by well-known engineering techniques, such as proper insulation of the nacelle. As a rule of thumb, aerodynamic noise from a wind turbine blade increases with the fifth power of the relative wind speed, as seen from the moving tip of the blades. With the tip speed being the most significant parameter, aerodynamic noise has been controlled by lowering the tip speed to a maximum of about 60 m s^{-1}. However, in recent years, the biggest development of wind turbines has taken place offshore, with the result that the latest generation of wind turbines operate at tip speeds up to 80 m s^{-1}. Thus, for turbines erected near the shore or for offshore turbines tested at land sites, noise has again become a subject of great concern with respect to public acceptance. This is best illustrated by the increasing number of conferences concerning wind turbine noise; for example, in 2005 the Initiative for Noise Control Engineering in Europe (INCE/Europe) initiated a biannual conference series on wind turbine noise, which in 2009 took place in Aalborg, and in 2011 is scheduled to take place in Rome.

Through the years, several models have been proposed to explain and predict wind turbine noise. Some of the models are somewhat simplistic, whereas others make use of complex CFD solvers that have not yet matured to be applied to compute noise emission for realistic rotors (see Wagner et al. [61] for a thorough review of various models). As a compromise between computing speed and accuracy, the most commonly used models are based on semiempirical relations. As a basis, most models employ the experimental results and scaling laws on airfoil self-noise by Brooks et al. [62] together with the turbulence inflow model proposed by Amiet [63]. This includes, for example, the models of Fuglsang and Madsen [64] and Zhu et al. [65, 66] and the model employed in the SIROCCO project [67], as well as further developments by Moriarty et al. [68] and Lutz et al. [69].

In the following, we show some of the features of a typical semiempirical model, such as those referred to above. In the model, only aerodynamic noise is considered (i.e., mechanical noise is not considered). Aerodynamic noise can be divided into 'airfoil self-noise' and 'turbulence inflow noise'. The former is a result of the interaction of the boundary layer of the airfoil with the trailing edge and the latter results from the interaction of the existing turbulence in the wind with the airfoil. In the model, the airfoil self-noise prediction is based on the functions given by Brooks et al. [62]. In total, five airfoil self-noise mechanisms were identified and studied separately:

- turbulent boundary layer trailing edge noise,
- separation-stall noise,
- laminar boundary layer vortex shedding noise,
- tip vortex formation noise, and
- trailing edge bluntness vortex shedding noise.

As a result, scaling laws were proposed, yielding the sound pressure level at the observer position as a function of frequency for the 1/3 octave band spectrum. The scaling laws for the different mechanisms are all of similar form:

$$\mathrm{SPL}_i = 10 \log \left(\frac{\delta_i^* M^{f(i)} L \bar{D}_h}{r^2} \right) + F_i(\mathrm{St}) + G_i(\mathrm{Re}) \quad [47]$$

where δ_i^* is the boundary layer displacement thickness, M is the Mach number, $f(i)$ is the raised power that depends on the particular noise mechanism i, L is the airfoil section semi-span, $\bar{D}_h$ is a sound directivity function, and r is the distance to the observer. The additional terms $F_i(\mathrm{St})$ and $G_i(\mathrm{Re})$ are functions of the 'Strouhal number' $\mathrm{St} = f\delta^*/U$ and the 'Reynolds number' Re. The nature of dependency is different for each noise mechanism but it is impressive that all the formulas look so much alike.

For turbulent inflow, the prediction equation is normally based on the work of Amiet [63]. This model takes the following form:

$$L_p = 10 \log \left(\rho_0^2 c_0^2 l \frac{\Delta L}{r^2} M^3 I^2 \hat{k}^3 \left(1 + \hat{k}^2\right)^{-7/3} \right) + 58.4 + 10 \log \left(\frac{K_c}{1 + K_c} \right) \quad [48]$$

where l is turbulence length scale, I is turbulence intensity, ρ_0 is density, c_0 is speed of sound, ΔL is blade segment semi-span, $\hat{k}$ is corrected wave length, and K_c is low-frequency correction.

Taking into account all the variable dependencies, the problem of predicting the noise spectrum at a given observer position for a given airfoil reduces to identifying the following quantities:

- The boundary layer thickness δ^* at the trailing edge of the airfoil
- The relative wind speed defining M and Re
- The boundary layer transition type (forced or natural), leading to tripped or untripped flow
- Miscellaneous input parameters to the turbulence inflow noise model, such as turbulent length scale and intensity, in the model reduced to the knowledge of the height from the ground z and the roughness length z_o.

Here we do not go into the theory behind the empirical correlations, and for details about the nature of each of the modeled noise mechanisms, we refer the reader to the original work of Brooks et al. [62] and Amiet [63] or the text book of Wagner et al. [61].

As mentioned above, an important parameter for the calculation of airfoil self-noise is the boundary layer thickness at the trailing edge. This can be calculated by use of the viscous–inviscid interactive computing program XFOIL [70]. It is important to note that the scaling laws shown above are deduced from experiments based only on the NACA 0012 airfoil. For this reason, an independent calculation of δ^* for each airfoil type is vital. This was carried out for different values of the Reynolds number and angle of attack and the computed boundary layer thickness was stored in a database and subsequently determined by interpolation.

Essentially, the code consists of a 'traditional' BEM code, to compute the relative velocities along each blade element defining the rotor, coupled with the routines to predict the noise contribution for each noise source along the span of the rotor blades. In short, the prediction code works as follows. First, the relative velocities seen by the blade elements are computed, just like in an ordinary BEM computation. Next, a table looking up in the boundary layer thickness database is made and the sound pressure level L_p and the noise spectrum at the observer position are calculated for each noise mechanism and for each blade element. Finally, the sound pressure levels are added for all elements, all blades, and all mechanisms and converted to sound power levels L_w referring to the hub of the wind turbine.

The main advantage of the semiempirical model is that it is fast to run, even on a PC, and that it gives a surprisingly reliable result. It is also fairly easy to couple the prediction code to an optimization algorithm and use it as a tool to optimize the rotor with respect to both performance and noise.

References

[1] Lanchester FW (1915) A contribution to the theory of propulsion and the screw propeller. *Transactions of the Institution of Naval Architects* 57: 98.
[2] Betz AD (1920) Maximum der theoretisch möglichen Ausnützung des Windes durch Windmotoren. *Zeitschrift für das gesamte Turbinenwesen* 26: 307–309.
[3] Glauert H (1935) Airplane propellers. Division L. In: Durand WF (ed.) *Aerodynamic Theory*, vol. IV, pp. 169–360. Berlin, Germany: Springer.
[4] Rankine WJM (1865) On the mechanical principles of the action of propellers. *Transactions of Institution of Naval Architects* 6: 13.
[5] Froude RE (1889) On the part played in propulsion by difference of fluid pressure. *Transactions of Institution of Naval Architects* 30: 390–405.
[6] Froude W (1878) On the elementary relation between pitch, slip and propulsive efficiency. *Transactions of Institution of Naval Architects* 19: 47.
[7] van Kuik GAM (2007) The Lanchester-Betz-Joukowsky limit. *Wind Energy* 10: 289–291.
[8] Wilson RE and Lissaman PBS (1974) *Applied Aerodynamics of Wind Power Machines*. Corvallis, OR: Oregon State University.
[9] Shen WZ, Mikkelsen R, Sørensen JN, and Bak C (2005) Tip loss corrections for wind turbine computations. *Wind Energy* 8(4): 457–475.
[10] Spera DA (1994) *Wind Turbine Technology*. New York, NY: ASME Press.
[11] Hansen MOL (2008) *Aerodynamics of Wind Turbines*. London, UK: Earthscan.
[12] Snel H and Schepers JG (1994) Joint investigation of dynamic inflow effects and implementation of an engineering method. *ECN-C-94-107*, Netherlands Energy Research Foundation ECN, Petten, The Netherlands.
[13] Schepers JG and Snel H (1995) Dynamic inflow: Yawed conditions and partial span pitch control. *ECN-C-95-056*, Netherlands Energy Research Foundation ECN, Petten, The Netherlands.
[14] Snel H and van Holten T (1995) Review of recent aerodynamic research on wind turbines with relevance to rotorcraft. *AGARD Report CP-552*, ch. 7, pp. 1–11, AGARD Advisory Group for Aerospace Research & Development.
[15] Viterna LA and Corrigan RD (1981) *Fixed-Pitch Rotor Performance of Large HAWT's*. DOE/NASA Workshop on Large HAWTs. National Aeronautics and Space Administration, Cleveland, Ohio.
[16] Øye S (1991) Dynamic stall, simulated as a time lag of separation. *Proceedings of 4th IEA Symposium on the Aerodynamics of Wind Turbines*. 20–21 November 1990, ETSU-N-118. Harwell, UK.
[17] Leishman JG and Beddoes TS (1989) A semi-empirical model for dynamic stall. *Journal of American Helicopter Society* 34(3): 3–17.
[18] Joukowsky NE (1912) Vortex theory of a rowing screw. *Trudy Otdeleniya Fizicheskikh Nauk Obshchestva Lubitelei Estestvoznaniya* 16(1): 1–31.
[19] Margoulis W (1922) Propeller theory of Professor Joukowski and his pupils. *NACA Technical Memorandum No. 79*.
[20] Leishman JG (2002) Challenges in modelling the unsteady aerodynamics of wind turbines. *Wind Energy* 5: 85–132.
[21] Voutsinas SG (2006) Vortex methods in aeronautics: How to make things work. *International Journal of Computational Fluid Dynamics* 20(1): 3–18.
[22] Katz J and Plotkin A (1991) *Low-Speed Aerodynamics*. New York, NY: McGraw-Hill.
[23] Cottet G-H and Koumoutsakos PD (2000) *Vortex Methods: Theory and Practice*. Cambridge, UK: Cambridge University Press.
[24] Sørensen JN and Myken A (1992) Unsteady actuator disc model for horizontal axis wind turbines. *Journal of Wind Engineering and Industrial Aerodynamics* 39: 139–149.
[25] Sørensen JN and Kock CW (1995) A model for unsteady rotor aerodynamics. *Journal of Wind Engineering and Industrial Aerodynamics* 58: 259–275.

[26] Vermeer LJ, Sørensen JN, and Crespo A (2003) Wind turbine wake aerodynamics. *Program Aerospace Science* 39: 467–510.
[27] Hansen MOL, Sørensen JN, Voutsinas S, et al. (2006) State of the art in wind turbine aerodynamics and aeroelasticity. *Program Aerospace Science* 42: 285–330.
[28] Brouckaert, J-F (ed.) (2007) *Wind Turbine Aerodynamics: A State-of-the-Art. VKI Lecture Series 2007-05*. Belgium: von Karman Institute for Fluid Dynamics.
[29] Sørensen JN and Shen WZ (2002) Numerical modelling of wind turbine wakes. *Journal of Fluids Engineering* 124(2): 393–399.
[30] Leclerc C and Masson C (2004) Towards blade-tip vortex simulation with an actuator-lifting surface model. *AIAA-2004-0667*, American Institute of Aeronautics and Astronautics, USA.
[31] Mikkelsen R (2003) Actuator Disc Methods Applied to Wind Turbines. PhD Dissertation. DTU Mechanical Engineering.
[32] Troldborg N (2008) Actuator Line Modelling of Wind Turbine Wakes. PhD Dissertation. DTU Mechanical Engineering.
[33] Ivanell SA (2009) Numerical Computations of Wind Turbine Wakes. PhD Dissertation. KTH, Royal Institute of Technology.
[34] Spalart P and Allmaras S (1994) A one-equation turbulence model for aerodynamic flows. *La Recherches Aerospace* 1(1): 5–21.
[35] Jones WP and Launder BE (1972) The prediction of laminarization with a two-equation model of turbulence. *International Journal of Heat and Mass Transfer* 15: 301–304.
[36] Menter FR (1993) Zonal two-equation $k-\omega$ models for aerodynamic flows. *AIAA Paper 93-2906*, American Institute of Aeronautics and Astronautics, USA.
[37] Lesieur M, Metais O, and Comte P (2005) *Large-Eddy Simulations of Turbulence*. Cambridge, UK: Cambridge University Press.
[38] Spalart PR, Jou W-H, Stretlets M, and Allmaras SR (1997) Comments on the feasibility of LES for wings and on the hybrid RANS/LES approach, advances in DNS/LES. *Proceedings of the First AFOSR International Conference on DNS/LES*.
[39] Sørensen, JN (ed.) (1999) VISCWIND: Viscous effects on wind turbine blades. *Report ET-AFM-9902*. Lyngby, Denmark: Department of Energy Engineering, DTU.
[40] Chaviaropoulos PK, Nikolaou IG, Aggelis K, et al. (2001) Viscous and aeroelastic effects on wind turbine blades: The VISCEL project. *Proceeding of 2001 European Wind Energy Conference and Exhibition*. Copenhagen, 2–6 July.
[41] Sørensen NN and Hansen MOL (1998) Rotor performance predictions using a Navier-Stokes method. *AIAA Paper 98-0025*, American Institute of Aeronautics and Astronautics, USA.
[42] Duque EPN, van Dam CP, and Hughes S (1999) Navier-Stokes simulations of the NREL combined experiment phase II rotor. *AIAA Paper 99-0037*, American Institute of Aeronautics and Astronautics, USA.
[43] Sørensen NN, Michelsen JA, and Schreck S (2002) Navier-Stokes predictions of the NREL phase VI rotor in the NASA-AMES 80 ft × 120 ft wind tunnel. *Wind Energy* 5: 151–169.
[44] Schreck S (2002) The NREL full-scale wind tunnel experiment introduction to the special issue. *Wind Energy* 5(2–3): 77–84.
[45] Sørensen NN (2009) CFD modelling of laminar-turbulent transition for airfoils and rotors using the γ–Re$_\theta$ model. *Wind Energy* 12(8): 715–733.
[46] Sørensen JN (2011) Aerodynamic aspects of wind energy conversion. *Annual Review of Fluid Mechanics* 43: 427–448.
[47] Sørensen, JN, Hansen, MOL and Hansen, KS (eds.) (2007) The science of making torque from wind. *Journal of Physics: Conference Series* 75.
[48] Ainslie JF (1985) Development of an eddy viscosity model for wind turbine wakes. *Proceeding of 7th BWEA Wind Energy Conference*. Oxford, 27–29 March.
[49] Crespo A and Hernández J (1996) Turbulence characteristics in wind-turbine wakes. *Journal of Wind Engineering and Industrial Aerodynamics* 61(1): 71–85.
[50] Ivanell S, Sørensen JN, Mikkelsen R, and Henningson D (2008) Analysis of numerically generated wake structures. *Wind Energy* 12(1): 63–80.
[51] Ivanell S, Mikkelsen R, Sørensen JN, and Henningson D (2010) Stability of the tip vortices of a wind turbine. *Wind Energy* 13(8): 705–715.
[52] Troldborg N, Larsen GL, Madsen HA, et al. (2010) Numerical simulations of wake interaction between two wind turbines at various inflow conditions. *Wind Energy* DOI: 10.1002/we.433.
[53] Troldborg N, Sørensen JN, and Mikkelsen R (2009) Numerical simulations of wake characteristics of a wind turbine in uniform flow. *Wind Energy* 13(1): 86–99.
[54] Crespo A, Hernandez J, and Frandsen S (1998) A survey of modelling methods for wind-turbine wakes and wind farms. *Wind Energy* 2: 1–24.
[55] Theodorsen T (1948) *Theory of Propellers*. New York, NY: McGraw-Hill Book Company.
[56] Okulov VL and Sørensen JN (2008) Refined Betz limit for rotors with a finite number of blades. *Wind Energy* 11: 415–426.
[57] Okulov VL and Sørensen JN (2010) Maximum efficiency of wind turbine rotors using Joukowsky and Betz approaches. *Journal of Fluid Mechanics* 649: 497–508.
[58] Fuglsang P and Madsen HA (1999) Optimization method for wind turbine rotors. *Journal of Wind Engineering and Industrial Aerodynamics* 80: 191–206.
[59] Fuglsang P and Thomsen K (2001) Site-specific design optimization of 1.5–2.0 MW wind turbines. *Journal of Solar Energy Engineering* 123: 296–303.
[60] Xudong W, Shen WZ, Zhu WJ, et al. (2009) Shape optimization of wind turbine blades. *Wind Energy* 12(8): 781–803.
[61] Wagner S, Bareiss R, and Guidati G (1996) Wind turbine noise. *EUR 16823*. Berlin, Germany: Springer.
[62] Brooks TF, Pope DS, and Marcolini MA (1989) Airfoil self-noise and prediction. *NASA Reference Publication 1218*. USA: National Aeronautics and Space Administration.
[63] Amiet RK (1975) Acoustic radiation from an airfoil in a turbulent stream. *Journal of Sound and Vibration* 41: 407–420.
[64] Fuglsang P and Madsen HA (1996) Implementation and verification of an aeroacoustic noise prediction model for wind turbines. *Risø National Laboratory Publication R-867(EN)*, Risø National Laboratory, Denmark.
[65] Zhu WJ, Heilskov N, Shen WZ, and Sørensen JN (2005) Modeling of aerodynamically generated noise from wind turbines. *Journal of Solar Energy Engineering* 127: 517–528.
[66] Zhu WJ, Sørensen JN, and Shen WZ (2005) An aerodynamic noise propagation model for wind turbines. *Wind Engineering* 29(2): 129–143.
[67] Schepers JG, Curvers APWM, Oerlemans S, et al. (2005) SIROCCO: Silent Rotors by Acoustic Optimisation. *First International Meeting on Wind Turbine Noise: Perspectives for Control*.
[68] Moriarty P, Guidati G, and Migliore P (2005) Prediction of turbulent inflow and trailing-edge noise for wind turbines. *AIAA Paper 2005–2881, Proceedings of the 11th AIAA/CEAS Aeroacoustics Conference*. Monterey, CA.
[69] Lutz T, Herrig A, Würz W, et al. (2007) Wind-tunnel verification of low-noise airfoils for wind turbines. *AIAA Journal* 45(4): 779–785.
[70] Drela M (1989) XFOIL: An analysis and design system for low Reynolds number airfoils. *Conference on Low Reynolds Number Aerodynamics*. University Notre Dame.

Further Reading

[1] Burton T, Sharpe D, Jenkins N, and Bossanyi E (2001) *Wind Energy Handbook*. New York, NY: Wiley.
[2] Hansen AC and Butterfield CP (1993) Aerodynamics of horizontal-axis wind turbines. *Annual Review of Fluid Mechanics* 25: 115–149.
[3] Hansen MOL (2008) *Aerodynamics of Wind Turbine*. London, UK: Earthscan.
[4] Hansen MOL, Sørensen JN, Voutsinas S, et al. (2006) State of the art in wind turbine aerodynamics and aeroelasticity. *Progress in Aerospace Sciences* 42: 285–330.
[5] Hau E and von Renouard H (2006) *Wind Turbines: Fundamentals, Application, Economics*. Berlin, Germany: Springer.
[6] Leishman JG (2002) Challenges in modeling the unsteady aerodynamics of wind turbines. *Wind Energy* 5: 86–132.
[7] Manwell F, McGowan JG, and Rogers AL (2010) *Wind Energy Explained: Theory, Design and Application*. West Sussex, UK: Wiley.
[8] Snel H (1998) Review of the present status of rotor aerodynamics. *Wind Energy* 1: 46–69.

[9] Sørensen, JN and Sørensen, JD (eds.) (2011) *Wind Energy Systems: Optimising Design and Construction for Safe and Reliable Operation.* Cambridge, UK: Woodhead Publishing Series in Energy No. 10.
[10] Sørensen JN (2011) Aerodynamic aspects of wind energy conversion. *Annual Review of Fluid Mechanics* 43: 427–448.
[11] Spera DA (1994) *Wind Turbine Technology.* New York, NY: ASME Press.
[12] Vermeer LJ, Sørensen JN, and Crespo A (2003) Wind turbine wake aerodynamics. Progress in Aerospace Sciences 39: 467–510.
[13] De Vries O (1979) Fluid dynamic aspects of wind energy conversion. *AGARD Report AG-243*, AGARD Advisory Group for Aerospace Research & Development.

2.09 Mechanical-Dynamic Loads

M Karimirad, Norwegian University of Science and Technology, Trondheim, Norway

© 2012 Elsevier Ltd. All rights reserved.

2.09.1	Introduction	244
2.09.2	Dynamic Analyses	244
2.09.3	Load Cases	246
2.09.4	Loads	247
2.09.4.1	Aerodynamic Loads	247
2.09.4.2	Hydrodynamic Loads	249
2.09.4.3	Gravitational Loads	251
2.09.4.4	Inertial Loads	251
2.09.4.5	Control Loads	251
2.09.4.6	Mooring System Loads	252
2.09.4.7	Current Loads	253
2.09.4.8	Ice Loads	253
2.09.4.9	Soil Interaction Loads	253
2.09.5	Case Studies: Examples of Load Modeling in the Integrated Analyses	254
2.09.5.1	Onshore Wind Turbine: Wind-Induced Loads	254
2.09.5.1.1	Power production and thrust load	254
2.09.5.1.2	Tower shadow, downwind, and upwind rotor configuration	255
2.09.5.1.3	Turbulent versus constant wind loads	256
2.09.5.2	Offshore Wind Turbine: Wave- and Wind-Induced Loads	258
2.09.5.2.1	Aerodynamic and hydrodynamic damping	259
2.09.5.2.2	Effect of turbulence on the wave- and wind-induced responses	259
2.09.5.2.3	Servo-induced negative damping	260
2.09.5.2.4	Comparison of power production of TLS and CMS turbines	261
2.09.6	Conclusions	262
Appendix A: Environmental Conditions		262
Appendix B: Wind Theory		263
Appendix C: Wave Theory		265
References		267

Glossary

CMS A spar-type offshore wind turbine which is moored by a catenary mooring system.
Limit state A limit state is a set of performance criteria (e.g., vibration levels, deformations, strength, stability, buckling, collapse) that should be considered when the wind turbine is subjected to loads.

Parked turbine To survive in storm conditions, wind turbines are shut down and the blades are usually feathered to be parallel to the wind.
Servo-induced The actions and loads introduced by the controller.

Nomenclature
Roman symbols

a axial induction factor
a' rotational induction factor
a_X water particle acceleration in the wave propagation direction
c_w scale parameter
C_d hydrodynamic quadratic drag coefficient
C_D aerodynamic drag coefficient
C_L aerodynamic lift coefficient
C_m hydrodynamic added mass coefficient
dm mass of a small section

D aerodynamic drag force per length
D_{ch} characteristic diameter
D_{cyl} cylinder diameter
D_{tower} tower diameter
f frequency in hertz
f_W Weibull probability density function
F_C centrifugal force
$F_{Generalized}$ generalized force vector
F_S shear force
F_T tension force
h mean water depth
h_{agl} height above ground level
H wave height

H_S significant wave height
I_t turbulent intensity
k wave number
k_w shape parameter
K_{surge} surge stiffness
l length scale
L aerodynamic lift force per length
L_B blade length
$L_{tendons}$ length of tendons
M total mass
M_B blade mass
$n_{tendons}$ number of tendons
$\dot{r}$ structural velocity vector
$\ddot{r}$ structural acceleration vector
R^D damping force vector
R^E external force vector
R^I inertia force vector
R^S internal structural reaction force vector
S spectrum
t time
T thrust force
T_C controller torque
T_P wave peak period
u water particle velocity in x-direction (wave propagation direction)
u_C current velocity
u_m modified axial velocity component
V wind velocity
V_{rel} relative velocity
V_{Annual} annual mean wind speed
x position vector including translations and rotations
z vertical coordinate axis (upward)
z' scaled vertical coordinate axis (upward)

Greek symbols

α angle of attack
ς regular wave elevation
ς_a regular wave amplitude
λ wavelength
μ mass per length
ρ_a air density
ρ_w water density
σ standard deviation
θ_{cone} blade cone angle
ω frequency (rad s^{-1})
∇ submerged displacement

2.09.1 Introduction

The demand for renewable and reliable energy due to global warming, environmental pollution, and the energy crisis deeply challenges researchers today. Wind, wave, tidal, solar, biological, and hydrological forces are potential resources for generating the desired power. Among these sources, wind seems to be the most reliable and practical source, with its annual increase rate of 25–30% [1, 2]. The International Energy Agency (IEA) suggests that with concentrated effort and technology innovation, wind power could supply up to 12% of global demand for electricity by 2050 [3].

For several decades, the land-based wind turbines have been used to generate green energy. Presently, the best onshore sites are already in use, and neighbors have been complaining aplenty in an overcrowded Europe. Land-based wind turbines are associated with visual and noise impacts that make it increasingly difficult to find appropriate and acceptable sites for future growth. Hence, wind engineering has moved offshore to find suitable sites for generating green electricity via ocean wind resources [4, 5]. Offshore wind turbines offer some advantages in that they cannot be seen or heard. Moreover, the offshore wind is steadier and stronger, which helps produce more electricity.

Following a number of large research projects, offshore wind turbines were mounted in Sweden, Denmark, and the Netherlands in the early 1990s [6]. Today, offshore wind power is approximately 1% of total installed capacity, but this capacity has been increasing very rapidly. By the end of 2007, 1100 MW capacities were installed offshore by five countries: Sweden, Denmark, Ireland, the Netherlands, and the United Kingdom [7].

A variety of concepts for fixed offshore wind turbines have been introduced; these include monopiles, tripods, guided towers, suction buckets, lattice towers, gravity-based structures, piled jackets, jacket monopile hybrids, harvest jackets, and gravity pile structures [8]. Most of these concepts were developed in the past decade for water depths of 5–50 m and have been used to build structures that now produce electrical power. It is not feasible to go further based on fixed mounted structures, because the cost increases rapidly and practical issues such as installation and design are affected by depth. In deepwater zones, the use of floating wind turbines (FWTs) provides more options for a proper solution for a specific site.

Several concepts for FWTs based on semisubmersible, spar, tension leg platform (TLP), and ship-shaped foundations have been introduced [9]. Each of these concepts has its advantages and disadvantages, which should be considered based on site specifications such as water depth, environmental conditions (Metocean), distance to shore, and seabed properties. **Figure 1** shows the wind turbine development.

2.09.2 Dynamic Analyses

Frequency domain, time domain, and hybrid time–frequency domain analyses are widely used for dynamic response analysis of mechanical systems. The frequency domain analysis is very fast. However, it is not possible to use the frequency domain methods for a wind turbine due to nonlinear wave and wind loading, control, strong coupling of rotor platform, geometrical updating, and large deformation. Hence, the integrated time domain analysis is necessary for such structures. As the environmental conditions are stochastic, the aerodynamic and hydrodynamic loads, and consequently the responses of wind turbines, are stochastic. We can

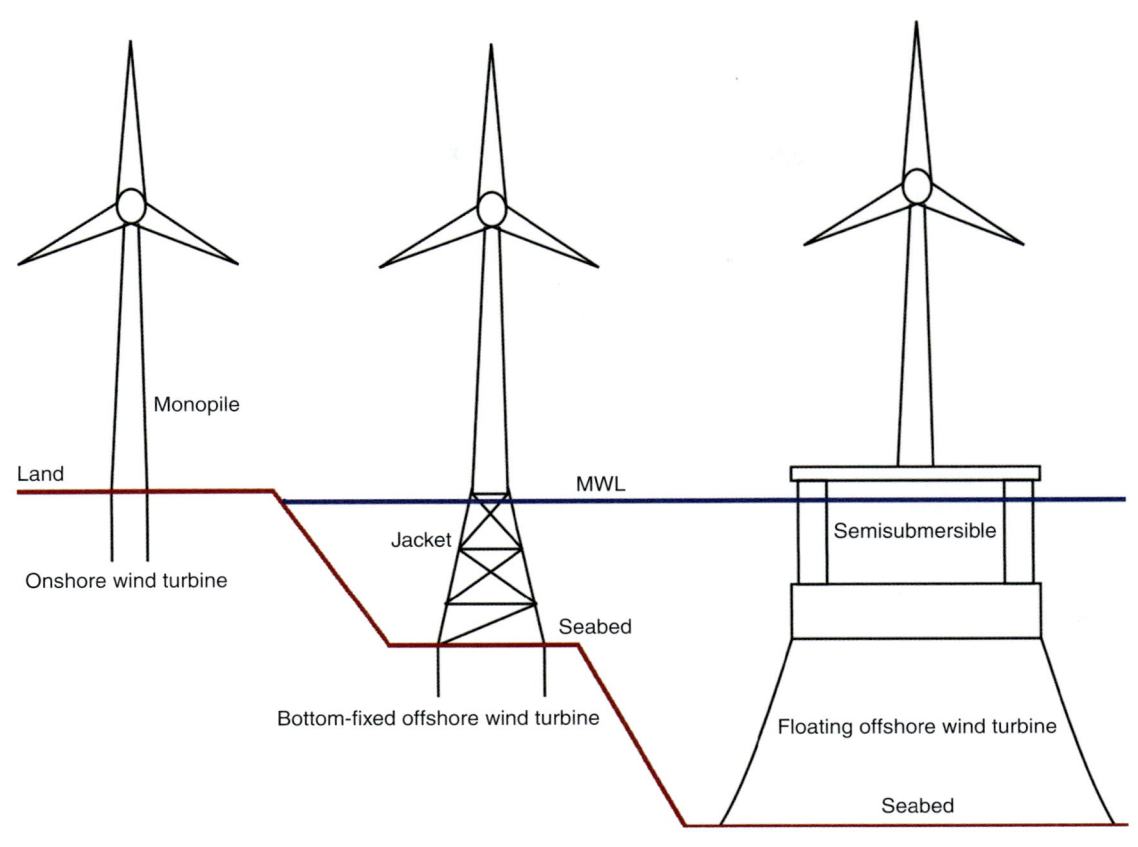

Figure 1 Wind turbine development (onshore and offshore).

distinguish mainly generalities from a time domain analysis: maximum, high- and low-frequency responses, strange peaks, and very slow variations. The time series can be transformed into the frequency domain and presented in spectral format to make it easier to follow the nature of the response. International Electrotechnical Commission (IEC) recommends 1 h stochastic time domain simulations for offshore wind turbines to ensure statistical reliability. The first part of the time domain stochastic simulation, which is influenced by transient responses, should be eliminated before transforming to the frequency domain.

The fatigue and ultimate limit states are two important factors in the design of structures. The environmental conditions can be harsh and induce extreme responses for a structure. For a land-based wind turbine, the fatigue is the key parameter in design, and the extreme responses that occur in operational conditions are linked to the rated wind speed. However, for an FWT, the extreme responses can occur in survival conditions.

The time domain analysis should be applied for solving the equations of motion for nonlinear systems. For a wind turbine, because the nonlinearities involved in the loading are dominant, the linearization of the equations of motion does not accurately represent the dynamic structural responses. Even if linear elastic theory is used to model the structure, the loading is nonlinear. Consequently, the responses are nonlinear as well. The aerodynamic loading is inherently nonlinear and the aerodynamic lift and drag-type forces for a parked or an operating wind turbine are fully nonlinear. The hydrodynamic drag forces are similar to aerodynamic forces in nature and add nonlinearities. The instantaneous position of the wind turbine should be accounted for when calculating the hydrodynamic and aerodynamic forces. The geometrical updating introduces nonlinear loading that can excite the resonant motions. It was shown that both the hydrodynamic inertial and drag forces need to be updated considering the instantaneous position of the system. The aerodynamic damping, wave-induced aerodynamic damping, hydrodynamic damping, and wind-induced hydrodynamic damping need to be considered for an FWT. The coupled time domain analysis is the reliable approach to account for all of these damping phenomena. For an operating wind turbine, the control algorithm controls the output power by controlling the rotational speed of the rotor or the attack angle of the blades by feathering the blades. Time domain analysis is necessary to implement the control loops. For FWTs, a mooring system is used to keep the structure in position. Taut, slack, and catenary mooring systems are some of the options that can be applied depending on the water depth and the floating concept. The mooring lines are nonlinear elastic elements; the nonlinear force–displacement or finite element (FE) modeling can be used to model mooring systems in a dynamic analysis.

To analyze the structural integrity and power performance of wind turbines, dynamic response analysis considering the system and environmental loads is needed. Different approaches can be applied to perform such an analysis:

- Time/frequency domain
- Uncoupled/integrated analysis

- Linear/nonlinear modeling
- Rigid/elastic body modeling
- Steady/turbulent wind simulation
- Linear/nonlinear wave theory.

For a wind turbine, considering both onshore and offshore wind turbines, nonlinear stochastic time domain analysis tools that can be used with hydro-aero-servo-elastic simulations are needed. The following issues, related to mechanical-dynamic loads, highlight the importance of doing integrated time domain analysis for wind turbines.

1. Aerodynamic forces
    - Lift and drag excitations considering the relative velocity
    - Aeroelasticity
2. Nonlinear hydrodynamic excitation forces
    - Inertial and drag forces considering the instantaneous position of the system
    - Hydroelasticity
3. Damping forces
    - Aerodynamic damping
    - Hydrodynamic damping
    - Wave-induced aerodynamic damping
    - Wind-induced hydrodynamic damping
4. Mooring system forces
    - Nonlinear FEs
5. Control (actuation) loads.

The response of wind turbines may consist of three kinds of responses: quasi-static, resonant, and inertia-dominated responses. When the frequency of the excitation is much less than the natural frequencies, the response is quasi-static; the dynamic response is close to the response due to static loading. For example, the mean wind speed can create quasi-static surge responses. The resonant responses can occur if the excitation frequencies are close to the natural frequencies of the system. The nonlinear hydrodynamic and aerodynamic forces can excite the natural frequencies and create the resonant responses. The inertia-dominated response happens when the loading frequencies are much higher than the natural frequencies. For an FWT, the rigid body motions can be inertia-dominated as the wave frequencies are greater than the platform natural frequencies.

2.09.3 Load Cases

The IEC issued the 61400-3 standard, which describes 35 different load cases for design analysis [10]. An appropriate combination of wind and wave loading is necessary for design purpose in an integrated analysis. In the IEC standard, different load cases are introduced for offshore and onshore wind turbines to assure the integrity of the structure in installation, operation, and survival conditions. The defined load cases are given below:

- Power production
- Power production plus fault condition
- Start-up
- Normal shutdown
- Emergency shutdown
- Parked
- Parked plus fault condition
- Transport, assembly, maintenance, and repair.

The power production case is the normal operational case in which the turbine is running and is connected to an electrical load with active control. The power production plus fault condition involves a transient event triggered by a fault or loss of electrical network connection while the turbine is operating under normal conditions. If this case does not cause immediate shutdown, the resulting loads could affect the fatigue life. Start-up is a transient load case. The number of occurrences of start-up may be obtained based on the control algorithm behavior. Normal shutdown and emergency shutdown are transient load cases in which the turbine stops generating power by setting to the parked condition. The rotor of a parked wind turbine is either in the standstill or idling condition. The ultimate loads for these conditions should be investigated. Any deviation from the normal behavior of a parked wind turbine resulting in a fault should be analyzed. All the marine conditions, wind conditions, and design situations should be defined for the transport, maintenance, and assembly of an offshore wind turbine. The maximum loading of these conditions and their effects should be investigated.

When combining the fault and extreme environmental conditions in the wind turbine lifetime, the realistic situation should be proposed. Fatigue and extreme loads should be assessed with reference to material strength, deflections, and structure stability. In some cases, it can be assumed that the wind and waves act from one direction (single directionality). In some concepts, multidirectionality of the waves and wind can be important. In the load case with transient change in the wind direction, it is suggested that codirectional wind and wave be assumed prior to the transient change. For each mean wind speed, a single value for the significant wave height (e.g., expected value) can be used [10]. **Appendix A** addresses the environmental conditions.

2.09.4 Loads

The dynamic equilibrium of a spatial discretized FE model of a wind turbine can be expressed as the following equation:

$$R^{I}(r,\ddot{r},t) + R^{D}(r,\dot{r},t) + R^{S}(r,t) = R^{E}(r,\dot{r},t) \qquad [1]$$

where R^I is the inertia force vector; R^D is the damping force vector; R^S is the internal structural reaction force vector; R^E is the external force vector; and r, $\dot{r}$, $\ddot{r}$ are the structural displacement, velocity, and acceleration vectors, respectively.

This equation is a nonlinear system of differential equations due to the displacement dependencies in the inertia and the damping forces and the coupling between the external load vector and structural displacement and velocity. Also, there is a nonlinear relationship between internal forces and displacements. All force vectors are established by an assembly of element contributions and specified discrete nodal forces.

The external force vector (R^E) accounts for the weight and buoyancy, drag and wave acceleration terms in the Morison formula, mooring system forces, forced displacements (if applicable), specified discrete nodal forces, and aerodynamic loads.

The aerodynamic loads including the drag and lift forces are calculated by considering the instantaneous position of the element and the relative wind velocity. The blade element momentum (BEM) theory is used to present the aerodynamic loads on the tower, nacelle, and rotor including the blades and hub. The aerodynamic damping forces can be kept on the right-hand side or moved to the damping force vector on the left-hand side. In the present formulation, the aerodynamic drag and lift forces and hydrodynamic drag forces accounting for the relative velocity are put on the right-hand side in the external force vector.

The inertia force vector (R^I) can be expressed by the following:

$$R^{I}(r,\ddot{r},t) = [M^{S} + M^{H}(r)]\ddot{r} \qquad [2]$$

where M^S is the structural mass matrix and $M^H(r)$ is the displacement-dependent hydrodynamic mass matrix accounting for the structural acceleration terms in the Morison formula as added mass contributions in local directions.

The damping force vector (R^D) is expressed as the following:

$$R^{D}(r,\dot{r},t) = [C^{S}(r) + C^{H}(r) + C^{D}(r)]\dot{r} \qquad [3]$$

where $C^S(r)$ is the internal structural damping matrix, $C^H(r)$ is the hydrodynamic damping matrix accounting for the radiation effects for floating and partly submerged elements, and $C^D(r)$ is the matrix of specified discrete dashpot dampers, which may be displacement-dependent.

The dynamic equilibrium equations (eqn [1]) can be solved in the time domain through step-by-step numerical integration, for example, based on the Newmark-beta methods. The equations of motions can be written in the form of the d'Alembert's principle as $F_{\text{Generalized}}(t,x,\dot{x},\ddot{x}) = 0$, in which the generalized force vector $F_{\text{Generalized}}(t,x,\dot{x},\ddot{x})$ includes all the environmental forces, inertial and gravitational forces, mooring system, and soil interaction (if applicable) and all kind of stiffness and damping forces (including aerodynamic, hydrodynamic, and structural stiffness and damping). x is the position vector including translations and rotations. The primary loads for an offshore wind turbine are as follows (see **Figure 2**):

- Aerodynamic loads
- Hydrodynamic loads
- Gravitational loads
- Inertial loads
- Control loads
- Mooring system loads
- Current loads
- Ice loads
- Soil interaction loads.

Appendixes B and **C** address the wind and wave theories, respectively.

2.09.4.1 Aerodynamic Loads

The aerodynamic loads are highly nonlinear and result from static and dynamic relative wind flow, dynamic stall, skew inflow, shear effects on the induction, and effects from large deflections. The complex methods for calculating the aerodynamics are based on solving the Navier–Stokes (NS) equations for the global compressible flow in addition to accounting for the flow near the blades. The extended BEM theory can be used to consider advanced and unsteady aerodynamic effects for aero-elastic time domain calculation. Approaches of intermediate complexity, such as the vortex and panel methods, can also be applied [11]. Computational fluid dynamics (CFD) methods are the most accurate, but are very time consuming. The advanced BEM theory is fast and gives good accuracy compared to CFD methods.

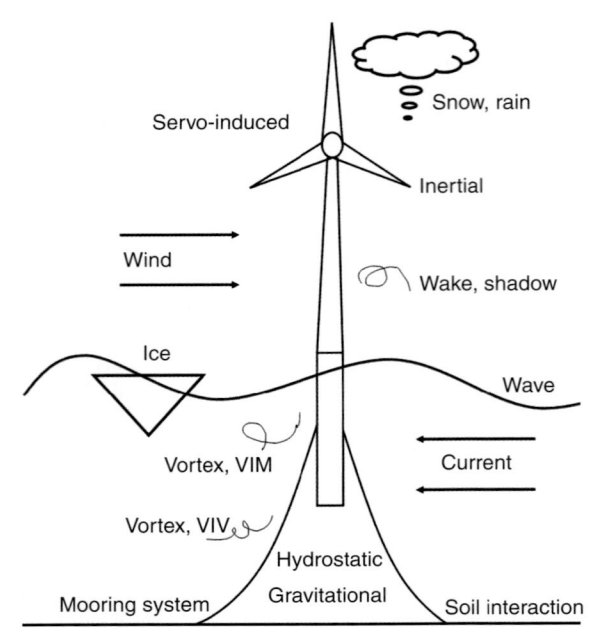

Figure 2 System and environmental loads for a wind turbine.

The BEM method relies on airfoil data; therefore, the results obtained using this method are no better than the input. It is proposed using NS methods to extract airfoil data and applying them in less advanced methods (e.g., BEM theory).

The aerodynamic forces consist of the lift and drag forces. The lift forces, skin friction, and pressure viscous drags are the main sources of the aerodynamic forces for the slender parts of a wind turbine. For slender structures, the 2D aerodynamic theory is applicable. Through the BEM theory, the lift and drag coefficients are used to model the aerodynamic forces. For a parked wind turbine, the aerodynamic forces are calculated directly using the relative wind speed. However, for an operating wind turbine, the induced velocities and wake effects on the velocity seen by the blade element need to be determined.

As mentioned above, the wind turbine blades and the tower are long and slender structures. The spanwise velocity component is much lower than the streamwise component, and. therefore, in many aerodynamic models, it is assumed that the flow at a given point is two-dimensional (2D) and the 2D aerofoil data can be applied. **Figure 3** illustrates a transversal cut of the blade element viewed from beyond the tip of the blade. In this figure, the aerodynamic forces acting on the blade element are also depicted. The blade element moves in the airflow at a relative speed V_{rel}. The lift and drag coefficients are defined as follows [11, 12]:

$$C_L(\alpha) = \frac{L}{\frac{1}{2}\rho_a V_{\text{rel}}^2 c}$$

$$C_D(\alpha) = \frac{D}{\frac{1}{2}\rho_a V_{\text{rel}}^2 c}$$

[4]

where D and L are the drag and lift forces (per length), c is the chord of the airfoil, ρ_a is the air density, α is the angle of attack, and V_{rel} is the relative velocity [13, 14].

$$V_{\text{rel}} = V\sqrt{(1-a)^2 + \left(\frac{r\omega}{V}(1+a')\right)^2}$$

[5]

$$\alpha = \phi - \beta$$

[6]

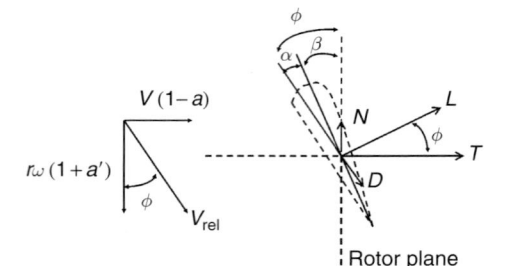

Figure 3 Forces on a blade element.

$$\tan(\phi) = \frac{V}{r\omega}\left(\frac{1-a}{1+a'}\right) \quad [7]$$

where a and a' are the axial and rotational induction factors, respectively, V is the upstream wind velocity, T is the thrust force, r is the distance of the airfoil section from the blade root, and ω is the rotational velocity (rad s^{-1}). a and a' are functions of ϕ, C_L, C_D, and the solidity (fraction of the annular area that is covered by the blade element). The aerodynamic theories to calculate the wind loads for operational and parked conditions are very similar. For a parked wind turbine, the rotational speed (ω) is zero as the blades are fixed and cannot rotate. ϕ is 90 degrees, which means the relative wind velocity and the wind velocity are parallel.

The aerodynamic loads can be divided into different types [13]:

- Static loads, such as a steady wind passing a stationary wind turbine
- Steady loads, such as a steady wind passing a rotating wind turbine
- Cyclic loads, such as a rotating blade passing a wind shear
- Transient loads, such as drive train loads due to the application of the brake
- Impulsive loads, that is, loads with short duration and significant peak magnitude, such as blades passing a wake of tower for a downwind turbine
- Stochastic loads, such as turbulent wind forces
- Resonance-induced loads, that is, excitation forces close to the natural frequencies.

The mean wind induces steady loads, whereas the wind shear, yaw error, yaw motion, and gravity induce cyclic loads. Turbulence is linked to stochastic loading. Gusts, starting, stopping, feathering the blades, and teetering induce transient loads. Finally, the structure's eigen frequencies can be the source of resonance-induced loading.

The following effects need to be included in the aerodynamic model [14]:

- Deterministic aerodynamic loads: steady (uniform flow), yawed flow, shaft tilt, wind shear, tower shadow, and wake effects
- Stochastic aerodynamic forces due to the temporal and spatial fluctuation/variation of wind velocity (turbulence)
- Rotating blades aerodynamics, including induced flows (i.e., modification of the wind field due to the turbine), three-dimensional flow effects, and dynamic stall effects
- Dynamic effects from the blades, drive train, generator, and tower, including the modification of aerodynamic forces due to vibration and rigid body motions
- Subsystem dynamic effects (i.e., the yaw system and blade pitch control)
- Control effects during normal operation, start-up and shutdown, including parked conditions.

The aerodynamic performance of a wind turbine is mainly a function of the steady-state aerodynamics. However, there are several important steady-state and dynamic effects that cause increased loads or decreased power production compared to those expected from the basic BEM theory. These effects can especially increase the transient loads. Some of the advanced aerodynamic subjects are listed [13]:

1. Nonideal steady-state aerodynamic issues
    - Decrease of power due to blade surface roughness (for a damaged blade, up to 40% less power production)
    - Stall effects on the airfoil lift and drag coefficients
    - The rotating condition affects the blade aerodynamic performance. The delayed stall in a rotating blade compared to the same blade in a wind tunnel can decrease the wind turbine life.
2. Turbine wakes
    - Skewed wake in a downwind turbine
    - Near and far wakes. The turbulence and vortices generated at the rotor are diffused in the near wake and the turbulence and velocity profiles in the far wake are more uniformly distributed
    - Off-axis flows due to yaw error or vertical wind components.
3. Unsteady aerodynamic effects
    - Tower shadow (wind speed deficit behind a tower due to tower presence)
    - Dynamic stall, that is, sudden aerodynamic changes that result in or delay the stall
    - Dynamic inflow, that is, changes in rotor operation
    - Rotational sampling. It is possible to have rapid changes in the flow if the blades rotate faster than the turbulent flow rate.

2.09.4.2 Hydrodynamic Loads

Hydrodynamic loads on the floater consist of nonlinear and linear viscous drag effects, currents, radiation (linear potential drag) and diffraction (wave scattering), buoyancy (restoring forces), integration of the dynamic pressure over the wetted surface (Froude–Krylov), and inertia forces. A combination of the pressure integration method, the boundary element method, and the Morison formula can be used to represent the hydrodynamic loading. The linear wave theory may be used in deepwater areas, while in shallow water the linear wave theory is not accurate as the waves are generally nonlinear. It was shown that [15] for offshore wind turbines, nonlinear (second-order), irregular waves can better describe waves in shallow waters. Considering the instantaneous position of the structure in finding the loads add some nonlinearity. These hydrodynamic nonlinearities are mainly active in the resonant responses, which influence the power production and structural responses at low natural frequencies.

Considering the size and type of the support structure and turbine, wave loading may be significant and can be the main cause of fatigue and extreme loads that should be investigated in coupled analysis. Hence, the selection of a suitable method of determining the hydrodynamic loads can have an important effect on the cost of the system and its ability to withstand environmental and operational loads.

The panel method, Morison formula, pressure integration method, or combination of these methods can be used to calculate the hydrodynamic forces. The selection of the method should be concept-dependent. Some of the hydrodynamic aspects for an FWT that may be considered depending on the concept and site specification are listed below [16, 17]:

- Appropriate wave kinematics models
- Hydrodynamic models considering the water depth, sea climates, and support structures
- Extreme hydrodynamic loading, including breaking waves, using nonlinear wave theories and appropriate corrections
- Stochastic hydrodynamic loading using linear wave theories with empirical corrections
- Consideration of both slender and large-volume structures depending on the support structure of the FWT.

The Morison formula is practical for slender structures where the dimension of the structure is small compared to the wavelength, that is, $D_{ch} < 0.2\lambda$ [16], where D_{ch} is the characteristic diameter and λ is the wavelength. In other words, it is assumed that the structure does not have significant effect on the waves. The hydrodynamic forces through the Morison formula include the inertial and quadratic viscous excitation forces. The inertial forces in the Morison formula consist of diffraction and Froude–Krylov forces for a fixed structure. For a floating structure, the added mass forces are included in the Morison formula through relative acceleration as well and the damping forces appear through the relative velocity.

Equation [8] shows the hydrodynamic forces per unit length on the floater based on the Morison formula, which was extended to account for the instantaneous position of the structure for FWTs [16].

$$dF = \frac{\rho_w}{2} C_d D_{cyl} |u_r| u_r + \rho_w \frac{\pi D_{cyl}^2}{4} C_m \dot{u}_r + \rho_w \frac{\pi D_{cyl}^2}{4} C_m \dot{u}_W \quad [8]$$

$$u_r = u_W - u_B \quad [9]$$

where ρ_w is the mass density of seawater, D_{cyl} is the cylinder diameter, $\dot{u}_r$ and u_r are the horizontal relative acceleration and velocity between the water particle velocity u_W and the velocity of the body u_B (eqn [9]), respectively, and C_m and C_d are the added mass and quadratic drag coefficients, respectively.

The first term is the quadratic viscous drag force, the second term includes the diffraction and added mass forces, and the third term is the Froude–Krylov force (FK term). A linear drag term $C_1 u_r$ can be added to the Morison formula as well, where C_1 is the linear drag coefficient. The positive force direction is in the wave propagation direction. C_d and C_1 have to be empirically determined and are dependent on many parameters as the Reynolds number, Keulegan–Carpenter (KC) number, a relative current number, and surface roughness ratio [16].

For large-volume structures, the diffraction becomes important. The MacCamy–Fuchs correction for the inertia coefficient in some cases can be applied. Based on the panel method (BEM), the added mass coefficient for a circular cylinder is equal to 1, which corresponds to the diffraction part of the Morison formula. The Froude–Krylov contribution can be found by pressure integration over the circumference; for a cylinder in a horizontal direction, the added mass coefficient is equal to 1. Therefore, the inertia coefficient for a slender circular member is 2. It is possible to use the pressure integration method to calculate the Froude–Krylov part of the Morison formula and just apply the diffraction part through the Morison formula.

For an FWT, the instantaneous position should be accounted for when updating the hydrodynamic forces. Hence, the original Morison formulation should be changed using the relative acceleration and velocities. The relative velocity will be applied to the quadratic viscous part. The pressure integration method and the Morison formula use the updated wave acceleration at the instantaneous position. The geometrical updating adds some nonlinear hydrodynamic loading that can excite the low natural frequencies of the spar.

Based on second-order wave theory, the mean drift, slowly varying (difference frequency) and sum frequency forces, drift-added mass, and damping can be added to the above linear wave theory. The Morison formula combined with the pressure integration method is a practical approach to model the hydrodynamic forces for a spar-type wind turbine. Using the modified linear wave theory accounting for the wave kinematics up to the wave elevation and the pressure integration method in transversal directions (Froude–Krylov), the mean drift forces were considered in this chapter. Moreover, the sum frequency forces were considered by using the instantaneous position of the structure to calculate the hydrodynamic forces.

2.09.4.3 Gravitational Loads

Like any other structure, for larger wind turbines, the significance of gravitational loads is greater. The gravitational forces result in harmonic varying shear forces and bending moments for operating turbines that have an important contribution in the blade fatigue life (**Figure 4**). For a pitch-controlled turbine, gravity loads will cause bending moments in both edgewise and flapwise directions. The nacelle and rotor weight is usually comparable with the tower weight and has a significant influence on the design of tower and installation of the system. The gravitational loads are deterministic and depend on the mass distribution and instantaneous position of the structure, that is, the blade azimuth. For an FWT, the gravitational force can have a significant influence on the hydrostatic stability of the system.

The rotor of a 5 MW wind turbine with a rated rotational speed of 12 rpm will be exposed to 1.6×10^8 stress cycles from gravitational loads, in 25 years operation. The blades of such a large turbine are more than 60 m long and each more that 17 tonnes. For large onshore and offshore turbines, the gravitational loads are very important in the fatigue limit state checks. The shear force (F_S) at the blade root due to the gravitational forces can be calculated as:

$$F_S = M_B\, g \sin(\omega t)$$
$$M_B = \int_0^{L_B} dm = \int_0^{L_B} \mu(r) dr \quad [10]$$

Equation [10] shows that the blade root is exposed to tensile and compressive stresses in each rotor rotation.

2.09.4.4 Inertial Loads

The deterministic inertial forces include centrifugal, Coriolis, gyroscopic, breaking, and teetering loads. These loads occur when, for example, the turbine is accelerated or decelerated.

- Centrifugal loads: A rotating blade induces centrifugal loads. If the rotor is preconed backward, the normal component of the centrifugal force gives a flapwise bending moment in the opposite direction to the bending moment caused by the thrust and consequently reduces the total flapwise bending moment.
- Gyroscopic loads: The gyroscopic loads on the rotor occur whenever the turbine is yawing during operation. This will happen regardless of the structural flexibility and will lead to a yaw moment about the vertical axis and a tilt moment about a horizontal axis in the rotor plane. For an FWT, it is necessary to provide sufficient yaw stiffness, that is, through the mooring system.
- Breaking loads: When a breaking torque is applied at the rotor shaft, rotor deceleration due to this mechanical breaking introduces edgewise bending moments.
- Teetering loads: For two-bladed turbines, sometimes the whole rotor is mounted on a single shaft hinge allowing fore–aft rotation or teetering that can only transmit in-plane blade moments to the hub. Flapwise blade moments are not transmitted to the low speed shaft.

Centrifugal load on a blade segment can be considered as follows (**Figure 5**):

$$F_C = dm\, r\omega^2 \quad [11]$$

If the blade is preconed backward with a cone angle of θ_{cone}, the $F_C \sin(\theta_{cone})$ will help to reduce the flapwise bending moments.

2.09.4.5 Control Loads

Wind turbine control is usually divided into passive control and active control. The control improves the turbine's performance and reduces loads. Active control needs external energy or auxiliary power and applies some loads on the wind turbine parts such as blades. Generally, a wind turbine controller should maximize the energy production while minimizing the fatigue damage of the drive train and other components due to changes in wind direction and speed (gust and turbulence), as well as start–stop cycles. Wind turbines usually use variable-speed rotors combined with active collective blade pitch. Actuation loads result from operation and control of wind turbines. These loads are in several categories including torque control from a generator/inverter, yaw and pitch actuator loads (**Figure 6**), and mechanical breaking loads.

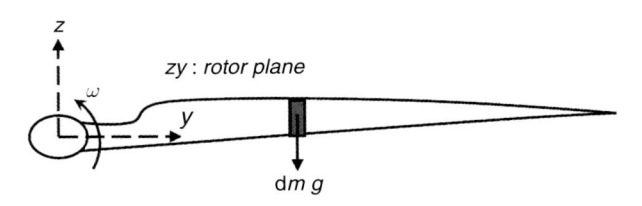

Figure 4 Gravitational load for a wind turbine's blade.

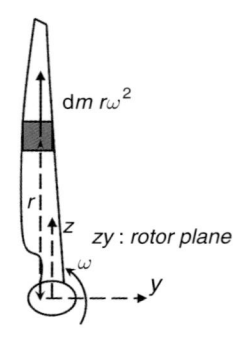

Figure 5 Centrifugal load for a rotating blade.

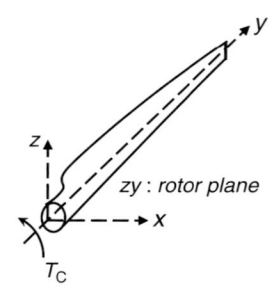

Figure 6 Actuation load resulted from feathering a blade.

2.09.4.6 Mooring System Loads

The mooring system forces are nonlinear time- and position-dependent restoring forces. Nonlinear spring or FE modeling is usually applied. Drag forces on the mooring lines can contribute to the damping effect on the platform motions. If inertia and the damping effects of the mooring system are neglected, it is possible to model the mooring system as a nonlinear spring. The mooring system such as catenary, slack, taut, and tension leg can be chosen depending on the floater, concept, water depth, offshore site, and environmental conditions. The idea is to use the proper mooring system to keep the structure in position while having a limited influence on the power production.

As an example, for a conventional TLP (**Figure 7**), the total tension (F_T) and the surge stiffness can be calculated as:

$$F_T = F_B - F_W = \rho_w \nabla g - Mg$$

$$K_{surge} = \frac{FT}{n_{tendons} \times L_{tendons}} \quad [12]$$

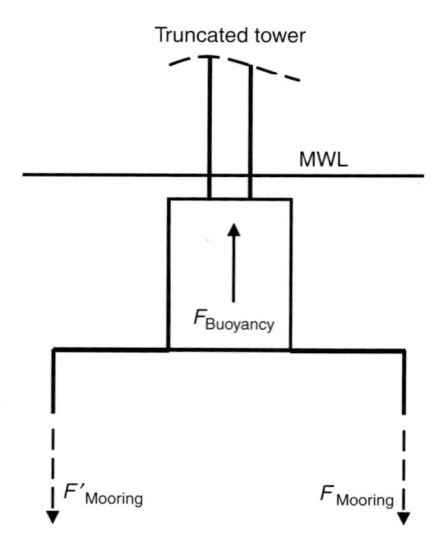

Figure 7 Mooring loads in a TLP concept.

2.09.4.7 Current Loads

The current loads on the offshore wind turbines can be modeled using the Morison's equation. Different current profiles have been suggested as a function of the water depth and sea current velocity. The velocity and the acceleration in Morison's equation need to be taken as the resulting combined current and wave velocity and acceleration, respectively. It is assumed that the floater is slender compared to the wavelength and the Morison's equation is valid. If the current is relatively stationary, then the fluid acceleration due to the current can be neglected (**Figure 8**). Usually, the current is assumed unidirectional, which means there is no change of direction with depth. The current velocity has a vertical gradient due to the boundary layer along the seabed.

2.09.4.8 Ice Loads

Ice can cover both the nonrotating parts of the turbine and the rotating parts (mainly the blades). The blades of a shutdown turbine can be covered by ice with an ice thickness up to several centimeters. The aerodynamic forces of a blade covered by ice increase due to the extra roughness compared with the smooth blade. Loads due to masses of ice frozen on the wind turbine and possible impact loads of the ice should be taken into account [18]. Sea ice may develop and expose the turbine support structure to loads for offshore wind turbines. It is current practice to distinguish between static ice loads and dynamic ice loads. Loads from laterally moving ice should be based on relevant full-scale measurements, model experiments, which can be reliably scaled, or on recognized theoretical methods [18].

2.09.4.9 Soil Interaction Loads

Slab or pile foundations are usually chosen for onshore wind turbines based on the soil conditions at the specific site. A slab foundation is normally preferred when the top soil is strong enough to support the loads from the wind turbine. When assessing whether the top soil is strong enough to carry the foundation loads, it is important to consider how far below the foundation base the water table is located. For fixed offshore wind turbines, the foundation is a more comprehensive structure to carry and transfer the aerodynamic, current, waves, and ice loads to the supporting soil. Monopile, gravity-based, and tripod are three basically foundations for bottom-fixed offshore turbines [18]. Pile foundations use lateral loading of the soil to withstand the loads induced in the supported structure (**Figure 9**). Under static lateral loading, typical soils, such as sand or clay, generally behave as a plastic

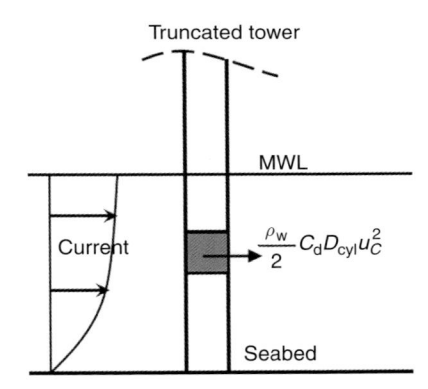

Figure 8 Current load applied on a segment of a bottom-fixed monopile. If the current is relatively stationary, then the fluid acceleration due to the current can be neglected.

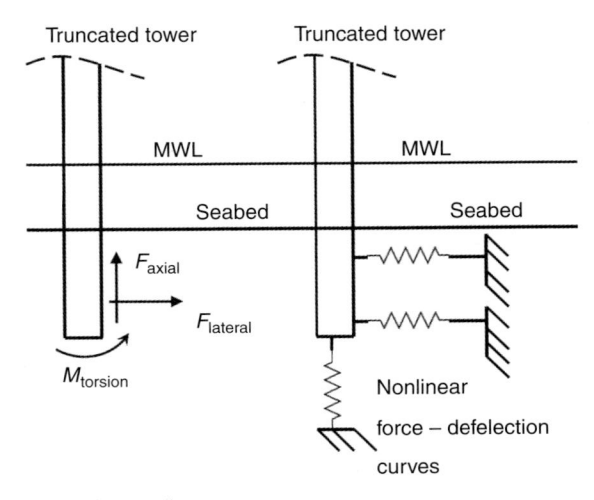

Figure 9 Soil interaction loads for a bottom-fixed monopile.

material, which makes it necessary to nonlinearly relate soil resistance to pile/soil deflection [18]. Nonlinear spring/damper models can be used to model the soil interaction loads.

2.09.5 Case Studies: Examples of Load Modeling in the Integrated Analyses

In this section, several examples of load modeling for both onshore and offshore wind turbines are presented.

2.09.5.1 Onshore Wind Turbine: Wind-Induced Loads

The National Renewable Energy Laboratory (NREL) 5 MW wind turbine [4, 5] has been chosen as an example of an onshore turbine to study some of the aerodynamic loads by wind-induced dynamic response analysis. The tower of the wind turbine on the base has a diameter of 6 m and thickness of 0.027 m. It has a diameter of 3.87 m and thickness of 0.019 m at the top [5]. The wind turbine properties, the blade structural properties, and blade aerodynamic properties are listed in **Tables 1–3**.

2.09.5.1.1 Power production and thrust load

The pitch-regulated variable-speed wind turbine is the state-of-the-art wind machine device. Depending on the wind speed, the status of the wind turbine is divided into four regions:

- The wind speed is too low for cost-effective operation of the wind turbine, so the rotor is parked.
- The wind speed is greater than the cut-in wind speed, but still less than the maximum capacity of the generator. Therefore, the turbine should extract as much energy from the wind as possible. The rotational speed of the rotor is kept below the rated rotor speed to optimize the efficiency of the turbine. The blade pitch is constant in this region.

Table 1 NREL 5 MW wind turbine properties [5]

Rating	5 MW
Rotor orientation, configuration	Upwind, three blades
Rated rotational speed	12.1 rpm
Rotor, hub diameter	126 m, 3 m
Hub height	90 m
Cut-in, rated, cutout wind speed	$3\,\mathrm{m\,s^{-1}}$, $11.4\,\mathrm{m\,s^{-1}}$, $25\,\mathrm{m\,s^{-1}}$
Rotor mass	110 000 kg
Nacelle mass	240 000 kg
Tower mass	347 460 kg

Table 2 Blade structural properties [5]

Length	61.5 m
Overall (integrated) mass	17 740 kg
Second mass moment of inertia	11 776 047 kg m^2
First mass moment of inertia	363 231 kg m

Table 3 Blade aerodynamic properties [5]

Section	Airfoil
1 and 2	Cylinder 1
3	Cylinder 2
4	DU40_A17
5 and 6	DU35_A17
7	DU30_A17
8 and 9	DU25_A17
10 and 11	DU21_A17
12, 13, 14, 15, 16, and 17	NACA64_A17

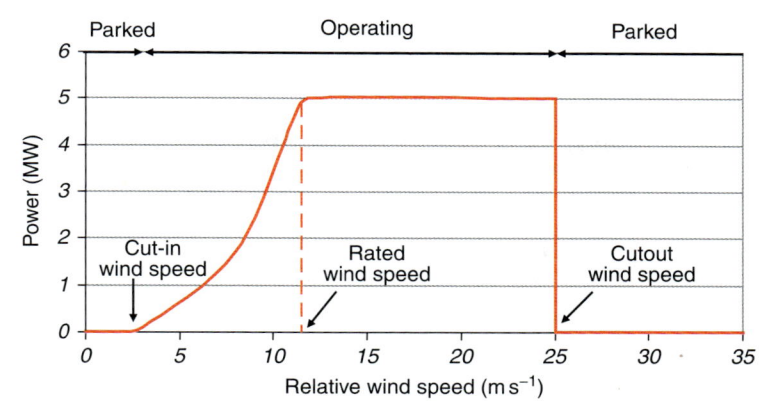

Figure 10 Power versus wind speed for NREL 5 MW (onshore) wind turbine.

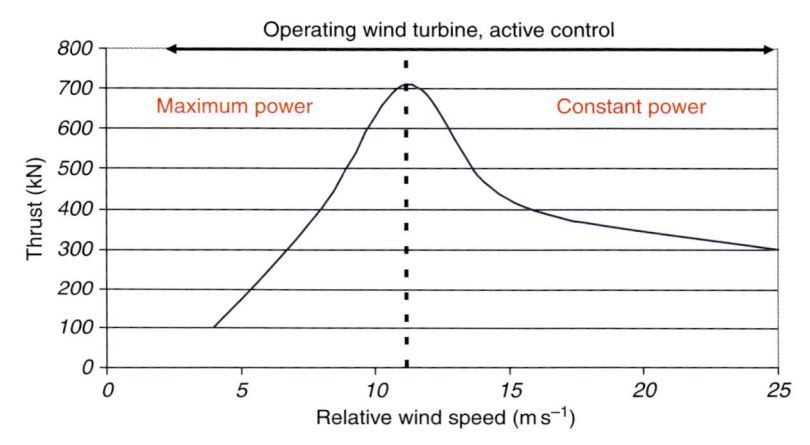

Figure 11 Thrust force versus wind speed for NREL 5 MW (onshore) wind turbine.

- The wind speed is above the rated wind speed. The pitch controller turns the blades toward less aerodynamic torque such that the energy extracted from the wind fits the capacity of the generator. The rotational speed of the rotor is constant.
- The wind speed is too high for safe operation of the wind turbine. After passing the cutout wind speed, the rotor is parked.

In operational conditions, the wind turbine produces electricity, and the control is active. During survival conditions, the wind turbine is parked (shut down) and the control is inactive. In parked configuration, the blades are feathered and set parallel to the wind to decrease the aerodynamic loads on the blades. **Figures 10** and **11** show the power curve and thrust load as a function of wind speed for a NREL 5 MW (onshore) wind turbine. The maximum thrust for a bottom-fixed wind turbine usually occurs in operational condition related to rated wind speed. For below-rated wind speed, the target of controller is to maximize the power and for overrated wind speed, the target of controller is to minimize the loads while maintaining the rated power.

2.09.5.1.2 Tower shadow, downwind, and upwind rotor configuration

The effect of the presence of the turbine tower on the flow field is modeled by the tower shadow. The potential flow and jet wake models for the tower shadow effect of upwind and downwind rotors in HAWC2 code are chosen. The potential flow model is appropriate for upwind rotors. The modified flow velocity component in the axial direction (u_m) based on the potential flow model is:

$$u_m = V_0 \left(1 + \left(\frac{D_{tower}}{2}\right)^2 \frac{x^2 - y^2}{x^2 + y^2}\right) \quad [13]$$

where D_{tower} is the tower diameter, x and y are the lateral and axial Cartesian coordinates in tower cross section with respect to tower center (y: from hub toward the nacelle for the upwind rotor), and V_0 is the ambient undisturbed flow velocity.

In the case of the download rotor, the flow separation and generation of eddies that take place are less amenable to analysis, so empirical methods are used. HAWC2 code uses the Jet wake model for tower shadow of downwind rotors. In this model, the modified axial velocity component (u_m) is defined as:

$$u_m = \frac{\sqrt{3}}{2}\sqrt{\frac{J_M \sigma}{\rho_a y'}}\left(1 - \tanh^2\left(\frac{\sigma x'}{y'}\right)\right) \qquad [14]$$

where σ is an empirical constant equal to 7.67 and x' and y' are lateral and axial nondimensional (with respect to tower diameter) Cartesian coordinates in tower cross section. y' is toward the hub from the nacelle for the downwind rotor and ρ_a is the air density. Using the correlation between the initial tower wake deficit and the drag coefficient of the tower (C_D), the momentum deficit behind the tower (J_M) is defined by:

$$J_M = \frac{V_0^2 D_{tower}}{2}\frac{\rho_a}{\pi}\left[\frac{1}{8} + \frac{16}{3\pi}\right]C_D^2 \qquad [15]$$

Changes are applied to the NREL 5 MW upwind turbine to make it a downwind turbine. The simplest way to make a downwind turbine from an upwind is to hang over the rotor behind the tower. This ensures that the aerodynamic properties of the blades and airfoils are applied correctly. An upwind turbine has a shaft tilt and hub cone angle in order to prevent the blades from hitting the tower due to large aeroelastic deflections. In a downwind turbine, these values can be set to zero as the rotor is behind the tower.

Downwind and upwind turbines with/without modeling the tower shadow are considered to study the effect of rotor configuration on the loads and responses. **Figure 12** compares the electrical power for the following cases:

- Downwind turbine with modeling the tower shadow (jet model)
- Downwind turbine without modeling the tower shadow
- Upwind turbine with modeling the tower shadow (potential model)
- Upwind turbine without modeling the tower shadow.

The constant wind speed of 17 m s^{-1} is chosen. Comparison shows that the tower shadow has an impulsive effect on the power performance for both the upwind and downwind turbines. The mean value of the power is less affected by the tower shadow. For the downwind turbine, the effect of tower shadow on the power production and aerodynamic loads is more obvious. When a blade passes the tower, the velocity seen by the blade will change due to the tower presence. As the rated rotational speed of the NREL turbine is 12.1 rpm, the third rotor harmonic has a period of $T_{3P} = 60/(12.1 \times 3) = 1.65$ s. This means that each of the three blades passes the tower with a period of 1.65 s. The impulse presented in the power when modeling the tower shadow is associated with this period (see **Figure 12**).

The mean and standard deviation of the bending moment at the bottom of the tower (overturning moment) have been plotted for upwind and downwind turbines with and without tower shadow to illustrate the tower shadow and rotor configuration effects on the wind-induced loads (**Figures 13 and 14**). As it is discussed above, the tower shadow does not have a significant effect on the mean value of the loads and responses. However, the standard deviation is significantly affected by the tower shadow and rotor configuration.

2.09.5.1.3 Turbulent versus constant wind loads

The bending moment (overturning moment) associated with turbulent and constant wind loads for a 5 MW wind turbine is compared in **Figure 15**. The tower of the wind turbine is fixed to the ground. The relative effect of the tower shadow and turbulence

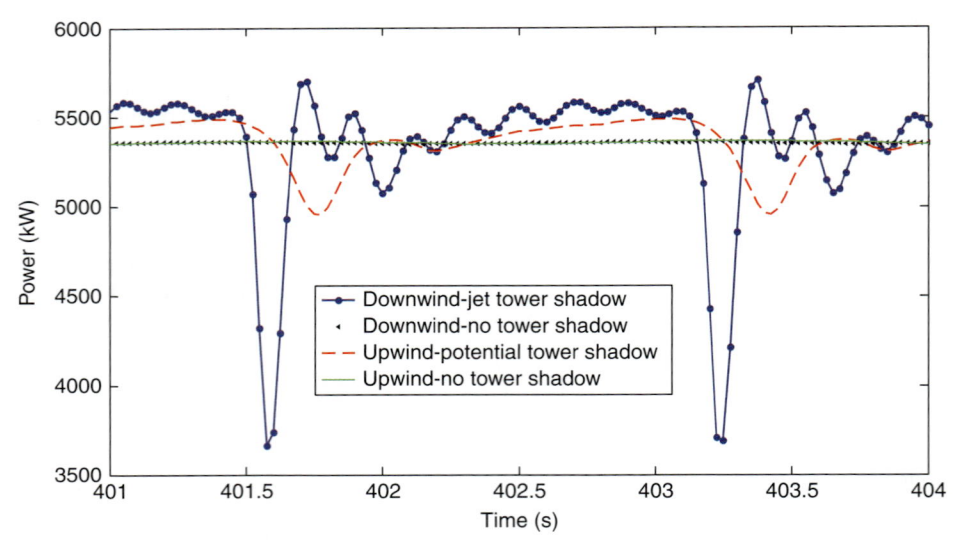

Figure 12 Effect of tower shadow on the power for upwind and downwind onshore turbines.

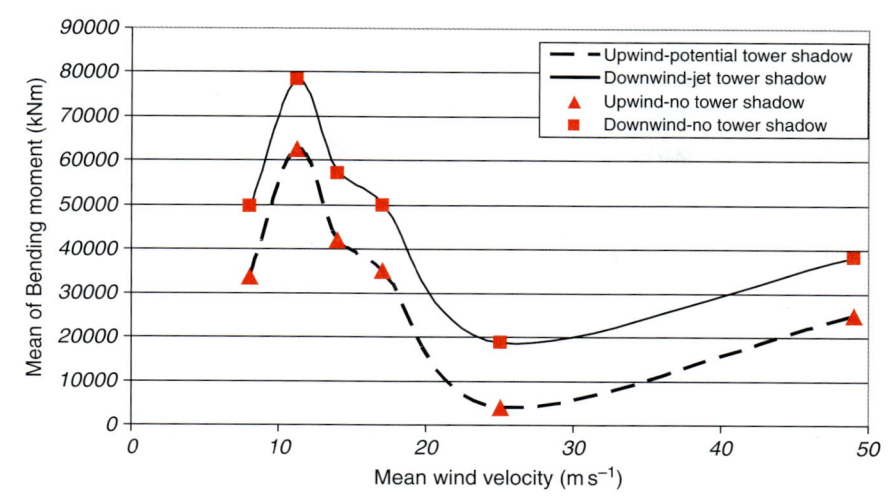

Figure 13 Effect of tower shadow on the mean value of the bending moment for the upwind and downwind onshore turbines.

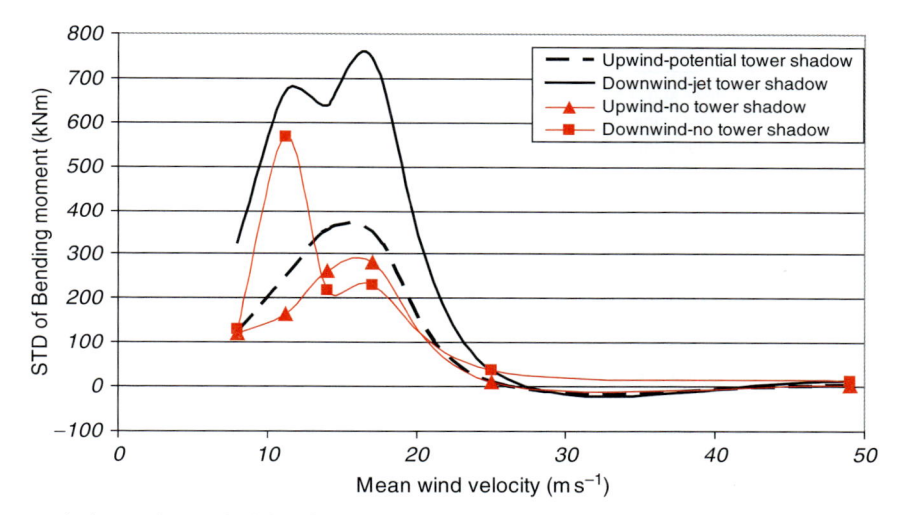

Figure 14 Effect of tower shadow on the standard deviation of the bending moment for the upwind and downwind onshore turbines.

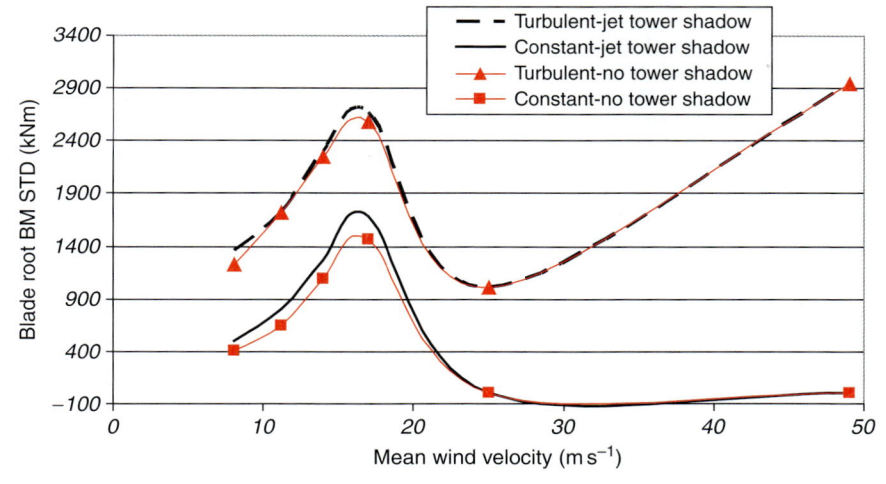

Figure 15 Effect of turbulent versus constant wind loads on the blade root bending moment for an onshore 5 MW downwind turbine.

is studied as well. As discussed in the previous section, the tower shadow is a deterministic variation of wind velocity. However, the turbulence is a stochastic phenomenon. The results show that the effect of the turbulence on the bending moment is greater than the effect of the tower wake deficit. For storm condition, the wind turbine is parked, and, hence, the effect of the tower shadow on the responses is negligible. Under operational condition, the effect of the tower shadow on the responses is notable. The dynamic responses in harsh conditions are strongly affected by the turbulence. Thus, the proper modeling of the turbulent wind is necessary in the ultimate limit state analysis of wind turbines.

2.09.5.2 Offshore Wind Turbine: Wave- and Wind-Induced Loads

Two case studies for wave- and wind-induced analysis of offshore wind turbines are presented. A catenary moored spar (CMS) and tension leg spar (TLS) type FWTs are discussed herein. The CMS and TLS types are similar to the Hywind and Sway, the Norwegian FWTs. In **Tables 4** and **5**, the CMS and TLS wind turbines characteristics are listed, respectively. **Figure 16** shows the schematic layout of the CMS and TLS wind turbines.

CMS: The NREL 5 MW upwind wind turbine [4, 5] has been chosen and mounted on a 120 m draft spar platform. The characteristics of the NREL upwind turbine are mentioned in **Tables 1–3**. The mooring system consists of three sets of mooring lines that are located around the structure. Three fairleads are located on the circumference of the spar. Each mooring line consists of a clump

Table 4 Catenary moored spar (CMS) FWT properties

Total draft	120 m
Diameter above taper	6.5 m
Diameter below taper	9.4 m
Spar mass, including ballast	7 593 000 kg
Total mass	8 329 230 kg
Center of gravity (CG)	−78.61 m
Pitch inertia about the CG	2.20×10^{10} kg m^2
Yaw inertia about the centerline	1.68×10^{8} kg m^2
Rating	5 MW
Rotor configuration	Three blades
Rotor, hub diameter	126 m, 3 m
Hub height	90 m
Cut-in, rated, cutout wind speed	3 m s^{-1}, 11.4 m s^{-1}, 25 m s^{-1}
Rotor mass	110 000 kg
Nacelle mass	240 000 kg
Tower mass	347 460 kg

Table 5 Tension leg spar (TLS) FWT properties

Wind turbine	5 MW
No. of blades	Three bladed
Blade length	61.5 m
Hub height	90 m
Controller	Collective blade pitch
Rated wind speed	11.2 m s^{-1}
Draft	120 m
Diameter above taper	6.5 m
Diameter below taper	9.4 m
Center of buoyancy	−62 m
Displacement	8126 m^3
Total mass	7682×10^3 kg
Center of gravity (CG)	−80 m
Pitch/roll inertia about (CG)	2.18×10^{10} kg m^2
Yaw inertia about centerline	1.215×10^{8} kg m^2
Leg length	Up to 200 m
Leg diameter	1.0 m
Leg thickness	0.036 m
Pretension	7.624 MN

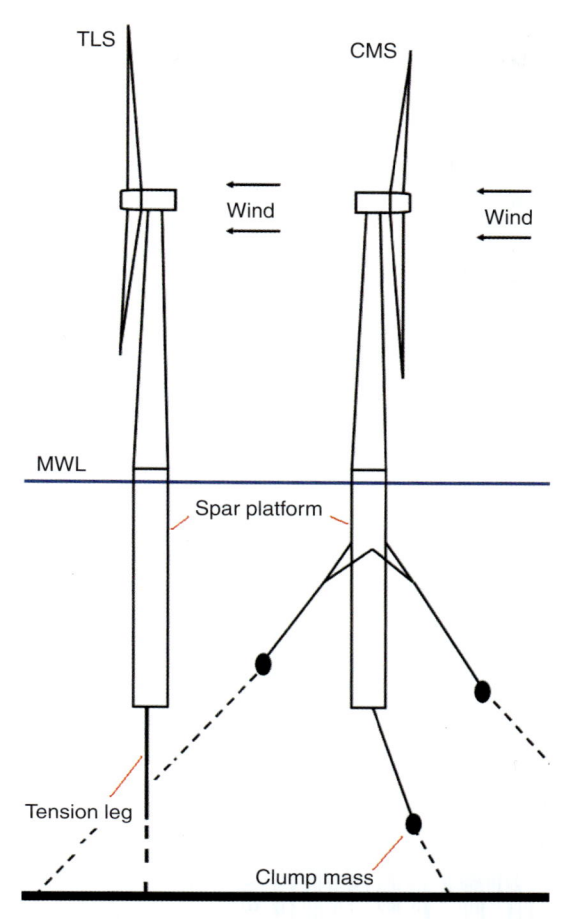

Figure 16 Schematic layout of a CMS offshore wind turbine and a TLS offshore wind turbine. The TLS wind turbine presented in the figure has a downwind rotor.

mass and four line segments (two segments make the delta for each). The purpose of the delta line configuration is to provide sufficient passive yaw stiffness.

TLS: The NREL 5 MW upwind wind turbine [4, 5] has been modified to make a downwind turbine and mounted on a 120 m draft spar platform. The characteristics of the NREL upwind turbine are mentioned in **Tables 1–3**. In a downwind turbine, the shaft tilt and hub cone angles are set to zero and the rotor is behind the tower. In the single leg TLS concept, a pretensioned leg connects the bottom of the spar to the seabed.

2.09.5.2.1 Aerodynamic and hydrodynamic damping

Figure 17 shows the effect of the hydrodynamic and aerodynamic damping forces on the dynamic nacelle surge motion of CMS wind turbine in below-rated operational conditions [19]. In the left part of **Figure 17**, the quadratic viscous hydrodynamic effects are compared for two different drag coefficients. As the structure is inertia-dominated, the increase of the drag coefficient does not affect the wave frequency responses. However, the resonant responses were decreased. In the right part of **Figure 17**, the wave-induced response and wind- and wave-induced response are compared to show the effect of the aerodynamic damping. The aerodynamic damping decreased the resonant responses. However, the wave frequency responses were not affected by the wind loads in this case. An operating rotor has a significant aerodynamic damping through power take-off which can be important for an FWT to reduce the responses and stabilize the system.

2.09.5.2.2 Effect of turbulence on the wave- and wind-induced responses

Figure 18 shows the nacelle surge time history (turbulent wind case) and nacelle surge spectrum (constant and turbulent wind cases) of CMS wind turbine under harsh environmental conditions [20]. All of the smoothed spectra in the present study were obtained based on time domain simulations by applying a Fourier transformation. The nacelle surge motion in a survival condition is dominated by the pitch resonant response. The comparisons between the turbulent and constant wind cases show that the turbulent wind excites the rigid body pitch and surge natural frequencies. The resonant response is dominant in both pitch motion and nacelle surge motion. Resonance should not be confused with instability. A resonant motion requires external excitation and grows linearly and not exponentially as in the case of instability.

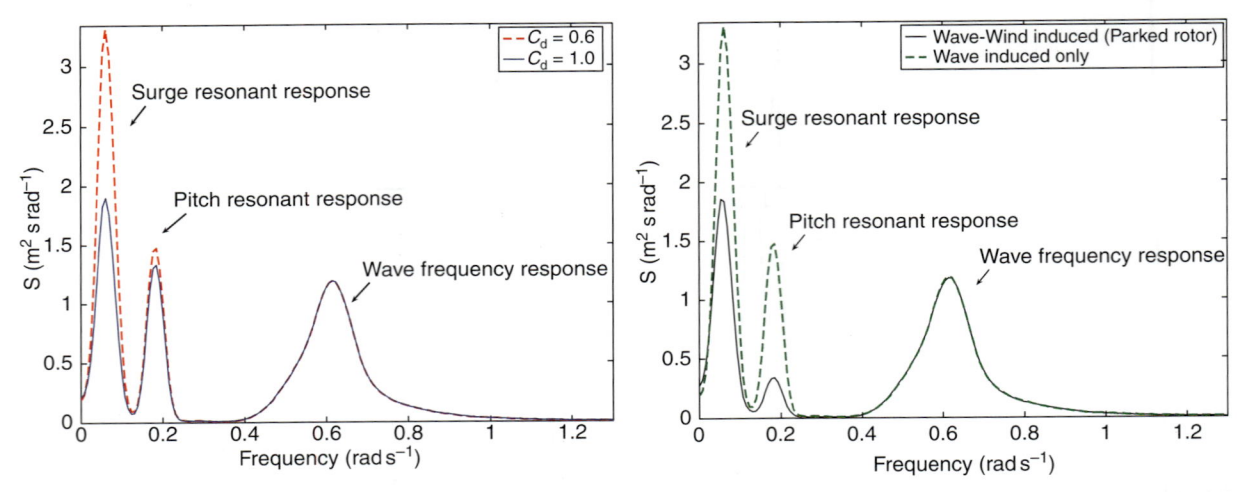

Figure 17 Left: nacelle surge motion spectrum of CMS wind turbine in a wave condition with $H_S = 3$ m and $T_P = 10$ s, based on a 1 h time domain simulation in HAWC2 (wave-induced). Right: nacelle surge motion spectrum of CMS wind turbine (H_S=3 m, T_P=10 s, and V=8 m s^{-1}), based on a 1 h time domain simulation in HAWC2 (constant wind). Reproduced with permission from Karimirad M and Moan T (2010) Effect of aerodynamic and hydrodynamic damping on dynamic response of a spar type floating wind turbine. *European Wind Energy Conference EWEC 2010*. Warsaw, Poland, 20–23 April.

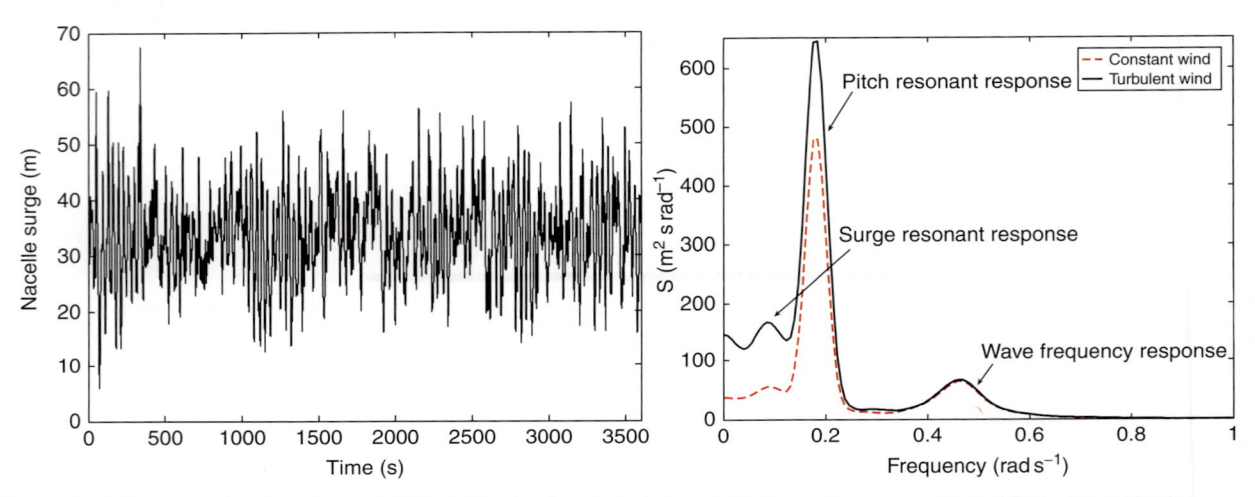

Figure 18 Left: nacelle surge time history of CMS wind turbine (turbulent wind case). Right: nacelle surge spectrum of CMS wind turbine for turbulent and constant wind cases. $H_S = 14.4$ m, $T_P = 13.3$ s, $V = 49$ m s^{-1}, and $I_t = 0.1$. Reproduced with permission from Karimirad M and Moan T (2011) Wave and wind induced dynamic response of catenary moored spar wind turbine. *Journal of Waterway, Port, Coastal, and Ocean Engineering*.

In **Figure 19** [20], the effect of wind and wave loads on the bending moments at the tower–spar interface of CMS wind turbine for different mean wind speeds is illustrated. The statistical characteristics are based on five 1 h samples. The maximum responses correspond to the up-crossing rate of 0.000 1 and are obtained by extrapolation. The up-crossing rate of a process at a defined level is the frequency of passing that level. The up-crossing rate of 0.000 1 for a process at a defined level means that the process (e.g., structural response) passes that level by a rate of 0.000 1 (Hz). For higher response levels, the up-crossing rate is lower. The maximum responses for an FWT can happen in storm condition. However, for an onshore wind turbine, the maximum responses are linked to the rated wind speed load cases. The responses of an FWT in survival conditions are mainly governed by wave loads.

2.09.5.2.3 Servo-induced negative damping

The blade pitch control of an operating turbine can introduce negative damping in an FWT. For example, if the relative wind speed experienced by the blades increases due to the rigid body motion of the system, then, if a conventional controller is used, the blades will feather to maintain the rated electrical power. Thus, the thrust force will decrease, which will introduce negative damping for overrated wind speed load cases. However, this is not the case in fixed wind turbines since the frequency of the blade pitch controller is normally less than the frequencies associated with the relative rotor motions induced by the structural responses.

Figure 20 [21] shows the comparison between the nacelle surge motion of TLS wind turbine with the untuned and tuned controller to avoid negative damping in the overrated constant wind condition ($V = 17$ m s^{-1}, $H_S = 4.2$ m, and $T_P = 10.5$) for a downwind TLS. This is an example to highlight the servo-induced loads. The tuned controller has much lower pitch resonant

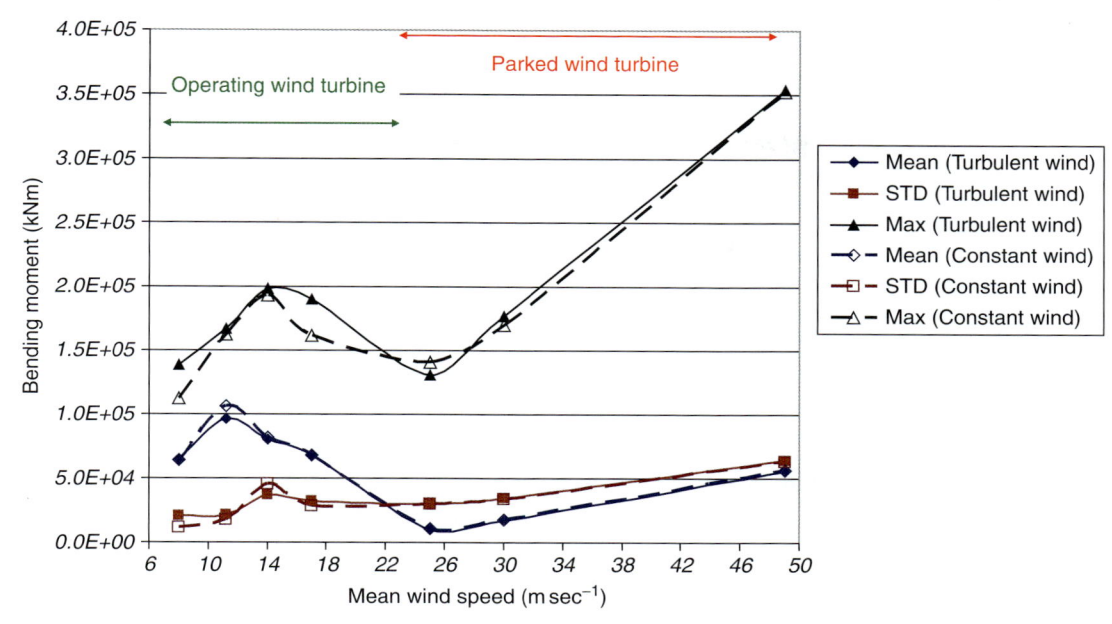

Figure 19 Bending moment at the tower–spar interface of CMS wind turbine (wave- and wind-induced) for constant and turbulent wind cases. The statistical characteristics are based on five 1 h samples. The maximum responses correspond to the up-crossing rate of 0.000 1 and are obtained by extrapolation. Reproduced with permission from Karimirad M and Moan T (2011) Wave and wind induced dynamic response of catenary moored spar wind turbine. *Journal of Waterway, Port, Coastal, and Ocean Engineering.*

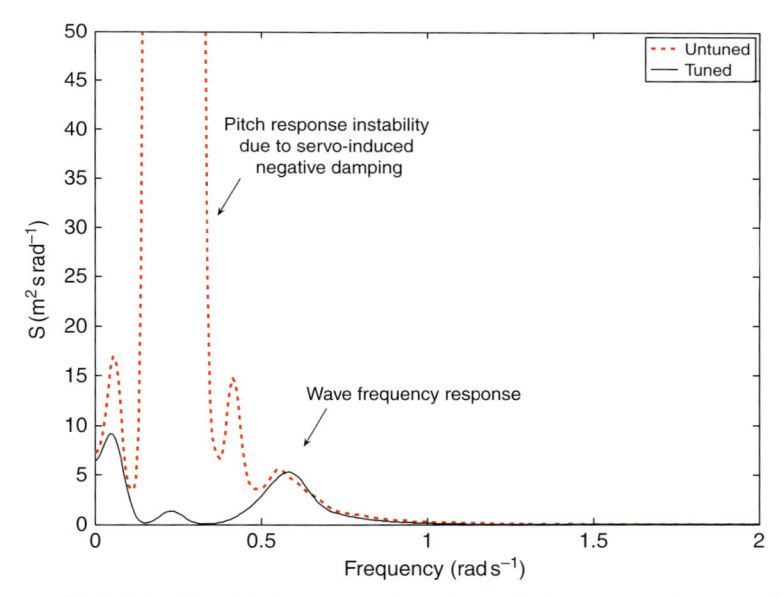

Figure 20 Nacelle surge spectra of TLS wind turbine, with the untuned and tuned controller in the overrated constant wind condition ($V = 17$ m s^{-1}, $H_S = 4.2$ m, and $T_P = 10.5$). The motion response instabilities due to servo-induced negative damping. Reproduced with permission from Karimirad M and Moan T (2011) Ameliorating the negative damping in the dynamic responses of a tension leg spar-type support structure with a downwind turbine. *European Wind Energy Conference EWEC 2011.* Brussels, Belgium, 14–17 March.

response. In the overrated wind speed range and due to the negative damping effect of the controller, the pitch resonant was dominant. After tuning the controller gains, the pitch resonant response is positively damped out.

2.09.5.2.4 Comparison of power production of TLS and CMS turbines

Figure 21 shows the power production of CMS and TLS FWTs. The properties of the two systems are defined in **Tables 4** and **5**. The electrical power produced by these FWTs is close. However, to compare the concepts it is necessary to consider other parameters such

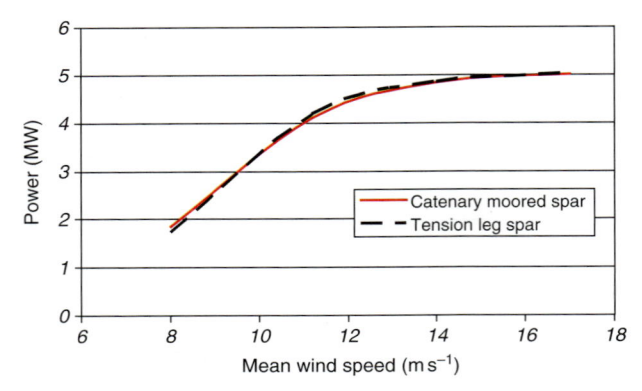

Figure 21 Comparison of power production of TLS and CMS offshore wind turbines.

as structural responses, fatigue life, and cost of produced electricity. The cost should include the design, construction, installation, maintenance, operation, and other practical issues.

2.09.6 Conclusions

The fast development of wind technology has introduced new challenges for researchers. This includes larger wind turbines with more elastic responses, floating and fixed offshore wind turbines with comprehensive dynamic loads, innovative concepts, and similar aspects. Advanced aero-hydro-servo-elastic numerical tools are needed to perform integrated analysis for today's wind turbines. This chapter made an introduction to mechanical-dynamic loads for both onshore and offshore wind turbines with a focus on the wave- and wind-induced loads to assess the structural integrity and power performance of FWTs. Several case studies were provided for both fixed and FWTs to support the presented discussion.

Appendix A: Environmental Conditions

To design, install, and operate wind turbines in a safe and efficient manner, it is necessary to have realistic metocean (meteorological and oceanographic) data available for the conditions to which the installation may be exposed.

A.1 General

The first step in performing rational structural dynamic analysis is setting realistic environmental conditions. The most important for a wind turbine are the wind and wave at the wind park site. However, at some offshore locations, other parameters may be important (e.g., air and sea temperature, tidal conditions, current, and ice conditions).

The wave and wind are random in nature. This randomness should be represented as accurately as possible to calculate reasonable hydro-aero-dynamic loading. Both the waves and the wind have long-term and short-term variability. The simulation time depends on the natural periods of the system. Wave-induced motions of common floating structures have been carried out considering a 3 h short-term analysis [22]. In wind engineering, the 10 min response analysis can cover all the physics governing a fixed wind turbine. When it comes to FWTs, the correlation between the wave and wind should be accounted for. For each environmental condition, the joint distribution of the significant wave height, wave peak period, wave direction, and mean water level (MWL, relevant for shallow water) combined with the mean wind speed, wind direction, and turbulence should be considered.

A.2 Joint Distribution of Wave Conditions and Mean Wind

The wave and wind show long-term and short-term variability. The long-term variability of the wind can be defined by the mean wind speed and direction. The short-term variability of the wind is usually defined by the turbulence. In an offshore site, the ocean waves can be wind-generated and swell. The waves are usually defined by the peak period and significant wave height. The correlation between the waves and wind should be considered for stochastic analysis of FWTs. Site assessments containing metocean data are needed to develop the joint distribution of the waves and wind for the analysis. The joint distribution can include the wave and wind characteristics, such as the mean wind speed, turbulence, direction of the waves and wind, significant wave height, and wave peak period. However, development of the joint distribution requires measurement of simultaneous wave and wind time histories at the offshore sites for several years. Currently, limited site assessments considering the correlated wave and wind time series are available. These data are missing the correlation between the turbulence and wave/mean wind characteristics. The offshore wind turbine is a new technology, and large metrological/oceanological studies for determining the proper joint distribution of wave and wind characteristics are needed.

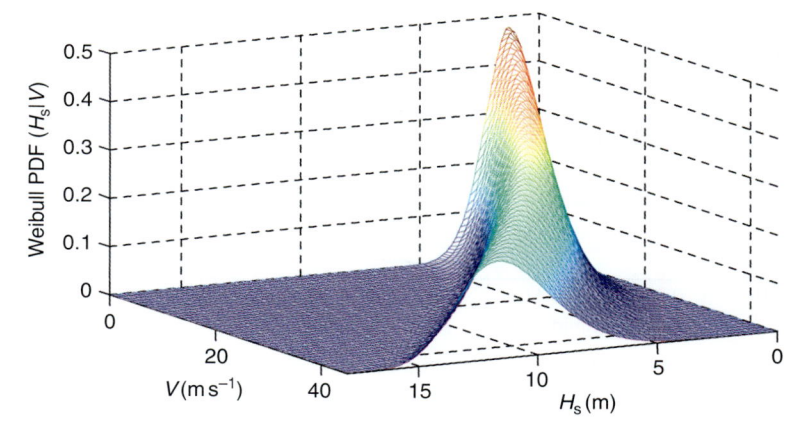

Figure 22 The Weibull probability density function of the significant wave height (H_S) given the mean wind speed at the nacelle (V) for the Statfjord offshore site at 59.7°N and 4.0°E and 70 km from the shore.

In this chapter, the wind and wave were assumed to have the same direction. The correlation between the mean wind speed, significant wave height, and wave peak period was considered, which can be done by fitting the analytical functions to the site assessments by considering a mathematical distribution for the mean wind speed and significant wave height. It is possible to model the significant wave height as a Weibull distribution whose parameters were functions of the mean wind speed [23].

Figure 22 illustrates the Weibull probability density function of the significant wave height (H_S) given the mean wind speed at the nacelle (V) for the representative offshore wind park, Statfjord offshore site at 59.7°N and 4.0°E and 70 km distance from the shore.

The significant wave height increased with the increase of the wind speed. For higher wind speeds, the Weibull distribution was negatively skewed. For each wind speed, a range of significant wave heights was possible. Smaller wind speeds had a narrower range of significant wave heights. The IEC 61400-3 standard recommends the use of the median significant wave height at each wind speed for dynamic response analysis of offshore wind turbines.

Appendix B: Wind Theory

The wind varies over space and time. It is important to know these variations to investigate the site energy resources for making electrical power, which is the first concern for a specific location. The spatial and temporal variations of the wind are defined as [24]:
Spatial variations:

- Trade winds emerging from subtropical, anticyclonic cells in both hemispheres
- Monsoons, which are seasonal winds generated by the difference in temperature between land and sea
- Westerlies and subpolar flows
- Synoptic-scale motions, which are associated with periodic systems such as travelling waves
- Mesoscale wind systems, which are caused by differential heating of topological features and called breezes.

Time variations:

- Long-term variability, which are annual variations of wind in a special site
- Seasonal and monthly variability
- Diurnal and semidiurnal variation
- Turbulence (range from seconds to minutes).

The temporal variations are usually represented by the energy spectrum of the wind. In **Figure 23**, the Van der Hoven wind speed spectrum [25] is shown. The yearly wind speed changes, pressure systems, and diurnal changes are influencing the left side of the wind speed spectrum. However, the turbulence shows itself in the right side of the spectrum.

The wind is characterized by its speed and direction. The wind energy is concentrated around two separated time periods (diurnal and 1 min periods), which allows the splitting of the wind speed into two terms: the quasi-steady wind speed (usually called the mean wind speed) and the dynamic part (the turbulent wind). In other words, the time-varying wind speed is considered to be made up of a steady value plus the fluctuations about this steady value. The steady value is assumed to be quasi-static; thus, its time dependency is negligible for the current purpose (the probabilistic dynamic response analysis). The long-term probability distribution of the mean wind speed is predicted by fitting site measurements to the Weibull distribution (eqn [16]). The Weibull probability density function (f_W) shows that the moderate winds are more frequent than the high-speed winds.

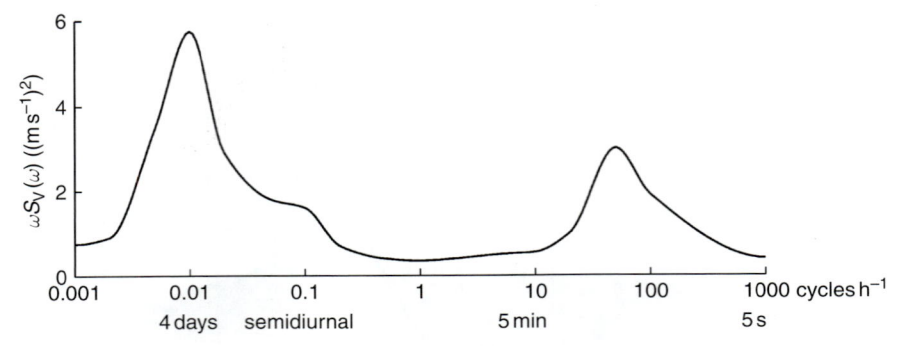

Figure 23 Van der Hoven wind speed spectrum. Reproduced with permission from Bianchi DF, Battista HD, and Mantz RJ (2007) *Wind Turbine Control Systems*. Germany: Springer.

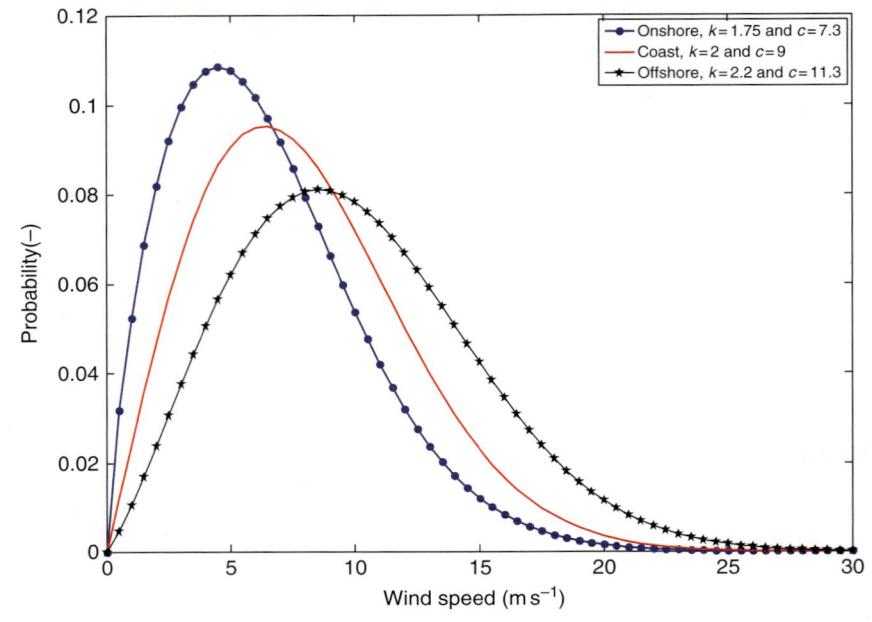

Figure 24 Weibull probability distribution of wind velocity for three different sites: onshore, coastal, and offshore considering typical values of shape and scale parameters. Reproduced with permission from Twidell J and Gaudiosi G (2008) *Offshore Wind Power*. Essex, UK: Multi-Science Publishing Co Ltd.

$$f\mathrm{W}(V) = \frac{k_\mathrm{w}}{c_\mathrm{w}} \left(\frac{V}{c_\mathrm{w}}\right)^{k_\mathrm{w}-1} \exp\left(-\left(\frac{V}{c_\mathrm{w}}\right)^{k_\mathrm{w}}\right) \qquad [16]$$

where V is the wind speed, k_w is the shape parameter describing the variability about the mean, and c_w is a scale parameter related to the annual mean wind speed. In **Figure 24**, the Weibull probability distribution for three different areas, that is, onshore, coastal, and offshore, with typical values of shape and scale parameters is plotted [7].

An empirical formula for the annual mean wind speed (V_Annual) is given in eqn [17] by Lysen [26].

$$V_\mathrm{Annual} = c_\mathrm{w}(0.568 + 0.433/k_\mathrm{w})^{1/k_\mathrm{w}} \qquad [17]$$

The annual mean wind velocities corresponding to different sites in **Figure 24** are 6.5, 8, and 11.3 m s^{-1} for the onshore, coastal, and offshore sites, respectively. Considering the ratio between the offshore and onshore power corresponding to the present example can be up to 5, which confirms the possibility of generating more electrical power by moving offshore.

The mean wind speed is a function of height, which can be represented by different shear models such as the Prandtl logarithmic and power laws. In these mathematical models, a parameter called the roughness length or exponent accounts for the effect of the type of surface over which the wind blows [12].

The turbulence in the wind is caused by the dissipation of the wind kinetic energy into thermal energy via the creation and destruction of progressively smaller eddies or gusts. Turbulent wind may have a relatively constant mean over time periods of an hour or more, but over shorter times (minutes or less) it may be quite variable. Turbulent wind consists of longitudinal, lateral, and vertical components [13].

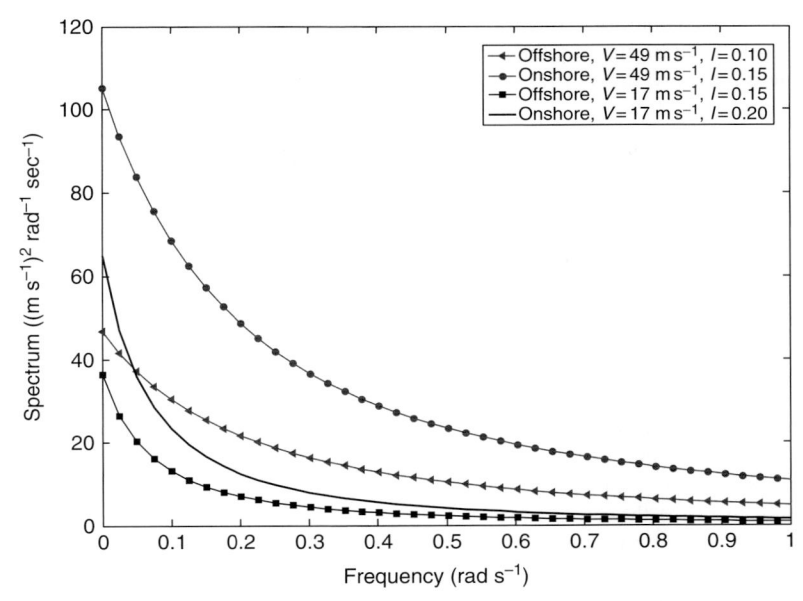

Figure 25 Kaimal spectra for onshore and offshore sites under operational and extreme environmental conditions, with the corresponding mean wind velocities and turbulence intensities for those conditions.

The dynamic part of the wind speed, turbulence, includes all wind speed fluctuations with periods below the spectral gap. The spectral gap occurs around 1 h, which separates the slowly changing and turbulent ranges. Therefore, all components in the range from seconds to minutes are included in the turbulence. The captured annual power is not affected by turbulence very much, but the turbulence has a major impact on aero-elastic structural response and electrical power quality. It is common to describe the wind turbulence in a given point in space using the power spectrum. The Kaimal and von Karman spectra are widely used. Both models depend on the mean wind speed and the topography of the terrain. One useful parameter is the turbulence intensity, which is defined as the ratio of the standard deviation of the wind speed to the mean wind speed. The turbulence intensity decreases with height. The turbulence intensity is higher when there are obstacles in the terrain; hence, the turbulence intensity for an offshore site is less than that for a land site.

The turbulent wind spectrum, such as the Kaimal spectrum (eqn [18]), is a function of the frequency, turbulence intensity, and mean wind speed [27].

$$S(f) = \frac{I_t^2 V_{10\,\text{min}} l}{\left(1+1.5\dfrac{f\,l}{V_{10\,\text{min}}}\right)^{5/3}} \qquad [18]$$

where $I_t = \sigma/V_{10\,\text{min}}$ is the turbulent intensity, f is the frequency in hertz, $V_{10\,\text{min}}$ is the 10 min averaged wind speed, and l is a length scale. $l = 20\,h_{\text{agl}}$ for $h_{\text{agl}} < 30$ m or $l = 600$ m otherwise where h_{agl} is the height above ground level.

In **Figure 25**, the Kaimal spectra for onshore and offshore sites are plotted. The harsh and operational environmental conditions with their mean wind speed and turbulence intensity were considered. The spectrum under harsh conditions has much more energy compared to those under operational conditions, especially in the low frequency region. At the offshore site, the wind is steadier, and the turbulence is decreased, but at onshore sites, the obstacles in the terrain influence the boundary layer and make the wind more turbulent.

Appendix C: Wave Theory

In this section the regular wave theory, modified regular wave theory, and irregular wave theory are described.

C.1 Regular Wave Theory

In the regular wave theory, the wave is assumed to be sinusoidal with constant wave amplitude, wavelength, and wave period. Thus, the regular propagating wave is defined as $\zeta = \zeta_a \sin(\omega t - kx)$. ζ is the time- and position-dependent wave elevation. The linear wave theory, usually called the Airy theory, can be used to represent the wave kinematics. In the Airy theory, the seawater is assumed to be incompressible and inviscid. The fluid motion is irrotational. Then, a velocity potential exists and satisfies the Laplace equations. By applying the kinematic boundary conditions and the dynamic free-surface conditions, the velocity potential, and the wave kinematics can be found [16]. Based on the Airy theory, the horizontal water particle kinematics are described by eqns [19] and [20]. The dynamic pressure is presented in eqn [21].

$$u = \omega \zeta_a \frac{\cosh k(z+h)}{\sinh kh} \sin(\omega t - kx) \quad [19]$$

$$a_X = \omega^2 \zeta_a \frac{\cosh k(z+h)}{\sinh kh} \cos(\omega t - kx) \quad [20]$$

where u and a_X are the water particle velocity and acceleration in the x-direction (wave propagation direction), respectively, ω is the wave frequency, ζ_a is the regular wave amplitude, k is the wave number, the z axis is upward, and h is the mean water depth.

$$P_D = \rho_w g \zeta_a \frac{\cosh k(z+h)}{\cosh kh} \sin(\omega t - kx) \quad [21]$$

In deepwater, the water particles move in circles in accordance with the harmonic wave. In deepwater, the depth is greater than half of the wavelength ($h \geq \lambda/2$). Thus, the effect of the seabed cannot disturb the waves. For shallow water, the effect of the seabed transforms the circular motion into an elliptic motion.

When the wave amplitude increases, the wave particle no longer forms closed orbital paths. In fact, after the passage of each crest, particles are displaced from their previous positions. This phenomenon is known as the Stokes drift. The Boussinesq equations that combine frequency dispersion and nonlinear effects are applicable for intermediate and shallow water. However, in very shallow water, the shallow water equations may be used.

Linear wave theory represents the first-order approximation in satisfying the free-surface conditions. It can be improved by introducing higher-order terms in a consistent manner via the Stokes expansion [16]. In this chapter, the linear wave theory was applied.

The wave theory discussed here is just applicable for nonbreaking waves. The wave breaks when $H/h \geq 0.78$ in shallow water and when $H/\lambda \geq 0.14$ in deepwater [8]. H is the wave height and the h is the mean water depth. For extreme waves, when the height increases greatly, the nonlinear features of the wave kinematics cannot be captured through linear wave theory. However, the nonlinear methods are mainly applicable for deterministic waves; they are not suitable for stochastic wave fields. Fortunately, the probability of breaking waves is relatively small. Moreover, most of the waves break close to the coast and not at the offshore wind turbine site.

C.2 Modified Linear Wave Theory

The Airy wave theory is only valid up to the MWL surface and does not describe the kinematics above that level. Different mathematical models, such as constant stretching and Wheeler stretching, have been suggested to describe the wave kinematics above the MWL surface. In the constant stretching model, it is assumed that the wave kinematics are constant above the MWL. In the Wheeler stretching model, the vertical coordinate z is substituted by the scaled coordinate z' (eqn [22]). In this chapter, the Wheeler stretching model was used.

$$z' = (z - \zeta)\frac{h}{h + \zeta} \quad [22]$$

where ζ is the wave elevation and $\zeta = \zeta_a \sin(\omega t - kx)$. In the following section, the stretching in the stochastic context is explained.

C.3 Irregular Wave Theory

Wind-generated waves are forced waves that are sustained by receiving energy from the wind. Swell waves are free waves that do not receive wind energy due to the absence of wind or movement to a new free-wind location. The practical way to model ocean waves in ocean engineering assumes that the sea surface forms a stochastic wave field that can be assumed to be stationary in a short-term period. The stationary assumption of the wave is site-dependent [22]. For most practical offshore engineering purposes, this assumption works very well and gives good agreement with full-scale measurements. The wave field is assumed to be Gaussian, which gives a reasonably good approximation of reality in most cases. The stochastic model approved for the waves leads to a normally distributed water surface elevation. The wave crests follow the Rayleigh distribution if the wave elevation is assumed to be Gaussian and narrow-banded. However, some phenomena, such as slamming, can violate the Gaussian assumption.

Based on the Gaussian assumption, the stationary sea (represented by the wave elevation at a point in space) can be modeled by a wave spectrum. The Pierson–Moskowitz (PM) and Joint North Sea Wave Project (JONSWAP) spectra (eqns [23] and [24]) are examples of mathematical models to represent the ocean wave spectrum. For a fully developed wind sea, the PM spectrum can be used, and for a growing wind sea, the JONSWAP [28] spectrum can be used. Moreover, the Torsethaugen spectrum (two-peaked wave spectrum) is introduced to define a sea comprising wind-generated waves and swells.

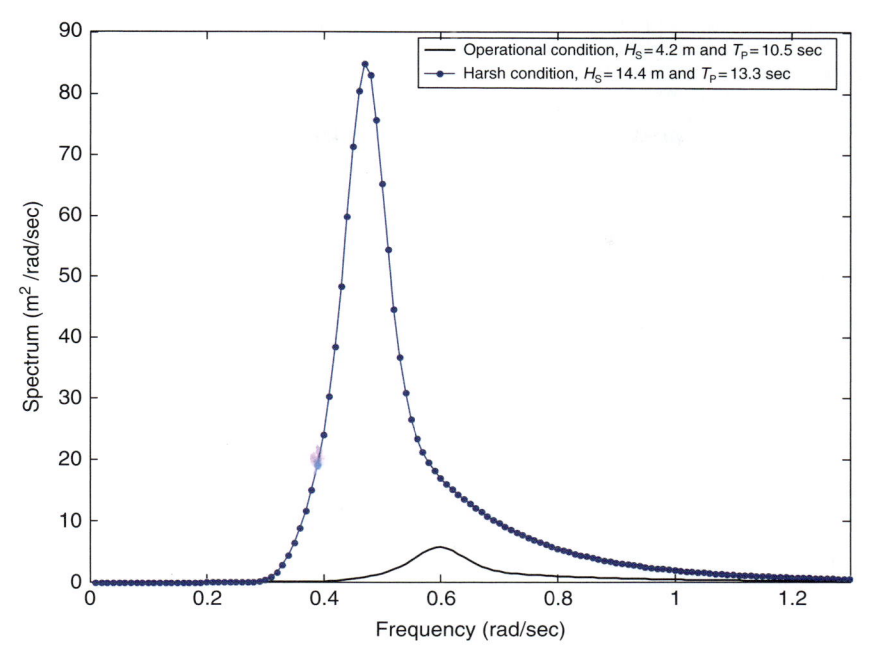

Figure 26 The JONSWAP wave spectrum for harsh and operational conditions.

$$S_{PM}(f) = \frac{5}{16} \frac{H_S^2}{T_P^4 f^5} \exp-\left(\frac{5}{4}(f\,T_P)^{-4}\right) \quad [23]$$

where H_S is the significant wave height, T_P is the wave peak period, and f is the frequency in hertz.

$$S_{JS}(f) = F_n\,S_{PM}(f)\,\gamma_{JS}\,\exp\left(\frac{-(f-f_P)^2}{2\,\sigma_{JS}^2\,f_P^2}\right) \quad [24]$$

$$\sigma_{JS} = \begin{cases} \sigma_a & \text{for}\,f \le f_P \;\;(\text{typically}:0.07) \\ \sigma_b & \text{for}\,f > f_P \;\;(\text{typically}:0.09) \end{cases} \quad [25]$$

$$F_n = \left[5\left(0.065\,\gamma_{JS}^{0.803} + 0.135\right)\right]^{-1} \quad \text{for}\; 1 \le \gamma_{JS} \le 10 \quad [26]$$

where γ_{JS} is the wave spectrum shape parameter, which is around 3.3 for seas that are not fully developed. For fully developed seas, γ_{JS} is taken to be 1. Therefore, the JONSWAP and PM spectra are the same for $\gamma_{JS}=1$. $f_P = 1/T_P$ is the wave peak frequency in hertz.

In **Figure 26**, the JONSWAP wave spectrum for operational and harsh environmental conditions is illustrated. The extreme sea state has much larger peaks, and it also covers a wider range of frequencies. The peak frequency of a harsh sea state is shifted to lower frequencies as well. This shift means that the probability of resonant motion occurrence is higher in extreme environmental conditions.

For a suitable wave spectrum representing the offshore site, the calculations may begin by converting the spectrum back into individual sinusoids using inverse fast Fourier transformation. Each sinusoid has a frequency and amplitude that can be derived from the energy density given by the wave spectrum. The phase angle is assigned randomly to each sinusoid.

In the stochastic context, the Wheeler stretching can be applied as well. For each regular wave, the stretching is applied, and the wave kinematics over the MWL is obtained. Then, the wave elevation, the velocities, and acceleration of regular waves are added together to obtain the irregular wave elevation, velocity, and acceleration for that particular time.

References

[1] Sclavounos PD, Lee S, DiPietro J, *et al.* (2010) Floating offshore wind turbines: Tension leg platform and taught leg buoy concept supporting 3–5 MW wind turbines. *European Wind Energy Conference (EWEC)*. Warsaw, Poland, 20–23 April.
[2] Henderson AR, Leutz R, and Fujii T (2002) Potential for floating offshore wind energy in Japanese waters. *ISOPE Conference*. ISBN 1-880653-58-3, Kitakyushu, Japan, 26–31 May.
[3] IEA (2008) *Renewable Energy Essentials: Wind*. http://www.iea.org/. (Accessed June 2010).
[4] Jonkman J (2009) Dynamics of offshore floating wind turbines-model development and verification. *Wind Energy* 12(5): 459–492.
[5] Jonkman J (2007) Dynamics modeling and loads analysis of an offshore floating wind turbine. *NREL, Technical Report, NREL/TP-500-41958*. Golden, CO: NREL.

[6] Tempel JVD (2006) Design of Support Structures for Offshore Wind Turbines. Doctoral Dissertation, Delft University of Technology.
[7] Twidell J and Gaudiosi G (2008) *Offshore Wind Power*. Essex, UK: Multi-Science Publishing Co Ltd.
[8] DNV (2007) Design of offshore wind turbine structures. DNV-OS-J101. Oslo, Norway: Det Norske Veritas.
[9] Roddier D, Cermelli C, and Weinstein A (2009) WINDFLOAT: A floating foundation for offshore wind turbine, Part I: Design basis and qualification process. Paper No. OMAE2009-79229. *Proceedings of the 28th International Conference on Offshore Mechanics and Arctic Engineering*. Hawaii, USA, May 31–June 5.
[10] IEC (2009), *International Standard 61400-3, Wind Turbines, Part 3: Design Requirements for Offshore Wind Turbines*. Geneva, Switzerland: IEC.
[11] Hansen MOL, Sorensen JN, Voutsinas S, *et al.* (2006) State of the art in wind turbine aerodynamics and aeroelasticity. *Progress in Aerospace Sciences Journal* 42: 285–330.
[12] Bianchi DF, Battista HD, and Mantz RJ (2007) *Wind Turbine Control Systems*. Germany: Springer.
[13] Manwell JF, McGowan JG, and Rogers AL (2006) *Wind Energy Explained, Theory, Design and Application*. Chichester, UK: John Wiley and Sons Ltd.
[14] Burton T, Sharpe D, Jenkins N, and Bossanyi E (2008) *Wind Energy Handbook*. Chichester, UK: John Wiley and Sons Ltd.
[15] Agarwal P and Manuel L (2009) Modeling nonlinear irregular waves in reliability studies for offshore wind turbines. Paper No. OMAE2009-80149. *Proceedings of the 28th International Conference on Offshore Mechanics and Arctic Engineering*. Hawaii, USA, May 31–June 5.
[16] Faltinsen OM (1995) *Sea Loads on Ships and Offshore Structures*. Cambridge, UK: Cambridge University Press.
[17] Henderson AR (2003) *Hydrodynamic Loading on Offshore Wind Turbines*. OWTES Task 4.2, The Netherlands: TUDelft.
[18] Det Norske Veritas/Risø National Laboratory (2002) *Guidelines for Design of Wind Turbines*, 2nd edn., Denmark: Jydsk Centraltrykkeri.
[19] Karimirad M and Moan T (2010) Effect of aerodynamic and hydrodynamic damping on dynamic response of a spar type floating wind turbine. *European Wind Energy Conference EWEC 2010*. Warsaw, Poland, 20–23 April.
[20] Karimirad M and Moan T (2011) Wave and wind induced dynamic response of catenary moored spar wind turbine. *Journal of Waterway, Port, Coastal, and Ocean Engineering*. doi: 10.1061/(ASCE)WWW.1943-5460.0000087. http://ascelibrary.org/wwo/resource/3/jwpexx/55.
[21] Karimirad M and Moan T (2011) Ameliorating the negative damping in the dynamic responses of a tension leg spar-type support structure with a downwind turbine. *European Wind Energy Conference EWEC 2011*. Brussels, Belgium, 14–17 March.
[22] Naess A and Moan T (2005) Probabilistic design of offshore structures. In: Chakrabarti S (ed.) *Handbook of Offshore Engineering*, ch. 5, pp. 197–277. Oxford, UK: Elsevier Ltd.
[23] Johannessen K, Meling TS, and Haver S (2001) Joint distribution for wind and waves in the Northern North Sea. Paper No. 2001-SH-06. *ISOPE Conference*, Stavanger, Norway, June 17–22.
[24] Spera DA (1998) *Wind Turbine Technology Fundamental Concepts of Wind Turbine Engineering*. New York, NY: ASME Press.
[25] Hoven VD (1957) Power spectrum of horizontal wind speed in the frequency range of 0.0007 to 900 cycles per hour. *Journal of Metrology* 14(2): 160–164.
[26] Lysen EH (1983) *Introduction to Wind Energy*. The Netherlands: SWD Publications, SWD 82-1.
[27] Hansen MOL (2008) *Aerodynamics of Wind Turbines*. 2nd edn., London, UK: Earthscan.
[28] Sagli G (2000) Model Uncertainty and Simplified Estimates of Long Term Extremes of Hull Girder Loads in Ships. Doctoral Dissertation, NTNU.

2.10 Electrical Parts of Wind Turbines

GS Stavrakakis, Technical University of Crete, Chania, Greece

© 2012 Elsevier Ltd. All rights reserved.

2.10.1	Introduction	270
2.10.2	Power Control	272
2.10.2.1	Pitch Control	273
2.10.2.1.1	Theory and implementation	273
2.10.2.1.2	Active stall-controlled wind turbines	276
2.10.2.2	Yaw System	277
2.10.3	Electricity Production	279
2.10.3.1	The Generator	279
2.10.3.2	Wind Turbine Generators	281
2.10.3.2.1	Asynchronous (induction) generators	281
2.10.3.2.2	Synchronous generators	285
2.10.3.3	Power Electronics	294
2.10.3.3.1	Harmonics	295
2.10.3.3.2	Ride through	295
2.10.3.3.3	Fixed-speed systems	295
2.10.3.3.4	Variable-speed systems	297
2.10.4	Lightning Protection	298
2.10.5	Small Wind Turbines	301
2.10.6	Outlook	303
2.10.7	Wind Turbine Industry	306
2.10.7.1	Major Wind Turbine Manufacturers	306
2.10.7.1.1	Vestas	306
2.10.7.1.2	Enercon	309
2.10.7.1.3	Gamesa	310
2.10.7.1.4	GE Energy	313
2.10.7.1.5	Siemens	314
2.10.7.1.6	Suzlon	314
2.10.7.1.7	Nordex	317
2.10.7.1.8	Acciona	317
2.10.7.1.9	REpower	319
2.10.7.1.10	Goldwind	322
2.10.7.1.11	WinWind	322
2.10.7.1.12	Windflow	322
2.10.7.1.13	Clipper	322
2.10.7.1.14	Fuhrländer	323
2.10.7.1.15	Alstom	323
2.10.7.1.16	AVANTIS	324
2.10.7.1.17	Sinovel	324
2.10.7.2	Subproviders	324
2.10.7.2.1	ABB	324
2.10.7.2.2	Weier	324
2.10.7.2.3	VEM	324
2.10.7.2.4	Phoenix Contact	325
2.10.7.2.5	Ingeteam	325
2.10.7.2.6	Maxwell	327
References		328
Further Reading		328
Relevant Websites		328

Glossary

Blade The part of a wind generator rotor that catches the wind.
Horizontal Axis Wind Turbine (HAWT) A 'normal' wind turbine design, in which the shaft is parallel to the ground, and the blades are perpendicular to the ground.
Hub The center of a wind generator rotor, which holds the blades in place and attaches to the shaft.
Induction motor An AC motor in which the rotating armature has no electrical connections to it (i.e. no slip rings), and consists of alternating plates of aluminum and steel.
Nacelle The protective covering over a generator or motor.
Permanent magnet A material that retains its magnetic properties after an external magnetic field is removed.
Pulse Width Modulation (PWM) A regulation method based on Duty Cycle. At full power, a pulse-width-modulated circuit provides electricity 100 percent of the time. At half power, the PWM is on half the time and off half the time. The speed of this alternation is generally very fast. Used in both solar wind regulators to efficiently provide regulation
Rotor (1) The blade and hub assembly of a wind generator. (2) The disc part of a vehicle disc brake. (3) The armature of a permanent magnet alternator, which spins and contains permanent magnets.
Slip ring Devices used to transfer electricity to or from rotating parts. Used in wound-field alternators, motors, and in some wind generator yaw assemblies.
Tip Speed Ratio (TSR) The ratio of how much faster than the wind speed, the blade tips are moving.
Transformer Multiple individual coils of wire wound on a laminate core. Transfers power from one circuit to another using magnetic induction. Usually used to step voltage up or down. Works only with AC current.
Yaw Rotation parallel to the ground. A wind generator yaws to face winds coming from different directions.
Wind generator A device that captures the force of the wind to provide rotational motion to produce power with an alternator or generator.

Nomenclature

$A(\gamma(t))$ turbine rotor swept area (time-varying due to yaw error)
B magnetic flux
C_P power coefficient
E electric field intensity
E electromotive force
f_e electrical frequency
N number of core windings
n_s rotor synchronous speed
P, P_m mechanical power
p number of generator pole pairs
R turbine rotor radius
S slip
$v(t)$ hub-height uniform wind speed across the rotor disk
$\gamma(t)$ rotor yaw angle
η flux linkage
$\theta(t)$ blade i pitch angle
λ tip speed ratio
ρ air density
$\omega(t)$ rotor angular velocity (mechanical)

2.10.1 Introduction

The quest of man for harnessing wind energy goes back into the centuries. Windmills have been used for many purposes but it is only lately that the wind power has been effectively exploited to produce electricity (**Figure 1**). Specifically, during the past 20 years, the wind power industry has evolved into the most important renewable energy sector.

A wind turbine is a complex machine. In order to design efficient and optimally operating wind turbines, knowledge from diverse scientific fields is required: aerodynamics, mechanical engineering, electrical and electronic engineering, materials and industrial engineering, civil engineering, meteorology, and automatic control among others.

A typical grid-connected wind turbine installation is shown in **Figure 2**. Though wind turbines can be operated in isolation, this configuration is of diminishing concern. Large offshore wind parks, comprising 10 MW wind turbines, seem to be the renewable future.

As seen in **Figure 2**, a typical wind turbine is erected on solid, concrete foundation and properly earthed. Its output of 690 V is connected through a transformer station to the 20 kV grid line. The wind turbine itself consists of the main tower, its three blades, and the nacelle. Inside the nacelle and the tower base are housed the various electrical and electronic parts necessary for the efficient and safe conversion of wind power to electrical energy. These include the power controls (pitch and yaw), the generator, and the power electronics. This is a typical example that is not always followed. The transformer station, for example, may be housed in the tower base.

The 'electrical system' of a wind turbine comprises all components for converting mechanical energy into electric power, as well as auxiliary electrical equipment and the control and supervisory system. The electrical system thus constitutes the second essential subsystem, following the mechanical one, in a wind turbine (**Figure 3**).

Electrical Parts of Wind Turbines 271

Figure 1 Seventeenth-century flour mill rebuilt by Acciona at the Guerinda wind park, Navarre, Spain. From Acciona leaflet, www.acciona-energia.com/.

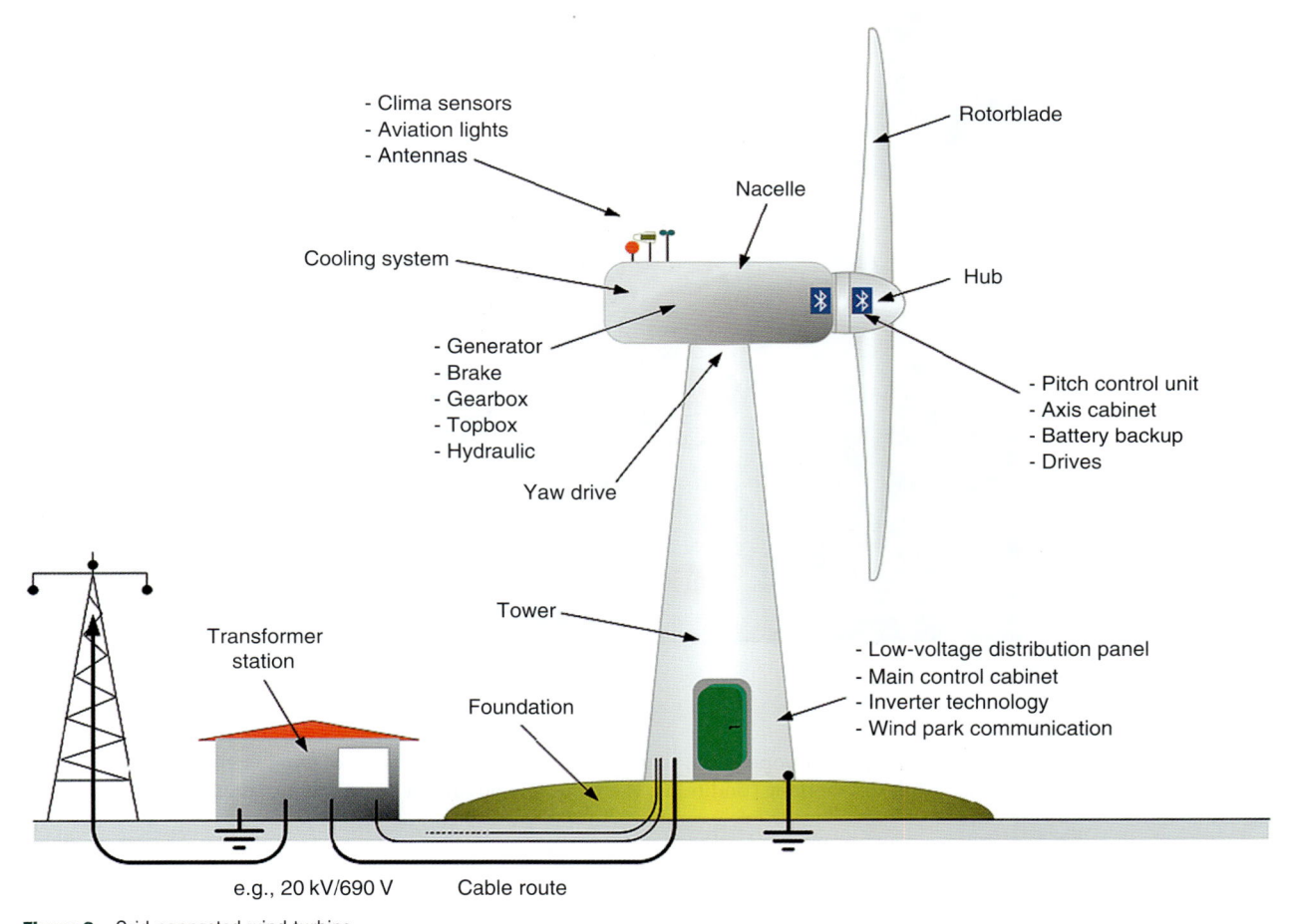

Figure 2 Grid-connected wind turbine.

The main components of the electrical subsystem are shown in **Figure 4**. They will be subsequently analyzed in functional order, that is, the power control/positioning components (pitch and yaw motors) first, followed by the generator, the power electronics and grid connection, and finally, the lightning protection elements.

From the electrical engineering point of view, wind turbines are nothing more than electricity-generating power plants, like hydroelectric ones or diesel-powered. Their electrical systems are similar and must meet the common standards for systems connected to utility grids. Therefore, similar safety, supervision, and power quality standards must be met.

Grid operation requirements are laid out by international and local institutions. On the global level, the International Electrotechnical Commission (IEC) has issued a set of general conditions that must be met by the wind farm operators.

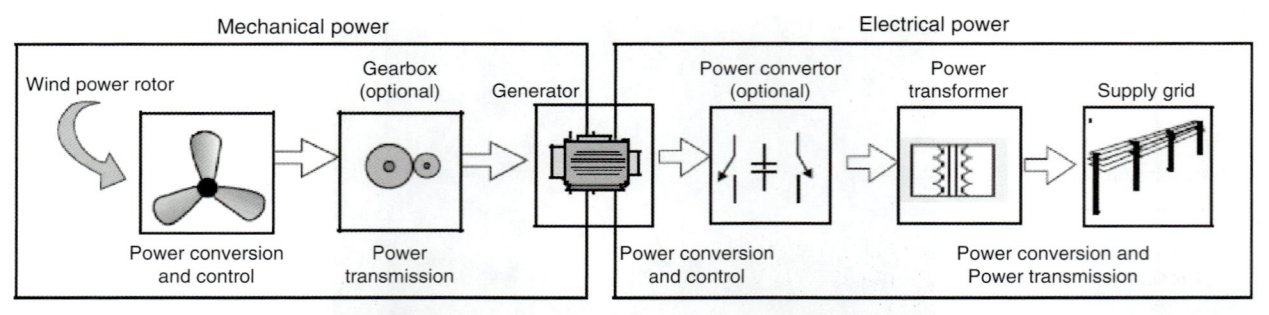

Figure 3 Subsystems of a wind turbine. From Blaabjerg F and and Chen Z (2006) *Power Electronics for Modern Wind Turbines*. San Rafael, CA: Morgan & Claypool.

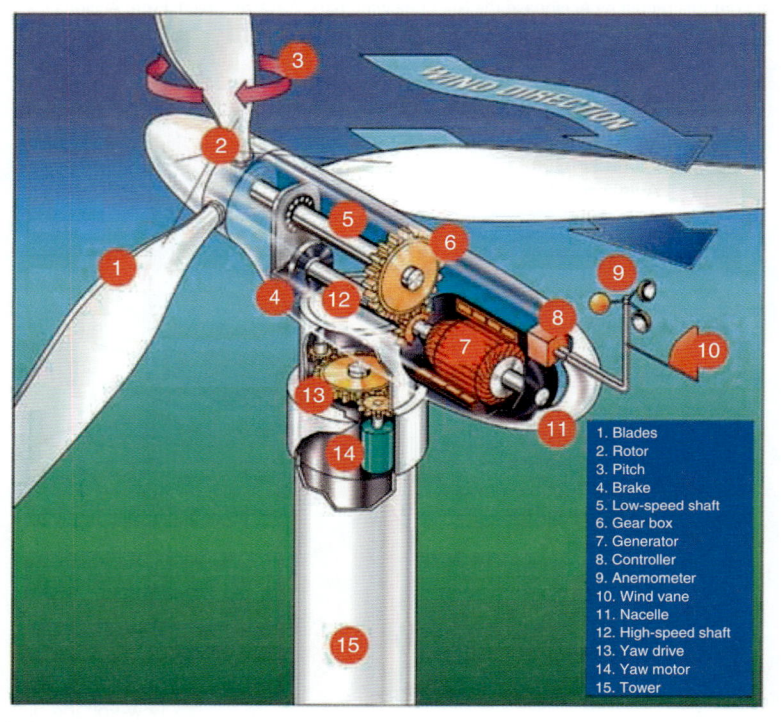

Figure 4 Wind turbine electrical parts.

1. Blades
2. Rotor
3. Pitch
4. Brake
5. Low-speed shaft
6. Gear box
7. Generator
8. Controller
9. Anemometer
10. Wind vane
11. Nacelle
12. High-speed shaft
13. Yaw drive
14. Yaw motor
15. Tower

Design of wind turbines is aimed at optimum operation, that is, at maximizing conversion of wind energy to electric power, while maintaining fault-free or fault-tolerant working conditions. Therefore, a wind turbine's performance must be judged on three factors:

1. Efficiency of wind power use (through the use of pitch and yaw control and generator selection)
2. Reliability (e.g., lightning protection)
3. Safety (grid connection regulations compliance).

Wind turbines have been rapidly evolved in the past years. Though a classification of various implementations may seem a little risky, nevertheless it may serve as a useful guide. In **Figure 5** is shown such a possible picture.

2.10.2 Power Control

Wind turbines are designed to produce electrical energy as cheaply as possible. Wind turbines are therefore generally manufactured so that they yield maximum output at wind speeds around $15\,\text{m}\,\text{s}^{-1}$ (30 knots or 33 mph). It does not pay to design turbines that maximize their output at stronger winds, because such strong winds are rare. In case of stronger winds, it is necessary to waste part of

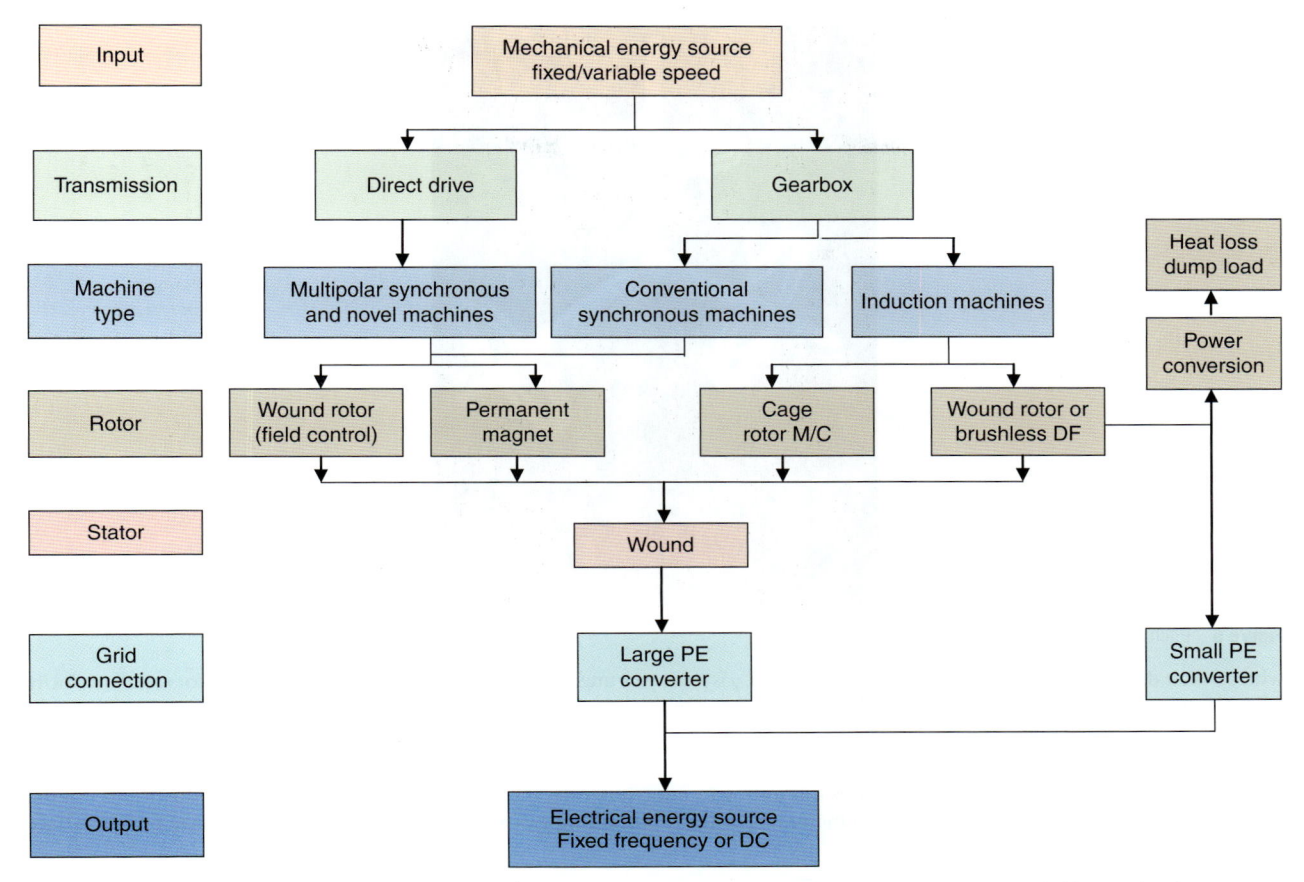

Figure 5 Wind turbine classifications. Modified from Wallace AK and Oliver JA (1998) Variable-speed generation controlled by passive elements. *International Conference on Electric Machines*. Istanbul, Turkey, 2–5 September [1].

the excess energy of the wind in order to avoid damaging the wind turbine, while in case of weaker speeds some sort of speed regulation is desirable. All wind turbines are therefore designed with some sort of power control.

There are different ways of doing this safely on modern wind turbines:

- Pitch control
- Stall control (passive or active)
- Yaw control.

2.10.2.1 Pitch Control

Pitch control refers to altering the pitch angle of the wind turbine's blades so that the rotor speed, and hence the rotor torque and generated electrical energy are kept at desired levels. This is one way to engineer a 'constant-speed' wind turbine, and can be implemented either by mechanical (hydraulic) or electrical (motor) mean. The latter is mostly employed at present, since, additionally, it is used to control each blade independently (**Figure 6**). Pitch control is also a safety mechanism since it can limit operating levels to the maximum of the given machine.

2.10.2.1.1 Theory and implementation

The ability of a wind turbine to extract power from wind is a function of three main factors:

1. Wind power availability
2. Power curve of the machine
3. Ability of the machine to respond to wind perturbations.

The equation for mechanical power, P_m, produced by a wind turbine is given by,

$$P_m = 0.5 \rho C_p \left(\frac{\omega R}{v}, \theta \right) A(\gamma) v^3 \quad [1]$$

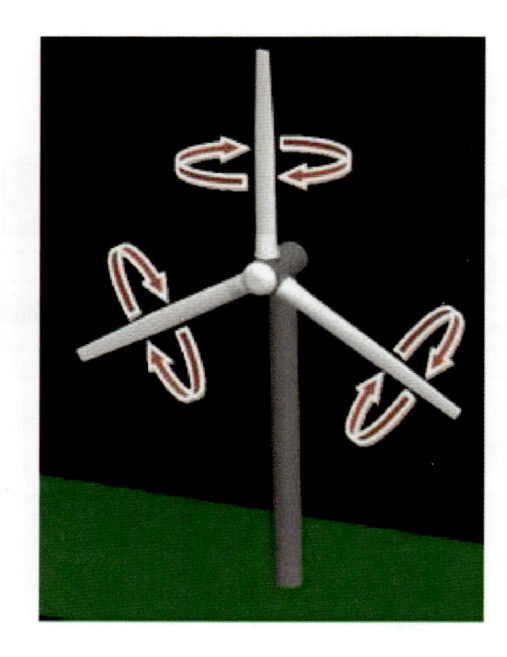

Figure 6 Pitch control.

where ρ is air density (kg m^{-3}), θ is blade pitch angle (rad), γ is rotor yaw angle (rad), v is wind velocity (m s^{-1}), ω is rotor angular velocity (rad s^{-1}), R is rotor diameter (m), $A(\gamma)$ is wind turbine rotor swept area (m^2), $C_p(\omega R/v, \theta)$ is power coefficient, and $\omega R/v = \lambda$ is tip speed ratio (TSR).

Looking at eqn [1], it is seen that in an actual turbine, power can be regulated through pitch angle, rotor speed, and yaw angle, and all other parameters being exogenous. It is interesting to note, however, that air density affecting power production is not the same in all wind sites since it decreases with increasing altitude. Excluding yaw variation, **Figure 7** shows a typical power surface

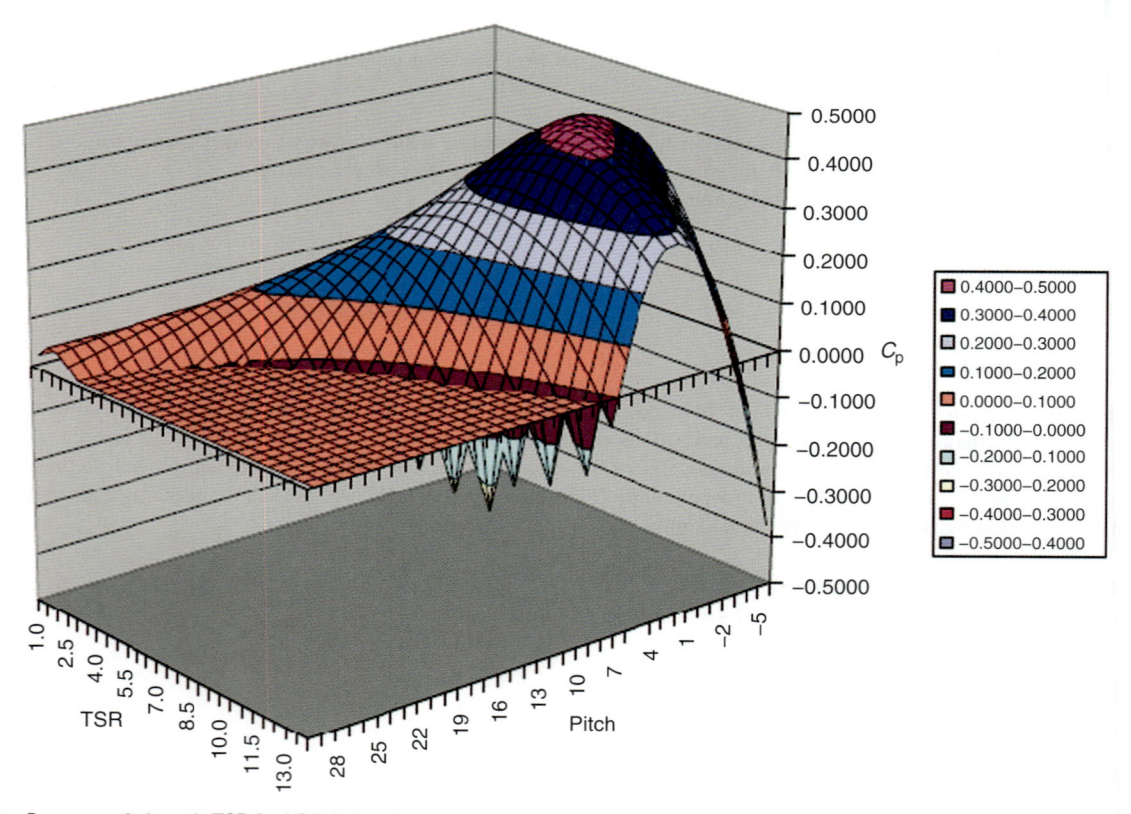

Figure 7 Power vs. pitch angle/TSR for NREL's CART machine. From Wright AD and Fingersh LJ (2008) Advanced control design for wind turbines part I: Control design, implementation, and initial tests. *Technical Report NREL/TP-500-42437*, March 2008: National Renewable Energy Laboratory, Golden, Colorado, USA.

plotted for various pitch angles and TSRs [2]. Such a surface is usually determined through simulation by using an aerodynamics code such as WT_Perf [3].

Power limitation in high winds is typically achieved by using pitch angle control. This action, also called 'pitch-to-feather', which corresponds to changing the pitch value such that the leading edge of the blade is moved into the wind (increase of θ). The range of blade pitch angles required for power control in this case is about 35° from the pitch reference. Therefore, for safe regulation, the pitching system has to act rapidly, with fast pitch change rates of the order of $5° \, s^{-1}$ resulting in high gains within the power control loop.

2.10.2.1.1(i) Implementation

On a pitch-controlled wind turbine, the turbine's electronic controller checks the power output of the turbine several times per second. When the power output becomes too high, it sends an order to the blade pitch mechanism that immediately pitches (turns) the rotor blades slightly out of the wind. Conversely, the blades are turned back into the wind whenever the wind drops again.

Presently, pitch motors are of very compact design. They are mounted on the outside flange ring of each blade (Enercon E-40, **Figure** 8) or inside the rotor hub (Lagerway, **Figure** 9). Meteorological data from anemometers and sensors atop the nacelle measure wind speed and other environmental conditions. The power supply, data, and control signals for the pitch system are transferred by a slip ring from the nonrotating part of the nacelle, or stationary-enclosed pivot behind the hub. The slip ring is

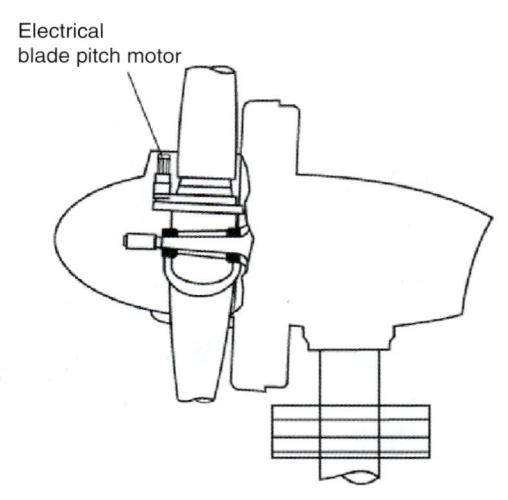

Figure 8 Enercon's pitch control. From Enercon, www.enercon.de.

Figure 9 Blade pitch system inside the rotor hub (Lagerwey LW-72). From Lagerwey, www.lagerweywind.nl.

Figure 10 Weier 10 kW pitch motor. From Weier, http://www.weier-energie.de/.

Figure 11 Bosch Rexroth Mobilex GFB pitch motor. From Bosch, http://www.boschrexroth.com.

connected to a central control unit, which includes clamps for distributing power, and control signals for the individual blade drive units. Each blade drive unit consists of a switched-mode power supply, a field bus, the motor converter, and an emergency system.

Pitch motors are manufactured in various sizes to suit wind turbines specifications. Output torques range from 3 to 1100 kNm, with corresponding ratios from 60 to over 1600 (**Figures 10** and **11**).

In case of power failure, emergency operation via batteries or capacitor bank is employed. 'Maxwell Techonologies' has recently introduced a series of ultracapacitor modules that promise a simple, solid state, high-reliability alternative to batteries for energy storage in this type of burst power application. Ultracapacitors offer excellent performance, with wide operating temperature range, long life, flexible management, and reduced system size; they are cost-effective as well as highly reliable, particularly when designed with a total systems approach (**Figure 12**).

2.10.2.1.2 Active stall-controlled wind turbines

An increasing number of larger, fixed-speed wind turbines (1 MW and up) are being developed with an 'active stall' (also called 'negative pitch') power control mechanism.

Technically, the active stall machines resemble pitch-controlled machines, since they have pitchable blades. In order to get a reasonably large torque (turning force) at low wind speeds, the machines will usually be programmed to pitch their blades much like a pitch-controlled machine at low wind speeds (often they use only a few fixed steps depending upon the wind speed).

When the machine reaches its rated power, however, an important difference from the pitch-controlled machines is evident: if the generator is about to be overloaded, the machine will pitch its blades in the opposite direction by a few degrees (3–5°) from what a pitch-controlled machine does. In other words, it will increase the angle of attack of the rotor blades in order to make the blades go into a 'deep stall', thus wasting the excess energy in the wind.

Only small changes of pitch angle are required to maintain the power output at its rated value, as the range of incidence angles required for power control is much smaller in this case than in the case of pitch control. Compared to the pitch-to-feather technique,

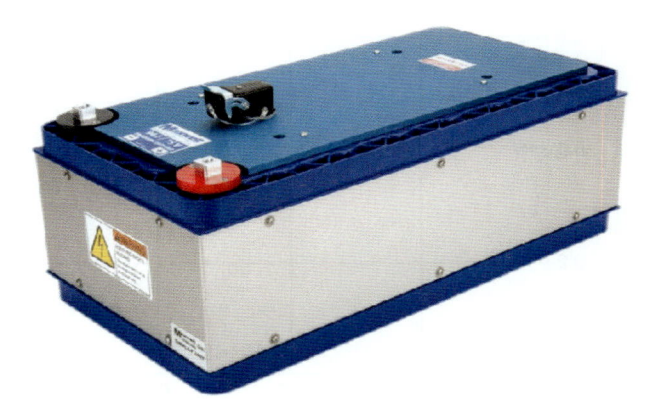

Figure 12 Ultracapacitor. From Maxwell, http://www.maxwell.com/ultracapacitors/products/modules/bmod0094-75v.asp.

the travel of the pitch mechanism is very much reduced; significantly greater thrust loads are encountered, but the thrust is much more constant, inducing smaller mechanical loads.

Additionally, in active stall one can control the power output more accurately than with passive stall, so as to avoid overshooting the rated power of the machine at the beginning of a gust of wind. Another advantage is that the machine can be run almost exactly at rated power at all high wind speeds. A normal passive stall-controlled wind turbine will usually have a drop in the electrical power output for higher wind speeds, as the rotor blades go into deeper stall.

Typical active stall representatives are the Danish manufacturers Bonus (1 MW and over) and NEG Micon (1.5 and 2 MW).

2.10.2.2 Yaw System

The rotor axis of a wind turbine rotor is usually not aligned with the wind, since the wind is continuously changing its direction (**Figure 13**).

The yawed rotor is less efficient than the nonyawed rotor and so it is vital to be able to dynamically align the rotor with the wind (**Figure 14**). Furthermore, unaligned rotors impose higher loads on the blades, causing additional fatigue damage. The output power losses can be approximated by,

$$\Delta P = \alpha \cos(\gamma) \quad [2]$$

where ΔP is the lost power, γ the yaw error angle, and α a suitable constant (**Figure 14**).

For these reasons, almost all horizontal-axis upwind turbines use forced yawing, that is, a mechanism which uses electric motors and gearboxes to keep the turbine yawed against the wind (**Figure 15**). Yaw control usually includes several drives and motors to distribute gear loading.

Active yaw is especially useful in providing maximum adaptability in complex terrains. The image in **Figure 16** shows the yaw mechanism of a typical 750 kW machine seen from below, looking into the nacelle.

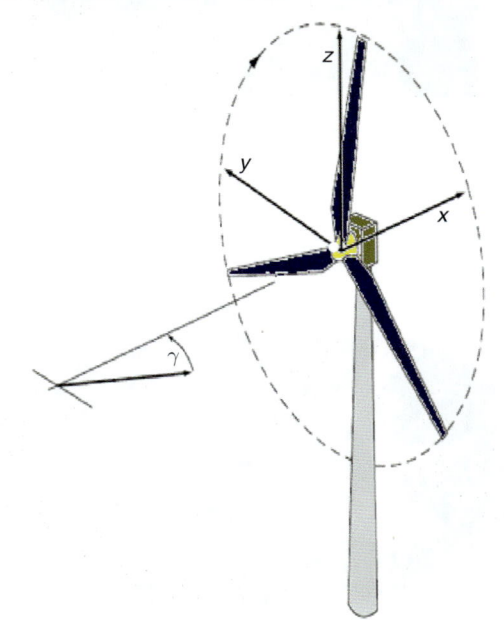

Figure 13 A wind turbine yawed to the wind direction.

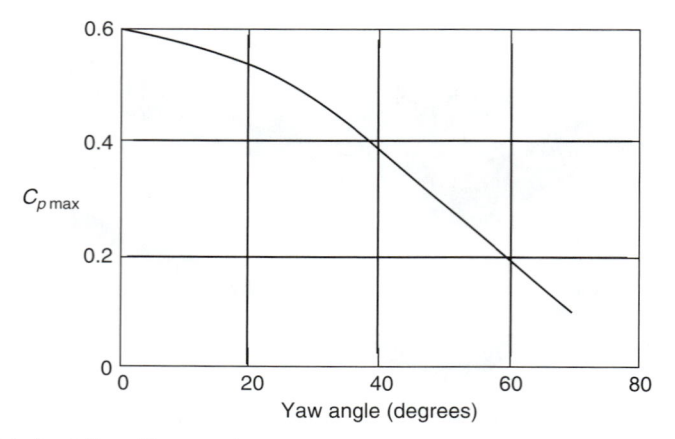

Figure 14 Maximum power coefficient variation with yaw angle γ.

Figure 15 Yaw control.

Figure 16 Yaw mechanism. From Windpower, www.windpower.org.

We can see the yaw bearing around the outer edge, and the wheels from the yaw motors and the yaw brakes inside. The yaw mechanism is activated by the electronic controller that checks the position of the wind vane on the turbine several times per second, whenever the turbine is running. However, in order to prevent large gyroscopic loads generated by the rotating rotor, the yaw rate is usually kept very low. Also the nacelle is often parked and the yaw drive is not operated unless the wind direction change reaches some predefined minimum.

In a novel approach described in Reference 4, a new yaw control technique through actively varying blade pitch angles is presented. It focuses on the feasibility of active yaw control through periodic state-space individual pitch control on the WindPACT 1.5 MW three-bladed upwind turbine. The periodic control technique has been used in many other control applications, particularly in the aerospace field. As the dynamic behavior of wind turbines is often periodic with the rotor revolution, due to asymmetric wind inflow, the control of turbine motion is more effective with periodic feedback gains. With the development of periodic state-space control and individual pitch algorithms, possibilities of controlling yaw through pitching the blades is made possible. One obvious benefit from controlling yaw through pitching the blades is that the motorized yaw drive can be removed. In addition to this, pitching the blades to yaw the rotor essentially takes advantage of asymmetric aerodynamic loads on the rotor plane. This means the rotor will be working with the wind through the blades instead of receiving rotational moments from the yaw motor. This could result in smoother continuous yaw responses and possibly a reduction in loads.

2.10.3 Electricity Production

To produce electricity, a wind turbine must conform to 'power quality' standards, such as voltage stability, frequency stability, and the absence of various forms of electrical noise (e.g., flicker or harmonic distortion) on the electrical grid. To accomplish this, a typical wind turbine's electrical system comprises a series of subsystems as shown in **Figure 17**.

2.10.3.1 The Generator

In a wind turbine, the generator plays a central role in the functional chain, since it is the actual 'converter' of mechanical into electric energy. However, since it has to face a highly fluctuating torque load, supplied by the wind turbine rotor, it is significantly different from other generators used in electrical grids.

It is outside the scope of this chapter to give a detailed description of how generators work, but only the most important features will be outlined. The interested reader can consult any standard textbook for further insight, as for example [5].

Generators are known by many names: DC (direct current), synchronous, induction, permanent magnet (PM), brushless, and so on. Although, these different types look dissimilar, the physical properties underlining their behavior are quite similar: in fact the torque-producing characteristics of all types stem from the fact 'the flux distributions of the stator and the rotor tend to align'.

The generator operation is based on the principle of 'electromagnetic induction' discovered in 1831 by Michael Faraday, a British scientist. Faraday discovered that if an electric conductor, like a copper wire, is moved through a magnetic field, electric current will flow (be induced) in the conductor. So the mechanical energy of the moving wire is converted into the electric energy of the current that flows in the wire.

Faraday's law can be stated in mathematical terms as,

$$\oint_C \mathbf{E} ds = -\frac{d}{dt} \int_S \mathbf{B} da \qquad [3]$$

where **E** is the electric field intensity around the closed contour C and **B** is the magnetic flux.

Equation [3] states in words that the line integral of the electric field intensity **E** around a closed contour C is equal to the rate of change of the magnetic flux passing through that contour. In magnetic structures with windings of high electrical conductivity (**Figure 18**), it can be shown that the E field in the wire is extremely small and can be neglected, so that the left-hand-side (LHS) of eqn [3] reduces to the negative of the induced voltage or 'electromotive force' e at the winding terminals. Additionally, the flux on the right-hand-side (RHS) of eqn [3] is dominated by the core flux φ. Since the winding links the core flux N times, eqn [3] reduces to,

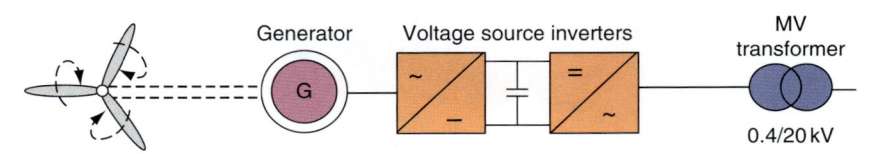

$$e(t) = N \frac{d\varphi(t)}{dt} = \frac{d\eta(t)}{dt} \qquad [4]$$

Figure 17 Wind turbine electrical system.

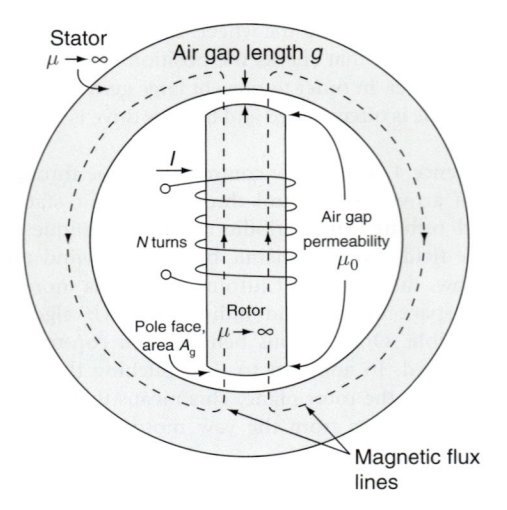

Figure 18 A simple synchronous machine. From Fitzgerald AE, Kingsley C, Jr., and Umans SD (2003) *Electric Machinery*. New York, NY: McGraw-Hill.

Equation [4] can be used to determine the voltages induced by time-varying magnetic fields. Electromagnetic energy conversion occurs when changes in the flux linkage η result from mechanical motion. In generators, a time-varying voltage is generated in windings or set of coils, by any of the following three ways:

1. by mechanically rotating the windings through a magnetic field,
2. by mechanically rotating a magnetic field past the windings, or
3. by designing the magnetic circuit so that the reluctance varies with rotation of the rotor.

This set of coils is termed the 'armature winding'. In general they carry alternating current (AC).

In AC generators, such as synchronous or induction machines, the armature winding is usually on the stationary part of the generator called the 'stator' (**Figure 19**).

In DC generators, the armature is wound on the rotating member, called the rotor. In this case, a rotating mechanical contact must be used in order to supply current to the rotor winding (**Figure 20**).

Synchronous and DC generators include a second set of windings that carry DC and are used to produce the main operating flux. This is referred to as 'field winding'. The field winding on a DC generator is on the stator, while on a synchronous machine it is found on the rotor. An alternative to DC is to use 'PMs' for the production of DC magnetic flux.

Figure 19 Stator winding assembly of a wind turbine.

Figure 20 DC motor armature.

2.10.3.2 Wind Turbine Generators

In principle, any type of generator can be used in a wind turbine. However, there are a number of factors that influence this choice, as well as specific performance criteria that must be met by the overall wind turbine electricity producing system, in order to be able to connect to the grid safely and effectively.

To satisfy grid criteria, downstream inverters can be used, even if the generator supplies AC of variable quality or even DC.

AC generators fall into two basic categories: 'synchronous' (from Greek συν+χρόνος: concurrent) and 'asynchronous' or 'induction'. In synchronous machines, rotor winding currents are supplied directly from the stationary frame through a rotating contact. In induction machines, rotor currents are induced in the rotor windings by a combination of the time variation of the stator currents and the relative motion of the rotor with respect to the stator.

There are three different concepts for the generators of wind power plants; the following points describe them:

- Synchronous generators: the output voltage of the generator is transmitted to an inverter via a power rectifier. The output frequency of the inverter is 50/60 Hz.
- Asynchronous generators with slip-ring rotor: an inverter supplies power to the rotor so that the stator side is regulated to 50/60 Hz.
- Asynchronous generators: the power supply network forces the 50/60 Hz frequency onto the stator. The voltage is provided in the oversynchronous area.

Specifically, the three main types of wind turbine generating systems currently in wide use are:

1. The 'direct-grid squirrel-cage induction' generator, used in constant-speed wind turbines. The wind turbine rotor is coupled to the generator via a gearbox. Power control is effected either using the passive stall effect (in constant speed machines) or by active pitch control.
   - The doubly fed (wound rotor) induction generator (DFIG), used in variable-speed machines. The rotor winding is fed using a back-to-back voltage source converter. Gearboxes are used to connect to the wind turbine rotor. Active pitch control is used to limit rotor speed.
   - Direct-drive synchronous generator, also allowing variable-speed operation. The synchronous generator can have a wound rotor or can be excited using PMs. It is a multipole low-speed generator, with no need for a gearbox to be coupled to the wind turbine rotor. Active pitch control is used.

In the sequel, all types of generators will be presented, even though some are in less common use than others today.

2.10.3.2.1 Asynchronous (induction) generators

'Asynchronous' or 'induction' generators were not the first choice for most applications, until the wind power industry found a suitable use for them.

In the induction generator, the stator windings are essentially the same as those of a synchronous one. However, the rotor windings are electrically short-circuited and frequently have no external connections; currents are 'induced' by transformer action from the stator windings.

An important fact for operating an induction generator is that the rotor must be supplied with a magnetizing current for generating and maintaining its magnetic field. This is called 'reactive power' and depends on active power. When a grid is present, reactive power can be taken from it; otherwise, capacitors must provide power factor compensation.

The synchronous speed, n_s, of the rotor of an induction generator is given by:

$$n_s = \frac{f}{p} \qquad [5]$$

where f is grid frequency in Hz and p the number of poles. Due to slip, s, the generator rotor speed is a few percent above the slip,

$$s = \frac{n_s - n_m}{n_s} \quad [6]$$

where n_m denotes mechanical speed. The electrical efficiency of induction generators is a function of the nominal slip. In megawatt turbines, the nominal slip is below 1%. Due to absorption of reactive power from the grid, power factor cos φ is comparatively low (~0.87). Smaller induction machines have higher nominal slip with correspondingly poorer efficiency.

2.10.3.2.1(i) Fixed-speed squirrel-cage induction generators (SCIGs)

In this type of generator, the rotor windings are solid aluminum bars that are cast into the slots of the rotor and that are shorted together by cast aluminum rings at each end of the rotor (**Figure 21**).

Squirrel-cage induction generators were used in early fixed-speed wind turbine designs with active or passive stall control. They consisted of the rotor, a squirrel-cage induction generator, and a gearbox interconnection. The generator stator winding is connected to the grid (**Figure 22**). The generator slip varies with the generated power, so the speed is not, in fact, constant; however, as the speed variations are very small (just 1–2%), it is commonly referred to as a 'fixed-speed' turbine. Since a squirrel-cage generator always draws reactive power from the grid, this is undesirable, especially in weak networks. The reactive power consumption of squirrel-cage generators is therefore nearly always compensated by capacitors.

A machine that utilized this design was NEG Micon's NM72 1500 kW, three-bladed, upwind turbine (currently managed by Vestas). It had a synchronous rotational speed of 1200 revolutions per minute (rpm), rated speed at rated power of 1214 rpm, and rated voltage of 600 V. It used an active stall aerodynamic power regulation system. The wind speed input to the pitch controller determined the range of pitch angle and the gain for the power regulation controller. The output power of the generator, P_{elec}, actively controlled the pitch angle in high wind speeds.

The fixed-speed squirrel-cage design has been utilized extensively in small turbine sizes. This is due to its robust design, since it is built with very few components. The weakest part is the gearbox, which has to withstand a lot of torque fluctuations, whose energy cannot be stored because of the almost fixed-speed nature of the overall design. These fluctuations are of course transmitted on to the grid voltage. In a wind park, these are smoothed out and do not pose a problem.

Another drawback is that the reactive power cannot be controlled. This means that the reactive power consumption of the wind turbine will increase when the power production increases. If the reactive power consumption is to be compensated for more, electronically switched capacitors or a Static Var Compensator can be used. In this case, there is the risk that the generator will be self-excited leading to severe overvoltages.

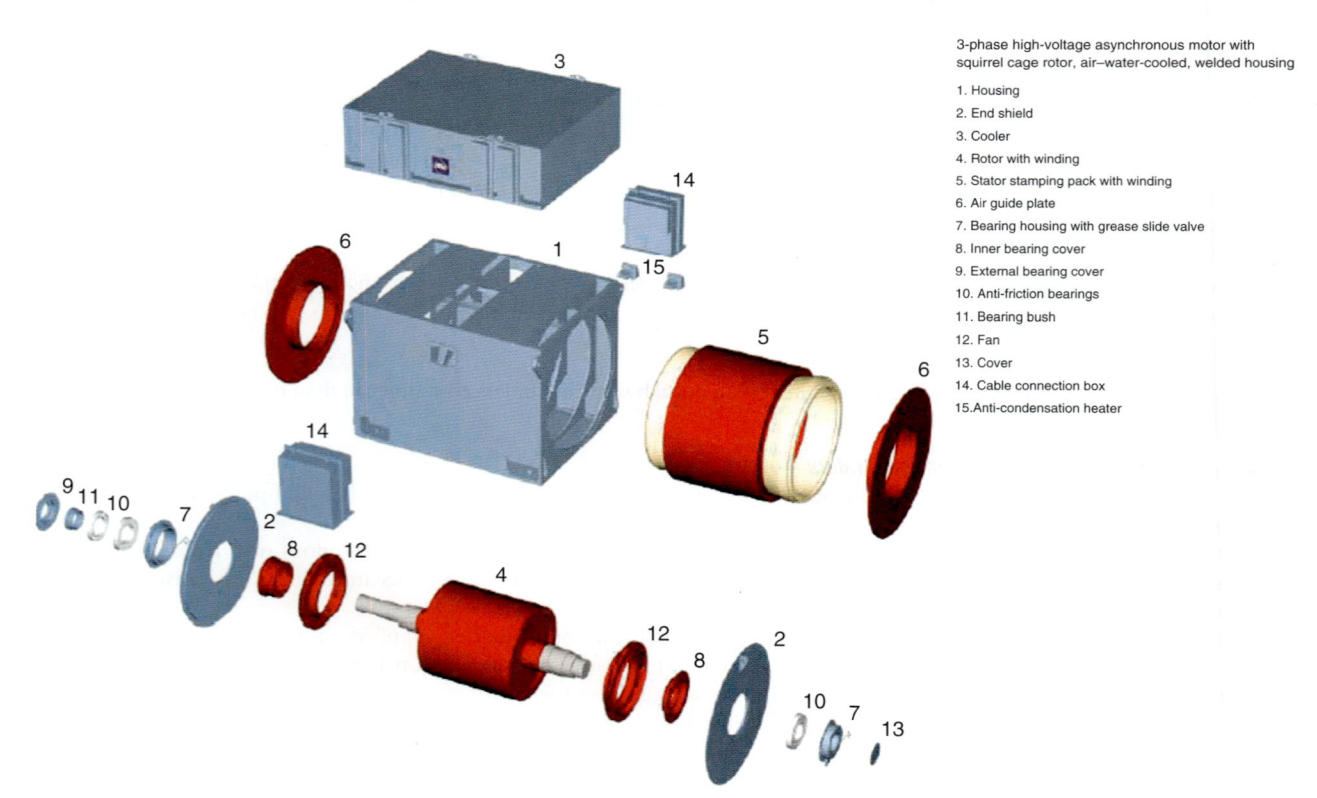

Figure 21 Three-phase asynchronous squirrel-cage generator (drawing by VEM motors). From Vem motors leaflet, www.vem-group.com.

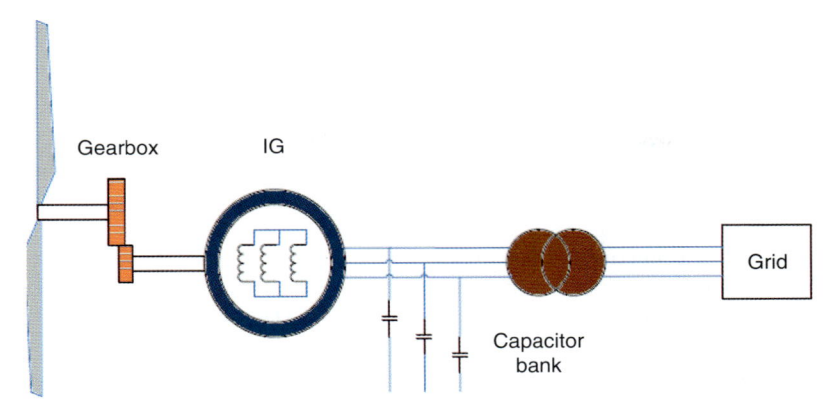

Figure 22 Squirrel-cage generator interconnection.

A method to increase efficiency is to employ two different generators, a small one for low wind speeds and a larger one for higher wind speeds. In **Figure 23** can be seen the effect of using such a configuration [6], where the generators change occurs at 6.5 m s^{-1}. Suslon's S64 1.25 MW wind turbine is an example of such a configuration.

Another possibility is to change the rotational speed of a squirrel-cage motor in steps by means of 'pole reconnection'. This requires two separate windings for the stator with different number of pole pairs. The advantages of this design are questionable and they have been implemented only in low-wind areas. Siemens' generator is an example of such a configuration.

A variation of this design is the 'semi-variable-speed turbine', in which the rotor resistance of the squirrel-cage generator can be varied instantly using fast power electronics (**Figure 24**). So far, Vestas alone has succeeded in commercializing this system, under

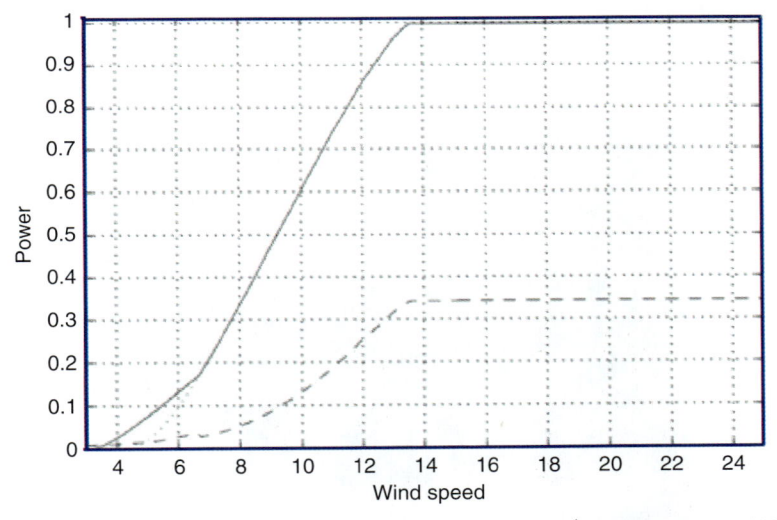

Figure 23 Two megawatt double-generator fixed-speed machine power lines (wind speed in m s^{-1}, power in per unit of 2 MW), solid line: active power, dashed line: reactive power drawn. From Lundberg S (2003) Configuration Study of Large Wind Parks. Licentiate Thesis, Chalmers University of Technology.

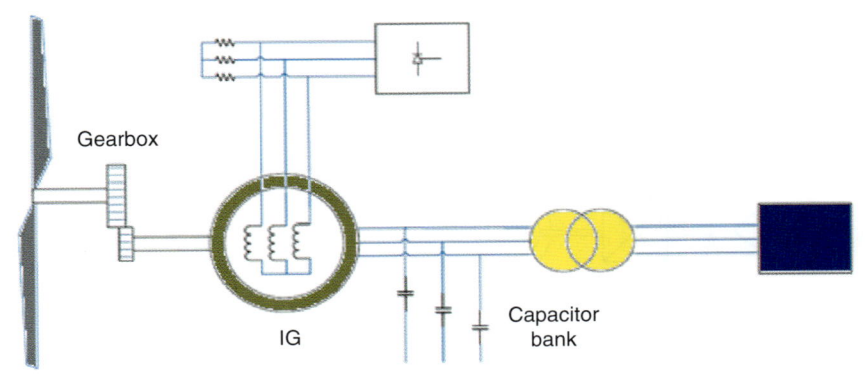

Figure 24 Vestas 'semi-variable'-speed induction generator.

the trade name OptiSlip®. A number of turbines, ranging from 600 kW to 2.75 MW, have now been equipped with this system, which allows transient rotor speed increases of up to 10% of their nominal value.

2.10.3.2.1(ii) Slip-ring induction generators

The rotor of an induction generator can also be designed with additional slip rings as a so-called 'slip-ring' configuration (**Figure 25**). The slip-ring rotor allows the electrical characteristics of the rotor to be influenced externally. By changing the electric resistance in the rotor circuit, greater slip can be attained and consequently greater compliance for direct coupling to the grid. By using an inverter in the rotor circuit, variable-speed operation is possible.

The external resistors will only be connected in order to produce the desired slip when the load on the wind turbine increases. Using external resistors instead of a rotor with higher slip has a positive effect on the cooling of the generator. Actual examples of this idea include Suslon's FlexiSlip® system, employed in their larger turbines (**Figure 26**).

2.10.3.2.1(iii) Doubly fed induction generator

A doubly fed induction generator (DFIG) is basically a standard, wound rotor induction machine with its stator windings directly connected to the grid and its rotor windings connected to the grid through a converter (**Figure 27**).

The AC/DC/AC converter is divided into two components: the rotor side and the grid side. These converters are voltage-sourced converters that use forced-commutated power electronic devices to synthesize an AC voltage form a DC source, that is, a capacitor. A coupling inductor is used to connect the grid-side converter to the grid. The three-phase rotor winding is connected to the rotor-side converter by slip rings and brushes and the three-phase stator windings are directly connected to the grid (**Figure 28**).

The control system generates the pitch angle command and the voltage command signals V_r and V_{gc} for the rotor- and grid-side converters in order to control the power of the wind turbine, the DC voltage, and the reactive power (voltage at grid terminals).

The system works in either subsynchronous or supersynchronous mode:

- In the subsynchronous operating mode (partial load range), the stator of the DFIG feeds all generated electrical power to the grid and additionally makes slip power available, which is fed from the frequency converter to the rotor via the generator's slip rings.

Figure 25 Slip-ring rotor.

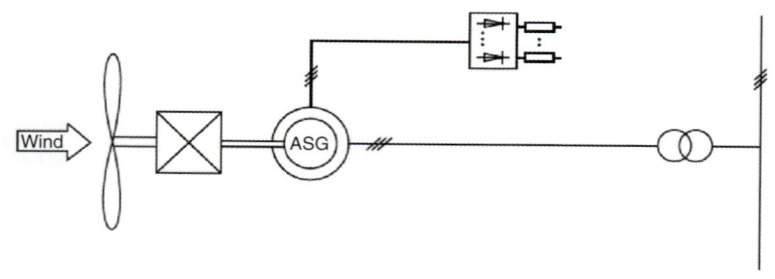

Figure 26 Slip-ring induction generator with resistors.

Figure 27 Bolting up a double-fed induction generator (photo by VEM motors). From Vem motors leaflet, www.vem-group.com.

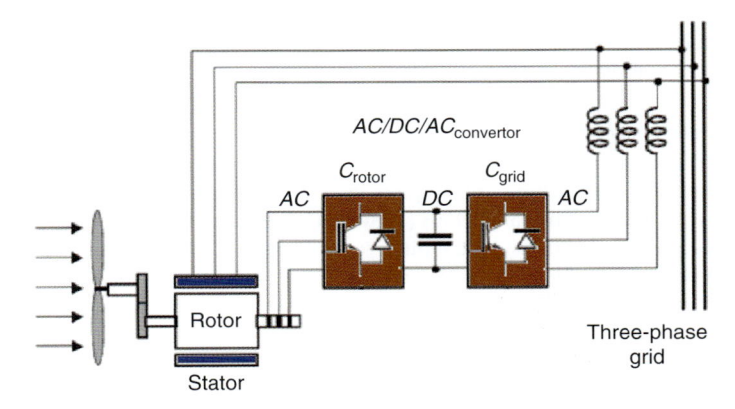

Figure 28 Geared double-fed induction generator.

- In the supersynchronous operating mode (nominal load range), total power consists of the components fed by the stator of the DFIG plus slip power, which is fed from the rotor to the grid via the frequency converter.

These different operational modes require a complex control system for the inverter. On the other hand, the controlled DFIG offers the advantage of separate active and reactive power control. A further advantage is the fact that only about a third of the nominal generator power flows via the inverter, resulting in much smaller and economical design, while at the same time it increases efficiency.

Though this concept was proved satisfactory since its first implementation in the experimental Growian turbine, it was not pursued further due to high costs. Today, however, it is being offered as an off-the-shelf generator system and is one of the main choices in many large wind turbines in the megawatt range.

2.10.3.2.2 Synchronous generators

Synchronous generators have a rotor (pole wheel) that is excited with DC conducted to it via stationary carbon 'brushes' with contact rotating 'slip rings' (**Figure 29**). An alternating voltage is generated in the stator windings. This voltage is sinusoidal with frequency in cycles per second (Hz) equal to the rotor speed in revolutions per second, that is, the electric frequency of the generated voltage is 'synchronized' with the mechanical speed, a fact that explains the designation of this type of generator.

The rotors of most synchronous wind turbine generators have 'salient', or projecting poles with 'concentrated windings'. In order to explain the reason for this, it is necessary to have a look at the relationship involving frequency, number of poles, and rotor speed of revolution (for details, see Reference 5).

The coil voltage of a multipole machine passes through a complete cycle every time a pair of poles sweeps by, or (poles/2) times each revolution. The electrical frequency f_e of the voltage generated in a synchronous machine is therefore,

Figure 29 Salient pole rotor (left) and rotor.

$$f_e = \left(\frac{\text{poles}}{2}\right)\frac{n}{60}\text{Hz} \qquad [7]$$

where n is the mechanical speed in revolutions per minute.

Hence, for a grid frequency of 50 Hz, 1500 rpm is required with two pole pairs, whereas in a 60 Hz grid, the rotational speed needed is 1800 rpm. Increasing the pole pairs decreases the necessary rpm. In wind turbines, rotational speeds are comparably low, and are sometimes increased by appropriate gearboxes. Salient pole machines (as opposed to 'cylindrical' or 'nonsalient pole' ones) are more suited 'mechanically' to these conditions.

The efficiency of a synchronous machine is generally higher than a similar induction one by 1–2%. Efficiency, as usual, increases with rated power, but in wind turbines size must also be taken into account. Faster rotating generators are usually lighter, but at the expense of more complicated gearbox design.

As has been repeatedly pointed out, the generator is but a part in the conversion chain, so let us look at the various options for connecting a synchronous generator to its inputs and outputs.

2.10.3.2.2(i) Fixed-speed direct-grid coupling

Even though this is an outdated option, it is presented for the sake of completeness (**Figure 30**).

Perhaps the best-known example of a machine utilizing this kind of setup was Boeing's 'second-generation' MOD-2 2.5 MW turbine, built in collaboration with NASA in the early 1980s (**Figure 31**). It was an upwind, two-blade machine with a diameter of 91.4, rotating at 17.5 rpm. For economical reasons, partial pitch control was used. Its generator produced 4.16 kV, line to line [7].

Coupling a synchronous generator directly to the grid is a hard case. It possesses, however, a critical characteristic: it has the ability to remain in synchronism during and after major voltage sags, a property termed 'transient stability' [8]. The main parameters influencing this condition are:

- Rotor inertia/turbine power during the fault
- Depth of voltage sag
- Duration of voltage sag

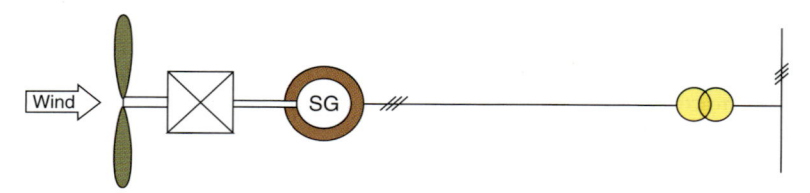

Figure 30 Synchronous generator directly couple to the grid.

Figure 31 Boeing's MOD-2 wind turbine.

- Short circuit impedance of the grid to which the generators are connected.

Other advantages of this setup include:

- Simplicity and compatibility with current technology for feeding the three-phase grid.
- Easy control of reactive power via DC rotor excitation.

These advantages are overbalanced by the following disadvantages:

- Very small load angles are possible for compensating the dynamic loads exerted by the wind rotor.
- Poorly damped oscillations in response to grid frequency fluctuations or sudden load peaks.
- Difficulty in synchronizing with the grid, complex automatic synchronization equipment needed.

To partly overcome poor damping, active electric damping was proposed in Reference 7. This solution uses two independent stator coils and suitable control forming an integrated generator controller.

It must be noted that despite the advances made in variable-speed machines today, cost considerations may dictate the use of this combination despite its considerable drawbacks.

2.10.3.2.2(ii) Variable-speed direct-grid coupling

A promising new type of synchronous generator machine directly coupled to the grid is a variable-speed wind turbine equipped with a 'hydrodynamically controlled gearbox'. This new type of gearbox effects variable-speed operation by continuously controlling the gearbox ratio. The product named WinDrive® is developed by the German mechanical engineering firm Voith [9] (**Figure 32**), and has presently been installed in DeWind's 8.2 machine (**Table 1**).

The idea of a hydrodynamic gearbox is not new. In fact, it was first developed by Hermann Föttinger in 1905. Its basic principle is as follows: in an enclosed housing containing a liquid, two bladed wheels (the pump wheel and the turbine wheel) face one another but are not in direct contact (**Figure 33**). The impeller is connected to the driving machine, the turbine wheel to the driven. The rotation of the pump wheel sets the liquid in motion which in turn transmits the mechanical power to the blades of the turbine wheel. The only connecting element is the liquid. As a result, wear-free and smooth power transmission is effected.

This basic setup has been successfully employed in other industries (e.g., oil rigs) and is now being tested in a complete configuration in wind turbines. Hereby follows a short description of its structure, which is quite complex. Details can be found in Reference 10.

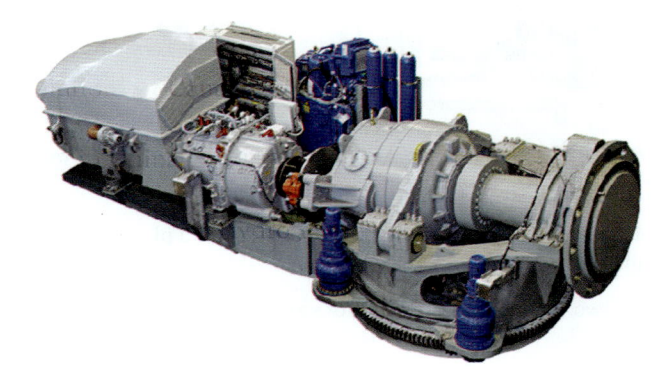

Figure 32 Complete power train of the DeWind 8.2. From left to right: synchronous generator, WinDrive, gear. Diameter 1.3 m, length 1.7 m (© Voith Turbo Wind Gmbh). From Yoh Y (2006) A new lightning protection system for wind turbines using two ring-shaped electrodes. *IEEJ Transactions on Electrical and Electronic Engineering.* 1: 314–319.

Table 1 DeWind 8.2 technical data

Rated power	2 MW
Rotor diameter	80 m
Swept area	5027 m^2
Rotor speed range	11.1–20.7 min^{-1}
Gear ratio	1:25
WinDrive ratio	1:3 to 1:5.5
Generator speed	1500 min^{-1} at 50 Hz; 1800 min^{-1} at 60 Hz
Output voltage	4.16–13.8 kV

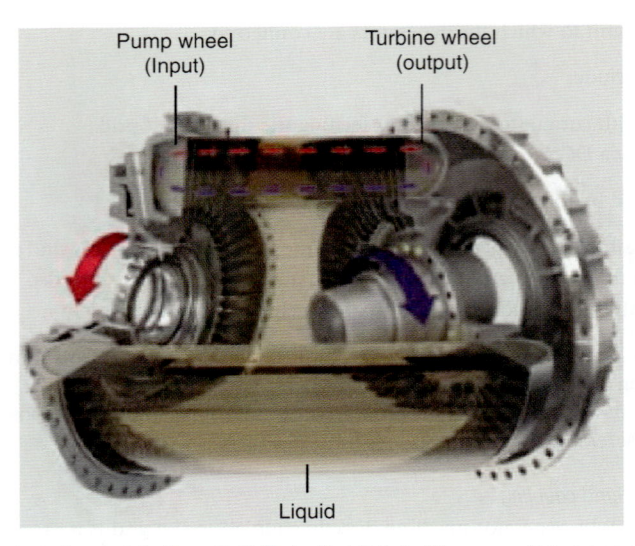

Figure 33 Visualization of the hydrodynamic principle. From Voith Turbo GmbH & Co KG, www.voithturbo.com.

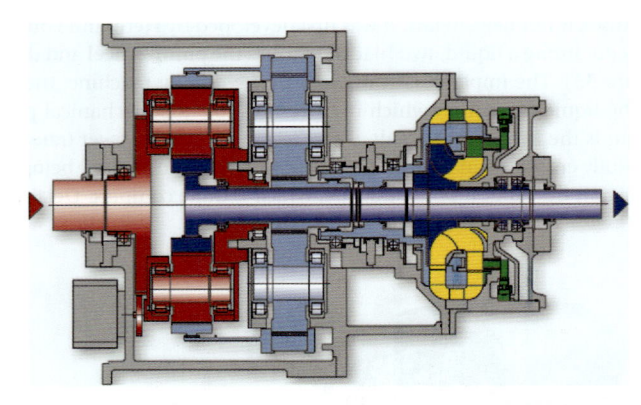

Figure 34 Longitudinal section of WinDrive showing its power flow. From Voith Turbo GmbH & Co KG, www.voithturbo.com.

The structure of the WinDrive is based on a torque converter combined with a planetary gear designed as a superimposed gear, comprising two interactive elements (**Figure 34**):

- The superimposed gear (red) adds two variable speeds: the rotor's and the correction speed within the WinDrive that add up to a constant output speed.
- The torque converter supplies the variable correction speed. It is flooded by hydraulic oil (yellow) and consists of a pump wheel, which is driven by the main shaft, a turbine wheel (light blue), which supplies the correction speed to the superimposed gear, and the adjustable guide vanes (green), which change the transmission behavior of the torque converter.

In weak winds, the generator is connected to the grid at low rotor speed. When rated speed is reached, the rotor speed is not increased further, due to strength and noise considerations. With increasing wind velocity, the drive train torque is continuously regulated by the hydrodynamic gearbox (**Figure 35**). Protection from wind gusts is ensured by the very fast adjustment of the guide vanes, which is of the order of 20 ms.

The combination of variable-speed operation and the direct-grid coupling capability of the synchronous generator result in the following properties:

- Very good network input quality
- Reduced torque dynamics, due to temporary storage of energy in the driveline
- No need for voltage transformer, due to high voltage levels of synchronous generators
- High energy output from maximum speed range
- Equalization of peak loads by dynamic decoupling of input and output side
- Vibration damping

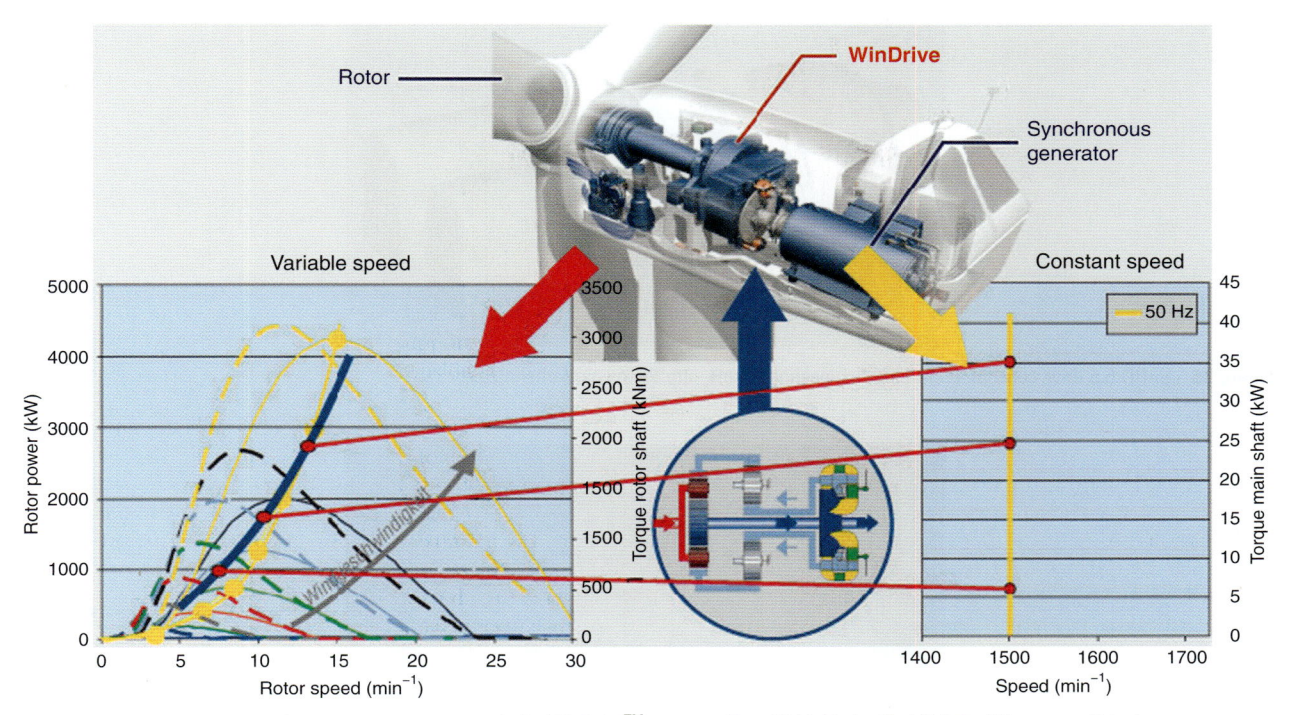

Figure 35 Variable rotor speed-constant generator speed: the WinDrive™ concept. From Voith Turbo GmbH & Co KG, www.voithturbo.com.

- Driveline weight reduction by 20%
- Nacelle volume reduction by 10%.

These properties make this system suitable in the following situations:

- In remote areas, remote industrial plants or small islands
- In offshore wind farm clusters connected to the main shore grid using conventional, thyristor-based high-voltage DC technology.

Disadvantages include:

- Complex construction, equaling or surpassing power electronics equivalent
- Weight (5.2 tons).

Whether mechatronics will succesfully replace power electronics, remains to be verified. For the moment, the WinDrive system, installed on the Edwin 8.2 wind turbine, has been operated in three experimental wind farms: Cuxhaven (Germany), Argentina, and Texas (60 Hz version). A promising sign is the start of a new WinDrive development for a 6.5 MW offshore wind turbine for wind power plant manufacturer BARD (**Figures 36** and **37**).

2.10.3.2.2(iii) Direct-drive variable-speed indirect-grid coupling

As mentioned earlier, the use of a direct-drive synchronous generator is among the main technological choices today. The generator is either connected directly to the turbine rotor operating at small rotating speeds (5–30 rpm) or uses a single-stage gearbox and operates at middle speeds. It has a large number of poles (>60) with classical excitation or PMs. The connection to the power grid is carried out using full-size power converters of equal power rating to the generator. Wind power is limited by individual active rotor blade pitching. Due to the large number of poles and slow rotating speed, the generator must develop large torque, so it must have large weight and diameter. This puts an extra degree of difficulty on the construction of the nacelle.

The development and application of direct-drive generators is closely tied to the development and cost of the power converter. Additionally, reduction of cost of PMs and their availability on the market have significantly influenced the development of such machines.

The direct-drive concept is a serious alternative to the standard design that uses gears. Nevertheless, its implementation problems cannot be overlooked. As the size of the turbine increases, its assembly raises considerable questions. Maintaining an accurate gap between rotor and stator becomes a problem as the large diameter rotor can only be assembled from several ring segments. Moreover, it is not easy to cool the generator. On the other hand, this gearless design can claim less maintenance and service costs.

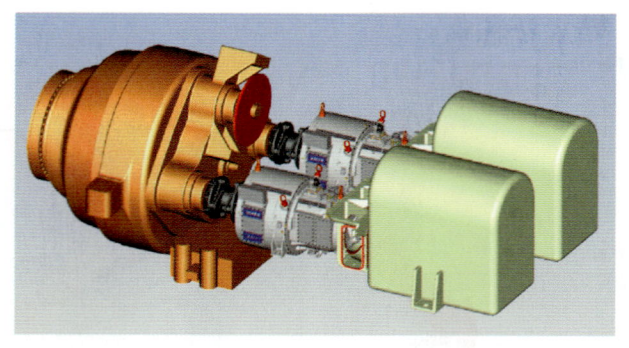

Figure 36 BARD 6.5 drive concept. From Bard Engineering GmbH, http://www.bard-offshore.de.

Figure 37 BARD 5.0 offshore wind energy system. From Bard Engineering GmbH, http://www.bard-offshore.de.

2.10.3.2.2(iii)(a) **Electrically excited** The first to develop a successful direct-drive synchronous generator was patented by Enercon. They called it 'annular generator'. This generator has proven to be very effective and is employed in all sizes of their wind turbine range (**Figure 38**).

The generator is electrically excited and has 84 poles. A 500 kW machine needs a rotor with diameter of 4.8 m. The nominal power is reached at a speed of 38 rpm, but has a usable range of 20–40 rpm. The generator stator uses a single-layer basket copper winding, consisting of continuous, individual round wires gathered in bundles and varnish insulated (**Figure 39**). The magnetic field is excited via 'pole shoes' located on the disk rotor (**Figure 40**). In order to prevent overheating, the hottest areas of the annular generator are constantly monitored by temperature sensors, which activate an optimized temperature control system.

The generator produces a nominal frequency of 16⅔ Hz, which is then fed to the grid via a DC-link circuit with an inverter which has virtually no harmonics (**Figure 41**). Electrical efficiency of the whole system is specified at 0.94. The output voltage, being at 20 kV, is suitable for direct use in medium-voltage grids. Because of its synchronous nature, reactive power output ($\cos \varphi$) is regulated.

2.10.3.2.2(iii)(b) **Permanent magnet** An alternative to electrically excited synchronous generators is that of a PM. Their main advantage is the lack of exciter power, resulting in greater efficiency in the partial load range and consequently increased revenues for wind power producers. Furthermore, great power density means reduced mass and compact design, while the lack of slip rings improves reliability and maintenance. Lastly, employing magnets instead of copper coils in the generator reduces electrical losses and current flow through the rotating parts of the generator.

On the other hand, the lack of exciter frequency results in poor $\cos \varphi$ values and dictates the use of complicated inverter technology or special filters. High cost of the material for PMs (neodymium iron or samarium cobalt) is another problem, though this is currently on the decline.

There are generally three types of PM machines: radial, axial, and transversal flux. In wind turbines, however, only the first two designs are currently used. General theory about PM machines can be found, amongst others, in Reference 11.

Figure 38 Enercon's direct-drive synchronous generator. From Enercon brochure, www.enercon.de.

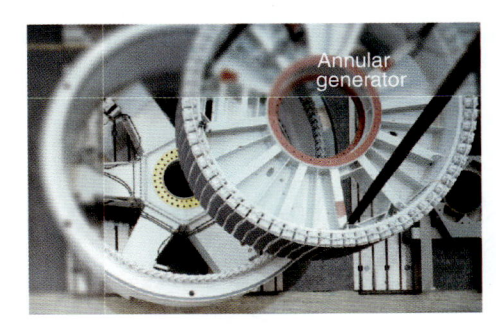

Figure 39 Enercon's annular generator. From Enercon brochure, www.enercon.de.

Figure 40 Rotor's pole shoes. From Enercon brochure www.enercon.de.

- Radial flux permanent magnet

The radial flux type (radial flux permanent magnet, RFPM) is the classic type and mostly used in wind turbines. The rotor can have buried or surface-mounted magnets, the poles can be skewed, have pole shoes, etc. The stator is quite similar to other AC machines both for windings and tooth shape. It is common but not necessary to use semi-closed slots. Magnetic slot wedges is also an option. Two-layer fractional windings are mostly used even though the simplicity of concentrated windings is spreading. The active materials are placed along the air gap (**Figure 42**). For large diameters, this means that the active material becomes a thin shell around the air gap, thus most of the volume to the machine is air or supporting structures to transfer the torque to or from the shaft to the rotor rim. Since the force is acting at a large radius, a high torque is produced.

- Axial flux permanent magnet

Axial flux machines are magnetized in the axial direction. The air gap is radial to the shaft. Compared to RFPM, given the same outer diameter and the same force/area, axial flux permanent magnet (AFPM) have a lower (torque/volume of active material). The advantage of AFPM is the possibility to use the volume of the machine more efficiently. AFPM are usually disk-shaped, with large diameter and short length (**Figure 43**).

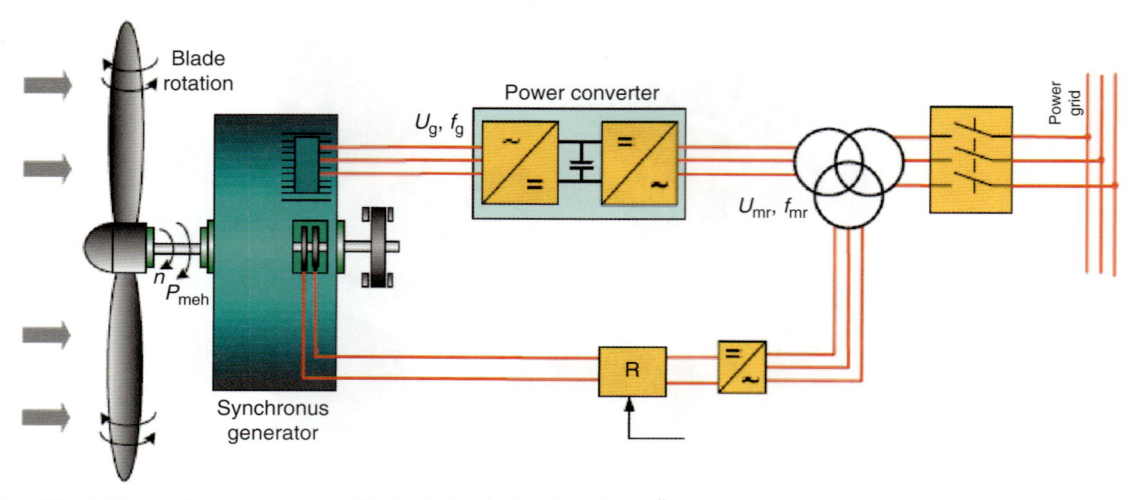

Figure 41 Direct-drive synchronous generator with classical excitation. From Ban D, Žarko D, Mađerčić M, *et al.* (2007) Generator technology for wind turbines, trends in application and production in Croatia. In: Taleski R (ed.) *ZBORNIK NA TRUDOVI, Mako-Cigre 2007. knjiga I., Ohrid, 7-9.oktombri 2007.5. SOVETUVANJE!*.

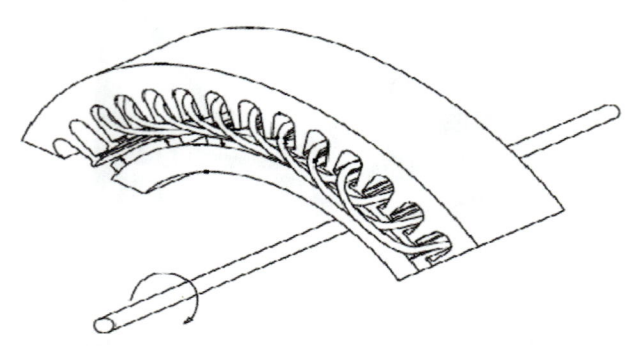

Figure 42 Radial flux permanent magnet magnetization. From Bang D, Polinder H, Shrestha G, and Ferreira JA (2008) Review of generator systems for direct-drive wind turbines. *Proceedings, EWEC*: European Wind Energy Association, Brussels.

Figure 43 An axial flux permanent magnet. From Bang D, Polinder H, Shrestha G, and Ferreira JA (2008) Review of generator systems for direct-drive wind turbines. *Proceedings, EWEC*: European Wind Energy Association, Brussels.

Several disks can be connected in series and make a multidisk machine. The rotor can be made with surface-mounted or buried magnets. The stator can likewise use various teeth and windings designs. It may employ ironless stators, a fact that reduces iron losses, which makes it possible to cool the windings more effectively and eliminates the attractive forces between the magnets in the rotor and the iron in the stator. It, however, increases the need for magnets. AFPM types are not used in machines with power over 1 MW.

Figure 44 Lagerwey's permanent magnet wind turbine. From Lagerwey, www.lagerweywind.nl.

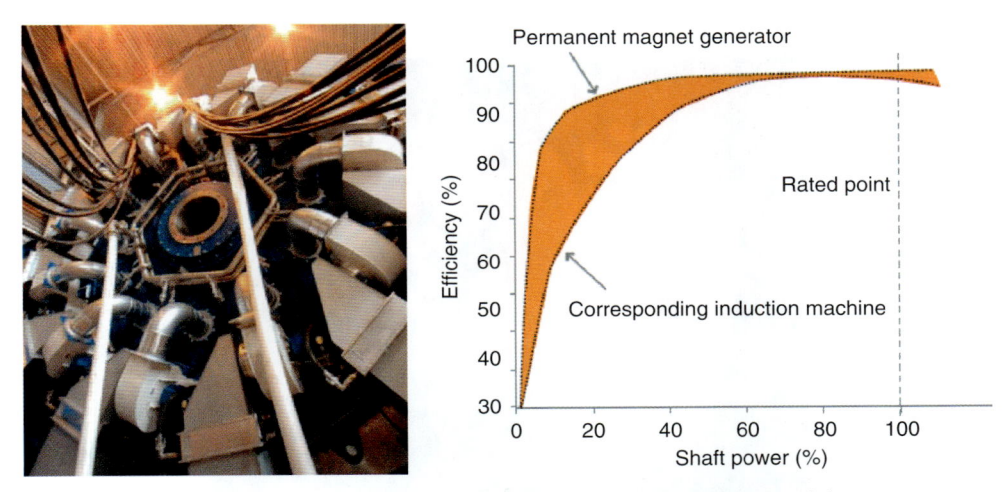

Figure 45 The switch permanent magnet generator and performance. From The Switch brochure, www.theswitch.com.

It was the Dutch firm Lagerwey who first used a PM generator developed by ABB, in a large wind turbine (**Figure 44**).

The Finnish firm, The Switch, manufactures a 3800 kW, 17.5 rpm low-speed PM wind generator. Its rated frequency is 17.5 Hz, maximum speed is 21 rpm, $\cos\varphi$ is 0.85, has a diameter of 6.6 m, and weighs 85 tons (**Figure 45**). The company claims its generator produces 20% more energy than corresponding induction machines.

2.10.3.2.2(iv)   Planetary gearbox medium-speed PM

Directly driven generators are operated in low speeds and thus have disadvantages, such as large diameter, heavy weight, and high cost. With increasing rated power levels, and the associated decrease of wind turbine rotor speeds, these systems are becoming even larger and more expensive, thus presenting higher technical difficulties of transport and assembly.

To overcome these shortcomings, a mixed solution, introduced by Areva Multibrid, is proposed. Their system, termed the M5000, consists of a single-stage planetary gearbox and a medium-speed PM generator (**Figures 46** and **47**) [12, 13].

In this technology, the generator, gearbox, main shaft, and shaft bearing are integrated in a common enclosure. The common generator-gearbox housing is supported by a tubular bedplate structure. A double-tapered roller-bearing connects the rotor with the machine housing. The helical planetary gear train ensures the optimal lubrication of all shafts and wheels (**Figure 48**).

The PM synchronous generator is directly installed in the machine housing and its rotor is directly mounted on the output shaft of the gearbox with no bearings (data in **Table 2**).

Similarly to other indirect to grid configurations, a back-to-back pulse-width modulator (PWM) full-scale power electronic converter is used to interface between the stator of the PM generator and the grid. This consists of a generator-side converter, a grid-side converter, and a DC-link capacitor. The use of the full-scale converter facilitates the operation of the wind turbine at its maximum efficiency (**Figure 50**).

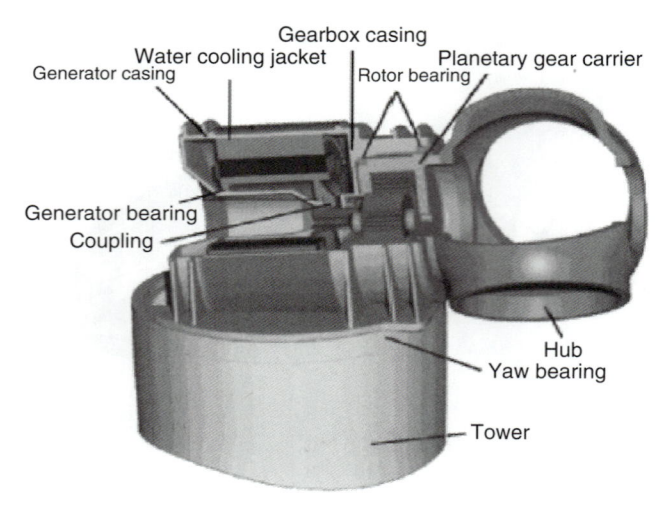

Figure 46 Configuration of Multibrid's generator design. From Li H, Chen Z, and Polinder H (2009) Optimization of multibrid permanent-magnet wind generator systems. *IEEE Transactions on Energy Conversion* 24: 82–92.

Figure 47 Combined gearbox – permanent magnet generator system. From Multibrid, www.multibrid.com.

Figure 48 Rotor bearing/gearbox of AREVA Multibrid M5000. From Multibrid, www.multibrid.com.

2.10.3.3 Power Electronics

Power electronics is of increasing importance in current wind turbines. Surely, they are most needed in variable-speed types, since the generator frequency has to be decoupled from the grid. However, even in fixed-speed machines, thyristors are used as soft starters.

Power electronics serve two parallel purposes:

1. To ensure compliance of the wind turbine's generated power waveform with the grid requirements
2. To protect the wind turbine elements from possible grid faults (voltage drop or rise, etc.).

The most important grid-related properties of a wind turbine's electricity production system are briefly discussed. These are not applicable of course in stand-alone systems.

Table 2 AREVA Multibrid M5000 technical data

Rated power	5315 kW[a]
Speed range	58.6–146.9 min^{-1}
Cooling	Water cooled
Power factor (grid)	0.9 inductive, 0.9 capacitive

[a] The actual power curve is as shown in Figure 49.

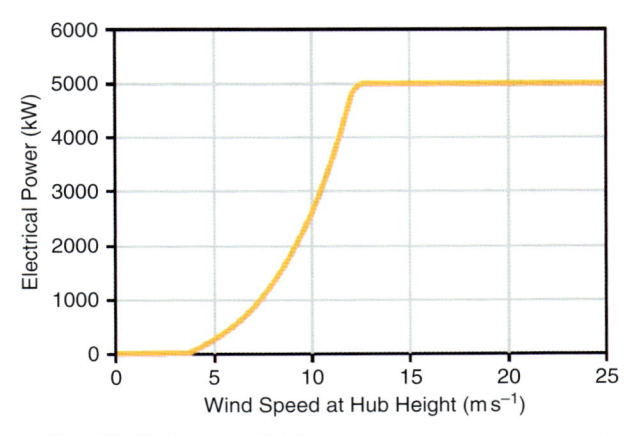

Figure 49 Multibrid M5000 power curve. From Multibrid, www.multibrid.com.

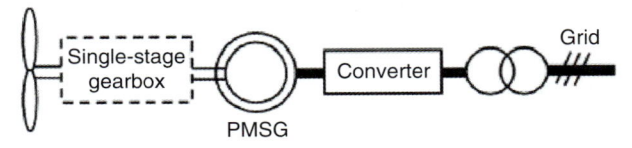

Figure 50 Interconnection of the planetary gear PM synchronous generator.

2.10.3.3.1 Harmonics
Only variable-speed wind turbines inject significant harmonic currents into the network. Fixed-speed wind turbines, particularly those with power factor correction capacitors, alter the harmonic impedance of the distribution network and, in some circumstance, create resonant circuits. This may be important if fixed- and variable-speed wind turbines are installed in the same wind farm. It is noted in IEC (2000b) [26] that harmonic currents have been reported from a few installations of fixed-speed induction generator wind turbines but there is no known instance of customer annoyance or equipment damage due to harmonic currents from fixed-speed wind turbines.

2.10.3.3.2 Ride through
The emergence of new grid codes poses a new challenge: the ride-through capability during voltage sags, that is, the wind farms should be able to continuously supply the network during voltage sags. One such grid code voltage sag profile for ride through is shown in **Figure 51** [14].

The compliance of the various types of wind turbines to the grid requirements depends on the specific type. In **Table 3** is summarized the response of various configurations to the most important grid conditions [15].

2.10.3.3.3 Fixed-speed systems
As already discussed, fixed-speed systems employ induction generators directly connected to the grid. This configuration dictates the need for power electronics aiming at two targets:

1. Smooth connection–disconnection from the grid
2. Compensation of generator no-load reactive power consumption.

These two requirements are met by the use of soft starters and capacitor banks (**Figure 52**).

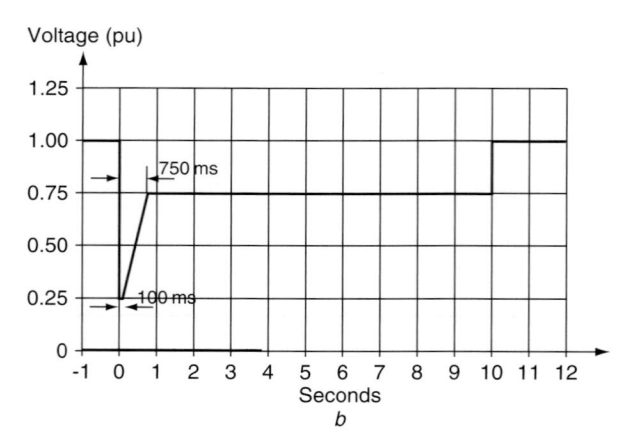

Figure 51 Voltage sag response requirement. From Molinas M, Naess B, Gullvik W, and Undeland T (2005) Cage induction generators for wind turbines with power electronics converters in the light of the new grid codes. In EPE 2005, *11th European Conference on Power Electronics and Applications*, Dresden, Germany.

Table 3 Grid-related performance of wind turbines

	FSS – SR/ASR	VSS – PR, DFIG	VSS – PR, full-power PEC
Steady-state voltage impact	Uncontrolled	Controlled	Controlled
Flicker	Medium	Low	Low
THD to the grid		Medium/high	Medium/high
Start-up voltage disturbances	Medium	Low	Low
Fault response	Uncontrolled	Semi-controlled	Controlled

ASR, active stall-regulated turbine; DFIG, doubly fed induction generator; FSS, fixed-speed system; PEC, power electronic converter; PR, pitch-regulated turbine; SR, stall-regulated turbine; THD, total harmonic distortion; VSS, variable-speed system.

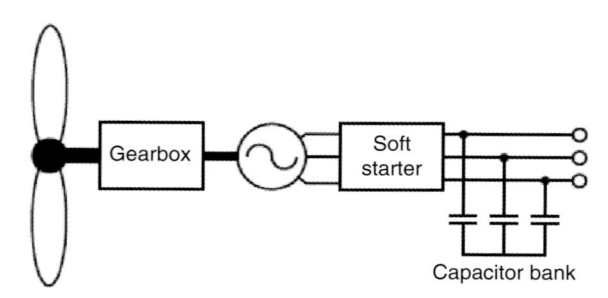

Figure 52 Electronics in fixed-speed systems. From Hansen LH, Helle L, Blaabjerg F, *et al.* (2001) Conceptual survey of generators and power electronics for wind turbines. *Risø Report R-1205*: Risø National Laboratory, Roskilde, Denmark.

2.10.3.3.3(i) Soft starter

The soft starter is an electronic device aiming at reducing transient currents during connection or disconnection from the grid. The latter happens when the generator speed exceeds the synchronous speed. Using thyristors controlled by their firing angle, the generator is smoothly connected to the grid over a predefined number of grid periods (**Figure 53**).

The commutating devices are two thyristors for each phase, connected antiparallel. The relationship of the firing angle, α, and the soft-starter amplification is nonlinear and also depends on the power factor of the connected element. For resistive loads, α varies between 0 and 90°, while in the case of an inductive load between 90 and 180°.

Usually, when the generator is completely connected to the grid, a contactor (K_{byp}) bypasses the soft starter in order to reduce the losses. In this way, the device produces varying harmonics as the firing angle of the thyristors is altered, but since they are only used for a few seconds during the connection of the induction generator, for this short period the effect of the harmonics is considered to be harmless and may be ignored (IEC, 2000b). If the antiparallel thyristors are not by-passed, then their harmonic currents need to be assessed.

2.10.3.3.3(ii) Capacitor banks

For the power factor compensation of the reactive power in the generator, AC capacitor banks are used. The generators are normally compensated into whole power range. The switching of capacitors is done as a function of the average value of measured reactive power during a certain period. In order to reduce the current at connection/disconnection of capacitors, a coil, L, can be connected in

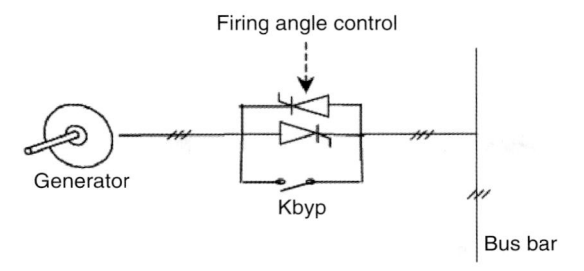

Figure 53 Soft-starter configuration. From Hansen LH, Helle L, Blaabjerg F, *et al.* Conceptual survey of generators and power electronics for wind turbines. *Riso Report R-1205*: Riso National Laboratory, Roskilde, Denmark.

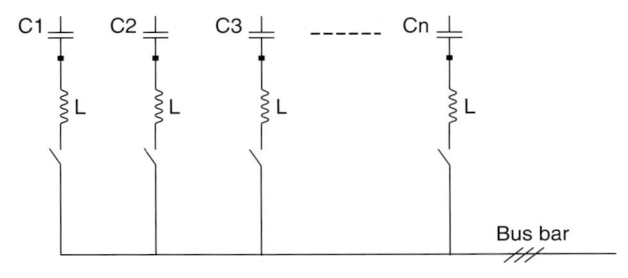

Figure 54 Capacitor layout. From Hansen LH, Helle L, Blaabjerg F, *et al.* Conceptual survey of generators and power electronics for wind turbines. *Riso Report R-1205*: Riso National Laboratory, Roskilde, Denmark.

series (**Figure 54**). The capacitors may be heavy-loaded and damaged in the case of overvoltages to the grid and thereby they may increase the maintenance cost. The capacitor banks are usually mounted in the bottom of the tower or in the nacelle.

2.10.3.3.4 Variable-speed systems

In variable-speed systems, the generator is normally connected to the grid by a power electronic system. For synchronous generators and for induction generators without rotor windings, a 'full-power converter' is connected between the stator of the generator and the grid, where the total power production must be fed through the power electronic system [16, 17]. For induction generators with rotor windings, the stator of the generator is connected to the grid directly. Only the rotor of the generator is connected through a 'partial power converter' thus allowing for the nominal power of the converter to be up to 30% of the power rating of the wind turbine.

2.10.3.3.4(i) Partial power converters

Various configurations have been used for partial load converters in slip-ring induction generators [18]. These include:

- Simple uncontrolled diode rectifier at the machine slip-rings and a line-commutated phase-controlled thyristor inverter [19] (**Figure 55**). This configuration suffers from poor power factor and harmonic distortion problems, generator operation limited only at supersynchronous speeds and nonharmonic distortion currents injected to the network.
- Cycloconverters, implemented in very large wind turbines [20], interface the rotor circuit to the bus. In this case, the generator operating region is extended below synchronous speed, although the overall speed control range is typically restricted between ± 15% of synchronous speed. In addition, reactive power control at the output is possible and improved efficiency and torque behavior can be achieved through the implementation of field-oriented control schemes. Yet, the high cost and complexity of the cycloconverters render this solution unfavorable.

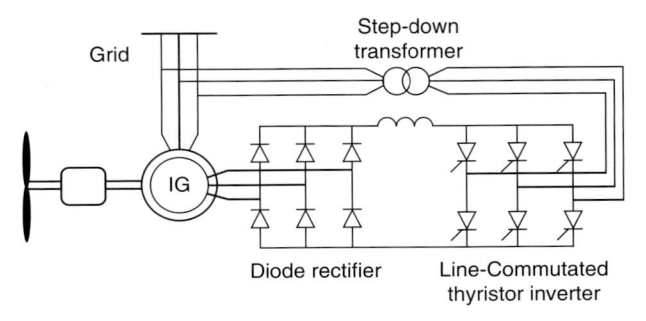

Figure 55 Slip-ring power conversion. From Kundur P (1994) *Power System Stability and Control.* New York, NY: McGraw Hill, Inc.

2.10.3.3.4(ii)   Full-power converters

The back-to-back PWM voltage source inverter (VSI) is a bidirectional power converter consisting of two conventional PWM VSIs. The topology is shown in **Figure 56**.

To achieve full control of the grid current, the DC-link voltage must be boosted to a level higher than the amplitude of the grid line–line voltage. The power flow of the grid side converter is controlled in order to keep the DC-link voltage constant, while the control of the generator side is set to suit the magnetization demand and the reference speed.

The PWM VSI is the most frequently used three-phase frequency converter. Many manufacturers produce components especially designed for use in this type of converter (e.g., a transistor pack comprising six bridge-coupled transistors and antiparalleled diodes). Due to this, the component costs can be low compared to converters requiring components designed for a niche production.

A technical advantage of the PWM VSI is the capacitor decoupling between the grid inverter and the generator inverter. Besides affording some protection, this decoupling offers separate control of the two inverters, allowing compensation of asymmetry both on the generator side and on the grid side, independently. The inclusion of a boost inductance in the DC-link circuit increases the component count, but a positive effect is that the boost inductance reduces the demands on the performance of the grid-side harmonic filter, and offers some protection of the converter against abnormal conditions on the grid.

2.10.4   Lightning Protection

In the past 10 years, the importance of effective lightning protection has been acknowledged by the wind turbine manufacturers, the wind turbine owners, governmental energy agencies, as well as the lightning research community [21].

The increasing number and height of installed turbines have resulted in a greater than anticipated incidence of lightning damage with consequent repair costs beyond acceptable levels. The influence of such events on operational reliability becomes a concern as the capacity of wind turbines increases and turbines move offshore. This is particularly important in wind farm installations, since the potential of large production lost due to one lightning flash is unacceptable. In **Figure 57** are shown the global areas with intense thunder activity.

Unlike other electrical installations, such as overhead lines, substations, and power plants, where protective conductors can be arranged around or above the installation, wind turbines pose a different protection problem due to their physical size and nature, that is, rotating blades with diameters exceeding 100 m. In addition, there is extensive use of insulating composite materials, such as glass fiber-reinforced plastic, as load-carrying parts. The lightning protection system has to be fully integrated into the different parts of the wind turbines to ensure that all parts likely to attract lightning are able to withstand its impact and

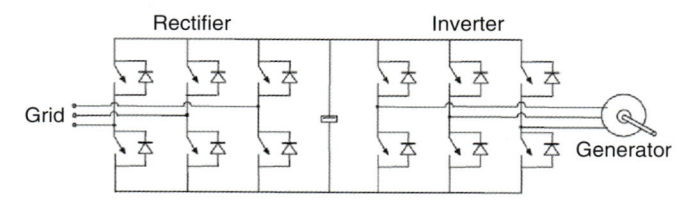

Figure 56   Back-to-back PWM VSI. From Hansen LH, Helle L, Blaabjerg F, *et al*. Conceptual survey of generators and power electronics for wind turbines. *Riso Report R-1205*: Riso National Laboratory, Roskilde, Denmark.

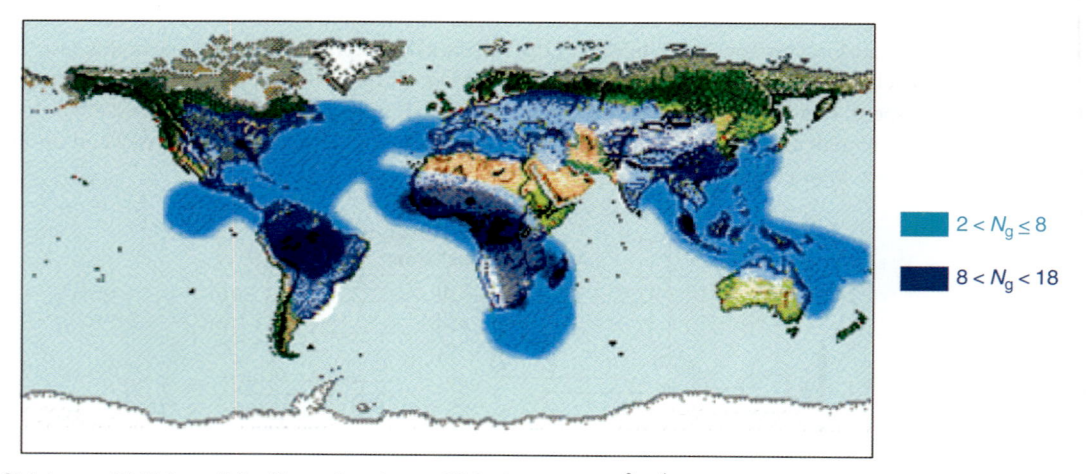

Figure 57   Global map of lightning activity. N_g, number of ground lightning strikes $km^{-2} yr^{-1}$. From ABB brochure: ABB Lightning Protection Group. 22, rue du 8 Mai 1945, 95340 – Persan, France, www.abb.com.

that the lightning current may be conducted safely from the attachment points to the ground without unacceptable damage or disturbances to the system.

Lightning develops when the upper atmosphere becomes unstable due to a convergence of a warm, solar-heated, vertical air column on a cooler upper air mass. These rising air currents carry water vapor, which, on meeting cooler air, usually condenses and gives rise to convective storm activity. Pressure and temperature are such that the vertical air movement becomes self-sustaining, creating the basis of a cumulonimbus cloud formation with its center core capable of rising to over 15 000 m. To generate lightning, the cloud must be 3–4 km deep. The taller the cloud, the more frequent the lightning. The center column of the cumulonimbus can have updrafts exceeding 120 km h^{-1}, creating intense turbulence with violent wind shears. Updrafts also lead to electric charge separations that ultimately lead to the lightning discharge. The earth's surface is positively charged and the lower atmosphere takes on an opposing negative space charge. As rain droplets carry charge away from the cloud to the earth, the storm cloud takes on characteristics of a dipole with the bottom of the cloud negatively charged and the top of the cloud positively charged.

The average energy released in a discharge is 55 kWh, a significant amount of energy by modern generation standards. The danger of the discharge lies in the fact that all of the energy is expended in only 100–300 µs, and the peak discharge current is reached in only 1–2 µs. Channeling the energy from the wind turbine blade through the nacelle and tower to ground takes proper design coordination. The difference between positive and negative lightning is that the positive lightning leader is neither stepped nor are there multistrikes. There is only one return stroke, after which a continuous current flows to discharge the cloud.

Because lightning is a natural phenomenon, a statistical approach is useful in its analysis and the design of protective systems. Data from the International Council of Large Electrical Systems (CIGRE) indicate that:

- 5% of negative lightning impulses exceed 90 kA (average is 33 kA)
- 5% of positive lightning impulses exceed 250 kA (average is 33 kA)
- 5% of negative restrikes exceed a rate of current rise 161 kA µs^{-1}.

The IEC 62305 series introduces four lightning protection levels with design rules based on a lightning protection system that guards against strikes of minimum and maximum values. Probability of exceeding limits shows probabilities that these maximum and minimum values may be exceeded.

In general, lightning protection for wind power generation includes a lightning pole on the nacelle, an independent lightning pole tower, and a receptor on the top end of a blade. However, the lightning pole on the nacelle cannot obtain enough height owing to weight and wind pressure, and an independent lightning tower greatly increases construction costs. The third solution, the receptor on the blade is recommended in IEC's reports [22], but is far from being a complete solution. Despite the existence of such receptors, dielectric accidents still occur in wind turbine components, such as blades, generator, transformer, and low-voltage circuits.

According to IEC, the most frequent accident is dielectric breakdown on low-voltage circuits including electric and telecommunication equipment. In general, electric and electronic equipment for wind turbine are set up close to or inside a wind tower. Once lightning strikes, assuming it hit a receptor of one of the blades, a lightning current surge propagates through a down-conductor in the blades, a carbon-brush or arc horn near the bearings, and the grounding conductor inside the wind tower (or the current may flow through the conductive tower itself) (**Figure 58**).

Therefore, to achieve complete lightning protection in accordance with IEC 61024-1 [23], a sophisticated system of lightning current arresters must be utilized.

There are special requirements for protecting the power supply system between the generator and transformer station at the 400/690-V level. It consists of a Class I and Class II arrester wired in parallel.

A typical Class I arrester uses spark gap technology with lightning current carrying capacity (I_{imp}) at 50 kA (with a 10/350-µs waveform) per channel (**Figures 59 and 60**). These qualities let the spark gap satisfy the relevant requirements of the IEC standard. It connects in parallel with Class II arresters based on metal oxide varistors. Both the Class I and II components must have an arrester-rated voltage (U_c) of 440 V.

These components function on the principle of active energy control. During a lightning strike, the Class II arrester initially handles all conduction because of its rapid response time. This device has a characteristic curve that graphs conducted current versus voltage. Designers can use this information to determine when the Class I arrester should trigger so as to keep from exceeding the maximum permissible energetic strain of the Class II device. Thus, once triggered, the Class I arrester handles the massive current from a lightning event, preventing an overload of the Class II arrester. This combination and coordination of Class I and II arresters allows fast response and high current handling capability. A Class II plug-in module can be hot swapped when necessary. In **Figure 61** are shown the most important electrical pieces that must be safeguarded against lightning strikes.

Furthermore, in wind turbines, surge voltage arresters safeguard the I/O of the measuring equipment leads coming in from outside. These carry signals that are important for steering the blades into the wind or for system start-up or shutdown. Finally, wind turbines within a wind park are networked to facilitate the exchange of data. A master system captures fault and status reports and transmits these to a main control center. The data communication interfaces to the telecommunications system must be equipped with pluggable surge voltage protection devices (**Figure 62**).

A novel lightning protection system for wind turbines is described in Reference 24. It uses two ring-shaped electrodes attached to the wind turbine. They are of several meters diameter, one vertically attached to the nose cone and the other laterally placed on the top of the wind tower, below the nacelle. The pair of rings is arranged with a narrow gap of no more than 1 m in order to avoid

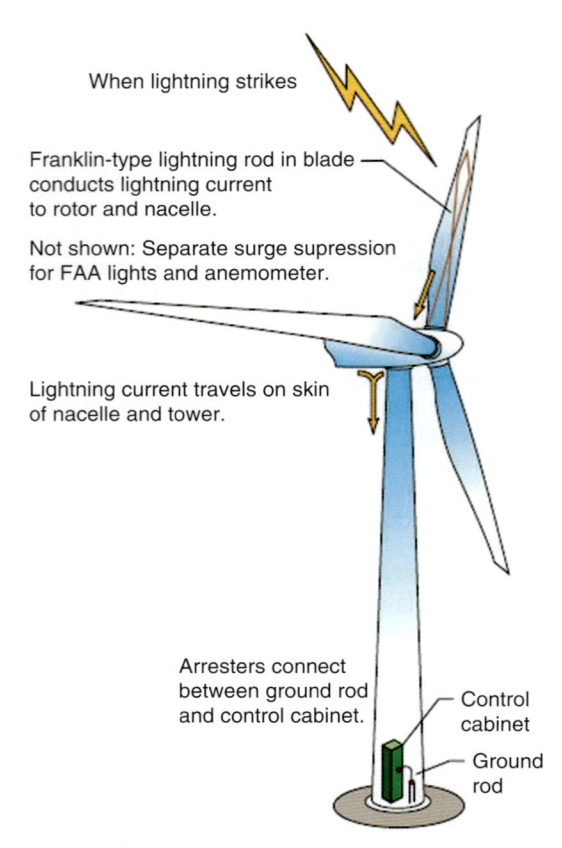

Figure 58 Lightning course. From ABB brochure: ABB Lightning Protection Group. 22, rue du 8 Mai 1945, 95340 – Persan, France, www.abb.com.

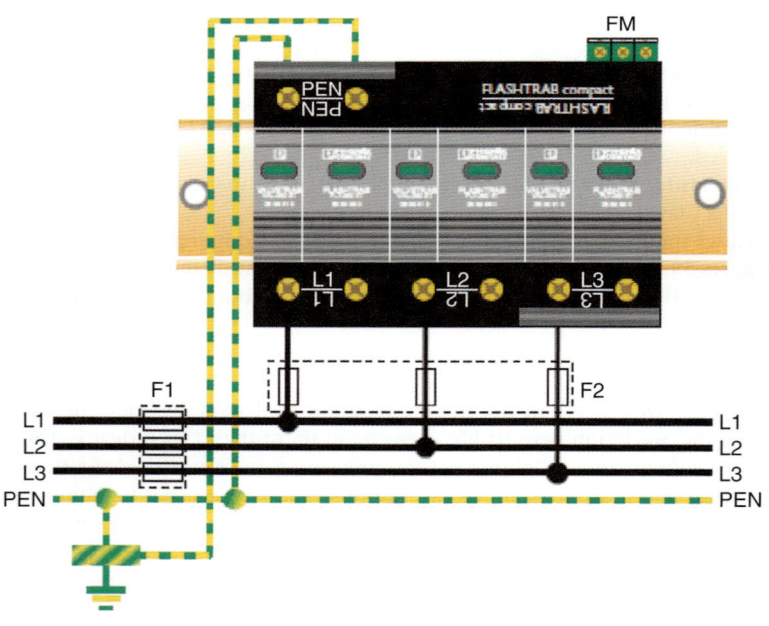

Figure 59 Branch wiring of a Class I arrester. From Phoenix Contact brochure http://www.phoenixcontact.co.uk/industries/27707.htm.

mechanical friction during rotation of the blades and the nacelle's circling. When lightning strikes a blade, the current reaches the upper ring from a receptor through a conductive wire. Then the electric field between the two rings gets higher, sparks over, and the lightning current flows downwards propagating along the lower ring and the grounding wire, which is located outside the wind tower, and is safely led to a grounding electrode (**Figure 63**).

Figure 60 Arrester combination for four-conductor networks. From Phoenix Contact brochure http://www.phoenixcontact.co.uk/industries/27707.htm.

2.10.5 Small Wind Turbines

Even though megawatt machines dominate the market today, it is an undisputable fact that small wind turbines (SWTs) have also a significant role to play in renewable energy production.

Small wind system technology can be subdivided into categories as shown in **Table 4** (CIEMAT, see Relevant Websites). The two main designs are the horizontal-axis wind turbines and vertical-axis wind turbines. They can be connected to the grid, or alternatively used to charge batteries off-grid.

However, in spite of the maturity reached on the development of the large- and medium-sized wind technology for wind farms, the state of the art for SWTs is far from technological maturity and economical competitiveness. Average costs for current stand-alone wind turbines vary from 2500 to 6000€ per installed kW, while in distributed generation, a SWT can vary from 2700 to 8000€ per installed kW, the additional cost mainly due to the power converter required for grid connection. Both these figures contrast with the specific costs of large wind turbines, which are in the region of $1500€\,kW^{-1}$.

Most of the SWTs that are currently deployed around the world have three blades, but there are also models with two, four, or more. Rotor diameter is below 20 m, but most of the commercial SWTs have a rotor diameter below 10 m. These turbines are mounted typically on 12–24 m towers.

For the rotor, technology trends are toward advanced blade manufacturing methods based mainly on alternative manufacturing techniques such as injection moulding, compression moulding, and reaction injection moulding. The advantages are shorter fabrication time, lower parts cost, and increased repeatability and uniformity, but tooling costs are higher.

A synchronous PM generator based on PMs is the standard choice for small machines, since they have better magnetic properties than ferrite ones and result in less overall weight. Induction generators, on the other hand, are still in the competition. Even though their employment in small machines directly connected to the grid was scarce, lately interest in them, mainly due to economic reasons, has reemerged. The reason is that expensive power electronics can, in this case be omitted.

Another costly component for grid-connected small machines is the inverter. Most designs use off-the-shelf industrial inverters, also used in PV systems, although wind-specific products have started to appear.

This kind of turbines utilize simple power control mechanisms, which are usually limited to just a yawing regulation. However, more advanced methods, such as active stall and pitch control, have started to appear, since these systems became increasingly available in low-cost versions.

The most recent developments in the field of SWTs can be summarized as follows (details at Relevant Websites):

- active pitch controls to maintain energy capture at very high wind speeds,
- vibration isolators to dampen sound,
- advanced blade design and manufacturing methods,
- alternative means of self-protection in extreme winds,
- adapting a single model to either on-grid or off-grid use,
- software and wireless display units,

302 Electrical Parts of Wind Turbines

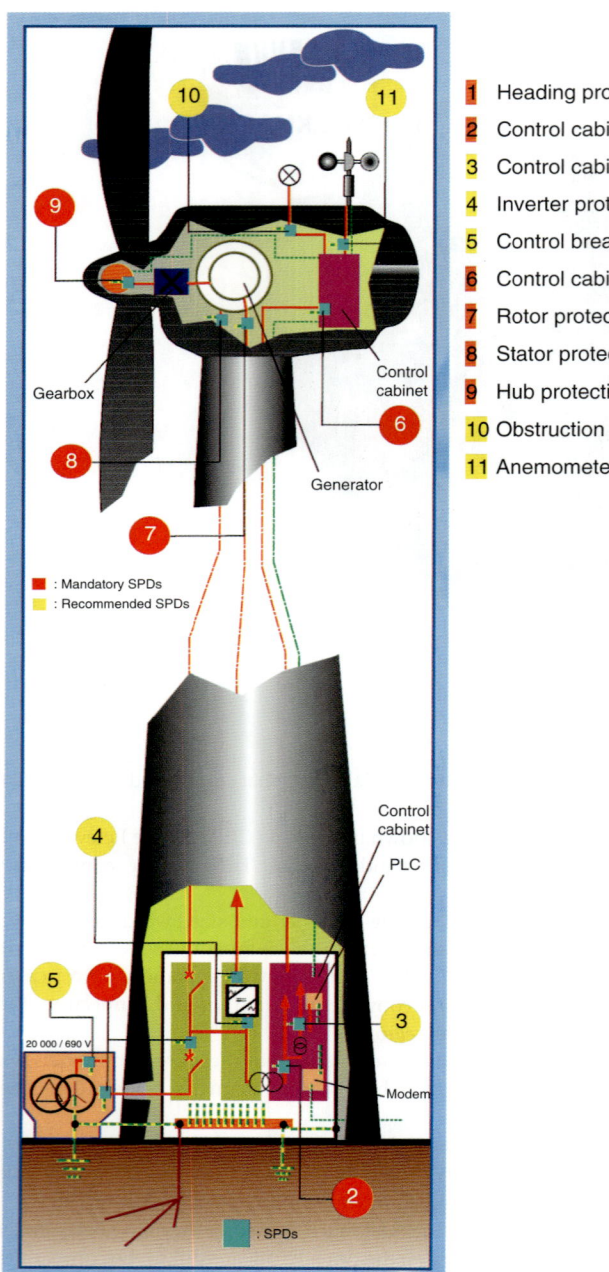

	Unit	Typical voltage
1	Heading protection	690
2	Control cabinet protection	230
3	Control cabinet protection	24
4	Inverter protection for rotor circuit	380/480/690
5	Control breaker protection	230
6	Control cabinet protection	230
7	Rotor protection	380/480/690
8	Stator protection	690
9	Hub protection	24/28/230
10	Obstruction lighting protection	230
11	Anemometer	24

Figure 61 Main lightning protection areas. From ABB brochure: ABB Lightning Protection Group. 22, rue du 8 Mai 1945, 95340 – Persan, France, drawing by ABB, www.abb.com.

- inverters integrated into the nacelle (rotor hub),
- electronics designed to meet stronger safety and durability standards,
- systems wired for turnkey interconnection,
- attempts to make SWT more visually attractive, and
- integrating turbines into existing tower structures, such as utility or lighting poles.

The industry is by no means small, since there exist over 400 models offered by more than 150 manufacturers worldwide (see Relevant Websites). This has led to the adoption of new operation standards by the IEC (61400-02, 2nd ed.) in 2006.

An interesting novel development is Madesta's 20 kW tower wind turbine. In this design, the air stream is directed into a vertically standing tower where a generator is installed. Wind is then speeded up just before its interaction with blades of the

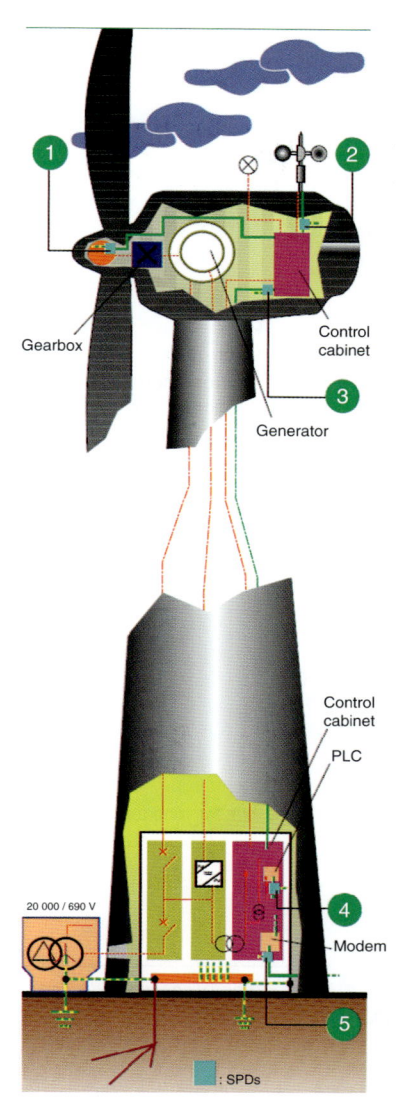

Figure 62 Data communication lines lightning protection points. From ABB brochure: ABB Lightning Protection Group. 22, rue du 8 Mai 1945, 95340 – Persan, France, drawing by ABB, www.abb.com.

generator increasing its kinetic energy (**Figure 64**). Designers claim an increase in power production, especially in low speeds, compared to horizontal generators (**Figure 65**).

2.10.6 Outlook

Currently, the three main categories (with minor subcategories) of generator/converter pairs currently dominating the wind turbine market are shown in **Table 5**. Market share of the various types is shown in **Figure 66**.

Larger PM generators seem to be dominating the current trend. Research directions in this area include [25]:

- Decreasing air gap, increasing poles in direct-drive AFPM generators
- Overcoming transportation problem of large (>4.2 m) generators
- Improving mechanical integrity (bearing arrangement, magnetic imbalance)
- Enhancement of medium-speed, geared Multibrid concept
- Further development of radial or transverse flux machines.

Increasing turbine size and moving offshore are the future outlook of the wind turbine industry. Two important research projects currently in progress are:

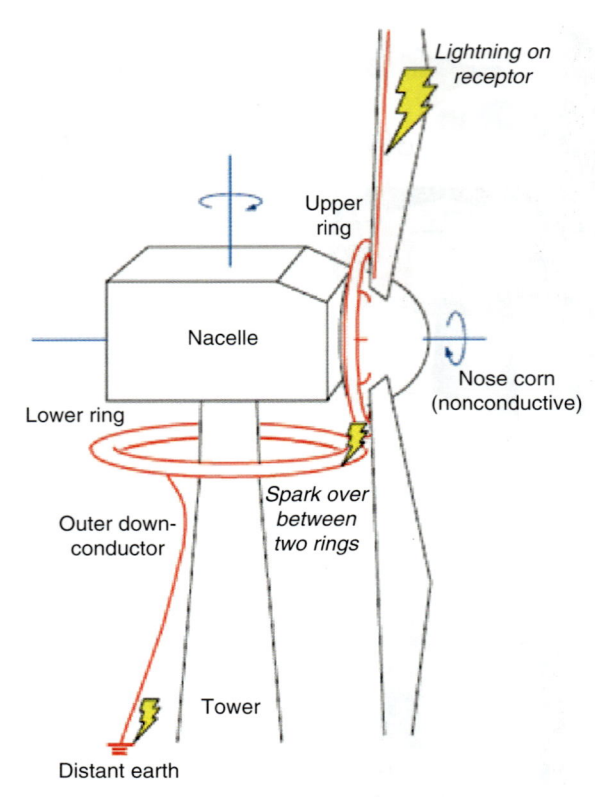

Figure 63 Two ring protection system. From Yoh Y (2006) A new lightning protection system for wind turbines using two ring-shaped electrodes. *IEEJ Transactions on Electrical and Electronic Engineering* 1: 314–319.

Table 4 Small wind turbine classification data

Rated power	Rotor swept area	Subcategory	Annual energy production (kWh)[a]	Height (m)
$P_{rated} < 1$ kW	$A < 5$ m^2	Pico wind	~1 000	10–18
1 kW $< P_{rated} < 7$ kW	$A < 40$ m^2	Micro wind	~50 000	12–20
7 kW $< P_{rated} < 50$ kW	$A < 200$ m^2	Mini wind	~100 000	15–40
50 kW $< P_{rated} < 100$ kW	$A < 300$ m^2	?	~200 000	30–100

[a]Annual energy consumption per household ~4000 kWh.

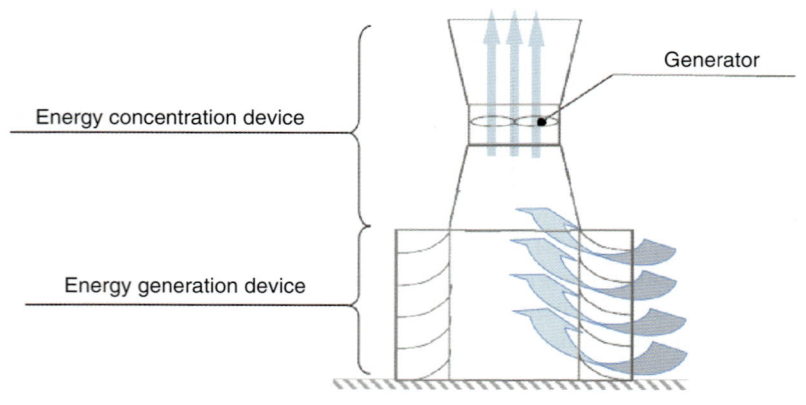

Figure 64 Madesta's concept. From Madesta brochure, http://www.madesta.com/.

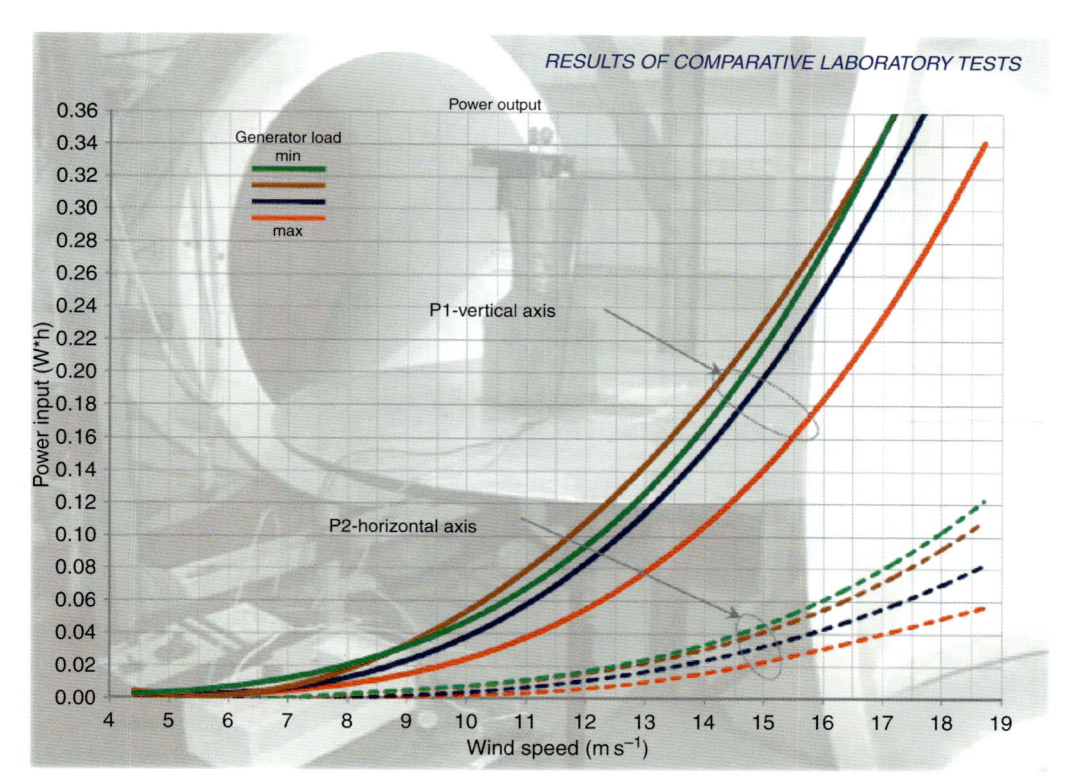

Figure 65 Comparison chart. From Madesta brochure, http://www.madesta.com/.

Table 5 Main categories of generator/converter pairs

Description	Speed control (%)	Efficiency	Cost[a] (%)	Advantages	Disadvantages
Squirrel-cage induction generator	100 ± 0.5	0.96	100	Robust, reliable, low cost	Low efficiency, excitation current
Double-fed asynchronous generator with static inverter, harmonic filter, and reactive power compensation	100 ± 25	0.94	160	Best compromise of controllability, cost, and performance	Poor reliability
Direct-drive synchronous generator with permanent magnet excitation, static inverter (AC-DC-AC), and harmonic filter	100 ± 50	0.94	450	Inherently grid compliant, affordable power electronics	Average reliability, large rotor size

[a]Compared to base price.

1. A 10 MW prototype floating offshore wind turbine has been commissioned by Norway's Enova to Sway AS. The turbine is standing on a floating tower and has a rotor diameter of 145 m. The tower pole is filled with a ballast beneath the water creating a low center of gravity. It will be anchored to the seabed with a single pipe and a suction anchor. The turbine can tilt 5–8°, and turns around a subsea swivel with the wind (**Figure 67**).
2. US's Clipper Windpower is another company involved in building a 10 MW wind turbine. Under the name 'Britannia', the firm has commissioned the design of a 144 m diameter machine, which, unlike Sway's prototype, is to be founded on solid grounds, even though offshore. The turbine parts, that is, controls, drive-train, gearbox, and blades seem to be based on the firm's Liberty turbine, but details are still undisclosed. The design will need to avoid the foundation problems faced by recently built offshore wind farms. The problem is based on the grouting used at the top of each turbine's monopile. The grouting supports the tower by holding the monopile foundations in place. It is beginning to fail as a result of the high stress levels imposed on the turbine above sea level.

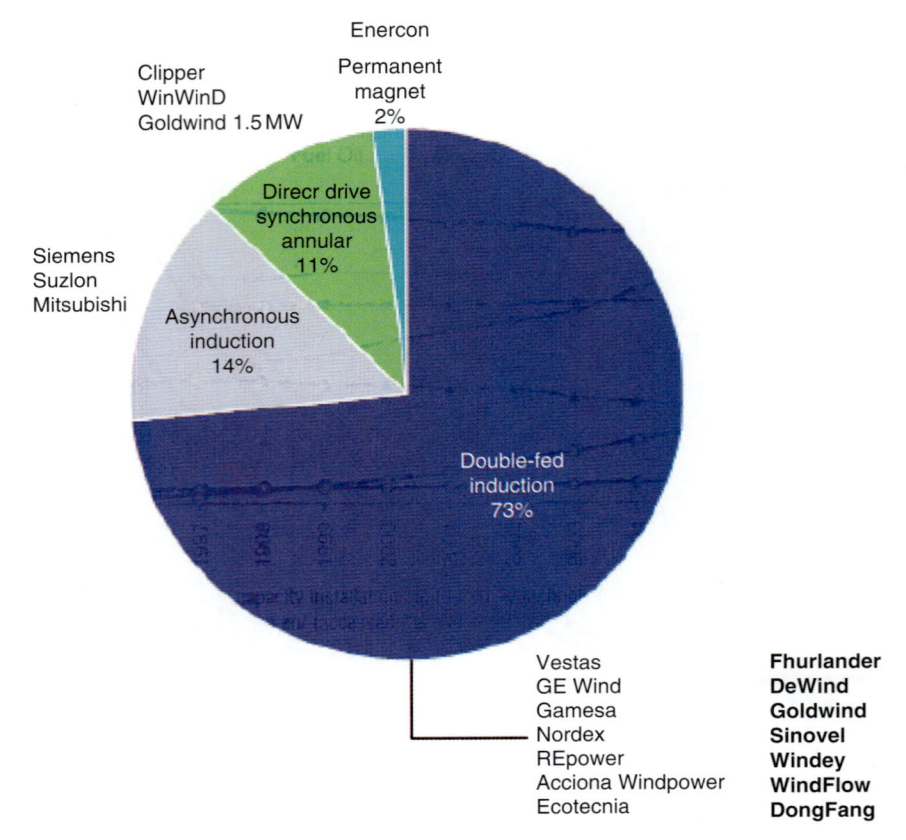

Figure 66 Wind turbine type market share. From EER, www.emerging-energy.com.

Figure 67 Sway concept. From SWAY website, www.sway.no.

2.10.7 Wind Turbine Industry

2.10.7.1 Major Wind Turbine Manufacturers

The relevant data for the foregoing electrical system elements will be described for each one of the major world wind turbine manufacturers. According to latest data (October 2010), the top 10 are shown in **Figure 68**. As it can be seen, Vestas keeps its established leading position, while Chinese manufacturers are strongly coming up in the world market.

Pertinent data are shown for typical models of each manufacturer, as described in their official documentation (see Relevant Websites for more up to date information).

2.10.7.1.1 Vestas

Vestas is a leading Danish company manufacturing wind turbines since 1970, even though the company dates back to 1898. With over 20 000 employees, they have installed more than 5500 MW of wind power worldwide. Their range of turbines spans the whole wind spectrum, climbing up to the 3 MW class (**Figure 69** and **Table 6**).

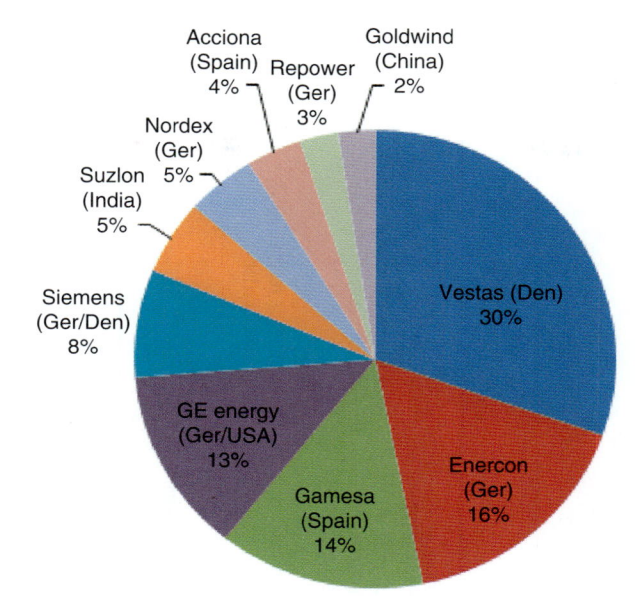

Figure 68 World distribution of wind turbine market.

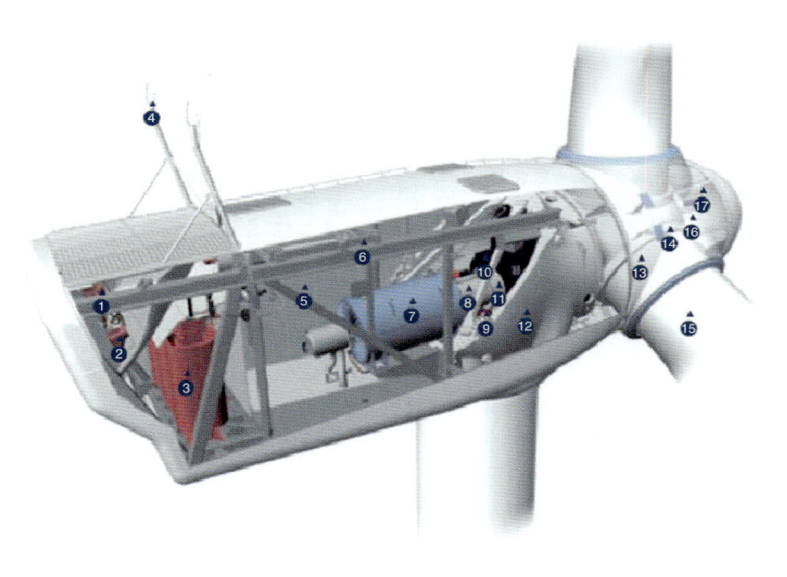

1. Oil cooler
2. Generator cooler
3. Transformer
4. Ultrasonic wind sensors
5. VMP-Top controller with converter
6. Service crane
7. Optispeed generator
8. Composite disc coupling
9. Yaw gears
10. Gearbox
11. Parking brake
12. Machine foundation
13. Blade bearing
14. Blade hub
15. Blade
16. Pitch cylinder
17. Hub controller

Figure 69 Vestas V90 nacelle components. From Vestas brochure, www.vestas.com.

Vestas has introduced a number of innovations in their wind turbines:

ActiveStall® is a hydraulic power control system for minimizing loads and controlling output. It provides fail-safe protection in all conditions and, above its rated wind speed, maintains a steady output. Employed in the 1.65 MW model.

Table 6 Wind turbine data: Vestas

Turbine type/size	Cut-in speed ($m\,s^{-1}$)	Cut-out speed ($m\,s^{-1}$)	Drive train	Power control	Generator type	Grid connection	Thunder protection
V82/1.65 kW	4	25	Three-stage, one planet, two parallel	ActiveStall®	690 V, squirrel-cage asynchronous. Fixed speed		
V80/1.8 MW	3.5	20	Three-stage planetary, helical	Common blade pitch control, ActiveStall®	690 V, wound rotor, external resistors asynchronous Semi-variable speed OptiSlip®	Active and reactive power regulation, fault ride-through	
V90/3 MW	4	25	Three-stage planetary, helical	Independent blade pitch control OptiTip® Yaw control	690 V, 4-pole, doubly fed, asynchronous Variable speed		
V112/3 MW	3	25		OptiTip®	Permanent magnet with full-scale converter, OptiSpeed®	Diode grid-side rectifier, IGBT rotor-side inverter	

IGBT, isolated gate bipolar transistor.

OptiTip® is a microprocessor-controlled pitch regulation system. It constantly adjusts the angle of the turbine blades to ensure the optimal position in relation to the prevailing winds. This technology is used in all their turbines except the V82-1.65 MW.

OptiSpeed® allows the rotor speed to vary within a range of approximately 60% in relation to nominal rpm. Thus, with OptiSpeed®, the rotor speed can vary by as much as 30% above and below synchronous speed. This minimizes both unwanted fluctuations in the output to the grid supply and the loads on the vital parts of the construction. Finally, OptiSpeed® helps to deliver better quality power to the grid, with rapid synchronization, reduced harmonic distortion, and less flicker.

Vestas grid support features full load and static phase compensation to enhance reactive power regulation. Additionally, grid support provides continuous active and reactive power regulation to maintain voltage balance in the grid, as well as fault ride-through in the event of disturbances.

2.10.7.1.2 Enercon

Enercon of Germany began its road to innovative wind turbine manufacturing in 1984. The first E-15/16 wind turbine with a rated power of 55 kW featured gearboxes, while the changeover to gearless technology was made in 1992 with the first Enercon E-40/500 kW.

Enercon has recently (2010) entered the multimegawatt class with the experimental E82/3 MW and E126/7.5 MW models. Previous models fully cover the kW to 2 MW range (see **Table 7**).

Enercon is the inventor of many breakthroughs, such as follows:

Annular generator. A key component in Enercon's gearless, direct-drive wind generator design. This low-speed synchronous generator is directly connected to the rotor. Generator output voltage and frequency vary with the speed and are converted via the Grid Management System to be fed into the grid. It allows rotational speed control to be optimized; the annular generator is coupled in a flexible way to the grid. By individual blade pitching and through electrical excitation via the turbine control system, rotational speed and power output are constantly checked and optimized.

Grid Management System. The electrical power produced by the annular generator passes into the grid management system that comprises a rectifier (DC link) and a modular inverter system. The inverter system defines the essential performance characteristics for output to the grid and ensures that the power output corresponds to grid specifications. Furthermore, voltage, frequency and power are converted accordingly and inverter voltage (400 V) is stepped up to the appropriate medium voltage required by the grid or the wind farm network (**Figure 70**). The Grid Management System offers

Table 7 Wind turbine data: Enercon

Turbine type/size	Cut-in speed (m s^{-1})	Cut-out speed (m s^{-1})	Drive train	Power control	Generator type	Grid connection	Thunder protection
E70/2.3 MW	2	28–34 (with storm control)	Direct drive	Independent blade pitch Active yaw	Enercon's annular generator	Enercon converter	Integrated in the blades
E82/2 MW	2	28–34 (with storm control)	Direct drive	Independent blade pitch Active yaw	Enercon's annular generator	Enercon converter	Integrated in the blades

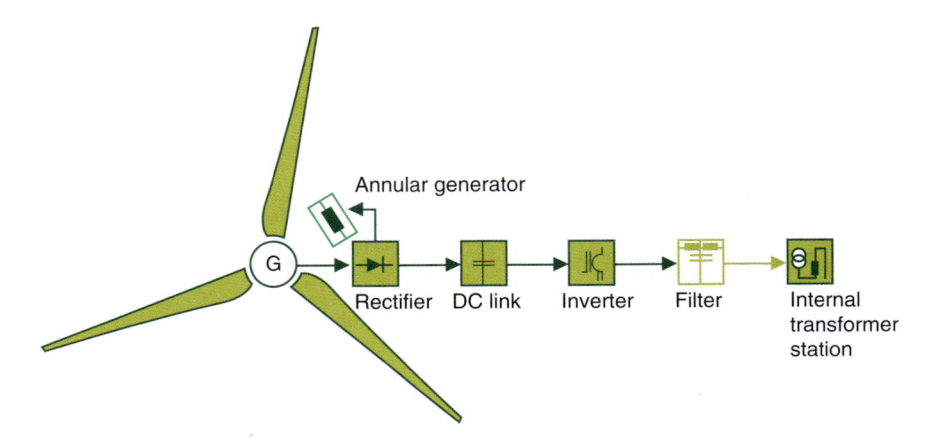

Figure 70 Enercon's system layout. From Vestas brochure, www.vestas.com.

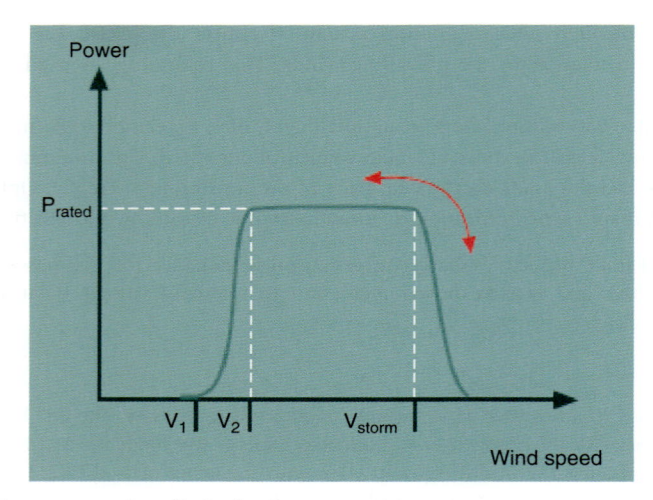

Figure 71 Enercon's storm control power curve. From Vestas brochure, www.vestas.com.

numerous performance features, for example, reactive power management and optimum contribution to maintaining voltage levels. Due to special control dynamics, the system also supports the grid in critical situations such as short circuits or bottlenecks.

Enercon storm control. A special storm control feature enabling reduced turbine operation in the event of extremely high wind speeds, and preventing the otherwise frequent shutdowns and resulting yield losses. In **Figure 71** is shown the power curve diagram with storm control that demonstrates that the wind turbine does not shut down automatically when a certain cut-out wind speed V_{storm} is exceeded, but merely reduces the power output by lowering the rotational speed. This is achieved by turning the rotor blades slightly out of the wind. Once the wind speed drops, the blades turn back into the wind, and the turbine immediately resumes operation at full power.

2.10.7.1.3 Gamesa

Gamesa is a Spanish company specialized in sustainable energy technologies, mainly wind power. Gamesa is the market leader in Spain and is positioned among the most important wind generator manufacturers in the world. It has installed wind turbines in 20 countries spreading out over four continents.

Gamesa offers a wind turbine range in the 850 kW sector and wind turbines in the multimegawatt sector (2.0 MW and the new platform Gamesa G10X-4.5 MW) (see **Table 8**).

All machines are equipped with pitch control. The 'active yaw system' is equipped with five hydraulic brake clamps that can be regulated gradually, in order to avoid fatigues and failures (**Figure 72**). It uses four electrical motors operated by the wind turbine controller based on information received from the anemometers mounted on top of the nacelle.

Their gearbox comprises three combined steps, one planetary and two parallel helicoidal (**Figure 73**).

Generator. The low power models use a 4-pole DFIG with variable speed regulation through rotor current control (**Figure 74**). Furthermore, active and reactive power control is effected as usual through control of rotor current amplitude and phase resulting in low harmonic content and minimal losses.

Transformer. Three-phase, dry encapsulated type with voltage range 6.6–34.5 kV. It is mounted inside the nacelle, thereby reducing energy losses and improving visual impact (**Figure 75**).

Safety system. Includes low-voltage protection, fuses in stator and rotor bush-bar, neutral current relay, medium-voltage protection, medium-voltage switchgear, spark sensors, and surge arrester.

Lightning protection. Gamesa uses a 'total lightning protection' system, in accordance with standard IEC 61024-1. Lightning is conducted from both sides of the blade tip down to the root joint and from there across the nacelle and tower structure to the grounding system located in the foundations.

Gamesa's 4.5 MW G128 machine is their top of the range and includes a number of innovative features.

CompacTrain®, the proprietary wind turbine drive train, consists of a semi-integrated main shaft and a two-stage planetary gearbox with mid-speed range output. This integrated design makes the unit more compact, with fewer components. Mid-range speed output improves reliability with no high-speed rotating mechanical components.

The generator is of PM type (**Figure 76**). Individual blade pitch control and active yaw are implemented.

Table 8 Wind turbine data: Gamesa

Turbine type/size	Cut-in speed ($m\ s^{-1}$)	Cut-out speed ($m\ s^{-1}$)	Drive train	Power control	Generator type	Grid connection	Thunder protection
G58/850 kW	3	23	One planetary stage Two helical	Variable speed Pitch control	690 V, 4-pole doubly fed generator GBT converter PWM modulation	Low-voltage ride-through: active crowbar and oversized converter Active and reactive power regulation	Total lightning protection IEC 61024-1
G90/2 MW	3	25	One planetary stage Two parallel	Variable speed Pitch/active yaw control	690 V, 4-pole doubly fed generator IGBT converter PWM modulation	Low-voltage ride-through: active crowbar and oversized converter Active and reactive power regulation	Total lightning protection IEC 61024-1
G128/4.5 MW	3	35	Two planetary stages	Variable speed Individual pitch/active yaw control	660 V, permanent magnet Full converter with independent modules	Full reactive power regulation	Total lightning protection IEC 61024-1

IGBT, isolated gate bipolar transistor; PWM, pulse-width modulator.

312 **Electrical Parts of Wind Turbines**

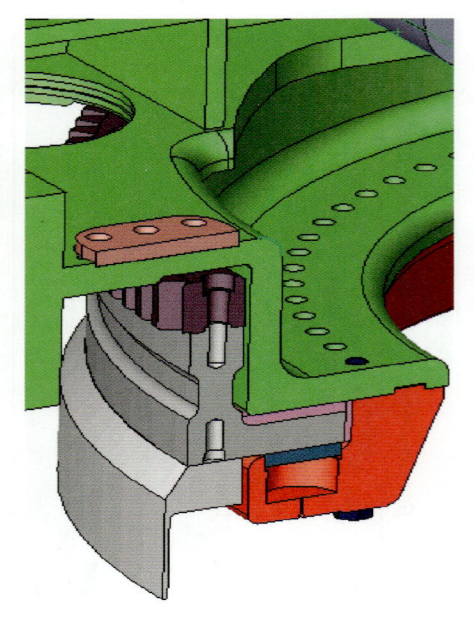

Figure 72 Gamesa's active yaw system. From Gamesa brochure, www.gamesacorp.com/en.

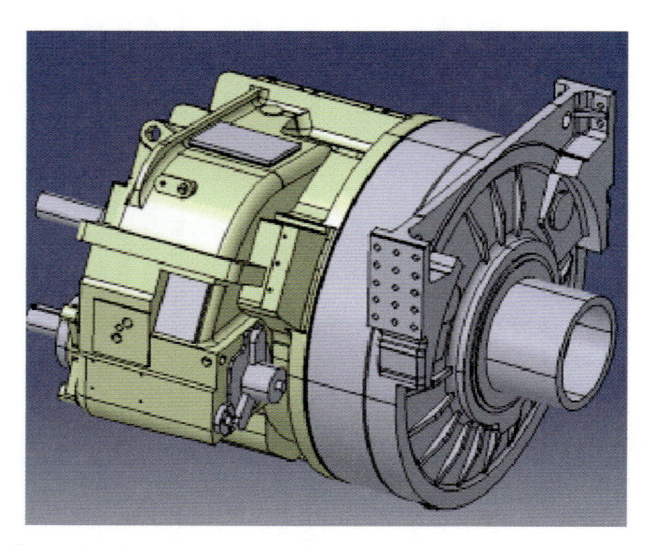

Figure 73 Gamesa's gearbox. From Gamesa brochure, www.gamesacorp.com/en.

Figure 74 Gamesa Eolica 2 MW turbine generator. From Gamesa brochure, www.gamesacorp.com/en.

Electrical Parts of Wind Turbines 313

Figure 75 Gamesa Eolica transformer. From Gamesa brochure, www.gamesacorp.com/en.

Figure 76 G128's permanent magnet generator. From Gamesa brochure, www.gamesacorp.com/en.

Gamesa's GridMate® full converter system comprises six independent systems connected in parallel to the liquid-filled MV transformer, which continue to function in the event of individual failure (**Figure 77**). A conventional back-to-back VSC converter rated at 690 V with 1700 V IBGT's connects the system to the grid.

2.10.7.1.4 GE Energy

GE Energy is a major US company supplying power generation and energy delivery technologies for traditionally fueled plants as well as those driven by renewable resources such as wind, solar, and biogas. It was founded in 1900 and operates in more than 100 countries worldwide. It employs ~40 000 people and revenue was $21.8 billion in 2007.

Their wind power sector manufactures a range of onshore and offshore wind turbines in the 1.5 and 2.5 MW range, as shown in **Table 9**. More than 13 500 units have been installed in all continents.

GE Energy has incorporated a number of patented features in their wind turbine range that include:

- WindCONTROL© System for voltage and power regulation so that reactive and active power are regulated and supplied to the grid. Additionally, power frequency droop, power ramp rate limiters, and integrated capacitor/reactor bank control are possible.

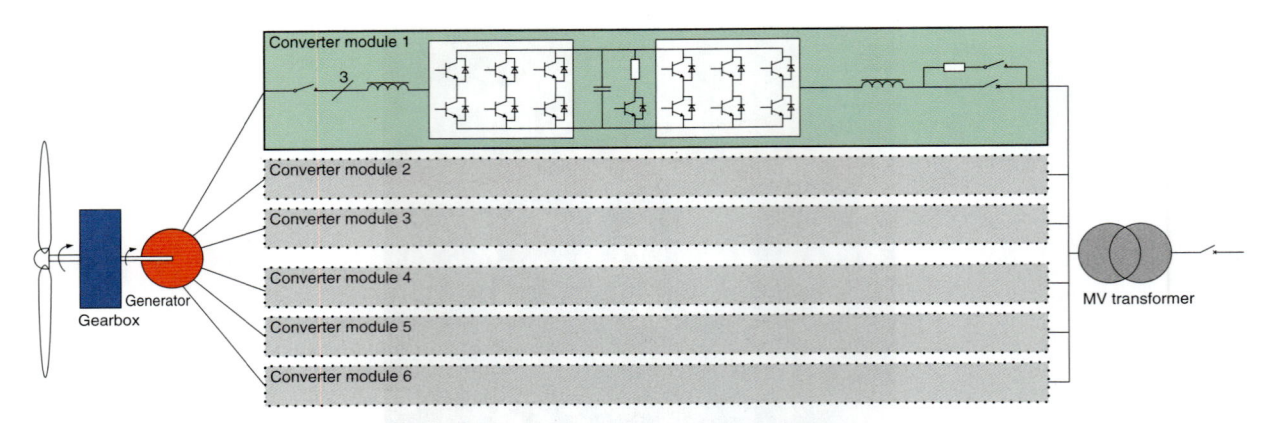

Figure 77 G128's modular generator structure. From Gamesa brochure, www.gamesacorp.com/en.

- Wind FREE© Reactive Power Feature provides reactive power even in no wind conditions, which eliminates the need for grid reinforcements in such conditions (VAR-generating equipment).
- WindRIDE-THRU© Feature provides low-voltage, zero-voltage, and high-voltage ride-through of grid disturbances, thus guaranteeing uninterrupted turbine operation in all conditions, meeting present and future transmission reliability standards.
- WindINERTIA© Control provides temporary boost in power for underfrequency grid events, similar to conventional synchronous generators with no additional hardware.

The 1.5 MW machine uses doubly-fed asynchronous generators made by the German firm VEM Sachsenwerk Gmbh (**Figure 78**). It employs pitch control.

2.10.7.1.5 Siemens

The German giant Siemens is manufacturing wind turbines as part of their renewable energy sector. Their installed machines total more than 6000 worldwide. Thanks to its wide know-how, Siemens machines are equipped with in-house technology.

Siemens produces machines in the 2.5–3.6 MW range, see **Table 10**. Their generator range comprises squirrel-cage induction generators (either fixed-speed or pole-changing) for their gearbox-based models and a PM generator for their direct-drive 3 MW machine. In this model, an outer rotor (the rotor spins on the outside of the stator) is designed (**Figure 79**). This feature allows the rotor to operate within narrower tolerances, decreasing the dimensions of the nacelle (**Figure 80**). Improved dual cooling system improves energy efficiency.

Siemens also manufactures a complete line of power converters by the brand name SIMOVERT MASTERDRIVES. They cover an output range from 45 to 6800 kW and operate as voltage DC-link converters utilizing fully digital technology. They are made for all of the voltages encountered (400, 500, or 690 V) and are quiet tolerant with respect to the specific line conditions. The rectifier–regenerative feedback unit, active front end (AFE), ensures clean voltage. AFE is a self-commutated, actively controlled line-side converter. It filters out harmonics and ensures a sinusoidal current with reduced line stressing. Furthermore, the AFE circuit principle permits line voltage fluctuations to be actively compensated. Inductive reactive power can be generated and therefore the power factor can be influenced via the line-side converter.

Power control. The blades are mounted on pitch bearings and can be feathered 90° for shutdown purposes. Each blade has its own independent fail-safe pitching mechanism allowing fine-tuning to maximize power output. On smaller fixed-speed machines, stall control is employed.

NetConverter®. A proprietary grid connection system that is compliant with current grid codes such as ride-through capability for all normal faults.

Lightning protection. Based on the international standard IEC 61400-24 Lightning Protection Level I.

2.10.7.1.6 Suzlon

Suzlon, an India-born company, was founded in 1995. It presently employs over 14 000 people in 21 countries and operates across the Americas, Asia, Australia, and Europe. It has a fully integrated supply chain with manufacturing facilities in three continents, and sophisticated R&D capabilities in Denmark, Germany, India, and The Netherlands. It is the market leader in Asia.

In May 2007, Suzlon acquired a stake in Repower Systems AG, a German-based firm. Suzlon is also closely collaborating with Hannsen Transmissions, a Belgian gearbox maker.

Their wind turbines span a range of 600 kW–2.1 MW (see **Table 11**). A direct-drive transmission system is used that comprises a three-stage gearbox consisting of one planetary and two helical stages (**Figure 81**).

Suzlon machines employ yaw motors and drives to turn the wind turbine rotor against the wind as well as pitch drives to start and stop the wind turbine generator. They use synchronous generators (**Figure 82**). The small (650 kW) machines use a 4-pole,

Table 9 Wind turbine data: GE Energy

Turbine type/size	Cut-in speed ($m\,s^{-1}$)	Cut-out speed ($m\,s^{-1}$)	Drive train	Power control	Generator type	Grid connection	Thunder protection
1.5 SLE/1.5 MW	3.5	20/25	Three-stage planetary/helical	Variable speed Independent pitch control	690 V, DFIG	Low-voltage ride-through: active crowbar and oversized converter Active and reactive power regulation	
2.5 XL/2.5 MW	3.5	25		Variable speed Independent pitch/active yaw control	Permanent magnet Full power conversion	Low-voltage ride-through: active crowbar and oversized converter Active and reactive power regulation	

DFIG, doubly fed induction generator.

Figure 78 VEM's double-fed 1.5 MW induction generator. From VEM brochure, www.vem-group.com.

Table 10 Wind turbine data: Siemens

Turbine type/size	Cut-in speed ($m\,s^{-1}$)	Cut-out speed ($m\,s^{-1}$)	Drive train	Power control	Generator type	Grid connection	Thunder protection
SWT-82/2.3	3–5	25	Three-stage planetary/helical	Variable speed independent pitch control, active yaw	690 V, induction generator	Low-voltage ride-through	IEC 61400-24 lightning protection level I
SWT-107/3.6	3.5	25	Three-stage planetary/helical	Variable speed Independent pitch control, active yaw	690 V, induction generator	Low-voltage ride-through	IEC 61400-24 lightning protection level I
SWT-101/3	3.5	25	Direct drive	Variable speed Independent pitch control, active yaw	Permanent magnet		IEC 61400-24 lightning protection level I.

Figure 79 Siemens direct-drive permanent magnet generator. From Siemens brochure, www.energy.siemens.com/hq/en/power-generation/renewables/wind-power/.

1500 rpm, squirrel-cage type with 2.5% slip at full load. Copper bars are used in the rotor slots and they are circuited at the ends by short circuit rings.

The larger ones (1.5, 2.1 MW) use a 4-pole, 50 Hz, 1500 rpm slip-ring type with wound rotors. The rotor winding is similar to stator windings, being balanced to reduce the vibration levels of the generator.

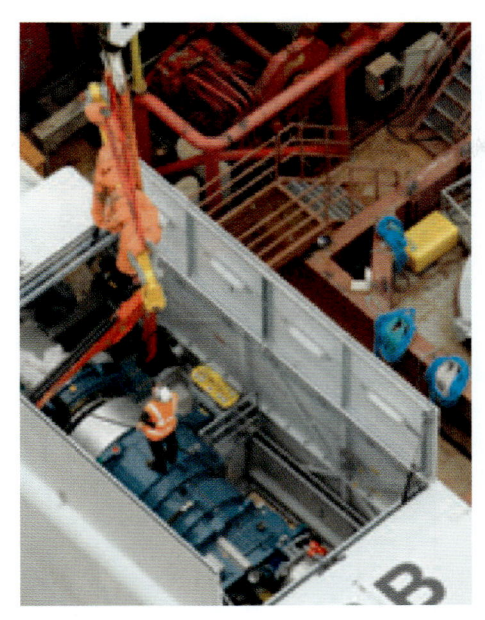

Figure 80 Siemens SWT 101 nacelle arrangement. From Siemens brochure, www.energy.siemens.com/hq/en/power-generation/renewables/wind-power/.

An interesting feature is implemented in their 250 kW and 1.25 MW machines namely a 'dual-speed' squirrel-cage generator.

The generator's stator uses special silicon steel laminations to minimize losses, while adequate cooling ducts are provided in the stator stack to maintain temperature within limits. Windings are fitted with 'resistance temperature detectors' of PT-100 type.

The effects of wind fluctuations/gusts on power outputs are damped by high slip arrangements in the generators. The generators voltage is 690 V. In-rush currents during start-up are limited by means of soft starters. The wind turbines are provided with various protection schemes to isolate the wind turbines in the event of any faults, including lightning arrestors.

Furthermore, Suzlon uses a sophisticated control system, incorporating among others:

- The Suzlon FlexiSlip that controls the power output of the asynchronous generator over a slip range of up to 16%. This reduces mechanical loads in the turbine and consequently lowers component and maintenance costs, and,
- IXYS, a system designed for short-time pulse operation to synchronize the generator speed of the wind turbine to the synchronous speed of the grid.

2.10.7.1.7 Nordex

Nordex is a Danish company launched in 1985. It has set new standards with several innovative products: the first megawatt machine in 1995 and the development and the first wind turbine with a capacity of 2.5 MW in 2000. They have presently installed over 4100 turbines with total capacity of 5.72 GW. They produce two lines of wind turbines: 1.5 and 2.5 MW models (see **Table 12** and **Figure 83**).

All their machines employ a two-stage planetary plus spur gearbox coupled to doubly-fed asynchronous generators. Torque power is split onto the planetary gears to ensure good transmission. The power is brought together again in the spur gear.

Power control is enforced by individual active blade pitch control and active yaw control.

Pitch control incorporates a number of innovative features such as:

- optimized emergency power supply with battery charging management,
- automatic lubrication system, and,
- ventilated water protection.

The yaw drive uses four induction motors for smooth operation. Nordex uses an intelligent control scheme to ensure low-strain yawing in extreme conditions.

The use of the doubly-fed generator means only 25–30% of the generated power has to be fed into the grid. In their new, third, generation slip-rings are incorporated in the rotor shaft The converter uses isolated gate bipolar transistor (IGBT) technology and is controlled by a microprocessor-based power electronics module using pulse-width modulation.

2.10.7.1.8 Acciona

A Spanish company founded in 1989. It is a multifaceted group, with 38% of its assets coming from the energy sector. The installed wind capacity was 6300 MW in December 2009.

Table 11 Wind turbine data: Suzlon

Turbine type/size	Cut-in speed (m s^{-1})	Cut-out speed (m s^{-1})	Drive train	Power control	Generator type	Grid connection	Thunder protection
S52/600 kW	4	25	One planetary/two helical	Independent active pitch Yaw control	Induction	Suzlon control system: reactive power control, low-voltage ride-through	
S64/1.25 MW	3.5	25	Three-stage: one planetary/two helical	Independent active pitch Yaw control	Double-speed squirrel-cage induction	Suzlon control system: reactive power control, low-voltage ride-through	
S82/1.5 MW	4	20	Three-stage: one planetary/two helical	Suzlon FlexiSlip active pitch Yaw control	Slip-rings induction, rotor resistance control via FlexiSlip	Suzlon control system: reactive power control, low-voltage ride-through	
S88/2.1 MW	4	25	Three-stage: one planetary/two helical	Suzlon FlexiSlip active pitch Yaw control	Slip-rings induction, rotor resistance control via FlexiSlip	Suzlon control system: reactive power control, low-voltage ride-through	

Figure 81 Suzlon's generator. From Suzlon brochure, www.suzlon.com.

Figure 82 Hansen's W4 gearbox. From Suzlon brochure, www.suzlon.com.

Table 12 Wind turbine data: Nordex

Turbine type/size	Cut-in speed ($m\,s^{-1}$)	Cut-out speed ($m\,s^{-1}$)	Drive train	Power control	Generator type	Grid connection	Thunder protection
N90/2.5 MW	3	25	Three-stage: two-stage planetary and one-stage spur	Independent active pitch Yaw control	Double-fed asynchronous	IGBT converter, PWM	Aluminum rotor blade tip. In accordance with DIN EN 62305
S70/1.5 MW	3	25	Three-stage: two-stage planetary and one-stage spur	Independent active pitch Yaw control (4 motors)	Double-fed asynchronous	IGBT converter, PWM	In accordance with DIN EN 62305

IGBT, isolated gate bipolar transistor; PWM, pulse-width modulator.

Acciona manufactures wind turbines and builds wind farms all over the world (**Figure 84**). Their wind turbine range comprises a 1.5 MW and a 3 MW series (**Figure 85** and see **Table 13**).

All their models are built on the same design. Power control is effected by individual blade pitch control. The active yaw system uses a gear ring integrated into the tower and four to six geared motors integrated into the nacelle. Active hydraulic braking is employed. The generators are three-phase asynchronous double-fed induction type with wound rotor and excitation by collector rings. Generated power is at medium voltage (12 kV) to reduce losses and avoid the need for a transformer.

Acciona uses Ingeteam's INGECON-W control system, capable of continuously optimizing its power production in a wide range of wind speeds. IGBT pulse-width modulation is used in the power converter.

2.10.7.1.9 REpower

REpower, founded in 2001, is a powerful German wind turbine manufacturer. Their product portfolio comprises several types of turbines with rated outputs ranging between 2.05 and 6.15 MW, with more than 2000 turbines installed worldwide (see **Table 14**).

320   **Electrical Parts of Wind Turbines**

Figure 83   Nordex S-70's nacelle (courtesy Nordex). From Nordex brochure, www.nordex-online.com/en.

Figure 84   Acciona's Cathedral Rocks wind park in South Australia. From Acciona brochure, www.acciona-energia.com/.

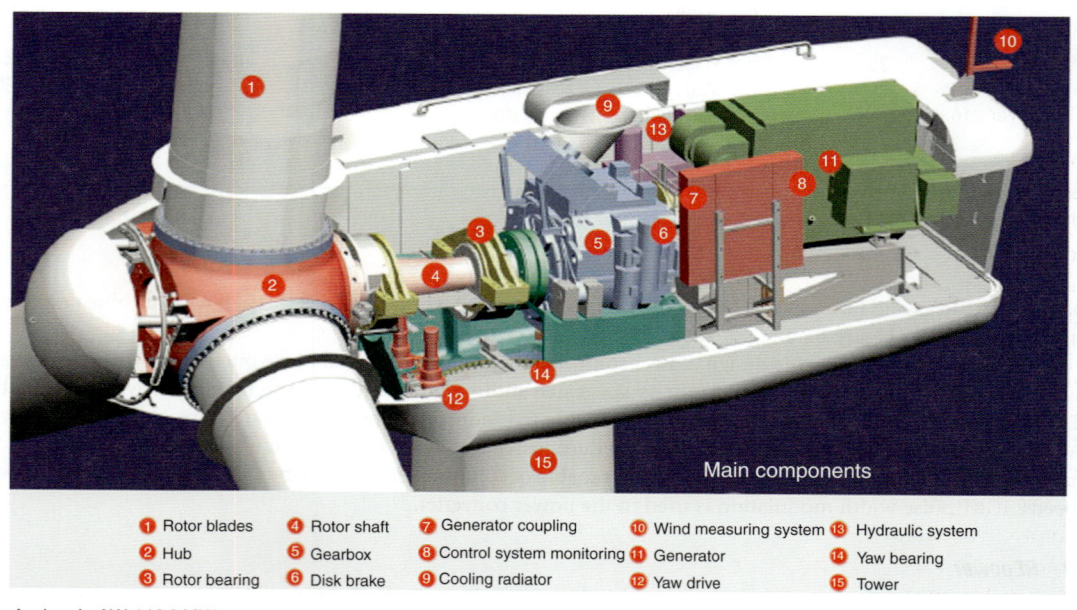

① Rotor blades   ④ Rotor shaft   ⑦ Generator coupling   ⑩ Wind measuring system   ⑬ Hydraulic system
② Hub   ⑤ Gearbox   ⑧ Control system monitoring   ⑪ Generator   ⑭ Yaw bearing
③ Rotor bearing   ⑥ Disk brake   ⑨ Cooling radiator   ⑫ Yaw drive   ⑮ Tower

Figure 85   Acciona's AW 119 3 MW turbine nacelle. From Acciona brochure, www.acciona-energia.com/.

Table 13 Wind turbine data: Acciona

Turbine type/size	Cut-in speed (m s^{-1})	Cut-out speed (m s^{-1})	Drive train	Power control	Generator type	Grid connection	Thunder protection
AW 82/1.5 MW	3	20	Three-stage: two planetary, one helical	Independent active pitch Yaw control (four motors)	6-Pole doubly fed asynchronous, slip-ring excitation, 12 kV	IGBT converter, PWM INGECON-W	
AW 119/3 MW	3	20	Three-stage: two planetary, one helical	Independent active pitch Yaw control (six motors)	6-Pole doubly fed asynchronous, slip-ring excitation, 12 kV	IGBT converter, PWM INGECON-W	

IGBT, isolated gate bipolar transistor; PWM, pulse-width modulator.

Table 14 Wind turbine data: REpower

Turbine type/size	Cut-in speed (m s^{-1})	Cut-out speed (m s^{-1})	Drive train	Power control	Generator type	Grid connection	Thunder protection
MM82/ 2 MW	3.5	25	Three-stage: two planetary, one spur	Individual blade pitch Yaw control	690, 4-pole, doubly fed asynchronous	IGBT with PWM	Fully integrated
3.4M104/ 3.4 MW	3.5	25	Three-stage: two planetary, one spur	Individual blade pitch Yaw control	690 V, 4-pole, doubly fed asynchronous	IGBT with PWM	Fully integrated
5M/5 MW	3.5	30	Three-stage: two planetary, one spur	Individual blade pitch Yaw control	660 V, 6-pole, doubly fed asynchronous	IGBT with PWM	Fully integrated

IGBT, isolated gate bipolar transistor; PWM, pulse-width modulator.

REpower's 6 MW test machine has been installed onshore at the German–Danish frontier in spring 2009.

REpower is participating in the 'Beatrice Demonstrator Project' to test the performance of its 5 MW turbine on the open sea. Two such turbines have been installed near the Beatrice oil field in Moray Firth, 25 km off the Scottish East coast and at a water depth of over 40 m. The demonstrator project is part of the European Union-supported 'DOWNWinD' project, which is Europe's largest research and development program in the field of renewable energies.

All of REpower's machines are designed on the same principles:

The pitch system uses a fail-safe design with separate control and regulation systems for each rotor blade, a virtually maintenance-free electronic system and a high-quality, generously dimensioned blade bearing with permanent track lubrication. It is protected by means of an integrated deflector in the spinner while maximum reliability is ensured via redundant blade angle detection, which uses two separate measuring systems.

The yaw system employs an externally geared, low friction, four-point bearing, driven by oversized, high-quality, gear motors. Hydraulic holding brakes with fail-safe function are implemented.

The drive system consists of a three-stage combined planetary/spur wheel gearbox using elastomer bearings in the torque multiplier for structure-borne sound insulation. It achieves low temperature levels due to effective oil cooling system, which uses a three-stage oil filter system.

The generators are doubly fed asynchronous, optimized for variable speed range and with high overall efficiency. They are fully enclosed with air/air heat exchanger for optimized temperature level. The converter uses IGBT pulse-width modulation and is water-cooled.

Lightning protection is according to IEC regulations with internal and external lightning protection. External protection includes blade receptors and a lightning rod at the weather mast. Reliable protection of bearings is achieved by defined lightning conduits coupling for the galvanic insulation of the generator system from the gear system. Overvoltage arrester is used in the electric system.

2.10.7.1.10 Goldwind

China's Goldwind Science & Technology Co. Ltd. was established in 1998. Technology was mainly provided under licenses from REpower and Vensys, which they acquired in 2008.

Goldwind has been manufacturing turbines in the medium-size range, up to 1.5 MW. However, recently the company has been installing, totally self-made, experimental 3 MW machines, while researching on 5 MW models (see Table 15).

Goldwind turbines feature independent pitch control. Each of the three pitch drives consists of motor gear units with synchronous belt systems. Belt drives are insensitive to torque shocks and resistant to moist or dirty environments and completely wear-free. The electric drives are robust AC motors controlled by inverters. Operation in emergency situations is assured by ultracapacitors, which have significant advantages over lead–acid batteries, such as no maintenance and 20 years lifetime.

Their direct-drive permanent magnet generator is characterized by an 'external rotor design' featuring maximum air gap diameter and low magnet temperatures. The generator cooling system is completely passive, while the maximum cooling effect is achieved at high wind speeds when maximum power is produced and consequently maximum heat losses occur.

Special attendance has been given to safety features of the frequency converter: safe operation is guaranteed by a heavy-duty switch located directly at the generator terminals. This switch is able to disconnect the permanent magnet generator under all circumstances. Furthermore, no power electronics are located in the nacelle while the passive diode rectifier is in the tower base.

2.10.7.1.11 WinWind

WinWind is a new company based in Finland, founded in 2002. It currently employs 300 personnel and claims an installed capacity of 150 MW.

It manufactures two turbine sizes: the 1 MW WWD-1 and the 3 MW WWD-3. Both designs are similar and employ the new Multibrid® concept. As described earlier, this is an integrated design using a planetary gear and PM synchronous generator, housed in a common casing. As a result, increased reliability is claimed. The planetary gear is manufactured by Moventas Wind Oy, while the generator is made by Siemens.

Both machines use full-power frequency converters employing IGBT bridges on both the generator and the grid side, as well as blade pitch control.

2.10.7.1.12 Windflow

Windflow is a New Zealand company founded in 2001. Its current workforce numbers 50 people.

Windflow manufactures a single 500 kW wind turbine, which is however a two-blade design, unlike most manufacturer's three-blade types (Figure 86). The machine is light, small, inexpensive, and especially suited to strong wind areas (IEC Class 1A).

To meet the tough requirements resulting from strong gusts, Windflow uses a patented torque limiting gearbox with a hydraulic system to limit torque fluctuations and allowing the generator shaft to rotate at a constant speed. Furthermore, the two-bladed design permits teetering (a see-sawing motion), an important element because it significantly reduces the bending forces on the turbine shaft, gearbox, tower, and foundations. The Windflow 500 turbine's rotor is designed to teeter up to 6° on either side of the normal plane of rotation in response to varying wind forces. Pitch-teeter coupling is an important feature of the Windflow 500 design, which, unlike many other two-bladed designs, stabilizes teetering during operation.

A self-exciting synchronous generator, configured to run in either VAr import or export modes that are fully controllable and do not require heavy-duty power electronics.

2.10.7.1.13 Clipper

Clipper Windpower is a rapidly growing, company engaged in wind energy technology, turbine manufacturing, and wind project development. Clipper employs over 750 people and manages over 6500 MW of wind resource development assets.

The company's wind turbine model is the 2.5 MW Liberty® (Figure 87). This is a horizontal-axis, three-blade, upwind, pitch-regulated, variable-speed machine. It features Clipper's own Quantum Drive® distributed drive train, a two-stage, helical load-splitting gearbox, four separate MegaFlux® PM synchronous generators, and optimized controls for variable-speed operation with full power conversion. Low-voltage ride through is also possible, thus enhancing weak grid situations.

Table 15 Wind turbine data: Goldwind

Turbine type/size	Cut-in speed $(m\,s^{-1})$	Cut-out speed $(m\,s^{-1})$	Drive train	Power control	Generator type	Grid connection	Thunder protection
S48/ 750 kW	4	25	Two-stage: planetary, spur	Stall control, active yaw	690 V, asynchronous		
GW70/ 1.5 MW	3	25	Direct drive	Ultracapacitor pitch control	Synchronous permanent magnet		

Figure 86 WindFlow's two-bladed machine. From Windflow brochure, www.windflow.co.nz.

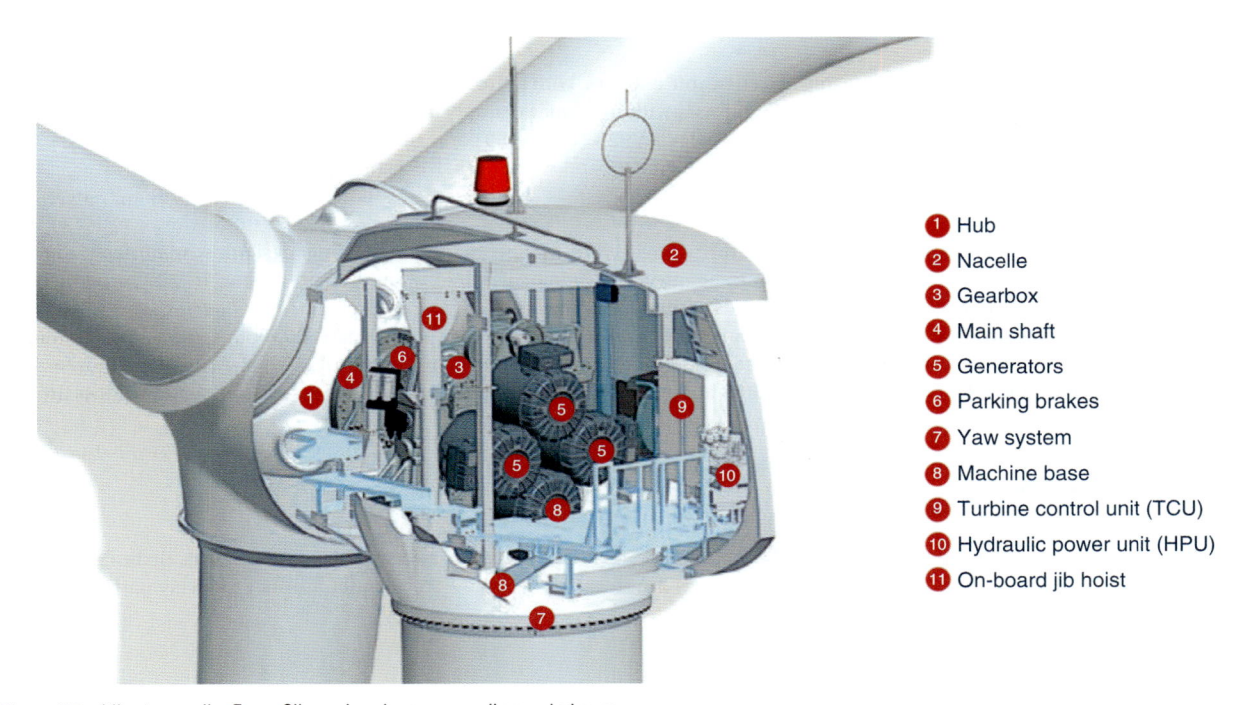

1. Hub
2. Nacelle
3. Gearbox
4. Main shaft
5. Generators
6. Parking brakes
7. Yaw system
8. Machine base
9. Turbine control unit (TCU)
10. Hydraulic power unit (HPU)
11. On-board jib hoist

Figure 87 Liberty nacelle. From Clipper brochure, www.clipperwind.com.

2.10.7.1.14 Fuhrländer
Fuhrländer AG is an independent German company with roots in metal processing and service industries for 40 years. They are currently manufacturing turbines in the range 30 kW to 2.5 MW.

Their top range FL2500 is based on an asynchronous generator with slip-ring motor using an indirect converter. Blade pitch is controlled independently. Yaw control is effected by four-gear motors.

2.10.7.1.15 Alstom
Alstom is the world leader in transport and energy infrastructure. They have recently acquired Ecotècnia, a firm established in 1981 operating wind farms with more than 2100 MW and 1800 wind turbines primarily in Spain, France, Italy, Portugal, the United Kingdom, and Japan.

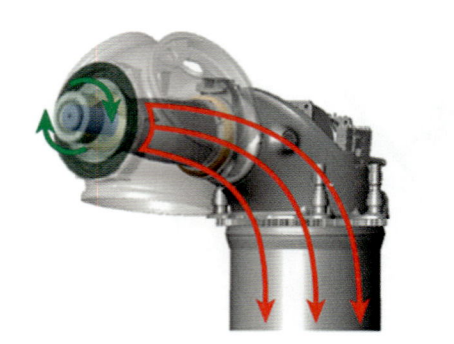

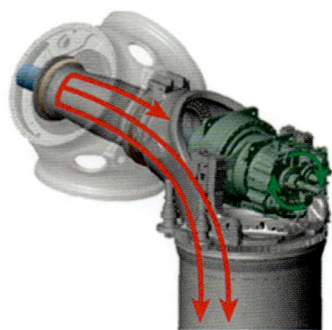

Figure 88 Alstom's pure torque concept. From Alstom brochure, www.power.alstom.com.

Alstom wind turbines are based on a patented mechanical design concept: the ALSTOM PURE TORQUE™. In this design, the hub is supported directly by a cast frame on two bearings, whereas the gearbox is fully separated from the supporting structure (**Figure 88**).

As a consequence, the deflection loads (red arrows) are transmitted directly to the tower, whereas only torque (green arrows) is transmitted through the shaft to the gearbox.

Alstom manufactures two lines of wind turbines: the 1.67 MW Eco 80 series and the 3.0 MW Eco 100 series aimed at Class II (8.5 m s^{-1} average wind speed) and IIa (9 m s^{-1} average wind speed) sites. Both series feature modular nacelles consisting of three modules containing the mechanical components and the control systems, allowing independent verification of their integrity and operational status, resulting in faster and simpler onsite testing. Also, variable speed with autonomous pitch control in each blade and active/reactive power control by wound rotor and power electronics is employed.

2.10.7.1.16 AVANTIS

AVANTIS is a new group of enterprises focusing on renewable energies, with a strong emphasis on wind power. The group comprises companies from the United States, Brazil, Europe, and Asia with headquarters in Beihai, China.

AVANTIS manufactures two turbine models: the 2.5 MW AV928 (**Figure 89**) and the 2.3 MV AV1010 aimed at Class IIa sites. Both feature direct-drive PM generators. Independent pitch control and with full IGBT rectifier/inverter are standard.

2.10.7.1.17 Sinovel

Sinovel Wind Group Co. is a high-tech Chinese enterprise engaged in independently developing, designing, manufacturing, and marketing large-scale onshore/offshore wind turbines adapted to different wind zones and environment. In 2009, the installed capacity of Sinovel was 3510 MW, making her a serious contender in the wind turbine market.

Sinovel manufactures two basic types of wind turbines: the 3 MW SL3000 and the 1.5 MW SL1500. Both series employ advanced power-generating technologies such as variable-speed control, pitch-regulated system, and DFIG, while maintaining low-voltage ride-through capability and adaptability to all grid codes and requirements. Various configurations for different wind regimes are also available.

2.10.7.2 Subproviders

2.10.7.2.1 ABB

ABB Lightning Protection Group, a branch of ABB, provides a range of lightning arresters against overvoltages, dedicated to wind turbine installations. These include both Class I and Class II arresters (see Section 2.10.4 for definitions) for every part of the wind turbine installation (**Figure 90**).

2.10.7.2.2 Weier

Weier was founded 60 years ago and has been developing, designing, and producing electric machines such as motors, generators, and rotating inverters. Their 'Clean Energy' product range includes generators for wind power plants, natural gas block-type thermal power plants, hydroelectric power plants, and clean energy-saving motors.

Conventional designed generators range from 0.125 kW up to 1.5 MW for large and small wind power plants (**Figure 91**).

A comprehensive range of synchronous PM generators for small wind power plants is also manufactured. Electrical power output levels of 0.5–10 kW are available. They feature internal rotors for input speeds ranging from 0 to 1250 rpm and laminated stators.

Furthermore, Weier is manufacturing a full range of pitch motors for use in variable-speed wind turbines.

At present, Weier is developing large generators of 1–3 MW, and up to 5 MW in the near future. In addition, output and security management systems, as well as grid connections to the integrated network, are researched.

2.10.7.2.3 VEM

VEM is the second-largest manufacturer of electrical machinery in Germany producing rotating electrical machines for the following sectors: mechanical engineering, plant construction, the chemical, oil, and gas industries, energy and environmental engineering, wind power plant construction, transport engineering, steelworks and rolling mills, and ship-building.

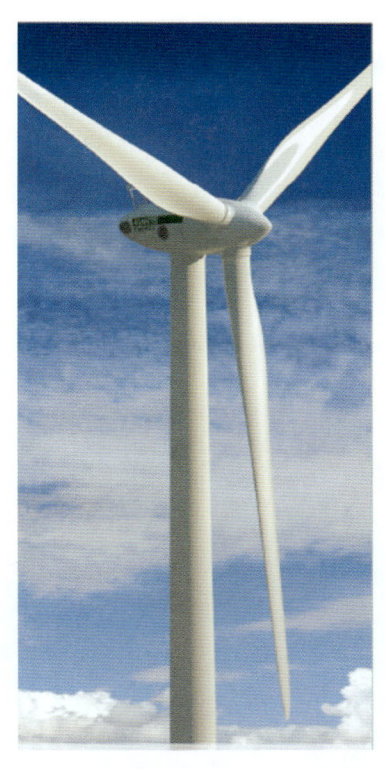

Figure 89 Avanti's AV928 wind turbine. From Avantis brochure, www.avantis-energy.com.

Figure 90 ABB's overvoltage protection arresters. From ABB brochure, www.abb.com/motors&drives.

The VEM series of wind power generators spans the whole spectrum: asynchronous squirrel-cage, double-fed asynchronous, and synchronous electrically or permanently excited. Furthermore low-speed synchronous machines for gearless or single-stage gear solutions are available on request. Output range covers 1–6 MW and voltage 690 V–12 kV (**Figure 92**). The cooling system is air-to-water or air-to-air.

The rotor design of double-fed generators generally comprises medium-voltage coils, while the main slip and earthing slip rings are generally made of stainless steel, enabling VEM wind power generators to operate without problems in coastal areas or offshore. Redundant earthing systems, combined with specially developed bearing insulation, also ensure safe control of the converter operation.

2.10.7.2.4 Phoenix Contact

Phoenix Contact is a leading German developer and manufacturer of industrial electrical and electronic technology. It offers a diverse product range including components and system solutions for industrial and device connection, automation, electronic interface, and surge protection (**Figure 93**).

2.10.7.2.5 Ingeteam

Ingeteam is a Spanish company, founded in 1974. It specializes in technology directed at the industry and energy sectors. Ingeteam's core business is based on power and control electronics, generator, motor and electric machine technology, and applications engineering.

326 Electrical Parts of Wind Turbines

Figure 91 Weier's 1 MW generator. From Weier brochure, www.weier-energie.de.

Figure 92 VEM's 5.4 MW wind turbine generator. From VEM brochure, www.vem-group.com.

Figure 93 Flashtrab arrester combination for four-conductor networks in a TN-C system.

Specifically for the wind energy sector they manufacture converters, generators (in collaboration with Indar Electric), control electronics, pitch controllers, as well as solutions to remote control and maintenance of wind parks.

Their standard range of power converters are PWM-controlled and principally based on IGBT power semiconductors, with a very low inductance DC bus. They are equipped with latest generation digital signal processing microprocessors, 32 bit parallel multiprocessing and include Advanced Vector Control algorithms on the PWM capable of applying rotor control (DFM) or stator

Figure 94 Ingeteam's 3 MW power converter. From Ingeteam Energy, S.A., www.ingeteam.com.

control (full converter) to the generator (**Figure 94**). Thus, total real and reactive power control is achieved. They include generator and grid-side disconnection switches.

Ingeteam has recently developed Ingecon® CleanPower concept, a new topology for variable speed control. The topology, named as xDFM, uses an additional generator acting as an exciter while the power converter is not directly connected to the grid. In this way, better power quality, grid fault tolerance, and other benefits are claimed.

Indar Electric's generators have output powers ranging from 850 kW to 6 MW and voltages from 690 V to 15 kV. They are doubly-fed asynchronous or PM synchronous as well as xDFM.

2.10.7.2.6 Maxwell

Maxwell Technologies is a fast growing company specializing in the manufacture of ultracapacitors for a wide range of industrial applications.

Ultracapacitors, also known as electric double-layer capacitors, or supercapacitors, are alternative energy storage devices that store energy by electrostatically (physically) separating positive and negative charges. This is in contrast to batteries that store energy via orbital electron exchange (chemically). The lack of chemical reaction permits ultracapacitors to be charged and discharged up to 1 000 000 times (compared to 100 or 1000 s of charge/discharge cycles in batteries) – and at a faster rate than batteries.

In particular, their new BMOD0094 P075 power module is directed for the safe operation and grid power quality for the most powerful wind turbine pitch drive and backup power generation systems. Based on compact, robust construction and top-grade components, it is designed for reliability and safety under harsh temperature, humidity, and vibration conditions. In addition, their smaller, cylindrical BOOSTCAP® range provides extended power availability, allowing critical information and functions to remain available during dips, sags, and outages in the main power source (**Figure 95**). Furthermore, they can relieve batteries of burst power functions, thereby reducing costs and maximizing space and energy efficiency.

Figure 95 BoostCap ultracapacitor. From Maxwell brochure, www.maxwell.com/ultracapacitors/index.asp.

References

[1] Wallace AK and Oliver JA (1998) Variable-speed generation controlled by passive elements. *International Conference on Electric Machines*. Istanbul, Turkey, 2–5 September.
[2] Wright AD and Fingersh LJ (2008) Advanced control design for wind turbines part I: Control design, implementation, and initial tests. *Technical Report NREL/TP-500-42437*. National Renewable Energy Laboratory (NREL), Golden, Colorado, USA.
[3] Buhl ML, Jr. WT_Perf user's guide. NREL codes. http://nwtc/designcodes/simulators/wtperf/WT_Perf.pdf.
[4] Wenxin Z and Karl AS (2007) Individual blade pitch for active yaw control of a horizontal-axis wind turbine. *45th AIAA Aerospace Sciences Meeting and Exhibit*. Reno, Nevada, 8–11 January.
[5] Fitzgerald AE, Kingsley C, Jr., and Umans SD (2003) *Electric Machinery*. New York, NY: McGraw-Hill.
[6] Lundberg S (2003) Configuration Study of Large Wind Parks. Licentiate Thesis, Chalmers University of Technology.
[7] Boeing Engineering and Construction Company (1979) Mod-2 wind turbine system concept and preliminary design report. vol. II, Detailed report. *NASA CR-159609*. NASA Lewis Research Center, Cleveland, Ohio.
[8] Kundur P (1994) *Power System Stability and Control*. New York, NY: McGraw Hill Inc.
[9] Voith Turbo. www.voithturbo.com/wind-technology_product.htm.
[10] Müller H, Pöller M, Basteck A, *et al.* (2006) Grid compatibility of variable speed wind turbines with directly coupled synchronous generator and hydro-dynamically controlled gearbox. *Sixth International Workshop on Large Scale Integration of Wind Power and Transmission Networks for Offshore Wind Farms*. Delft, NL: Offshore Wind Farms, 26–28 October.
[11] Hanselmann D (2003) *Brushless Permanent Magnet Motor Design*. Rhode Island, USA: The Writer's Collective.
[12] Siegfriedsen S and Bohemeke G (1998) Multibrid technology: A significant step to multi-megawatt wind turbines. *Wind Energy* 1: 89–100.
[13] Multibrid. www.multibrid.com.
[14] Tsili M and Papathanassiou S (2009) A review of grid code technical requirements for wind farms. *IET Renewable Power Generation* 3: 308–332.
[15] Petru T (2003) Modeling of Wind Turbines for Power System Studies. PhD Thesis, Chalmers University of Technology.
[16] Chen Z and Spooner E (1998) Grid interface options for variable-speed, permanent magnet generators. *IEE Proceedings Electric Power Applications* 145: 273–283.
[17] Chen Z, Arnalte S, and McCormick M (2000) A fuzzy logic controlled power electronic system for variable speed wind energy conversion systems. *8th IEE International Conference on PEVD'2000*. London, UK, September 2000, pp. 114–119.
[18] Papathanassiou S, Vokas G, and Papadopoulos M (1995) Use of power electronic converters in wind turbines and photovoltaic generators. *Proceedings ISIE '95*. Athens, July 1995.
[19] Lampola P (2000) *Directly Driven, Low-Speed Permanent-Magnet Generators for Wind Power Applications*. Espoo, Finland: Helsinki University of Technology, Laboratory of Electromechanics.
[20] Warneke O (1984) Use of a double-fed induction machine in the Growian large wind energy converter. *Siemens Power Engineering* VI, pp. 56–59.
[21] International Conference on Lightning Protection: Topic XI, *ICLP 2006*, 18–22 September 2006, Kanazawa, Japan.
[22] IEC 61400-24: Wind-turbine generator system – Part 24: Lightning protection. International Electrotechnical Commission, Geneva, Switzerland.
[23] IEC 61024-1-1:1993-09: Protection of structures against lightning – Part 1: General principles – Section 1: Guide A: Selection of protection levels for lightning-protection systems. International Electrotechnical Commission, Geneva, Switzerland.
[24] Yoh Y (2006) A new lightning protection system for wind turbines using two ring-shaped electrodes. *IEEJ Transactions on Electrical and Electronic Engineering* 1: 314–319.
[25] Sakki R (2009) Technology trends of wind power generators. *Nordic Conference IAS Technical Seminar on Wind Power Technologies*. Stockholm, Sweden, 13–15 September.
[26] IEC 61400-21 (2000) Wind turbine generator systems – Part 21: Measurement and assessment of power quality characteristics of grid connected wind turbines. IEC Draft 88/124/CDV.

Further Reading

[1] Burton T, Sharpe D, Jenkins N and Bossanyi E (2001) *Wind Energy Handbook*. Chichester, UK: Wiley.
[2] Elliott DL, Holladay CG, Barchet WR, *et al.* (1987) *Wind Energy Resource Atlas of the United States*. Golden, CO: Solar Energy Research Institute.
[3] Hansen M (2008) *Aerodynamics of Wind Turbines, Rotors, Loads and Structure*. London, UK: James & James Ltd.
[4] Hau E (2006) *Wind Turbines*. Berlin, Germany: Springer.
[5] Nelson V (2009) *Wind Energy: Renewable Energy and the Environment*. Boca Raton, FL: Taylor and Francis.
[6] Patel MR (1999) *Wind and Solar Power Systems*. Boca Raton, FL: CRC Press.
[7] Stiebler M (2008) *Wind Energy Systems for Electric Power Generation*. Berlin, Germany: Springer.
[8] Troen I and Petersen E (1991) *European Wind Atlas*. Risoe, Denmark: Risoe National Laboratory.
[9] White FM (1999) *Fluid Dynamics*. New York, NY: McGraw-Hill.
[10] Wind Energy Department of Risoe National Laboratory and Det Norske Veritas (2001) *Guidelines for Design of Wind Turbines*. Copenhagen, Denmark: Wind Energy Department of Risoe National Laboratory and Det Norske Veritas.
[11] Bertin JJ (2002) *Aerodynamics for Engineers*, 4th edn. New Jersey, NJ: Prentice Hall.
[12] Bianchi FD, De Battista H and Mantz Ricardo J (2007) *Wind Turbine Control Systems*. London, UK: Springer.

Relevant Websites

www.awea.org – American Wind Energy Association
www.canwea.ca – Canadian Wind Energy Association
www.ciemat.es/portal.do – Centro de Investigaciones Energéticas, Medioambientales y Tecnológicas (CIEMAT)
www.windpower.org/ – Danish Wind Energy Association
www.nrel.gov/wind – DOE National Renewable Energy Laboratory
www.ewea.org – European Wind Energy Association
http://www.iec.ch/ – International Electrotechnical Committee (IEC)
http://www.bwea.com/ – Renewable UK
www.allsmallwindturbines.com – Small wind turbines
www.thewindpower.net – The WindPower

2.11 Wind Turbine Control Systems and Power Electronics

A Pouliezos, Technical University of Crete, Hania, Greece

© 2012 Elsevier Ltd. All rights reserved.

2.11.1	Control Objectives	330
2.11.2	Wind Turbine Modeling	333
2.11.2.1	Mechanical Part	334
2.11.2.2	Electrical Part – Generators and Converters	336
2.11.2.2.1	Permanent magnet synchronous generators	337
2.11.2.2.2	Asynchronous (induction) generators	339
2.11.2.2.3	Doubly fed induction generator	339
2.11.2.2.4	Squirrel cage generator	340
2.11.2.2.5	Power converter	340
2.11.2.3	Full Model	341
2.11.3	Control	343
2.11.3.1	Overall Control Strategy	343
2.11.3.2	Pitch Control	345
2.11.3.2.1	Collective pitch control	345
2.11.3.2.2	Individual pitch control	348
2.11.3.3	Generator Control	352
2.11.3.3.1	Wound rotor doubly fed induction generator control	353
2.11.3.3.2	Asynchronous squirrel cage generator control	354
2.11.3.3.3	Permanent magnet synchronous generator control	356
2.11.3.4	Coupled Pitch–Generator Control	358
2.11.3.5	Grid Control	358
2.11.3.6	Yaw Control	360
2.11.3.7	Grid Issues	362
2.11.4	Fault Accommodation	364
2.11.5	Hardware	366
2.11.5.1	Sensors	366
2.11.5.2	Actuators	368
References		369
Further Reading		370
Relevant Websites		370

Glossary

Direct drive (DD) technology A design that eliminates the need for gearboxes. With fewer moving parts, DD technology can reduce maintenance costs and provide higher wind turbine availability.

Double fed induction generator (DF) Sometimes referred to as DFIG – has been widely used technology in wind turbines for ten years in thousands of commissioned wind turbines. It is based on an induction generator with a multiphase wound rotor and a multiphase slip ring assembly with brushes for access to the rotor. Recently, designs without the brushes have been introduced.

Fault ride-through (FRT) A requirement of network operators, such that the wind turbine remains connected during severe disturbances on the electricity system, and returns to normal operation very quickly after the disturbance ends.

Grid-connected A wind turbine is grid-connected when its output is channelled directly into a national grid.

Power curve The relationship between net electric output of a wind turbine and the wind speed measured at hub height.

Rated wind speed The lowest steady wind speed at which a wind turbine can produce its rated output power.

Reactive power An imaginary component of the apparent power. It is usually expressed in kilo-vars (kVAr) or mega-vars (MVAr). Reactive power is the portion of electricity that establishes and sustains the electric and magnetic fields of alternating-current equipment.

Nomenclature

$A(\gamma(t))$ turbine rotor swept area (time-varying due to yaw error) (m^2)
c_P power coefficient
c_T torque coefficient
C_d drive-train torsional damping constant
$i_{Sd}(t), i_{Sq}(t), i_{Rd}(t), i_{Rq}(t)$ stator/rotor (d, q) current components (A)

I_T lumped rotational inertia of the turbine (rotor, generator, etc.) (kg m^2)
K lumped stiffness coefficient of the turbine
K_d drive-train torsional spring constant
L_m stator/rotor mutual inductance (H)
L_S, L_R stator/rotor inductances (H)
p number of generator pole pairs
$q_r(t)$ generator rotor azimuth angle (rad)
$q_t(t)$ turbine rotor azimuth angle (rad)
R turbine rotor radius (m)
R_S, R_R stator/rotor resistances (Ω)
$T_e(t)$ generator electromagnetic torque (electrical) (N m)
$T_m(t)$ rotor aerodynamic torque (mechanical) (N m)
$V_{Sd}(t)$, $V_{Sq}(t)$, $V_{Rd}(t)$, $V_{Rq}(t)$ stator/rotor (d, q) voltage components (V)
$w(t)$ hub-height uniform wind speed across the rotor disk (m s^{-1})
$\beta_i(t)$ blade i pitch angle (rad)
$\gamma(t)$ rotor yaw angle (rad)
$\theta_S(t)$ stator flux position (Hz)
λ tip speed ratio
ρ air density (kg m^{-3})
$\psi_{Rd}(t) = L_R i_{Rd}(t)$ stator/rotor (d, q) flux components (weber (m^2 kg s^{-2} A^{-1}))
$\psi_{Rq}(t) = L_R i_{Rq}(t)$ stator/rotor (d, q) flux components (weber (m^2 kg s^{-2} A^{-1}))
$\psi_{Sd}(t) = L_S i_{Sd}(t)$ stator/rotor (d, q) flux components (weber (m^2 kg s^{-2} A^{-1}))
$\psi_{Sq}(t) = L_S i_{Sq}(t)$ stator/rotor (d, q) flux components (weber (m^2 kg s^{-2} A^{-1}))
$\omega(t)$ rotor angular velocity (mechanical) (rad s^{-1})
$\omega_e(t) = p\omega_m(t)$ electrical speed (electrical rad s^{-1})
$\omega_S(t) = d\theta_S(t)/dt$ stator field frequency (rad s^{-1})

Note: Tip speed ratio (TSR) is nondimensional. However, since $\lambda = \omega R/v$, the units appear to be (rad s^{-1})(m)(m^{-1} s) = rad. But the SI unit of frequency is given as hertz (Hz), implying the unit cycles per second; the SI unit of angular velocity is given as radian per second. Although it would be formally correct to write these units as the reciprocal second, the use of different names emphasizes the different nature of the quantities concerned. The use of the unit radian per second for angular velocity, and hertz for frequency, also emphasizes that the numerical value of the angular velocity in radian per second is 2π times the numerical value of the corresponding frequency in hertz. The following table summarizes these facts.

Derived quantity	Name	Symbol	Expressed in terms of SI base units
Plane angle	Radian	rad	m m^{-1}
Angular velocity	Radian per second	rad s^{-1}	m m^{-1} s^{-1} = s^{-1}

Hence, λ has units (s^{-1})(m)(m^{-1} s): non-dimensional.

2.11.1 Control Objectives

The conversion of wind energy into electrical power is not as straightforward as it might seem at first glance.

Wind speed is highly unpredictable and volatile. Furthermore, wind potential is not evenly distributed across the globe (**Figure 1**).

Wind generators cannot work optimally in every wind speed, thus they are designed for maximum production in a certain wind speed margin. Categorization of wind turbines follows IEC's 61400 classification as shown in **Table 1** [1].

In stronger than rated winds, the generator is in danger of being damaged, while at weaker winds the generator produces less than expected.

To increase power production in these 'nonrated' wind speeds, control and supervision systems are employed. In short, the most important objectives of a wind turbine control and supervision system are

- to maximize efficiency at every operating point;
- to minimize the structural load on the wind turbine;
- to meet strict power quality standards (power factor, harmonics, flicker, etc.); and
- to transfer the electrical power to the grid at an imposed level for a wide range of wind speeds.

To meet the above objectives, the control and supervisory system of large, variable-speed machines should consist of three main subsystems (**Figure 2**).

Smaller wind turbines which frequently have no blade pitch control have no active speed and power control. Instead, passive aerodynamic power control is achieved by exploiting blades stall effect while speed remains almost constant as it is fixed to the system frequency. But even in this simpler version, a supervisory control system is necessary for operation monitoring and controlling the operating sequence.

Control requirements depend mainly on the two ends of the wind power conversion process: the turbine rotor side and the grid side.

On the turbine generator end, we distinguish between fixed- and variable-speed operation. Although these modes require different control strategies, it is common in large megawatt turbines to adopt a discrete strategy, depending on the wind regime that the turbine is actually operating (**Figure 3**). Region 1 describes start-up when wind speeds are below cut-in speed. Region 2 is

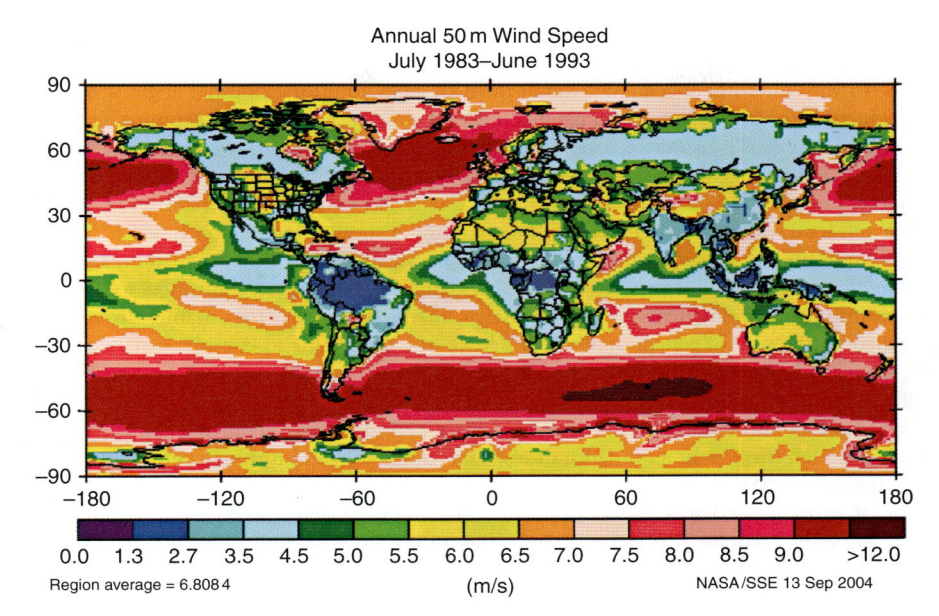

Figure 1 Global wind potential. Reproduced from NASA (www.nasa.gov).

Table 1 Categorization of wind turbines (IEC's 61400 classification)

Wind turbine class	I	II	III	IV
v_{ave} (average wind speed at hub height (m s^{-1}))	10.0	8.5	7.5	6.0
v_{50} (extreme 50-year gust (m s^{-1}))	70	59.5	52.5	42.0

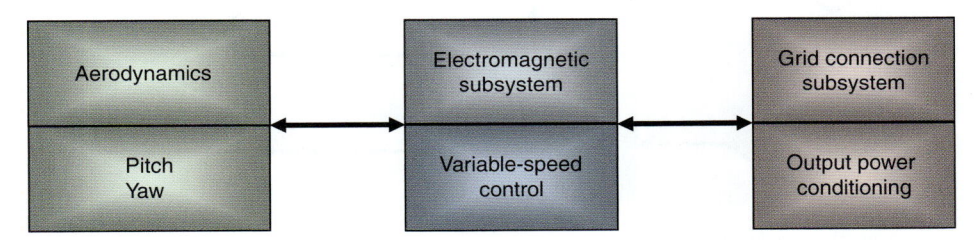

Figure 2 Overall control system. NREL (www.nrel.gov/wind).

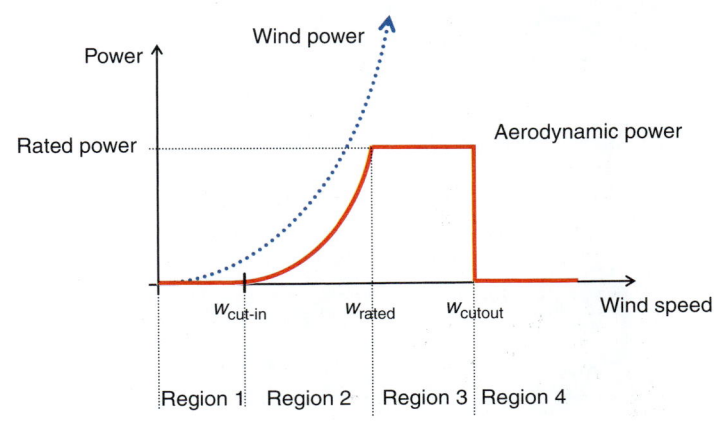

Figure 3 Wind turbine operational regions.

between cut-in and rated wind speeds, just before the turbine generates rated power. The main objective of a controller in this region is to capture the maximum amount of energy from the wind. This is achieved by keeping blade pitch approximately constant and using generator torque to vary the rotor speed. With small pitch changes about the optimal angle, a controller can also reduce dynamic loads in the structure. In Region 3, between rated and cutout wind speeds, wind power must be shed by the rotor to limit output power to the rated value. This is usually accomplished by keeping generator torque constant and commanding blade pitch angles. Structural fatigue loads can also be reduced in Region 3 via individual pitch commands. The overall goal of the control system is to meet different performance objectives in each operating region and make the transition between Regions 2 and 3 proceed smoothly to avoid load spikes. Finally in Region 4 the controller should stall the machine.

This strategy, as shown in the generic block diagram of **Figure 4**, is supervised by the wind turbine's supervisor system.

On the grid side, modern megawatt turbines employ full- or partial-load frequency converters to convert variable-frequency, variable-voltage current into constant-frequency, constant-voltage current (**Figure 5**). This enables decoupled regulation of active and reactive power, wherever the type of generator allows it. Hence, it is acceptable to consider generator control separately from grid control. Having said that however, it must be pointed out that the two subsystems may be coupled in the case of systems capable of tolerating grid faults.

It has been difficult to gather information on the design and field performance of industrial controllers employed in real wind turbines. Furthermore, although there is an abundance of research papers on wind turbine controllers, ranging from the simpler proportional-integral-derivative (PID) to more exotic fuzzy or neural versions, the performance of most of these is judged from computer simulations of mathematical models of the wind turbine system. Even though these models are sometimes quite complicated and therefore quite accurate, it is impossible for them to capture every detail of the real world. Another paradox is the well-known fact that despite an abundance of theoretical work on almost every type of controller available, industry, to the best of my knowledge, still uses the solid PID controller, with various modifications, on all machines.

Some of the material that follows is taken from the US's Department of Energy National Renewable Energy Laboratory (NREL) research. This is tested both on simulated environments and on their Controls Advanced Research Turbine (CART) (**Figure 6**). A short description of CART follows.

The CART is actually a Westinghouse WTG-600 two-bladed, teetered, upwind, active-yaw wind turbine. It is of variable speed, and each blade can be independently pitched with its own electromechanical servo. The pitch system can pitch the blades up to

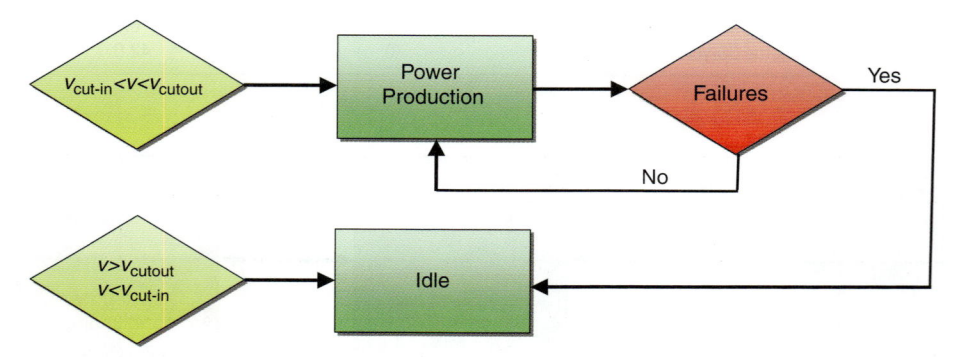

Figure 4 Wind turbine generic structure for supervisor control.

Figure 5 Power electronics converter.

Figure 6 NREL's CART (Controls Advanced Research Turbine). Reproduced from US's Department of Energy National Renewable Energy Laboratory NREL (www.nrel.gov/wind).

18° s^{-1} with pitch accelerations up to 150° s^{-2}. The squirrel cage induction generator with full-power electronics can control torque from minus rating (motoring) to plus rating (generating) at any speed. The torque control loop has a high-rated bandwidth of 500 rad s^{-1}. Rated electrical power is 600 kW at a low-speed shaft (LSS) speed of 41.7 rpm. Power electronics is used to command constant torque from the generator and full-span blade pitch controls the rotor speed.

The machine is equipped with a full complement of instruments that gather meteorological data at four heights. Blade root flap and edge strain gauges, tower-bending gauges, and low- and high-speed shaft (HSS) torque transducers gather load data. Accelerometers in the nacelle measure the tower's fore–aft and side–side motion. Absolute position encoders gather data on pitch, yaw, teeter, and LSS and HSS positions. These data are sampled at 100 Hz.

In order to design any controller, a model of the controlled process is usually needed. Non-model-based methods, collectively known as 'intelligent control', are also possible (fuzzy, neural, etc.). Models can be either linear or nonlinear, with linear models usually being linearizations of the corresponding nonlinear ones about an operating point.

As already stated, most controllers actually installed on wind turbines are of the standard PID type. Their tuning is necessarily based on linearized models of the processes involved. This fact imposes the first of the two main problems that designers are facing, namely, that of degraded performance in other operating points. This problem is usually faced by 'gain scheduling' methods, even though more advanced techniques, including nonlinear multi-input multi-output (MIMO) approaches, have been proposed. It is a general feeling, however, that these highly complex techniques do not greatly outperform a well-tuned PID controller.

The second major problem is that of the wind disturbance, the wind being highly stochastic and unpredictable in nature. A number of techniques have been proposed for overcoming this problem also, the most prominent of which is wind information ahead of the turbine. This information is then fedforward, thus making the whole system respond better to sudden wind fluctuations such as gusts or lulls.

Other problems include quality of sensor data (rotation speed, angle, etc.), a major source of performance degradation in every feedback control system. Solutions come in the form of suitable filters or better sensors.

Finally, additional control objectives such as load mitigation or energy maximization have to be cast in a multivariable framework and solved by vector optimal control or other performance-driven methods.

2.11.2 Wind Turbine Modeling

For control design purposes, it is imperative to establish a relation connecting the wind turbine system's inputs, outputs, and disturbances, possibly utilizing internal 'state variables'.

The output of the turbine is its actual rotating speed, which in turn affects the captured aerodynamic power. Control inputs are (wherever applicable) pitch angle and generator currents. Yaw angle control could also be included. Lastly, wind power is the disturbance term.

2.11.2.1 Mechanical Part

A process model should be as simple as possible for the specific control problem. Therefore, for simple, collective pitch control, a simple, scalar, spring-mass description is adequate, while in individual pitch control (IPC), possibly coupled with vibration attenuation, a more complex vector procedure is called for.

Let us therefore start with a spring-mass system describing in simple terms the wind turbine dynamics given by

$$I_T \frac{d^2 q(t)}{dt^2} + K q(t) = T_m(t) - T_e(t) \quad [1]$$

If K is neglected, a simpler form results:

$$I_T \frac{d\omega(t)}{dt} = T_m(t) - T_e(t) \quad [2]$$

What eqn [1] actually says is that rotor rotation is a balance between the aerodynamic torque applied by the wind and the electrical torque applied by the generator. Furthermore,

$$T_m(t) = \frac{1}{2} \rho A(t) R c_T(\omega(t), w(t), \beta(t)) w^2(t) \quad [3]$$

To complete the model, an expression for T_e is needed, which depends on the specific type of generator employed. Usually the expression for T_e involves (d, q) axis stator and rotor current components. Such a formula for the doubly fed induction generator (DFIG) is

$$T_e(t) = \frac{3}{2} p L_m \left(i_{Sq}(t) i_{Rd}(t) - i_{Sd}(t) i_{Rq}(t) \right) \quad [4]$$

Plugging eqns [3] and [4] into eqn [1] results in a highly nonlinear system in both the states and the control. Furthermore, the system is coupled since, for example, generator electromagnetic torque $T_e(t)$ affects rotor speed $\omega(t)$.

It is common in wind turbine control systems to use pitch angle $\beta(t)$ and generator current $i(t)$ in different operating regions. Therefore, let us look at these different situations, starting with the case in which generator electromagnetic torque is kept constant, $T_e(t) = \bar{T}_e$.

The only control input to this model will be rotor collective pitch. This means that the pitch angle $\beta(t)$ of each blade is identical. Since T_m is a continuous function of w, ω, and β, it can be expanded in a Taylor series about an equilibrium point as

$$T_m(w_0 + \delta w, \omega_0 + \delta \omega, \beta_0 + \delta \beta) = T_m(w_0, \omega_0, \beta_0) + \frac{\partial T_m}{\partial w} \delta w + \frac{\partial T_m}{\partial \omega} \delta \omega + \frac{\partial T_m}{\partial \beta} \delta \beta + \text{higher order terms} \quad [5]$$

$$\Rightarrow T_m(w, \omega, \beta) \cong T_m(w_0, \omega_0, \beta_0) + \alpha \delta w + \gamma \delta \omega + \eta \delta \beta \quad [6]$$

where subscript 0 denotes values at some equilibrium point, usually at rated configuration.

At equilibrium, acceleration is zero ($d^2 q(t)/dt^2 = 0$); therefore, aerodynamic and generator torque must cancel each other. Hence, using eqn [6], eqn [2] becomes

$$I_T \delta \ddot{q} = \alpha \, \delta w + \gamma \, \delta \omega + \eta \, \delta \beta + (T_m(w_0, \omega_0, \beta_0) - \bar{T}_e)$$
$$\Rightarrow I_T \delta \ddot{q} = \alpha \, \delta w + \gamma \, \delta \omega + \eta \, \delta \beta \quad [7]$$

Finally, since by definition $\dot{q} = \omega$, eqn [7] becomes

$$\delta \dot{\omega} = \frac{\gamma}{I_T} \delta \omega + \frac{\eta}{I_T} \delta \beta + \frac{\alpha}{I_T} \delta w \quad [8]$$

Equation [8] constitutes the linearized wind turbine model in terms of the deviation variables. We can rewrite eqn [8] in other forms, suitable for single-input single-output (SISO) or MIMO control. By Laplace-transforming eqn [8], for example, we get the transfer function

$$\tilde{\omega}(s) = \frac{\eta}{(sI_T - \gamma)} \tilde{\beta}(s) + \frac{\alpha}{(sI_T - \gamma)} \tilde{w}(s) \quad [9]$$

where the tilded variables denote deviation variables.

Alternatively, eqn [8] can be written in (trivial) state space form as

$$\dot{x}(t) = Ax(t) + Bu(t) + Gd(t)$$
$$y(t) = Cx(t) \quad [10]$$

where

$$x(t) = \tilde{\omega}(t), \ u(t) = \beta(t), \ d(t) = w(t)$$
$$A = \left[\frac{\gamma}{I_T}\right], \ B = \left[\frac{\eta}{I_T}\right], \ G = \left[\frac{\alpha}{I_T}\right], \ C = [1] \quad [11]$$

and measurement of rotor speed is assumed.

If IPC is possible, a more complicated multivariable model is needed. Furthermore, since individual pitching provides more degrees of freedom, other control goals besides constant speed may be fulfilled, such as blade load mitigation, especially in large megawatt turbines. Actually, it may not be an exaggeration to state that in current and future design control, interest has shifted from maximization of power capture to minimization of blade and tower load. At best, an optimal compromise between the two may be sought after.

Although many different versions of suitable models exist in the literature, we will outline the model used in NREL's laboratories [2], since, as explained, it is one of the few that has actually been field tested. This model uses 15 state variables in its more general form. In the sequel, a model aiming at ensuring stability and adequate damping of the first tower fore–aft mode will be presented. Other control objectives may require a different model to be employed, but the general control design procedure shown is still applicable.

The appropriate model uses nine state variables and its state space form is

$$\dot{x}(t) = Ax(t) + Bu(t) + B_d u_d(t)$$
$$y(t) = Cx(t) \quad [12]$$

where the state x, control u, and disturbance u_d are defined as follows:

$$x(t) = \begin{bmatrix} \tilde{q}_1(t) & \dot{\tilde{q}}_1(t) & \tilde{q}_2(t) & \dot{\tilde{q}}_2(t) & \dot{\tilde{q}}_4(t) & K_d(\tilde{q}_4(t) - \tilde{q}_{15}(t)) & \dot{\tilde{q}}_{15}(t) & \tilde{q}_7(t) & \dot{\tilde{q}}_7(t) \end{bmatrix}^T$$
$$u(t) = \begin{bmatrix} \tilde{\beta}_1(t) \\ \tilde{\beta}_2(t) \end{bmatrix}, \ u_d(t) = \begin{bmatrix} \tilde{w}_1(t) \\ \tilde{w}_2(t) \end{bmatrix} \quad [13]$$

The meaning of the various quantities is as follows (see also **Figure 7**): $x_1 (= \tilde{q}_1(t))$ is the blade 1 perturbed flap tip displacement; $x_2 (= \dot{\tilde{q}}_1(t))$ the blade 1 perturbed flap tip velocity; $x_3 (= \tilde{q}_2(t))$ the blade 2 perturbed flap tip displacement; $x_4 (= \dot{\tilde{q}}_2(t))$ the blade 2 perturbed flap tip velocity; $x_5 (= \dot{\tilde{q}}_4(t))$ the perturbed rotor rotational speed (Ω_{rot}); $x_6 (= K_d(\tilde{q}_4(t) - \tilde{q}_{15}(t)))$ the perturbed drive-train torsional spring force (ψ_{rot}, ψ_{gen}); $x_7 (= \dot{\tilde{q}}_{15}(t))$ the perturbed generator rotational speed (Ω_{gen}); $x_8 (= \tilde{q}_7(t))$ the perturbed tower-top first fore–aft mode deflection; $x_9 (= \dot{\tilde{q}}_7(t))$ the perturbed tower-top first fore–aft mode velocity, $u_i (= \tilde{\beta}_i(t))$ the blade i pitch perturbation angle; and $\hat{w}_i(t)$ the wind speed impinging on blade i.

Finally, matrices A, B, and B_d are obtained through linearization about the chosen operating point and C depends on the available measurements. The linearization is performed using any suitable software such as SymDyn [3].

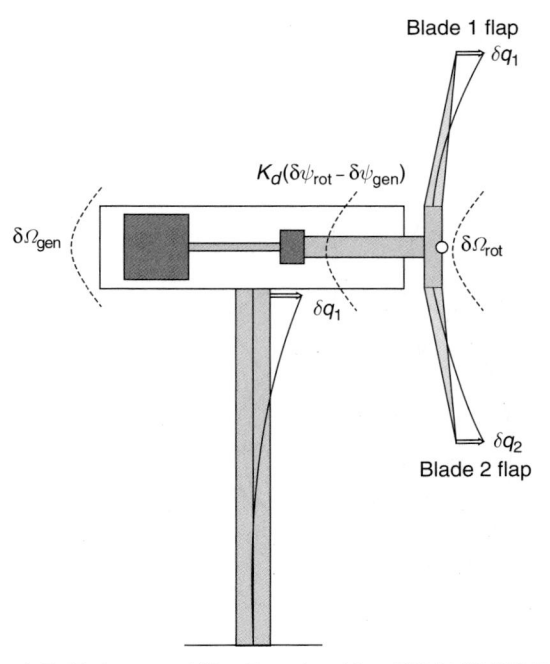

Figure 7 CART (Controls Advanced Research Turbine) state variables. Reproduced from Wright AD (2004) Modern control design for flexible wind turbines. *NREL Report No. TP-500-35816*. Golden, CO: National Renewable Energy Laboratory [2].

2.11.2.2 Electrical Part – Generators and Converters

The generator consists essentially of two elements: the field and the armature. The field winding carries direct current and produces a magnetic field which induces alternating voltages in the armature windings. The normal practice is to have the armature on the stator. Slowly rotating generators, such as those employed in wind turbines, have a rotor structure with a large number of salient (projecting) poles and concentrated windings. **Figure 8** shows the cross section of a three-phase synchronous generator with one pair of poles.

The magnitude of the stator magnetomotive force (MMF) wave and its relative angular position with respect to the rotor MMF wave depend on the load (MMF is defined as the line integral of the magnetic field intensity $\vec{H}$ in the machine's air gap). The electromagnetic torque on the rotor acts in a direction so as to align the magnetic fields. In a wind turbine generator, the rotor field leads the armature field due to the forward aerodynamic torque.

Voltage differential equations that describe the performance of AC machines are usually time-varying, except when the rotor is stalled. A change of variables is often used to reduce the complexity of these equations. This general transformation refers machine variables to a frame of reference that rotates at an arbitrary angular velocity.

This idea was contributed by Park [5], who in the 1920s formulated this concept, which in effect replaces all variables (voltages, currents, and flux linkages) associated with the stator windings of a synchronous machine with variables associated with fictitious windings rotating with the rotor. This, in effect, eliminates all time-varying inductances from the voltage equations. It was later discovered that this transformation admits a general structure applicable in all AC machines, be it synchronous or asynchronous. In this approach, all stator and rotor variables are referred to a frame of reference that may rotate or remain stationary. It is worth noting that in the case of synchronous machines this idea works only if the reference frame is fixed to the rotor.

The general equations of this transformation are [6]

$$\begin{bmatrix} f_{qs}(t) \\ f_{ds}(t) \\ f_{0s}(t) \end{bmatrix} = \begin{bmatrix} \cos\theta(t) & \cos\left(\theta(t)-\frac{2\pi}{3}\right) & \cos\left(\theta(t)+\frac{2\pi}{3}\right) \\ \sin\theta(t) & \sin\left(\theta(t)-\frac{2\pi}{3}\right) & \sin\left(\theta(t)+\frac{2\pi}{3}\right) \\ \frac{1}{2} & \frac{1}{2} & \frac{1}{2} \end{bmatrix} \begin{bmatrix} f_{as}(t) \\ f_{bs}(t) \\ f_{cs}(t) \end{bmatrix} = K f_{abcs}(t) \quad [14]$$

where

$$\omega(t) = \frac{d\theta(t)}{dt} \quad [15]$$

In eqn [14], f can represent voltage, current, flux linkage, or electric charge. Subscript s denotes stationary circuits. The frame of reference may rotate at any constant or varying angular velocity ω or remain stationary.

The inverse transformation is obtained by inverting K:

$$K^{-1} = \begin{bmatrix} \cos\theta & \sin\theta & 1 \\ \cos\left(\theta-\frac{2\pi}{3}\right) & \sin\left(\theta-\frac{2\pi}{3}\right) & 1 \\ \cos\left(\theta+\frac{2\pi}{3}\right) & \sin\left(\theta+\frac{2\pi}{3}\right) & 1 \end{bmatrix} \quad [16]$$

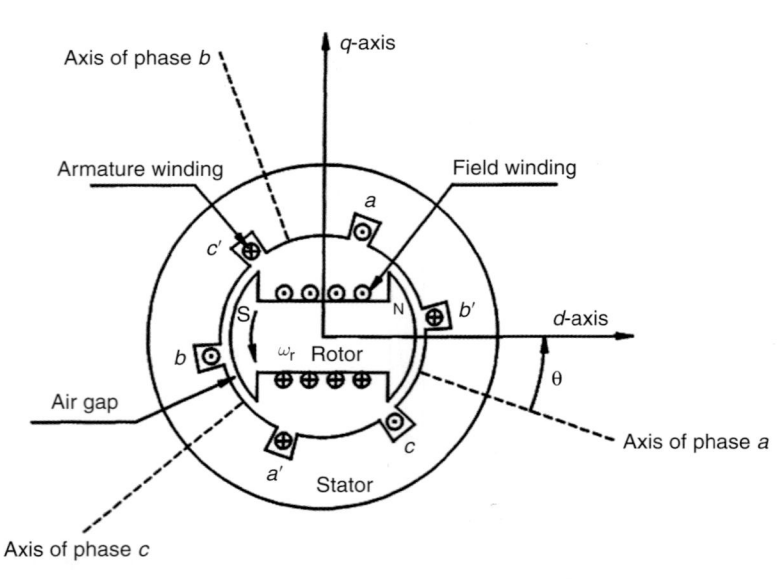

Figure 8 Three-phase synchronous generator. Reproduced from Kundur P (1994) *Power System Stability and Control*. New York, NY: McGraw-Hill, Inc. [4].

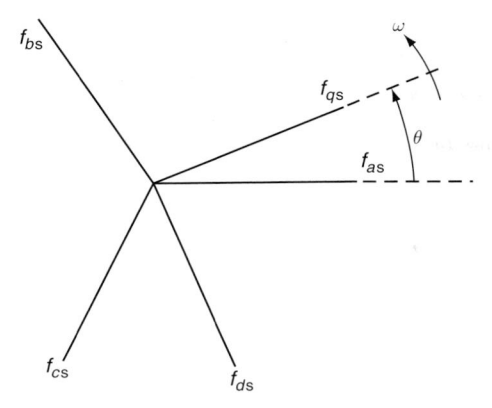

Figure 9 Trigonometric sketch of d–q transformation (eqn [14]). Reproduced from Krause PC, Wasynczuk O, and Sudhoff SD (2002) *Analysis of Electric Machinery and Drive Systems*. New York, NY: IEEE Press [6].

It is often convenient to visualize the transformation equations as shown in **Figure 9**. As seen, the transformation may be thought of as if the f_{ds} and f_{qs} variables are directed along paths orthogonal to each other and rotating at an angular velocity ω, whereas f_{is} may be considered as variables directed along stationary paths displaced by $120°$.

Electrical generators are systems that are generally controlled by power electronics. Two different types of self-commutated converters can be implemented: the voltage source inverter or converter (VSI or VSC) and the current source inverter (CSI). The first has a capacitor in the DC circuit and works with a relatively constant DC voltage; the second has an inductance in the DC circuit and works with a relatively constant DC current. The power production of the turbine is controlled by controlling the generator current. A chopper can be used to change the DC voltage and to keep it constant; it also provides an additional way to control generator torque. VSI converters are preferable in modern applications due to several advantages they present regarding control performance and power quality issues. These converters, as their name implies, use voltage as the control input.

The building block of VSC is the insulated gate bipolar transistor (IGBT). It is capable of handling large phase currents and can be used in converters rated up to 1700 V.

The generator-side converter or rectifier and the grid-side converter or inverter usually exploit pulse width modulation (PWM) techniques. In this case, the power converter comprises six valves with turn-off capability and six antiparallel diodes (**Figure 10**). The valves are typically realized by IGBTs because they allow for higher switching frequencies than classical gate turn-off thyristors (GTOs). The converter is fed from a DC source, usually a rectified three-phase AC source.

2.11.2.2.1 Permanent magnet synchronous generators

The main type of synchronous generator used in large wind turbines is the multipole permanent magnet synchronous generator (PMSG). In this concept, the PMSG is commonly directly driven, that is, the wind turbine is gearless, and connected to the grid through full-load frequency converters. The complicated electromagnetic construction of the permanent magnets presents a drawback of the whole design. Several types of PMSG exist, but the most widely used is the radial flux permanent magnet (RFPM) generator.

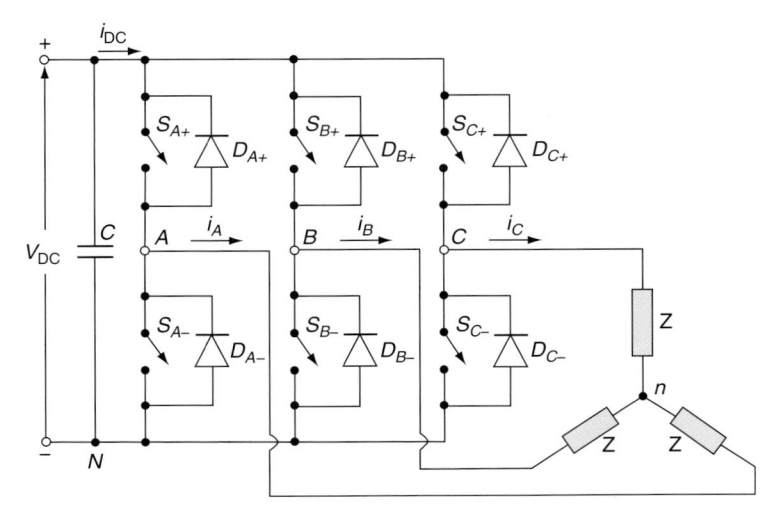

Figure 10 Three-phase inverter circuit.

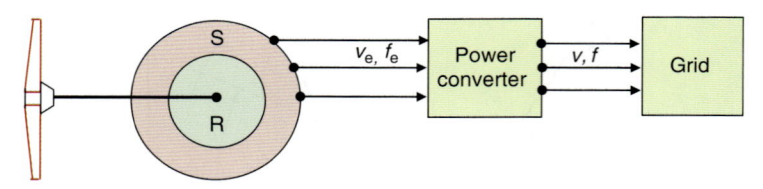

Figure 11 Permanent magnet synchronous generation grid connection.

Usually, the permanent magnets are placed in the generator rotor. In wind turbine applications, the stator is connected to the AC grid via full-scale frequency converters (**Figure 11**). In variable-speed machines, the use of frequency converters is essential, since the generator output frequency is time varying and equal to

$$f_e(t) = f_m(t)p \qquad [17]$$

where f_m is the turbine rotor frequency (mechanical) and p is the number of pole pairs. From eqn [17], the rated (=maximum) electrical frequency of the machine may be derived as

$$f_e^r = f_m^r p \qquad [18]$$

where superscript r denotes 'rated'.

In order to obtain a dynamic model of the PMSG, we consider a symmetrical, three-phase generator where the developed stator flux is sinusoidal. This in turn implies that the electromotive forces (EMFs) are also of the same type.

In the case of PMSG, the angular velocity of the stator space vectors, ω_e, is equal to the mechanical angular velocity ω. This means that the coordinate system rotates field synchronously and fixed to the rotor. Therefore, if the coordinate system is chosen to match the direct d-axis or field flux, the coordinate system represents the desired field flux orientation. Therefore, for studying synchronous machine characteristics, the transformation axes are defined as (**Figure 12**) [4]

- the direct (d) axis, centered magnetically in the center of the north pole; and
- the quadrature (q) axis, 90 electrical degrees ahead of the d-axis.

Then the equations describing its operation are given by [7]

$$\begin{aligned}\dot{\psi}_{ds}(t) &= -v_d(t) - R_s i_{ds}(t) - \omega_e(t)\psi_{qs}(t) \\ \dot{\psi}_{qs}(t) &= -v_q(t) - R_s i_{qs}(t) - \omega_e(t)\psi_{ds}(t)\end{aligned} \qquad [19]$$

and

$$\begin{aligned}\psi_{ds}(t) &= L_{ds} i_{ds}(t) + \psi_m \\ \psi_{qs}(t) &= L_{qs} i_{qs}(t)\end{aligned} \qquad [20]$$

where $V_G = [v_d \ v_q]^T$ is the terminal generator voltage vector, $\psi_G = [\psi_{ds} \ \psi_{qs}]^T$ is the stator flux vector, $i_G = [i_{ds} \ i_{qs}]^T$ is the machine current vector, and ψ_m denotes the magnitude of the permanent magnet flux linked to the stator windings.

Furthermore, the electric torque of the PMSG is

$$\begin{aligned}T_e(t) &= p\big(\psi_{ds}(t) i_{qs}(t) - \psi_{qs}(t) i_{ds}(t)\big) \\ &= p\big(\psi_m(t) i_{qs}(t) + (L_{ds} - L_{qs}) i_{qs}(t) i_{ds}(t)\big)\end{aligned} \qquad [21]$$

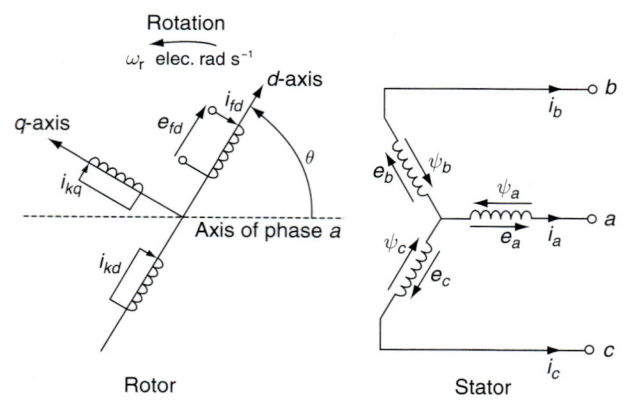

Figure 12 Stator and rotor circuits of synchronous machines. Reproduced from Kundur P (1994) *Power System Stability and Control*. New York, NY: McGraw-Hill, Inc. [4].

Finally, the active, $P_s(t)$, and reactive, $Q_s(t)$, power delivered by the stator are given by

$$P_s(t) = v_d(t)i_{ds}(t) + v_q(t)i_{qs}(t)$$
$$Q_s(t) = v_d(t)i_{qs}(t) - v_q(t)i_{ds}(t)$$
[22]

2.11.2.2.2 Asynchronous (induction) generators

An induction generator carries AC currents in both the stator and rotor windings. In a three-phase generator, the stator windings are connected to a balanced three-phase supply. The rotor windings are connected through slip rings to a passive external circuit. The distinctive feature of the induction generator is that the rotor currents are 'induced' by electromagnetic induction from the stator.

When current of frequency f_s Hz is applied to the stator, its windings produce a field rotating at synchronous speed given by

$$n_s = \frac{120 f_s}{p} \quad (\text{r min}^{-1})$$
[23]

where p is the number of poles (two per three-phase winding set).

Whenever there is relative motion between the stator field and the rotor, voltages are induced in the rotor windings. The rotor current reacting with the stator field produces a torque, which accelerates the rotor in the direction of the stator field rotation. The slip speed of the rotor is defined as

$$s = \frac{n_s - n_r}{n_s} \quad (\text{per unit of synchronous speed})$$
[24]

where n_r is rotor speed and n_s stator field speed. To act as a generator, the rotor speed must be greater than n_s, that is, with negative slip. The resulting torque is in this case opposite to that of rotation.

An induction machine differs from the synchronous one in the following points:

- The rotor has a symmetrical structure, making the (d, q) axes circuits equivalent.
- The rotor speed varies with load.

The above characteristics make a synchronously rotating reference frame an appropriate choice for transforming induction generator relationships.

2.11.2.2.3 Doubly fed induction generator

In the DFIG, the wound rotor has conventional three-phase windings brought out through three slip rings on the shaft so that they can be connected to a frequency converter.

As stated, the induction generator model can be expressed in (d, q) axes, rotating at synchronous speed ω_s. The q-axis is assumed to be 90° ahead of the d-axis in the rotation direction. If the d-axis is chosen so that it coincides with the phase axis a at $t = 0$, its displacement from axis a at any time is $\omega_s t$.

To express the dynamic equations describing the operation of the DFIG, expressed in the (d, q) frame, in state space form, let us choose the following state and control vectors:

$$x(t) = \begin{bmatrix} i_{ds}(t) \\ i_{qs}(t) \\ i_{dr}(t) \\ i_{qr}(t) \end{bmatrix}, \quad u(t) = \begin{bmatrix} V_{ds}(t) \\ V_{qs}(t) \\ V_{dr}(t) \\ V_{qr}(t) \end{bmatrix}$$
[25]

With this choice of variables, the DFIG can be expressed in standard control notation as [8]

$$\dot{x}(t) = A(\omega)x(t) + Bu(t)$$
[26]

$$y(t) = \frac{3}{2} p L_m (x_2(t) x_3(t) - x_1(t) x_4(t)) \equiv T_e(t)$$
[27]

where

$$A(\omega) = \begin{bmatrix} -\dfrac{R_S}{\sigma L_S} & \omega_S + \dfrac{p\omega L_m^2}{\sigma L_S L_R} & \dfrac{L_m R_R}{\sigma L_S L_R} & \dfrac{p\omega L_m}{\sigma L_S} \\ -\left(\omega_S + \dfrac{p\omega L_m^2}{\sigma L_S L_R}\right) & -\dfrac{R_S}{\sigma L_S} & -\dfrac{p\omega L_m}{\sigma L_S} & \dfrac{L_m R_R}{\sigma L_S L_R} \\ \dfrac{L_m R_S}{\sigma L_S L_R} & -\dfrac{p\omega L_m}{\sigma L_R} & -\dfrac{R_R}{\sigma L_R} & \omega_S - \dfrac{p\omega}{\sigma} \\ \dfrac{p\omega L_m}{\sigma L_R} & \dfrac{L_m R_S}{\sigma L_S L_R} & -\omega_S + \dfrac{p\omega}{\sigma} & -\dfrac{R_R}{\sigma L_R} \end{bmatrix}$$
[28]

$$B = \begin{bmatrix} \dfrac{1}{\sigma L_S} & 0 & -\dfrac{L_m}{\sigma L_S L_R} & 0 \\ 0 & \dfrac{1}{\sigma L_S} & 0 & -\dfrac{L_m}{\sigma L_S L_R} \\ -\dfrac{L_m}{\sigma L_S L_R} & 0 & \dfrac{1}{\sigma L_R} & 0 \\ 0 & -\dfrac{L_m}{\sigma L_S L_R} & 0 & \dfrac{1}{\sigma L_R} \end{bmatrix} \qquad [29]$$

and

$$\sigma = 1 - \dfrac{L_m^2}{L_S L_R}$$

2.11.2.2.4 Squirrel cage generator

The squirrel cage induction generator rotor consists of a number of uninsulated bars in slots, short-circuited by end rings at both ends. Thus, the squirrel cage model can be obtained from the corresponding DFIG by setting $V_{dr}(t) = V_{qr}(t) = 0$.

Let

$$u(t) = \begin{bmatrix} V_{ds}(t) \\ V_{qs}(t) \end{bmatrix} \qquad [30]$$

Then the relevant space state equations governing the electrical operation are

$$\dot{x}(t) = A(\omega)x(t) + B_1 u(t) \qquad [31]$$

where

$$B_1 = \begin{bmatrix} \dfrac{1}{\sigma L_S} & 0 \\ 0 & -\dfrac{L_m}{\sigma L_S L_R} \\ -\dfrac{L_m}{\sigma L_S L_R} & 0 \\ 0 & -\dfrac{L_m}{\sigma L_S L_R} \end{bmatrix} \qquad [32]$$

and $A(\omega)$ is given by eqn [28].

Equation [31] is complemented by the electromagnetic torque equation

$$y(t) \equiv T_e(t) = \dfrac{3}{2} p L_m (x_2(t) x_3(t) - x_1(t) x_4(t)) \qquad [33]$$

2.11.2.2.5 Power converter

To model the generator-side converter, it is common to neglect switching dynamics, ripple currents, and other fast dynamics in the electrical system and model the generator-side converter as a simple time delay. Thus, voltages on the generator clamps are given by

$$\begin{aligned} V_d^s(t) &= V_{c,d}(t - t_d) V_{dc}(t) \\ V_q^s(t) &= V_{c,q}(t - t_d) V_{dc}(t) \end{aligned} \qquad [34]$$

where $V_{c,d}$ and $V_{c,q}$ are the controller's outputs.

The dynamic equation for the DC-link voltage V_d is given by

$$\dfrac{dV_d(t)}{dt} = \dfrac{1}{CV_d(t)}(-P_c(t) + P_s(t)) \qquad [35]$$

neglecting the losses from the converters, where P_c and P_s are the active power from the grid-side converter and the stator-side converter, respectively, and C is the DC-link capacitance.

The grid is usually modeled as an infinite bus with voltage V_{grid} and frequency ω_{grid}. The grid-side converter voltage is given as

$$V_c(t) = m V_d(t) e^{ja} \qquad [36]$$

where m and a (phase angle between V_c and V_{ex}) are controlled by the amplitude and phase controllers on the grid side.

The currents through the grid-side converter are given as a function of the grid voltage,

$$\begin{aligned} i_{qc}(t) &= \dfrac{V_{dc}(t) - V_{dex}(t)}{X_t} \\ i_{dc}(t) &= -\dfrac{V_{qc}(t) - V_{qex}(t)}{X_t} \end{aligned} \qquad [37]$$

where X_t is the grid-side inductance and subscript c indicates values flowing through the grid-side converter while ex indicates values at the grid. Hence, the reactive power flowing into the grid, Q_{grid}, is given by

$$Q_{grid}(t) = V_{dex}(t)i_{qc}(t) - V_{qex}(t)i_{dc}(t) \quad [38]$$

while the active power flowing into the grid, P_c, is

$$P_c(t) = V_{qc}(t)i_{qc}(t) + V_{dc}(t)i_{dc}(t) \quad [39]$$

2.11.2.3 Full Model

For transient stability analysis, a dynamic mathematical model comprising every wind turbine subsystem is essential. The level of detail of this complete system varies, and is dependent on the particular application. Some, or all, of the modules shown in **Figure 13** can be included. However, most models are linearized versions of the nonlinear equations, around some suitable operating point, usually the nominal.

If driveshaft, rotor torque, tower, thrust, and wind speed are taken into account, the following state space model of the mechanical system is derived [9]:

$$\begin{bmatrix} \dot{\omega}_r(t) \\ \dot{\omega}_g(t) \\ \dot{\phi}_\Delta(t) \\ \dot{x}_t(t) \\ \ddot{x}_t(t) \end{bmatrix} = \begin{bmatrix} -\frac{D_s + \gamma_r}{I_r} & \frac{D_s}{I_r N_g} & -\frac{K_s}{I_r} & 0 & -\frac{\alpha_r}{I_r} \\ \frac{D_s}{I_g N_g} & -\frac{D_s}{I_g N_g^2} & \frac{K_s}{I_g N_g} & 0 & 0 \\ 1 & -\frac{1}{N_g} & 0 & 0 & 0 \\ 0 & 0 & 0 & 0 & 1 \\ \frac{\gamma_t}{M_t} & 0 & 0 & -\frac{K_t}{M_t} & -\frac{D_t}{M_t} -\frac{\alpha_t}{M_t} \end{bmatrix} \begin{bmatrix} \omega_r(t) \\ \omega_g(t) \\ \phi_\Delta(t) \\ x_t(t) \\ \dot{x}_t(t) \end{bmatrix} + \begin{bmatrix} \frac{\eta_r}{I_r} & 0 \\ 0 & -\frac{1}{I_g} \\ 0 & 0 \\ 0 & 0 \\ -\frac{\eta_t}{M_t} & 0 \end{bmatrix} \begin{bmatrix} \beta(t) \\ T_e(t) \end{bmatrix} + \begin{bmatrix} \frac{\alpha_r}{I_r} \\ 0 \\ 0 \\ 0 \\ \frac{\alpha_t}{M_t} \end{bmatrix} w(t)$$

or

$$\dot{x}_0(t) = A_0 x_0(t) + \begin{bmatrix} B_0^\beta & B_0^T \end{bmatrix} \begin{bmatrix} \beta(t) \\ T_e(t) \end{bmatrix} + G_0 w(t) \quad [40]$$

where subscripts r and g denote corresponding turbine rotor and turbine generator quantities and the rest of the variables are depicted in **Figures 14** and **15**.

Equation [40] can be augmented with actuator dynamics, for example,

$$\begin{bmatrix} \dot{x}_0(t) \\ \dot{x}_\beta(t) \\ \dot{x}_T(t) \end{bmatrix} = \begin{bmatrix} A_0 & \begin{bmatrix} B_0^\beta & 0 \end{bmatrix} & B_0^T \\ 0 & A_\beta & 0 \\ 0 & 0 & A^g \end{bmatrix} \begin{bmatrix} x_0(t) \\ x_\beta(t) \\ x_T(t) \end{bmatrix} + \begin{bmatrix} 0 & 0 \\ B_\beta & 0 \\ 0 & B_T \end{bmatrix} \begin{bmatrix} \beta_{ref}(t) \\ T_{ref}(t) \end{bmatrix} + \begin{bmatrix} G_0 \\ 0 \\ 0 \end{bmatrix} w(t) \quad [41]$$

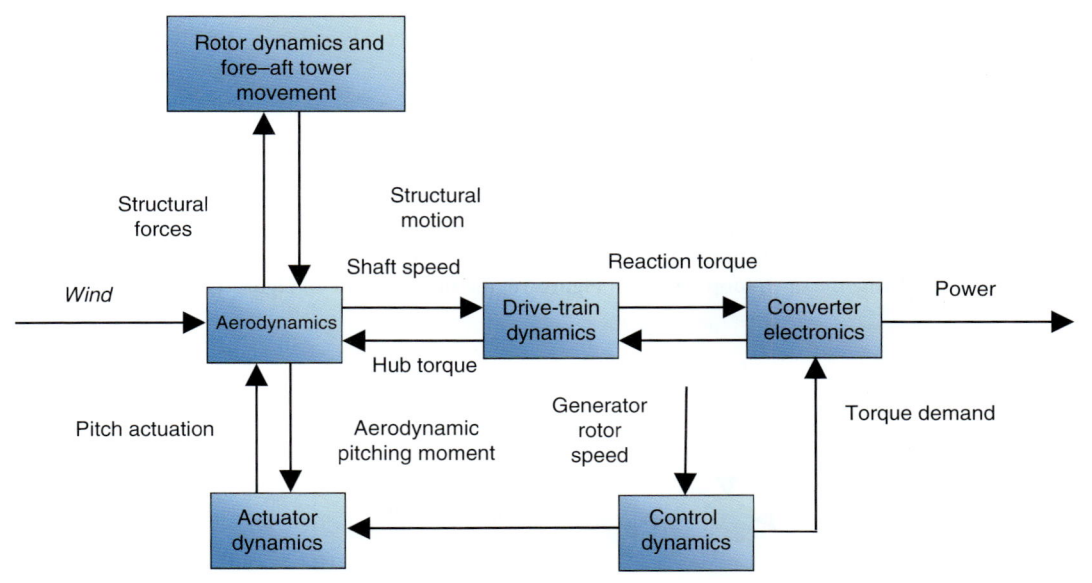

Figure 13 Full system interconnection. Reproduced from Henriksen LC (2007) Model Predictive Control of a Wind Turbine. MSc Thesis, Technical University of Denmark [9].

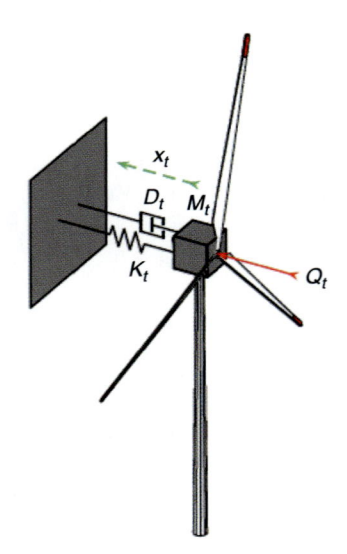

Figure 14 Wind tower variables. Reproduced from Henriksen LC (2007) Model Predictive Control of a Wind Turbine. MSc Thesis, Technical University of Denmark [9].

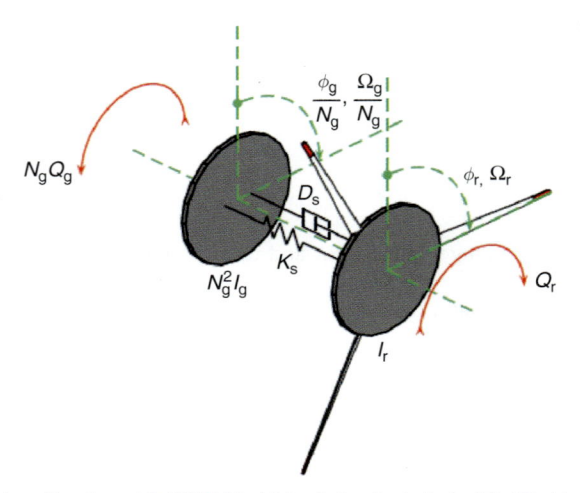

Figure 15 Drive variables. Reproduced from Henriksen LC (2007) Model Predictive Control of a Wind Turbine. MSc Thesis, Technical University of Denmark [9].

Equation [40] can be further extended if generator dynamics are added. In this case, however, it may not be possible to get linear expressions, since in some cases generator torque is bilinearly related to the control variables (see, e.g., Reference [4]).

On the other hand, if simpler models are desired, one can attempt to use black box identification through step response data. In Reference [10], such a procedure is described whereby a PID pitch angle controller for a fixed-speed active-stall wind turbine is designed using the root locus method. The purpose of this controller is to enable an active-stall wind turbine to perform power system stabilization. Considering the open-loop system of **Figure 16**, the step response of **Figure 17** was obtained.

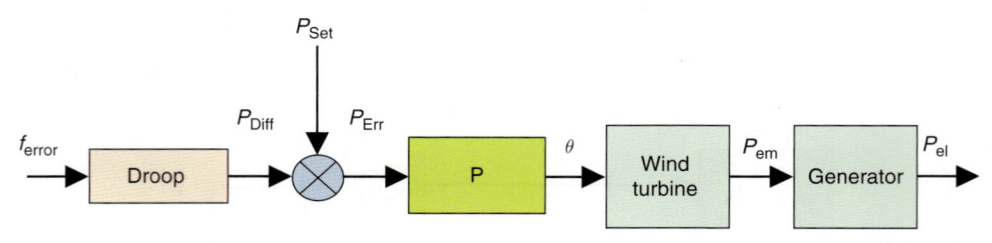

Figure 16 Open-loop block diagram for wind turbine identification. Reproduced from Jauch C, Islam SM, Sorensen P, and Jensen BB (2007) Design of a wind turbine pitch angle controller for power system stabilisation. *Renewable Energy* 32: 2334–2349 [10].

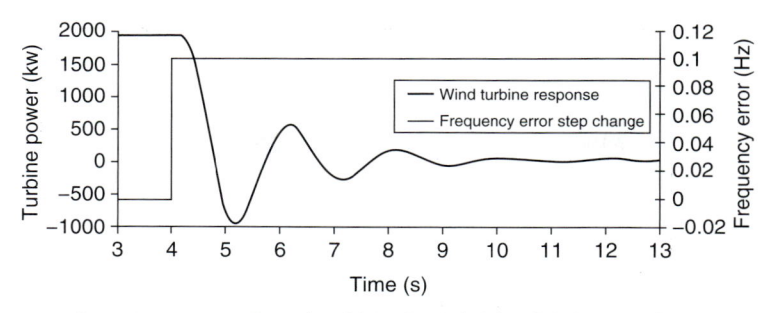

Figure 17 Wind turbine power open-loop step response. Reproduced from Jauch C, Islam SM, Sorensen P, and Jensen BB (2007) Design of a wind turbine pitch angle controller for power system stabilisation. *Renewable Energy* 32: 2334–2349 [10].

As seen, the response resembles a second-order transfer function response,

$$\frac{f_{err}(s)}{P_e(s)} \equiv G(s) = \frac{K\omega_n^2}{s^2 + 2\zeta\omega_n + \omega_n^2} \quad [42]$$

Identification of parameters K, ζ, and ω_n is straightforward from the characteristics of the step response, such as overshoot and settling time. As is often the case, a set of such transfer functions must be obtained corresponding to different operating points due to the nonlinearity of the process.

2.11.3 Control

2.11.3.1 Overall Control Strategy

As outlined previously, current wind turbines aim at maximizing power output while maintaining grid quality standards. However, in isolated areas, such as islands, power limitation may be imposed by the grid operator.

The basic relation concerning this goal is the well-known equation connecting mechanical power P_m and power coefficient C_p:

$$P_m(t) = 0.5\rho C_p(\lambda, \beta) A(\gamma) v^3(t) \quad [43]$$

$$\lambda(t) = \frac{\omega(t)R}{v(t)}, \text{ tip speed ratio (TSR)} \quad [44]$$

From eqn [43] it can be clearly seen that power maximization depends mainly on C_p and secondarily on $A(\gamma)$, with all other parameters being external disturbances. Since the yaw angle γ is regulated independently in its optimum position, P_m depends on λ (or equivalently ω) and β.

The graph of $C_p(\lambda, \beta)$ is a three-dimensional surface, obtained for each turbine by modeling or experiments. **Figure 18** shows such a typical curve, drawn using [11]

$$C_p(\lambda, \beta) = \sum_{i=0}^{4} \sum_{j=0}^{4} \alpha_{ij} \beta^i \lambda^j \quad [45]$$

If β is fixed, P_m depends only on λ. **Figure 19** shows a graph relating P_m and ω for various v.

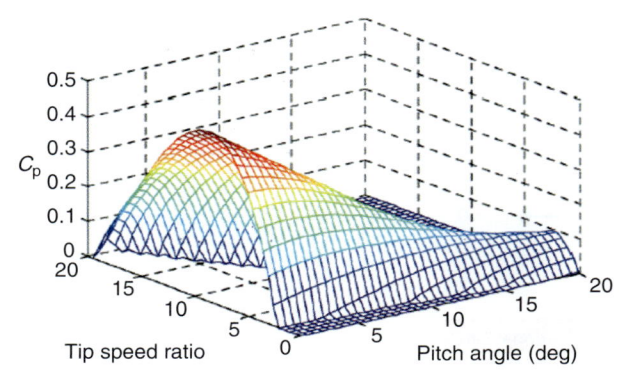

Figure 18 $C_p(\lambda, \beta)$ surface. Reproduced from Li S, Haskew TA, and Xu L (2010) Conventional and novel control designs for direct driven PMSG wind turbines. *Electric Power Systems Research* 80: 328–338 [11].

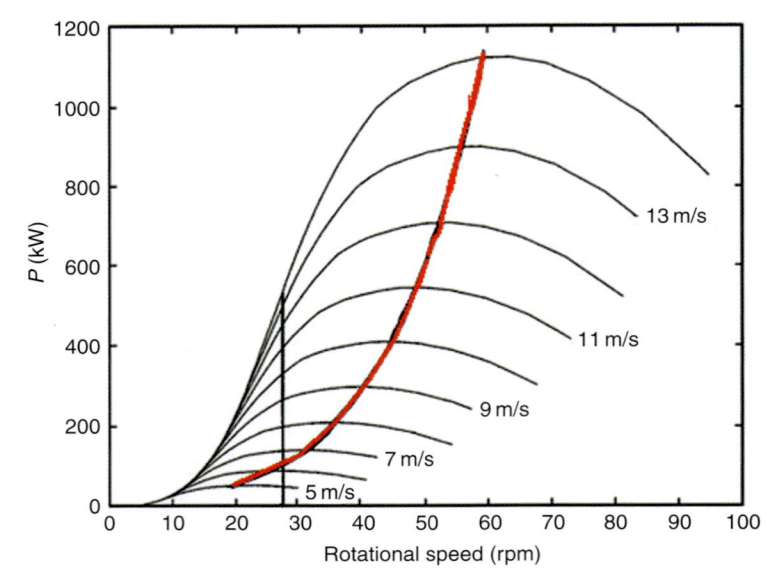

Figure 19 P_m vs. ω for the NTK 500-41 wind turbine.

Now, from eqn [44] it follows that

$$\omega^*(t) = \frac{\lambda^* v(t)}{R} \qquad [46]$$

is a suitable wind-dependent optimal speed trajectory (set point) for less than rated wind speeds (red line in **Figure 19**).

As explained in the introduction, the control process of the wind turbine consists mainly of two phases: (1) a constant pitch, variable torque and (2) a variable-pitch, constant torque. Other, less important from a control viewpoint, processes include start-up and shutdown and transition from phase (1) to phase (2). These phases are traditionally termed regions of operation in wind turbine design, as shown in **Figure 3**. **Figure 20** shows a generic control block diagram of the whole process, depicting the most important control loops.

In variable-speed machines, the generator is connected to the grid by a power electronics system. For synchronous generators and for induction generators without slip rings, this system is connected between the stator of the generator and the grid, where the total

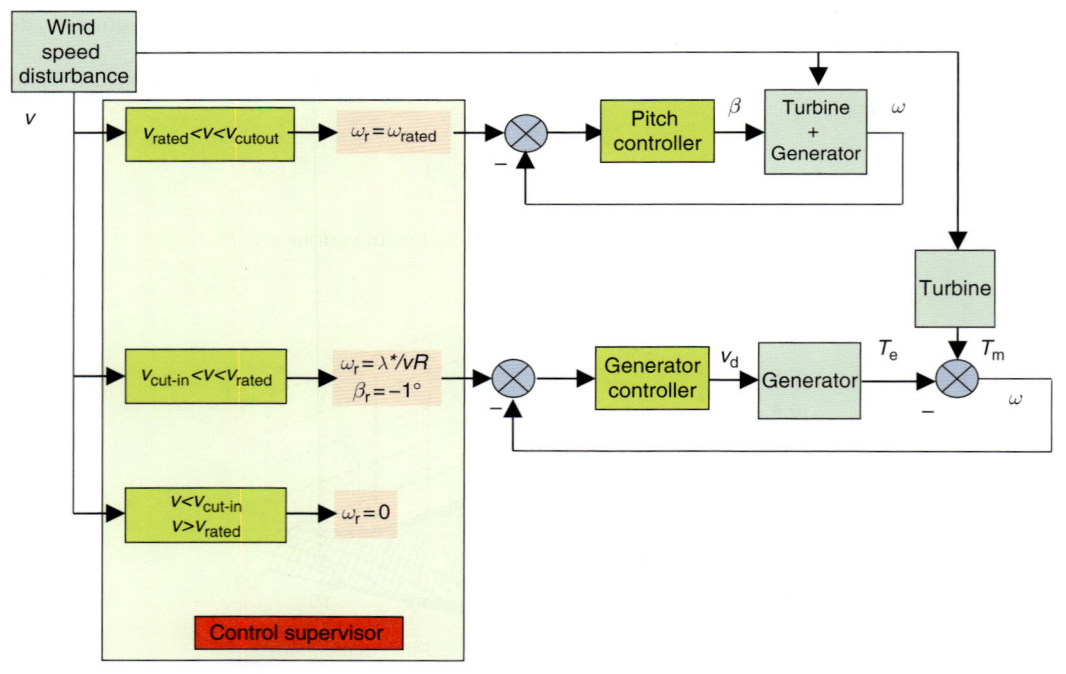

Figure 20 Overall wind turbine control block diagram.

power production must be fed through it. For induction generators with slip rings, the stator of the generator is connected to the grid directly and the rotor of the generator is connected to the grid by an electronic inverter. This has the advantage that only a part of the power production is fed through the inverter; therefore, the nominal power of the inverter system can be less than the nominal power of the wind turbine.

There are two different types of inverter systems: grid commutated and self-commutated. The grid commutated inverters are mainly thyristor inverters, for example, 6 or 12 pulse. This type of inverter produces integer harmonics like the 5th, 7th, and so on (frequencies of 250 Hz, 350 Hz, and so on), which in general must be reduced by harmonic filters. On the other hand, thyristor inverters are not able to control the reactive power. Self-commutated inverter systems are mainly pulse width modulated, where IGBTs are used. This type of inverter has the advantage that in addition to the control of active power, reactive power is also controllable. One disadvantage is the generation of interharmonics, in the range of some kHz, necessitating filters to reduce their effect. In modern wind turbines, transistor-based inverter systems are usually used.

Figure 21 [12] shows a schematic of the wind turbine control processes where the main elements (inputs, outputs, and controls) are clarified (modified from Reference [13]).

Figure 21 depicts a doubly fed generator configuration whose rotor windings are connected to the grid by a partial power converter, but it is nevertheless quite representative of all configurations. As seen, there are two main control blocks, a mechanical (wind turbine) and an electrical (generator and grid). As explained these blocks are quite decoupled. Let us look at the signals involved in some detail.

Reference signals. The reference signals influencing the control system operation are the requirements of the grid, at some point M, as expressed by the quantities P_g^* (active power set point) and Q_g^* (reactive power set point) and the converter's DC voltage V_{DC}^*.

The active power set point may influence both the mechanical and electrical converter, but is usually set at the rated power of the turbine. Special circumstances may dictate a value less than the rated, for example, in cases where maximum power cannot be absorbed by the grid.

Reactive power usually influences only the grid-side portion of the converter, since rotor and grid control are also decoupled by suitable transformations. Its value is usually zero unless the turbine operates in a weak grid or a grid fault situation demands grid voltage support from the wind park.

The converter's reference DC voltage depends on the size of the converter, the stator/rotor voltage ratio, and the modulation factor of the power converter.

Control signals. The control mechanism generates two control signals: pitch angle β and converter modulation signals pulse width modulated based on the desired generator power P_e^*. These control signals affect essentially the rotational speed in two distinct ways depending on the region where the turbine operates.

Disturbance signals. The main disturbance signal is wind speed v. However, in this case, wind speed is a 'measurable' disturbance, a fact that is utilized in the control algorithms in order to generate the control signals. Even though most current wind sensors do not provide accurate measurements, the employment of new, laser-based equipment will surely correct this deficiency.

Measurement signals. In order to keep controlled variables in their reference limits, a number of measurements must be made (apart from wind speed). Although specific measurements depend on machine configuration and control strategy, it can safely be stated that generated active and reactive power, P_G and Q_G, DC-link voltage, V_{DC}, generator speed, ω_m, and rotor current, i_{AC}, are usually measured.

2.11.3.2 Pitch Control

2.11.3.2.1 Collective pitch control

Pitch control is used in both fixed- and variable-speed machines, serving similar purposes. In a fixed-speed pitch-regulated turbine, an induction generator is connected directly to the AC network and rotates at a nearly constant speed. In a variable-speed turbine, pitch control comes into play in operating Region 3, where again the electrical power is at rated levels.

As the wind speed varies, the power produced will vary roughly as the cube of the wind speed. At the rated wind speed, the electrical power generated becomes equal to the rating of the turbine. As the wind speed rises above the rated wind speed, the blades are pitched in order to reduce the aerodynamic efficiency of the rotor and limit the power to the rated value. The usual strategy is to pitch the blades in response to a set-point error, such as the power error or rotational speed error, defined as the difference between the rated value and the actual value achieved, as measured by a transducer.

Most pitch controllers use the simple linearized model in eqn [9], which is reproduced here:

$$\tilde{\omega}(s) = \frac{\eta}{(sI_T - \gamma)}\tilde{\beta}(s) + \frac{a}{(sI_T - \gamma)}\tilde{w}(s) \qquad [9]$$

The control block diagram for this problem is shown in **Figure 22**.

An example of synthesizing such a proportional integral (PI) pitch controller is detailed in Reference [14]. The turbine data refer to NREL's CART design. The goal of this controller is to regulate rotational speed to 41.7 rpm (rated speed for the CART).

Since this is a typical disturbance attenuation problem, the disturbance to output transfer function of **Figure 22** is found by plugging in the controller transfer function into eqn [9],

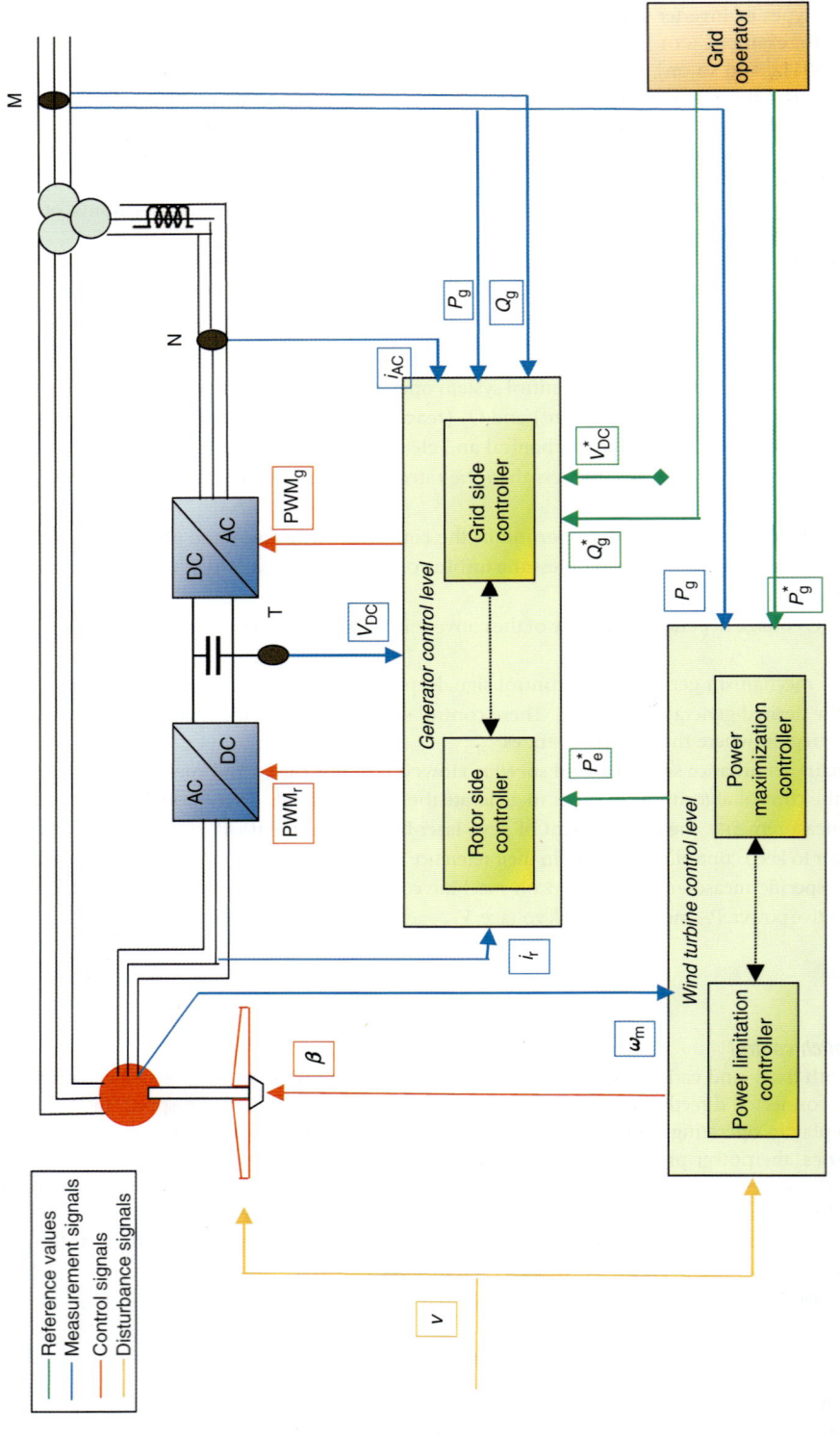

Figure 21 Schematic of wind turbine control. Reproduced from Hansen A, Jauch C, Sørensen P, et al. (2003) Dynamic wind turbine models in power system simulation tool DIgSILENT. *Report Risø-R-1400(EN)*. Roskilde, Denmark: Risø National Laboratory [12].

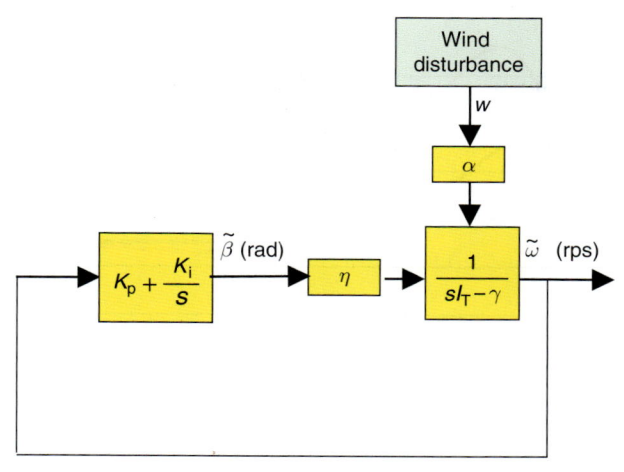

Figure 22 Pitch control block diagram.

$$T(s) \equiv \frac{\tilde{\omega}(s)}{\tilde{w}(s)} = \frac{\frac{\alpha}{sI_T - \gamma}}{1 - \frac{\eta}{sI_T - \gamma}\left(\frac{K_P s + K_I}{s}\right)} = \frac{\alpha s}{s^2 I_T - (\gamma + \eta K_P)s - \zeta K_I} = \frac{\frac{\alpha}{I_T}s}{s^2 - \frac{(\gamma + \eta K_P)}{I_T}s - \frac{\eta}{I_T}K_I} \quad [47]$$

To proceed let us substitute for the constants $\gamma/I_T = -0.194$, $\eta/I_T = -2.65$, and $\alpha/I_T = 0.069$ (for linearization about $w_0 = 18 \text{ m s}^{-1}$, $\omega_0 = 41.7$ rpm, $\theta_0 = 11°$). With these values, the denominator of eqn [47] becomes

$$s^2 + (0.194 + 2.65 K_P)s + 2.65 K_I = 0$$

A simple way to choose the controller parameters is to relate them to the standard second-order damping ratio ζ and the natural frequency coefficient ω_n. This means

$$K_I = -\frac{\omega_n^2 I_T}{\eta}, \quad K_P = -\frac{2\zeta\omega_n I_T - \gamma}{\eta} \quad [48]$$

Usually the damping ratio is in the range 0.6–0.8 for underdamped response and $\omega_n \approx 0.6 \text{ rad s}^{-1}$ for acceptable attenuation time. In **Figure 23** are shown responses for $\omega_n = 0.6 \text{ rad s}^{-1}$ and $\zeta = 0.3$ (red), 1 (blue), and 2 (green) for a wind unit step disturbance (from 17 to 18 m s^{-1}). Calculated controller gains are $K_I = 0.136$ and $K_P = 0.38$.

Although simple, this controller suffers from poor performance in different operating points, that is, different from the ones that it is designed for. This is illustrated in **Figure 24** for $\zeta = 1$, where a much greater overshoot is observed (red line) compared to the one previously attained (blue line).

This problem can be overcome by an approach termed 'gain scheduling'. In this method, the overall controller gain is not constant but varies depending on the actual operating point [13, 15]. The relationship for the multiplying factor is

$$g_K(\beta_i) = \frac{1}{\left(1 + \frac{\beta_i}{\beta_K}\right)} \quad [49]$$

where β_K is a pitch angle chosen as follows.

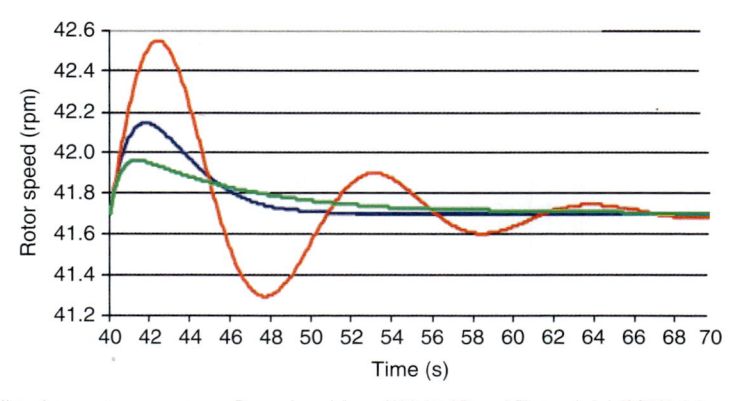

Figure 23 Pitch control unit disturbance step responses. Reproduced from Wright AD and Fingersh LJ (2008) Advanced control design for wind turbines part I: Control design, implementation, and initial tests. *Technical Report NREL/TP-500-42437*. Golden, CO: National Renewable Energy Laboratory [14].

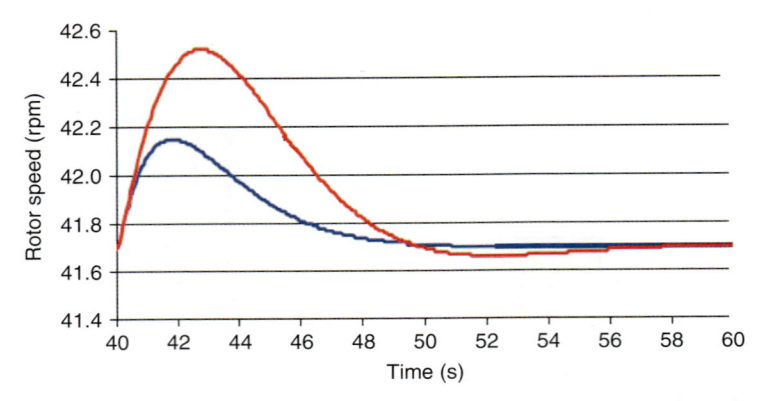

Figure 24 Pitch control at different operating points. Reproduced from Wright AD and Fingersh LJ (2008) Advanced control design for wind turbines part I: Control design, implementation, and initial tests. *Technical Report NREL/TP-500-42437*. Golden, CO: National Renewable Energy Laboratory [14].

An operating point in the beginning of Region 3 is chosen. For the turbine examined, this may be $w_0 = 13.7 \text{ m s}^{-1}$, $\omega_0 = 41.7$ rpm, and $\beta_0 = 0.53°$. At this operating point, the controller gains are calculated as $K_I = 0.78$ and $K_P = 2.35$. Next an operating point is found at which η is doubled. Simulation studies have shown that around $w_0 = 14.1 \text{ m s}^{-1}$, $\omega_0 = 41.7$ rpm, and $\beta_0 = 2.62°$, η is doubled. Thus,

$$g_K(\beta_i) = \frac{1}{\left(1 + \dfrac{\beta_i}{2.62}\right)} \qquad [50]$$

Figure 25 shows the revised controller in actual implementation. **Figure 26** shows the improved performance of this controller at different operating points. An alternative method for computing the parameters for use in the above expression is described in Reference [15] based on a best-fit least-squares estimate of the pitch sensitivity for various blade pitch angles.

This controller is in operation on all wind regimes but takes effect only when winds approach regime 3. When the controller starts operation in this way, a phenomenon known as 'integrator windup' is observed. This results in a momentary large overshoot in the rotor speed and a corresponding long settling time. This problem can be treated by the addition of an additional gain term in the integrator whose value can be found through trial and error. The modified diagram is shown in **Figure 27**. The results are depicted in **Figure 28**, where the benefits of the anti-windup mechanism are clearly observed.

2.11.3.2.2 Individual pitch control

For IPC, eqn [12] is used. The capability of individually regulating blade pitch allows us to add to the standard control objective of speed regulation the following:

- first drive-train torsional mode stabilization;
- enhanced damping of the tower first fore–aft mode;
- stabilization of rotor first symmetric and asymmetric flap mode; and
- attenuation of blade flap wind shear response.

Control action is usually calculated as a function of states or measurements, that is,

$$u(t) = K(t)x(t) \text{ or } u(t) = K(t)y(t) \qquad [51]$$

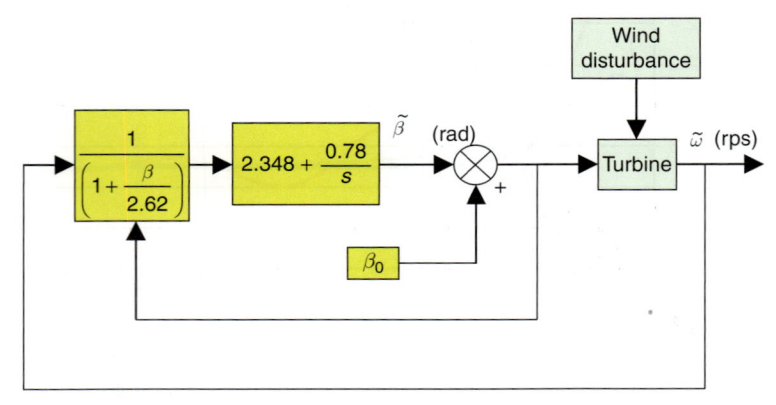

Figure 25 Gain scheduling pitch controller.

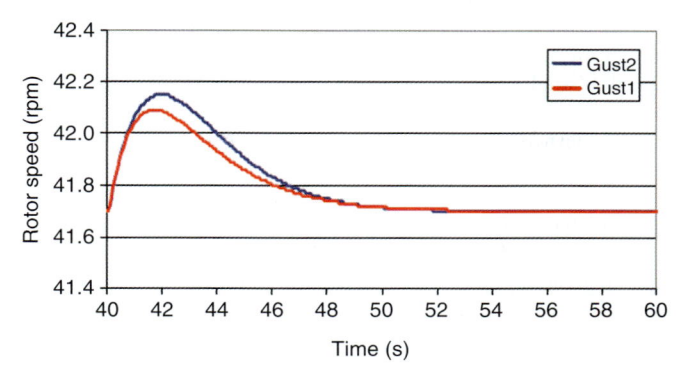

Figure 26 Gain scheduler performance. Reproduced from Wright AD and Fingersh LJ (2008) Advanced control design for wind turbines part I: Control design, implementation, and initial tests. *Technical Report NREL/TP-500-42437*. Golden, CO: National Renewable Energy Laboratory [14].

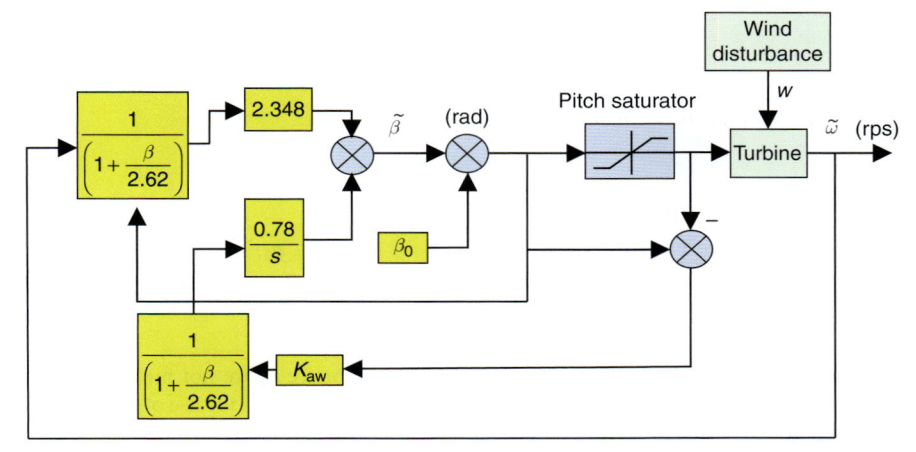

Figure 27 Anti-windup, gain scheduling pitch controller.

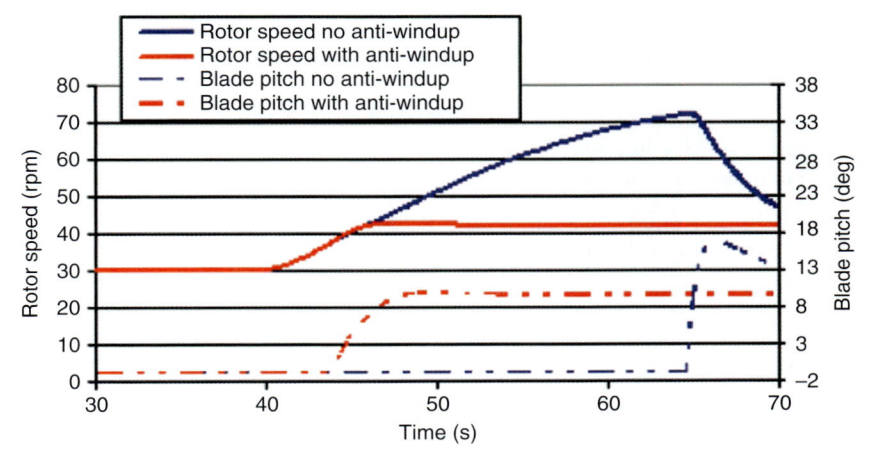

Figure 28 Anti-windup results. Reproduced from Wright AD and Fingersh LJ (2008) Advanced control design for wind turbines part I: Control design, implementation, and initial tests. *Technical Report NREL/TP-500-42437*. Golden, CO: National Renewable Energy Laboratory [14].

There are a variety of methods for calculating the time-varying feedback matrix. A rather simple, yet quite powerful technique is the well-known linear quadratic regulator (LQR) method. In this method, $K(t)$ is calculated as the (constant) matrix that minimizes the infinite horizon criterion,

$$J = \int_0^\infty \{x^T(t)Qx(t) + u^T(t)Ru(t)\}\, dt \qquad [52]$$

subject to the plant dynamics given by eqn [12]. The matrices Q and R are design matrices used for weighting the importance of control effort and state departure from equilibrium. What actually eqn [52] means is that its minimization will result in minimization of the relevant 'deflection' angles and consequently of the loads experienced by the blades and tower.

Before proceeding with the details of solving eqn [52], let us address two other problems that are inherent in our formulation: the problem of the wind disturbance and the problem of state estimation.

- **Wind disturbance**

Wind can be thought of as a highly stochastic disturbance input. Disturbance rejection or attenuation is the primary goal of any control system. How one achieves this goal depends on whether the disturbance can be measured, forecasted, or is completely unpredictable. In the following, one such method will be outlined, namely, the disturbance accommodation control (DAC) [16]. In this method, the disturbance is modeled as a dynamic system of known structure, such as

$$\dot{z}_d(t) = F z_d(t); \quad z_d(0) = z_d^0 \text{ (unknown)} \qquad [53]$$

This model is then 'augmented' with the original system to form the plant-disturbance model given by

$$\begin{bmatrix} \dot{x}(t) \\ \dot{z}_d(t) \end{bmatrix} = \begin{bmatrix} A & B_d \\ 0 & F \end{bmatrix} \begin{bmatrix} x(t) \\ z_d(t) \end{bmatrix} + \begin{bmatrix} B \\ 0 \end{bmatrix} u(t)$$

$$y(t) = \begin{bmatrix} C & 0 \end{bmatrix} \begin{bmatrix} x(t) \\ z_d(t) \end{bmatrix} \qquad [54]$$

Furthermore, if the feedback control law is calculated as

$$u(t) = G x(t) + G_d z_d(t) \qquad [55]$$

and eqn [55] is substituted in eqn [54], we get

$$\begin{bmatrix} \dot{x}(t) \\ \dot{z}_d(t) \end{bmatrix} = \begin{bmatrix} A & B_d \\ 0 & F \end{bmatrix} \begin{bmatrix} x(t) \\ z_d(t) \end{bmatrix} + \begin{bmatrix} B \\ 0 \end{bmatrix} \{G x(t) + G_d z_d(t)\} = \begin{bmatrix} A + BG & B_d + BG_d \\ 0 & F \end{bmatrix} \begin{bmatrix} x(t) \\ z_d(t) \end{bmatrix} \qquad [56]$$

- **State estimation**

A usual problem associated with eqn [55] is that the full state x and disturbance z_d are not measured; therefore, they must be retrieved (estimated) from the available measurement vector y. The standard procedure is the use of observers, either in their 'full' or 'reduced' version. The full version is given by

$$\dot{\hat{x}}(t) = A \hat{x}(t) + B u(t) + K(y(t) - \hat{y}(t)); \quad \hat{x}(0) = 0$$

$$\hat{y}(t) = C \hat{x}(t) \qquad [57]$$

As seen, eqn [57] uses the same inputs and outputs as the actual system to generate the state estimates. The gain matrix K determines how fast the estimate will converge to the true value, since it can be proved that the estimation error's equation is

$$\dot{e}(t) = (A - KC) e(t) \Rightarrow e(t) = e^{(A - KC)t} e(0) \qquad [58]$$

Thus K can be chosen by either specifying its eigenvalue set or solving an LQR problem.

Now let us use eqn [57] to design a full-state estimator for the augmented system (eqn [56]). We get

$$\begin{bmatrix} \dot{\hat{x}}(t) \\ \dot{\hat{z}}_d(t) \end{bmatrix} = \begin{bmatrix} A & B_d \\ 0 & F \end{bmatrix} \begin{bmatrix} \hat{x}(t) \\ \hat{z}_d(t) \end{bmatrix} + \begin{bmatrix} B \\ 0 \end{bmatrix} u(t) + K(y(t) - \hat{y}(t))$$

$$\hat{y}(t) = \begin{bmatrix} C & 0 \end{bmatrix} \begin{bmatrix} \hat{x}(t) \\ \hat{z}_d(t) \end{bmatrix} \qquad [59]$$

and eqn [55] becomes

$$u(t) = G \hat{x}(t) + G_d \hat{z}_d(t) \qquad [60]$$

Gain matrices G and K exist if certain conditions on original matrices A, B, and C are fulfilled [17]. Coefficient matrix G_d can be chosen to minimize.

$$\|B G_d + B_d\| \qquad [61]$$

Now, for the problem at hand, the linearization is performed around $w_0 = 18 \text{ m s}^{-1}$, $\theta_0 = 12°$, and $\omega_0 = 42 \text{ rpm}$, which are rated values for the CART turbine. Measurement matrix C is

$$C = \begin{bmatrix} 0.5 & 0 & -0.5 & 0 & 0 & 0 & 0 & 0 \\ 0 & 0 & 0 & 0 & 0 & 1 & 0 & 0 \\ 0 & 0 & 0 & 0 & 0 & 0 & 0 & 0 \end{bmatrix} \qquad [62]$$

where it is assumed that perturbed generator speed, tower-top fore–aft deflection, and the rotor first asymmetric mode deflection are measured.

The rest of the system matrices are evaluated using standard linearization routines. Wind disturbance is modeled as

$$\dot{z}_d = \begin{bmatrix} 0 & 1 & 0 \\ -\omega^2 & 0 & 0 \\ 0 & 0 & 0 \end{bmatrix} \quad [63]$$

With this formulation, the disturbance vector is

$$u_d = \begin{bmatrix} 1 & 0 & 0 \\ 0 & 0 & 1 \end{bmatrix} z_d \quad [64]$$

Note that in this way the first two states of eqn [63] model the azimuth-dependent wind component, while the third state models a uniform step wind disturbance.

Design feedback matrix G in eqn [60] was found through eqn [52], with

$$Q = \begin{bmatrix} 0 & 0 & 0 & 0 & 0 & 0 & 0 & 0 & 0 \\ 0 & 0 & 0 & 0 & 0 & 0 & 0 & 0 & 0 \\ 0 & 0 & 0 & 0 & 0 & 0 & 0 & 0 & 0 \\ 0 & 0 & 0 & 0 & 0 & 0 & 0 & 0 & 0 \\ 0 & 0 & 0 & 0 & 0.0001 & 0 & 0 & 0 & 0 \\ 0 & 0 & 0 & 0 & 0 & 1\times 10^{-12} & 0 & 0 & 0 \\ 0 & 0 & 0 & 0 & 0 & 0 & 1 & 0 & 0 \\ 0 & 0 & 0 & 0 & 0 & 0 & 0 & 10 & 0 \\ 0 & 0 & 0 & 0 & 0 & 0 & 0 & 0 & 0.1 \end{bmatrix}, \quad R = \begin{bmatrix} 1 & 0 \\ 0 & 1 \end{bmatrix} \quad [65]$$

It has to be remembered that these weight matrices balance orders of magnitudes of variables involved as well as weighting their relative importance. Design estimator matrix K in eqn [59] is similarly calculated through a suitable LQR formulation with

$$Q_e = \begin{pmatrix} 500 & & & & & & & & & & & \\ & 50\,000 & & & & & & & & & & \\ & & 500 & & & & & & & & & \\ & & & 50\,000 & & & & & & & & \\ & & & & 120 & & & & & & & \\ & & & & & 800 & & & & & & \\ & & & & & & 220 & & & & & \\ & & & & & & & 20 & & & & \\ & & & & & & & & 2500 & & & \\ & & & & & & & & & 10^5 & & \\ & & & & & & & & & & 10^6 & \\ & & & & & & & & & & & 10^5 \end{pmatrix}, \quad R_e = \begin{pmatrix} 1 & & \\ & 1 & \\ & & 1 \end{pmatrix} \quad [66]$$

Note that Q_e is 12 × 12 to accommodate the nine system states plus the three disturbance states.

The resulting system was simulated in the FAST and ADAMS simulation environments using a turbulent wind inflow. The results are shown in **Figures 29** and **30**.

As seen, generator speed is kept well within the set point of 42 rpm, while blade pitch slightly exceeds its mechanical limits. One way to alleviate this could be to use generator torque as an additional control input.

The described multivariable linear quadratic Gaussian (LQG) approach may seem quite complicated, while at the same time requiring considerable computer power to work online. These problems have led to an alternative formulation, leading to an 'almost decoupled' system, on the lines of generator control.

This d–q axis representation transforms the three blade root load signals into a mean value and variations about two orthogonal axes (the 'direct' and 'quadrature' axes). Recently, it has been shown that it is possible to treat the d- and q-axis as being almost independent. This means that conventional classical design techniques can be applied to generate a SISO controller that can be applied separately to the d- and q-axis. A conventional PI controller in series with a simple filter provides very satisfactory control action. In practice, there is some interaction between the two axes, but this can be accounted for by introducing a simple azimuthal phase shift into the d–q axis transformation, that is, adding a constant offset to the rotor azimuth angle used in the transformation. The direct transformation is given by [18]

$$\begin{bmatrix} \beta_d \\ \beta_q \end{bmatrix} = \frac{2}{3} \begin{bmatrix} \cos\theta & \cos\left(\theta + \frac{2\pi}{3}\right) & \cos\left(\theta + \frac{4\pi}{3}\right) \\ \sin\theta & \sin\left(\theta + \frac{2\pi}{3}\right) & \sin\left(\theta + \frac{4\pi}{3}\right) \end{bmatrix} \begin{bmatrix} \beta_1 \\ \beta_2 \\ \beta_3 \end{bmatrix} \quad [67]$$

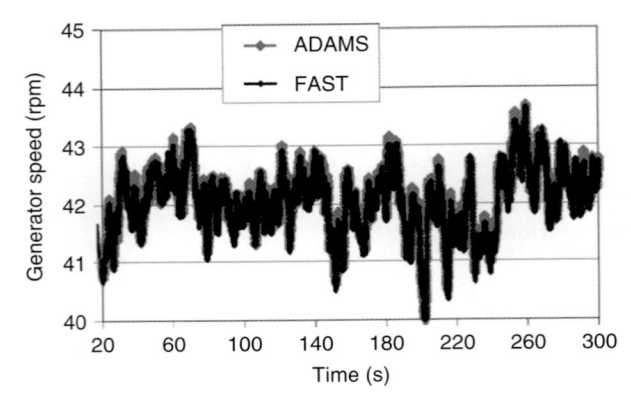

Figure 29 Generator speed response. Reproduced from Wright AD (2004) Modern control design for flexible wind turbines. *NREL Report No. TP-500-35816.* Golden, CO: National Renewable Energy Laboratory [2].

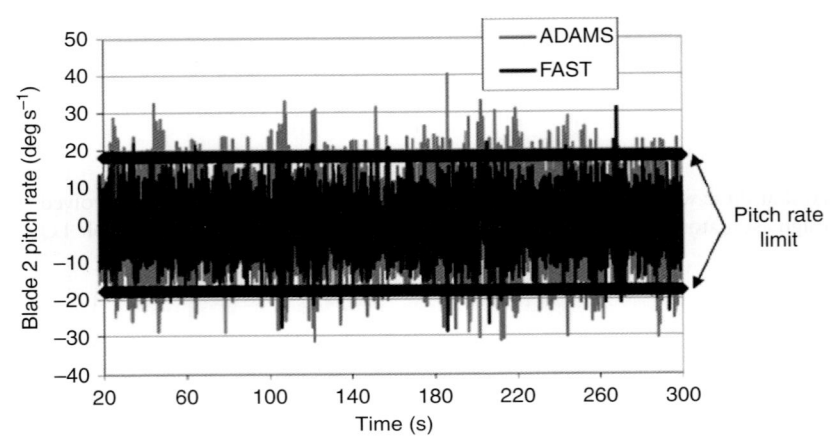

Figure 30 Control effort: pitch rate. Reproduced from Wright AD (2004) Modern control design for flexible wind turbines. *NREL Report No. TP-500-35816.* Golden, CO: National Renewable Energy Laboratory [2].

while the inverse relations are

$$\begin{bmatrix} \beta_1 \\ \beta_2 \\ \beta_3 \end{bmatrix} = \begin{bmatrix} \cos\theta & \sin\theta \\ \cos\left(\theta + \frac{2\pi}{3}\right) & \sin\left(\theta + \frac{2\pi}{3}\right) \\ \cos\left(\theta + \frac{4\pi}{3}\right) & \sin\left(\theta + \frac{4\pi}{3}\right) \end{bmatrix} \begin{bmatrix} \beta_d \\ \beta_q \end{bmatrix} \quad [68]$$

where θ is the angle of blade 1 and the direct axis formation. The inverse transformation [68] is used to generate the individual pitch demand increments for the three blades from the d–q axis pitch demands generated by the LQG algorithm.

2.11.3.3 Generator Control

Generator control is active in Region 2 so as to speed up the turbine rotor and bring it closer to its optimal value (**Figure 20**). It could also be used in Region 3, whenever pitch angle saturates, in order to slow down the rotor speed.

Electrical generators are systems that are generally controlled by power electronics. Hence, controlled electrical generators are systems whose inputs are stator and rotor voltages, having as state variables the stator and rotor currents or fluxes [19]. They are composed of an electromagnetic subsystem, which outputs the electromagnetic torque decelerating the generator rotor coupled to the turbine rotor.

As explained earlier, control of wind turbine AC generators falls into two main categories. The first comprises synchronous and induction generators without slip rings, controlled by full power converters, whereas the second refers to induction generators with slip rings that are controlled by partial power converters.

2.11.3.3.1 Wound rotor doubly fed induction generator control

The stator of the DFIG is directly connected to the grid while the rotor is connected through a power electronics converter (**Figure 31**). The aim of the controller is to regulate stator active and reactive power through a variable-frequency and variable-magnitude rotor voltage supplied to the slip rings.

The power converter consists, as usual, of two converters, that is, a machine-side converter and a grid-side converter. A DC-link capacitor is placed between them, as energy storage, in order to keep the voltage variations (or ripple) in the DC-link voltage small. With the machine-side converter it is possible to control the torque or the speed of the DFIG and also the power factor at the stator terminals, while the main objective of the grid-side converter is to keep the DC-link voltage constant.

The DFIG is described by the differential equations [41]. In order to design efficient controllers, it is useful, as mentioned previously, to transform these equations in a suitable decoupled form. This is achieved by using a (d, q) reference frame that is synchronized with the stator flux, that is, the d-axis is aligned with the stator flux vector. Consequently,

$$\psi_{ds} = \psi_s, \quad \psi_{qs} = 0$$

while the electromagnetic torque is given by

$$T_e = -p \frac{L_m}{L_s} i_{qr} \psi_s \qquad [69]$$

The dynamics of stator flux is controlled only by the stator voltage. Stator voltage is imposed by the network; stator flux is established very quickly. We can thus admit the following simplifying relation and consider that the flow of the stator evolves in a static way. Thus, according to the reference frame carried by the stator vector voltage and neglecting the effect of stator resistance, we have the following relationships:

$$\psi_{ds} = V_s = V_{qs} = V \text{ (grid voltage)}$$

$$V_{ds} = \psi_{qs} (=0)$$

Furthermore, stator active and reactive power are now given by

$$P_s(t) = -\frac{V_s(t) L_m}{L_s} i_{qr}(t) \qquad [70]$$

$$Q_s(t) = \frac{V_s^2(t)}{L_s} - \frac{V_s(t) L_m}{L_s} i_{dr} \qquad [71]$$

while

$$\psi_{dr}(t) = \left(L_r - \frac{L_m^2}{L_s}\right) i_{dr}(t) + \frac{V_s(t) L_m}{\omega_s L_s}$$

$$\psi_{qr}(t) = \left(L_r - \frac{L_m^2}{L_s}\right) i_{qr}(t) \qquad [72]$$

Inspection of eqns [69]–[71] reveals that, as designed, stator reactive power depends on i_{dr}, while stator active power depends on only i_{qr}. Then eqn [26] reduces to

$$\begin{bmatrix} \dot{i}_{dr}(t) \\ \dot{i}_{qr}(t) \end{bmatrix} = \begin{bmatrix} -\frac{R_R}{\sigma L_R} & \omega_s - \frac{p\omega}{\sigma} \\ -\omega_s + \frac{p\omega}{\sigma} & -\frac{R_R}{\sigma L_R} \end{bmatrix} \begin{bmatrix} i_{dr}(t) \\ i_{qr}(t) \end{bmatrix} + \begin{bmatrix} 0 & \frac{1}{\sigma L_R} & 0 \\ -\frac{L_m}{\sigma L_s L_R} & 0 & \frac{1}{\sigma L_R} \end{bmatrix} \begin{bmatrix} V_s(t) \\ V_{dr}(t) \\ V_{qr}(t) \end{bmatrix} \qquad [73]$$

If eqn [73] is expanded,

$$\dot{i}_{dr}(t) = -\frac{R_R}{\sigma L_R} i_{dr}(t) + \left(\omega_s - \frac{p\omega}{\sigma}\right) i_{qr}(t) + \frac{1}{\sigma L_R} V_{dr}(t)$$

$$\dot{i}_{qr}(t) = \left(-\omega_s + \frac{p\omega}{\sigma}\right) i_{dr}(t) - \frac{R_R}{\sigma L_R} i_{qr}(t) + \frac{1}{\sigma L_R} V_{qr}(t) - \frac{L_m}{\sigma L_s L_R} V_s(t) \qquad [74]$$

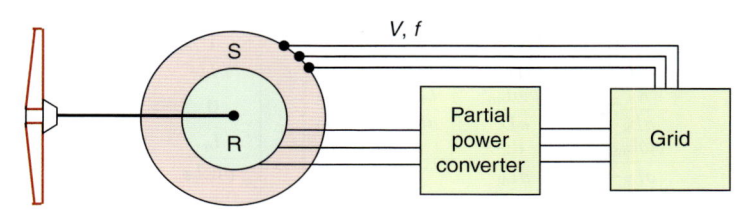

Figure 31 Schematic of doubly fed induction generator wind turbine control.

we see that the equations are still decoupled. However, we can regard the coupling terms as disturbances. Taking Laplace transforms of both sides of eqn [74] gives

$$\left(s + \frac{R_R}{\sigma L_R}\right) I_{dr}(s) = \left(\omega_S - \frac{p\omega}{\sigma}\right) I_{qr}(s) + \frac{1}{\sigma L_R} V_{dr}(s)$$

$$\Rightarrow I_{dr}(s) = \left(s + \frac{R_R}{\sigma L_R}\right)^{-1} \frac{1}{\sigma L_R} V_{dr}(s) + \left(s + \frac{R_R}{\sigma L_R}\right)^{-1} \left(\omega_S - \frac{p\omega}{\sigma}\right) I_{qr}(s)$$

$$\Rightarrow I_{dr}(s) = H_V(s) V_{dr}(s) + H_{IQ}(s) I_{qr}(s) \qquad [75]$$

and

$$\left(s + \frac{R_R}{\sigma L_R}\right) I_{qr}(s) = \left(-\omega_S + \frac{p\omega}{\sigma}\right) I_{dr}(s) + \frac{1}{\sigma L_R} V_{qr}(s) - \frac{L_m}{\sigma L_S L_R} V_s(s)$$

$$\Rightarrow I_{qr}(s) = \left(s + \frac{R_R}{\sigma L_R}\right)^{-1} \frac{1}{\sigma L_R} V_{qr}(s) + \left(s + \frac{R_R}{\sigma L_R}\right)^{-1}$$

$$\times \left[\left(-\omega_S + \frac{p\omega}{\sigma}\right) I_{dr}(s) - \frac{L_m}{\sigma L_S L_R} V_s(s)\right]$$

$$\Rightarrow I_{qr}(s) = H_V(s) V_{qr}(s) + H_{ID}(s) I_{dr}(s) + H_{VS}(s) V_s(s) \qquad [76]$$

By keeping the first terms of the right-hand side of eqns [75] and [76], separate PI controllers for i_{qr} and i_{dr} can be designed, resulting in the individual control of active and reactive power through eqns [70] and [71] [20].

To calculate the stator current set points i_{qr}^* and i_{dr}^*, first note that reactive power is usually maintained at 0. Thus, from eqn [71],

$$i_{dr}^* = -\frac{V_s}{L_m}$$

To set the stator quadrature current reference, eqn [69] is used. This gives

$$T_e(t) = -p \frac{L_m}{L_s} i_{qr}(t) \psi_s(t) \Rightarrow i_{qr}^* = -\frac{L_s}{p L_m \psi_s} T_e^* \qquad [77]$$

Therefore, i_{qr}^* is obtained through T_e^*. Stator flux cannot be directly measured and is usually estimated by

$$\hat{\psi}_s(t) = \frac{E_g}{\omega_1}$$

Now, T_e^* is related to ω, through eqn [2],

$$I_T \frac{d\omega(t)}{dt} = T_m(t) - T_e(t)$$

In steady state, the time derivative vanishes, hence $T_m = T_e = P_m/\omega_m$. Substituting $T_e^* = P_m^*/\omega_m^*$ into eqn [77] gives

$$i_{qr}^* = -\frac{L_s}{p L_m \hat{\psi}_s} \frac{P_m^*}{\omega_m^*} \qquad [78]$$

where P_m is given by eqn [43] and ω^* by eqn [46].

Let us not forget that electrical ($\omega_e = \omega_s$) and mechanical ($\omega_m = \omega$) speed must be available to the control system (measured) since they are needed in the relevant Park transformations [21]. Furthermore, stator voltage V_S is also needed to complete the disturbance term in eqn [74].

The complete DFIG power control system is shown in **Figure 32**.

2.11.3.3.2 Asynchronous squirrel cage generator control

Squirrel cage control is developed similar to the DFIG case. To effectively decouple stator currents, the rotor field is chosen to lie on the d-axis. Hence i_{ds} is aligned with Ψ_{rd} and i_{qs} is perpendicular to it. Furthermore, $V_{rd} = V_{rq} = 0$.

Thus the equations describing the dynamic model of the squirrel cage are [22]

$$\begin{bmatrix} \dot{i}_{sd} \\ \dot{i}_{sq} \\ \dot{i}_{rd} \\ \dot{i}_{rq} \end{bmatrix} = -\begin{bmatrix} \frac{R_S}{\sigma L_S} & \omega_S + \frac{p\omega L_m^2}{\sigma L_S L_R} & \frac{L_m R_R}{\sigma L_S L_R} & \frac{p\omega L_m}{\sigma L_S} \\ -\left(\omega_S + \frac{p\omega L_m^2}{\sigma L_S L_R}\right) & \frac{R_S}{\sigma L_S} & -\frac{p\omega L_m}{\sigma L_S} & \frac{L_m R_R}{\sigma L_S L_R} \\ \frac{L_m R_S}{\sigma L_S L_R} & -\frac{p\omega L_m}{\sigma L_R} & \frac{R_R}{\sigma L_R} & \omega_S - \frac{p\omega}{\sigma} \\ \frac{p\omega L_m}{\sigma L_R} & \frac{L_m R_S}{\sigma L_S L_R} & -\omega_S + \frac{p\omega}{\sigma} & -\frac{R_R}{\sigma L_R} \end{bmatrix} \begin{bmatrix} i_{sd} \\ i_{sq} \\ i_{rd} \\ i_{rq} \end{bmatrix} + \begin{bmatrix} \frac{1}{\sigma L_S} & 0 & -\frac{L_m}{\sigma L_S L_R} & 0 \\ 0 & \frac{1}{\sigma L_S} & 0 & -\frac{L_m}{\sigma L_S L_R} \\ -\frac{L_m}{\sigma L_S L_R} & 0 & \frac{1}{\sigma L_R} & 0 \\ 0 & -\frac{L_m}{\sigma L_S L_R} & 0 & \frac{1}{\sigma L_R} \end{bmatrix} \begin{bmatrix} V_{sd} \\ V_{sq} \\ 0 \\ 0 \end{bmatrix} \qquad [79]$$

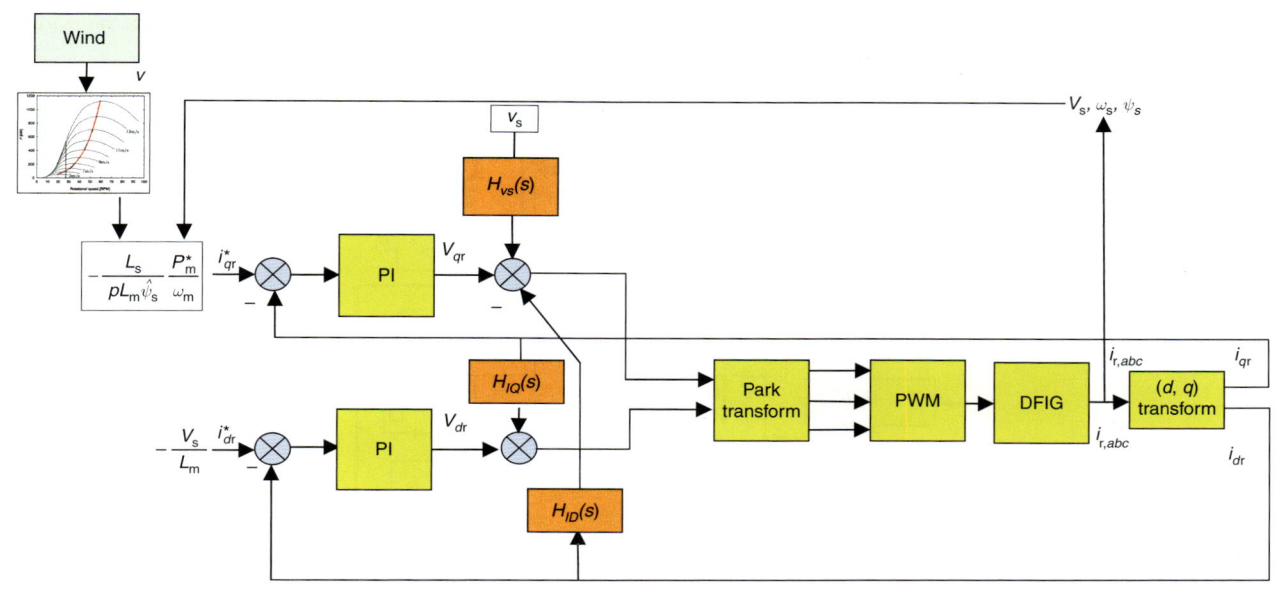

Figure 32 Control block diagram of doubly fed induction generator (the v vs. ω^* graph is shown in detail in **Figure 19**).

while generator torque is now given by

$$T_e(t) = \frac{3}{2}p\frac{L_m}{L_r}i_{Sq}\psi_{Rd} \qquad [80]$$

Utilizing the convenient use of the (d, q) reference frame, eqn [79] can be Laplace-transformed to yield

$$\begin{bmatrix} \psi_{Rd}(s) \\ I_{Sq}(s) \end{bmatrix} = \begin{bmatrix} 1 & -M(s)N(s) \\ P(s)R(s) & 1 \end{bmatrix}^{-1} \begin{bmatrix} 0 & M(s) \\ P(s) & 0 \end{bmatrix} \begin{bmatrix} V_{Sd}(s) \\ V_{Sq}(s) \end{bmatrix} \qquad [81]$$

$$\Rightarrow X(s) = G(s)U(s) \qquad [82]$$

where

$$G(s) = \begin{bmatrix} 1 & -M(s)N(s) \\ P(s)R(s) & 1 \end{bmatrix}^{-1} \begin{bmatrix} 0 & M(s) \\ P(s) & 0 \end{bmatrix}, \; U(s) = \begin{bmatrix} V_{Sd}(s) \\ V_{Sq}(s) \end{bmatrix} \qquad [83]$$

with

$$M(s) = \frac{1}{(R_S + \sigma L_S s)\dfrac{1 + L_R/R_R s}{L_m} + \dfrac{L_m}{L_R}s}$$

$$N(s) = \omega_s \sigma L_S$$

$$P(s) = \frac{1}{(R_S + \sigma L_S s)}$$

$$R(s) = \omega_s \left(\sigma L_S \frac{1 + L_R/R_R s}{L_m} + \frac{L_m}{L_R} \right)$$

and, as before,

$$\sigma = 1 - \frac{L_m^2}{L_S L_R}$$

Equation [82] can be used to derive a feedback control law of the form $U(s) = KX(s)$. However, a better approach is to decouple eqn [82], so that simpler, scalar, PI algorithms can be used to control the ψ_{Rd} and i_{Sq} components independently. Reference trajectories are calculated using eqn [80].

The schematic of squirrel cage control is shown in **Figure 33**, while the overall control block diagram of the generator-side converter is shown in **Figure 34**.

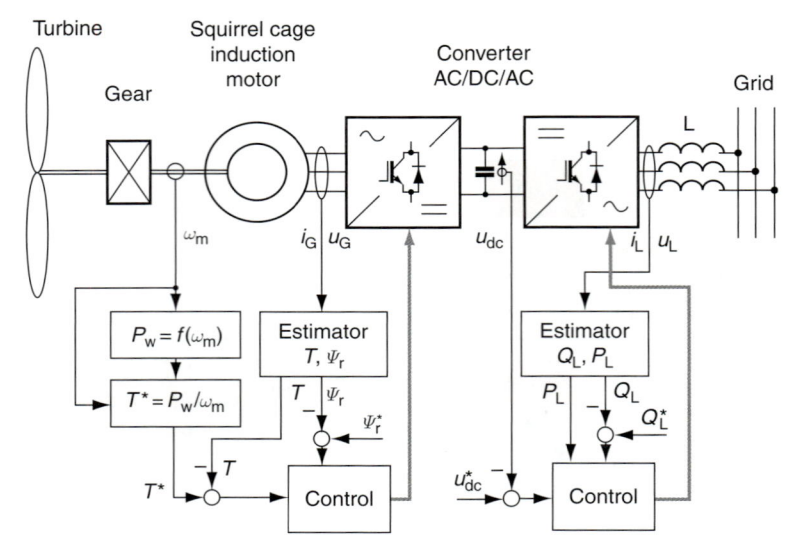

Figure 33 Torque control electromagnetic subsystem. Reproduced from Sikorski A and Kuzma A (2009) Cooperation of induction squirrel-cage generator with grid connected AC/DC/AC converter. *Bulletin of the Polish Academy of Technical Sciences* 57: 317–322 [26].

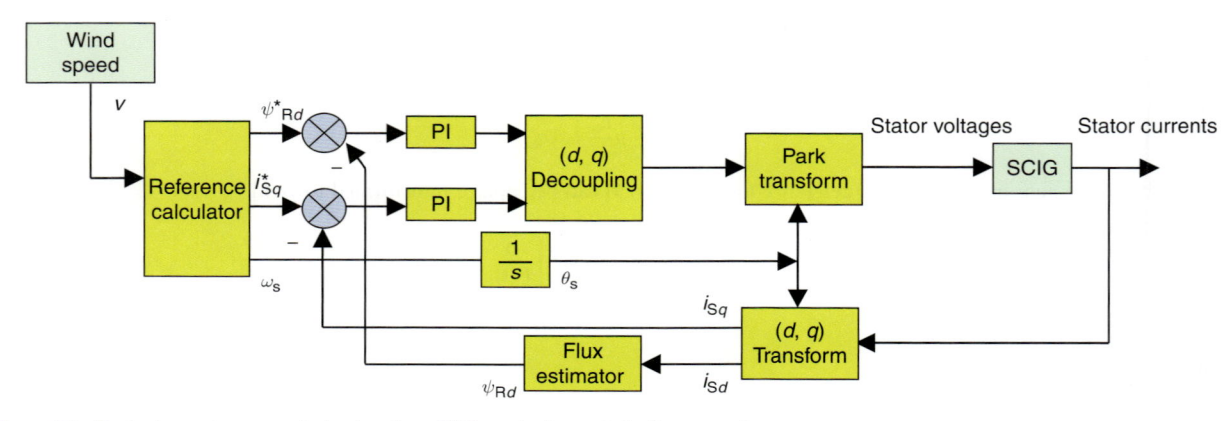

Figure 34 Squirrel cage torque control subsystem. SCIG, squirrel cage induction generator.

A suitable choice of the PI parameters may result in a millisecond rated electromagnetic subsystem (EMS) time constant, τ_G. This control structure allows very fast and accurate torque response, permitting the whole subsystem to be assimilated to a first-order element. This allows one to neglect this subsystem's involvement in the overall operation.

2.11.3.3.3 Permanent magnet synchronous generator control

As already discussed, PMSGs are controlled by full-scale power electronic converters. The generator-side converter controls the voltage and the electric frequency at the PMSG terminals, which corresponds to the desirable rotational speed of the wind turbine. In this respect, it operates as a VSC with voltage V_{Sd} and frequency f_s.

By working in the (d, q) reference frame, decoupled control of active and reactive power is possible. Thus, active power can be controlled by influencing the d-axis component of the stator current, while the reactive power can be controlled by influencing the q-axis components of the stator current. Let us rearrange eqns [22], so that identification of state, control, and disturbance elements is clear.

Inspection of eqns [19]–[21] reveals that these expressions are nonlinear (to be precise bilinear), coupled, and time varying. Substituting eqn [20] into eqn [19] gives

$$L_{ds}\dot{i}_{ds}(t) = v_d(t) - R_s i_{ds}(t) + \omega_e(t) L_{qs} i_{qs}(t)$$
$$L_{qs}\dot{i}_{qs}(t) = v_q(t) - R_s i_{qs}(t) - \omega_e(t)[L_{ds} i_{ds}(t) + \psi_m]$$

[84]

We can rewrite eqn [84] in state space form as

$$\begin{bmatrix} \dot{i}_{ds}(t) \\ \dot{i}_{qs}(t) \end{bmatrix} = \begin{bmatrix} -\frac{R_s}{L_{ds}} & 0 \\ 0 & -\frac{R_s}{L_{qs}} \end{bmatrix} \begin{bmatrix} i_{ds}(t) \\ i_{qs}(t) \end{bmatrix} + \begin{bmatrix} \frac{1}{L_{ds}} & 0 \\ 0 & \frac{1}{L_{qs}} \end{bmatrix} \begin{bmatrix} v_d(t) \\ v_q(t) \end{bmatrix}$$
$$+ \begin{bmatrix} 0 & \frac{\omega_e(t) L_{qs}}{L_{ds}} \\ -\frac{\omega_e(t) L_{ds}}{L_{qs}} & 0 \end{bmatrix} \begin{bmatrix} i_{ds}(t) \\ i_{qs}(t) \end{bmatrix} + \begin{bmatrix} 0 \\ -\frac{1}{L_{qs}} \end{bmatrix} \omega_e(t) \psi_m \quad [85]$$

or

$$\dot{x}(t) = A_1 x(t) + B u(t) + N \omega_e(t) x(t) + G \omega_e(t) \psi_m \quad [86]$$

where the various quantities are obvious from comparing eqns [85] and [86]. In this way, eqn [84] is split into a linear part (A, B), a coupling term (N), and a disturbance term (G).

Most industrial controllers choose to retain the linear terms and treat the rest as disturbances accommodated by a PI block. This idea is unfortunately termed 'vector decoupled control'. Taking Laplace transform of the linear part of eqn [85] gives the transfer function of interest,

$$\begin{bmatrix} I_{ds}(s) \\ I_{qs}(s) \end{bmatrix} = \begin{bmatrix} \frac{1}{L_{ds}s + R_s} & 0 \\ 0 & \frac{1}{L_{qs}s + R_s} \end{bmatrix} \begin{bmatrix} V_d(s) \\ V_q(s) \end{bmatrix} \quad [87]$$

Figure 35 shows the PMSG control schematic, while Figure 36 depicts the overall control block diagram for controlling torque.

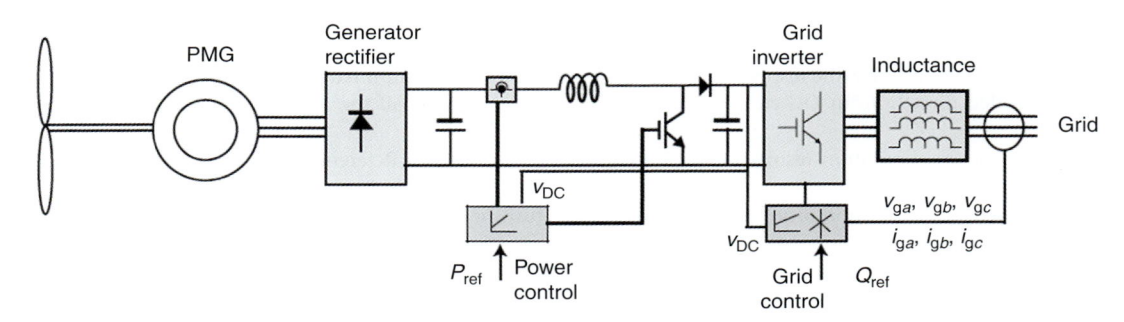

Figure 35 Schematic of permanent magnet synchronous generator control.

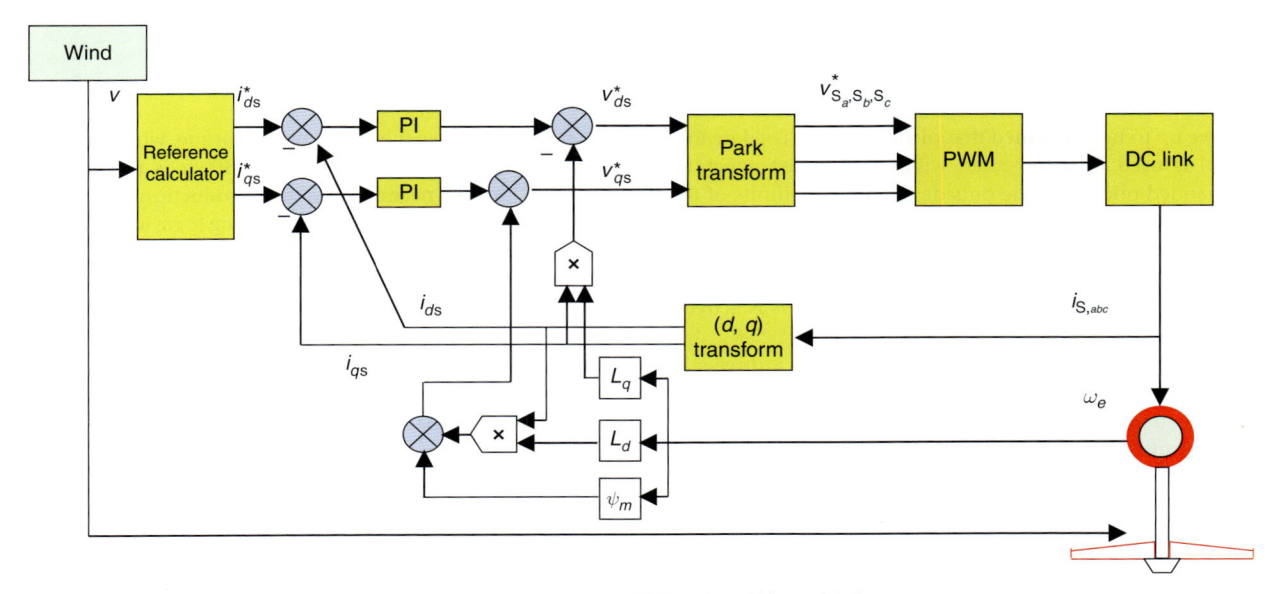

Figure 36 Permanent magnet synchronous generator torque controller. PWM, pulse width modulation.

Equation [87] can be used to tune the PI parameters for a given system. The reference calculator block must utilize wind speed information to calculate stator current set points i_{ds}^* and i_{qs}^*.

Normally, the difference between the d- and q-axis mutual inductance is very small for a PMSG with greater than 100 pole pairs [23] and the stator winding resistance is much smaller than the synchronous reactance. Adopting this simplifying condition, eqn [21] becomes

$$T_e(t) = p\psi_m i_{qs}(t) \qquad [88]$$

Using eqn [88] the current trajectory can be calculated in terms of the torque trajectory.

Various approaches exist for the latter calculation, the most common being

$$T_e^*(t) = k(\omega^*)^2 = \frac{1}{2}\rho\pi R^5 \frac{C_p^*}{(\lambda^*)^3}(\omega^*)^2 \qquad [89]$$

Using eqn [46], eqn [89] becomes

$$T_e^*(t) = k\omega^2 = \frac{1}{2}\rho\pi R^5 \frac{C_p^*}{(\lambda^*)^3}\left(\frac{\lambda^* v(t)}{R}\right)^2 = \frac{1}{2}\rho\pi R^3 \frac{C_p^*}{\lambda^*} v^2(t) \qquad [90]$$

Finally, plugging eqn [90] into eqn [88] gives the desired expression,

$$p\psi_m i_{qs}^*(t) = \frac{1}{2}\rho\pi R^3 \frac{C_p^*}{\lambda^*} v^2(t)$$

$$\Rightarrow i_{qs}^*(t) = \frac{1}{2}\rho\pi R^3 \frac{C_p^*}{p\psi_m \lambda^*} v^2(t) \qquad [91]$$

Since in variable-speed wind turbines with PMSG, the generator is connected to a simple diode rectifier, the stator reactive power is set to zero [24]. This results in

$$i_{ds}(t) = 0 \qquad [92]$$

This also makes $V_{ds}(t)=0$. In this case, the respective control system can be greatly simplified as the only control variable is $i_{qs}(t)$. This can be easily controlled directly from DC current by suitably switching on and off the DC chopper according to simple PWM techniques.

In **Figure 37** are shown simulation results for such a controller, described in Reference [25], for a permanent magnet wind turbine generator.

The machine used in the simulation is a 2.5 MW wind turbine. The rotor's radius is $R = 40$ m, the moment of inertia $J_T = 9.193 \times 10^6$ kg m^2, and $C_p^* = 0.474$. Controller parameters were manually calculated as $K_p = 0.8$ and $K_I = 100$. Simulation time was 150 s with a wind profile shown in **Figure 37(a)**. Wind speed is well below the rated speed of 14 m s^{-1}. Machine speed and tip speed ratio are shown in **Figures 37(b)** and **37(c)**. As seen, λ is kept well within its optimum value of 7.5, while rotor speed tracks incoming wind. Stator d current, shown in **Figure 37(d)**, is also kept at its set value of 0 A as stated above. Lastly, **Figure 37(e)** shows the fluctuation of stator q current, trying to track its set point (red line) produced by the reference calculator.

2.11.3.4 Coupled Pitch–Generator Control

We have up to now assumed that pitch control is used in above-rated winds to decrease the aerodynamic torque, while generator control is used in below-rated winds to increase generator production. However, as seen in **Figure 30**, it is possible that commanded pitch rates are outside the physical limits of the turbine (18° s^{-1}), thus necessitating the introduction of generator control in the opposite direction, that is, braking. To accomplish this in a decoupled fashion, some switching logic which ensures that only one of the control loops is active at any one time should be designed. Alternatively, both control loops can be run together, but coupled with terms that drive one or the other loop into saturation when far above or below the rated wind speed. Thus most of the time, only one of the controllers is active, but they can be made to interfere constructively when close to the rated point.

In Reference [2], simulations were run using a three-state generator control model and a nine-state IPC model. Generator control poles were chosen so as not to interfere with speed control. In fact, generator control was used to add damping to the first drive-train torsion mode. In **Figures 38** and **39**, the performance of this approach looks promising as pitch rate is kept within limits.

2.11.3.5 Grid Control

Since modern power electronics effectively decouples the generator from the grid side, grid control is essentially the same, regardless of the generator type used in the wind turbine.

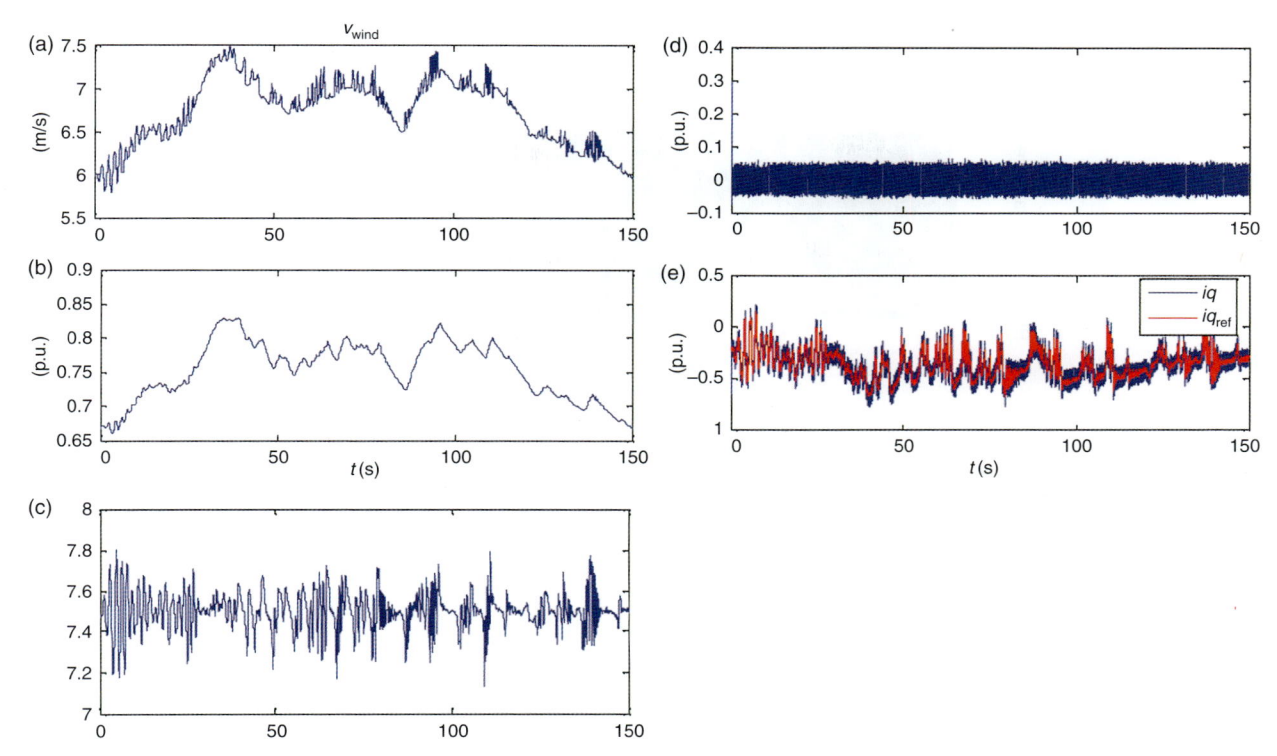

Figure 37 Permanent magnet synchronous generator control graphs. Reproduced from Fuglseth TP (2008) Modelling a 2.5 MW direct driven wind turbine with permanent magnet generator. *Report for the Final Examination Project of the Nordic PhD Course on Wind Power.* Norway: Department of Electrical Power Engineering, Norwegian University of Science and Technology [25].

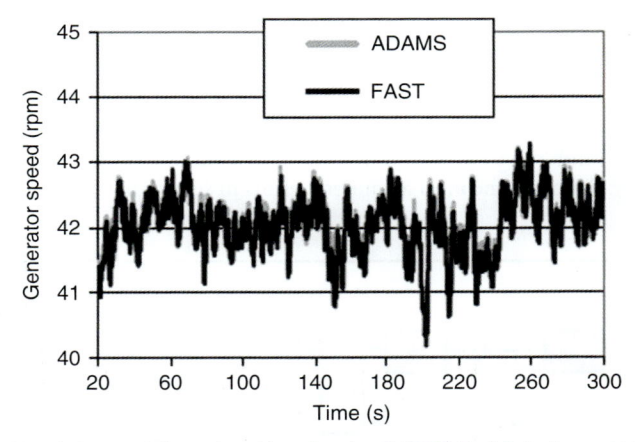

Figure 38 Generator speed using torque–pitch control. Reproduced from Donders S (2002) Fault Detection and Identification for Wind Turbine Systems: A Closed-Loop Analysis. Master's Thesis, University of Twente [41].

The DC/AC grid converter transfers the energy from the DC link to the three-phase grid. The converter is controlled by the main voltage control loop of the capacitor (DC link). The above loop is created for two reasons:

- to provide an appropriate voltage value to make it possible to shape the sinusoidal current transferred to the grid under fixed conditions (grid voltage value, current, and inductance of grid choke); and
- to protect the converter against overvoltages that may occur due to the differences between the delivered and received energy from the DC link.

If the reference frame (x, y) for the grid converter subsystem is chosen in synchronous coordinates with grid angular frequency, then active and reactive power injected to the grid are given by

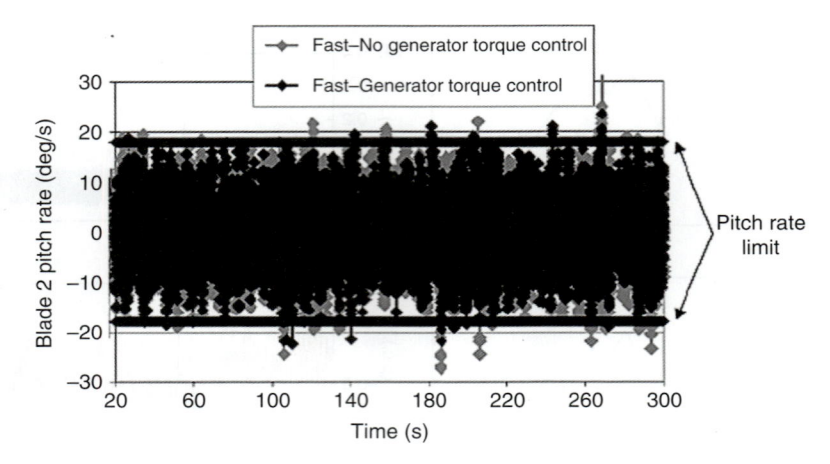

Figure 39 Pitch rate using torque–pitch control. Reproduced from Donders S (2002) Fault Detection and Identification for Wind Turbine Systems: A Closed-Loop Analysis. Master's Thesis, University of Twente [41].

$$P_{grid}(t) = \frac{3}{2}V_x(t)i_x(t)$$

$$Q_{grid}(t) = -\frac{3}{2}V_x(t)i_y(t)$$

[93]

hence y-axis current can control reactive power, while x-axis current controls active power. When the current set value i_y^* equals zero, then the currents flowing into the grid remain in phase with the corresponding voltages in the supply grid, that is, only active power is generated.

If there is no particular active power demand from the system operator, P_{grid}^* may be given by a maximum power point (MPP) characteristic. Q_{grid}^* is typically set to zero but in case the grid voltage is disturbed from its rated value, and voltage grid support is demanded from the wind turbine, the reactive power reference can be provided by a voltage controller.

A possible control scheme is shown in **Figure 40**, where classical PI controllers are used for regulating i_x and i_y. Forward and inverse transforms are shown, while angle φ_0, used in transformation operations, is reproduced in phase-locked loop (PLL) [26]. The capacitor voltage error $u_{dc}^* - u_{dc}$ determines the amplitude and direction of the i_x^* component directly proportional to the set value of the active power.

2.11.3.6 Yaw Control

Yaw control is necessary in upwind turbines to fully capture incoming wind power. As shown in **Figure 41**, power variation is proportional to the square of cos γ; therefore, incorrect alignment results in substantial loss of electricity production [28].

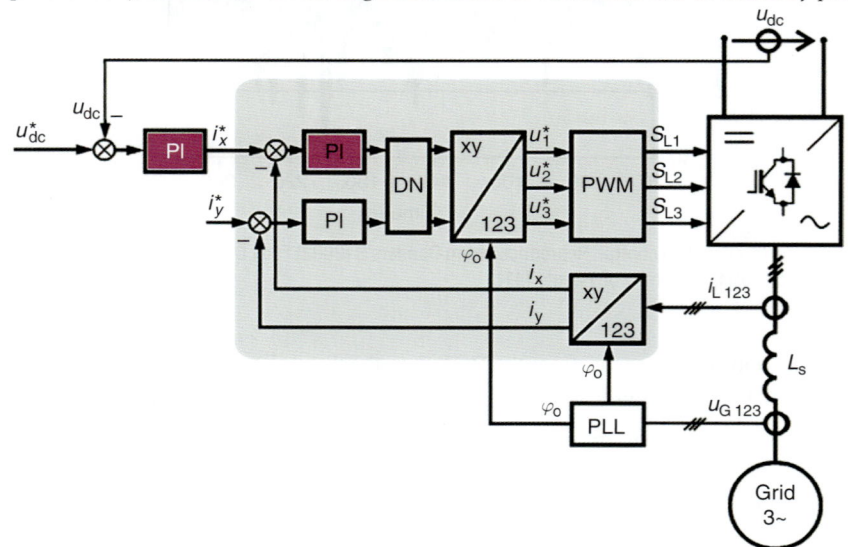

Figure 40 DC/AC converter control. Reproduced from Sikorski A and Kuzma A (2009) Cooperation of induction squirrel-cage generator with grid connected AC/DC/AC converter. *Bulletin of the Polish Academy of Technical Sciences* 57: 317–322 [26].

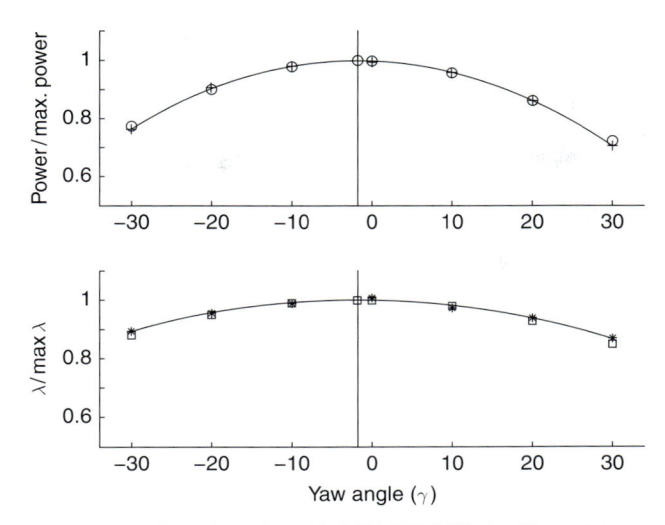

Figure 41 Yaw angle vs. power and tip speed ratio. Reproduced from Medici D (2004) Wind turbine wakes – control and vortex shedding. *KTH Mechanics Technical Report*. Stockholm, Sweden: Royal Institute of Technology [27].

Even though yawing may be accomplished mechanically, either by using a wind vane located on the nacelle or by free yawing downwind, nearly all modern megawatt turbines use motorized yawing.

The yaw subsystem consists of the following parts:

Azimuth bearing. This ensures easy running, long service life, and adequate damping. A four-point ball bearing or friction bearings are used. The latter have the advantage that no complicated brakes or rings are needed.

Yaw drive. Even though the yaw drive could be either hydraulic or electrical, current trends are toward the latter. Furthermore, electric yaw drives with integrated brakes are being manufactured.

Yaw brakes. These are essential for absorbing yawing moments. They are usually integrated into the drive system. Two or more yaw brakes are common in larger turbines. These act on a brake ring on the inside of the tower or on a ring in the nacelle.

Controlling yaw is a sensitive process, since it requires accurate placement of the nacelle, without unnecessary movement. The control algorithm usually utilizes the yaw error measurement from a nacelle-mounted wind vane to calculate a control signal for the yaw actuator, a mechanical or hydraulic servo. Sensorless techniques are also found in the literature [29]. Frequently the demand signal will simply be a command to yaw at a slow fixed rate in one or the other direction. The yaw vane signal must be heavily averaged, especially for upwind turbines where the vane is behind the rotor. Because of the slow response of the yaw control system, a simple dead-band controller is often sufficient (**Figure 42**). The yaw motor is switched on when the averaged yaw error exceeds a certain value, and switched off again after a certain time or when the nacelle has moved through a certain angle.

More complex control algorithms are sometimes used, but the control is always slow-acting, and does not demand any special design considerations. One exception is the case of active yaw control to regulate aerodynamic power in high winds. In this case, rapid yaw rates are required, resulting in large yaw loads.

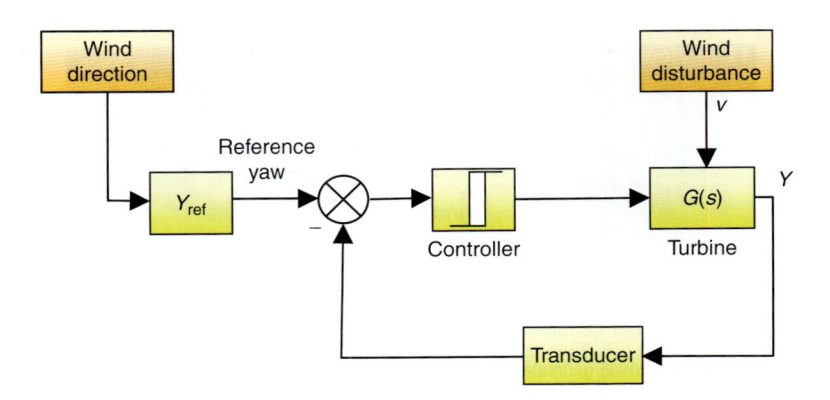

Figure 42 Yaw control.

As mentioned, special concern should be given to the yaw rate, especially for flexible blades. Since the rotor has angular momentum, when the brake is applied, the wind turbine will tend to rotate about the yaw axis. The rate of yaw gives a torque,

$$T_y = \frac{d\gamma}{dt} \qquad [94]$$

in the direction perpendicular to the plane of rotation of the rotor. Therefore, a large change in the angular momentum of the rotor, due to a large change in wind direction or a change in yaw due to shutdown for overspeed, results in a force perpendicular to the plane of rotation. For flexible blades, this force could be large enough such that the blades could strike the tower. In the worst case, the blades break off at the root.

Yaw control is also useful in emergency operations since wind turbines can be damaged when they are stopped as a result of supervisory control action, either due to high winds or fault conditions. In these circumstances, even though very little active control is usually done, the yaw angle may be changed to accommodate changes in wind direction.

Mitsubishi has recently developed its Smart Yaw® system against typhoons, following the collapse of a wind turbine in Miyakojima caused by Typhoon Maemi [30]. This system ensures yaw control even during power interruption, by yawing using the wind vane effect, that is, by changing the turbine standby position to downwind direction (**Figure 43**). Hence, since the wind load acting on the rotor is used for driving the yaw, it is effective even at power failure. It must be noted that during this operation the yaw brake is in effect in order to prevent excessive yawing rate.

The Smart Yaw concept was found to reduce blade loads by 25% and tower load by 30%, leading to a decrease of blade and tower weight by 15%.

Yaw control has also been investigated in the context of reducing structural dynamic loads [28]. Since the yaw controller is parked most of the time, large dynamic loads appear in its components and the tower because of its stiffness. It may be better to make it flexible, for instance, with mechanical suspension devices. An alternative is to use the yaw motor continuously. The same dynamic behavior as with a spring and damper suspension can theoretically be obtained with feedback of the yaw angle. The disadvantage of this concept is the increased demands on the yaw servo. Furthermore, continuous operation leads to increased wear. The ratings of the motor, for example, the maximum torque and speed, may have to be improved. However, continuous yaw control may have more potential by actively attenuating structural dynamic oscillations, since the yaw motion is dynamically coupled with the tower and the blades.

Two different structural modes were investigated: the teeter motion of the turbine and the lateral tower bending. Among others an active linear quadratic (LQ) control was implemented. The results showed that the lateral tower motion is highly dependent on the yaw dynamics. It can be reduced with a passive spring and damper suspension system, but the efficiency is significantly improved when the angular position of the rotor is taken into account. A periodic LQ controller achieves the same damping as a passive scheme, but requires only 10% of the control effort. Moreover, it reduces the tower torque more effectively. It is the yaw motion rather than the yaw torque that is limiting. The teeter angle is significantly more difficult to control. Because of the aerodynamic damping, it is difficult to change the natural teeter motion. However, there may be some cases where the aerodynamic damping is sufficiently low to consider continuous yaw control. The aerodynamic damping is much less important for the lateral tower bending.

2.11.3.7 Grid Issues

Large-scale integration of wind turbines significantly impacts grid operation. Traditionally, wind turbines were not required to participate in frequency and voltage control. However, in recent years, grid codes have been defined to specify the requirements that wind turbines must meet in order to be connected to the grid. Examples of such requirements include the capability of contributing to frequency and voltage control by continuously adjusting active and reactive power supplied to the transmission system, the

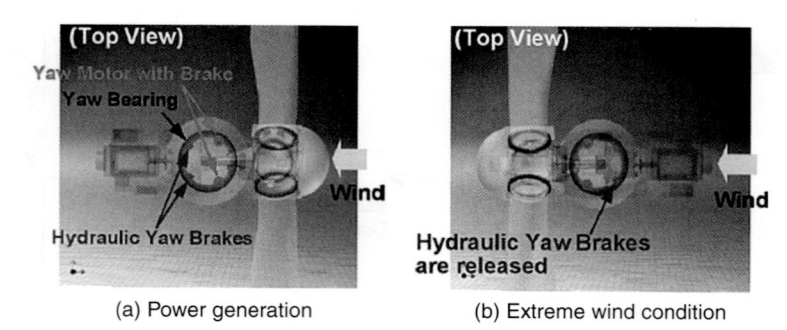

Figure 43 Smart yaw operation. (a) In normal power generation, the yaw controller directs the turbine against the wind. (b) In extreme winds, hydraulic yaw brake is released. Reproduced from Kuroiwa T, Karikomi K, Hayashi Y, et al. (2004) New products and technologies of Mitsubishi wind turbines. *Mitsubishi Heavy Industries Technical Review* 41: 170–174 [30].

power regulation rate that a wind farm must provide, and capability of providing power in grid voltage dips (low-voltage ride through (LVRT)). In general, grid connection requirements can be categorized as

1. power control and frequency range;
2. power factor and voltage control; and
3. transient fault behavior, voltage operating range.

As has already mentioned, wind turbine generating systems can be divided into two main categories: fixed speed and variable speed. A fixed-speed machine generally uses a squirrel cage induction generator which consumes reactive power and cannot contribute to voltage control. Therefore, wind farms with this type of generators use static capacitor banks to provide reactive power.

Variable-speed turbines can offer the ability to regulate the power factor, by either consuming or producing reactive power. Doubly fed machines can be controlled to provide frequency and voltage control with a back-to-back converter in the rotor. This type of generators have some difficulties to ride-through voltage dips, because they generate high voltages and currents in the rotor circuit and the power converter could be damaged. This is the most extended variable-speed wind turbine technology and manufacturers already offer this type of wind turbines with fault ride-through capabilities.

Synchronous generator versions connect through a full-scale converter to the grid. This provides maximum flexibility, enabling full real and reactive power control and fault ride-through capability during voltage dips.

Grid requirements vary from country to country. It can generally be stated that the more penetrated is renewable energy in a country's grid, the stricter are the codes regulating grid connection. The following is an outline of the regulations in Denmark, a country where at some periods 100% of the supplied energy is from renewable sources:

1. *Power control and frequency range*. Controlled limitation of active power is demanded to limit the reactive power demand of wind farms after a fault. In addition, power limitation is demanded to ensure supply and demand balance if a part of Denmark becomes an island due to a fault. It must be possible to reduce power to less than 20% of nominal power within less than 2 s. This corresponds to a ramp rate of 40% of rated power per second. In a transient fault situation, the full power decrease and a subsequent power increase must be possible within approximately 30 s. Normal operation between 49 and 50.3 Hz is required. Beyond the outer limits of 47 and 53 Hz, the turbines have to disconnect within 300 ms. Frequency control is not required.
2. *Power factor and voltage control*. Wind farms are required to have sufficient reactive power compensation to be neutral in reactive power at any operating point. This requirement has to be fulfilled at the grid connection point. In the 150 kV system, steady-state operation has to be possible under full load in the voltage range between 0.95 and 1.13 pu. If the voltage reaches 1.2 pu at the grid connection point (irrespective of the voltage level), the wind farm has to start performing voltage reduction within 100 ms of detection. Voltage reduction can be achieved by switching in reactors to increase the reactive power demand of the wind farm.
3. *Transient fault operation*. No specific voltage operating ranges and respective trip times in transient fault situations are specified. Wind farms have to stay connected and stable under permanent three-phase faults on any arbitrary line or transformer and under transient two-phase fault on any arbitrary line. In the wake of a fault, the voltage can be down to 70% of the initial voltage for duration of up to 10 s, which must not lead to instability of the wind farm (**Figure 44**). The controllability of the wind farm must be sustained for up to three faults within 2 min, or for up to six faults if the delay between the faults is 5 min, each fault happening during steady-state operation. This requirement makes sure that the turbines are fitted with sufficient auxiliary power supplies.

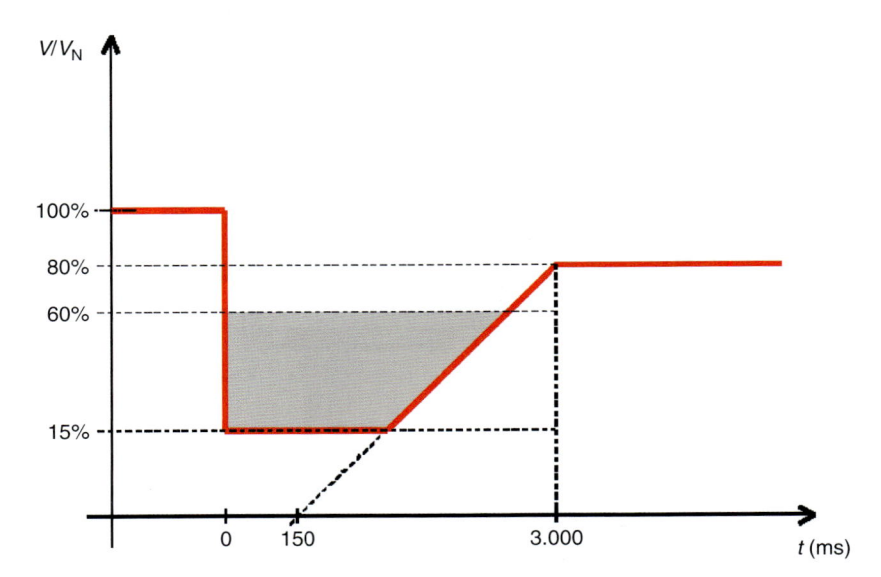

Figure 44 Typical low-voltage ride-through capability.

When the voltage directly after a fault falls below 60–80% for longer than 2–10 s, it is likely that the turbines have accelerated so much that the grid cannot get them back to normal speed. In such a case, a fast reduction of the active power and a fast increase of reactive power have to be conducted. If this does not successfully reestablish the grid voltage, the wind farm has to be disconnected.

As already stated, power electronic converters are essential in keeping with the above requirements. Their intrinsic ability to decouple turbine and grid operation effectively allows the wind turbine to remain in operation during voltage dips and separately control active and reactive power.

In PMSGs, these are achieved as follows: When voltage drops to unacceptable levels, the inverter switches off the IGBTs and remains in the waiting state to resume operation when the fault is cleared. On the generator side, the rectifier can be bypassed while the stator feeds a resistor, so that excessive acceleration of the rotor is avoided. Furthermore, since the generator does not directly experience the low-voltage spikes, no large transient currents are developed in the generator stator or rotor.

2.11.4 Fault Accommodation

Reliability is a major concern in every industrial design. While maximizing power production represents one pillar of the wind conversion process, uninterrupted operation becomes more and more imperative, especially now that wind parks are moving offshore and inspection and maintenance costs are expected to be much higher. While foundation and transmission costs are an intrinsic property of the offshore location, reducing the inspection and maintenance costs is a key objective of offshore development.

A wind turbine operates unattended for about 13 years in a design life of 20 years. A motor vehicle's operation by comparison amounts to just 4 months. In this respect, the wind turbine is a unique power generating system as the power train components are subject to highly irregular loading from turbulent wind conditions, and the number of fatigue cycles experienced by the major structural components can be far greater than for other rotating machines [31].

The main components to be monitored and some possible faults are shown in **Figure 45** [32].

Machine maintenance can be classified into three schemes:

1. breakdown maintenance;
2. preventive maintenance, based on the average component lifetime; and
3. predictive maintenance, based on the operating health of a component.

Currently, often preventive maintenance is applied, combined with breakdown maintenance. A component is replaced after the average lifetime. However, since the lifetime estimate of a component is always on the low side in order to minimize the number of failures, this often leads to unnecessary component replacement and a waste of money. These problems can be overcome by the utilization of condition monitoring systems (CMSs), which can be more beneficial than corrective and preventive maintenance since they allow early warnings of mechanical and electrical defects to prevent major component failures.

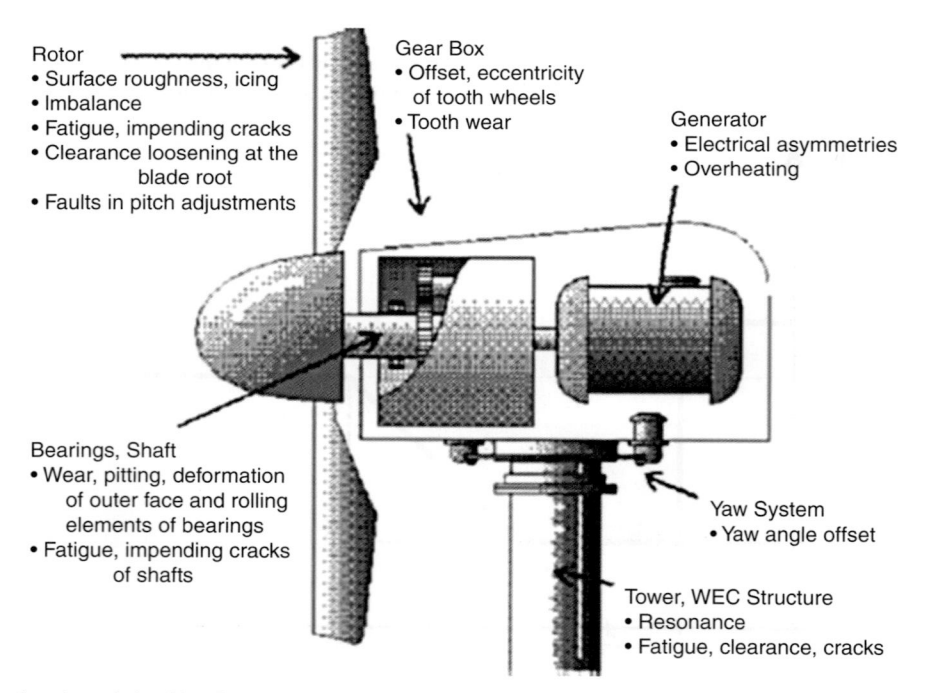

Figure 45 Fault locations in a wind turbine. Reproduced from Hameed Z, Hong YS, Cho YM, *et al.* (2009) Condition monitoring and fault detection of wind turbines and related algorithms: A review. *Renewable and Sustainable Energy Reviews* 13: 1–39 [32].

Wind power systems usually have a high rate of availability, but this is because of frequent maintenance. The goal of a well-designed CMS is to minimize the frequency of maintenance and enhance reliability with minimum number of faults, damages, downtimes, and smaller duration of repairs.

Modern wind turbine control systems are equipped with condition monitoring and fault detection systems. These systems detect and isolate faults and determine the current operating conditions of the wind turbine. The available information can then be utilized for predictive maintenance. Most condition monitoring and fault detection systems in wind turbines are signal-based and utilize vibration analysis to detect and isolate faults. Numerous signal-based approaches utilized in wind turbines can be found in Reference [32].

CMSs may utilize the following techniques [33]:

1. *Vibration analysis.* This is the most widely used methodology, especially for rotating equipment (wheels and bearings).
2. *Oil analysis.* This is for safeguarding the oil quality (contamination by parts, moist) and for safeguarding the components involved. Oil analysis is usually executed off-line.
3. *Thermography.* This is applied for monitoring and failure identification of electronic and electric components.
4. *Physical conditions of materials.* Here the focus is on crack detection and growth.
5. *Strain measurements.* These are very useful for lifetime prediction and safeguarding of the blades. Optical fiber sensors are a promising development in this area, if cost effectiveness can be guaranteed.
6. *Acoustic monitoring.* This has been successfully applied for monitoring bearing and gearboxes using acoustic sensors.
7. *Process parameters.* Detection or comparison of process parameter signals, which directly result in an alarm when the signals exceed predefined limit values, is a well-known technique applied also in wind turbines. Although still used in a primitive way, as control systems become more sophisticated and the diagnostic capabilities improve this method promises better safeguarding capabilities.
8. *Performance monitoring.* This is strongly related to the previous method; it relies on the relationship between power, wind velocity, rotor speed, and blade angle. In case of large deviations, an alarm is generated. Similar to estimation of process parameters, more sophisticated methods, including trending, are not often used.

CMS is usually carried out on the component level, although attempts have been made to address the wind turbine as a whole. In this respect, the following subsystems are usually being monitored [32]:

1. *Rotor.* The health of the rotor is obviously of utmost importance and early warning of possible failures is very useful. Numerous techniques exist in this area including monitoring of power characteristic [34], spectral and order analysis [34], strain monitoring-based algorithm [35], optical fiber-based algorithm [35], inertial sensing [36], optical coherence tomography [36], acoustic emission based on pattern recognition [37], acoustic emission based on continuous sensor [37], structural neural systems [37], and vibration/stress wave monitoring [37].
2. *Pitch mechanism.* Modern wind turbines are equipped with independent blade pitch control mechanisms. To detect faults in the servomotors, two main approaches are applied: trend analysis based on process residuals and trend analysis based on model parameters [33].
3. *Gearbox and bearings.* The nature of the problem here facilitates the use of spectral analysis [38] for monitoring the overall spectral energy of the gearbox vibration. A more advanced alternative is to monitor the vibration's cepstrum [39].
4. *Generator.* Bearing faults and stator insulation breakdown constitute the main faults in this area. Monitoring the different components of the generator, that is, transducers, signal conditioning boxes, stator and rotor currents, stator voltages, rotor speed, and windings temperature, helps in identifying possible incipient faults in this component [40].

Only a few model-based fault diagnosis approaches exist for wind turbines. These are mainly research approaches, tested on simulated environments.

In Reference [41], a time-domain, model-based, pitch fault detection and isolation (FDI) scheme is proposed for a horizontal axis wind turbine that uses pitch-to-vane control. In particular, two FDI scenarios are considered: estimation of an unknown actuator gain and that of an unknown actuator delay. Two feasible FDI algorithms that are based on the Kalman filter are presented: the discrete-time Kalman filter and the interacting multiple-model (IMM) estimator. Both algorithms provide a reliable estimate of the wind speed by including it in an augmented system state. They have been applied for online estimation of an unknown actuator gain. The discrete-time Kalman filter requires this gain together with the wind to be included in an augmented system state. The IMM estimator requires a suitable model set that describes a fault-free and a faulty horizontal axis wind turbine (HAWT) to be defined instead. The discrete-time Kalman filter has a superior performance in the detection and identification of an unknown pitch actuator gain. The performance of the IMM estimator is slightly lower, but still good enough for FDI purposes. However, the IMM estimator is a more versatile algorithm: it has been applied successfully to estimate an unknown actuator delay, which affects the system behavior in a nonlinear way.

In Reference [42], the blade root moment sensor FDI issue for three-bladed wind turbines with horizontal axis is investigated. A wind turbine model based on the closed-loop identification technique, where the wind dynamics is included, is utilized. The FDI scheme is based on the residuals generated by dual Kalman filters. Both additive faults and multiplicative faults are considered. For the additive fault case, the mean value change detection of the residuals and the generalized likelihood ratio test are utilized. For multiplicative faults, they are handled via the variance change detection of the residuals. The fault isolation issue is resolved with the help of dual sensor redundancy.

In Reference [43], fault diagnosis and fault-tolerant control algorithms are developed for improving the reliability of wind turbines. The study is based on the model of a variable-speed, variable-pitch 4.8 MW wind turbine. The analysis focuses on sensor and actuator faults, which are included in the model of the wind turbine. In the diagnosis of the faults, model-based fault diagnosis algorithms are primarily developed, due to their improved resilience toward making incorrect decisions compared to signal-based approaches. Additionally, only the already available sensor information is utilized in the diagnosis of the faults. To obtain a fault-tolerant control system, different approaches are utilized depending on the nature of the faults. For faults that affect the dynamics of the system, active and passive fault-tolerant controllers are designed and compared. To access the performance of the designed algorithms, only Monte Carlo simulations are performed; therefore, the validity of the proposed approach remains to be verified on real machines.

2.11.5 Hardware

2.11.5.1 Sensors

A typical commercial wind turbine has surprisingly few sensors for its size and complexity. In fact, most turbines utilize only rotor speed and wind measurements, which are typically used in feedback loops for basic control in both Regions 2 and 3. Since the gearbox ratio is known, speed can be measured on either the high-speed (generator) or low-speed (rotor) shafts.

Wind speed and direction are needed in various parts of the supervisory and control system. Yaw control requires information about wind direction, while wind speed data are needed in the supervisory system. Although it might seem logical to use wind speed information in the power control system, inaccuracies in estimating the actual rotor speed have not allowed to progress in this direction. Instead, generator power is used as an indirect measurement of wind speed.

The wind measuring system consists of the sensor and the data processing system. Sensors for the combined measurement of wind speed and direction are available in numerous forms. Usually, wind speed is recorded by a cup anemometer (**Figure 46**). Wind direction is determined with the aid of a small wind vane.

New ultrasonic anemometers allow inertia-free measurement of running variable dimensions with higher precision and accuracy. Their working principle is as follows: the speed of propagation of sound in calm air is superposed by the velocity components of airflow in wind direction. A wind velocity component in the direction of the propagation leads to an increase in the

Figure 46 Wind anemometers. Speed, combined. Direction, ultrasonic. Courtesy of Thies. (http://www.thiesclima.com/wind_e.html) [44].

speed. A wind velocity component opposite to the direction of propagation, on the contrary, leads to a reduction of the speed of propagation. The speed of propagation resulting from the superposition leads to different propagation times of the sound at different wind velocities and directions over a fixed measurement path. As the speed of sound is very dependent on the air temperature, the propagation time of the sound is measured on both of the measurement paths in both directions. In this way, the influence of the temperature-dependent speed of sound on the measurement result can be eliminated. By combining the two measuring paths, which are at right angles to each other, one obtains the measurement results of the sum and the angle of the wind velocity vector. Afterward, one receives the angle and the sum of the wind velocity by transformation into polar coordinates.

The serial or analogue output of the data is carried out alternatively as instantaneous value or as gliding mean value with selectable time frame. If necessary, the sensor arms and the ultrasonic sensors are automatically heated in case of critical ambient temperatures, thus minimizing the possibility of malfunction.

It must be stressed however that it is virtually impossible to obtain a good measurement of the wind speed encountering the blades because of the spatial and temporal variability and also because the rotor interacts with and changes the wind input. Not only does turbulent wind cause the wind to be different for the different blades, but also the wind speed input is different at different positions along each blade.

Recently, a hub-mountable, forward-looking, multiple point reporting remote laser wind sensor (LWS) called the Vindicator® LWS has been manufactured by Catch the Wind, Inc. (**Figure 47**). The wind sensor utilizes wind measurements taken 150 m ahead of the turbine.

Furthermore, nearly all grid-connected wind turbines have power measurement devices for keeping track of a turbine's energy generation. Other sensors that are sometimes found on wind turbines and whose measurements are used in more advanced wind turbine controllers include

- strain gauges on the tower and blades;
- accelerometers;
- position encoders on the drive shaft, blade pitch, and yaw actuation systems; and
- torque transducers.

Micronor manufactures the MR200W series yaw position transducers, which monitor yaw position, direction, speed, and cable twist. The unit can be multifunctional and integrate any combination of electromechanical limit switches, encoder, resolver, or potentiometer. Anti-backlash polyoxymethylene (POM) pinion gear optimizes coupling to the turbine's large bull gear (**Figure 48**).

Figure 47 Vindicator laser wind sensor. Reproduced from Catch the Wind. http://www.catchthewindinc.com [45].

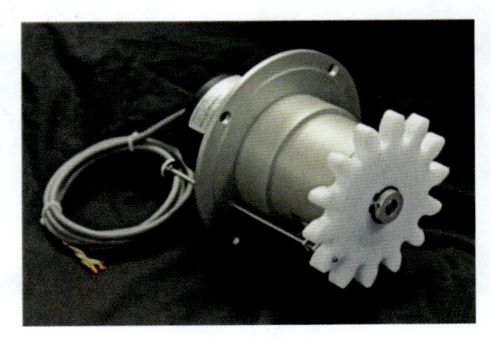

Figure 48 Micronor's MR200W yaw position transducer. Reproduced from Micronor. http://www.micronor.com [46].

2.11.5.2 Actuators

Modern utility-scale wind turbines typically have three main types of actuators.

A yaw motor, which turns the wind turbine to align it with the wind, is nearly always included on large turbines, resulting in active yaw control. However, due to dangerous gyroscopic forces, it is not usually desirable to yaw the turbine at a high rate. Most large turbines yaw at rates of less than $1\ °s^{-1}$. Thus, investigation of advanced controllers for yaw control is not of as much interest as the investigation of advanced controllers for other actuators.

Yaw motors are usually asynchronous type with planetary gears and motor brakes (**Figure 49**).

A collective pitch actuation system commonly consists of an electric or hydraulic actuator in the nacelle, driving a pushrod which passes through the center of the gearbox and hollow main shaft. The pushrod is attached to the pitchable blade roots through mechanical linkages in the hub. The actuator in the nacelle is often a simple hydraulic cylinder and piston.

An alternative arrangement is to use an electric servomotor to drive a ballnut which engages with a ballscrew on the pushrod. Since the pushrod turns with the rotor, loss of power to the motor causes the ballscrew to wind the pitch to feather, giving fail-safe pitch action. This requires a fail-safe brake on servomotor to ensure that the ballnut stops turning if power is lost.

IPC requires separate actuators in the hub for each blade. These can be either electric or hydraulic. Power can be transmitted by either slip rings or a rotary transformer in the case of electric actuators, or a rotary hydraulic joint for hydraulic actuators (**Figure 50**).

A hydraulic actuator is usually controlled by a proportional valve controlling the flow of oil to the actuator cylinder, while in the case of an electric actuator, the motor controller usually requires a torque demand signal.

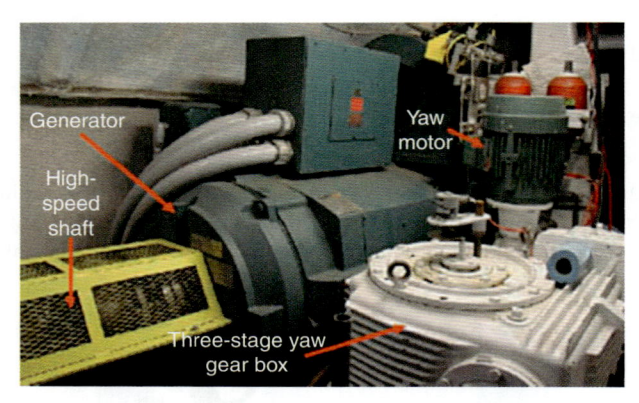

Figure 49 NREL's CART3 nacelle interior (courtesy J. Fingersh [47]). Reproduced from Pao LY and Johnson KE (2009) A tutorial on the dynamics and control of wind turbines and wind farms. *2009 American Control Conference.* St. Louis, MO, June 10–12 [47].

Figure 50 NREL's CART3 individual pitch motors and circuitry (courtesy J. Fingersh [47]). Reproduced from Pao LY and Johnson KE (2009) A tutorial on the dynamics and control of wind turbines and wind farms. *2009 American Control Conference.* St. Louis, MO, June 10–12 [47].

References

[1] International Electrotechnical Commission. www.iec.ch.
[2] Wright AD (2004) (2004) Modern control design for flexible wind turbines. *NREL Report No. TP-500-35816*. Golden, CO: National Renewable Energy Laboratory.
[3] Stol KA and Bir GS (2003) User's guide for SymDyn, Version 1.2. *NREL/EL-500-33845*, http://wind.nrel.gov/designcodes/symdyn/symdyn.pdf. Golden, CO: National Renewable Energy Laboratory.
[4] Kundur P (1994) *Power System Stability and Control*. New York, NY: McGraw-Hill, Inc.
[5] Park RH (1929) Two-reaction theory of synchronous machines – generalized method of analysis, Part I. *AIEE Transactions* 48: 716–727.
[6] Krause PC, Wasynczuk O, and Sudhoff SD (2002) *Analysis of Electric Machinery and Drive Systems*. New York, NY: IEEE Press.
[7] Ackermann T (2005) *Wind Power in Power Systems*. Chichester, UK: John Wiley & Sons Ltd.
[8] Bose BK (2001) *Modern Power Electronics and AC Drives*. Englewood Cliffs, NJ: Prentice-Hall.
[9] Henriksen LC (2007) Model Predictive Control of a Wind Turbine. MSc Thesis, Technical University of Denmark.
[10] Jauch C, Islam SM, Sorensen P, and Jensen BB (2007) Design of a wind turbine pitch angle controller for power system stabilisation. *Renewable Energy* 32: 2334–2349.
[11] Li S, Haskew TA, and Xu L (2010) Conventional and novel control designs for direct driven PMSG wind turbines. *Electric Power Systems Research* 80: 328–338.
[12] Hansen A, Jauch C, Sørensen P, et al. (2003) Dynamic wind turbine models in power system simulation tool DIgSILENT. *Report Risø-R-1400(EN)*. Roskilde, Denmark: Risø National Laboratory.
[13] Hansen MH, Hansen A, Larsen TJ, et al. (2005) Control design for a pitch-regulated variable-speed wind turbine. *Report Riso-R-1500 (EN)*. Roskilde, Denmark: Riso National Laboratory.
[14] Wright AD and Fingersh LJ (2008) Advanced control design for wind turbines part I: Control design, implementation, and initial tests. *Technical Report NREL/TP-500-42437*. Golden, CO: National Renewable Energy Laboratory.
[15] Jonkman JM (2007) Dynamics Modeling and Loads Analysis of an Offshore Floating Wind Turbine. PhD Dissertation, University of Colorado (also NREL Technical Report NREL/TP-500-41958).
[16] Balas MJ, Lee YJ, and Kendall L (1998) Disturbance tracking control theory with application to horizontal axis wind turbines. *Proceedings of the 1998 ASME Wind Energy Symposium*, pp. 95–99. Reno, Nevada, 12–15 January.
[17] Kwakernaak H and Sivan R (1972) *Linear Optimal Control Systems*. New York, NY: Wiley Interscience.
[18] Bossanyi EA (2003) Individual blade pitch control for load reduction. *Wind Energy* 6: 119–128.
[19] Leonhard W (2001) *Control of Electrical Drives*. New York, NY: Springer Verlag.
[20] Petersson A (2003) Analysis, Modeling and Control of Doubly-Fed Induction Generators for Wind Turbines. Licentiate Thesis, Chalmers University of Technology.
[21] Poitiers F, Machmoum M, Le Doeuff R, and Zaim ME (2001) Control of a doubly-fed induction generator for wind energy conversion systems. *Proceedings Aupec 2001*, p. 101. Perth, Australia, September 23–26.
[22] Kanellos FD, Papathanassiou SA, and Hatziargyriou ND (1999) Dynamic analysis of a variable speed wind turbine equipped with a voltage source AC/DC/AC converter interface. Electromotion '99, Patras, Greece, 8–9 July.
[23] Bana Sharifian MB, Mohamadrezapour Y, Hosseinpour M, and Torabzade S (2009) Maximum power control of variable speed wind turbine connected to permanent magnet synchronous generator using chopper equipped with superconductive inductor. *Journal of Applied Sciences* 9: 777–782.
[24] Kim H-W, Kim SS, and Ko H-S (2010) Modeling and control of PMSG-based variable-speed wind turbine. *Electric Power Systems Research* 80: 46–52.
[25] Fuglseth TP (2008) Modelling a 2.5 MW direct driven wind turbine with permanent magnet generator. *Report for the Final Examination Project of the Nordic PhD Course on Wind Power*. Norway: Department of Electrical Power Engineering, Norwegian University of Science and Technology.
[26] Sikorski A and Kuzma A (2009) Cooperation of induction squirrel-cage generator with grid connected AC/DC/AC converter. *Bulletin of the Polish Academy of Technical Sciences* 57: 317–322.
[27] Medici D (2004) Wind turbine wakes – control and vortex shedding. *KTH Mechanics Technical Report*. Stockholm, Sweden: Royal Institute of Technology.
[28] Ekelund T (2000) Yaw control for reduction of structural dynamic loads in wind turbines. *Journal of Wind Engineering and Industrial Aerodynamics* 85: 241–262.
[29] Farret FA, Pfischer LL, and Bernardon DP (2000) Active yaw control with sensorless wind speed and direction measurements for horizontal axis wind turbines. *Proceedings of the 2000 Third IEEE International Caracas Conference on Devices, Circuits and Systems*. Cancun, Mexico, 15–17 March.
[30] Kuroiwa T, Karikomi K, Hayashi Y, et al. (2004) New products and technologies of Mitsubishi wind turbines. *Mitsubishi Heavy Industries Technical Review* 41: 170–174.
[31] Morthorst PE (2003) Cost and prices. In: Chandler H (ed.) *Wind Energy: The Facts*, pp. 93–110. Brussels, Belgium: European Wind Energy Association, wwww.ewea.org.
[32] Hameed Z, Hong YS, Cho YM, et al. (2009) Condition monitoring and fault detection of wind turbines and related algorithms: A review. *Renewable and Sustainable Energy Reviews* 13: 1–39.
[33] Verbruggen TW (2003) Wind turbine operation and maintenance based on condition monitoring WT-OMEGA; *Final Report, ECN-C-03-047*. Energy Research Centre of the Netherlands, 1755 ZG Petten, The Netherlands, April 2003.
[34] Caselitz P and Giebhardt J (2005) Rotor condition monitoring for improved operational safety of offshore wind energy converters. *Journal of Solar Energy Engineering* 127: 253.
[35] www.smartfibres.com/shm
[36] Lading L, McGugan M, Sendrup P, et al. (2002) *Fundamentals for Remote Structural Health Monitoring of Wind Turbine Blades – A Preproject*. Roskilde, Denmark: Risø National Laboratory.
[37] Dutton AG, Blanch MJ, Vionis P, et al. (2001) Acoustic emission condition monitoring of wind turbine rotor blades: Laboratory certification testing to large scale in-service deployment. *Proceedings of the 2001 European Wind Energy Conference*. Copenhagen, Denmark, 2–6 July.
[38] Caselitz P and Giebhargt J (1999) *Advanced Condition Monitoring System for Wind Energy Converters*. Kassel, Germany: Institut fur Solare Energieversorgungstechnik e.V.
[39] Caselitz P, Giebhardt J, and Mevenkamp M (1997) Application of condition monitoring systems in wind turbine converters. *Proceedings of EWEC*. Dublin, Ireland, 6–9 October.
[40] Popa LM, Jensen B-B, Ritchie E, and Oldea I (2003) Condition monitoring of wind generators. *Industry Applications Conference*, pp. 1839–1846. Salt Lake City, UT, 12–16 October.
[41] Donders S (2002) Fault Detection and Identification for Wind Turbine Systems: A Closed-Loop Analysis. Master's Thesis, University of Twente.
[42] Wei X and Verhaegen M (2008) Fault detection of large scale wind turbine systems: A mixed H_-/H_∞ index observer approach. *Proceedings of the 16th IEEE Mediterranean Conference on Control and Automation*, pp. 1675–1680. Ajaccio, France, June 25–27.
[43] Esbensen T and Sloth C (2009) *Fault Diagnosis and Fault-Tolerant Control of Wind Turbines*. Aalborg, Denmark: Aalborg University.
[44] *Thies*. http://www.thiesclima.com/wind_e.html.
[45] *Catch the Wind*. http://www.catchthewindinc.com.
[46] *Micronor*. http://www.micronor.com/.
[47] Pao LY and Johnson KE (2009) A tutorial on the dynamics and control of wind turbines and wind farms. *2009 American Control Conference*. St. Louis, MO, June 10–12.

Further Reading

[1] Eggleston DM and Stoddard FS (1987) *Wind Turbine Engineering Design*. New York, NY: Van Nostrand Reinhold.
[2] Gipe P (1995) *Wind Energy Comes of Age*. New York, NY: John Wiley and Sons.
[3] Harrison R, Hau E, and Snel H (2000) *Large Wind Turbines, Design and Economics*. Chichester, UK: John Wiley and Sons.
[4] Johnson L (1985) *Wind Energy Systems*. Englewood Cliffs, NJ: Prentice-Hall.
[5] Le Gourieres D (1982) *Wind Power Plants Theory and Design*. Oxford, UK: Pergamon Press.
[6] Twiddell JW and Weir AD (1986) *Renewable Energy Sources*. London, UK: E. & F. N. Spon.
[7] Troen I and Petersen EL (1991) *European Wind Atlas*. Risoe, Denmark: Risoe National Laboratory.
[8] Elliott DL, Holladay CG, Barchet WR, *et al.* (1987) *Wind Energy Resource Atlas of the United States*. Golden, CO: Solar Energy Research Institute.
[9] Martin OL (2000) *Hansen: Aerodynamics of Wind Turbines, Rotors, Loads and Structure*. London, UK: James & James Ltd.
[10] Frank M (1999) *White, Fluid Dynamics*. New York, NY: McGraw-Hill.
[11] Bruce RM, Young DF, and Okiishi TH (1994) *Fundamentals of Fluid Mechanics*. New York, NY: John Wiley & Sons Inc.
[12] Abott IH and von Doenhoff AE (1959) *Theory of Wing Sections*. New York, NY: Dover Publications, Inc.
[13] Katz J and Plotkin A (2001) *Low-Speed Aerodynamics*, 2nd edn. New York, NY: Cambridge University Press.
[14] Bertin JJ (2002) *Aerodynamics for Engineers*, 4th edn. Upper Saddle River, NJ: Prentice-Hall.
[15] Bertagnolio F, Sørensen N, Johansen J, and Fuglsang P (2001) *Wind Turbine Airfoil Catalogue*. Roskilde, Denmark: Risø National Laboratory.

Relevant Websites

http://www.awea.org – American Wind Energy Association.
http://www.canwea.ca – Canadian Wind Energy Association.
http://www.ciemat.es/portal.do – Centro de Investigaciones Energéticas, Medioambientales y Tecnológicas (CIEMAT).
http://www.windpower.org – Danish Wind Industry Association.
http://www.nrel.gov/wind – DOE National Renewable Energy Laboratory.
http://www.ewea.org – European Wind Energy Association.
http://www.bwea.com – RenewableUK.

2.12 Testing, Standardization, Certification in Wind Energy

F Van Hulle, XP Wind Consultancy, Leuven, Belgium

© 2012 Elsevier Ltd. All rights reserved.

2.12.1	Introduction	371
2.12.1.1	Brief History of Standardization in Wind Energy	371
2.12.1.2	Wind Energy Technology-Specific Issues	372
2.12.1.3	Overview and Status of International Wind Energy Standards	372
2.12.2	**Standards with Design Requirements for Wind Turbines**	373
2.12.2.1	Wind Turbine Design-Related IEC Standards	374
2.12.2.1.1	IEC 61400-1: Wind turbines – Part 1. Design requirements	374
2.12.2.1.2	IEC 61400-2: Wind turbines – Part 2. Design requirements for small wind turbines	374
2.12.2.1.3	IEC 61400-3: Wind turbines – Part 3. Design requirements for offshore wind turbines	375
2.12.2.1.4	IEC 61400-4: Wind turbines – Part 4. Design and specification of gearboxes	375
2.12.2.1.5	IEC 61400-24: Wind turbines – Part 24. Lightning protection	375
2.12.2.1.6	IEC 61400-25: Wind turbines – Part 25. Communication for monitoring and control of wind power plants (six standards)	375
2.12.2.2	Other Standards Related to Wind Turbine-Specific Design Aspects	376
2.12.2.2.1	Personnel safety: EN 50308	376
2.12.2.2.2	Offshore wind turbine support structures: DNV-OS-J101	376
2.12.2.2.3	Small wind turbine performance and safety standards (United Kingdom and United States)	376
2.12.3	**Testing Methods for Wind Turbines and Wind Plants**	376
2.12.3.1	Introduction	376
2.12.3.2	Wind Speed Measurement	377
2.12.3.3	Power Performance Testing	377
2.12.3.4	Mechanical Load Measurements	378
2.12.3.5	Acoustic Noise Measurements	379
2.12.3.6	Electrical Characteristics and Power Quality Measurements	380
2.12.3.7	Rotor Blade Testing	380
2.12.3.8	Safety and Function Testing	381
2.12.3.9	Measurement Quality	382
2.12.4	**Certification in the Wind Industry**	383
2.12.4.1	General Aspects of Certification in Wind Energy	383
2.12.4.2	Certification Systems in Wind Energy	383
2.12.4.2.1	Wind turbine type certification	384
2.12.4.2.2	Wind energy project certification	386
2.12.4.2.3	Other certification systems for wind energy	388
2.12.5	**Conclusions**	388
References		388
IEC Standards (to be purchased via IEC or the National Standardization Institutes)		389
Relevant Websites		389

2.12.1 Introduction

At the end of 2010, the global wind industry had produced and installed wind power plants at an annual rate in the order of 36 GW, representing a capex value of approximately 65 billion USD. At the same time, the globally operating wind power capacity amounted close to 200 GW. This power source comes in the form of wind plants consisting of up to hundreds of wind turbines dispersedly installed over land and sea. The wind plants are designed for unattended operation during 20 years in all possible weather situations. The increasing penetration demands for increasing reliability and power plant capabilities. This chapter describes the approach that has been developed and implemented by the wind power industry together with the research community for ensuring quality and safe and economic operation during the lifetime of the wind plant, notably testing and certification and the related standardization.

2.12.1.1 Brief History of Standardization in Wind Energy

Testing and certification in the field of wind power has evolved already from the early days in parallel with the industrial development, and was mainly promoted by specialized research institutes. In the 1980s, methods for functional wind turbine tests (e.g., power performance, acoustic noise) and certification processes using simplified design criteria and rules were set up in various countries (Denmark, The Netherlands, United States, Canada, and Germany) to be used in local spatial approval procedures and national incentive schemes and to support the early industrial development. These methods were drawing upon the experience with the testing of large 'national' wind turbine prototypes that were built in the 1970s and 1980s in various countries (Denmark, Sweden, Germany, United Kingdom, and Italy).

Wind turbine test stations in Europe and North America established platforms for exchange of testing practices in both formal and informal circuits. This resulted, for example, in recommended practices for testing issued under International Energy Agency (IEA) in areas like power performance testing, acoustic measurements, power quality, and anemometry. The development of harmonized practices in certification took considerable advantage from international research projects developing common wind turbine design methods and benchmarking wind turbine design tools in Europe and the United States. Since the end of the 1980s, the International Electrotechnical Commission (IEC) took up the results of the European and American standardization efforts in wind energy under the Technical Committee TC88, establishing the 61 400 series of wind energy standards, in all fields deemed relevant (design, testing, and certification). This process was assisted by various dedicated research efforts, for example, by the European Wind Turbine Standards project (EWTS), which elaborated aspects not yet covered or insufficiently covered by IEC.

As a result, there is today a well-established practice of testing and certification of most aspects relevant to wind turbine projects, which leads to worldwide recognition of the results and products by the relevant market parties. Major future challenges arise from the continuous upscaling of the technology and the expected massive expansion of offshore wind energy bringing the need for new measurement and assessment methods.

2.12.1.2 Wind Energy Technology-Specific Issues

The characteristics of wind energy technology and the constraints arising from the site-specific external conditions lead to specific issues related to testing and certification. Some important ones are highlighted here:

- *Heavy external design conditions*: Wind turbine standards and certification have to take account of the fact that wind power plants need to operate unattended and remain within their design limits for 20 years during a wide range of design conditions, including extreme events. Moreover, these conditions are very site specific.
- *Short product cycle – fast developing product size*: The high rate of introduction of new and larger wind turbine types puts pressure on the speed of certification. The modular approach to certification is a practical solution to that.
- *Wind turbine siting*: Because of the closeness of wind turbines to habitation and other risk-sensitive areas, sufficiently rigorous safety approach has to be followed in safety requirements to limit the risk below a set level, but at the same time being rational and workable.
- *Large wind turbine sizes*: The average wind turbine sizes have been increased considerably, and are such that they involve severe constraints on locations of testing and on the size of testing facilities for blades and other major components (e.g., offshore structures). The large sizes also pose challenges for calibration methods in mechanical load measurements.
- *Wind variability*: Most of the wind turbine testing involves measurement of the wind conditions. Specific testing methods for accurate, traceable measurements are not straightforward because of the spatial and temporal variability of the wind vector. Increasing wind turbine sizes make this issue more complex.
- *Workers risk*: Being large structures involving working at great heights in environments with electrical and mechanical risks poses specific requirements for personnel and labor safety.
- *New electrical functionalities*: With increasing penetration of wind power in power systems, new network requirements and wind power plant functionalities are developed bringing about the need for new corresponding test and verification procedures. Moreover, certain aspects such as electrical characteristics at wind farm level cannot be tested physically, bringing the need for combination of physical testing and modeling.

Many of the above issues are in principle very challenging; however, several have been solved satisfactorily. This chapter intends to demonstrate how these issues have been addressed with the development and implementation of proper standards, resulting in a comprehensive approach in the sector to deal with quality and safety.

2.12.1.3 Overview and Status of International Wind Energy Standards

Testing and certification according to a set of dedicated standards is a major element of ensuring safety and adequate functionality of design and operation of wind turbines according to a traceable quality. In this respect, the approach in wind energy is not different from the approach in any other power generation technology.

This chapter intends to present an overview and status of internationally available wind energy standards. This is done in regard to the relevant stages in the wind turbine life cycle. Broadly speaking, a distinction should be made in

Table 1 Availability of international standards (mainly IEC wind energy standards of the series IEC 61400) for different aspects in the various stages in turbine life

Stage in wind turbine life	Design					Certification (type certification, project certifcation, component certifcation)	Testing				Other
	Wind turbines	Small wind turbines	Offshore wind turbines	Gearboxes	Protective measures		Power performance	Acoustics	Loads and components (blades)	Electrical	Communication
Design and manufacturing	x	x	x	x	x	x			x		
(Proto)type testing					x	x	x	x	x	x	x
Installation and commissioning	x	x	x		x	x	x	x	x	x	x
Network connection						x				x	x
Operation and maintenance	x	x	x		x	x	x	x		x	x
Decommissioning											

x = standard available.
Gray-shaded cell = not applicable case.

- design requirements and the related standards;
- testing methods and the related standards; and
- certification methods and related procedures and standards.

The wind energy standards that have been developed within the IEC are covering all these three categories. **Table 1** presents an overview of the fields covered by the specific wind energy standards developed in IEC and other international wind energy specific standards (e.g., European Standards (EN standards)). The gray-shaded cells indicate cases that are not applicable. The mark up in the cell indicates where an international wind energy standard is available. In the next sections, for the particular areas mentioned in the table, the applicable standards will be described, and where relevant ongoing work will be mentioned. Moreover, other relevant national or regional standards will be indicated, where appropriate.

Thus, in general, it can be concluded that the majority of relevant aspects pertinent to the important stages in the lifetime of wind turbines can be covered with international standards. This is not surprising as engineering characteristics and their method of measurement or specification in principle are globally applicable. In the more detailed discussion in the next sections, it will be indicated where it is more appropriate to also take account of local (national) standards. This is specifically applicable in the electrotechnical area where local codes are applied.

The mutual recognition of testing and certification practices is very important in the international wind energy market. This recognition has been a continuous concern during the development of the international approach. Formally, the recognition of test results and certification is ensured by the process of accreditation (according to the International Organization for Standardization (ISO) 17025 for testing and ISO 45011 for certification) and international agreements between accreditation bodies. This is a system that functions pretty well in wind energy. In addition to this, specific networks have been set up in the industry to establish a high-quality profile in measurements. Examples in the area of testing are the Measnet network in Europe and the Regional Test Center Initiative in the United States. Examples in the field of certification include the Microgeneration Certification Scheme (MCS) developed by the Department of Energy and Climate Change (DECC) in the United Kingdom and the Small Wind Certification Council (SWCC) initiative in the United States, both in the area of small wind turbines.

2.12.2 Standards with Design Requirements for Wind Turbines

Wind power technology has diverse engineering aspects (structural, mechanical, electrical, control systems) and for each of them a range of engineering standards apply. However, in this section, only standards that are developed exclusively for wind turbine systems are discussed, mainly IEC standards, complemented by specific other standards.

2.12.2.1 Wind Turbine Design-Related IEC Standards

The most comprehensive documents laying down design requirements for wind turbines are the standards for wind turbines developed under the technical committee TC88 (Wind Turbines). The wind energy standards are of the series IEC 61400. The available published standards include (situation end of 2010)

- Part 1: Design requirements (for wind turbines in general).
- Part 2: Design requirements for small wind turbines.
- Part 3: Design requirements for offshore wind turbines.
- Part 4: Design and specification of gearboxes.
- Part 24: Lightning protection.
- Part 25: Communication for monitoring and control of wind power plants (six standards).

Other aspects that are presently work in progress under IEC TC88 include

- Part 5: Rotor blades.
- Part 26: Time-based availability for wind turbines.
- Part 27: Electrical simulation models for wind power generation (this topic could be considered partly design related, partly testing related).

The available standards as listed above are explained briefly in this section.

2.12.2.1.1 IEC 61400-1: Wind turbines – Part 1. Design requirements

The standard, now in its third edition, specifies essential design requirements to ensure the engineering integrity of wind turbines. It is relevant for all wind turbine subsystems such as structural parts, control and protection mechanisms, electrical systems, and mechanical systems. In principle, it applies to wind turbines of all sizes, but states that for small wind turbines IEC 61400-2 may be applied. Equally, it is mainly geared toward horizontal axis turbines but in principle does not preclude its applicability to vertical axis machines.

Some basic features of the standard are discussed below:

- The structural safety in general is based on probabilistic design methods as described in the ISO standard 2394 General principles on reliability for structures, including the use of partial safety factors for loads and materials.
- For the calculation of the loads, a system of load cases is defined as a combination of design situations (operational states of the wind turbine) and external conditions (e.g., wind conditions). For the various load cases, the standard indicates how to evaluate the different limit states: ultimate, fatigue, accidental, serviceability, also depending on the type of loads considered (aerodynamic, inertia, other). The design life is assumed to be 20 years.
- The standard contains descriptions for the wind and turbulence model. It gives a system of wind turbine classes that specify the average wind speed, reference wind speed, and turbulence values for four normal classes and one special class (see **Table 2**).
- For the design of control and protection systems, the principle is that the wind turbine should remain safe with a single failure in the protection system.
- Electrical safety refers mainly to existing standards.

2.12.2.1.2 IEC 61400-2: Wind turbines – Part 2. Design requirements for small wind turbines

Small wind turbines may require a different approach; therefore, a specific standard was set up that is applicable to wind turbines (of all concepts) with a rotor swept area smaller than 200 m^2. The structure of the standard is similar to IEC 61400-1, but it is geared

Table 2 Basic parameters for wind turbine classes

Wind turbine class		I	II	III	S
V_{ref}	(m^{-1}s)	50	42.5	37.5	values specified by the designer
A	I_{ref} (–)		0.16		
B	I_{ref} (–)		0.14		
C	I_{ref} (–)		0.12		

Source: Data from IEC 61400-1 Edition 3.
The parameter values apply at hub height. V_{ref} is the reference wind speed averaged over 10 min; the average wind speed in the standard classes is 20% of the value of V_{ref}. A, B, and C are designating turbulence categories. The value of the turbulence (I_{ref}) applies at 15 m s^{-1}.

toward more simplicity in order to be applicable to small turbines. Presently, an update of the standard is being prepared by a maintenance team (MT2) under TC88.

2.12.2.1.3   IEC 61400-3: Wind turbines – Part 3. Design requirements for offshore wind turbines

This standard is specifically focused on the design of offshore wind turbines. In principle this is for bottom-mounted offshore wind turbines, not for floating constructions, for which a separate standard will be prepared (new work item is proposed). For many aspects, the requirements of IEC 61400-1 apply; however, because of the application offshore, striking differences with respect to IEC 61400-1 include

- The standard prescribes how the marine conditions should be taken into account. This relates to wave conditions and the correlation between wind and waves, which is decisive for the loading on the structure. A further elaboration of wave conditions is made in various types of sea states (normal, severe, and extreme), sea currents (subsurface and near-surface currents, currents induced by breaking waves), water level, sea ice, marine growth, seabed movement, and scour. The wind conditions are like in Part 1, but the inclination angle has to be assumed zero.
- The standard gives guidance for the assessment of external conditions at an offshore site.
- The types of loads to be analyzed include gravitational/inertial loads, aerodynamic loads, actuation loads (like, e.g., yawing), hydrodynamic loads, and sea ice loads.
- The system of load cases is much more complex than for the onshore wind turbines, because of all possible sea states and ice states. The standard indicates the relevant wind models that have to be taken into account, depending on the wind turbine design situation (power production, occurrence of fault, etc.) and the corresponding wave, directionality, sea current, water level, type of analysis, and partial safety factors.
- In the analysis, a basic division is made between rotor–nacelle assembly (RNA) and support structure.
- For foundation design, the standard makes reference to ISO 19900/01/02/03 series.

2.12.2.1.4   IEC 61400-4: Wind turbines – Part 4. Design and specification of gearboxes

In fact, the standard for gearboxes is published as an ISO document being the result of a common IEC/ISO project. The document was drafted by a combined committee of the American Wind Energy Association (AWEA) and American Gear Manufacturers Association (AGMA), with members representing international wind turbine manufacturers, operators, researchers, consultants, and gear, bearing, and lubricant manufacturers. Based on data from field experience, the standard actually describes the differences in operation and loading of gearboxes between use in wind turbines and in other gear applications. The standard is instrumental for developing clear specifications of the information needs between wind turbine and gearbox manufacturers for wind turbine applications and discusses issues specific to wind turbine applications and gear design.

2.12.2.1.5   IEC 61400-24: Wind turbines – Part 24. Lightning protection

This standard was developed to inform designers, purchasers, operators, certification agencies, and installers of wind turbines on the state-of-the-art of lightning protection of wind turbines. Wind turbines pose a lightning protection problem different from other devices due to their physical size and nature, and due to extensive use of insulating composite materials, such as glassfibre reinforced plastic. The standard prescribes how the lightning protection system should be fully integrated into the different parts of the wind turbines to ensure that all parts likely to be lightning attachment points are able to withstand the impact of the lightning and that the lightning current may be conducted safely from the attachment points to the ground without unacceptable damage or disturbances to the systems.

2.12.2.1.6   IEC 61400-25: Wind turbines – Part 25. Communication for monitoring and control of wind power plants (six standards)

This standard number represents a series of six standards relevant for the operational stage, focusing on the communications between wind power plant components and actors, such as wind turbines, a supervisory control and data acquisition (SCADA) system, or a condition monitoring system (CMS). It defines wind power plant information models and an information exchange model, and deals with the mapping of these two models to a standard communication profile. The standard enables connectivity between a heterogeneous combination of client and servers from different manufacturers and suppliers. The structure of the above-described approach is reflected in the division of the different parts of IEC 61400-25:

- Part 25-1: Overall description of principles and models.
- Part 25-2: Information models.
- Part 25-3: Information exchange models.
- Part 25-4: Mapping to communication profile.
- Part 25-5: Conformance testing.
- Part 25-6: Logical node classes and data classes for condition monitoring.

2.12.2.2 Other Standards Related to Wind Turbine-Specific Design Aspects

Other standards of international relevance specifying design requirements for wind turbines exist. The most relevant to mention here are related to the following aspects.

2.12.2.2.1 Personnel safety: EN 50308

This European Standard EN 50308 specifies requirements for protective measures relating to the health and safety of personnel, relevant in the stages of commissioning, operation, and maintenance of wind turbines. The standard specifies requirements regarding

- hardware provisions being a part of the turbine such as platforms, ladders, and lighting; and
- manuals and warning signs to accommodate safe and quick operation, inspection, and maintenance.

The requirements and/or measures specified account for many types of hazards: hazards of mechanical, thermal, or electrical origin, noise hazards, or hazards caused by neglecting ergonomic principles in machine design. The document in principle is related to onshore wind turbines. For offshore applications, the document only draws attention to additional provisions and procedures that may be necessary for offshore turbines. Also, the document does not include requirements for provisions and procedures for lifts and suspended access equipment (SAE) in wind turbine towers.

2.12.2.2.2 Offshore wind turbine support structures: DNV-OS-J101

This standard issued by Det Norske Veritas (DNV; guideline on the design of offshore wind turbine structures) is applicable for the design of offshore wind turbine structures and also for meteorological masts. As such it is a complete stand-alone specification and provides principles, technical requirements, and guidance for design, construction, and in-service inspection of offshore wind turbine structures. However, it is not applicable for support structures and foundations for transformer stations for wind farms (there the DNV-OS-C101 applies).

2.12.2.2.3 Small wind turbine performance and safety standards (United Kingdom and United States)

For completeness sake, two national standards are mentioned here, drafted specifically for small wind turbines, namely one for the United Kingdom issued by the British Wind Energy Association (BWEA) (nowadays by Renewable Energy UK) and one for the United States. However, unlike the document titles suggest, these standards are not specifying design requirements (for which they make a reference to the IEC standard). They mainly deal with specification of performance, acoustic, and duration tests, and are rather a guideline in certification of small wind turbines. Therefore, it is not further discussed in this section; some of the content is discussed in Section 2.12.4.

2.12.3 Testing Methods for Wind Turbines and Wind Plants

2.12.3.1 Introduction

This section deals with current state-of-the-art methods and related standards for testing of wind turbines and wind plants (wind farms). In principle, any new wind turbine type will at least undergo all the tests performed at a representative prototype or specimen as described here. It is clear that for new wind turbine types, primary functional aspects such as functioning of control and safety systems, power performance, and mechanical loads are essential elements that without doubt need an experimental verification, from the point of view of both the wind turbine manufacturer and the future wind owner. As such, the described tests are applied for new wind turbine types, for example, in the so-called prototype testing and type characteristic measurements, but also apply for existing wind turbines and wind energy projects, for example, related to regular check for approval or performance verification. The methods are applicable both for development testing by manufacturers or for third-party testing, for example, in the frame of type or project certification. In principle, the described methods apply for wind turbines irrespective of the size. Small wind turbines however may require a different approach. Where relevant, this will be discussed below in the description of the individual test.

Table 3 gives an overview of the main fields covered by testing and the related standards' main standardized tests.

Although the described tests are covering fairly well the potential scope of aspects of wind turbines that could be tested, other tests may be of relevance, for example, specific tests of individual components and construction details.

Per specific test, the following sections will explain

- what exactly is tested and the purpose of the test;
- existing test procedure and/or standard; and
- brief description of testing methodology.

Wind speed measurement is an element that is common to most of the below described tests. As indicated earlier, the method of measurement of the wind speed is far from obvious. Therefore, it was considered useful before discussing the individual testing

Table 3 Overview of state-of-the-art wind turbine tests, applicable standards, and link with wind turbine certification (according to IEC 61400-22)

Testing method	Applicable IEC standard	Link with certification
Safety and function	IEC 61400-22 (Annex)	Type testing, mandatory
Power performance	IEC 61400-12-1	Type testing, mandatory
Mechanical loads	IEC 61400-13	Type testing, mandatory
Rotor blade tests	IEC 61400-24	Type testing, mandatory
Acoustic noise emission	IEC 61400-11	Type characteristic measurement, optional
Power quality	IEC 61400-21	Type characteristic measurement, optional

methods to devote a specific section to the discussion of some critical aspects of wind turbine measurements and the related technique (anemometry).

2.12.3.2 Wind Speed Measurement

Most of the testing in the area of wind energy makes use of measurement techniques (sensors, data acquisition) according to normal engineering practice also used in other disciplines. An important exception to this is the measurement of the wind speed. Important physical reasons related to turbine size bring about significant challenges, which increase with wind turbine size. Classical sensors such as anemometers measure the wind vector in a point whereas the parameters to be characterized (power, loading) are related to a large surface (rotor swept area) and atmospheric wind has very low spatial coherence. The consequences on accuracy are exacerbated by the strong dependence of the parameters on wind (power depends on the cube of the wind speed). Also, with increasing wind turbine sizes, the positions for measuring wind speed become higher and higher, with corresponding increased costs for the measurement mast. Remote sensing techniques (like, e.g., light detection and ranging (LIDAR)) bring significant advantages in this respect, as they avoid the need for construction of high meteorological masts.

Despite the limitations, the current accepted practice is to measure the wind speed with a cup anemometer, as the best available technical compromise. Alternative wind measurement techniques are being used in various applications, each with its specific pros and cons (sonic anemometer, propeller anemometer, sound detection and ranging (SODAR), LIDAR). However, there is not yet an internationally accepted agreement for the use of these types of anemometers in the industrial commercial standardized testing of wind turbines. Hence, current standards recommend the use of the cup anemometer for measuring the wind speed, complemented by a separate wind vane for measuring the wind direction. A lot of research has been done during the past 30 years to understand the problems of the cup anemometer and to develop optimal solutions to go around its limitations [1]. In this respect, the research work done in the frame of the European AccuWind project may be mentioned, which developed a methodology for classifying cup anemometers according to the sensitivity of their accuracy to various influences such as inflow angle, temperature, and air density [2]. The method provides guidance to the user on the choice of the right instrument for a specific application (e.g., in complex terrain). Hence it could be concluded that the physical limitations of the instrument are largely solved by

- objective methods and minimum requirements for calibration;
- requirements on the mounting of the cup anemometer; and
- classification of cup anemometers.

2.12.3.3 Power Performance Testing

In power performance testing, the relationship between the electrical power output of the wind turbine and the wind speed is established, also called the power curve of the wind turbine.

The power curve is a unique and essential performance characteristic of the wind turbine as generation unit. For the wind turbine manufacturer, it is a basic performance measure of the product and therefore is used in the process of turbine development, for example, for optimizing control settings. For the developers and owners, a measured power curve enables an unambiguous statement (by calculation) of the expected annual energy output of the wind turbine at a given site and wind regime, plus a quantitative value of the uncertainty in power output. Therefore, it is a critical element in any energy output assessment of wind energy projects, and is a basis for commercial agreements in wind energy development. As a consequence, an accurate uncertainty assessment in the measurement is of high importance. Furthermore, power performance is a mandatory test in the type certification according to IEC 61400-22 and most other certification schemes (see Section 2.12.4). It is also used for product verification in order to allow statement of conformity of actual product with the documented wind turbine type.

The test procedure for power performance testing is described in the IEC 61400-12-1 Edition 1.0. An update of the document (Edition 2.0) is under preparation. Additional requirements for the measurement of the power curve are described by Measnet, the network of qualified measurement institutes. Additional specifications for small wind turbines are given in the earlier-mentioned AWEA and BWEA standards. The method in these documents is largely based on IEC; however, it makes adaptations to cater for the non-grid-connected aspects, exclude the effects of potentially fluctuating battery voltage, and enable a fast determination of the power curve (1 min averages).

Conceptually, the power performance test procedure is relatively simple. At the wind turbine electrical system, current and voltage are measured as well as a number of additional signals (status, blade pitch angle, rotational speed, control settings where relevant). The wind speed and wind direction are measured on a separate meteorological mast at hub height and some other heights in order to establish the wind shear. Furthermore, the atmospheric pressure and temperature are measured to enable data normalization to standard air density.

The standard procedure prescribes the scanning frequency and averaging time and statistical values that shall be kept by the data acquisition system. The data flow is processed with the so-called method of bins. The standard also states the minimum required number of values of power and wind speed in all the wind speed bins over the whole relevant measurement range (between cut-in and cut-out wind speed) in order to ensure that there are representative values of power over the whole range of relevant wind speeds. This often is an issue for the high wind speeds (above 20 m s^{-1}) that rarely occur during test campaigns. Therefore, a special procedure is described in the standard on how to extrapolate measured curves to high wind speeds.

The measurement involves some special issues:

- It has to be ensured that the measured wind speed is uniquely defined. It is recognized that the method is a compromise because the wind is only measured at a point, whereas the effective output of the wind turbine is determined by the wind field seen by the entire rotor disk. The anemometer has to be located close to the wind turbine but not so close that the measurement is affected. Therefore, the measurement procedure includes detailed rules for the distance between the mast and the wind turbine. Furthermore, there are strict rules on angular measurement sectors around the mast from which data have to be rejected when wind is blowing from these directions, because of potential disturbing effects of the wind turbine on the wind measurement.
- Measuring the wind at the wind turbine nacelle would be practical, but is problematic because of the disturbing wake effects. A new IEC standard is in preparation to prescribe how to carry out power performance testing with nacelle anemometers.
- Disturbing influences of the terrain should be avoided, and the standard prescribes the requirements for the test site. If the terrain deviates from these (e.g., in complex terrain), a so-called site calibration shall be carried out to establish correction factors.
- Turbulence influences the power output; therefore, rules for data filtering are prescribed.
- A number of applications would welcome wind farm power curves (e.g., project verification, short-term forecasting). To cater for that need, the IEC TC88 intends to develop a specific standard for wind farm power curve measurements.

The output of the test is typically a graph of power output versus wind speed and a corresponding table with prescribed format. The values to be reported also include the uncertainty on the measured power per wind speed bin.

2.12.3.4 Mechanical Load Measurements

In a mechanical load campaign, the principal loads (forces and moments) on a wind turbine are measured, which essentially consist of blade root loads, rotor loads, and tower loads. The selection of the locations for measuring these forces and moments ensures that the design mechanical stresses can be determined in any part and location of the wind turbine.

The measured loads are used for different purposes. The actual measurement of loads on a wind turbine (proto)type is of high value, because it gives a real-world check and benchmarking for the output of analytical design methods (aeroelastic models and codes) that have to deal with a large number of parameters often with high uncertainties. These uncertainties increase with the scale of the machine. Thus, measurements enable verification/validation of the outputs of the design software tools that calculate the ultimate and fatigue loading and stresses and the corresponding strength and stress reserve margins in the structural components of the wind turbine. In principle, loads measured according to the standard can also be used as a reference for direct determination of design loads in specific conditions. Therefore, mechanical load measurements are mandatory type tests in the process of wind turbine certification. Furthermore, dedicated load measurement campaigns are helpful in the process of prototype development testing.

The procedure for measuring the mechanical loads of wind turbines is described in the standard IEC 61400-13, which in its present version dating from 2001 is a technical specification. A new version which will be a full standard is presently under development. The document is aimed at the test engineer who will design and implement the test program to meet the specific design or certification needs. The specification provides specific guidance on load measurements on key structural components and load paths.

A mechanical load measurement campaign is quite complex and involves accurate measurement of a large number of signals. The loads – basically forces and moments – are measured with the help of strain gauges and accelerometers applied on selected locations. The standard sets a minimum set of fundamental load quantities to be measured:

- On at least one blade, the flap and lead-lag bending moments are measured in the blade root.
- The rotor loads include the tilt moment, the yaw moment, and the rotor torque (moments around three perpendicular axes).
- The tower loads include tower bottom bending in two perpendicular directions (fore-and-aft and lateral).

In principle, from such a set of measured loads, the loading in any part of the wind turbine structure can be derived by calculation, with the help of the exact knowledge of the load path geometry from the design, in other words, the exact dimensions within the wind turbine structure. For meteorological quantities, the standard prescribes as a minimum the measurement of wind speed and wind direction at hub height, as well as air temperature and air density. Furthermore, a number of wind turbine operation quantities shall be measured including electrical power, rotor speed, pitch angle, yaw position, and rotor azimuth. Other status signals relevant for the operation are recommended.

Before and during the measurement campaign, all individual load measurement chains – sensor, amplifier, cable, data acquisition system – have to be calibrated, to establish a unique and traceable relationship between the measured signal and the actual physical force or moment. This is not always possible or practical by applying calibrated external forces – for example, by pulling at the blade or tower with a known force – because of the large size of the components of modern wind turbines. Therefore, blade root loads are mostly calibrated by measuring the effect of the blade's own weight during slow rotation of the rotor, which is then showing a sinusoidal variation of the signal from the blade root strain gauge. Tower loads, on the other hand, are calibrated with the help of shunt calibration, which is measuring the effect of the eccentric overhanging mass of the nacelle on the tower bottom strain gauges during a full rotation of the nacelle with the yawing system.

The load measurement campaign is structured in such a way that it reflects the design load cases of the wind turbine design standard (IEC 61400-1). Therefore, measurement load cases are defined corresponding to relevant design load cases, namely, the combinations of wind turbine operational state and corresponding external (wind) conditions and both in steady-state operation and during transients (braking, yawing, start-up, and shutdown).

The so-called capture matrix is used to organize the measured time series. The capture matrix has two objectives: it can be used as a guideline for programming the data acquisition system for automatic and unattended operation of the measurement system and it can be used as a tool to decide when the measurement requirements are fulfilled, in other words when there are sufficient load data at different wind speed and turbulence values in order to reach. The standard prescribes minimum amounts of data to be collected per wind speed and turbulence bin.

Test reports of mechanical load campaigns are very extensive because of the complexity of the system and the large amount of data. The standard gives guidance for such reports. In general, the practice is to divide the report into two parts. The first part describes the measurement setup, including site, instrumentation, and the details about the calibration of all measurement chains. The second part describes the data and the results of their processing and analysis, including typical time histories, load statistics, frequency spectra, fatigue load spectra, and equivalent loads. An uncertainty analysis has to be included as well.

2.12.3.5 Acoustic Noise Measurements

In a sound measurement campaign for wind turbines, the apparent A-weighted sound power levels, spectra, and tonality at integer wind speeds from 6 to $10 \, \text{m s}^{-1}$ of an individual wind turbine are determined, possibly including the directivity. The wind speed range is chosen such that it is considered representative of wind conditions under which potential nuisance can be caused by the wind turbine.

The measured acoustical emissions by wind turbines are important in various stages of project development and project implementation and for different stakeholders, wind turbine manufacturers, project developers, wind farm operators, planners, and regulators. The measurement of acoustic noise emission is a type characteristic measurement in wind turbine certification systems (see Section 2.12.4), thus is optional in the certification process.

The test procedure for acoustic noise emission measurements is laid down in the IEC 61400-11 Edition 2.1. Besides, there is a standard IEC 61400-14 prescribing the method for making a declaration of acoustic noise emission for particular wind turbine type based on a series of measurements at the similar type at various locations. Specific aspects of acoustic measurements are specified in the BWEA standard for small wind turbines.

A measurement setup in general consists of acoustic measurements, wind measurements, and wind turbine power measurements. Performing the measurements at positions within a prescribed reference distance to the wind turbine minimizes the influence of terrain effects, atmospheric conditions, or wind-induced noise. In order to reduce the wind noise generated at the microphone and avoid the influence of different ground types, the microphone has to be positioned on a board placed on the ground. There are a number of options for determining the wind speed corresponding to the acoustic measurements. The preferred method is to derive the wind speed from the measured power output of the wind turbine, using its (known) power curve. The limitation of this method of course is the fact that it does not work at wind speeds above the rated speed (because in that range the power does not change any more). The standard gives rules on how to deal with power rating situations that could interfere with this wind speed range. The standard also gives recommendations on how to determine the relevant wind speed values with the help of a meteorological mast or by using the nacelle anemometer as a reference.

The measurement campaign consists of taking simultaneous measurements of sound pressure levels and wind speeds over short periods of time and over a wide range of wind speeds. The measured wind speeds are converted to corresponding wind speeds at a reference height of 10 m and a reference roughness length of 0.05 m. The sound levels at standardized wind speeds of 6, 7, 8, 9, and $10 \, \text{m s}^{-1}$ are determined and used for calculating the apparent A-weighted sound power levels. The directivity is determined by comparing the A-weighted sound pressure levels at three additional positions around the turbine with those measured at the reference position. For each of the representative measurement cases, the background noise is measured with stopped wind turbine.

The presence of audible tones in the noise at different wind speeds has to be determined on the basis of a narrowband analysis, and the standard gives procedures on how to determine tonality taking account of background noise, masking noise levels, and audibility of the tones.

Information to be provided in a measurement report includes characterization of the wind turbine and the site, description of the instrumentation, and details about the acoustic and nonacoustic data and an uncertainty analysis.

2.12.3.6 Electrical Characteristics and Power Quality Measurements

Electrical tests measure essential characteristics of the power output of wind turbines such as power variations, voltage variations, harmonic contents (read definition), and fault-ride-through capabilities.

Electrical power quality measurements are mainly intended to determine the impact and mutual influences of the connection of the wind turbine on electrical characteristics of the local network, in other words to characterize the grid-friendliness of a wind turbine or wind plant. The measurement of the power quality is considered as optional type characteristic measurement in the frame of wind turbine type and project certification according to IEC 61400-22 (see Section 2.12.4). The output of the tests is used in the process of grid connection, for example, to obtain the formal authorization to connect and feed-in power into the network. The test results (together with other relevant information) enable the grid operator to assess whether the generation unit/facility complies with the requirements of the local network connection code (grid code). With increasing wind penetration in networks these requirements are becoming extensive and increasingly complex. In some cases, it will be necessary to complement tests at wind turbine level with simulations in order to enable one to produce the relevant answers at wind farm level for aspects that cannot be tested at wind farm level, such as fault-ride-through capability.

The international standard for the measurement of power quality is the IEC 61400-21 (Edition 2). Measurements according to this standard address most of the relevant power quality parameters, both in normal operation and during network faults. The standard defines and specifies these parameters, and provides measurement procedures for measuring and quantifying the characteristics as well as for assessing compliance with power quality requirements, including estimation of the power quality expected from the wind turbine type when deployed at a specific site, whether or not in wind farms. In addition, network operators may prescribe test methods, which in general can be very different depending on country, power system, and so on. For example, network operators in Spain and Germany established specific procedures for assessing wind power plant capabilities in the frame of a system of additional incentives (bonus) for wind plants equipped with functionalities enabling grid services (reactive power, fault-ride-through, etc.). It goes beyond the scope of this chapter to discuss such local requirements. Finally, it can be mentioned that a standard is under development under IEC for dynamic models of wind turbine to be used in grid integration processes and integration studies. The provisional title is IEC 61400-27 Edition 1.0 Electrical simulation models for wind power generation.

The measurements aim in general to verify the characteristic power quality parameters for a substantial part of the operational range of the assessed wind turbine, at least up to a wind speed of $15\,\mathrm{m\,s^{-1}}$. This enables a practical approach and is expected to enable sufficient scope of verification of the characteristic power quality parameters of the assessed wind turbine. The power quality characteristics to be measured include

– voltage fluctuations during continuous operation and during switching operations;
– current harmonics, interharmonics, and higher frequency components;
– response to voltage dips;
– characteristics of active power (maximum measured power, ramp rate limitation, set-point control);
– reactive power (reactive power capability, set-point control);
– grid protection (protection levels and disconnection times for over- and undervoltage and frequency in the grid); and
– reconnection time.

The standard contains a detailed format for reporting the characteristic measured values.

2.12.3.7 Rotor Blade Testing

In full-scale rotor blade testing, an entire rotor blade is mounted on a test rig – most often in a specialized laboratory – and is subjected to a series of static and fatigue loads representative of the design loads. The test objective is to experimentally verify that a specific blade type possesses the strength (fatigue and ultimate) and service life as foreseen in the design.

The blades of a wind turbine rotor are among the most critical components of the wind turbine. Blade tests are therefore considered as mandatory tests in wind turbine type certification (see Section 2.12.4). The need for specific tests will depend on the level of uncertainty in the design assessment due to the use of new materials, new design concepts, new production processes, and so on, and the possible impact on the structural integrity. Furthermore, rotor blade testing is helpful in the process of prototype development, and therefore rotor blade manufacturers usually have their own testing facilities.

The procedure for testing rotor blades is documented in the IEC/TS 61400-23 Wind turbine generator systems – Part 23: Full-scale structural testing of rotor blades. The document recognizes the wide range of methods (dictated by the test system hardware) that were developed over time at various testing laboratories. Therefore, it did not intend to be a restrictive standard that favors one method to the exclusion of all others. The primary emphasis is to identify and describe commonly accepted practices among the various laboratories and to give guidance in establishing blade test criteria. Therefore, rather than being a full-scope standard, it presently is a technical specification under IEC TC88 that includes many different methods and provides guidelines on recommended practices.

Full-scale rotor blade tests are quite complex, involving sophisticated and at the same time massive test infrastructure and test equipment. Also many different methods can be applied, depending on the specific purpose. Blade tests normally distinguish between static testing and fatigue testing. In static testing, the blade should be loaded to each of its most severe design load conditions. In fatigue testing, a test loading is being generated giving fatigue damage equivalent to the design loads, on selected critical areas in the blade construction. The fatigue test loads will generally be chosen in such a way that, for practical reasons, the test time is reduced and still is representative of a loading during a 20 years lifetime.

The test loads are mechanically put to the blade in such a way that their application and distribution adequately represent the load situations leading to the different design loads. These include the following load components along the length of the blade:

- flatwise and edgewise bending moment;
- shear loading in flatwise and edgewise direction;
- torsional moment; and
- radial load.

Application of test loads should consider the relevant combination of those loads (e.g., flatwise and edgewise). Also, the relevant load factors have to be put to the magnitude of the test loads in order to take test and design considerations into account. Practically, the test loads are applied with hydraulic actuators, cranes, and so on. The load distribution for static loading is done with the help of the so-called whiffletree (Figure 1). Given the fact that rotor blades with a length of more than 60 m and a weight of 20 tonnes are no longer exceptional, it is clear that the technical and space requirements and related investments for test facilities are becoming very high.

2.12.3.8 Safety and Function Testing

In safety and function testing, the behavior of a wind turbine as predicted in the design is experimentally verified for relevant design situations. More specifically, the functioning of the control and protection systems is tested under relevant test conditions.

The experimental verification of the adequate functioning of control and safety systems on a prototype or representative sample of a wind turbine type is of primary importance in the testing stage of the wind turbine, and is the basis for the actual confidence in the reliable and safe functioning of the machine in all relevant design situations. Therefore, a safety and function test is the very first of the mandatory type testing modules in type certification of wind turbines.

The general requirements for safety and function testing are specified in the IEC 61400-22. The actual test plan has to include elements such as physical quantities to be measured, instrumentation, data acquisition system, operational settings of the wind turbine, and external conditions. Also the test plan shall identify the criteria for acceptable wind turbine behavior. As the contents of

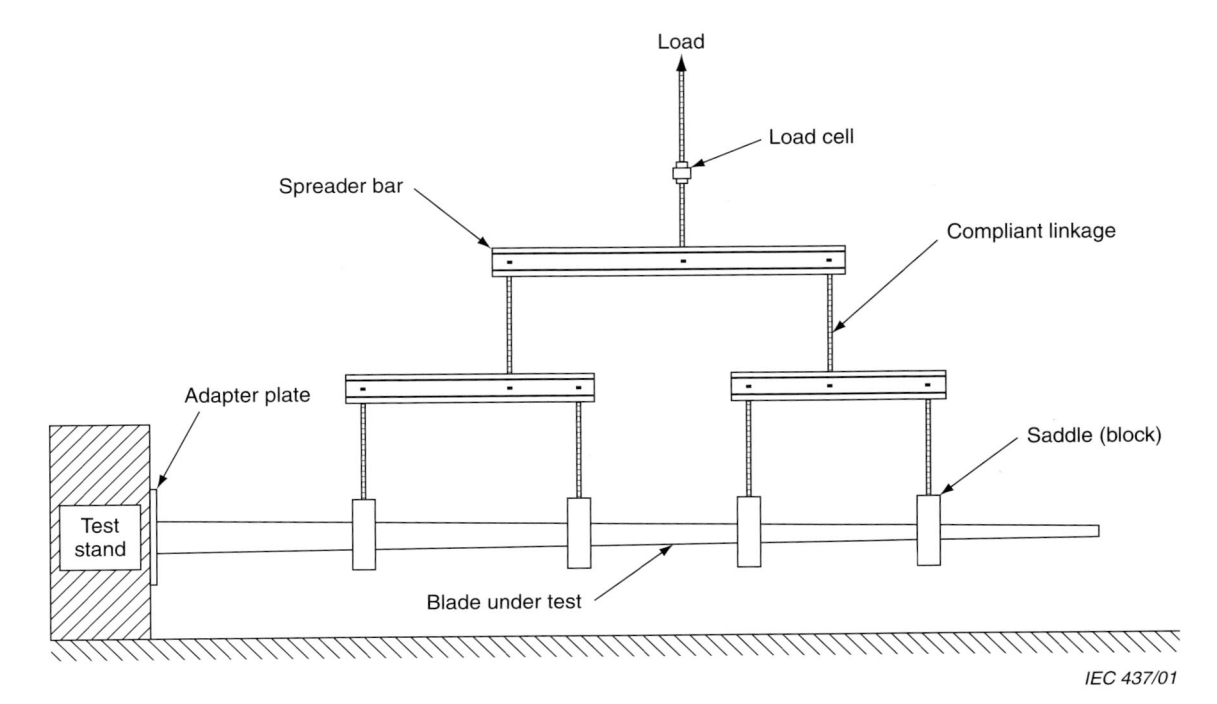

Figure 1 Whiffletree for load distribution.

a safety and function test are very specific to the design of the wind turbine, its plan is subject to an agreement between the wind turbine manufacturer and the certification body.

The setup of the actual test is relatively straightforward. For practical reasons, it is often combined with other tests, for example, power performance measurements and/or mechanical load measurements, to take advantage of the availability of a number of relevant signals, such as meteorological signals from the meteorological mast, rotational speed, and some mechanical signals where needed.

As a minimum, a safety and function test includes the testing of the primary and secondary protection functions in connection with critical situations such as grid failure, emergency shutdown, wind turbine overspeed, and single fault in the primary protection system. It also has to include the testing and verification of the proper operation of the wind turbine control functions in relation with important design criteria/values, for example, pitch position for a pitch-regulated turbine, functioning of brake and yaw mechanism according to the design specifications.

Other important aspects to be tested may include

- operating vibration levels and vibration protection, below and above rated power;
- overspeed protection at rated wind speed or above;
- start-up and shutdown above rated wind speed; and
- yaw control including cable twist.

The tests – depending on the complexity of the wind turbine – normally can be carried out within a couple of days. Completion also depends on the availability of the relevant wind speed 'window' that enables one to carry out the relevant components of the test – for example, there may be a minimum wind speed to carry out a brake test. On the other hand, some relevant test situations can be 'faked', that is, for different sensors it is possible to adjust the set point to simulate conditions triggering actuation of certain mechanisms such as overspeed protection.

A safety and function test according to IEC 61400-22 also includes an inspection by the certification body of the aspects of the personnel safety described in the design documentation. These include

- on-site availability of safety instructions;
- assembly and functioning of climbing facilities;
- adequacy of access ways and passages;
- safe layout of standing places, platforms, and floors;
- adequate mounting and safety of handrails and fixing points;
- availability and suitability of lighting where necessary;
- safety of electrical and earthing system including proper marking of conductive components;
- fire prevention and control concept;
- functioning, visibility, and easy access of emergency stop buttons;
- provision of alternative escape routes;
- provision for emergency stay on an offshore wind turbine for 1 week; and
- offshore-specific safety equipment for an offshore wind turbine.

The IEC 61400-22 standard prescribes the minimum requirements for the test report.

2.12.3.9 Measurement Quality

As should be clear from the introductory section, many of the above testing methods have been developed by national research institutes in Europe and the United States. Indeed, in the early years of industrial wind power technology development and even before, wind turbine testing was an integral part of the research and development activities, and was embedded in a frame of development of know-how and even fundamental research. The need was recognized to establish harmonized testing procedures. Nowadays, as demonstrated above, for many aspects, agreed test methods exist, and are implemented on a routine basis for every new wind turbine type that enters the market. Besides the research institutes that were strongly involved in the standardization of the test procedures into standards (ECN (Netherlands Energy Research Foundation), Risø, CRES (Centre for Renewable Energy Sources), CIEMAT (Centro de Investigaciones Energéticas, Medioambientales y Tecnológicas), DEWI (Deutsche Windenergie-Institut), etc.), several specialized testing institutes have been founded that nowadays supply high-quality testing services to the wind power industry.

The way for independent quality assessment in measurement is accreditation according to the ISO 17025, which leads to a formal third-party statement of competence that the testing 'laboratories'

- work under an appropriate management system ensuring quality;
- employ competent and adequate staff for the test activities; and
- utilize and implement adequate testing procedures.

The prominent testing institutes active in important wind energy markets obtained accreditations for operating the relevant measurement procedures in accordance with the requirements of ISO EN 17025 from national accreditation institutes including

DAkkS (Deutsche Akkreditierungstelle GmbH, Germany), ENAC (Entidad Nacional de Acreditación, Spain), DANAK (Danish Accreditation and Metrology Fund, Denmark), UKAS (United Kingdom Accreditation Service, United Kingdom), RvA (Raad voor Accreditatie, Netherlands), and ESYD (Hellenic Accreditation System, Greece).

In the year 1997, an international network of measurement institutes was established called Measnet, striving for harmonized and recognized measurement methods in wind energy. Nowadays, it is a network of 18 institutes engaged in the field of wind energy and wanting to ensure high-quality measurements, uniform interpretation of standards and recommendations as well as interchangeability of results. Within the Measnet network, assessment teams perform assessments for the admission of new members and for the periodical quality confirmations of Measnet members. A basic requirement for Measnet members is accreditation according to the ISO/IEC 17025 for the Measnet-approved measurements. To date, the Measnet-approved measurement procedures include anemometer calibration, power performance measurements, power quality measurements, and acoustic noise measurements.

In the United States, under the Department of Energy (DOE) a similar system of recognized test laboratories for small wind turbines has recently been established, namely the Regional Test Centers.

2.12.4 Certification in the Wind Industry

2.12.4.1 General Aspects of Certification in Wind Energy

Certification in wind energy is the formal statement of compliance namely that a certain system (wind turbine, wind energy project, CMS) is meeting the requirements of well-defined standards. In the case of wind turbines, for example, it is the statement by a competent third party (a certification body) that the design is in conformity with the requirements of standards or other normative documents such as the ones discussed in Section 2.12.2. In very general terms, the purpose of certification in the wind energy sector is to ensure that wind turbine systems during their expected lifetime do not cause harm to persons and the environment (safety) and produce energy in an efficient manner (reliability and economy). In practice, wind turbine certification focuses on overall product integrity and incorporates verification of sufficient fatigue and ultimate load capacity, safety system functionality, and personnel safety measures. With such a broad objective, certification is asked by many stakeholders in the field:

- manufacturing industry: third-party quality statement, indispensable for selling the product;
- developers, owners, and operators: enabling making informed choices; conformity check of the delivered project in the case of high-risk projects such as offshore;
- authorities: confidence in safety-related aspects for permitting process; eligibility for incentive programs; and
- financing and insurance: reduction of the financing risk.

Nowadays, any new wind turbine type on the market passes through certification, and its implementation in offshore projects is gaining speed. An approach to certification has been developed that is quite pragmatic and serves the purposes of multiple stakeholders. As will be shown further in this chapter, this approach has a certain degree of flexibility, notably by the modular approach. This enables issuing conformity statements about parts of the assessment and so does not hinder the ongoing technical development for aspects not yet ready to enter the certification stage. It can be safely stated that certification has contributed to the increasing quality and reliability of wind power technology, although it can never guarantee that failures will not occur.

As the wind industry is growing strongly, the market for certification services has grown significantly too. As a consequence, more certification providers are operating in the different markets all over the world, and there is a strong tendency to using a similar approach to certification.

In the 1980s, the first certification systems for wind energy were developed by research institutes (e.g., Risø, ECN) and major certification bodies (notably Germanischer Lloyd, DNV) and these practices have more or less converged to the approach as described in the present IEC Standard 61400-22 (IEC 61400-22 is the formal successor of the IEC-WT-01, which has been in use for a long time). This document nowadays is the principal guideline for certification in wind energy, besides the certification regulations of major certification bodies. Inside Europe, these are, for example, the guidelines issued by Germanischer Lloyd and DNV. Outside Europe, these include the documents issued by C-WET (Centre for Wind Energy Technology) in India and Underwriters Laboratory (UL) in the United States. There are some specific 'niche activities' in certification with their specific documents (offshore, small wind turbines, condition monitoring), as will be shown further in this chapter.

This section will further focus on the contents of the various certification systems used in wind energy today.

2.12.4.2 Certification Systems in Wind Energy

Certification is the assessment of the conformity of a product, project, type, and so on to certain criteria and standards. Thus any certification system basically consists of certification procedures and the relevant standards and criteria. Nowadays, there are several systems of certification in the wind industry, depending on the application and scope, each of them issuing a specific certificate. These are the following, and they will be discussed further in detail in this section:

- type certification;
- project certification;
- other certification: for example, CMSs, component certification;

- certification of small wind turbines; and
- certification of power plant capabilities/conformity to grid code requirements.

2.12.4.2.1 Wind turbine type certification

In order to ensure that every wind turbine of a given type is in conformity with the relevant standards and requirements, the practice of 'type certification' has been adopted. This process includes an evaluation of the design (based on documents) and evaluation of principal functional and structural characteristics from type testing and an evaluation of the manufacturing quality.

The principal modules of type certification are shown in **Figure 2**. Each of the principal modules – design evaluation, type testing, and manufacturing evaluation – results in a specific conformity statement. The final evaluation makes a combined assessment of the outcome of these three evaluations, and results in a decision of the certification body to issue a type certificate.

Design evaluation includes a number of aspects, as shown in **Figure 3**. As the control characteristics and safety concept are decisive for many other aspects of the wind turbine design, the evaluation starts with this module. A new element introduced with the IEC 61400-22 as compared to former versions of the standard is the evaluation of the design basis, which identifies all requirements, assumptions, and methodologies that are essential for the design, and the design documentation including codes and standards, design parameters, assumption, methodologies and principles, and other relevant requirements (e.g., for manufacturing, operation and maintenance (O&M)).

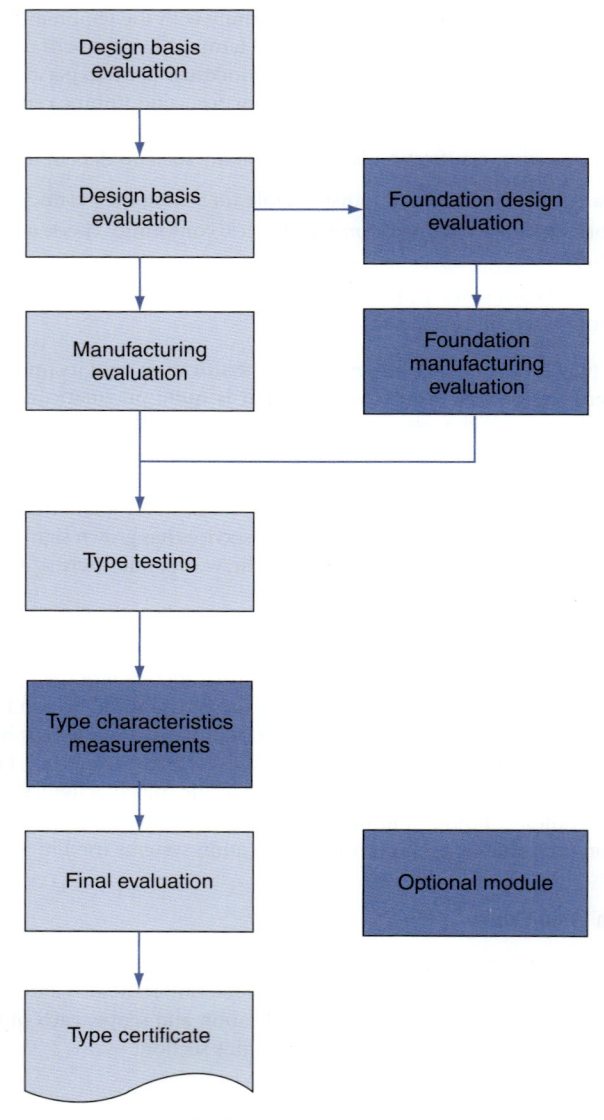

Figure 2 Modules of type certification according to IEC 61400-22. The process leads to the issuing of a type certificate after the final evaluation of the outcome of the different constituting modules and their respective conformity statements.

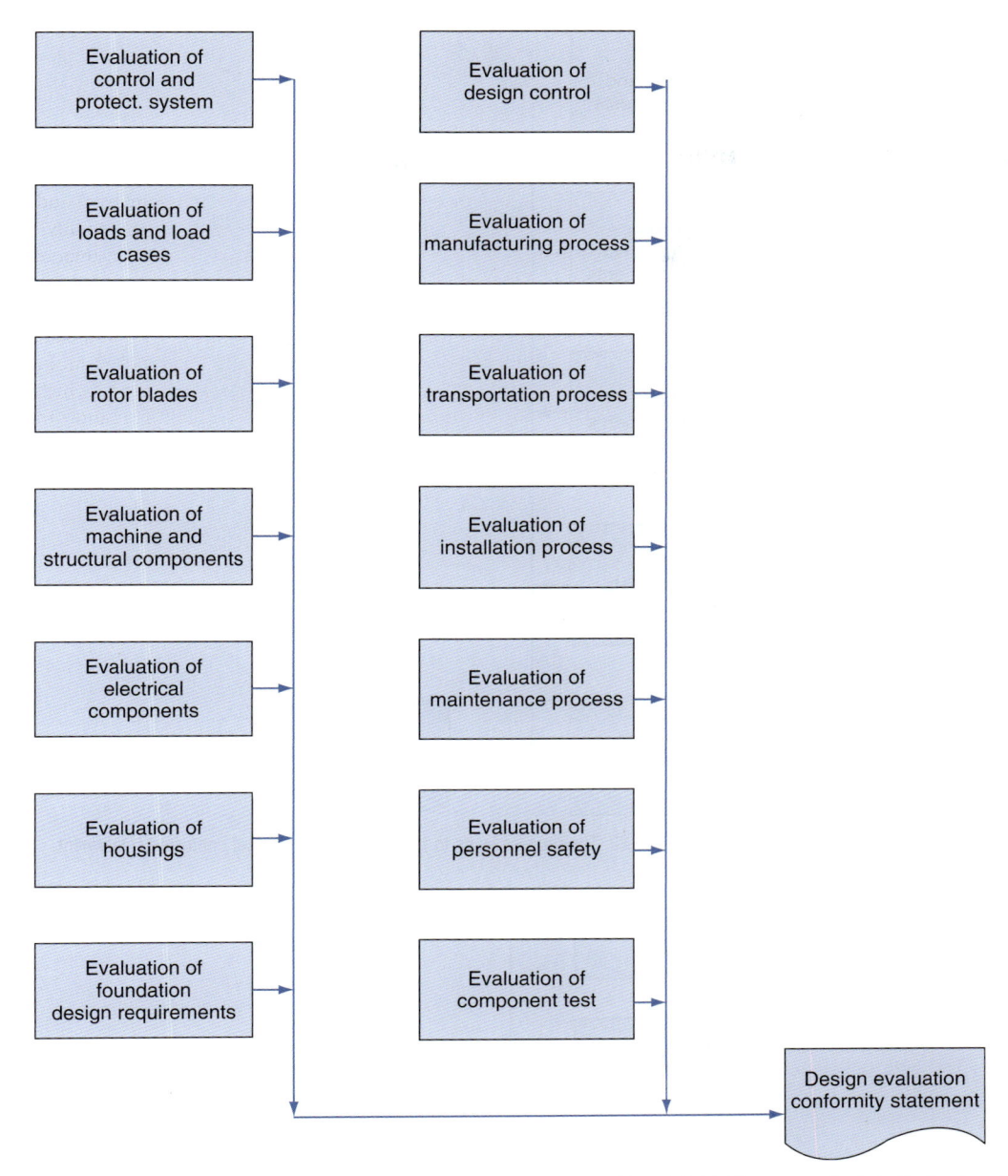

Figure 3 Elements of design evaluation in wind turbine type certification according to IEC 61400-22. The process leads to the issuing of a design evaluation conformity statement.

Type testing evaluation comprises the assessment of data and results from the experimental verification (test) of important functional, structural, and performance characteristics. The mandatory modules of type testing are shown in **Figure 4**. Besides, certification may also involve the assessment of the results of the measurement of so-called type characteristics such as acoustic noise emission and power quality, as shown in **Figure 5**.

The evaluation of manufacturing quality is based on the evaluation of the quality system – which is accepted if the wind turbine manufacturing company has ISO 9001 certification. In addition, an inspection shall be carried out that verifies on the basis of at least one specimen of the wind turbine that it is manufactured according to the certified design. The inspection is done with emphasis on aspects identified during design evaluation as deserving special attention.

Prototype certification excludes several of the abovementioned modules and has limited validity. Basically, it is used for wind turbines that are not yet ready for manufacture and is limited to a specific site.

2.12.4.2.2(i) Procedures and standards used in type certification
Reference procedures to be used for type certification are the ones described in IEC 61400-22. Other procedures often used are the earlier-mentioned documents of major certification bodies in and outside Europe.

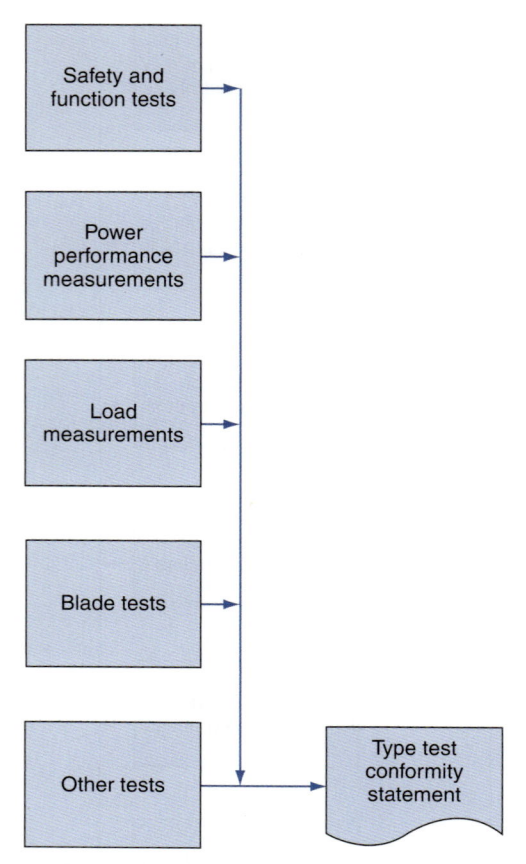

Figure 4 Elements of type testing according to IEC 61400-22. The process leads to the issuing of a type test conformity statement.

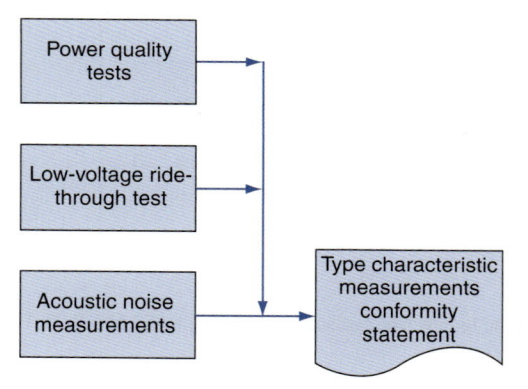

Figure 5 Elements of type characteristic measurements according to IEC 61400-22. The process leads to the issuing of a type characteristic measurements conformity statement.

Many aspects are checked as well in the areas of design as in testing and manufacturing. For each of these aspects, a multitude of standards and criteria may apply. Important standards and criteria for wind turbine design are discussed in Section 2.12.2. With respect to testing, the standards discussed under Section 2.12.3 are used as criteria in type certification.

The type certificate issued is the statement that the wind turbine type with declared technical characteristics has been assessed according to the specified certification procedure and complies with design requirements as stated in a specific design standard. The certificate also specifies the wind turbine class for which the type has been certified, corresponding to the IEC classification as described in Section 2.12.2.

2.12.4.2.2 Wind energy project certification

The practice of project certification in wind energy has been introduced with the arrival of large high-risk projects, such as offshore wind energy. Whereas type certification mainly focuses on the product itself, project certification aims at the assessment of wind

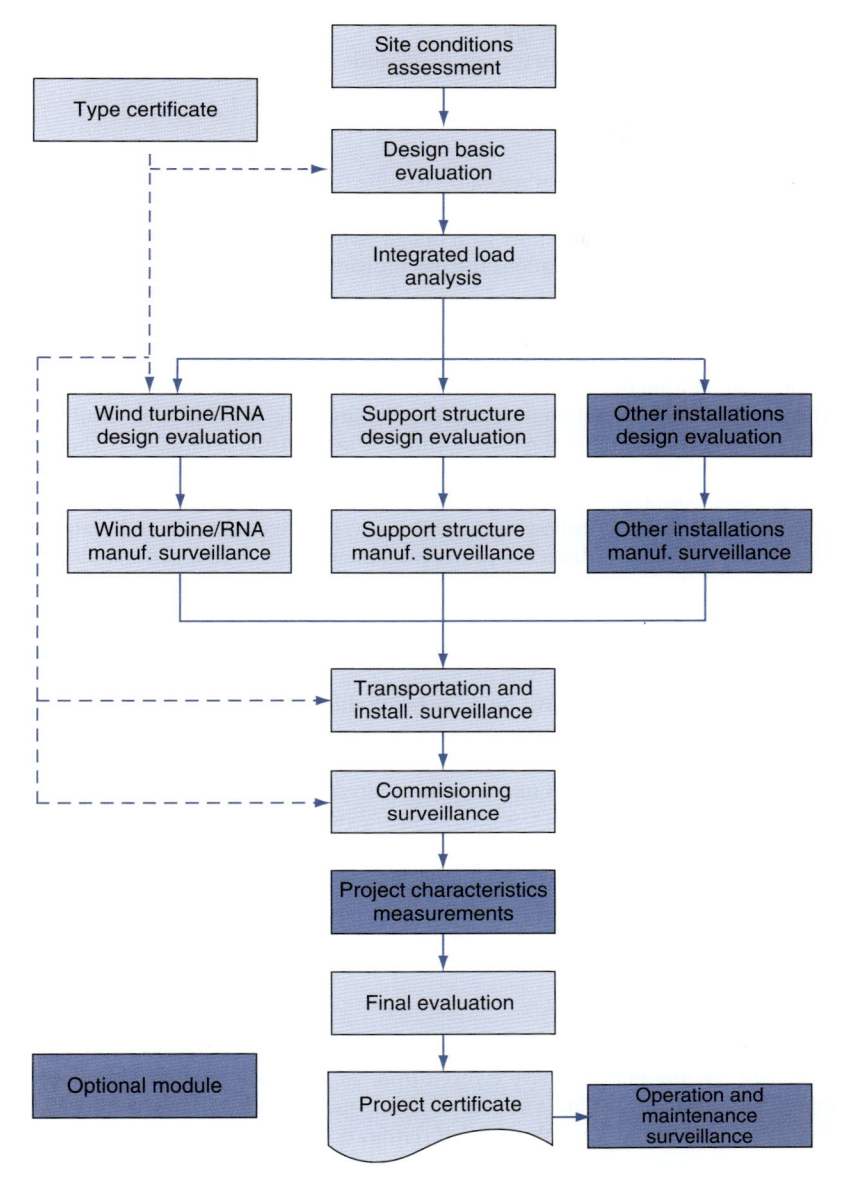

Figure 6 Mandatory and optional modules of wind turbine project certification according to IEC 61400-22.

energy projects where the (type-certified) turbines are implemented with the specific site conditions, with specific foundations and including the processes of transportation, installation, and commissioning. The modules of project certification as given in IEC 61400-22 are shown in **Figure 6**. It shows that in project certification a large number of elements need to be assessed in order to enable issuing relevant statements of compliance and certificates.

Project certification builds further on type certification; however, a lot of assessment work has to be done anew, because now the compliance of the wind turbine design should be assessed for site-specific conditions (wind, ocean, grid, etc.). Therefore, the first step in project certification is an evaluation of the design basis, which includes the site conditions. Then, the design of the major parts of the wind turbine, namely, RNA and support structure (tower, foundation), is evaluated for the site-specific load spectrum and other conditions. For the wind turbine, for example, additional effects are the site-specific turbulence caused by the wind farm wake effects.

Project characteristic measurements to be evaluated in project certification include

– measurement of grid connection compatibility: check of compliance with local grid code requirements;
– power performance verification; and
– acoustic noise emission verification.

2.12.4.2.3 Other certification systems for wind energy

Besides the type and project certification, a number of specific certification systems have been developed to cover the growing needs in the wind energy industry. The following can be mentioned in this respect:

2.12.4.2.3(i) Component certificates

Any major component like a tower, a blade, or a gearbox can be certified according to specific application and load spectra. As for type certification, the purpose of wind turbine component certification is to confirm that a major component of a specific type is designed, documented, and manufactured in conformity with design assumptions, specific standards, and other technical requirements. These modules are similar as for type certification. The specific contents of a module depend on the actual component. The resulting certificate specifies the methods.

2.12.4.2.3(ii) Certification of small wind turbines in the United States and the United Kingdom

In principle, the certification of small wind turbines is covered by the IEC 61400-22. However, in some markets, a specific approach is being followed for the small machines, enabling a faster process involving a manpower effort that is in balance with the substantially lower product cost as compared to large wind turbines. In the United Kingdom, where there is a strong growing market for small wind turbines, a number of industry stakeholders under the umbrella of the MCS platform (Microgeneration Certification Scheme) established by DECC have developed a certification scheme for small wind turbines (power output not higher than 50 kW at 11 m s^{-1}). The scheme is basically following the philosophy of the certification of the larger turbines, but concentrates on a simplified design assessment, specific guidance for power performance evaluation, and mandatory acoustic noise measurements. The requirements are specified in a BWEA document [3]. The scheme also includes a duration test. In the United States, a similar approach is followed, this time under the auspices of the SWCC (Small Wind Turbine Certification Council).

2.12.4.2.3(iii) Certification of condition monitoring systems

The design and operation of CMSs is to a large extent integrated with the design of wind turbines; however, in principle, a CMS remains a system external to the wind turbine. Condition monitoring in the first place focuses on components in the wind turbine drivetrain and is implemented to prevent damage in the relevant components by early detection of altered dynamic behavior (vibrations). As wind turbines equipped with CMS may involve reduced insurance risk, introduction of certified CMSs in wind turbines is promoted by insurance companies. Hence, several certifying bodies are offering certification schemes for CMSs.

Rules for certifying CMSs are described in a specific regulation issued by Germanischer Lloyd. The certification of the CMS involves the evaluation of the system itself (including functioning, installation, operation, and manufacturing) and the evaluation of the monitoring body.

2.12.5 Conclusions

As wind power comes of age, the value of internationally agreed approaches in design, testing, safety, and operational procedures becomes all the more apparent. Testing practices have evolved from *ad hoc* experimenting with prototypes to a rational set of high-quality reproducible testing services covering a variety of testing needs offered by highly qualified testing companies in a competitive environment. At the same time, a whole range of certification services is offered on the market, enabling the wind turbine manufacturers to choose between different suppliers, even processing one single wind turbine type in parallel through different certifiers.

The existing framework of testing methodologies, standards, and certification systems has been described in this chapter. This is a system of quality and safety assurance that is an integrated part of wind energy implementation. The challenges are to make the system suitable for the future generation of wind plants. Important characteristics of the future wind turbine fleet requiring innovation are large wind turbine dimensions, offshore applications, and wind power plant capabilities. These features should give direction to the future elaboration of the system of quality and safety assurance in the wind industry and also necessitate continuous efforts from the research community to develop the required new tools for design and testing.

References

[1] Hunter R (1999) *Recommended Practices for Wind Turbine Testing. Part 11: Wind Speed Measurement and Use of Cup Anemometry*. IEA.
[2] Dahlberg J-Å, Pedersen TF, and Busche P (2006) *ACCUWIND – Methods for Classification of Cup Anemometers Risø-R-1555(EN)*. May.
[3] British Wind Energy Association Standard 2008-02, Small Wind Turbine Performance and Safety Standard.

IEC Standards (to be purchased via IEC or the National Standardization Institutes)

The following list contains all relevant IEC wind turbine standards as valid at the start of the year 2011.

IEC 61400-1 Edition 3.0 (2005) Wind turbines – Part 1: Design requirements.
IEC 61400-2 Edition 2.0 (2006) Wind turbines – Part 2: Design requirements for small wind turbines.
IEC 61400-3 Edition 1.0 (2009) Wind turbines – Part 3: Design requirements for offshore wind turbines.
ISO 81400-4 Edition 1.0 (2006) Wind turbines – Part 4: Design and specification of gearboxes.
IEC 61400-24 Edition 1.0 (2010) Wind turbines – Part 24: Lightning protection.
IEC 61400-25-1 Edition 1.0 (2006) Wind turbines – Part 25-1: Communications for monitoring and control of wind power plants – Overall description of principles and models.
IEC 61400-25-2 Edition 1.0 (2006) Wind turbines – Part 25-2: Communications for monitoring and control of wind power plants – Information models.
IEC 61400-25-3 Edition 1.0 (2006) Wind turbines – Part 25-3: Communications for monitoring and control of wind power plants – Information exchange models.
IEC 61400-25-4 Edition 1.0 (2008) Wind turbines – Part 25-4: Communications for monitoring and control of wind power plants – Mapping to communication profile.
IEC 61400-25-5 Edition 1.0 (2006-12) Wind turbines – Part 25-5: Communications for monitoring and control of wind power plants – Conformance testing.
IEC 61400-25-6 Edition 1.0 (2010) Wind turbines – Part 25-6: Communications for monitoring and control of wind power plants – Logical node classes and data classes for condition monitoring.
IEC 61400-12-1 Edition 1.0 (2005) Wind turbines – Part 12-1: Power performance measurements of electricity producing wind turbines.
IEC 61400-11 Edition 2.1 (2006) Wind turbine generator systems – Part 11: Acoustic noise measurement techniques.
IEC/TS 61400-14 Edition 1.0 (2005) Wind turbines – Part 14: Declaration of apparent sound power level and tonality values.
IEC/TS 61400-13 Edition 1.0 (2001) Wind turbine generator systems – Part 13: Measurement of mechanical loads.
IEC 61400-21 Edition 2.0 (2008) Wind turbines – Part 21: Measurement and assessment of power quality characteristics of grid connected wind turbines.
IEC/TS 61400-23 Edition 1.0 (2001) Wind turbine generator systems – Part 23: Full-scale structural testing of rotor blades.
IEC 61400-22 Edition 1.0 (2010) Wind turbines – Part 22: Conformity testing and certification.

Relevant Websites

http://www.awea.org – American Wind Energy Association.
http://www.cwet.tn.nic.in – Centre for Wind Energy Technology.
http://www.dnv.com – Det Norske Veritas.
http://www.gl-group/com/en/certification/renewables – GL Renewables Certification.
http://www.iec.ch – International Electrotechnical Commission.
http://www.measnet.org – International Network for Harmonised and Recognised Measurements in Wind Energy.
http://www.renewableenergyworld.com – Renewable Energy Network for News and Information.

2.13 Design and Implementation of a Wind Power Project

T Wizelius, Gotland University, Visby, Sweden; Lund University, Lund, Sweden

© 2012 Elsevier Ltd. All rights reserved.

2.13.1	Introduction	392
2.13.2	Project Management	393
2.13.3	Finding Good Wind Sites	394
2.13.4	Feasibility Study	394
2.13.4.1	Impact on Neighbors	395
2.13.4.2	Grid Connection	395
2.13.4.3	Land for Wind Power Plants	395
2.13.4.4	Opposing Interests	395
2.13.4.5	Local Acceptance	396
2.13.4.6	Permission	396
2.13.5	Project Development	396
2.13.5.1	Verification of Wind Resources	396
2.13.5.2	Land Lease	397
2.13.5.3	Micro-Siting and Optimization	397
2.13.5.4	Environment Impact Assessment	397
2.13.5.5	Public Dialogue	397
2.13.5.6	Appeals and Mitigation	398
2.13.6	Micro-Siting	398
2.13.6.1	Wind Wakes	398
2.13.6.2	Energy Rose	399
2.13.6.3	Wind Farm Layout	399
2.13.6.4	Optimization	401
2.13.6.4.1	Park efficiency	402
2.13.6.4.2	Conflicting projects	403
2.13.7	Estimation of Power Production	403
2.13.7.1	Long-Term Wind Climate	403
2.13.7.1.1	Annual variations	403
2.13.7.2	Wind Data	403
2.13.7.2.1	Frequency distribution	404
2.13.7.2.2	Wind speed and height	404
2.13.7.2.3	Turbulence	406
2.13.7.3	Wind Data Sources	406
2.13.7.3.1	Historical meteorological data	406
2.13.7.3.2	Onsite measurement data	406
2.13.7.3.3	Data from meteorological modeling	406
2.13.7.3.4	Long-term correlation	407
2.13.8	Planning Tools	407
2.13.8.1	The Wind Atlas Method	407
2.13.8.1.1	Roughness of terrain	409
2.13.8.1.2	Hills and obstacles	409
2.13.8.1.3	Fingerprint of the wind	411
2.13.8.1.4	Wind atlas calculation	411
2.13.8.1.5	Sources of error	412
2.13.8.1.6	Loss and uncertainty	412
2.13.8.2	Wind Measurements	412
2.13.8.3	Pitfalls	413
2.13.8.3.1	Extreme temperatures	413
2.13.8.3.2	Extreme wind speeds	413
2.13.8.3.3	Wind power and forest	413
2.13.8.3.4	Wind resource maps	414
2.13.8.3.5	Upgrading of wind turbines	415
2.13.9	Choice of Wind Turbines	416
2.13.9.1	Wind Turbine Size	416
2.13.9.2	Type of Wind Turbines	417

2.13.9.3		Wind Turbines Tailored to Wind Climate	418
2.13.9.3.1		Nominal power versus rotor diameter	418
2.13.9.3.2		IEC wind classes	418
2.13.9.3.3		Grid compatibility	418
2.13.9.4		Supplier	418
2.13.10		**Economics of Wind Power Plants**	**420**
2.13.10.1		Investment	421
2.13.10.1.1		Wind turbines	421
2.13.10.1.2		Foundation	421
2.13.10.1.3		Access roads	421
2.13.10.1.4		Grid connection	421
2.13.10.1.5		Land lease	422
2.13.10.1.6		Project development	422
2.13.10.1.7		Total investment	422
2.13.10.2		Economic Result	422
2.13.10.2.1		Depreciation	422
2.13.10.2.2		Operation and maintenance	423
2.13.10.3		Revenues	423
2.13.10.4		Calculation of Economic Result	423
2.13.10.4.1		Cost of capital	424
2.13.10.4.2		Present value and IRR	424
2.13.10.4.3		Payback time	424
2.13.10.4.4		Levelized cost of energy	424
2.13.10.4.5		Cash flow analysis	424
2.13.10.5		Risk Assessment	424
2.13.10.6		Financing	425
2.13.11		**Documentation**	**425**
2.13.11.1		Project Description	425
2.13.11.2		Environment Impact Assessment	426
2.13.11.3		Economic Reports	426
2.13.11.3.1		Wind data report	426
2.13.11.3.2		Economic prospect	426
2.13.11.3.3		Real budget	426
2.13.12		**Building a Wind Power Plant**	**427**
2.13.12.1		Selection of Suppliers	427
2.13.12.2		Contracts	427
2.13.12.3		Supervision and Quality Control	427
2.13.12.4		Commissioning and Transfer	428
2.13.13		**Operation**	**428**
2.13.13.1		Maintenance	428
2.13.13.2		Condition Monitoring	428
2.13.13.3		Performance Monitoring	429
2.13.13.4		Decommissioning and Site Restoration	429
2.13.14		**Business Models**	**429**
2.13.15		**Summary and Conclusion**	**429**
References			**430**
Further Reading			**430**

2.13.1 Introduction

To develop a wind power project includes many different steps and processes that can vary depending on the preconditions; planning, the acquisition of consents, agreements and contracts, financing, installation, and finally operation of the wind power plants. During the feasibility study, the developers will have to decide after each step if it is worth to continue or if it is better to end the project at an early stage and find a better site to develop. The demands from authorities have also to be fulfilled so that necessary permission will be given, and the documentation of the estimated production good enough to convince banks and investors (see **Figure 1**).

The determining factor for the prospects of a wind farm development decision is the outcome of the economic calculation. If the preconditions are good enough, the wind turbine has to be sited, or the wind power plant designed, to optimize the efficiency and output and at the same time minimize impacts on the environment.

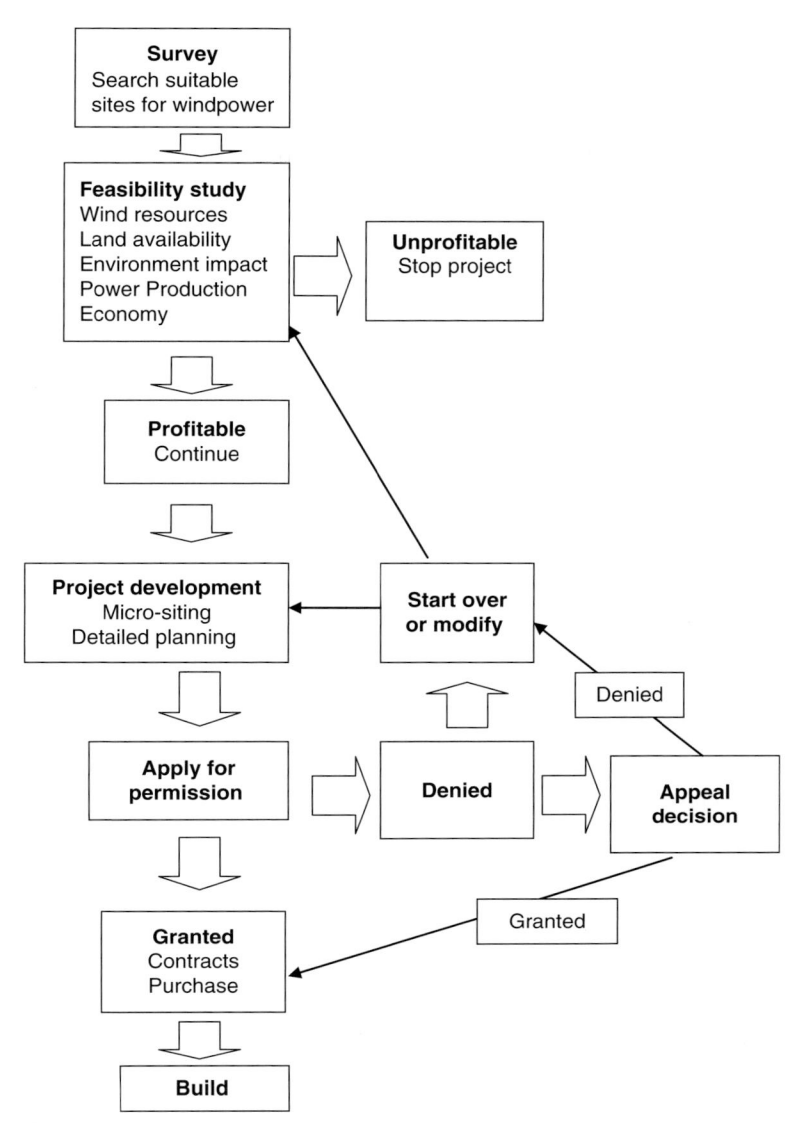

Figure 1 Project development process.

The aims of this chapter are to describe and discuss the most important issues related to the design and implementation of a wind power project. The different steps in the project development process are described. The principles governing the configuration of a wind farm, the so-called micro-siting, as well as pitfalls that should be avoided are discussed. Different methods to assess the wind resources and estimate the annual energy production are reviewed. Factors that govern the choice of wind turbines are described as well as how economic calculations are made. Finally, the building and operation phases are summarized. The focus of this chapter lies in the design of wind power plants.

2.13.2 Project Management

How a wind power project should be managed depends on who is in charge of the project. If a large corporation plans to invest in wind power, the management of the corporation will give the task of developing a wind power plant to a technical consultancy firm; an experienced wind power developer. Another option is to order a turnkey wind power plant from a developer or a manufacturer, and then give the same company the task to operate the plant as well. With a single contractor who is responsible for delivering a turnkey wind power plant including the wind turbines, foundations, access roads, and grid connection, the responsibility is very clear.

If the company's business idea is to develop and operate wind power plants, it would manage the project by its own staff, and engage some external experts and subcontractors if necessary. It will use project financing and also has to negotiate loans from banks

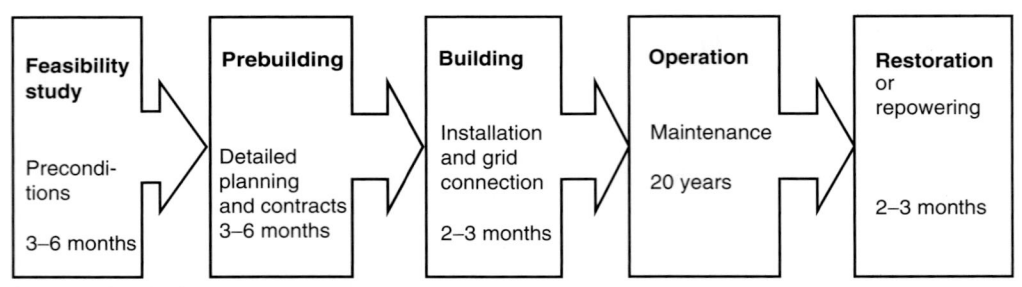

Figure 2 Windpower project development stages.

and raise equity. If a new company is formed for wind power development, the partners have to select a suitable business model, a project manager, and CEO and raise seed capital to hire experts and finance the venture until the first project has been developed and sold. To manage the project development is a complex task. A detailed project plan and timeline has to be worked out. First, a feasibility study has to be made to find out if the project will be viable. When the decision to go ahead has been taken, the development consists of three phases: 'pre-building', 'building', and 'operation' (see **Figure 2**) [1,2].

2.13.3 Finding Good Wind Sites

If the task is to develop one or a few wind turbines or large wind power plants within a specified geographical area – a country, region, or municipality – the first step is to make a survey of the area to find suitable places, followed by an evaluation to choose the most promising sites for feasibility studies.

The most important precondition for a good wind power project is that there are good wind conditions at the site. The first step always is to study wind resource maps for the area, if there are any available. If there are no such maps, information about wind conditions can be found, for example, by analyzing data from meteorological stations.

It is the long-term wind conditions, the regional wind climate that has to be found and evaluated. This means the average wind speed for at least a 10-year period, the frequency distribution of these wind speeds, and also if possible the quality of the wind – the turbulence intensity.

When good sites for wind turbines are looked for, many different aspects have to be considered. The most important one is of course the wind resource. Local conditions like hills, orography, buildings, and vegetation influence the wind and have to be considered in a more detailed calculation of how much energy wind turbines will be able to produce at a specific site [3].

The wind turbines have to be transported to the site, installed, and connected to the grid. The distance to existing roads and/or harbors, the costs for building access roads, ground conditions that influence the design and cost of the foundation, and the distance to and capacity of the grid are thus important factors that have to be considered in the evaluation of a site. When the wind turbines have been installed, they should not disturb people who live close by. In Europe and North America, there are rules about the maximum noise level (in dBA) that is acceptable and this defines the minimum distance to buildings in the vicinity of the site [4].

Permission from authorities to install wind turbines is also necessary. The rules and regulations for permissions are specific for each country. As a common rule, the authorities will check that wind turbines will not interfere or create conflicts with other kinds of enterprises or interests. It is therefore both wise and necessary for a wind power developer to check what kind of opposing interest there may be at a potential site. It can be an airport, air traffic in general (turbines are quite high), military installations (radar, radio links, etc.), nature protection areas, archaeological sites, and so on. Information about opposing interests can usually be supplied by the county administration or by the municipality. If there are municipal, regional, or national plans for wind power, this screening of opposing interest may already have been made.

A good site for wind power development is thus not only defined by the available wind resource but also by available infrastructure; roads and power grid and by the absence of strong opposing interests.

2.13.4 Feasibility Study

When a site with apparently good wind resources has been identified, the first thing is to verify and specify the wind resources.

Wind resource maps are made with a rough resolution, often with a 1×1 km grid, so the wind data are smoothed out. They cannot be used to calculate the production of wind turbines at specific sites. There are other methods for doing this, like the wind atlas method [3]. For larger projects, it is usually necessary also to make wind measurements at the hub height of the planned wind turbines, using a wind measurement mast. A wind measurement mast is, however, not installed until the feasibility study has come to the conclusion that it is worthwhile to realize the project. These wind data are also necessary for the economic calculations, and is usually also a demand from the institutions that will finance the project. As a first step in the feasibility study, a wind atlas calculation can be used for the evaluation of a site (see Section 2.13.8).

Then other preconditions for wind power have to be scrutinized. The following matters have to be clarified:

Neighbors: Noise and flickering shadows should not disturb neighbors. Can the turbine(s) be sited so that such disturbances can be avoided?

Grid connection: Is there a power grid with capacity to connect the wind turbine(s) within a reasonable distance?

Land: Who owns the land in the area? Are there landowners willing to sell or lease land for wind turbines?

Opposing interest: Are there any military installations, airports, nature conservation areas, or other factors that could stop the project?

Local acceptance: What opinion do local inhabitants have about wind power in their neighborhood?

Permission: Is the chance of obtaining necessary permissions reasonably good?

2.13.4.1 Impact on Neighbors

To avoid neighbors being disturbed, a minimum distance of 400 m to the closest dwellings will eliminate this problem. For a large wind power plant, this distance may have to be increased. The site where the turbines will be installed should be quite large and have an open terrain. A good rule of thumb is to have a minimum distance of 400 m for single turbines or 4 times the total height (hub height + ½ rotor diameter) if the turbines are very large and a few hundred meters extra for wind power plants with many turbines. With such distances, the impacts from noise should be well within acceptable limits. During micro-siting, more exact calculations can be made of impacts of noise and also shadow flicker on neighbors.

2.13.4.2 Grid Connection

Power lines are usually indicated on maps, so it is quite easy to estimate the distance from the turbine(s) to the grid. However, it is also necessary to know the voltage level, since that sets a limit to the amount of wind power (MW) that can be connected to the power grid. There are several technical factors to take into consideration (the dimensions of the lines, voltage level, power flows, distance to the closest transformer station, loads, etc.), and only electric power engineers can make these kinds of calculations [5].

There are, however, some rules of thumb that give an idea of how many MW of wind power that can be connected to power lines with different voltage levels. One such rule is that grid connection capacity increases with the square of the voltage level (when voltage level is doubled, wind power capacity can be increased 4 times). Around 3.5 MW can be connected to a 10 kV line, and 15 MW to a 20 kV line, 60 MW to a 40 kV line, and so on. Close to the transformer station, more wind power can be connected than close to the end of a power line [6].

There are also technical rules, the so-called grid codes. There are no harmonized rules on an international level. To get this information right, it is best to consult the grid operator.

2.13.4.3 Land for Wind Power Plants

What kind of landowners there are in an area is usually quite easy to guess. In an agricultural district, local farmers usually own the land. In that case, it is quite probable that it will be possible to find landowners who are prepared to lease or sell some land for installation of wind turbines. The land can be tilled like before, but there will be additional revenues. Not only the soil but also the wind can be harvested, and to make money out of air is usually considered as a good business idea. In other cases, companies, municipalities, or the state can own the land. Information on landownership can be found in the land registry. Often landowners make contact with developers to get some wind turbines on their land.

Access to land is necessary to be able to install and operate wind power plants, so an agreement with the landowner(s) should be made at an early stage. If several landowners are involved, a common agreement should be made, although the land lease contracts will be individual. Land lease contracts can be signed already during the feasibility study, with a paragraph included with the precondition that the agreement comes into force only if the project is realized.

2.13.4.4 Opposing Interests

The possibility of realizing a project can be stopped by the so-called opposing interests. The first thing to check is that if there are any military installations close to the site that can be disturbed by wind turbines. Military installations for radar or signal surveillance, radio communication links, and similar equipment are secret, so they cannot be found on maps. The developer should make contact with the appropriate military command to find out if they will oppose wind turbines at the site. If so, the chances are nil. The developer can in such a case ask the military to suggest a site that will not interfere with their interests.

Wind turbines are high structures and can pose a risk to air traffic, especially if there is an airport close by. There are strict rules on how high structures close to the flight routes to and from an airport may be. These rules are available from national aviation authorities. There are also rules and regulations for warning lights for air traffic, which depend on the height of the turbines.

In most countries, there are areas that are classified as national or international interests, to protect nature or cultural heritage, like national parks, nature reservations, bird protection areas, and so on. In such areas, and sometimes also in the vicinity of such areas, it will be difficult to get the permissions necessary for wind turbine installations. Protected areas are usually indicated on public maps.

2.13.4.5 Local Acceptance

The attitude of the local inhabitants to a proposed wind power project in their vicinity is largely dependent on how the developer performs. In Europe, according to opinion polls and experience, most people have a very positive opinion about wind power [7]. On the local level, however, there always seems to be some people who strongly oppose wind turbines in their neighborhood.

How local inhabitants react often depends on how they learn about the project. If they get good information at an early stage, most of them will be positive. When the developer has decided to realize the project, it is important to create a dialogue with local authorities as well as the public, and to take the opinions of the local inhabitants about distance to dwellings and other practical details into serious consideration. When the turbines are on line, it is valuable to have local support and people will keep an eye on the turbines and report when some problems occur.

There are, however, also persons who are dedicated opponents to wind power, as well as organizations for these wind power opponents. Their view is that wind turbines will turn the beautiful landscapes in the countryside into industrial areas and spoil the view of the unbroken horizon at the seacoast. Even if these opponents are few, they can delay, increase the costs, and even stop projects that are planned by appealing against the building and environment permissions given by the authorities.

This makes it even more important to give proper and good information to all that will be affected by wind power projects. To make efforts to give information in local languages, if inhabitants do not speak the same language as the developers, and to create some local benefits for those who will live close to the wind power plants, like work opportunities, dividends to village councils or other local organizations, is well invested money. This will make the inhabitants in the vicinity feel concerned and not exploited by the project developers.

2.13.4.6 Permission

To spend time and money on projects that cannot be built is a bad business. To evaluate the prospect for getting the necessary permissions from authorities is thus a very important part of the feasibility study. The developer has to be familiar with all the rules and regulations that can be applied to a wind power project, and how the authorities interpret them. If there are any municipal or regional plans with designated areas for wind power development, these give a good idea of the chances to get the necessary permissions approved.

2.13.5 Project Development

When the site where the wind power plant will be installed has been identified in the feasibility study, now the exact number and location of the turbine(s) within this area have to be decided. Usually, there are several factors to consider: how much power that can be connected to the grid, specification about minimum annual production, maximum investment costs, and demands on economic return from the investors/owners. The developer's task is to plan an optimized wind power plant within the limits of given conditions and restrictions. The first task during the prebuilding phase is to confirm and specify the details of the feasibility study. All the assumptions made should be reexamined and justified to avoid expenditure on nonviable projects.

In many countries, the only permission needed, up to a certain size of a project, is a building permit from the municipality. For large projects, there can be a demand for a permission or license from higher levels, the county administration, or even the government. There is also a risk that permission will not be granted. This sets a limit to how much that can be invested during this prebuilding phase.

2.13.5.1 Verification of Wind Resources

Reliable data on the wind resources at the site are essential. This is necessary to make the project bankable. It is also necessary for the optimization of the wind farm. To get these data, a full year of data from hub height, and some more heights as well to be able to find the wind profile, is demanded. To install one or for very large projects, a couple of 80–100 m high meteorological masts is quite expensive. If there is any doubt about the outcome of the permission process, project developers postpone these measurements until permissions are granted. This, however, delays the project, so it is a matter of corporate strategy to evaluate risks and benefits of the timing of these measurements.

There are, however, other and cheaper and also quite reliable methods to verify the wind resources. If the terrain is not too complex, there are synoptic weather stations within reasonable distance, and even better a number of wind turbines that have been operating in the same region for a number of years, the wind resources at a site can be calculated and evaluated by the use of the so-called wind atlas software. There are also new wind measuring equipment installed on the ground like Sodar [8], which uses sound impulses, and Lidar [8], that uses light (laser beams) to measure the wind (see Section 2.13.8).

2.13.5.2 Land Lease

How large an area that will be needed depends on the size and layout of the wind farm. Limits are set by the capacity of the grid and the size of the project. How much wind power that can be installed on a given piece of land can be found by an estimate of the wind catchment area. The distance between wind turbines should be 4–7 rotor diameters, depending on the predominant wind direction. To make such an estimate, circles with a radius of say 2.5 rotor diameters (for an in-row distance between turbines of 5 diameters) can be used, and fitted into an area without overlap (see **Figure** 3). The wind catchment area for a group of three wind turbines with 64 m rotor diameter and with in-row distances of 5 rotor diameters would then be around 13 ha.

The project developer has to sign land lease contracts with all the landowners within the area needed for the wind farm. The terms of a land lease contract is a matter of negotiation between the landowner and the developer. In Sweden, the lease usually is set at 3–4% of the gross annual income from the wind power plant. In the United States, the annual land lease usually is in the range of 2000–4000 $ MW^{-1} installed [9].

It is wise to make a fair deal that is in accordance with other similar contracts. It is always valuable to have someone living close to the site that has the wind power plants under surveillance. Landowners can of course also develop and operate their own wind power plants. In countries like Denmark, Germany, Sweden, the United States, and Canada, many farmers own and operate wind turbines sited on their own land.

2.13.5.3 Micro-Siting and Optimization

The developer's task is to optimize the wind turbine(s) within the limits set by the local preconditions. To find the best solution, wind turbines of different size (hub height and rotor diameter) and nominal power should be tested (theoretically) at several sites within the area. For these different options, the production should be calculated and the economics analyzed. The impact on neighbors and environment has to be checked. Finally, the developer has to choose the best option.

In practice, there are always boundary conditions to consider. Dwellings (minimum distances to avoid disturbance), buildings, groves, and other shelters, roads, power grid, topography, land property borders, coastlines, and so on, define these conditions and limit the area available for wind power plants.

With the aid of know-how, good judgment, a constructive dialogue with neighbors and authorities, and high-quality wind data and wind power software, the developer will find the best solution for the project; a detailed plan that should be realized.

2.13.5.4 Environment Impact Assessment

In Europe and the United States, it is compulsory to make an environment impact assessment (EIA) for large wind power plants. In other countries this is not a legal demand. Still, it could be worthwhile to analyze the impacts on environment as a part of the development process. It should be considered to be good practice and thus give some additional goodwill for the project developer and plant operators, in countries where there is no formal demand to make an EIA.

The EIA is a process, a public dialogue [10]. It results in an EIA report, which is evaluated by the authorities who will decide if the project will get the permission to build the wind turbines. Often, it is necessary to engage external consultants to do the EIA itself, or to make special reports on birdlife and other impacts.

2.13.5.5 Public Dialogue

The developer can start by making rough outlines for a few different options for a wind power installation, and invite people in the surrounding area (1–2 km from the site) to an information meeting for a preliminary dialogue. Local and regional authorities, the grid operator, and the local media should also be invited. The developer can inform about wind power in general, the environmental benefits, local wind resources, possible impact, and finally present some outlines and ask the audience about their opinions. Representatives from the local and/or regional authorities can state their opinions about the proposed project, and describe how a decision will be taken.

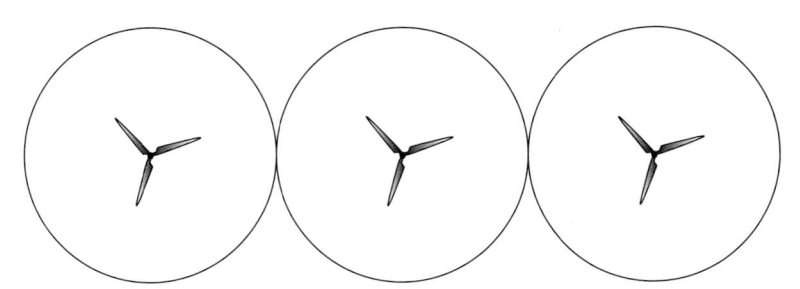

Figure 3 Distance between Wind Turbines. A distance circle with a radius of 2.5 D (rotor diameters) can be used if a proper distance between the wind power plants is set to 5 rotor diameters.

The developer should also have a preliminary dialogue with the municipality, county administration, the grid operator, and other relevant authorities in separate meetings. The project should at this stage be presented as a rough outline, the point of an early dialogue is to keep a door open so that the project can be adapted and modified to avoid unnecessary conflicts.

In many countries, wind power developers have applied a practice for planning that is in accordance with the intentions of the EIA process. Most developers organize local information meetings at an early stage to try to secure that the public will be well informed and have a positive attitude to the plans. Sometimes, they also offer people living in the area to buy shares in the wind power plants. This information meeting is also the first step in the EIA process (early dialogue).

The developer has to present several different options for the siting of wind turbines, and also discuss practical matters of the construction process, building of access roads, power lines, and so on. Also a so-called zero-option, that is, the consequences if the project will not be built, has to be shown. The developer can of course argue for the preferred option, but should be sensitive to the opinions that are put forward. The fact that local inhabitants know the area they live in very well has often proved to be useful for the developer.

By this dialogue, the project is made concrete and is designed to minimize impacts on the environment and neighbors. After that the time is due to compile the EIA document. Agreements to finance the project and a power purchase agreement (PPA) must be negotiated and suppliers of equipment and contractors selected.

The project development process, as well as the purchase of wind turbines and ancillary work, has to be financed. This is another task for the project developer to work out. The wind power project should give the best possible return on the investment, but has also to be compatible with the demands of authorities so that necessary permission will be granted.

2.13.5.6 Appeals and Mitigation

When the relevant authorities and political bodies have processed the applications, the developer will eventually get the necessary permissions granted. It takes another couple of weeks before they have become unappealable. After that the actual building of the wind power plant can start.

It may, however, happen that some neighbors, interest groups, or even an authority will raise an appeal against the decision. The developer then has to wait until the court has tried the appeal. Such legal processes can delay a project for years and sometimes also set a definite stop to it. This risk is another good reason to inform all concerned parties, adapt the project to avoid nuisances, even if it will reduce the economic results a little bit. If the permissions are appealed, the costs will be much higher.

2.13.6 Micro-Siting

When a good area for a wind power plant has been identified, land lease contracts are signed, and the prospects to get the necessary permissions seem good, the project has to be specified in detail. The number and size of wind turbines, and their exact position, have to be defined. A wind power plant can be configured in many different ways, but there is often a best way to do it, that will optimize the return on the investment. This fine-tuning of the layout of wind power plants is called micro-siting.

2.13.6.1 Wind Wakes

If only one wind turbine will be installed, the position of the turbine will be based on the roughness of the terrain, distance to obstacles, and the height contours of the surrounding landscape. If more than one turbine will be installed at a site, the turbines will also have an impact on each other. How large this impact will be depends on the distance between the turbines and the distribution of the wind directions at the site. On the down-wind side of the rotor, a wind wake is formed; the wind speed slows down and regains its undisturbed speed some 10 rotor diameters behind the turbine (see **Figure 4**). This factor has to be taken into account when the layout for a group with several wind turbines is made.

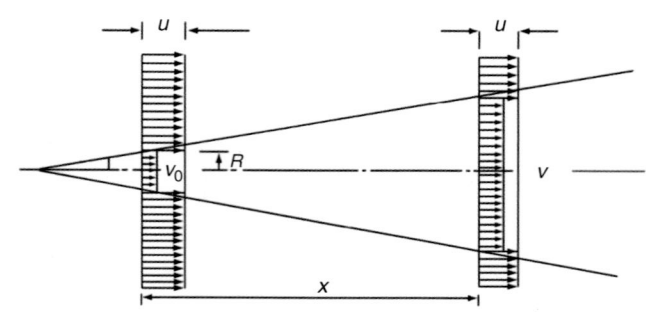

Figure 4 Wind wake. The wind speed (u) is retarded by the rotor (v_0). Behind the rotor the wind speed increases again (v) as the wake gets wider. Reproduced from Jenson NOA (1983) Note on wind generator interaction. *Risoe-M–2411*. Roskilde, Denmark: Risoe National Laboratory.

The wind speed is retarded by the wind turbine rotor, and behind the rotor, the wind speed increases again until it regains its initial speed. The extension of the wind wake determines how the individual turbines will be sited in relation to each other in a group of turbines. The diameter of the wind wake increases by about 7.5 m for each 100 m downwind of the rotor, and the wind speed will increase with the distance until the wake decays completely.

The relation between the wind speed v and the distance x behind the rotor is described by the formula:

$$v = u \left[1 - \frac{2}{3} \left(\frac{R}{R + \alpha x} \right)^2 \right]$$

where v is the wind speed x meter behind the rotor, u is the undisturbed wind speed in front of the rotor, R is the radius of the rotor, and α is the wake decay constant (how fast the wake widens behind the rotor).

The wake decay constant α depends on the roughness class. On land, this value is usually set to 0.075 (m), and on off shore, the value is set to 0.04 (m). Several more advanced models for calculations of wind wakes have been developed since this was formulated in 1986, by N.O. Jensen [11,12] from Risö, but this one shows the principle of wind wakes quite well.

2.13.6.2 Energy Rose

To minimize the impact of wakes from other wind turbines, a so-called energy rose gives the best guidance. A regular wind rose shows the average wind speeds or the frequency of the wind from different directions. An energy rose shows the energy content of the wind distributed to wind directions (see **Figure 5**). Since it is the energy in the wind that is utilized by wind turbines, this is the best guidance. An energy rose can be created with wind atlas software (see **Figure 5**).

2.13.6.3 Wind Farm Layout

Small groups with two to four wind turbines are often put on a straight line, perpendicular to the predominant wind direction. The distance between turbines is measured in rotor diameters, since the size of the wind wake depends on the size of the rotor. A common rule of thumb is to site the turbines 5 rotor diameters apart if they are set in one row. Larger wind power plants can have several rows of turbines. In that case, the distance between rows usually is 7 rotor diameters (see **Figures 6** and **7**) [4].

This ideal model for the layout can be applied in an open and flat landscape and offshore. The actual layout of a wind farm is, however, often formed by the limits set by local conditions, like land use, distance to dwellings, roads, and the power grid. If there are height differences on the site, this will also influence how the turbines should be sited in relation to each other to optimize power production. It is usually not reasonable to increase the distance between turbines to eliminate the impact from wind wakes completely; it is an inefficient use of land.

In areas where one or two opposing wind directions are very dominant, the in-row distance between the turbines can be reduced to 3–4 rotor diameters (see **Figure 8**).

In large wind farms with several rows of wind turbines, the in-row distance should be 5 and the distance between rows 7 rotor diameters. In offshore wind farms, these distances should be 6 in-row and 8–10 between rows ideally. Wind wakes

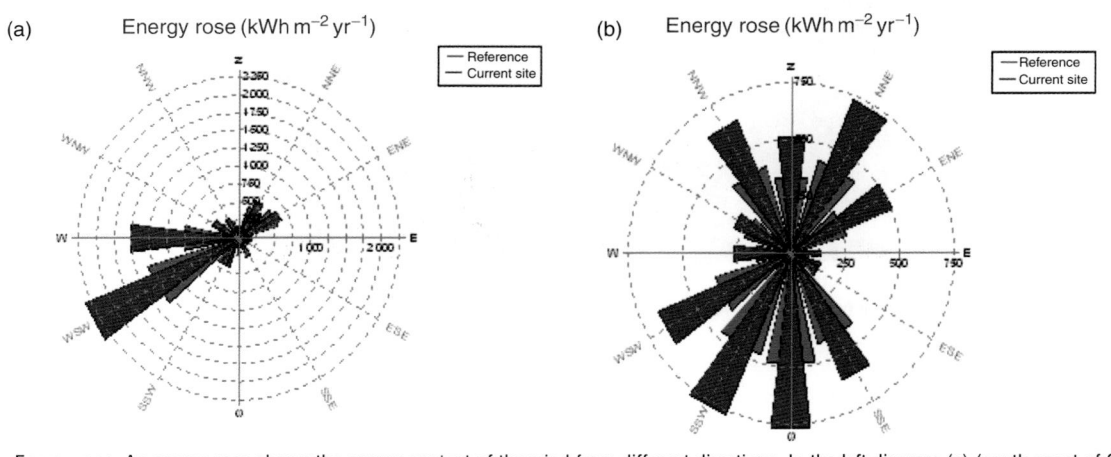

Figure 5 Energy rose. An energy rose shows the energy content of the wind from different directions. In the left diagram (a) (south coast of Sweden) most energy is in the winds from WSW and W. A line of wind turbines should then be installed on a line from NNW to SSE. The in-row distance can be quite short. The diagram to the left, (b), (island in the northern Baltic sea), energy comes from more directions, but it shows that the line of turbines should be oriented from W to E. Both are very windy sites, close to the open sea.

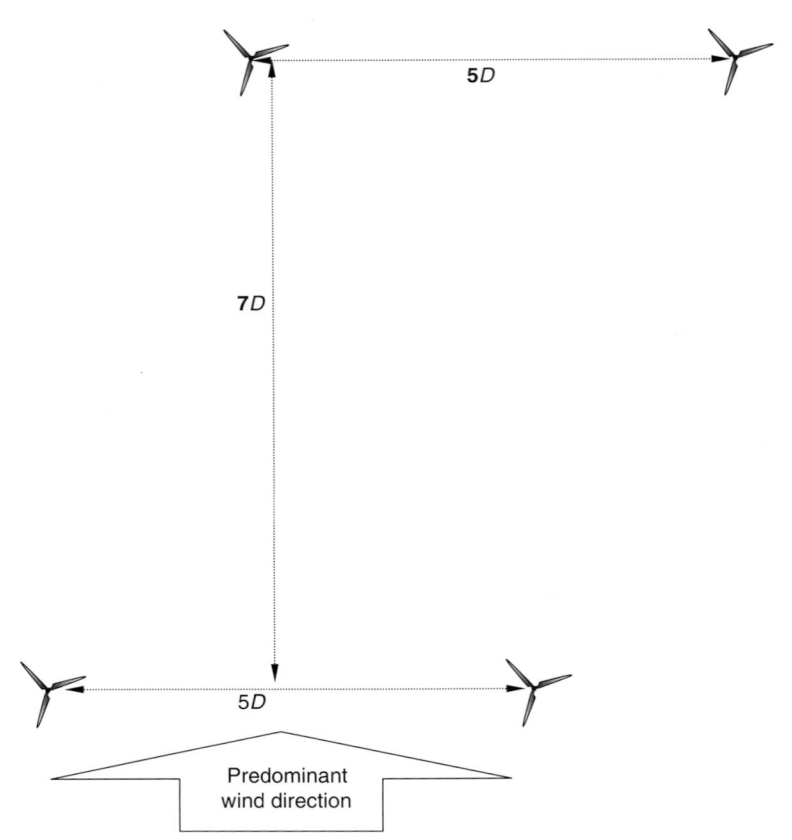

400 Design and Implementation of a Wind Power Project

Figure 6 Wind farm layout. The rule of thumb for a wind farm layout is to have an in-row distance of 5D (rotor diameters) and a between-row distance of 7D.

Figure 7 Standard wind farm lay out. In this wind farm, sited on Öland in Sweden, the rows are perpendicular to the predominant wind direction. The in-row distance is 5D and the distance between rows 7D. Photo Courtesy: T. Wizelius.

survive longer at sea, since the turbulence over water is lower. It is the turbulence in the surrounding wind that destroys the wakes (see **Figure 9**).

If the area is not absolutely flat, the optimal configuration will be irregular, where the distance between turbines differ and the turbines are not set along straight lines. In practice, the layout is also guided by aesthetical and practical concerns; along a coastline, road, headland, regular pattern, or in an arc like the offshore Middelgrunden wind farm outside Copenhagen (see **Figure 10**).

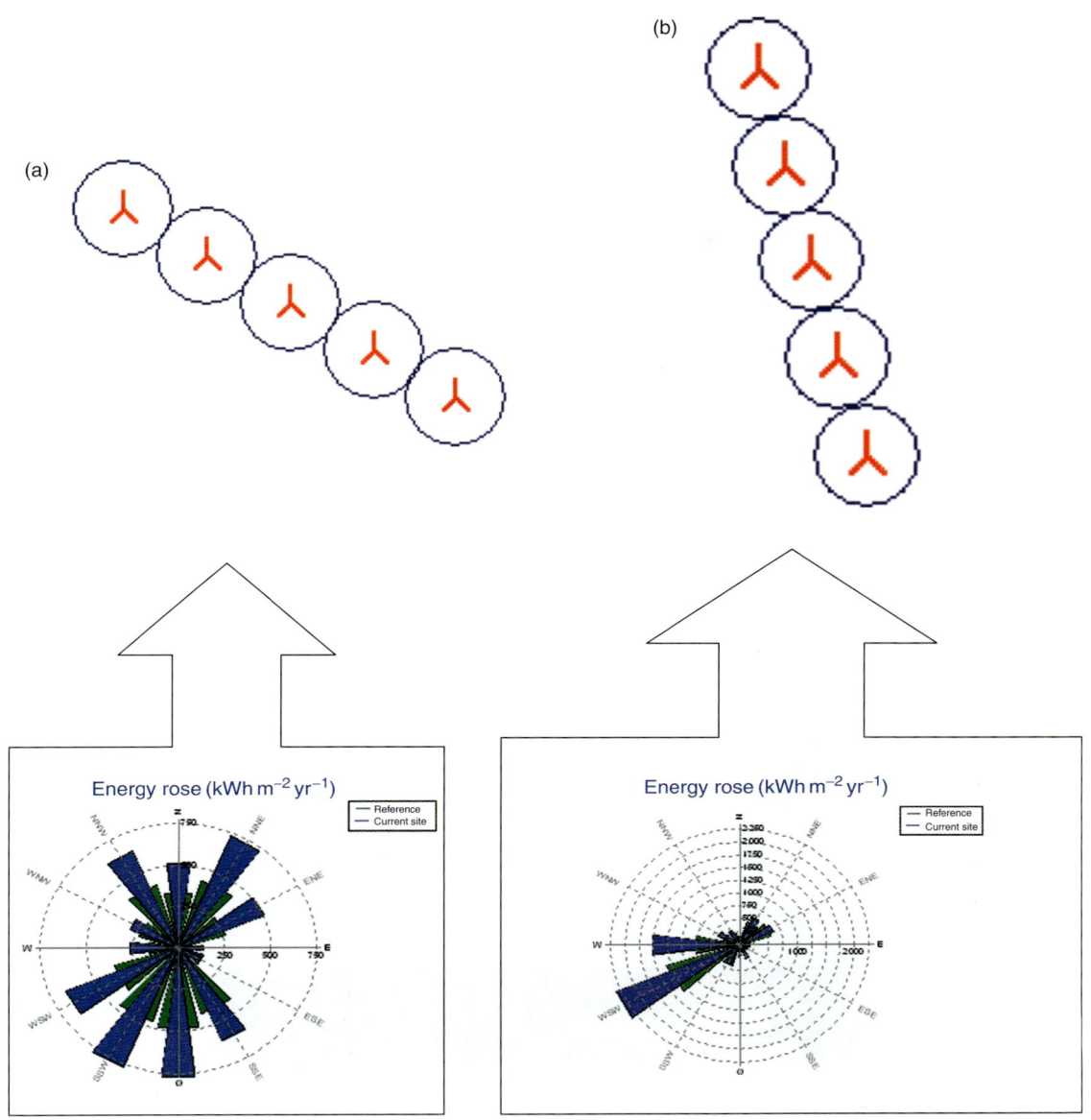

Figure 8 In-Row Distance. The standard in-row distance is 5D (rotor diameters), like in (a). If the wind mainly comes from one and the same direction (or from two opposite directions only), like it does in regions with trade winds, the distance can be reduced to 4D, (b). If several rows are installed, the in-row distance should be increased to 4–5D, and the distance between rows to 8–10D.

2.13.6.4 Optimization

A project developer should of course optimize the layout of a wind power plant. It is, however, important to be aware of what parameters that should be optimized. For the owner and operator of the wind farm, it is neither the installed power in MW nor the total power output that should be optimized (maximized), but the cost-efficiency. It is the production cost for each kWh of electric energy that should be minimized. At the same time, the area available for development has to be utilized in an efficient way. For the landowner and for the supplier as well, it is most profitable to install as many turbines as possible on the land. The owner/operator has the choice to optimize the rate of return on investment, or the cash flow generated by the wind power plant.

The available land area and the capacity of the grid restrict the maximum power that can be installed. The developer, or rather the customer who has ordered a wind power plant, may have restrictions when it comes to the total investment cost. It is the relation between these factors that will set the framework for the optimization of the wind power plant configuration. The wind turbines themselves should also be tailored to fit the wind resources and other conditions at the site.

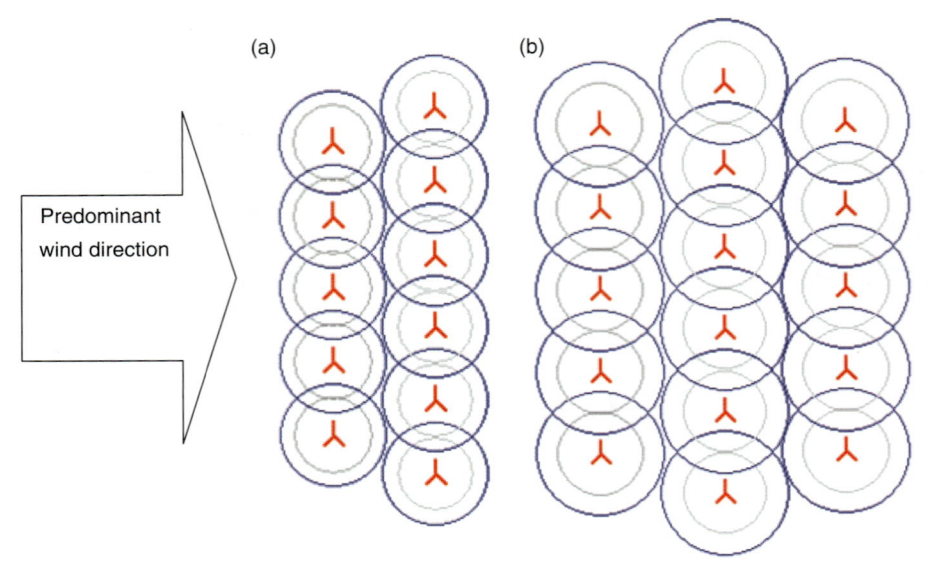

Figure 9 Large wind farm layout. In wind farms with several rows of turbines the in-row distance should be 5 rotor diameters (small circle), and the distance between rows 7 rotor diameters (large circle), (a). Offshore the distances should be 6 diameters in-row and 8–10 between rows, (b).

Figure 10 Middelgrunden offshore wind power plant. The wind turbines in the offshore windpower plant Middelgrunden just outside Copenhagen are sited no more than three rotor diameters from each other, which is too close to get an optimal production. In this case, aesthetic concerns were given much weightage. These wind power plants are visible from the Danish parliament building. Photo courtesy: T. Wizelius.

2.13.6.4.1 *Park efficiency*

In the optimization process, park efficiency is the key concept. When many turbines are installed at the same site, the wind turbines will inevitably steal some wind from each other. How large these array losses will be depends on the configuration of the wind farm, that is, the positions and distances (in rotor diameters) between the wind turbines.

Park efficiency is defined as the relation between the actual production of a wind power plant in relation to what the production would be without any array losses caused by other turbines [8]. The closer the turbines are sited in relation to each other, the lower the park efficiency. To aim at a park efficiency of 100% is not realistic; it would be bad use of available land. But it should be as high as possible. With the same number of turbines in the same area the park efficiency can be optimized, by following the rules of thumb described above, but also by finetuning the position of turbines and checking the park efficiency by calculations using wind power software.

Looking at costs, a loss of 10% of production – a park efficiency of 90% – can be compensated by breaking up the necessary investment for access roads, grid connection, cranes, and so on, on more capacity. However, the wind wakes that reduce output will also increase wear and tear on the turbines, since they will be exposed to more turbulence from the wind wakes of neighboring turbines. To install wind turbines too close to each other is bad practice, to optimize the technical lifetime of the wind turbines should also be included in the cost-efficiency calculation. A park efficiency of 90% may be acceptable, but it is likely more cost-efficient to keep the park efficiency in the region up to 90% or higher.

2.13.6.4.2 Conflicting projects

A delicate situation occurs when several project developers operate in the same area. If a new wind power plant is installed in front of existing wind turbines, especially if it is in the prevalent wind direction, it will reduce the power output of the existing wind power plant. How much depends on the distance. This is, however, a question for the planning authorities. A distance of 15 rotor diameters or more is recommended in such cases. Often, there are planning regulations that set a minimum distance, usually a number of kilometers, between wind power plants.

The capacity of the grid is another sensitive question. There is always a limit to how much power that can be fed into the grid. If too much capacity is connected, the wind turbines have to be cut out from the grid when they all produce at full power. This is a lose–lose situation that should be avoided. It is up to the grid operator to regulate how much power that can be connected, and if the capacity already connected is close to this limit, it is often better to look for another site.

With several projects in the planning stage, and a limited grid capacity, it is important that the grid operator has clear and transparent rules for which projects that will get the right to connect wind power plants to the grid.

2.13.7 Estimation of Power Production

To calculate how much a wind turbine will produce at a given site, two things have to be known:

1. The power curve of the wind turbine(s).
2. The frequency distribution of the wind speed at hub height at the site.

The power curve shows how much power the turbine will produce at different wind speeds. It is shown as a table, graph, or as a bar chart, and is available from the manufacturers. These power curves are verified by independent and authorized control agencies. The power curves are, however, valid only under specified conditions, in an open landscape. If turbulence is too high or the wind gradient exponent too big, production will be reduced. There is a risk for this, especially in forest areas or close to forest edges [13].

It is necessary to have detailed information about the winds at the site. It is not sufficient to know the annual average wind speed. It is also necessary to know the frequency distribution of the wind speeds, that is, how many hours a year the wind speed will be 1, 2, 3, ... 30 m s^{-1}. These data should represent the wind speed distribution during a normal year, that is, average values for a 5- to 10-year period. The data also have to be recalculated to the hub height of the turbines. Then the power produced at each wind speed is multiplied with the number of hours this wind speed occurs. There will, however, always be some losses. The wind turbines have to be stopped for regular service, some power is needed to operate the turbines, and there are losses in cables, transformers, and so on.

2.13.7.1 Long-Term Wind Climate

Most wind turbines are certified for a technical life of 20 years. From the data collected by wind measurements, the wind speed and the frequency distribution during the coming 20 years have to be estimated. This prognosis has to be based on solid assumptions.

If the wind is measured very accurately for 12 months, the only thing we know for sure is the wind's characteristics during this specific period. What conclusions can be drawn from these facts about the wind's power density in coming years?

2.13.7.1.1 Annual variations

The wind speed, frequency distribution, and averages vary significantly in different years. Also long-term averages for 5- and 10-year periods can vary a lot. How the power density at a site will vary in the long term is important to know if the power of wind is going to be utilized. The longer the period that are compared, the less will the variation be, which is reasonable from a statistical point of view. However, today when climate change no longer is just a threat but a fact, the uncertainty of prognoses for future winds has increased. The power in the wind, energy content, or power density can vary by as much as 30% in different 10-year periods (see **Figure 11**).

To get good background data for a prognosis, measured data for a much longer period than 1 year is necessary. It is, however, no sensible strategy to measure the wind for 5–10 years before a decision to develop a wind farm is taken. In most cases, the long-term average wind speed will not differ more than 10% from a single year, in 90% of the case (90% confidence interval). In Europe, the standard deviation of the long-term wind speed is about 6% [7]. The power density, that is the available wind energy, will however differ much more, since the power in the wind is proportional to the cube of the wind speed.

Wind data from a site that have been logged for a shorter period have to be adapted to a so-called normal wind year that is an average for a period of 5–10 years, before it can be used to calculate the power density at the site and the energy production of a wind power plant.

2.13.7.2 Wind Data

The mean wind speed at the site is a first criterion for the evaluation of a site. However, to calculate the power density and energy content of the wind at a site, it is not only sufficient to know only the mean wind speed but it is also necessary to know all the different wind speeds that occur and their duration; the frequency distribution of the wind speeds has to be found. The turbulence intensity is also necessary to know.

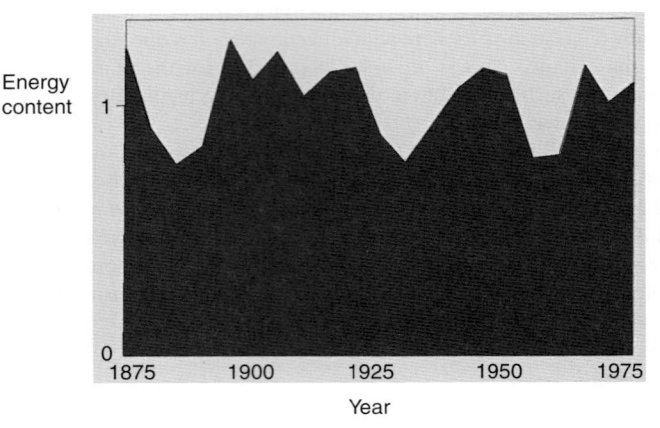

Figure 11 The energy content in the wind during 5-year periods in Denmark. This diagram shows how the energy content of the wind has varied during the 5-year periods from 1875 till 1975 at Hesselö in Denmark, compared to the average for the whole 100-year period. Source: European Wind Atlas, Risö, Denmark.

2.13.7.2.1 Frequency distribution

Data on wind speeds are sorted into a bin diagram, with wind speed on the *x*-axis and the duration (in hours or percent) on the *y*-axis (see **Figure 12**).

The power density of the wind (energy content) at two different sites with exactly the same mean wind speed can differ considerably. This is due to differences in the frequency distribution of the wind (see **Figure 13**).

A 1 MW turbine with a nominal wind speed of 14 m s^{-1}, installed at a site with an average wind speed of 6.2 m s^{-1}, will produce around 10% more when the shape parameter $k = 1.5$ than for $k = 2.5$, although the average wind speed is the same.

2.13.7.2.2 Wind speed and height

As a general rule, wind speed will increase with height. How large this increase will be depends on the roughness of the terrain. In areas with high roughness, the wind speed will increase more with height than over a smooth terrain. But the wind speed at a specific height, for example, 50 m above ground level (agl), will always be higher in an area with low roughness, if all other factors are equal.

For wind turbines it is the wind speed at hub height that is of interest. This height varies for different models and manufacturers. Available wind data often represent a different height than the hub height. It is, however, not very difficult to recalculate these data for other heights.

If the average wind speed at a height (h_o) is known and the wind speed at hub height (h) has to be found, the following relation can be used:

$$\frac{v}{v_o} = \left(\frac{h}{h_o}\right)^\alpha$$

where v_o is the known wind speed at the height h_o and v is the wind speed at the height h. The value of the exponent α depends on the roughness of the terrain and on general geographic conditions. These are based on the wind atlas for Denmark.

Roughness class 0 (open water): $\alpha = 0.1$.
Roughness class 1 (open plain): $\alpha = 0.15$.

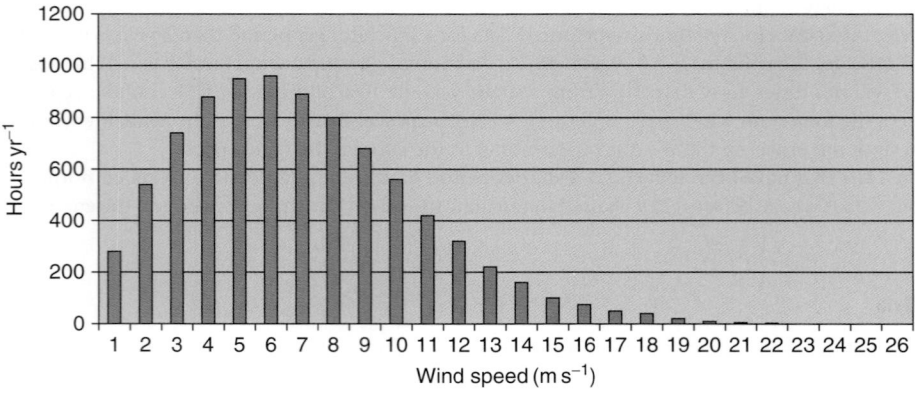

Figure 12 Frequency distribution of wind speeds. A frequency distribution of wind speeds can look like this. The most common wind speeds are 5–6 ms^{-1}. During 950 hours a year, 11% of the time, the wind speed is 6 ms^{-1}.

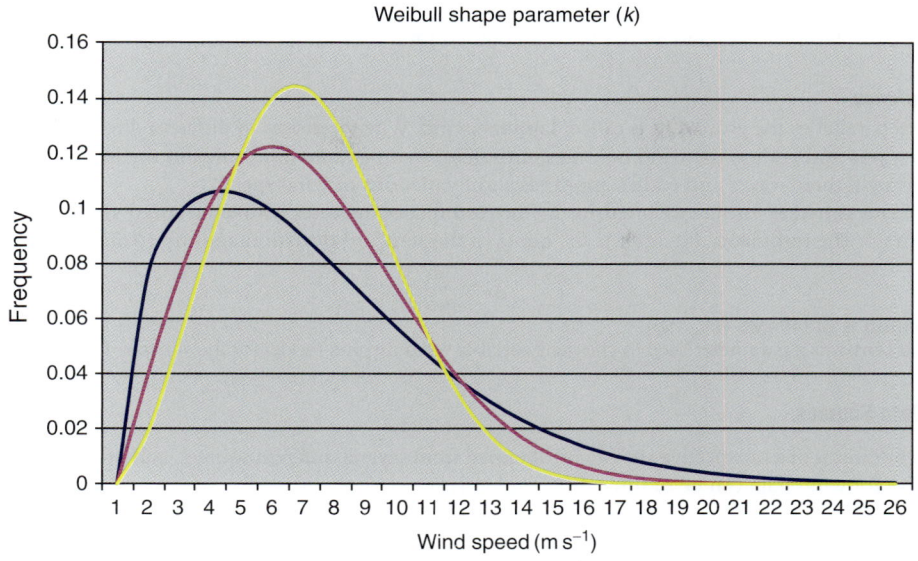

Figure 13 In this diagram the scale parameter A is 7, and the average wind speed 6.2 ms^{-1}. The shape parameters are 1.5 (lowest), 2.0 (middle), and 2.5 (highest).

Roughness class 2 (countryside with farms): $\alpha = 0.2$.
Roughness class 3 (villages and low forest): $\alpha = 0.3$.

With the wind speeds at two different heights known, the wind gradient exponent (also called 'Hellman Exponent') can be calculated by:

$$\alpha = \frac{\log\left(\dfrac{v}{v_o}\right)}{\log\left(\dfrac{h}{h_o}\right)}$$

It important to be aware that there is a high possibility of inaccuracy using this simple power law equation, especially in a complex terrain.

The so-called wind profile varies with the roughness of the terrain (see Section 2.13.8.1.1). The smoother the surface of the ground is, the higher is the wind speed, if the geostrophic wind (undisturbed by friction against the earth surface) is the same (see **Figure 14**).

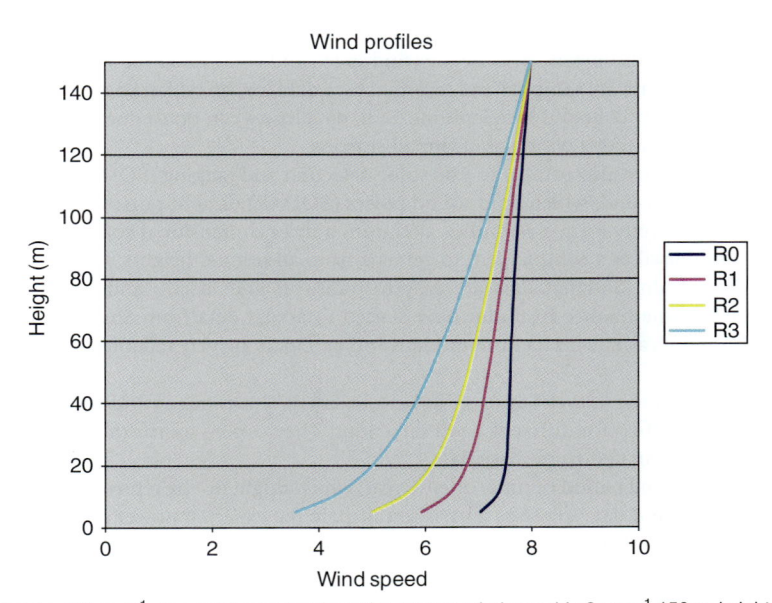

Figure 14 Wind speed and height at 8 m s^{-1}. In a wind climate where the average wind speed is 8 m s^{-1} 150 m height above ground level (agl), the wind speed at hub height (30–80 m agl) will be higher when roughness is low. At 60 m agl, the wind speeds will be 6.4 (R3), 7.0 (R2), 7.3 (R1), and 7.6 (R0) (from left to right).

When an area is covered by forest, the wind profiles do not start at the ground level, but at ¾ of the height of the trees. This distance is called the displacement height and has to be accounted for in this kind of terrain.

2.13.7.2.3 Turbulence

When the air moves parallel to the ground, it is called 'laminar' wind. When it moves in different directions around the prevailing wind direction, in waves and eddies, the wind becomes 'turbulent'. Temperature differences in the air can also create turbulence. When wind is measured, these waves and eddies appear as short variations of wind speed.

The turbulence is measured as turbulence intensity, I. Since turbulence increases with wind speed, the speed has to be annotated as well, I_{15} for 15 m s^{-1}. The turbulence intensity is the quota of the standard deviation and the 10 min average wind speed [8].

$$I_u = \frac{\sigma}{u_{ave}}$$

The standard deviation is the RNMS [$u_{ave} - u_n$].

The turbulence intensity is a parameter used to choose a suitable wind turbine model for the site (see **Table 3** in Section 2.13.9.3.2).

2.13.7.3 Wind Data Sources

The data on wind conditions at a prospective site can be obtained from several different sources, and preferably from a combination of them. The sources for wind data can be of three different kinds:

- Historical meteorological data
- Onsite measurement data
- Data from meteorological modeling.

2.13.7.3.1 Historical meteorological data

National meteorological institutes have collected data on winds for many decades and have a lot of wind data in their archives. Wind measurements have been made on many different locations, so there is a wide geographical spread of data. There are very long time series of wind data. However, these data are rarely from representative sites, since the main interest in the wind conditions have been at sea, harbors, and airports. The standard height for measurements, 10 m agl, is also quite low. However, these archived data are very valuable for reference and for the calculation of long-term wind conditions. The basic data are usually public and free of charge; for special data treatment and time series; there can be charges.

2.13.7.3.2 Onsite measurement data

A wind measurement mast at the prospective site will collect the most accurate data on wind conditions. Ideally, the measurement mast should have the same height as the hub height of the wind turbine(s). Since the cost increases with height, this may be prohibitive for smaller projects. The measured data can in such case be recalculated to hub height. The best data will be collected at the top of the mast, since the mast itself affects the wind. The wind should, however, be measured at two or more different heights to make it possible to calculate the wind gradient exponent.

There are many good wind measurement masts with equipment to collect wind data for wind power plants available, which are quite easy to install at the site. Cup anemometers measure the wind speed and wind vanes the wind direction. Also temperature and air pressure should be recorded. The data are sampled and recorded by a data logger, which has to be very robust and well insulated from the rain. The data can be remotely collected by telephone. Still, data losses can occur due to power failures and water ingress. Measurement data should cover 1 year to get wind data from all seasons.

Lately, other types of equipment have also come into use; sonic detection and ranging (SODAR) and light detection and ranging (LIDAR). These are installed on the ground, which send sound pulses (SODAR) or light pulses (LIDAR) up into the air. A Sodar or Lidar can get measurement data not only form a point but also from a three-dimensional space. Sodars/Lidars have not replaced measurement masts, but are often used as a complement to get data from additional heights, nearby sites in an area, or to get data on the turbulence in complex terrain. Sodars/Lidars are easy to transport and install, and less expensive to use than a high measurement mast. From 2010, some finance institutes have started to accept data from Sodars and Lidars as good enough for making projects bankable. This is logical, since data from modern Sodars/Lidars are very reliable, and probably even better than data from wind measurement masts [14].

From these measurement data, all the relevant factors can be calculated. The average wind speed, the frequency distribution of the wind, and these can also be specified for different wind directions. They can be transformed to different heights and also the turbulence intensity can easily be calculated from these data.

Since all the data cover only a limited period of time, often 1 year, which might not be representative for an average year, the data have to be correlated to long-term wind data to use as a basis to calculate the expected power production of a wind power plant at the site. Such long-term corrected data should be used for all calculations, including turbulence, and so on.

2.13.7.3.3 Data from meteorological modeling

On most sites, it is possible to calculate the power density and energy content of the wind without using measuring equipment at the specific site. Instead, the wind data from measuring masts at other sites, within 10–50 km distance from the site to be developed, can be used. These data come from the measuring mast used in the meteorological agencies, which also have historical long-term data. These wind data can be recalculated to represent the wind climate at the site where wind turbines will be installed. These calculations are made with the so-called wind atlas method [3], which is described in Section 2.13.8.1.

There are also the so-called mesoscale models available, but these are very complicated and are handled by specialists. These models are mainly used to create wind resource maps for countries or regions, but can also be used with higher resolution for specific sites. Mesoscale and wind atlas models can also be combined, as in the so-called KAMM–WAsP model [15].

2.13.7.3.4 Long-term correlation

The winds can differ much from year to year and the measurement period could have been exceptionally windy or calm. To find out if the data collected during 1 year are representative for an average year; these 1-year data have to be compared to long-term wind data. To do this, it is necessary to have a reference site, at a site with the same wind climate, where the wind has been measured for several years.

The measured wind data have to be compared with corresponding data from the same measurement period in the same region, where long-term data are also available. Then, it can be checked how representative the data from the measurement period are, compared to the long-term data from this second measuring mast. The national meteorological institutes have collected wind data for decades from a large number of meteorological stations in different parts of their countries. Finally, the collected wind data can be adjusted so that they will correspond to a normal year; the long-time average.

If the wind speed is measured with a wind measurement mast at a site during a shorter period, for example, during 6–12 months, the wind energy during a normal year can be calculated by using wind data from a close measuring mast with long-term data available, if there is a correlation between the wind at the two sites.

Usually, these data are available from an official meteorological station in the same region. If not, there may be useful satellite data available, from NCEP/NCAR [16], where wind data sets from 1948 up to now in a 2.5 degree longitude/latitude grid. There are several ways to correlate measured data to predict the wind for a coming period of years. These so-called measure–correlate–predict (MCP) methods can be used for long-time correlation:

- Comparing the wind speed factors
- Linear regression
- Matching Weibull parameters.

The first method is quite simple. The average wind speed for the site is compared to the average wind speed at the reference site for the same time period. Then the long-term average wind speed at the reference site is found, and the quota of the long-term and measurement period mean wind speed is multiplied with the measured mean wind speed at the site [17].

Linear regression fits the measured data to the long-term data with a graph, parameters can then be fine-tuned to get a better fit. To use this method, software that can compare the time series is necessary [17].

Matching Weibull parameters is an empirical method, which manipulates the Weibull form and scale parameters and thus also the frequency distribution. On locations with a bad Weibull fit, this method should be used with caution [17].

2.13.8 Planning Tools

When it comes to actual planning, there are many very good tools available, which makes work easier. These software are basically geographical information systems (GISs), with many special features developed for wind power project development. These tools perform all the calculations needed.

2.13.8.1 The Wind Atlas Method

On most sites, it is possible to calculate the power density and energy content of the wind without using measuring equipment at the specific site. Instead, the wind data from an existing measuring mast, with long-term data, can be recalculated to represent the site with the so-called wind atlas method [3].

The wind atlas method was developed in the 1980s by researchers from Risoe in Denmark. The scientists made careful measurements of how the wind was influenced by different kinds of terrain, hills, and obstacles. From these empirical data, they developed models and algorithms to describe the influence of the terrain, hills, and different kinds of obstacles.

These algorithms were then entered into a computer program, WAsP, that can be utilized to calculate the energy content at a given site by using long-term wind data from an existing wind measuring mast and with information that describes obstacles, height contours, and the roughness of the terrain within a radius of 20 km from the site where the wind turbine will be installed.

A wind atlas program works in two steps. The first step is to convert normal long-term (5–10 years) wind data (wind speed and direction) from a regular wind measurement mast to the so-called wind atlas data. The wind data from the measuring masts are normalized to a common format, so that data from different masts are comparable and can be used by the program.

Wind measurement masts often stand close to buildings and are surrounded by different types of terrain and often also by hills and mountains. The program can 'delete' the influence from obstacles, orography (height contours), and terrain (roughness), so that the measured wind data are converted to what they would be if the terrain had been plain (roughness class 1) without any hills or obstacles, at 10 m agl.

The first set of wind atlas data consists of the frequency distribution of the wind in 12 sectors (N, NNW, WNW, etc.) 10 m agl in roughness class 1. These data are then recalculated to other heights: 25, 50, 100, and 200 m. Together, these data describe the regional wind climate in an area with a radius of approximately 20–100 km (the size of the area depends on local conditions) where the geostrophic winds, that is, winds unaffected by friction against the ground, are the same.

The second step is to calculate the energy content of the wind and how much a specific wind turbine can be expected to produce at a given site. The same procedure is followed, but the other way around. Within a reasonable distance from the measuring mast, which has been used to process the wind atlas data, the properties of the winds at 200 m height should be the same.

By entering data about the roughness of the terrain within 20 km radius from the site, data about hills and obstacles, and data about the wind turbine (hub height, rotor swept area, and power curve that describes how much the turbine will produce at different wind speeds), the program calculates the frequency distribution of the wind at hub height. Finally, the program calculates how much the wind turbine can produce at that site during a normal (average) wind year (see **Figure 15**).

There are several different computer software for wind power applications that are based on the wind atlas method. WAsP has been developed by Risoe National Laboratory in Denmark and is the basis for all wind atlas programs [18]. It can be used to make wind resource maps, wind atlases for whole countries, as well as production calculations for single wind turbines or large wind power plants.

The program WindPRO can do the same calculations as WAsP and has additional modules for noise, shadow and visual impact, planning tools, and many other functions, as well as a comprehensive database with wind turbine models and wind atlas data for regions and countries. It has been developed by Energi og Miljödata in Denmark [19].

The program WindFarm that has been developed in the United Kingdom by the company ReSoft [20], and WindFarmer from GL Garrad Hassan [21], can do all the calculations necessary for project development, including optimization and visualizations. There

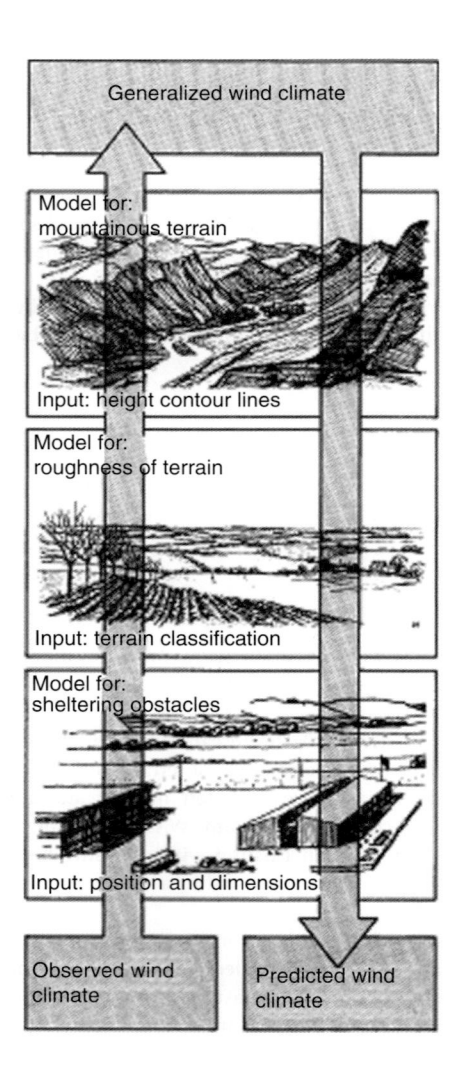

Figure 15 Wind Atlas Method.

is also a freeware called RETScreen that can be found on a website developed by CANMET Energy Technology Centre in Canada, with education, databases, and software for different renewable energy sources [22].

All of these programs are easy to work with and give reliable results, if the operator understands them and is an experienced user. They can be used to calculate how much a wind turbine of a specific brand/model can produce at a given site, as well as the sound propagation, park efficiency, and visual impact. It is also possible to create wind resource maps with some of these programs.

In complex terrain and where available data are unreliable (in mountain areas, large lakes, and at sea), this method cannot be applied and it is necessary to make on site wind measurements. For large projects, banks and other financing institutions will also demand wind data from a meteorological mast installed at the site.

In many countries, the state-owned meteorological institute has prepared wind atlas data for some hundreds of measurement masts in different parts of the country. Wind atlases with wind atlas data are available for most countries in Europe and for many countries on other continents as well. Many of them are available on the Internet [23].

2.13.8.1.1 Roughness of terrain

The wind is retarded by friction against the ground surface. How much depends on the character of the terrain where the wind turbine will be sited and in the surrounding landscape. To calculate how much energy a wind turbine at a specific site can be expected to produce, wind data from one or several measuring masts within a reasonable distance from the site are used. These data (giving mean wind speed and frequency distribution for an average year) have to be adapted to the specific conditions at the chosen site; the roughness of the terrain. The roughness in classified into five different classes (see **Table 1**).

How much a wind turbine can produce depends not only on the character of the terrain at the site but is also influenced by the terrain in a large area. The terrain conditions close to the site have the greatest impact on the turbine's production. The roughness usually varies in different sectors and thus also with the wind direction. In calculations, an area with 20 km radius around the turbine site is divided into 12 sectors, 30 degrees each, with the wind turbine in the center. A roughness classification is then done sector by sector or by setting roughness values to areas of different character directly on a map.

The classification of the area close to the site should always be made in the field, since maps do not give an exact picture of reality; symbols for buildings, roads, and so on, are larger/wider than they actually are to make them visible on the map. Significant changes could also have occurred since the map was drawn (new buildings, roads, etc,). For distances more than 1000 m, the classification can be made at the desk on a map or directly in the software (see **Figure 16**).

2.13.8.1.2 Hills and obstacles

If a wind turbine is sited on the top of a hill or on a slope, this could increase its power production.

The speedup effect from hills has most impact at lower heights above the hilltop. The height of this effect increases with the size of the hill (see **Figure 17**). Steep slopes, however, can have the opposite effect; if the inclination is larger than ~25 degrees, the slope can create turbulence that will decrease production. If the surface is rough or complex, this could happen with inclinations of 10–20%, and if the slope is covered by trees or forest, there will be no hilltop effect if the slope is >5 degrees. A wind atlas program will calculate the impact of hills and obstacles on the production. In a complex terrain, it is always necessary to make wind measurements on site, not only to get correct wind data but also to measure the turbulence.

Buildings and other obstacles close to a wind turbine (<1000 m) affect the wind that the turbine will use. How much an obstacle affects the production depends on the height, width, and distance from the turbine and its character (porosity). Buildings and other obstacles that are situated 1000 m from the site or more shall not be classified as obstacles, but as elements in the roughness classification.

Table 1 Roughness classes

Roughness class	Character	Terrain	Obstacles	Farms	Buildings	Forest
0	Sea, lakes	Open water	–	–	–	–
1	Open landscape, with sparse vegetation and buildings	Plain to smooth hills	Only low vegetation	0–3 km^{-2}	–	–
2	Countryside with a mix of open areas, vegetation, and buildings	Plain to hilly	Small woods, alleys are common	Up to 10 km^{-2}	Some villages and small towns	–
3	Small towns or countryside with many farms woods and obstacles	Plain to hilly	Many woods, vegetation, and alleys	Many farms >10 km^{-2}	Many villages, small towns, or suburbs	Low forest
4	Large cities or high forest	Plain to hilly	–	–	Large cities	High forest

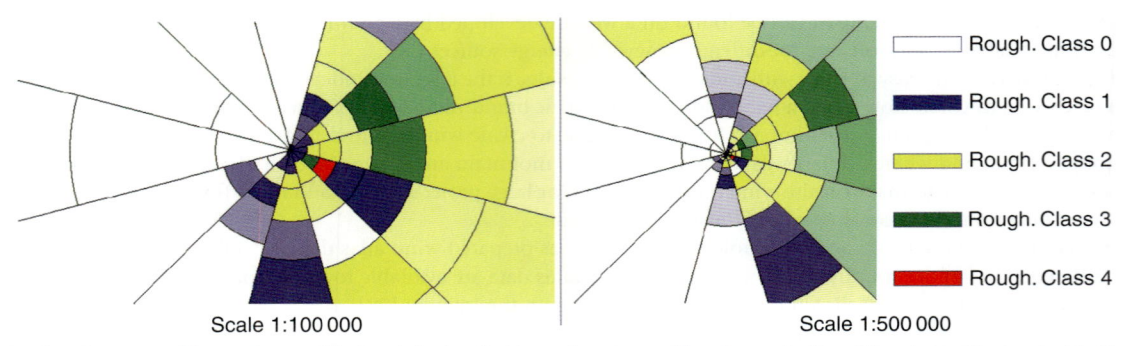

Figure 16 Roughness rose. The roughness of the terrain is classified for each sector, and then the production of the wind turbine is calculated for each of these sectors. Reproduced from WindPRO2.

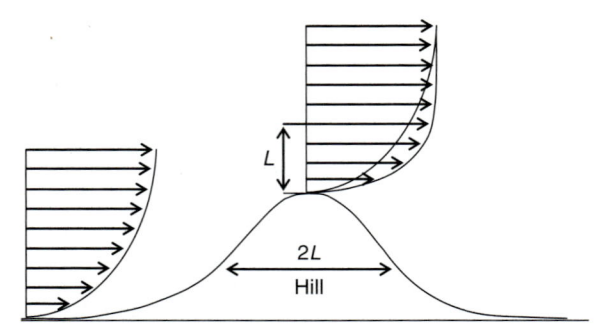

Figure 17 Increase of wind speed on hills. When wind is passing over a smooth hill, wind speed will increase to the hilltop. To get this effect, the inclination of the hill should be less than 40°, and if the hillside is uneven and rough, or covered with trees, The wind flow can be disturbed at inclinations of even 5°. On the leeside of a hill, the wind speed will decrease. The wind can accelerate around the sides of hill in a similar way. The marked area of the wind profile (to the right) shows the increase compared to the wind profile in front of the hill (to the left). (Illustration: S. Piva after Troen (1989)).

If there are large obstacles close to the turbine, the production will be affected. For large wind turbines, the impact from obstacles is comparatively small, since the impact depends on the difference between the turbine's hub height and the height of the obstacle. The turbulence from an obstacle will spread to twice the obstacles height (see **Figure 18**). The rotor of a turbine with 80 m hub height and a 80 m rotor diameter has its lowest point 40 m agl, which means that an obstacle has to be more than 20 m high to cause turbulence within the rotor swept area.

Information on obstacles (within 1000 m from the site), hills, and if the terrain is complex with height contour lines are entered into the program. The wind speed will change each time the roughness of the terrain changes. The wind atlas program recalculates wind atlas data to wind data at hub height for each sector. This is illustrated by an energy rose, which is used as a basis for the layout of the wind farm.

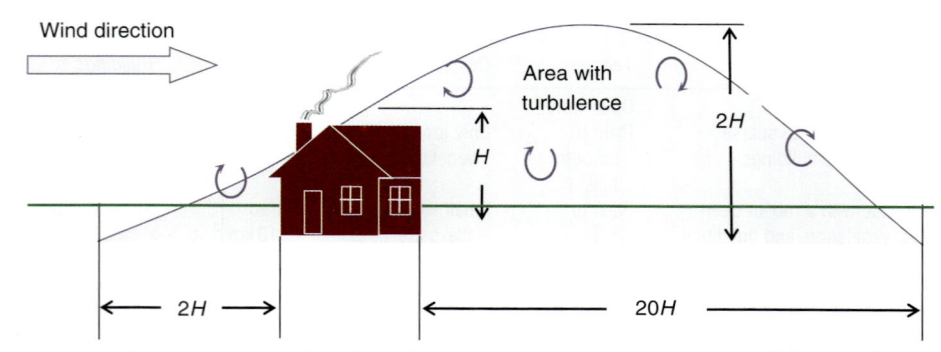

Figure 18 Turbulence from obstacles close to an obstacle the turbulence will increase and the wind speed will decrease. The turbulence is spread not only further on the leeside of an obstacle, but also on the side where the wind comes from turbulence will appear, since the obstacle interferes with the airflow. The areas with turbulence will of course vary with the wind direction. Illustration: S. Piva after Gipe.

2.13.8.1.3 Fingerprint of the wind

The energy rose is the fingerprint of the wind, at a specific height. When a wind atlas calculation is made, it will produce tables and diagrams where the energy produced by the wind turbines at the site is specified for wind directions and wind speeds. These calculations are made before the wind turbines are installed, and by analyzing the energy rose and other data from these calculations, the configuration of the wind power plant can be optimized by moving the turbines around until the best results are achieved. In different countries and regions, these fingerprints differ, as these two examples from the west coast of Sweden and Sri Lanka, respectively (see **Figures 19** and **20**).

At the west coast of Sri Lanka, with a monsoon climate, the corresponding diagrams look quite different.

2.13.8.1.4 Wind atlas calculation

First, the input for the project, maps, and height contours for the area are loaded. Then roughness is defined and wind turbines are entered on the map. Often, meteorological data are available in a database, as well as wind turbine models. This wind atlas software then calculates the estimated production of the wind turbines and park efficiency, and there are even tools that can find the most efficient configuration that will optimize the production of a specified number of turbines within a limited area. There are also modules that calculate noise levels in noise-sensitive areas, and shadow flicker.

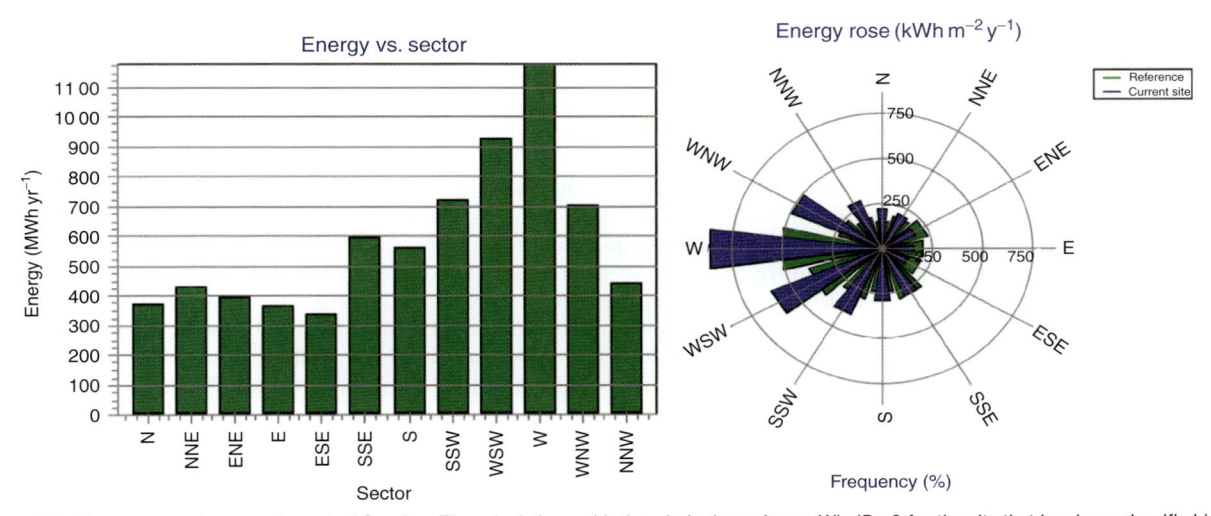

Figure 19 Energy vs. sector – west coast of Sweden. The calculations with the wind atlas software WindPro2 for the site that has been classified in *Figure 12*, on the west coast of Sweden, shows how much energy that is produced by the wind turbine from different wind directions – sectors.

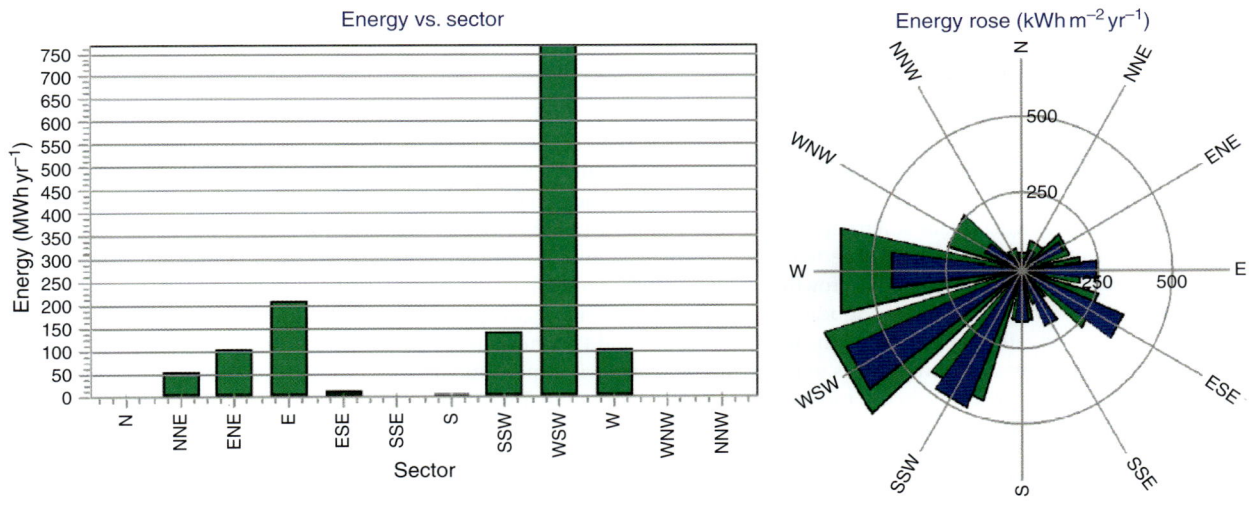

Figure 20 Energy vs. sector – west coast of Sri Lanka. In Sri Lanka, with a monsoon climate and trade winds, the energy rose shows that almost all energy is produced by winds in the sector SSW–W.

The wind atlas program first calculates the wind's frequency distribution at hub height for each sector, and then multiplies the frequency distributions with the wind turbines power curve. The results are weighted according to the frequency for each wind direction and finally summarized.

If the terrain is not extremely complex, this method gives very accurate results. It takes, however, quite long practice and experience on how different kinds of terrain in a region should be classified, as well as experience on how far from the measurement mast the wind atlas data still are representative, to make accurate calculations with this method.

If there are other wind turbines on line in the area, the production of these can be entered as a reference in the calculation. If these turbines have been in operation for a couple of years, and their average production is known, these figures can be entered in the program. Then a calculation is made with the software, and the results can be compared. If the actual production is the same as that calculated, then the calculation for the turbines in the project should also be correct. If not, the quota of actual/calculated production can be multiplied with the calculated production of the new turbine to make it more accurate.

If a wind measurement mast, a Sodar, or a Lidar at the site has collected the wind data (see Section 2.13.7.2), these data can also be entered into the software. Such onsite data will give the best estimation of the power production. With these kind of data, and after adjusting them to long-term wind data, a local wind resource map can be created, which shows how the wind will vary within the siting area, depending on the character of the local terrain, heights, and obstacles.

2.13.8.1.5 Sources of error

The accuracy of the calculation depends of course on the quality of the data that are entered into the program. Wind atlas data are based on measured data from different periods. Which sequence of years the data are based on is indicated in the database and can vary for different measuring masts. These periods can be too short or not be representative for the long-time averages. The wind data, as well as the transformation of these to wind atlas data, can be impaired by faults, due to technical faults of the measuring equipment, and so on, or systematic errors when the data were registered. There is a certain amount of rounding when data are transformed to Weibull parameters that are used in the software.

The roughness classification is never absolutely correct, and the roughness can change during the seasons and the lifetime of the turbine. The power curve of the turbine is a third source of error. The form of the power curve depends on the conditions when it was measured, and does not give an exact relation between wind speed and power. In a different surrounding with other terrain and wind regime, it may differ somewhat from the certified one. Special care should be taken in areas with tree cover and forests.

These and other factors are considered to create an error margin of 10% in the calculations, an estimation that has been confirmed by experience. The uncertainty with the wind resource estimation can be either too low or too high, from a statistical point of view. However, most of these factors are only on the negative side, caused by losses in the internal grid, the turbines own power consumption, and so on. Therefore, 10% should always be subtracted from the result of the calculation.

2.13.8.1.6 Loss and uncertainty

Instead of using the default reduction of 10%, losses and uncertainties can be calculated more in detail with wind atlas software. Seven different loss categories, with some subcategories, have been defined and agreed on [24]. These are wake effects, availability, turbine performance, electrical, environmental, curtailment, and others. The starting point is the gross annual production, AEP, without any losses and also the array losses excluded. From this the losses are deducted to get an estimate of the actual power production.

The loss category wake effects has two subcategories; wake effects all wind turbines (park efficiency, array losses) and future wake effects, that is, impacts from wind turbines planned but not yet built.

Availability has four subcategories; turbine (losses due to maintenance, etc.), balance of plant (faults in internal grid up to the substation), grid, and others.

Turbine performance has four subcategories; power curve, high-wind hysteresis (losses due to shutdown between cut out and subsequent restart), wind flow (turbulence, high wind shear, etc.), and others.

The loss category electrical has two subcategories; losses (up to the interface to external grid) and facility consumption (reductions of sold energy due to consumption for operation of plant, behind the meter).

The loss category environmental has six subcategories defining impacts on power production from climate and nature. Performance degradation not due to icing (blade soiling and degradation) and due to icing (reduced aerodynamic efficiency of blades), shutdowns (due to icing, lightning, hail, etc.), extreme temperatures (outside turbine's operating range), site access (due to remote location, weather, or force majeure events), and the growth or cutting down of trees in nearby forests (that will reduce or increase production).

The curtailment category has seven subcategories; wind sector management (commanded shutdowns to reduce loads), grid curtailment and ramp rate (due to limitations in external grid), and PPA curtailment (when power purchaser does not take power from the plant). There are also curtailments to reduce impacts on environment and neighbors, for noise, shadow flicker, birds, and bats. Finally, there is a category, other, for losses not accounted for in the first six categories.

2.13.8.2 Wind Measurements

Even if the wind atlas calculations give accurate results, when the assumptions for the calculations are valid, it is often necessary to also get wind data from a meteorological mast installed at the site, with one full year of data. This is often a demand from financing institutions, and prospective buyers of the wind power plant. For some sites, far from weather stations or in a complex terrain, there is no other way to get reliable data.

To get correct and detailed information about the power density and energy content of the wind at a specific site, a wind measurement mast can be installed. Anemometers mounted at different heights register the wind speeds and the wind directions by wind vanes. A so-called data logger collects the wind data. With these data, the average wind speed, the frequency distribution, power density, energy content, distribution of wind directions, wind profile, and turbulence intensity for the measurement period can be calculated. The ideal is to measure the wind at the hub height of the turbines to be installed, but it is easy to recalculate wind data to other heights. Instead of a meteorological mast, a Sodar or Lidar can be used. Such measuring instruments are far cheaper and give accurate results, with high resolution.

The precondition for accurate results is, however, always that the measuring equipment works according to specifications. The anemometers have to be calibrated, and installed correctly on the mast. During actual measurement, weather conditions can affect the results, especially snow and ice.

The insecurities involved in the measured data can be estimated with statistical methods.

Before wind measurement starts, it is important to make sure that the financiers will accept the wind measurement methods that will be used.

2.13.8.3 Pitfalls

Evaluations of wind turbine sites, analysis of wind data, wind power plant configurations, and calculations of estimated production are usually based on general standard assumptions. There are, however, sites where these assumptions do not apply. There are several factors that can upset the prognoses that the investments have been based on. Some of these have been described in the preceding paragraphs, but there are some more. The temperature and climate is one, extreme wind speeds is another, and the impact of trees and forests should also be considered. Wind resource maps should be interpreted critically, and finally, it is important to be aware of the risk to upgrade a wind farm before it is built, without adapting the wind turbine configuration accordingly.

2.13.8.3.1 Extreme temperatures

There are many places in mountainous areas and in arctic regions with very good wind resources. In some areas, there are also wind turbines installed, in the United States and in northern Scandinavia. The arctic climate conditions put some special demands on the wind turbines. Ordinary standard turbines would not survive for a long time, but they can be adapted to the strains that the climate will cause; special steel for towers, special oils for low temperature, heating systems for rotor blades and anemometers, ice detectors, and other special equipment can be used to increase availability and power production for wind turbines in a cold climate.

Extreme heat seems to be less of a problem, since most turbines have cooling systems installed. In a tropical climate, the humidity in the air can also be very high, and may make it necessary to install extra equipment for air conditioning inside the hub and where the control system is installed.

2.13.8.3.2 Extreme wind speeds

Most wind turbines are designed to survive extreme wind speeds of at least $60\,\mathrm{m\,s^{-1}}$, but only for a few seconds of time, that is, extreme gusts. For sites where the wind speeds can get higher than that, turbines can be designed for that as well. This will of course also increase the cost of the turbines. Several severe storms, hurricanes, and typhoons have passed over areas with many wind turbines installed, so the survival ability has been tested in practice.

In Denmark, most of the thousands of turbines installed survived the severe storms that occurred in the beginning of 2005, storms that felled tens of thousands of trees in southern Scandinavia. In India, a large number of turbines, in a wind farm I Gujarat 111 turbines were uprooted by a hurricane in 1998 [25]. In Japan as well, turbines on Miyaki island were felled to the ground by a typhoon. In August 2006, the typhoon Sangmei destroyed the wind farm Changnan Xiaguan with 28 turbines in China [26]. In areas where hurricanes and typhoons are parts of the normal climate, wind turbines should be designed to survive, even if it will make them more expensive. Another option is to avoid such areas to disqualify them in the feasibility study.

2.13.8.3.3 Wind power and forest

To avoid trees and forest has been the first commandment for wind power developers. This has been expressed in term like: Tree cover – Avoid like the plague! The reason is of course that forest has high roughness and retards the wind. Due to this the wind shear will increase, and the wind gradient exponent should not exceed 0.2 over the rotor swept area. Trees and forest edges also create much turbulence, and it is recommended to have a safe distance between wind turbines and forest edges. If the distance is too short, the power curve is not valid; calculations will overestimate the expected production (see **Figure 21**).

The following rules of thumb can be applied near forest edges:

Shear (wind gradient exponent) should not to exceed 0.20.

The height of trees in the vicinity of a wind turbine, from the turbines bottom flange, should not exceed the following limits, where

R is the distance from the turbine to the trees, Hh is the hub height and D is the rotor diameter [13].

For $R \leq 5D$, maximum height of trees: $\mathrm{Hh} - 0.67D$

For $5D < R \leq 10D$, maximum height of trees: $\mathrm{Hh} - 0.67D + 0.17D \times (R/5D - 1)$.

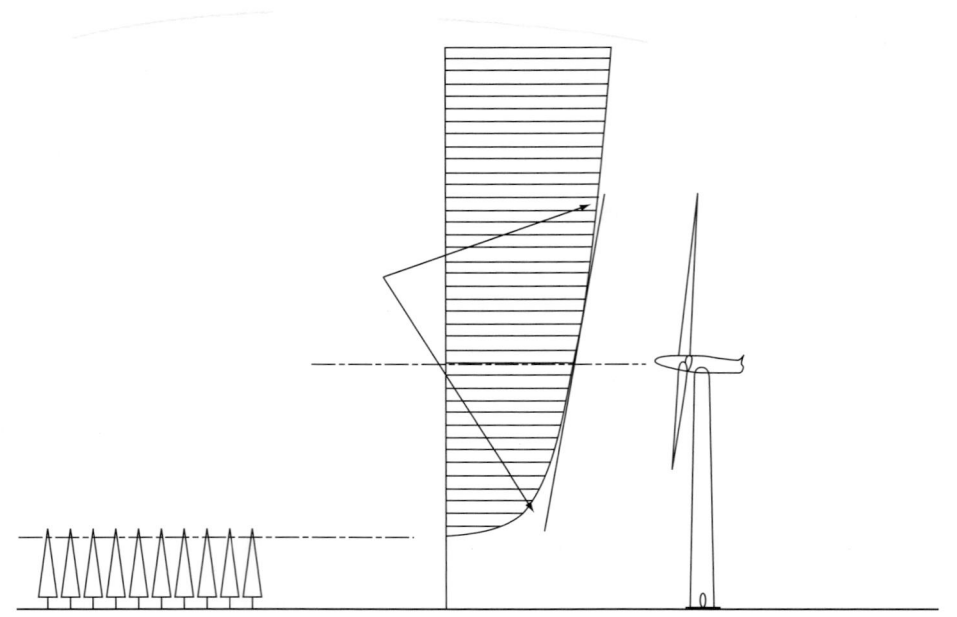

Figure 21 Distance to forest edges. Close to a forest edge the basic assumption that hub height measurement is representative of average wind speed over the rotor disk is not valid. Source: Bonus/Siemens.

If a turbine with a hub height of 60 m and a rotor diameter of 60 m is going to be installed at a site with a forest edge, where the trees are 20 m high (60−0.67 × 60 = 20 m), the distance to the edge should be at least 5 times the rotor diameter, 5 × 60 = 300 m. If the trees are 30 m, the minimum distance should be 588 m; $R = [30 − 60 + (0.67 \times 60) + (0.17 \times 60)](5/0.17)$, to avoid affecting the performance (the power curve) of the turbine. If the distance is given, say 500 m, the option in the second case would be to increase the hub height to 64 m. The first recommendation is thus to have a distance of >10D to forest edges, and if that is not feasible, to increase the distance or the hub height according to these rules.

In Germany and Sweden, wind turbines have been installed inside areas covered by forest. These installations are often made on hills and ridges in the woodlands, which often gives a very high production. On such sites, the turbines are operating high above the surrounding forests, often where the hill height plus the hub height is several hundred meters. Otherwise, there are serious pitfalls when wind turbines are installed in forests. To avoid too high wind shear and turbulence, towers have to be very high; the bottom end of the rotor should be above the so-called roughness sublayer, which ends at 2–3 times the height of the trees. If the trees are 20 m high, the rotor should pass at 60 m height, and the tower has to be some 90 m or even higher [26].

To develop wind power in forest has many drawbacks:

- Higher towers – higher cost
- Same wind speed at hub height – less energy in forest (due to turbulence, etc.)
- High turbulence and shear – more wear and tear – shorter lifetime, higher O&M costs.

Some manufacturers have developed control methods for such sites. One method is sector management, which means that the wind turbines are stopped when the wind comes from directions with too high turbulence, which of course will reduce the potential AEP. To avoid trees like the plague is still the best advice. Wind turbines installed too close to forest edges often produce 20–40% less power than expected. Hills and ridges in woodlands can, however, be very good sites for wind power. This is, however, not always the case, so onsite measurements are compulsory for all sites in forested areas.

2.13.8.3.4 Wind resource maps

Wind resource maps are usually made with meteorological models using high-capacity computers. These mesoscale models are usually very good. However, the input data also have to be correct. In specific type of terrain changes, like coastlines, or mountainous terrain, the reality may be too complex to be well described by a model. They usually cover large areas, like a country. The roughness of the terrain cannot be described in detail, but is taken from sources based on satellite data, or ground coverage maps.

In Sweden, a new wind resource map was published by the Energy Agency in 2007 [27]. According to this new map, the wind resources in a large forest covered region in the southern part of Sweden had very good wind resources. This was a big surprise, since the basic rule of thumb for most developers had been to avoid forest, since high roughness retards the wind and also creates turbulence. But with new heights in reach, with larger turbines, the retarding effect on wind speed by forests seemed to be offset.

This sparsely populated region became an Eldorado for developers, who made land lease contracts for large wind farms. Hundreds of wind turbines would be erected. But first, wind measurement masts were installed. After a year, when the winds had been measured, it turned out that the wind speed was around $1\,m\,s^{-1}$ less than indicated by the map in most of these areas. It turned out that input data for that region had been wrong, with too low roughness. And the wind resource map had to be recalculated.

Wind power developers with a long experience did not join this rush. They knew by their long experience that the wind map was too good to be true. And there were also a few wind turbines on line in the region, with very poor AEP. But many developers spent resources to develop projects that turned out to be almost worthless. So, it is important to have good knowledge and to interpret wind resource maps with a critical mind.

2.13.8.3.5 *Upgrading of wind turbines*

To develop a wind power project often takes a long time, especially the permission process. If permissions are appealed, a developer may have to wait for the permission to start the building phase for many years. During this time, the technical development of wind turbines continues. The wind turbines in the planning stage for a wind power project may not be available on the market when the building phase is about to start. The most cost-efficient turbines have become bigger than the ones the developer has got permission to build, and used for the wind farm configuration.

One example of this process is the offshore wind farm Lillgrund, in Öresund, between Malmö and Copenhagen. The project was started by the company Eurowind AB in 1997. The wind farm was originally planned for 1.5 MW turbines with 66 m rotor diameter. Within the planning area, sites for 48 turbines were identified and applied for. Since this was the first application for permission to build a large offshore wind farm in Sweden, the demands for investigations from the authorities were immense. However, all aspects asked for, impact on fish, flora on sea bottom, on water streaming, on shipping, radar, and many other aspects were thoroughly researched, which took several years. Finally, permission was granted in October 2003.

During this time, the first partner who had planned to finance the project had been involved in other plans, so the whole project was sold to the Swedish state-owned power company Vattenfall in 2004. The turbines the wind farm was planned for had become obsolete. Vattenfall opted for larger turbines and choose 2.3 MW turbines with proven offshore performance from the Danish offshore wind farm at Nysted, rather close by. And finally choose to increase the rotor diameter to 100 m.

New approval was then necessary from the environment court for the change in the original description of the project that had got the permission. However, Vattenfall kept the original layout for the wind farm. Since the layout pattern is governed by the size of turbines, and the distance between turbines in rows and between rows is measured in rotor diameters, this was a radical change of the layout. In the original plan they were following the rules of thumb (described in Section 2.13.6.3) but with larger turbines this was no longer the case. The in-row distance was reduced to 3.3 and the between rows distance to 4.3 rotor diameters (see **Figure 22**) [28].

Figure 22 Lillgrund wind farm layout. In the Lillgrund offshore wind farm, the in-row distance between the turbines is 3.3 rotor diameters, and the between-row distance 4.3 diameters. With such small distances between turbines the park efficiency will be very low. From Dahlberg J-Å (2009) Assessment of the Lillgrund windfarm. Power performance, Wake effects. Vattenfall/Swedish Energy Agency. http://www.vattenfall.com/en/reports-from-the-lillgrund-pr.htm (accessed 1 October 2010).

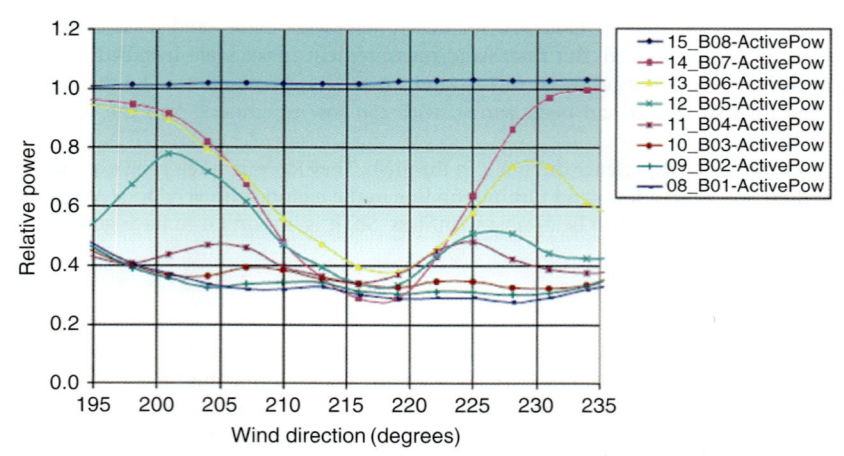

Figure 23 Lillgrund windfarm: Relative power loss for turbines in row B. Relative power for turbines in row B (**Figure 22**) in relation to angle of wind direction. With wind parallel to the row, all turbines behind the first in the row (15) will produce 60–70% less power than from the undisturbed wind. The losses will be similar in the other rows. From Dahlberg J-Å (2009) Assessment of the Lillgrund windfarm. Power performance, Wake effects. Vattenfall/Swedish Energy Agency. http://www.vattenfall.com/en/reports-from-the-lillgrund-pr.htm (accessed 1 October 2010).

This resulted in a very low park efficiency of no more than 77%. When the wind comes parallel to a row (with 4.3 diameter distance), the second turbine will produce 70% less than the first turbine in the row (see **Figure 23**) [28]. With the wind across the wind farm perpendicular to the rows (with 3.3 rotor diameter distance), the turbines in the wake of the first one will produce 80% less [28].

This wind farm would actually produce more power with fewer turbines. When the wind blows across the rows (3.3 rotor diameter distance), production would increase if every second row was cut out and feathered, and the distance between turbines would increase to 6.6 diameters, which could be done by sector management.

Even if it would take the engineers quite some time to rearrange the farm layout, recalculate the dimensions of the foundations, (where design depends on depth), and take a few more months to get permission for a new wind farm configuration, this would be nothing compared to the gains in cost-efficiency for the wind farm. Never use an old layout for new and larger turbines.

2.13.9 Choice of Wind Turbines

After more than 30 years of research and development and practical experience from thousands of wind turbines in operation, the wind power industry can be considered to be mature. There are no bad wind turbines that will break down in a few years, at least not among commercial grid-connected models. There is also a certification system that ensures the quality of the wind turbines. To make an investment in wind power is not more risky than any other investment in a reliable technology.

Many different types of wind turbines have been tested and commercialized during these last decades. The type that has proven most reliable, efficient, and has won the competition in the market is the horizontal axis three-bladed upwind wind turbine. Most wind turbines in commercial operation are of this type.

There is still a wide choice of wind turbines on the market. Most manufacturers market several different models and these models are often available in different versions. This wide choice makes it possible to install wind turbines that are tailored to match the conditions at specific sites.

What type of turbine that shall be used at a site depends on many different factors: the wind resource, the roughness of the terrain, the size of the available area, grid capacity, and the purpose of the project. The price and delivery times of wind turbines are of course also important parameters to consider.

2.13.9.1 Wind Turbine Size

There are wind turbines of several different sizes, where the size is defined by hub height, rotor diameter, and nominal power. Wind turbines can be classified into different size ranges. There are no official criteria for these subranges, but a reasonable classification is 200–500, 500–1000, 1000–2000, and >2000 kW. These sizes correspond to the technical development of wind turbines during the years.

The main parameter for the definition of size is the rotor diameter, or the rotor swept area. The bigger the swept area is, the more wind can be captured and transformed to power. Hub height and nominal power are secondary criteria. The choice of hub height is determined by the surrounding terrain and the nominal power by the wind resources at the site [1]. As the rotor diameter increases, higher hub heights will be necessary. For sites in forested areas, very high towers have been developed, up to 160 m (see **Figure 24**).

Figure 24 High tower in low-wind regime. This was the highest wind turbine tower in 2009; a 160 m high lattice tower for a Führländer wind turbine. It is installed in an area with high roughness in Germany. Photo courtesy: Führländer.

2.13.9.2 Type of Wind Turbines

Within the group of three-bladed upwind horizontal axis wind turbines, there are several different options. Taking the so-called Danish standard concept – stall-regulated rotor with a three-stage gearbox and an asynchronous generator – as the starting point, development has moved to more sophisticated technology. This has increased the efficiency, and also the complexity of wind turbines.

The power output of most wind turbines is now controlled by pitch or active stall by turning the blades of the rotor. The revolution speed of the rotor has become more or less variable to increase efficiency. This has been achieved adopting double-wound generators (two-speed) or by power electronics, which adapts variable voltage and frequency to the requirements of the grid.

Since the middle of the 1990s, gearboxes have been a problematic component. Considering the loads that gearboxes have to manage, it is not too surprising that many of them have had to be retrofitted or changed after a few years of operation. A lot of work has been done to develop the gearboxes as well as the drive train to make it more flexible and durable. There are also models without a gearbox, using a multipole direct drive ring generator. New concepts with a robust one- or two-stage gearbox between the rotor and a slow-running multipole generator have also been developed. However, no one would expect a gearbox of a truck to last forever – to change it after some 10 years would be quite natural. The same can be said about wind turbines, and this future cost can easily be included in the economic calculations. The trend in 2010 is, however, that more manufacturers opt for direct drive turbines [29].

Beside this choice of technology of the wind turbine itself, there is a choice also for towers, where there are tubular steel, concrete, or lattice towers to choose from. This choice will to a large extent depend on the climate and other factors. A lattice tower in northern Scandinavia is no option, since heavy icing in the winter could make it collapse. In tropical countries like India, the lattice towers have an advantage, and since they need regular maintenance, the bolts have to be checked with regular intervals; this is a better option in countries where the cost of labor is low. Lattice towers need less steel and are easier to transport, and the foundations also need less concrete than the gravity foundations for tubular steel towers.

When a developer has a large area for the installation of a wind power plant, there are also different options, not only for the configuration of the individual wind turbines. There is also a choice between a large number of small- or medium-sized wind turbines or fewer and bigger ones. The biggest wind turbines usually utilize the wind resources the best, both when it comes to power production per km^2 of land and for cost-efficiency. This is, however, not always the case for smaller areas, where it may be possible to install several small wind turbines but only a few big ones, so that the first option results in more installed power and higher production. It is always worthwhile to spend time and effort to optimize the configuration of a wind power plant.

The choice between a small and simple turbine and a huge high-tech one depends on the size of the project, the nature of the site, and the conditions in the country. The infrastructure – roads and power grid – is crucial. The most important parameter is the cost-efficiency. At some sites, a small, simple, and robust work-horse of a turbine may be the best choice, while the big high-tech turbines may be the best choice at other sites.

2.13.9.3 Wind Turbines Tailored to Wind Climate

Most manufacturers offer different options of their models. Often two or three different hub heights can be chosen, and there is also a choice between tubular steel, lattice, and precast concrete towers. This choice is mainly a matter of taste, cost, and transportation to the site. The choice of hub height should be based on the character of the terrain. In an open landscape or at the coast, the shortest tower will be sufficient, since the wind speed does not increase very much with height (see Figure 25).

In other kinds of terrain, with many trees, buildings, or close to forest edges, it makes sense and increases cost efficiency to have higher towers. There is a relation between heights and cost; a higher tower is more expensive, so the difference in wind speed has to increase production enough to pay back a higher investment.

2.13.9.3.1 Nominal power versus rotor diameter

Wind power plants can be tailored to the wind conditions at the site. Nowadays, there are wind turbines designed for sites with low-, normal-, and high-average wind speeds. Low-wind turbines have a large rotor diameter in relation to the rated power and have a low rated wind speed (where the wind turbine reaches its rated power). High-wind turbines have a small rotor diameter in relation to the rated power and a high rated wind speed. A measure used for this classification is the relation between the nominal power and the rotor swept area, A, in $kW\,m^{-2}$.

Enercon has the models E-48 and E-53, respectively, with 800 kW nominal power. The E-53 is a low-wind version, and E-48 is better for sites with strong winds. The Indian manufacturer Suzlon has two versions of its 1250 kW turbine, with 64 and 66 m rotor diameter, respectively. General Electric has three versions of its 1500 kW turbine, with 70.5, 77, and 82.5 m rotor diameter. The Vestas model V90, with 90 m rotor diameter, can be ordered with a 2 or 3 MW generator, for low-/normal- and high-wind sites, respectively (see Table 2).

The values of these specific ratings ($kW\,m^{-2}$) are in the range 0.28–0.58 among wind turbines available on the world market. The highest values are for offshore wind power plants. To adapt a wind turbine to the wind conditions at a site, the specific rating should be around 0.3 for average wind speed of $6\,m\,s^{-1}$, 0.4 for $7\,m\,s^{-1}$, and 0.45–0.6 for $8\,m\,s^{-1}$.

2.13.9.3.2 IEC wind classes

There is a system for wind turbine classes established by the International Electrotechnical Commission (IEC) (www.iec.ch). These classes are applied for the standardization and certification of wind turbines. These classes are numbered with class I for the toughest wind conditions and then up to class IV for sites with moderate winds (see Table 3).

Wind turbines are specified for different wind conditions, for example, IEC IIB, which means that the turbine may be used at a site with a mean wind speed $<8.5\,m\,s^{-1}$, and where the turbulence intensity is <0.16 at a wind speed of $15\,m\,s^{-1}$. The turbulence varies with wind speed, so the wind speed has to be specified. Turbulence is measured in 10 min averages.

The basic parameter used for defining IEC wind turbine classes is the reference wind speed (V_{ref}). A turbine for a reference wind speed V_{ref} is designed to withstand wind climates for which the extreme 10 min average wind speed, with a recurrence period of 50 years at the turbine's hub height, is lower or equal to V_{ref}. There can actually be higher extreme wind speeds than this; the other measure is the 3 s average, for extreme gusts [30].

2.13.9.3.3 Grid compatibility

The condition and capacity of the grid at the site, and the demands from the grid operator, may restrict the models that can be chosen. When only single turbines or small wind power plants are connected, the grid can absorb some spikes, consumption of reactive power, and other power quality problems, which could be caused by wind power plants without advanced equipment for grid compatibility. For large wind power plants with a significant nominal power and in areas with high wind power penetration, the demands from grid operators are stricter and limit the wind turbine models that can be chosen and the electrical equipment installed in transformers and substations on the wind farm operator's side of the grid interface.

2.13.9.4 Supplier

When the wind power plant has started to operate, it should continue to do so for some 20 years, with as few problems as possible. It is therefore important to choose a supplier and wind turbine models that have a good track record. A manufacturer with a good reputation for quality equipment, and who responds quickly to problems that may arise, will be of good help to keep the wind farm in operation. The best way to find this out is to get in touch with other experienced project developers and wind power plant operators.

When the market for wind turbines is growing fast, it may not always be possible to get orders for wind turbines accepted, especially for smaller projects and minor developers. Delivery times may also be very long. The question then is if it is worth changing the time-line of a project to wait for delivery from the desired manufacturer or to choose another option. Since the technical lifetime of

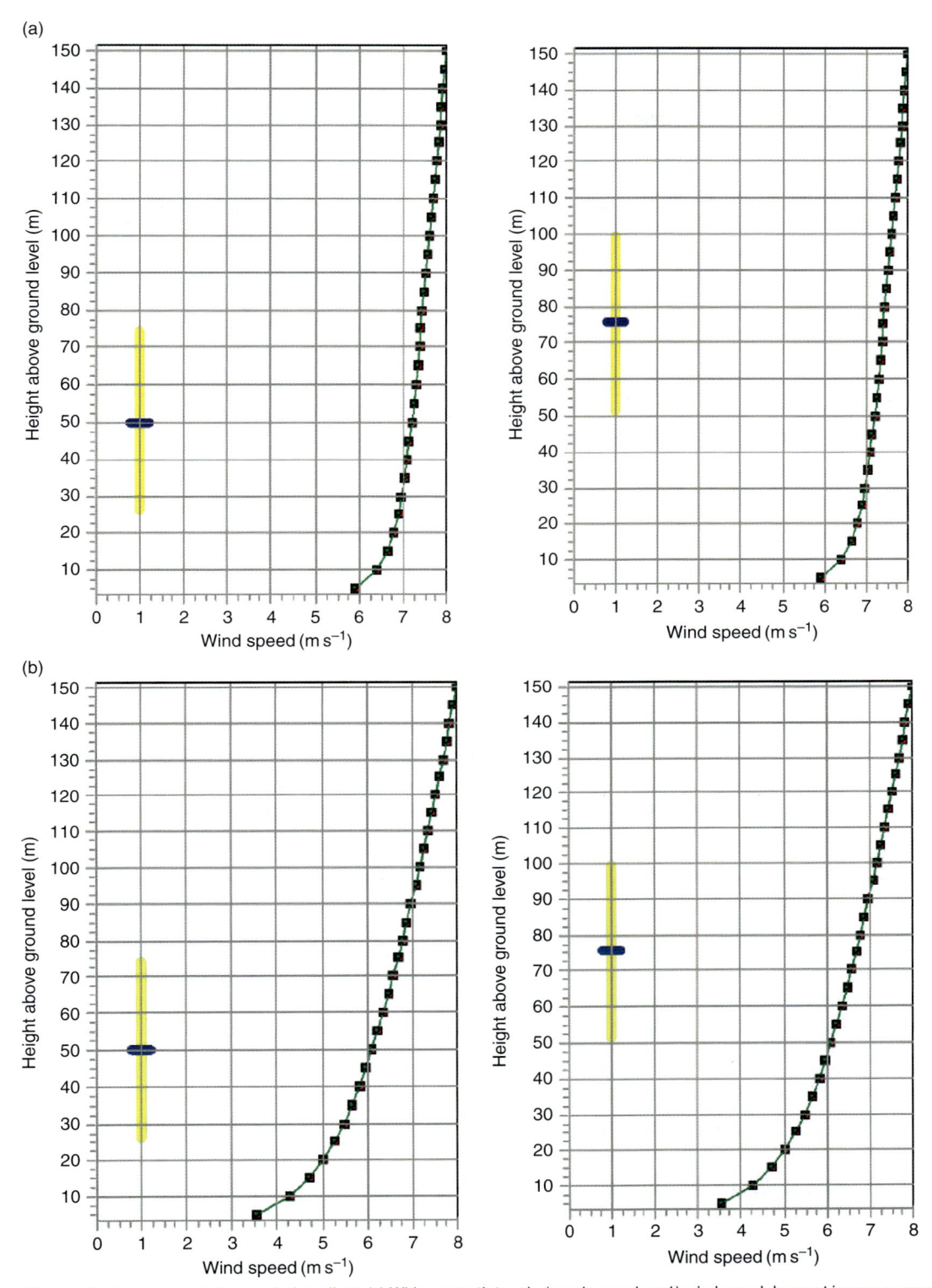

Figure 25 Choice of hub height in relation to wind gradient. (a) With a smooth terrain (roughness class 1) wind speed does not increase very much with height. At 50 m, the wind speed is 7.2 m s^{-1}, and at 75 m, it is 7.4 m s^{-1} (+3%). In this case, with a 50 m rotor diameter, the annual production will be 9% higher with a 75 m hub height, an increase from 2200 to 2400 MWh yr^{-1}. (b) When the terrain is roughness class 3, the wind speed at 50 m is 6.1. At 75 m height, it is 6.7 m s^{-1} (+10%). The wind regime is exactly the same in these examples, only the roughness of terrain differs. In this case, with a 50 m rotor diameter, the annual production will be 17% higher with a 75 m hub height, an increase from 1800 to 2100 MWh yr^{-1}.

Table 2 Nominal power versus rotor swept area

Wind turbine model	Rated power (kW)	Rated wind speed (m s^{-1})	Rotor diameter (m)	Rotor swept area (m^2)	kW m^{-2}
Enercon E-48	800	14	48	1810	0.44
Enercon E-53	800	13	52	2123	0.38
Suzlon S64-1250	1250	14	64	3215	0.39
Suzlon S66-1250	1250	14	66	3420	0.37
GE 1.5se	1500	12	70.5	3902	0.38
GE 1.5sle	1500	12	77	4416	0.34
GE 1.5xle	1500	12	82.5	5343	0.28
Enercon E70	2300	15	71	3959	0.58
Enercon E82	2000	12	82	5281	0.38
Vestas V90-1	1800	12	90	6362	0.28
Vestas V90-2	2000	13	90	6362	0.31
Vestas V90-3	3000	15	90	6362	0.47

Table 3 IEC classes for wind turbines

	IEC classes				
	I	II	III	IV	S
V_{ref} (m s^{-1})	50	42.5	37.5	30	Values to be specified by the designer
V_{ave} (m s^{-1})	10	8.5	7.5	6	
A I_{15}	0.18	0.18	0.18	0.18	
a	2	2	2	2	
B I_{15}	0.16	0.16	0.16	0.16	
a	3	3	3	3	

The values apply at hub height. '**A**' designates higher turbulence; '**B**' designates lower turbulence; I_{15} is the turbulence intensity at 15 m s^{-1}; a is the slope parameter in the normal turbulence model equation.

wind turbines is 20 years, it may be worth waiting for delivery from a manufacturer with a proven record, good after sales service, experience in operation and maintenance (O&M), and with spare parts available for the whole period of operation.

There is a wide choice of wind turbines available on the market, and more will come when new manufacturers start to export their products on the world market. Research is an ongoing process, and there are still technical developments towards even more cost-efficient wind turbines.

The project developer should never specify a manufacturer's model in the application procedure. From a planning point of view, it is sufficient to specify the number and size of turbines, hub height, and total height. There are several reasons for this. First, the preferred model may no longer be available when it is time to start the building process. Most manufacturers develop their turbines continually, and a specific model may have a larger rotor or other standard hub heights when time comes to order the turbines. If so, the permission is no longer valid. Therefore, in the application a margin should be added to the size of the turbines. Second, in a business venture, several different manufacturers should be asked for tenders.

The project developer needs to have a good knowledge and understanding of the interplay between site conditions, wind resources, and wind turbine specifications to choose the most suitable models for the wind power plants that are developed; wind turbines are tailored to the sites.

2.13.10 Economics of Wind Power Plants

To make a good decision about a wind power project, a thorough economic analysis is necessary. The wind power plant has to generate enough income to guarantee that the investors, or the banks that give credits, will get their money back and a decent return on their investments. Without a realistic and convincing budget, no investors will be willing to finance the wind power project.

The first task in a good economic analysis is to do a realistic calculation of how much electric power the wind power plant will produce at the chosen site. This is done with a so-called wind atlas program (software), like WindPRO, WAsP, and so on, or by onsite wind measurements that are normalized to long-term averages. The results of this calculation will show how many kWh the wind power plant can be expected to produce in a normal wind year; the average annual power production, the AEP, during the lifetime of the plant.

The next task is to make a budget for all the investments that will be necessary to realize the project, to estimate the investment costs. When a wind turbine has been installed and starts to produce power, the incomes have to cover the financial costs as well as the costs for O&M. The wind power plant should also generate a profit.

There are several different methods to calculate the returns on an investment; the annuity method, the present value method, the internal rate of return (IRR), and the payback time method. A cash flow analysis illustrates the annual returns on the investment during the lifetime of a wind power plant. All these calculations are, however, based on assumptions on future power production (the winds vary), power prices, interest rates, and so on, that cannot be accurately foreseen today. The economic analysis should therefore also include a sensitivity analysis that will estimate the risks and opportunities with the investment. Finally, a plan for the financing of the project that ensures that there always will be enough money available to pay interests, repayments of loans, and other bills has to be made. This is called a liquidity budget [31].

Basically, the financing can be done in two different ways, corporate financing or project financing. A wind power project can be financed by lending money from a bank, by private investors, and other ways. It also takes money to develop the project, to build access roads, deposits when wind power plants are ordered, and so on, before any incomes are generated. The developer or a building credit from a bank usually covers these costs [31].

2.13.10.1 Investment

The costs for the purchase of wind power plants, the installation at the site, and for grid connection are estimated by an investment budget. In a feasibility study, rounded estimations can be used. The purpose of the feasibility study is to evaluate if the project is worth realizing or not. After the decision is taken to fulfill the plans, a new more detailed investment budget is made based on tenders for wind turbines, access roads, foundations, grid connection work and equipment, and other ancillary works. This carefully calculated investment budget is then presented to the bank for application of loans and to prospective investors.

An investment budget has the following entries:

- Wind turbine(s)
- Foundation(s)
- Roads and miscellaneous
- Grid connection
- Land lease
- Project development.

2.13.10.1.1 Wind turbines

The price of different models and sizes of wind turbines can be found from price lists or directly from the manufacturers or their agents. During the final procurement (purchase process), prices and conditions can be negotiated. If the wind power equipment is manufactured in a foreign country (with another currency), the price will also depend on the exchange rate, which sometimes can change quite fast. The transport of the turbine to the site, mounting, installation, and grid connection is made by staff from the manufacturer and is normally included in the purchase price. The costs for mobile crane and some transports have to be covered by the developer. For wind power plants installed on land, the cost for the turbine amounts to about 75% of the total investment [32].

2.13.10.1.2 Foundation

The cost for the foundation varies a little between different manufacturers. The price for a rock-foundation and a gravity foundation is about the same, while foundations for lattice tower tend to be cheaper, since less concrete is needed for them. The manufacturer will give the technical specifications for the foundation (size, weight, etc.). The project developer will then ask a local building company to build the foundation. For offshore installations, the foundations are much more expensive.

2.13.10.1.3 Access roads

The cost for access roads depends on the size and weight of the turbine, ground conditions, and the lengths of the road that has to be built. At the sites where the individual turbines will be installed, it is necessary to prepare an open workspace approximately 50 m wide and 70 m long, for trucks, cranes, and so on. In many cases, it will be sufficient to reinforce existing roads, so that trucks and a mobile crane can get to the site. It is often easier and cheaper to prepare an access road when the soil is hard and dry. After the turbine has been installed, the road only has to carry an ordinary small van for the service crew and materials. This cost depends on local conditions. The costs for mobile crane and special transportation costs (by ferry, etc.) have to be covered by the project developer.

2.13.10.1.4 Grid connection

To connect the wind turbine to the electric power grid, a transformer and a cable or overhead line to the closest grid power line have to be installed. The cost depends on the size and model of the wind turbine, the distance to the grid, and the grid voltage. Large wind turbines often have an integrated transformer, either in the nacelle or in the bottom of the tower. If so, the price for the transformer is included in the price of the turbine. For large wind farms, an internal grid has to be built. A telephone line to monitor and control the turbine has to be connected as well.

2.13.10.1.5 Land lease

Wind power plants are often installed on land that is leased. In this case, the developer has to conclude a land lease contract with the landowner, which will give the owner/operator the right to use the land for a wind power plant for 25–35 years. The landowner will either get an annual fee or a down payment for the total period when the turbine is installed.

2.13.10.1.6 Project development

This entry includes costs for planning, the time the developer has to spend working with the project. This time is needed for business negotiations, information, economic calculations, and so on. Fees for building permission, interests during construction, and other similar costs are also included. This cost can vary widely, depending on the time needed for the development process, and what fee the developer and consultants will charge.

2.13.10.1.7 Total investment

It is often hard to calculate the total investment cost correctly, before the development actually starts. The budget should give a rough idea with a margin for unexpected costs added. The relative costs for different budget entries, based on actual figures from Denmark, differ greatly for developments onshore and offshore (see Table 4) [33].

For offshore wind farms, the investment costs are considerably higher than for wind power plants on land. The cost for foundations is much higher, as well as for the undersea cables that connect the wind farm to the grid on land. Figures are based on 600 kW wind turbines in Denmark 1997 (land) and offshore (Tunö knob in Denmark). These figures and relations will most likely differ in different countries and may also change with time.

2.13.10.2 Economic Result

It is of course just as important to find out the economic outcome after the wind power plant has begun to deliver power to the grid. Then the plant begins to generate revenues, but also draws some costs. To give a profit, the revenues have to be larger than the costs. To calculate the future costs is not so difficult, it is far trickier to calculate the revenues.

There are basically two kinds of costs, capital costs (interest and repayment of loans) and costs for O&M. The actual capital costs depend on how the project has been financed. There are basically two models for this, corporate financing or project financing. Corporate financing means that the wind power plant is owned and operated by a company, and treated like an investment within the company. It will be entered among other machinery in the company's balance sheet. With project financing the wind power plant is treated as an independent economic entity [31].

If the wind power plant has been financed by credits from a bank, the conditions are specified in the credit agreement. If private investors finance it, for example, in a share holding company formed to own and operate a wind power plant, the project will be financed by equity capital, but the stakeholders expect a good return on their investments. In these cases, the financing is made by a combination of loans and equity.

2.13.10.2.1 Depreciation

Commercial wind power plants are designed for a technical lifetime of 20–25 years. The actual technical lifetime is not well known, since few wind power plants have reached that age yet. How much retrofits that are necessary when a turbine gets old is also a factor of uncertainty. However, nowadays costs for retrofits during the lifetime of wind power plants are often included in the project budget.

Table 4 Cost structure for wind power plants on land and offshore (%)

	Land	Offshore
Wind turbines, ex works	68–84	49
Foundation	1–9	21
Electric installation	1–9	21[a]
Land	1–5	–
Road construction	1–5	–
Consultancy	1–3	3[b]
Financial cost	1–5	n/a
Design and management	–	6

[a] Trafo and sea cable (16) and internal electric grid (5).
[b] Environment Impact Assessment.

Table 5 Typical annual O&M costs: percent of investment

Years	1–2	3–5	6–10	11–15	16–20
600 kW wind turbine	1.0%	1.9%	2.2%	3.5%	4.5%

Source: Redlinger (2004).

Maintenance costs will, however, increase with age (see Table 5). Therefore, the economic lifetime may be shorter than the technical lifetime. After 15–20 years, the maintenance cost may be so high that it makes sense to replace a wind turbine with a new and more efficient model. In economic calculations, the depreciation time is usually set to 20 years, but owners usually opt to pay back loans on shorter terms, in 8–12 years. This means that the capital cost (loan plus interests) always should be paid back within 20 years. If the turbine continues to produce power without problems, the profits will be higher, unless the incomes are drained by cost for repairs and retrofits.

2.13.10.2.2 Operation and maintenance

When a wind power plant has been installed and connected to the grid, it starts to operate, and should do so for at least 20 years. Compared to other power plants, the cost for O&M of wind power plants are very low, since no staff is needed to operate the plants and no fuel is needed. However, wind power plants need regular service and maintenance, they have to be insured against accidents, and there are some administration costs as well.

A wind turbine needs regular service, just like any other machine. The service crew will make regular checks of the condition usually twice a year (depends on the manufacturer). The oil in the gearbox has to be checked regularly and changed after a couple of years. The service costs for the first 2 years are often included in the price, but oil and other materials are not included. After that period, the manufacturer or some service company offers a service contract to conduct regular service for an annual fee.

During the time of the warranty, which usually will last for 2–5 years, insurance for fire and responsibility is necessary. When the warranty runs out, a machine-insurance is usually added and the premium of insurance will increase.

To own and operate a wind power plant also takes some administrative work; invoices have to be paid, as well as taxes, and the bookkeeping has to be managed. Then there usually are some taxes and fees to be paid. The grid operator might take a fee for measuring the production that is fed into the grid.

2.13.10.3 Revenues

The basic incomes for a wind power installation are the revenues from selling the electric power. The owner has to make a PPA with a power trading company that buys and sells electric power. In many countries, the power market has been deregulated during the last years, while in others there is still a monopoly. The conditions for a PPA as well as the price per kWh can vary much in different countries.

There are also some special bonuses for wind-generated power in most countries that emanate from an ambition to support the development of renewable energy sources and to reduce emissions that harm the environment and cause external cost to society. Some countries have a CO_2 tax reduction (Denmark), others have green certificates (Sweden, Great Britain, Italy), or offer a special and long-term purchase price for the power, so-called Feed-in-Tariffs (FIT) (Germany, Spain).

Since rules, regulations, conditions, taxes, and market situations differ, a specific analysis has to be made for every country. Since rules and regulations are changed and the future market prices are not known, even this is a very complicated and uncertain task. National wind power associations, state energy authorities, or ministries can provide this kind of country-specific information on rules, tariffs, and so on.

2.13.10.4 Calculation of Economic Result

To calculate the economic result, an assumption about a price per kWh for the coming 20 years has to be made. This assumption has to be based on the facts that are known when the calculation is done. Since this calculation will be the basis for a decision about the investment, it should be supplemented with a 'sensitivity analysis', with a worst-case scenario, and also a best-case scenario. By doing this, the economic risk can be evaluated. The higher the estimated risk, the more expensive it is to lend money for the project; higher risk implies higher interest rate.

The economic result, that is, the annual profit is calculated in this way [4]:

$$P_a = I_a - C_a - OM_a$$

where P_a is annual profit, I_a is annual income, C_a is annual cost of capital, OM_a is annual cost for O&M.

The investment has been financed by a loan, which gives an annual cost for capital during the years when the loan has to be paid back to the bank, including the interest.

2.13.10.4.1 Cost of capital

The annual cost for capital is calculated by the annuity method. The annuity is the sum of amortization (pay back of loan) and interest where the sum of the amortization plus interest will be constant, that is, the same sum each year. The annual capital cost C_a is calculated by the so-called annuity formula (**Table 6**):

$$C_a = a \cdot C_i$$

where a is annuity and C_i is investment cost.

2.13.10.4.2 Present value and IRR

Another method to calculate the economic result for an investment in wind power plants is the 'present value' method, which also is called the 'discounting' method. With this method, the value of an annual income or expense that will occur for a specific number of years is given the value at a specific time, usually the day when the turbine starts to operate. If the present values of the revenues are larger than the present value of the investment and expenses, the investment will be profitable.

The IRR is the rate of return when the present value is set to zero. It gives a measure of the annualized effective return rate that can be earned on the invested capital, the yield on the investment.

2.13.10.4.3 Payback time

A third method to evaluate the economic preconditions for an investment in a wind power project is the pay off method. It is used to calculate how long it will take to get back the invested money. The simple payback time is calculated with this formula:

$$T = \frac{\text{Investment}}{\text{Anual net income}}$$

2.13.10.4.4 Levelized cost of energy

The actual cost to produce 1 kWh with wind power is an interesting figure. This energy cost is equal to the annual capital cost plus the annual O&M cost, divided by the annual production in kWh; this is called the levelized cost of energy [4].

$$E_{\text{cost}} = \frac{C_a + OM_a}{\text{kWh yr}^{-1}}$$

2.13.10.4.5 Cash flow analysis

A cash flow analysis is a good method to calculate the economic result year by year. It shows the cash flow during the economic lifetime of the wind power plant and can be made with the spreadsheet software (Excel, etc.). Information on calculated power production, power price, certificates and other bonuses, loans, interest rates, and other factors that have an impact on the economy are entered into the spreadsheet. Expected inflation rates and increases of power purchase prices can be entered, as well as rising costs for maintenance. The program then calculates the outcome year by year. The result can be presented in diagrams and tables showing the cash flow, annual revenues, capital costs, maintenance costs, and remaining surplus.

The interest rate has a great impact on the economic result. The higher the interest rate is, the longer time it will take to pay back the loans. The relation between the interest rate and the payback time can also be illustrated by a pay-off diagram.

2.13.10.5 Risk Assessment

The calculation of the economic result is based on several assumptions. The first one is the calculated power production. The second is the power price. What happens if these assumptions are wrong? To find this out, it is always wise to assess the risk with a sensitivity analysis.

Table 6 Annuity factors for different interest rates and pay-back time

Pay-back time interest rate	5 years	10 years	15 years	20 years
5 %	0.2310	0.1295	0.0963	0.0802
6 %	0.2374	0.1359	0.1030	0.0872
7 %	0.2439	0.1424	0.1098	0.0944
8 %	0.2505	0.1490	0.1168	0.1019
9 %	0.2571	0.1558	0.1241	0.1095
10 %	0.2638	0.1627	0.1315	0.1175

A realistic scenario for the worst things that can happen, a worst-case scenario, is made. This could be that the total power price will drop by 15% and that the power production will be 10% less than calculated (due to errors in the calculations, climate change, grid failures, or other reasons). These figures are then used in the same calculations that have been made. A similar best-case scenario should be made as well. The best case could be that the total power price will rise by 20% and power production will be 10% higher than calculated (due to errors in the calculations, climate change, or other reasons).

The worst risks for the power industry are unexpected increases of fuel prices. This can never be a problem for wind power since the fuel is free. There is, however, an uncertainty on the energy content of the wind that should be considered. The economic calculation for the base case is based on the expected power production during a normal wind year. During a specific year in the 20–25 years that the wind power plant will operate, the energy content in the wind can vary considerably. In some of these years, the wind power plants could produce 20% less than average. The estimated annual production for the 20-year period can also be too optimistic.

This uncertainty should also be included in the sensitivity analysis, and combined with the price uncertainty. The absolute worst case is that the price will drop by 15% and that production is 15% less than expected. The outcome of this case should be above the levelized cost of energy from the wind power plant. There is also a very best case, where prices as well as production will be higher than expected. There is a risk and a chance. To evaluate these is a matter for the investors and the owner/operator. To do that, a well-founded risk-analysis is necessary. Such risk assessment can be made by the wind power software, for example, the module Loss and Uncertainty in WindPRO [19].

2.13.10.6 Financing

Wind power plants have a high investment cost, but very low operational cost, since the wind which is used as fuel is free. In this respect, wind power is similar to hydropower. This means that in most cases significant loans are necessary to finance wind power projects.

The project developer has to search loan and grant options and find banks or other investors that offer interest rates and payback times that the project can afford. Most banks, nowadays, consider investments in wind power as any other investment, and do not add any extra risk premiums. Up to 70–80% can usually be financed this way, with the wind power plant as the sole security. The remaining funds have to be supplied from the company's strongbox, or by using some other asset as security (land, real estate, etc.), or from equity. If the last option has to be used, the developer has to conduct an equity drive and negotiate and execute agreements with equity investors. These will demand a higher return on investment than the banks.

How a wind power project is financed depends on what kind of owner it will have. In many countries, wind power plants are developed and owned by independent power producers (IPPs), and not by big utilities and power companies.

Big companies often have a good cash balance and a full strongbox and thus also the capital needed for the investment available within the company. This is called corporate financing. The other financing principle is called project financing and can be utilized by large corporations as well. In this case, the wind power project is treated as an independent economic entity. Small and medium enterprises, which have been formed for the sole purpose to own and operate wind power plants, usually have to take loans in a bank or other credit institution. A Limited company will raise some or all the money for the investment from equities [31].

2.13.11 Documentation

A wind power project has to be well documented. Well written, accurate, and reliable documents that describe the project are needed to inform the public, for the permission application, for financing, and also to find investors who are prepared to realize the project. Some of these documents are public, and some are internal documents for the project developing company.

2.13.11.1 Project Description

The project developer makes a feasibility study, which is an internal document. The project has, however, also to be made public, and for that a good project description has to be prepared. This is a document for the nonprofessional public, and should be understandable and also address the questions the public are expected to raise. A description of the project should describe the area, the number of wind turbines, and their siting. Impacts on neighbors, sound emission, shadow flicker, access roads, and new power lines should be described. Finally, the visual impact should be illustrated by photomontages.

An introduction with information and arguments for the necessity to develop renewable energy sources, on climate change and mitigation, the positive impact on global level, as well as a presentation of the developing company and who will own and operate the wind power plant when it is installed, should also be included in the project description.

This report should be nontechnical, have many maps and other illustrations, and some basic information on wind turbines, size, and annual production. If there are no good writers in-house, it is a good idea to engage a professional writer to compile this public report. To have a good project description will make it possible to get a good public dialogue, and it will create goodwill for the project development company.

2.13.11.2 Environment Impact Assessment

The project description can also be used for the dialogue with authorities in the permission process. For larger projects, there is also a demand for a formal EIA. The demand on an EIA may differ in different countries, and for different projects. What the EIA should cover is decided in the dialogue with authorities. This report should also start with a nontechnical description, and the project description can be reused for this. This is, however, a much more comprehensive report, often with technical and scientific reports from investigations made, on grid connection, access roads, bird life, and so on.

An EIA shall describe the impact of the wind power plant on the global, regional, and local environment. Each impact (sound, landscape, etc.) should be described on three levels: first, the present situation, then the impacts (change, consequences), and finally, precautions (measures that minimize impacts). The positive impact from wind power, by reducing GHG emissions, should always be included in the EIA.

Then the impact during different stages of development should be described. How will the building process be organized: preparatory work, access roads, power lines, working areas for cranes, excavators, trucks, storage places, and so on. Then the impact during operation should be described in detail: visual impact, sound propagation, shadow flicker, safety measures. Finally, the restoration of the site should be described: how the wind turbines will be dismantled and the ground restored and how this process will be financed.

In a complete EIA, at least two different options for siting and/or design of the project and a so-called zero-option shall be included. The different options and their environment impact shall be described in a way that makes it possible to compare them and to assess which option that will be the best for the environment. The zero-option shall describe the consequences if the project will not be realized. It could describe how the electric power that would be produced by the wind power plants will be supplied (by coal or natural gas and the emissions that will be generated).

Measures that will be taken to prevent, reduce, or compensate for impacts and other precautions shall be presented in a separate paragraph. Here measures to prevent damages during the building process should be described. Finally, a summary of the process of public consultation and dialogue with authorities that the EIA report is based on should be included.

When the application for permission is submitted, this EIA report will be public. It will be scrutinized by experts, as well as by eventual opponents. The EIA has to be of a high quality, and if competence to make a good EIA is lacking, there are consultants that can do this part of the job, and also some of the investigations that are included in the EIA.

2.13.11.3 Economic Reports

The economy of a wind power project is a business matter, and the business calculations of the developer are internal documents. However, to be able to finance projects, banks, finance institutes, and private investors will demand very detailed information on the project's economic viability and risks. Potential investors will also conduct a Due Diligence, and check that all contracts, with landowners and grid operators are legally correct, that all necessary permissions are granted, and that a PPA is signed on reasonable terms.

2.13.11.3.1 Wind data report
The annual energy production is the basis for the economic viability, and a wind data report is the core of the economic evaluation. The report that describes in detail how the wind resources have been estimated is thus the most important document. This document should describe in detail how the local wind climate has been researched. The demands on the methods from banks are very strict, at least for large projects. The method, the measuring equipment, certificates for calibration of anemometers used, as well as the measurement period, collected wind data, and how they have been transformed to long-term data has to be accounted for. As a rule, banks and other investors will demand a third-party evaluation of this report from well-established independent international consultant. Therefore, it is wise to consult potential financiers before measurements start and ask them to specify their demands.

2.13.11.3.2 Economic prospect
To finance the project, it is always necessary to have a well-founded and convincing documentation of the project's economic prospects. The developer has to prepare a budget, cash flow, balance sheet, and income statements to prove the case to banks and equity investors. This can be done in a prospect for potential equity investors, which describes the opportunities as well as the risks with an investment.

2.13.11.3.3 Real budget
None of the calculation methods described (in Section 2.13.10) are sufficient to work out a real budget for a wind power project. They are used to come to a conclusion on the economic feasibility of the project. To make a real budget, a much more detailed analysis, based on tenders, actual credit conditions from banks, the share of equity versus loans, and so on, has to be made. The interest rates have a large impact on the economic viability and result, and these are influenced by the perceived risks and opportunities of the investment. The real budget, and the outcome, is an internal report.

2.13.12 Building a Wind Power Plant

The building phase includes all activities from commencement of the works to prepare the site up to the handover of the operational wind power plant to the buyer/owner. Once all the initial stages have been concluded, and the status reviewed, the building stage can start.

For small- and medium-sized wind power plants, the time from placing an order for wind turbines and delivery to the site can vary from a few months to a year or more. In the meantime, the access roads, turbine foundations and substation, and the electrical infrastructure have to be built. Further, the installation is weather sensitive; to install the wind turbines during the rainy season is not a good idea, nor to do it in the windy season. Delays due to bad weather conditions will increase cost, but can be avoided by good planning.

The developer has to prepare the site and build the foundations. Wind turbine foundations of reinforced concrete have to harden for a month. The wind turbines are usually mounted and installed by the turbine supplier. To install the transformer (if it is not integrated in the turbine) and a power line to the grid is the task of the developer.

Wind turbines are large and heavy, so suitable site access for transport is required. The transport vehicles are also quite long, and may have problems with bends on the road and up and down hills. The supplier usually checks out the transport route to make it work; some trees may have to be felled in sharp curves, and telephone and power lines raised or temporarily removed. Onsite storage and assembly work will require an open space at the base of each tower of approximately 50×70 m. Heavy cranes will be required on site; a 2 MW turbine requires a crane with a capacity to lift several hundred tons for hoisting tower, nacelle, and rotor into position.

When the wind turbine components finally arrive, it does not take more than one day to mount it on site, if everything is well prepared and the weather allows. Once the wind turbines are installed, about 2 weeks are needed to complete the installation work, commission the system, and connect the wind power plant to the grid. The building phase for a small- or medium-sized wind power plant only lasts 2–3 months.

2.13.12.1 Selection of Suppliers

When all necessary permissions are granted and financing arranged, time is due to find a supplier of wind turbines and other equipment, entrepreneurs to build access roads, and other tasks that have to be done to realize the project. A review of technical specifications of wind turbines should be done to determine which model that would be most suitable for the project in terms of capacity, size, price, and availability.

In the procurement of wind turbines, tenders should be asked for from several different suppliers. A Tender Enquiry Document should include basic information about the project time plan and planning status, financial, technical and operational information, contractual issues, scope of supply, technical specifications, maintenance and repair conditions, and agreements for warranty and insurance.

The different tenders have to be evaluated to find the one that is most favorable. This is not always the supplier that offers the lowest price. The supplier's record, ability to offer good service and maintenance, and other factors should also be considered. At this stage, the supplier may ask for a down payment of 10–30% for the wind turbines that are ordered, when the contract is signed.

The developer has to negotiate and execute a turbine purchase agreement and warranty and place an order with the required deposit. To avoid problems on warranties, the supplier should make a formal statement that the delivered wind turbines are fit for the site where they will be installed. During the building phase, many different processes have to be coordinated, so a delivery schedule for the wind turbines should also be included in the turbine sales agreement.

2.13.12.2 Contracts

Contracts have also to be signed with landowners, the grid operator, and with a power company, utility, or third party that will buy the power. Contracts for credits from banks and other financial institutions should be signed as well. Then there are entrepreneurs who have to be contracted to build access roads, pads for cranes and equipment, transformers, cable ditches, and electrical work. Potential construction companies have to be investigated, cost estimates worked out, and construction contracts signed. It is good practice to engage local companies and entrepreneurs to build access roads, foundations, and other tasks. This gives benefits to the local community. Since all of these works have to be coordinated, a detailed timetable has to be worked out for all these contracts.

2.13.12.3 Supervision and Quality Control

It is common practice to assign a number of 'checkpoints' as part of the quality control process during production of wind turbines and construction of a wind power plant. These checkpoints give the owner an opportunity to audit the progress and quality of work and to verify that the components conform to the specifications. Checkpoints are mostly planned immediately following a project milestone, like factory acceptance test of components ready for shipment, site acceptance test when components are delivered to the site, and several inspections during building and installation.

2.13.12.4 Commissioning and Transfer

When the building phase is finished, before the wind power plant is handed over, an overall inspection and commissioning is carried out. Representatives of the contractor, the owner, and the grid operator perform these final commissioning inspections. The commissioning involves a comprehensive testing and monitoring plan. The main objective is to verify that the system is complete, installed correctly, and that it works properly.

The procedure for commissioning is formulated in mutual cooperation, with all the parties involved. Often some defects are discovered during the inspections, and these defects are listed. The parties decide what actions that should be done to clear this list, and sometimes a second inspection is required. When the commissioning has been approved, final project payment is made. The wind power plant is then transferred to the client, the owner/operator.

2.13.13 Operation

From the date of handover, the owner is responsible for the daily operation of the wind power plant. Now warranty and maintenance contracts become valid. The terms of warranties can vary for different suppliers. They can be valid from 2 and up to 12 years from the handover, and include repairs and modifications. Some warranties also cover technical availability of individual wind turbines and 95% of the certified power curve. Warranties do not cover actual performance since the available wind energy at the site cannot be accurately predicted; the winds can vary greatly in different years.

If the availability or performance is less than the warranted value, the supplier has to settle the difference. Beside the warranty, an insurance cover is required for third-party liability, machine breakdown, lightning strikes, fire, vandalism, and insurance for business interruption during unproductive days following a breakdown. Financial institutions demand good insurance as a precondition for loans. Machine insurance is not necessary until the warranty has expired.

The supplier insures damages during transport and installation of the wind turbines. After commissioning and transfer of a wind power plant, the owner takes over all risks, besides those covered by the warranty.

2.13.13.1 Maintenance

When the wind turbines have been installed, connected, and started to feed electric power to the grid, they will operate unattended. The owner or the one who is in charge of the operation can keep them under surveillance from his desk in the office, since the wind turbines control system is connected to the operator's PC. Simple operational disturbances can be attended to from a distance, and the turbine can be restarted from the PC.

When more serious disturbances occur, the operator has to visit the wind power plant to attend to the fault before the wind turbine can be restarted. When a fault occurs, the operator will get an alarm on his cell phone or PC.

Modern wind turbines require regular maintenance service twice a year. The wind turbine manufacturer can do this service. This is often included in the warranty for 2 years or longer. After that a contract for regular service should be negotiated with the manufacturer or an independent service company. It is also recommended for the owner/operator to create a contingency fund, to set aside money for major repairs that may have to be done after the warranty has expired.

For a wind turbine in the MW-class, planned preventive maintenance takes 2–3 working days for two technicians. They will inspect and test the control and safety devices, repair small defects, and replace or replenish gearbox lubrication. Oil samples are taken from the gearbox at regular intervals and are analyzed. Filters are replaced and gears are inspected for damage.

The requirement of repairing wind turbines varies widely between different wind power plants, but three to four mechanical or electrical faults a year that require a visit by a service engineer is a likely average. The downtime for each failure can last for 1–4 days. However, downtime can be much longer if spare parts are hard to find. This is often the case with older wind turbines that are no longer manufactured.

How much power the wind turbines produce is registered on a meter that the grid operator will take readings of. Settlements are usually made once a month, when the owner gets paid for the power that has been delivered to the grid the preceding month. Rules for how this is done should be included in the PPA.

2.13.13.2 Condition Monitoring

To reduce downtime due to technical faults, systems for condition monitoring have been introduced. A modern wind turbine has a comprehensive condition monitoring system from the start, which checks temperatures, rotational speeds, voltage, and many other parameters. When some parameter is outside specified values, the turbine is stopped and an alarm is sent to the operator.

Condition monitoring systems have some additional sensors, and software that analyzes vibrations, frequencies, and so on, and send an alarm when indications are found that some component might be worn out. The idea is to mend a problem before it results in a shutdown, and avoid the downtime by repairing or changing components before they cause the turbine to stop. For wind power plants in remote locations and offshore, where it takes a long time to be able to do repairs, this will save costs.

2.13.13.3 Performance Monitoring

Performance monitoring means that the performance is continually checked, in relation to the wind conditions, that is, that the turbine at all times will produce power according to its power curve [34]. The reasons for a turbine to underperform may be caused by other factors than faults on components, and these will not be identified by the control system or the condition monitoring system. One example is that the yaw system sets the turbine rotor disk a few degrees off from the perpendicular wind direction; another is a fault in the equipment that measures the power fed to the grid.

2.13.13.4 Decommissioning and Site Restoration

When a wind turbine after some 20–25 years of operation is worn out, it should be dismantled. Most of the parts can be recycled as scrap metal. The only components that cannot be recycled today are the rotor blades, but there are efforts to find methods for that as well. The scrap value of a turbine is about the same as the cost to dismount it. The foundation of reinforced concrete, built below ground level, can be left behind, if it does not affect ground conditions in a negative way. Otherwise, it can be removed and reused as filling material for roads or buildings.

When the wind power plant has been dismantled, it leaves no tracks behind. However, if it is a good site, a new generation of wind turbines will be installed. This repowering process has already started in Denmark, Germany, and Sweden, and will increase the installed capacity since new turbines have higher capacity than those that are replaced.

2.13.14 Business Models

Wind power project developers can apply several different business models. A company in the wind power business can specialize in one phase of development, while the other may work through the whole chain, from the feasibility study to the operation of wind power plants, and take the earnings from sale of electric power. There are significant differences in the company structure in different countries. In Europe, there are many companies which develop projects, and make an exit either when the permissions have been granted or when turnkey plants are installed and online. In India, manufacturers often develop their own projects, sell them when online, but also take charge of the operation during the wind power plants lifetime. In 2010, many large power companies, like Iberdrola from Spain, Dong from Denmark, and Vattenfall from Sweden develop large wind power plants on their own, for operation and sales of power.

The highest risk is usually in the first stages of development, when there is uncertainty if the project will get the necessary permissions and if the wind power plant can be connected to the grid. Companies specialized in the project development start with land lease contracts to secure access to land suitable for wind power plants. Some will even sell these contracts to other developers and make a very early exit. Most will, however, make a project description, and then apply for permission to build it. When permissions have been granted, there is an exit point, so the project developer may sell the project to another company. To enter the building phase, there are other competencies needed, and also a lot more capital and financing skills. This is thus also the entry point for companies that are specialized in the management of building wind power plants.

Finally, there are consultants who will do this work for a customer, often large power companies, but sometimes also on behalf of landowners who do not have these inhouse competencies.

2.13.15 Summary and Conclusion

To design and implement a wind power projects requires many different skills. The most important task is to identify good sites for wind power plants, where the energy content as well as the quality of the wind, that is, low turbulence, is high. From the power system's point of view, it is however an advantage that wind power plants are geographically well distributed, so that the variation of the output is smoothed out in the system, which makes it possible to have a high wind power penetration. The wind resource is thus not the only criteria, and since wind turbines can be tailored to suit the wind conditions at specific sites, it is possible to utilize wind power in many different regions.

The sites chosen for wind power development should also be uncontroversial. Sites where there are obvious conflicts with opposing interests should be avoided. Support from public opinion is important, as this can be earned with an open public dialogue and good information about how a project develops. It takes weeks and months to create such public thrust, but it can be lost in a moment. So it is always worth the effort to spend a reasonable time and resources on keeping the public informed, and to consider the opinions that are put forward.

The size of wind turbines seems to be ever increasing, and the wind power plants as well. Still there is no reason to focus just on larger turbines and wind farms. The size should be well adapted to local conditions, loads, and the capacity of the grid. There are advantages with distributed generation, as well as distributed ownership, and hopefully manufacturers will continue to manufacture turbines of different sizes.

The configuration of wind power plants, the micro-siting, is a very important aspect. Much can be gained by spending time and effort on this so as to avoid cramming a wind power area with too many wind turbines, which reduce park efficiency and also likely increase maintenance costs.

The methods to measure the wind and to calculate annual energy production are getting better and make it possible to increase the accuracy of the estimated power production. To get this right is important. When production does not live up to estimations, investors will become disappointed and it will reduce their confidence in wind power development.

The technical availability of wind turbines is high, and with increased use of systems for condition and performance monitoring, it will become even higher. For a good performance, and a cost-efficient operation of wind power during their technical lifetime, it is necessary to have a good management of the O&M as well, which will reduce downtime and also increase the lifetime of the wind power plants.

References

[1] Earnest J and Wizelius T (2011) *Wind Power Plants and Project Development*. New Delhi, India: PHI Learning Private Ltd.
[2] van de Wekken T (2008) Doing it right: The four seasons of wind farm development. *Renewable Energy World*, May 2008.
[3] Troen I and Petersen LE (1989) *European Wind Atlas*. Roskilde, Denmark: Risoe National Laboratory.
[4] Wizelius T (2007) *Developing Wind Power Projects*. London, UK: Earthscan.
[5] Ackerman T (ed.) (2005) *Wind Power in Power Systems*. Chichester, UK: Wiley.
[6] Burton T, Sharpe D, Jenkins N, and Bossany E (2002) *Wind Energy Handbook*. Chichester, UK: Wiley.
[7] EWEA (2009) *Wind Energy – The Facts*. Brussels, Belgium: EWEA.
[8] Manwell JF, McGowan JG, and Rogers AL (2009) *Wind Energy Explained: Theory, Design and Application*, 2nd edn., Chichester, UK: Wiley.
[9] Windustry (2009) Wind energy easements and leases: Compensation packages. Minneapolis, USA. www.windustry.org
[10] Donelly A, Dalal-Clayton B, and Hughes RA (2009) *Directory of Impact Assessment Guidelines*, 2nd edn., Nottingham, UK: International Institute for Environment and Development.
[11] Jensen NOA (1983) Note on wind generator interaction. *Risoe-M–2411*. Roskilde, Denmark: Risoe National Laboratory.
[12] Rathmann O, Barthelmie R, and Frandsen S (2006) *Turbine Wake Model for Wind Resource Software*. Roskilde, Denmark: Risö National Laboratory.
[13] Schou Nielsen B and Stiesdal H (2004) *Trees, Forests and Wind Turbines: A Manufacturer's View*. Presentation at Trees Workshop, British Wind Energy Association.
[14] Gustafsson D (2008) Remote Wind Speed Sensing for Site Assessment and Normal Year Correction. MSc Thesis, EKV746 KTH.
[15] Frank HP, Rathmann O, Mortensen NG, and Landberg L (2001) The numerical wind atlas. The KAMM/WAsP method. *Risö-R-1252(EN)*. Roskilde, Denmark: Risö National Laboratory.
[16] Earth System Research Laboratory. NCEP/NCAR data. www.esrl.noaa.gov.
[17] EMD. WindPRO. Module description. www.emd.dk.
[18] WAsP. www.wasp.dk.
[19] EMD. WindPRO. www.emd.dk.
[20] WindFarm – ReSoft. www.resoft.co.uk.
[21] WindFarmer. www.gl-garradhassan.com.
[22] RETScreen. www.retscreen.net.
[23] See www.windatlas.dk and www.nrel.gov/gis/wind.html.
[24] Jones S (2008) *Standard Loss Definitions for Wind Resource/Energy Assessments Global Energy Concepts (DNV) Paper*, AWEA. www.talentfactory.dk.
[25] Jargstorf B (2010) *Are Hurricanes a Constraint to Wind Development in the Caribbean? Factor 4 Energy Projects GmbH, Wismar, Germany*. Presentation at Caribbean Environment Forum, Jamaica 2010. www.cehi.org.lc.
[26] Gardiner B (2004) *Airflow Over Forests and Forest Gaps*. Presentation at Trees Workshop. British Wind Energy Association.
[27] Bergström H (2007) Wind resource mapping of Sweden – version 2007. http://www.geo.uu.se/luva.
[28] Dahlberg J-Å. (2009) Assessment of the Lillgrund windfarm. Power performance, Wake effects. Vattenfall/Swedish Energy Agency. http://www.vattenfall.com/en/reports-from-the-lillgrund-pr.htm (accessed 1 October 2010).
[29] De Vries E (2010) Are we closing in on the ultimate turbine? Technology latest. *Windpower Monthly Special Report*.
[30] International Electricity Commission (2005) Wind turbine generator systems: Part 1: Safety requirements. *International Standard 61400-1*, 3rd edn.
[31] Redlinger RY, Andersen PD, and Morthorst PE (2002) *Wind Energy in the 21st Century*. Hampshire, UK: Palgrave.
[32] Milborrow D (2012) *Wind Energy Economics in Elsevier Encyclopedia on Renewable Energy*, Wind Energy Volume.
[33] Krohn, S Morthorst, P-E, and Awerbuch, S (eds.) (2009) *The Economics of Wind Energy*. Brussels, Belgium: EWEA.
[34] McLaughlin D, Clive P, and McKenzie J (2009) Staying ahead of the wind power curve. *Renewable Energy World*.

Further Reading

Freris, L (ed.) (1990) *Wind Energy Conversion Systems*. Hempstead, UK: Prentice Hall International.
Gasch R and Twele J (2002) *Wind Power Plants: Fundamentals, Design, Construction and Operation*. Berlin, Germany: Solarpraxis.
Gipe P (1995) *Wind Energy Comes of Age*. New York, NY: Wiley.
Hau E (2006) *Wind Turbines – Fundamentals, Technologies, Applications, Economics*. Berlin, Germany: Springer.
Manwell JF (2010) *Wind Energy Explained – Theory, Design and Application*, 2nd edn., Chichester, UK: Wiley.
Mendonca M (2007) *Feed-in Tariffs: Accelerating the Deployment of Renewable Energy*, World Future Council. London, UK: Earthscan.
Petersen E, Mortensen L, Niels G, et al. (1997) Wind power Meteorology. *Risoe-I-1206 (EN)*. Roskilde, Denmark: Risoe National Laboratory.
Quaschning V (2005) *Understanding Renewable Energy Systems*. London, UK: Earthscan.

2.14 Offshore Wind Power Basics

M Kapsali and JK Kaldellis, Technological Education Institute of Piraeus, Athens, Greece

© 2012 Elsevier Ltd. All rights reserved.

2.14.1	Introduction	432
2.14.2	Offshore Wind Energy Status	432
2.14.2.1	History and Background	432
2.14.2.2	Offshore Wind Energy Activity	434
2.14.3	Offshore Wind Farms – Basic Features	440
2.14.3.1	Wind Turbine Design	440
2.14.3.2	Support Structures and Towers	441
2.14.3.2.1	Shallow water technology	441
2.14.3.2.2	Transitional water technology	446
2.14.3.2.3	Floating technology	449
2.14.3.3	Supplementary Equipment	450
2.14.3.3.1	Offshore substation	450
2.14.3.3.2	Onshore substation	451
2.14.3.3.3	Underwater cabling	451
2.14.4	Offshore Wind Farm Design, Installation, and Maintenance	452
2.14.4.1	Equipment Selection Requirements	452
2.14.4.1.1	Wind evaluation	454
2.14.4.1.2	Wave and current evaluation	454
2.14.4.2	Other Wind Farm Design Considerations	455
2.14.4.3	Installation and Transportation Facilities	456
2.14.4.4	O&M Facilities	458
2.14.5	Offshore Wind Energy Economic Considerations	459
2.14.6	Environmental and Social Issues	463
2.14.6.1	Noise Impacts	463
2.14.6.2	Visual Impacts	463
2.14.6.3	Impacts on Wild Life	463
2.14.7	Future Trends and Prospects	464
References		466
Further Reading		468
Relevant Websites		468

Glossary

Capacity factor Ratio between the real and the potential electricity production if the wind turbine had operated at rated capacity.

Conventional power generation Burning coal, oil or natural gas to generate power.

Fixed bottom structure Mounting the wind turbine's tower on the seabed.

Floating concept Mounting the wind turbine's tower on a floating platform.

Foundation In this Chapter the term 'foundation' refers only to the part of the installation being actually into the seabed. However, in some other cases, one may see the term 'foundation' to be used for the whole part of the installation below the tower of the offshore wind turbine.

Life cycle cost The sum of all recurring and one-time (non-recurring) costs over the full life cycle of a project. Broadly speaking, this cost includes the initial investment, installation costs, O&M costs (split into the fixed maintenance cost and the variable one), and remaining (residual) value at the end of the project's useful life.

Shallow water technology Offshore wind applications appropriate for shallow water depths (e.g. <30 m).

Support structure The construction between the tower and the foundation.

Transitional water technology Offshore applications appropriate for transitional water depths (e.g. between 30 m and 60 m).

Wind farm micrositing The exact determination of the turbines' installation positions inside a wind farm's site.

2.14.1 Introduction

As has been already described in detail in previous chapters of this volume, in recent years, there has been a spectacular increase in wind power installations worldwide. Wind power technology is generally considered as a mature and cost-effective means of achieving future carbon reductions and renewable energy targets, but issues such as the scarcity of appropriate on-land installation sites and visual and noise constraints often limit its development. As a result, a substantial shift of the focus toward the vast offshore wind resources has been made and an incipient market has emerged, that is, offshore wind energy.

Offshore wind energy, as implied by the name, concerns the electricity produced by wind turbines placed offshore and practically in the sea. Offshore wind power comprises a relatively new challenge for the international wind industry with a demonstration history of around 20 years and a 10-year commercial history for large, utility-scale projects. Currently, about 3 GW of offshore wind power is installed worldwide, with the majority of projects being located in European waters. During the year 2010, offshore wind power experienced a record growth with more than 800 MW being installed. Despite the progress met, however, in the field of offshore wind during the recent years, offshore installations represent at the moment only a very small percentage of the global wind power capacity, approximately 1.5%. Nonetheless, it is expected that a considerable part of the future expansion of wind energy utilization, at least in Europe, will come from offshore resources.

Compared with land-based installations, offshore wind energy has greater resource potential (wind speeds tend to increase significantly with distance from land) and minimal environmental effects, but marine conditions (weather, winds, waves, and water currents) pose considerable challenges to project development that require a new approach in terms of wind turbine technology, support structures, electrical infrastructure, and logistics for installation and maintenance. At present, offshore wind farms require strong foundations that must be firmly placed into the seabed. Also, many kilometers of cabling are needed to transfer the power output back to shore, and both construction and maintenance work must be carried out in reasonable weather conditions using special vessels and equipment. Furthermore, compared with land-based wind power projects, the construction of offshore wind turbines requires advanced engineering and use of materials that resist corrosive marine environment.

The costs of offshore wind are currently significantly higher than onshore ones and strongly depend on site-specific conditions such as water depth, distance from shore, and seabed properties. In general, offshore wind power follows the following simple principle: The further the distance from the shore, the greater the wind resources are, resulting in higher energy production. But further distance from shore implies greater water depths, which in turn increase the development and operation costs of such projects.

It should be mentioned that the development of offshore wind power projects has been based considerably on experience and technology from the oil and gas industry, while the wind turbines used, currently having capacity ratings up to 5 MW, comprise adaptations from land-based counterparts. In this context, although offshore wind turbine technology has been evolving at a fast pace over the last few years, there is clearly much that needs to be done. In future, much larger machines, specifically constructed for offshore use, are envisaged that will likely benefit from economies of scale and result in significant cost reduction.

All the above issues are extensively analyzed in this chapter. It should be noted, however, that this text has been written on a scientific basis adjusted to be also equally well-understood by anyone who is interested but is not an expert reader. Since other chapters cover the fundamental aspects of wind energy, mainly from the point of view of land-based installations, this chapter intends to present only issues that are different for offshore counterparts. In this context, it is recommended that this chapter is read in parallel with other chapters of this volume.

2.14.2 Offshore Wind Energy Status

Over the last 20 years, there has been a spectacular increase in wind power installations worldwide. The enormous growth of the onshore wind energy industry has been accompanied by the growth of offshore wind power technology, especially during recent years, with several countries (United Kingdom, Denmark, Netherlands, etc.) being the key drivers for its development. In this section, a review of the offshore global wind energy installations is undertaken, starting from the very first applications up until today.

2.14.2.1 History and Background

The first documented concepts of offshore wind turbines were developed by Hermann Honnef in Germany in 1932 [1]. The first concept of large-scale offshore wind farms was developed by Prof. William E. Heronemus off the coast of Massachusetts in 1972 [2], but they were never installed. Eventually, the first offshore wind power test facility was set up in Sweden in 1990. It was a single wind turbine of 220 kW rated power, at a distance of 250 m from the coast, supported on a tripod structure anchored to the seabed about 7 m deep.

The first full-scale development of offshore wind power projects was driven largely by commercial aspirations of the European wind industry, considering the oceans as a feasible solution to the shortage of onshore sites. The first offshore wind farm was commissioned in 1991 in Denmark and constructed by the utility company SEAS. This small wind farm, which is still in operation, consists of 11 stall-controlled wind turbines of total rated power 4.95 MW (450 kW each). It is located 1.5–3 km north from the coast of the island of Lolland, near the village of Vindeby (**Figure 1**). The total area of the wind farm is 3 km^2 and it has gravity-based foundation structure type. The wind turbines are placed in shallow water, 3–5 m deep, in two parallel rows, with the distance between each turbine being approximately 500 m. The cost of construction is stated as being approximately €10 million [4].

The world's second offshore wind farm (**Figure 2**) was built in 1994 in the Netherlands, at a depth of 5–10 m, with 800 m average distance from the shore. It consists of four wind turbines of 500 kW each, and the foundation type adopted for this project is monopile. Just after 1 year, in 1995, the world's third offshore wind farm (**Figure 3**) was commissioned between the Jutland peninsula and the small island of Tunø Knob in Denmark. It consists of 10 wind turbines of 500 kW each, sited 6 km far from the shore at a depth of 3–6 m. The turbines are placed in two rows, with a distance of 200 m between each turbine and 400 m between the two rows. The foundation structure of the wind farm is gravity-based type. Each turbine is a horizontal axis pitch regulated machine, orientated upwind with a tubular tower and a three-bladed rotor of 39 m diameter.

In the following 5 years, relatively small offshore wind power projects of 450–600 kW units rating were installed in the United Kingdom, the Netherlands, and Sweden, at distances of up to 3 km from the coast and depths of up to 8 m. Multimegawatt wind turbines appeared later, in a second phase, along with the opportunity of experiencing deeper waters in the sea. In 2001, the construction of the first large-scale offshore wind farm (**Figure 4**) of Middelgrunden with a total rated power of 40 MW (20 wind turbines of 2 MW each) ended 2 km outside of the harbor of Copenhagen in Denmark, where the seabed is situated between 2.5 and 5 m under sea level.

The demonstration project of Middelgrunden in Denmark led the way for two larger offshore wind power projects, that is, Horns Rev I (160 MW) in 2002 and Nysted (165.2 MW) in 2003. However, the construction costs of these projects were higher than

Figure 1 Vindeby offshore wind farm in Denmark [3].

Figure 2 Lely offshore wind farm in the Netherlands [5]. Photo by Martin Bond.

Figure 3 Tunø Knob offshore wind farm in Denmark. Vestas offshore wind turbines. Still: Bo Hovgaard.

Figure 4 Offshore wind farm outside the harbor of Copenhagen [7].

anticipated, while some unexpected failures occurred, resulting mainly from the turbines' exposure to harsh wind and wave conditions. These issues resulted in the deterioration of some of the initial enthusiasm for the expansion of the offshore wind power market, and thus in 2005 only one new project was installed. Nevertheless, the great efforts made by manufacturers and developers in order to identify and improve problems associated with this first phase of projects [8] eventually led to 13 new commercial offshore wind farm installations in 2008 and 2009.

2.14.2.2 Offshore Wind Energy Activity

Since the installation of the first offshore wind power project, both size and capacity of wind turbines have increased considerably during recent years (**Table 1**). While at land-based sites the size of wind turbines, in terms of height and rotor diameter, is often restricted due to visual impacts, these limits are not encountered in marine environments. The experience has grown significantly so that now many countries are building large, utility-scale offshore wind farms or at least have plans to do so. However, the vast majority of the existing large-scale commercial projects still use shallow water technology (located at less than 30 m water depth), but the idea of going deeper is gradually moving closer toward implementation.

Drivers of offshore wind power development vary from country to country, either determined by the availability of high wind resources or the limitation of land for new onshore installations. As of 2010, about 96% of global offshore wind farms are located in European waters, with almost 85% of the total installed capacity being located in the United Kingdom, Denmark, and The Netherlands (**Figure 5**). The new installations in 2010 (as of September) were more than 800 MW, with the cumulative global offshore wind power market finally reaching almost 3 GW, presenting a 40% increase over 2009 (**Figure 6**).

Table 1 Wind turbines' size and capacity evolution for selected models

Project	Year	Capacity of each turbine (MW)	Turbine type	Hub height (m)	Rotor diameter (m)
Irene Vorrink	1996	0.6	Nordtank	50	43
Scroby Sands	2004	2	Vestas V80	60	80
Nysted	2003	2.3	Siemens	69	80
Robin Rigg	2010	3	Vestas V90	80	90
Alpha Ventus	2009	5	Repower/Multibrid	92/90	126/116

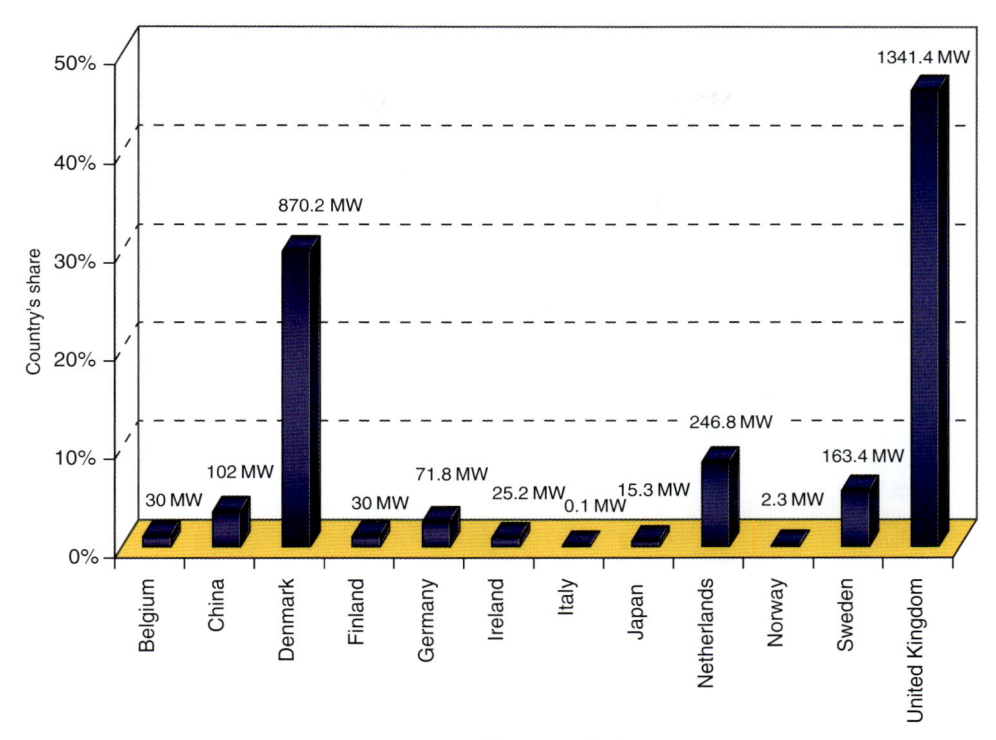

Figure 5 Cumulative offshore wind power percentage by country (as of September 2010).

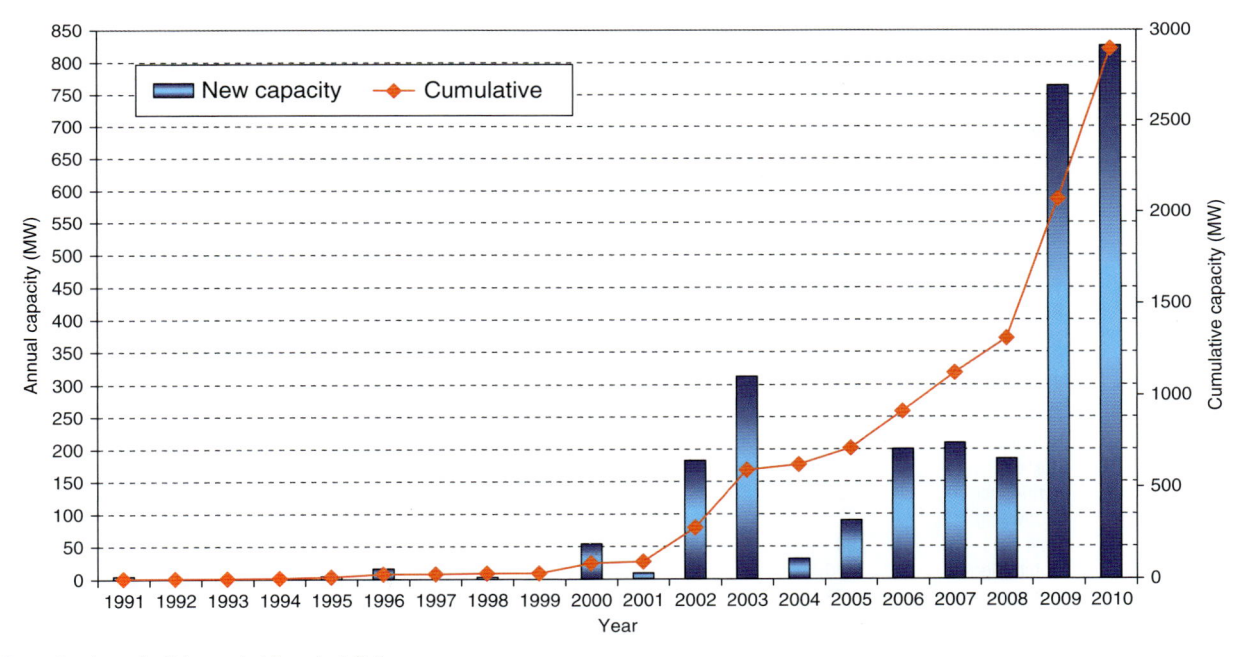

Figure 6 Annual offshore wind farm installations.

More specifically, by September 2010, the offshore wind power industry had developed a total of 45 projects, many of them large-scale and fully commercial in the waters of Belgium, China, Denmark, Finland, Germany, Ireland, Italy, Japan, The Netherlands, Norway, Sweden, and the United Kingdom. In terms of capacity, by 2010, offshore wind farms represented 1.5% of the total installed wind power in the world. **Table 2** contains information about all offshore wind farm installations up till now, showing capacity, distance from the shore, and water depth along with the installation year of each project.

Table 2 Operational wind farms in the world as of September 2010

Country	Project	Rated power (MW)	Average water depth (m)	Average distance from shore (km)	Number of wind turbines	Turbine capacity (MW)	Turbine manufacturer	Year online
Belgium	Thornton Bank	30	20	29	6	5	Repower	2008
China	Donghai Bridge	102	10	10.5	34	3	Sinovel	2010
Denmark	Vindeby	5	4	3	11	0.45	Bonus	1991
	Tunø Knob	5	3	6	10	0.5	Vestas	1995
	Middelgrunden	40	8	3	20	2	Bonus	2000
	Horns Rev I	160	10	16	80	2	Vestas	2002
	Samsø	23	20	3.5	10	2.3	Bonus	2002
	Frederickshavn	10.6	3	1	4	2.65	Vestas/Bonus/Nordex	2003
	Nysted	165.2	8	8	72	2.3	Bonus	2003
	Rønland	17.2	1	0.1	8	2.3/2	Bonus/Vestas	2003
	Horns Rev II	209	13	30	91	2.3	Siemens	2009
	Sprogø	21	11	1	7	3	Vestas	2009
	Avedøre	7.2	2	0.1	2	3.6	Siemens	2009
	Rødstand II	207	9	9	90	2.3	Siemens	2010
Finland	Kemi Ajos I + II	30	0	1	10	3	WinWinD	2008
Germany	Ems-Emdem	4.5	3	0.1	1	4.5	Enercon	2004
	Breitling	2.3	2	0.5	1	2.3	Nordex	2006
	Hooksiel	5	5	0.5	1	5	Enercon	2008
	Alpha Ventus	60	30	53	12	5	Repower/AREVA	2009
Ireland	Arklow Bank	25.2	15	10	7	3.6	GE	2004
Italy	Brindisi	0.08	108	20	1	0.08	Blue H	2008
Japan	Setana	1.32	10	0.2	2	0.66	Vestas	2004
	Kamisu	14	5	0.04	7	2	Hitachi	2010
The Netherlands	Lely	2	7.5	0.8	4	0.5	Nedwind	1994
	Irene Vorrink	16.8	2	0.1	28	0.6	Nordtank	1996
	Egmond aan Zee	108	20	10	36	3	Vestas	2006
	Princess Amalia	120	22	23	60	2	Vestas	2008
Norway	Hywind	2.3	220	10	1	2.3	Siemens	2009
Sweden	Bockstigen	2.75	7	3	5	0.55	Windworld	1998
	Utgrunden	10.5	7	7	7	1.5	Enron/GE Wind Energy	2000
	Yttre Stengrund	10	10	4	5	2	NEG-Micon	2001
	Lillgrund	110	6	10	48	2.3	Siemens	2007
	Vavern	30	7	4	10	3	WinWinD	2010
The United Kingdom	Blyth	4	6	1	2	2	Vestas	2000
	North Hoyle	60	9	8	30	2	Vestas	2003
	Scroby Sands	60	6	3	30	2	Vestas	2003
	Kentish Flats	90	5	9	30	3	Vestas	2005
	Barrow-in-Furness	90	15	7	30	3	Vestas	2006
	Beatrice	10	45	25	2	5	Repower	2007
	Burbo	90	10	5	25	3.6	Siemens	2007
	Lynn/Inner Dowsing	194.4	10	5	54	3.6	Siemens	2009
	Rhyl Flats	90	8	8	25	3.6	Siemens	2009
	Robin Rigg	180	5	9.5	60	3	Vestas	2009
	Gunfleet Sands	173	8	7	48	3.6	Siemens	2010
	Thanet	300	22.5	11.5	100	3	Vestas	2010

According to official data [9], it is expected that between 1 and 1.5 GW of new offshore wind power capacity will be fully connected in Europe during 2011. As seen in **Table 3**, there are 15 offshore wind energy projects (~4 GW) which are under construction and they are going to operate within 2011 and beyond. Furthermore, at least 37 projects have been given consent worldwide, among which many belong to countries without any offshore wind energy activity yet (i.e., the United States, Canada, and France) [10].

As mentioned above, up till now vast deployment has taken place in Northern Europe, a situation expected to continue for another 5 years. Before the end of 2014, more than 16 GW of additional capacity is estimated to be installed, with the United

Table 3 Wind farms under construction in the world, planned to operate in 2011 [10]

Country	Project	Rated capacity (MW)
Belgium	Bligh Bank Belwind I	165
Belgium	Thorntonbank	144
Denmark	Anholt	400
Denmark	Frederikshavn	12
Germany	Baltic 1	48.3
Germany	Bard 1	400
Germany	Borkum West II	400
Germany	Global Tech 1	400
Italy	Tricase	90
United Kingdom	Greater Gabbard 1	288
United Kingdom	Greater Gabbard 2	216
United Kingdom	Gwynt y Mor	576
United Kingdom	London Array	630
United Kingdom	Ormonde	150
	Total	3919.3

Kingdom and Germany being the two leading markets in the world. By 2020, offshore wind power capacity is expected to reach a total of 75 GW worldwide, with significant contributions from China and the United States [11], while the European target has been set to 40 GW by 2020 and 150 GW by 2030 [12].

Offshore wind power market is currently dominated by a few companies. On the demand side, 10 companies or consortia account for all 3 GW of offshore capacity presently in operation. Dong Energy (Denmark), Vattenfall (Sweden), and E.on (Germany) are the leading operators [11], all being giant European utilities.

On the supply side, Vestas and Siemens (formerly Bonus Energy A/S) are the leading wind turbine manufacturers worldwide in terms of installed capacity, with more than 2 GW turbines operating offshore (**Figure 7**), although there are several other manufacturers who are now developing new offshore wind turbine types which are close to commercial viability [8]. Both Repower Systems and AREVA Multibrid installed commercial turbines of 5 MW with a pilot project named Alpha Ventus in Germany in 2009. Sinovel also entered the market in 2009 with SL3000/90, the first offshore wind turbine manufactured in China and installed in the Donghai Bridge project in Shanghai. More recently, General Electric reentered the offshore wind market with the announcement of its 4.1 MW direct drive wind turbine, which is still under development [13].

The United Kingdom is the most important player in the offshore wind energy market, with almost 50% of the offshore wind power installations in the world being located in British waters. It has 12 operating wind farms (as of December 2010) and the plans for further development are considerable, since more than 2 GW of offshore wind farms are currently under construction and many more are at approval stage.

Thanet wind farm (**Figure 8**), which is the world's largest offshore wind power project up till now, is located in the United Kingdom's waters. The wind farm has 100 wind turbines that have a total capacity of 300 MW, enough to power more than 200 000 homes per year. The Thanet project is located approximately 12 km off Foreness Point, the most eastern part of Kent in England. Planning permission for the project was granted on 18 December 2006. Eventually, the wind farm was officially opened on 23 September 2010 and the total investment for completing the project is in the order of around £780 million (or ~€874 million based on present day currency conversion prices, that is, £1 = €1.121) [14]. The project covers an area of about 35 km^2, with the distance between wind turbines being approximately 500 m along rows and 800 m between rows. Each turbine has rotor diameter 90 m

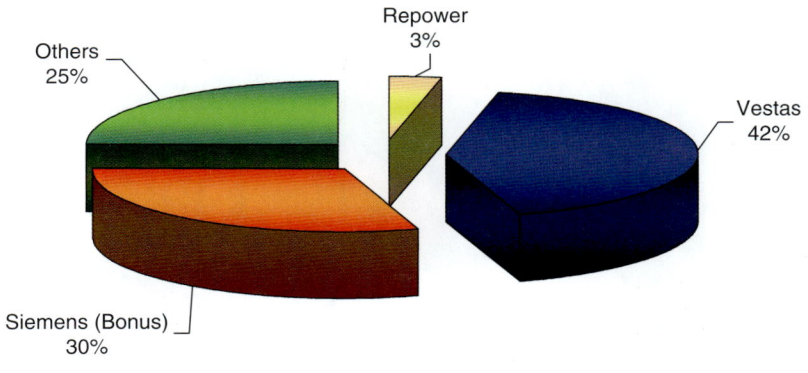

Figure 7 Wind turbine manufacturers' share until September 2010.

Figure 8 Thanet offshore wind power project in the United Kingdom [15].

and is 115 m tall at its highest point, with an average clearance above sea level of about 23 m. Two submarine power cables run from an offshore substation within the wind farm connecting to an existing onshore substation in Richborough, Kent.

The United Kingdom has also built the demonstration offshore wind farm called Beatrice, consisting of two wind turbines of 5 MW each. The turbines are placed in a water depth of 45 m at an average distance of 25 km from the shore, representing the deepest offshore wind turbine site in the world.

Denmark is the pioneer in offshore wind turbine development as it owns the first offshore wind farm in the word (i.e., Vindeby in 1991). At this time, it has 12 operating wind farms (September 2010), including the second biggest located at Horns Rev in the North Sea. The Horns Rev II project has rated capacity of 209 MW and consists of 91 turbines located 30 km far from the shore at an average water depth of 13 m.

Another big project called Rødsand II (**Figure 9**) was brought online recently (in October 2010) in the Baltic Sea with a generating capacity of 207 MW. It is located 4 km off the Danish island of Lolland, very close to the east of the existing 166 MW Rødsand I (also called Nysted, see **Figure 10**). Rødsand II covers an area of 35 km^2 at an average water depth of 9 m and consists of 90 wind turbines of 2.3 MW each. Each turbine has a hub height of 68 m and a rotor blade diameter of 93 m. The turbines are connected with 33 kV underwater cables leading to a substation. It should be noted that this project benefits from a perfect offshore combination, that is, considerable wind energy yield (~800 GWh per year, supplying 230 000 homes with electricity), closeness to the shore, shallow waters, and good soil conditions. The total investment for the completion of this project amounts to about €400 million [16].

The Netherlands is the second country immediately after Denmark that developed offshore wind farms. As of September 2010, the Netherlands has almost 247 MW offshore wind generating capacity, with the biggest wind farm being that of Princess Amalia (60 wind turbines of 2 MW each), lying approximately 23 km west of the village of Egmond aan Zee, in the North Sea. The wind turbine towers are placed on monopile foundations at 23 km average distance from the shore in 22 m water depth. The second

Figure 9 Rødsand II offshore wind power project in Denmark [16].

Figure 10 Nysted offshore wind power project in Denmark [16].

largest offshore wind farm in the Netherlands is the project of Egmond aan Zee, with 108 MW rated power (36 wind turbines of 3 MW each). It is located at an average distance from the shore of about 10 km, at a water depth of 20 m. Egmond aan Zee project started operation in October 2007 and is now generating enough electrical power for about 100 000 Dutch households.

Sweden currently obtains almost 7% of the total offshore wind power installations. The first Swedish and the fifth worldwide offshore wind farm named Bockstigen has been operating since 1998, 3 km far from the coast of Gotland. It was built as a demonstration project with 2.8 MW generating capacity (five wind turbines of 550 kW each). Each three-bladed turbine was installed on a 2.1 m diameter steel monopile foundation grouted into a 2.25 m diameter socket drilled in a 10 m deep hole in the seabed. While at earlier wind farms, attention was paid on the demonstration of the technical feasibility of offshore wind energy utilization, Bockstigen aimed at demonstrating its economic viability [17]. During the next decade, Sweden installed four more projects and as of September 2010 the offshore wind capacity reached almost 163 MW.

China, the world's largest onshore wind power developer, with a total of about 43 GW wind turbine installed capacity by the end of 2010, erected the first large-scale offshore wind farm (Donghai Bridge) outside Europe in 2009, adding 63 MW by year-end for a project that reached 102 MW upon completion in early 2010. Thus, although offshore wind power development in China has been much delayed, the year 2010 marked the start of the country's offshore wind power sector's transition from research and pilot projects to operational wind farms. Donghai Bridge project (**Figure 11**) is located on the east side of the Shanghai East Sea Bridge. It comprises 34 wind turbines of 3 MW capacity, and it is placed at an average distance of 10.5 km from the shore in 10 m water depth. According to the Chinese Renewable Energy Industries Association (CREIA) [19], China is planning to expand its offshore wind power installed capacity to 5 GW by 2015 and 30 GW by 2020.

Germany currently obtains almost 72 MW of offshore wind farm installations. Although Germany is one of the front-runners in the installation of renewable energy assets, the pace toward offshore wind farms was rather slow mainly because of limited coastline availability, the need to move into deeper waters, and skepticism concerning economic feasibility of such projects. Nevertheless, this status seems to change as the government has so far granted permission for 20 offshore wind farms with a total capacity of about 7 GW [10] while another 1.2 GW is currently under development (see also **Table 3**).

As of September 2010, Germany's only large-scale offshore wind farm is Alpha Ventus (**Figure 12**), which has been initially launched as a pilot project by the German government. This wind farm comprises the deepest large-scale operational offshore wind power project at this time, with an average distance from the shore of about 53 km. It officially began to operate in April 2010. It is situated in the North Sea, at 30 m average water depth. It consists of 12 wind turbines of 5 MW generating capacity, giving a total of 60 MW. The total

Figure 11 Donghai Bridge wind power project in China [18].

Figure 12 Alpha Ventus wind power project in Germany [20].

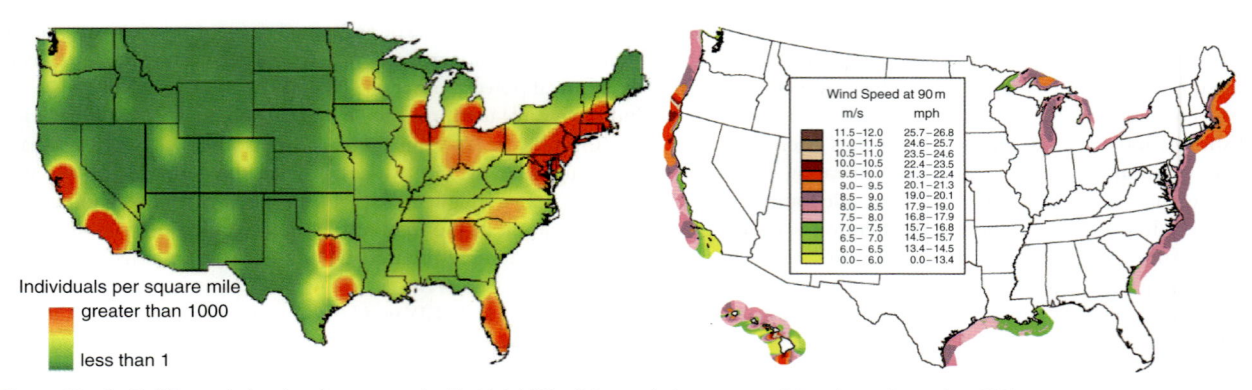

Figure 13 (Left) US population density compared with (right) US offshore wind resource at 90 m above the surface [21].

investment of Alpha Ventus is about €250 million (quite a high specific turnkey cost ≈4150 € kW^{-1}), and by the construction time of the project, it was the only wind farm in the world using tripods as foundations for supporting six of the turbines [20].

The United States has also ambitious offshore wind energy plans but none is yet implemented. Even though the United States is among the leaders in land-based wind energy capacity, no offshore wind power projects have been installed to date. However, about 20 projects of more than 2 GW are in the planning and permitting process. Most of these activities are located in the Northeast and Mid-Atlantic regions, although projects are being considered or approved also in wind-rich areas along the Great Lakes, the Gulf of Mexico, and the Pacific Coast. The deep waters off the West Coast, however, pose a technological challenge for the near term [8].

Figure 13 shows the potential offshore wind resources off the US coast compared with the density population. A very interesting relation may be obtained between these two maps, showing the great possibilities regarding offshore wind energy in the United States [22]. Specifically, most of the potential offshore wind resources are found relatively close to major urban load centers, where high energy costs prevail and where opportunities for wind development on-land are limited. This is especially true in the densely populated northeast, where nearly one-fifth of the national population live on less than 2% of the total land area [23].

2.14.3 Offshore Wind Farms – Basic Features

Most of the current offshore wind energy system designs have been drawn from offshore oil and gas extraction industry and from land-based wind energy installations. However, the combination of wind, waves, and in some cases ice has introduced a new set of unique engineering challenges (e.g., construction in the marine environment, towers and foundation design, and electrical transmission) that need to be fully addressed and tested. This section describes the principal components of an offshore wind energy system, that is, wind turbines, towers, foundations, and additional equipment required for the system's erection and commissioning.

2.14.3.1 Wind Turbine Design

The wind turbine is the energy producing component and the most visible part of an offshore wind farm installation. The standard wind turbine type operating today in marine environments consists of a hub and a blade rotor assembly connected through a drive train to the generator housed in a nacelle (**Figures 14** and **15**). The most commonly met applications are three-bladed horizontal axis machines, yaw-controlled, active blade-pitch-to-feather controlled, upwind rotors, with a diameter normally between 90 and 130 m.

Several types of commercial offshore wind energy applications have been developed so far, based on land-based proven technologies, but with some significant subsystem upgrades. These kinds of systems have special components and characteristics which must meet the needs of a more remote, harsh, and demanding environment (i.e., ocean conditions). The modifications from onshore installations include, among others, strengthening the tower to cope with the additional load from waves, incorporating enhanced corrosion protection systems to keep corrosive salty water and air away from the electrical parts of the wind turbine, and using warning lights, bright markers, and fog signals to ensure the safety of marine navigation. Also, lightning is generally considered as more risky offshore, so instead of incorporating systems to ease handling, the wind turbine blades are provided with better protection, the same used on the most problematic sites onshore.

Offshore wind generators are generally larger than the onshore ones in order to take advantage of the more consistent and stronger offshore winds. Also, locating wind farms offshore significantly reduces public concerns related to visual impacts, thus allowing the use of larger machines with greater power output than on-land.

A typical onshore wind turbine today has a tower height of about 60–80 m, while in offshore applications, the height may be considerably higher with rotor diameters reaching 130 m and even more. Offshore turbines installed today are generally between 2 and 5 MW, but prototypes up to 7 MW are currently being tested, indicating the manufacturing trends about the future wind turbines operating in maritime environments. Some examples are given in **Table 4**. This new generation of wind turbines is intended to acquire innovative operation and maintenance (O&M) concepts and higher technical reliability.

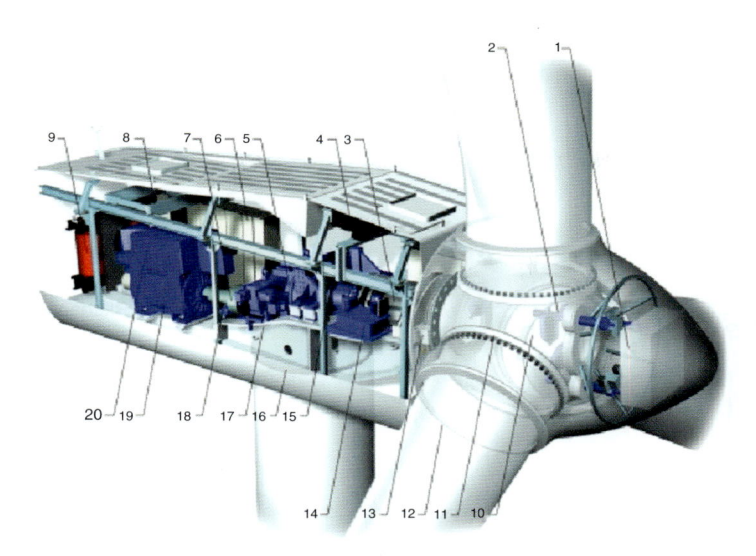

1. Hub controller
4. Oil cooler
7. Parking brake
10. Blade hub
13. Rotor lock system
16. Yaw ring
19. Generator

2. Pitch cylinder
5. Gearbox
8. Service crane
11. Blade bearing
14. Hydraulic unit
17. Machine foundation
20. Generator cooler

3. Main shaft
6. VMP-top controller
9. Transformer
12. Blade
15. Hydraulic shrink disk
18. Yaw gears

Figure 14 General layout of a horizontal axis wind turbine [24].

2.14.3.2 Support Structures and Towers

Offshore, the climate is considerably different from onshore, winds are less turbulent but stronger, and wind shear (i.e., the change in wind velocity resulting from the change in elevation) is lower; thus, shorter towers may be used than those in land-based applications for the same output. Offshore wind turbines are generally mounted on tubular steel or lattice towers (with a special offshore coating to withstand the harsh marine environment), which are fixed to a foundation so that turbines can capture winds well above the water's surface.

The selection of the offshore wind turbine support structure is based on site-specific conditions. Water depth, wind/wave conditions, currents, seabed properties (i.e., natural or man-made obstructions, slopes, stability, composition, etc.), and access requirements are the basic parameters affecting the design of the foundation type to be used.

So far, there is not a standard foundation type suitable for all kinds of seabed conditions. Various foundations have been used up till now (**Figure 16**), with the most common types being the monopile and the gravity-based one, both employed in shallow waters. Note that shallow water depths range between 0 and 30 m, transitional depths between 30 and 60 m, while beyond that point deep water concepts are introduced (see **Figure 17**). Thus, generally speaking, the support structures of offshore wind turbines may be classified into three main groups, that is, shallow water, transitional, and floating. Nevertheless, the latter type is still into the prototype phase and may be feasible as a future option in deep waters. **Figure 18** summarizes the main support structures for offshore wind turbines in terms of maturity and water depth.

2.14.3.2.1 Shallow water technology

As mentioned above, today, the majority of offshore wind power projects are located in shallow waters between 5 and 20 m (see also **Table 2**) and employ fixed bottom structures suitable for small to moderate depths. The basic concepts and some installation details of the main foundations in shallow waters such as monopiles, gravity based, and suction buckets are presented in the following.

2.14.3.2.1(i) Monopile foundation

A monopile (**Figure 19**) is a giant steel tube which is normally used in waters up to 30 m deep. It comprises the simplest and the most commonly employed foundation solution up till now mainly due to its low cost, the minimal footprint on the seabed, and low design requirements for transition from onshore to offshore. Besides, the installation of a monopile does not generally entail advanced techniques or significant preparation of the seabed as it is usually hammered into the ocean floor. The relatively simple shape of monopile keeps its construction cost down but calls for a large tube diameter of up to 6 m. The total weight of the structure may be more than 500 t. For the sake of reference, this type of foundation has been successfully installed at the 180 MW Robin Rigg project in the United Kingdom (**Figure 20**) and at the 160 MW Horns Rev I project in Denmark.

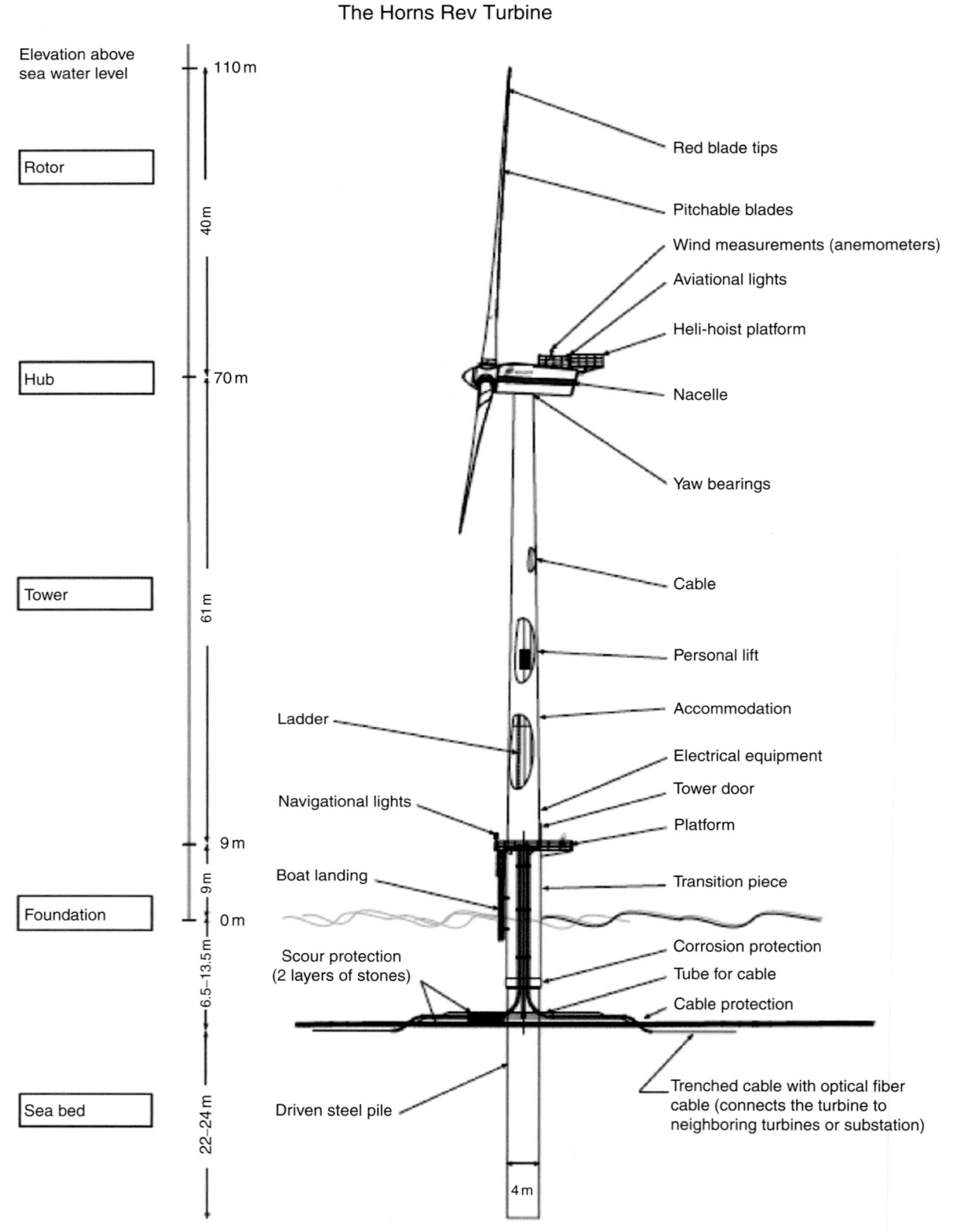

Figure 15 Principal components and dimensions of an offshore wind turbine [25].

Table 4 Current offshore wind turbine types (as of September 2010) [26]

Manufacturer	Rated capacity (MW)	Hub height (m)	Rotor diameter (m)	Status
AREVA Multibrid	5	90	116	Commercial
BARD	6.5	90	120	In progress
BARD	5	90	122	Commercial
GE	4.1	Site specific	113	In progress
Nordex	2.3	70/80/100/105	90	Commercial
Nordex	6	Unspecified	150	In progress
Repower	5	90–100	126	Commercial
Repower	6	85–95	126	In progress
Siemens	3.6	90	120	Commercial
Siemens	2.3	Site specific	93	Commercial
Sinovel	6	Unspecified	128	In progress
Sinovel	3	80/90/100/110	122	Commercial
Vestas	7	Site specific	164	In progress
Vestas	3	Site specific	112	Commercial
Vestas	3	Site specific	90	Commercial
WinWinD	3	80/88/100	90/100/103/109	Commercial

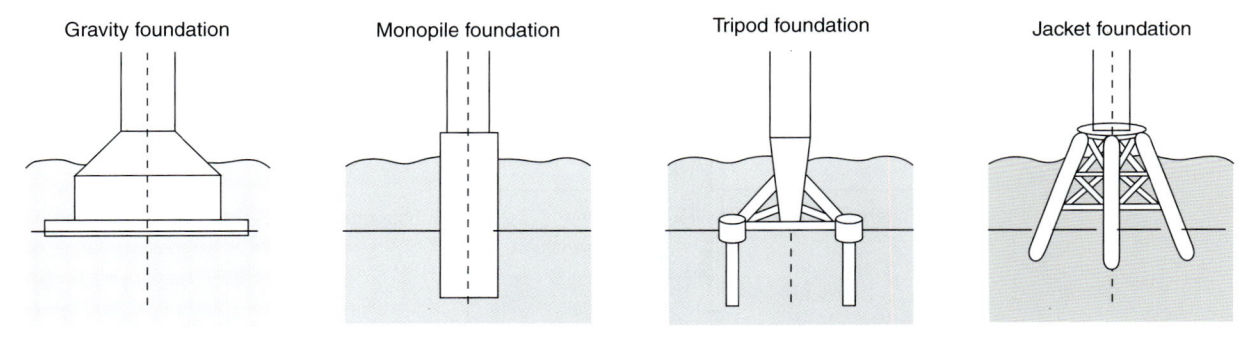

Figure 16 Overview of the main types of offshore support structures installed today [16].

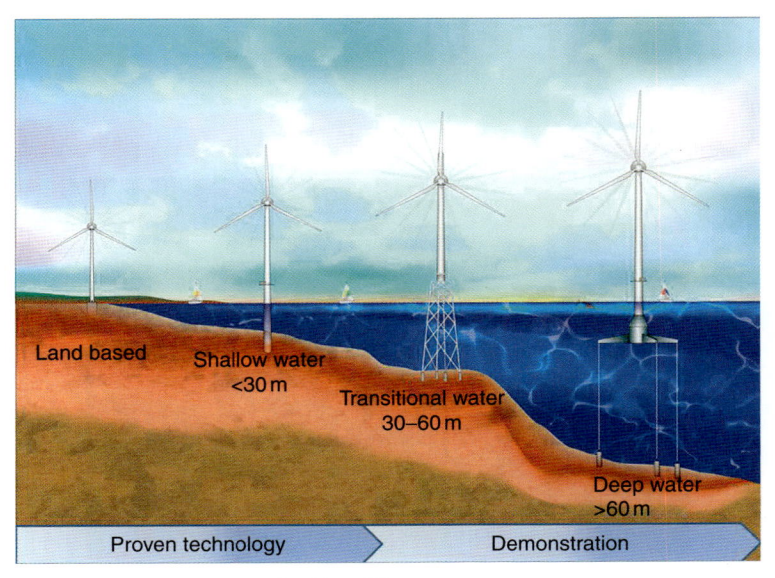

Figure 17 Substructure technology classes for offshore wind turbines [8].

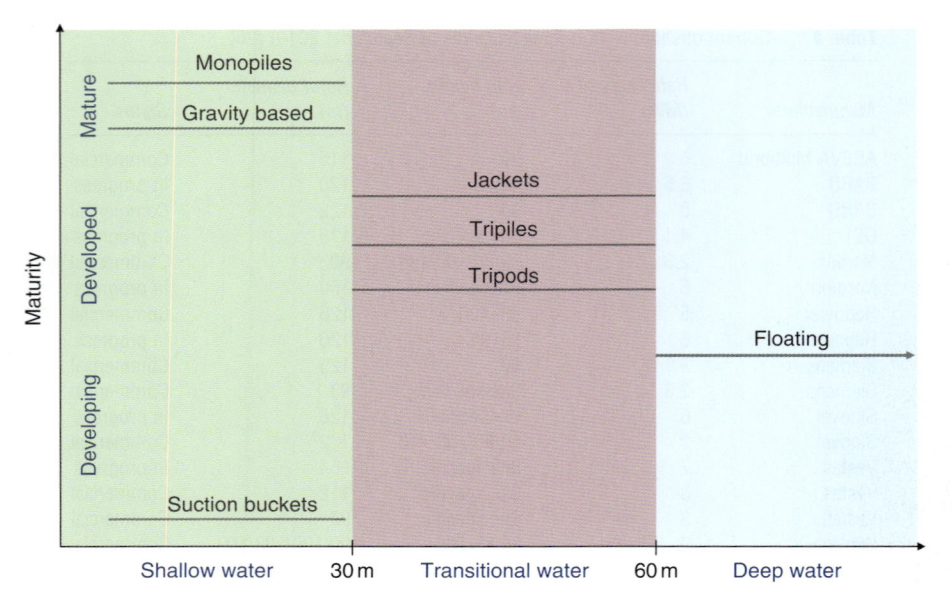

Figure 18 Main support structure technology in relation to water depth.

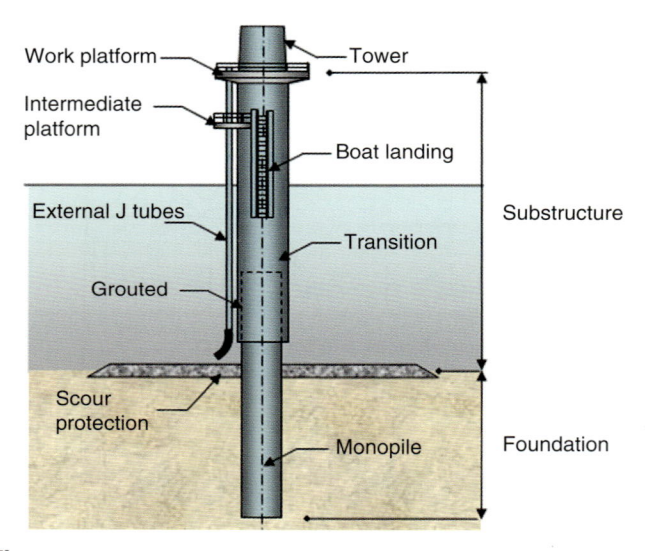

Figure 19 Monopile foundation [27].

Figure 20 Robin Rigg wind power project in the United Kingdom [16].

Figure 21 Grouted connection with gaps [28].

In case that the monopile is hammered into the seabed, the tube rests in the soil and a transition piece connects the support structure with the wind turbine tower (see **Figure 21**). Nevertheless, the transition piece represents a significant weakness of the monopile concept. As the tower vibrates over the years due to the dynamic loads from wind and waves, the grout (i.e., the material which is often used to connect the monopile with the transition piece) crumbles and must be refilled.

The only way to reduce the risk of grout crumbling is to employ a conical design concept for the transition piece [28] or to drill the monopile directly into the soil without the use of a transition piece [29]. However, the second choice is rarely used, due to the high cost associated with it. Drilling is an option only in case where hammering the monopile down is prohibitive due to unsuitable conditions of the soil.

Although monopile foundation is an appropriate choice for many projects located up to 30 m depth, in deeper waters it may be inapplicable. As a rule of thumb, going deeper implies increase in the wave, wind, and current loading of the structure. On top of that, the higher performance of the wind turbines, which is normally encountered in such cases, indicates the installation of larger machines with greater diameters and thus the implementation of more complex designs (e.g., tripods, jackets, or floating) to support the structure. The required size of the monopile increases disproportionately with the size of the wind turbine, a condition that may lead to technoeconomic unfeasible results.

2.14.3.2.1(ii) Gravity-based foundation

The gravity-based foundation comprises an alternative solution employed in shallow waters up to 20–30 m. Eleven concrete gravity-based structures, each one weighing an average of 908 t, were used to hold the wind turbines of the first offshore wind farm in the world, Vindeby in Denmark.

Today, gravity-based structures are still constructed in the same way. The basic difference with the monopile is that this type of foundation is not drilled or hammered into the seabed but rests on the top of the ocean floor. It is simply a large and heavy mass of material, normally the caisson of reinforced concrete, steel, or a composite. However, depending upon site geologic conditions, this foundation may require significant seabed preparation before its installation, for example, dredging, gravel, and scour protection (measures taken in order to avoid soil erosion).

These structures are constructed almost entirely onshore and they are transported on barges to the site of installation. They are lifted using heavy cranes, sunk, and filled with ballast to increase their resistance to loads. While these kinds of structures can weigh several hundred and even thousand tons, they can last up to 100 years without any significant maintenance requirements.

Figure 22 shows the installation of a gravity-based structure in the Rødstand II project in Denmark. This kind of structure has also been deployed successfully at projects such as the 165.2 MW Nysted and 23 MW Samsø in Denmark and more recently at the Thornton Bank in Belgium.

2.14.3.2.1(iii) Suction bucket foundation

While the suction bucket foundation concept has been widely used in practice in the oil and gas industry, it has not yet been used commercially as an alternative to support wind turbines offshore in shallow waters. However, a lot of research effort [30, 31] has been put on it, showing that this technology may be applied equally well as an offshore wind turbine foundation solution.

Figure 22 Installation of a gravity-based support structure at Rødstand II project in Denmark [29].

Figure 23 Suction bucket foundation [8].

Suction bucket foundation consists of a vertical steel skirt extending down from a horizontal base resting on the soil surface, as illustrated in **Figure 23**. The bucket is installed by means of suction. It is placed initially on the ocean floor with its self-weight providing a seal between the skirt tip and the soil. Then, further penetration is achieved by pumping out the water through an opening in the top lid of the bucket. The resulting differential pressure created between the inside and outside of the bucket forces it downward into the desired depth of the soil [32].

2.14.3.2.2 Transitional water technology

Transitional or intermediate water technology is used to support wind turbines at depths between 30 and 60 m. Generally, the advantage of employing wind turbines in these areas is that the visual impacts are minimized and wind generators demonstrate higher performance compared with shallow water sites. Due to the design adopted and the characteristics of such structures, the alternating tensile and compressive loads applied on their elements (e.g., piles) are less than those met at a compact foundation (e.g., monopiles and gravity based), a fact which makes them suitable for greater depths. However, transitional structures imply higher costs and a more difficult installation process but comprise a step toward floating systems and exploitation of the full wind resource met in deep waters. Current transitional water technology may be classified into three main types, that is, jacket, tripod, and triple support structures.

2.14.3.2.2(i) Jacket support structure

The jacket structure is a design commonly applied by the oil and gas industry for supporting rigs offshore, at water depths much greater than 100 m. A jacket is made up of four legs of more than 1 m diameter connected to each other with bracings (**Figure 24**). It also consists of a working platform, corrosion protection system, cables, and ladders. After a thorough preparation of the seabed, the legs are usually attached to the ground using piles to secure the structure but gravitation bases or suction anchors may also comprise a possibility [29].

The first successful attempt of installing a jacket structure was made quite recently, in 2007, in the Beatrice demonstrative project in the United Kingdom, at a water depth of 45 m. The latest in the world on jacket structures is the Alpha Ventus project in Germany, in 2009. This is the largest project installed in transitional waters so far. Although the average water depth on-site is almost 30 m, the project employs six 5 MW wind turbines on jackets and six 5 MW wind turbines on tripods. **Figure 25** shows the transportation on a barge of three from the six jackets used in the Alpha Ventus project.

2.14.3.2.2(ii) Tripod support structure

This structure got its name from the tripod well known to everyone, used by photographers. In offshore sites, however, it comprises a new and a rarely used concept so far. The whole structure is made of steel and consists of a central cylindrical section, bracings, and three supporting pile sleeves (**Figure 26**). Once the tripod is transported to the site of installation, the structure is lowered to the seabed and a pile is driven through each sleeve. For securing the structure to the seabed, the connection between the pile and the sleeve is filled with grout or concrete. Tripod structures' manufacture is relatively complex and time consuming, while the transportation and installation processes require large barges and heavy lifting cranes.

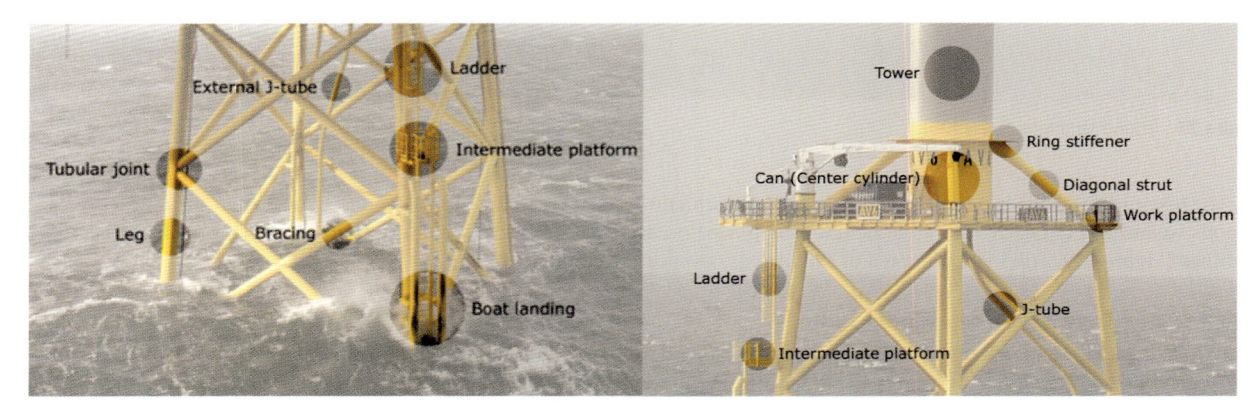

Figure 24 Jacket structure [29].

Figure 25 Jacket structures on their way to the site of Alpha Ventus [29].

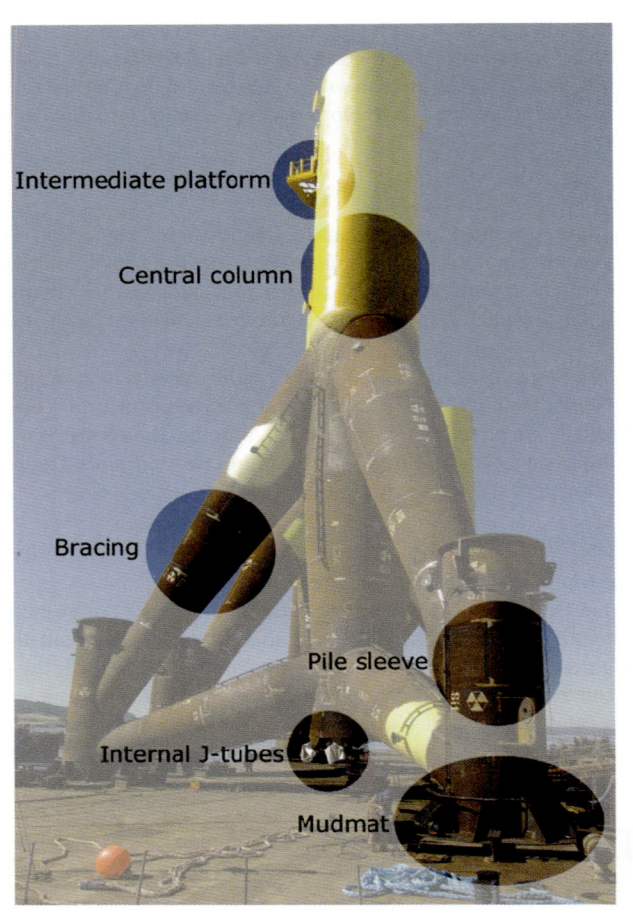

Figure 26 Tripod structure details [29].

The first and so far the last implementation of tripod structures has been in the Alpha Ventus offshore demonstration project. Six tripods weighing 710 t each with 45 m height were placed on 40 m long piles into the seabed to support six of the project's wind turbines (**Figure 27**). The triangular area of the tripods covers an overall area of 255 m^2 [33].

2.14.3.2.2(iii) Tripile support structure
The tripile comprises also a new type of supporting structure developed for offshore wind turbines. It consists of a single beam and three steel piles, which sit on a three-legged structure above the water's surface (**Figure 28**). The three legs are connected to the tower structure with a transition piece using grouted joints.

Figure 27 Left: The tripod structures used in Alpha Ventus project. Right: A floating crane lifts the 710 t tripod onto the anchoring area and sets it down on the seabed [33].

Figure 28 Left: Tripile structures [34]. Right: BARD 1 offshore wind farm in Germany [35].

The first tripile test support structure was installed in 2008, in the Hooksiel 5 MW project, in Germany. Also, the large-scale 400 MW offshore wind farm BARD 1 (**Figure 28**), which is presently under construction in Germany, employs this technology. The project is located in the North Sea, about 90 km northwest of the island of Borkum at 40 m water depth covering an area of 60 km^2 [35].

2.14.3.2.3 Floating technology

The fixed bottom foundation concepts discussed up to now are suitable for shallow to transitional or intermediate water depths of up to approximately 60 m. At deeper water sites, the above structures are inapplicable because as depth increases, loading also increases and this requires larger fixed bottom structural dimensions which are economically nonviable. In this context, a floating concept (i.e., mounting a wind turbine's tower on a floating platform) instead of a fixed bottom foundation may be a better choice. Nevertheless, floating wind turbines are still immature and are associated with increased technical risk, which tends to drive costs upward. For that reason, a lot of research effort has been put on developing a feasible concept [22, 36, 37], with a number of possible offshore wind turbine platform configuration permutations in terms of available anchors, moorings, buoyancy tanks, and ballast options being under investigation by the offshore industry [38].

Generally, the major advantages of moving deeper and developing floating systems are as follows:

- Higher and steadier wind speeds improve the energy performance of wind turbines.
- Steadier winds cause less wear on the wind turbine.
- There is reduced impact on ecosystems and humans (e.g., visual disturbance is nullified).
- There is greater potential for full system fabrication at shipyards and transportation to the site in one piece.
- The potential locations for installing such systems are increased since there is no depth limitation.

Typically, floating wind turbines are held in place by wires or chains anchored on the ocean floor with piles or suction anchors. However, the final design of a floating configuration and the selection of the most appropriate solution may vary significantly depending on a large number of parameters (e.g., mooring system cost and deployment complexity, on-site installation requirements, soil conditions, maintainability, and related costs). Generally speaking, one may classify floating structures into three main types (see **Figure 29**) based on the strategy used to ensure static stability [39], that is,

1. *Ballast stabilized*. Positioning and stabilization of the platform is achieved with the use of ballast weights attached below a buoyancy tank. Catenary mooring drag-embedded anchors are used to keep the platform in place [40, 41].
2. *Mooring line stabilized*. Positioning and stabilization of the platform is reached through prestressed mooring lines anchored to the seabed by suction piles. The prestressing of lines is used for stabilizing the wind turbine in heave, pitch, and roll [42].
3. *Buoyancy stabilized*. Positioning and stabilization of the platform is reached through the use of distributed buoyancy. The wind turbine stands on a platform which floats on the water surface and is held in place by mooring lines [42, 43].

The world's first full-scale floating wind turbine 'Hywind' (**Figure 30**) was installed in 2009 off the Norwegian coast by the oil company StatoilHydro at an average water depth of 220 m. The 'Hywind' concept incorporates a 2.3 MW wind turbine with 82.4 m rotor diameter manufactured by Siemens. The floating structure is a ballasted spar type consisting of a steel cylinder filled with a ballast of water and rocks. It extends 100 m beneath the sea's surface and is attached to the seabed by a three-point mooring spread. The primary intention for 'Hywind' is to test the performance of the structure and once this has been successfully achieved, Statoil will work on commercializing the concept for up to 700 m water depths. Furthermore, it should be mentioned that Statoil invested around 400 million kroner (or around €54 million) in the construction and further development of the pilot project and in research and development (R&D) related to the specific wind turbine concept [45]. This cost, however, seems unreasonably high, but this project is the first of its kind and its demonstrative nature required a lot of R&D and monitoring of its operational behavior. Future cost projections by StatoilHydro indicate that this will change in the near future and the floating concept will compete with the fixed bottom one.

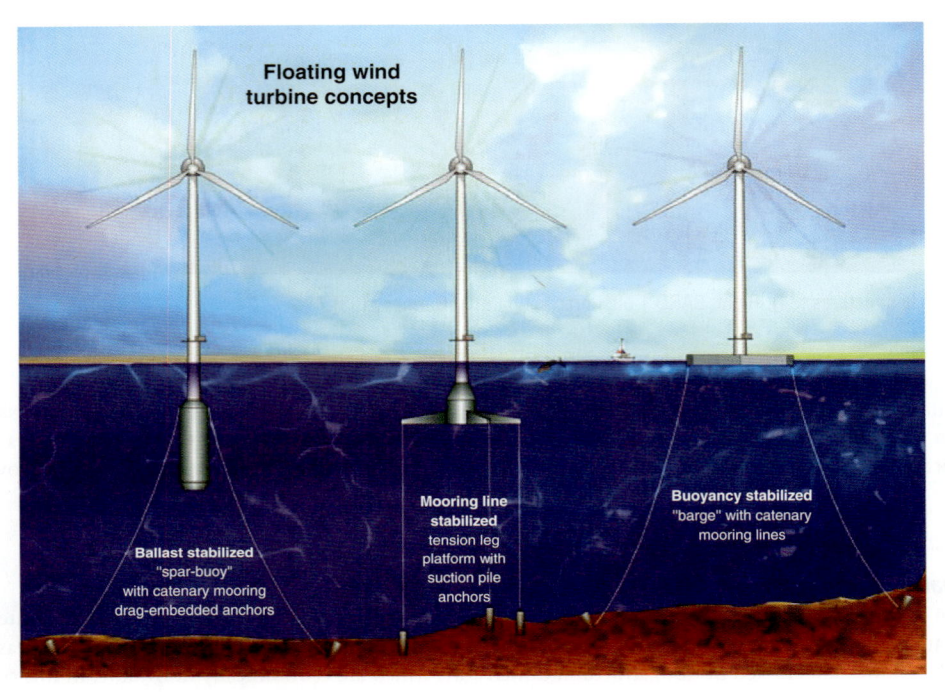

Figure 29 Floating support structure concepts for offshore wind turbines [39].

Figure 30 First deepwater floating wind turbine [44].

2.14.3.3 Supplementary Equipment

Except for the rotor/nacelle assembly and the support structure employed for an offshore wind power project, there exist additional elements such as an electrical collection system, transmission cables to the shore, and substations.

2.14.3.3.1 Offshore substation

On-site offshore substations are used to reduce electrical line losses and improve the overall electrical efficiency by increasing the voltage level (e.g., to 100–220 kV) from the collection system (see below) and then exporting the power to the shore. Apart from locating the lines from the collection system at a central point and transforming the energy produced to high voltage, the substation contains the necessary switching panels and other electrical facilities (e.g., power factor correction systems). The substation normally rests on a monopile or gravity-based foundation and may be also used as a service platform for the wind power plant with a boat docking facility and a helicopter landing station.

Typically, an offshore substation is installed in cases where the project is in the range of tens of megawatts, located quite far from shore, and the connection to the electric grid is not at the collection voltage. Nevertheless, a lot of the projects met today do not serve the above criteria, so they do not incorporate an offshore substation. **Figure 31** shows three central offshore transformer substations located in large-scale wind farms operating today in Denmark and the United Kingdom. Note that to date, no standard substation layout has yet evolved.

Figure 31 (a) Project Nysted in Denmark, 165 MW, tide range < 1m, low wave height. (b) Project Horns Rev I in Denmark, 160 MW, tide range 5 m, medium wave height, with helideck. (c) Project Barrow in the United Kingdom, 90 MW, tide range 10 m, high wave height [46].

2.14.3.3.2 Onshore substation

The role of an onshore substation is to forward the energy produced by the offshore wind farm to the electric power grid. Its design is mainly determined by the network operator and it typically consists of switchgear, metering, transformers, and associated plant. For projects not very far from shore, it may be possible to connect the collection system directly with an onshore substation instead of employing an offshore one.

2.14.3.3.3 Underwater cabling

Electrical cabling is divided into two main types, that is, collection and transmission (**Figures 32** and **33**), with its length being a major determinant in the setup cost of the project.

The power output of the wind farm is delivered to the offshore substation through interturbine (array) cables (or collection system). The cables are typically rated at 30–36 kV and are designed to connect multiple wind turbines by forming a string (collection circuit) before feeding the project's offshore substation. Then, the transmission of the power to the mainland grid is achieved with export cables of similar design with the collection system but with higher voltage (usually 100–220 kV). Typically, each collection and export circuit may be rated up to 3 and 150–200 MW, respectively. Suitable technologies for insulation of cables include cross-linked polyethylene, self-contained fluid-filled insulation, and ethylene propylene rubber.

The high level of reliability of subsea cables over a long period is ensured by safe laying and burying into marine floor by means of water jetting, air-lifting, excavating, and rock-sawing. The greatest damages of subsea cables come from ships' anchors, fishing gear, and exposure to mobile sand waves which can uncover a buried cable within a few days. In order to avoid the above hazards, cables are buried at least 2 m deep into the sea floor.

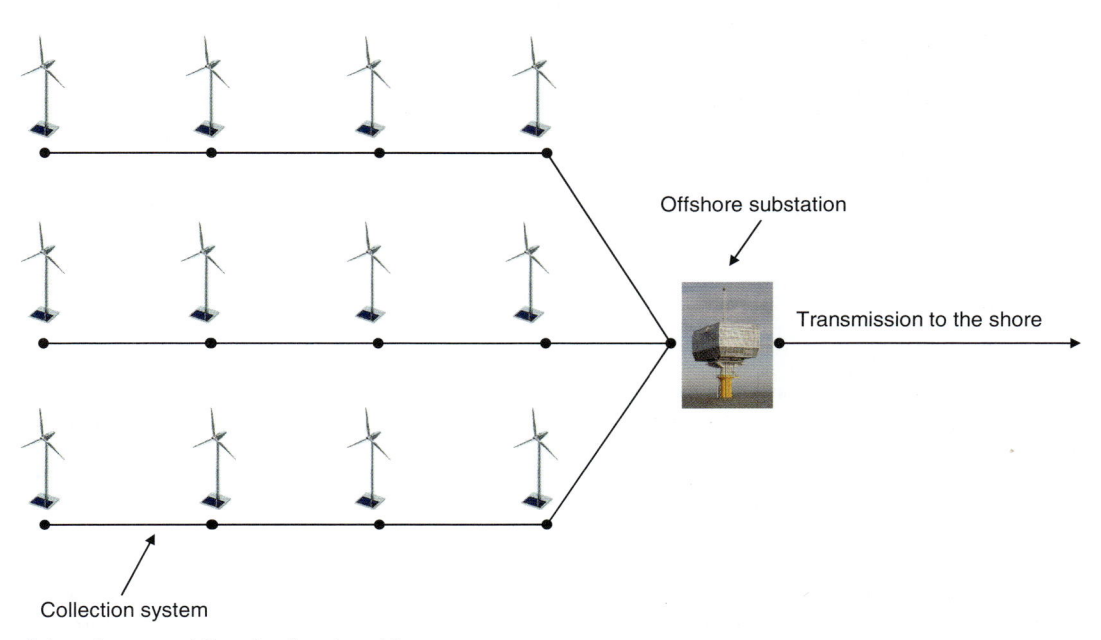

Figure 32 Schematic representation of underwater cabling.

Figure 33 Underwater cable with optic fiber option [47].

2.14.4 Offshore Wind Farm Design, Installation, and Maintenance

Offshore, the methods adopted for wind farm design, installation, and maintenance are fairly different from onshore, with great attention being given to issues concerning operation reliability, cost-effectiveness, and access. Capital costs are significantly higher than onshore, as well as risks, thus making the design procedure of a project and the selection of the suitable equipment critical with no room for mistakes.

In this context, not only the installation of an offshore project comprises a more difficult and more expensive task than onshore, but also the accessibility for maintenance purposes poses additional concerns. The harsh environmental conditions met in offshore sites may be the reason for the wind farm to be inaccessible by any transportation means for a long period of time. But even when the weather permits access to the project, maintenance cost is significantly higher than the equivalent work onshore. Specifically, O&M costs may be up to 3 times higher than those of land-based systems [48], exceeding 20% of the total life cycle cost of these projects [49]. For that reason, high operational reliability and adequate maintenance capability are both considered crucial for the technical and economic feasibility of offshore wind farms. The following section presents the key aspects concerning the offshore wind farm design, installation, and maintenance.

2.14.4.1 Equipment Selection Requirements

According to relevant international guidelines and standards (see corresponding chapter of this volume for further information) developed by several bodies and institutions (e.g., Germanischer Lloyd [50], BSH [51], and Det Norske Veritas [52]) concerning the design and construction of wind farms in offshore sites, the entire system – wind turbine, tower, support structure – is designed by taking into account the following:

- local environmental conditions (e.g., water depth, seabed features),
- loading (wind, wave, current), and
- long-term operational behavior.

Furthermore, the IEC 61400-3 international standard 'Design Requirements for Offshore Wind Turbines' provides the parameters that should be considered during the design in order to ensure the safety of systems and components of offshore wind turbines, inclusive of their support structures.

The most critical decision during the development of an offshore wind farm project is the selection of the site and the evaluation of local resources and conditions driven by technical feasibility constraints, economics, and regulatory issues. On top of that, the selection of the site largely affects the selection of a suitable wind turbine model and likewise the substructure and the foundation to be employed. Therefore, the selection of the wind turbine model is carried out in an early stage of the project development so as to determine the design and the selection criteria of the rest of the components of the wind farm (support structures, electrical infrastructure, etc.). Besides, offshore wind turbines are usually large in terms of capacity, so the selection is often limited to few commercially available models and it is based on efficiency, controllability, loading, reliability, serviceability, and maintainability criteria.

Similarly, the selection of support structures for the wind turbines depends on factors such as site-specific conditions, available technology, and applicability. Specifically, the support structure concept is primarily determined by the water depth and subsoil conditions, that is, if a shallow (e.g., monopile), transitional (e.g., tripile), or deep water (e.g., floating) technology is most suitable to be employed and if measures for preparation or further improvement of the soil need to be taken. Therefore, extensive on-site investigations are necessary in order to ascertain the seabed characteristics at each wind turbine location.

More specifically, on-site investigations require careful planning and include a combination of both geophysical and geotechnical measurements, which are the key determinants for the selection of the size and the type of the underwater structure. The geophysical investigation comprises the determination of water depth and seismic properties of the underlying soil layers through the use of remote sensing technology, often multibeam sonar and/or high-resolution seismic reflection. Accordingly, the geotechnical measurements are carried out with the use of cone penetrometers or borehole testing for identifying the physical properties of the seabed into which the foundations are to be installed.

Furthermore, a parameter that is also considered during the selection of suitable support structures is the available construction and installation technologies. For instance, the prefabrication of a large number of foundations on-land requires the availability of advanced construction and storage facilities as close as possible to the project's location so as to minimize transportation costs through the sea. Also, maintainability and decommissioning issues after the end of the project's lifetime (e.g., 20 years) are taken into account.

Except water depth and seabed characteristics, the determination of stochastic environmental conditions such as wind, waves, and currents is important not only in defining the loading forces imposed on a wind turbine's structural components but also in the design process of an offshore wind farm in terms of its long-term energy performance. At this point, it should be mentioned that an analysis of the mechanical–dynamic loads for offshore wind turbines' structural components is undertaken in the corresponding chapter of this volume, where one may obtain further information. However, for the sake of reference, one may categorize the primary loads for an offshore wind turbine and its support structure as follows (see also **Figure 34**):

- Aerodynamic loads
- Hydrodynamic loads
- Gravitational loads
- Inertial loads
- Control loads
- Mooring system loads
- Current loads
- Ice loads
- Soil interaction loads

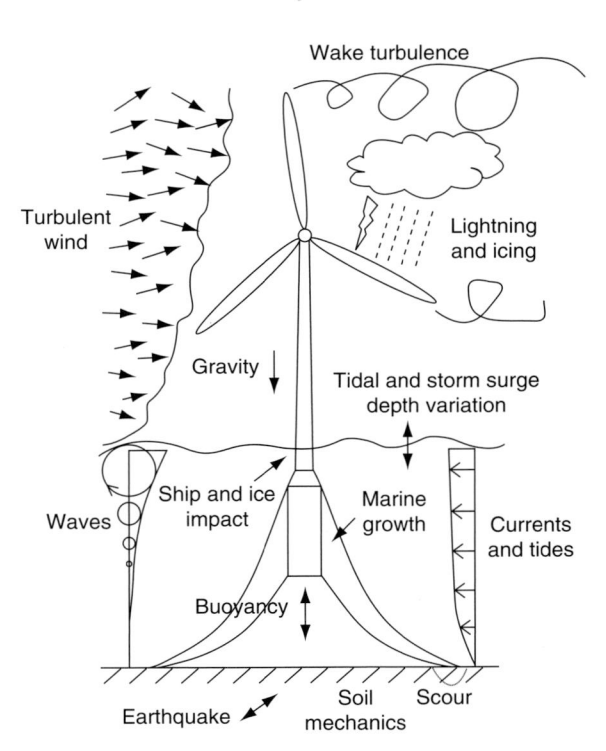

Figure 34 Loading sources for an offshore wind turbine [39].

2.14.4.1.1 Wind evaluation

As mentioned above, data concerning on-site wind conditions are important not only in determining the loading forces on a wind turbine's rotor and nacelle assembly but also in predicting the amount of future electricity production from wind generators, which will allow evaluation of the economic viability of a project. Furthermore, the knowledge of on-site analytical wind resource data dictates to a large extent the design of the layout of the plant as it depends not only on technical and cost parameters but also on the predicted energy production.

Generally speaking, among the most significant meteorological statistics that should be obtained when evaluating a candidate site are the wind speed time series (on hourly and 10-min basis, in preference at hub height), wind speed and direction probability density distributions, wind shear, turbulence intensity, and extreme wind gusts. In order to retrieve the above information, accurate field data, mapping, or databases are essential, depending, however, on the phase of the project development.

Specifically, one should either employ a meteorological mast or utilize offshore databases, including meteorological buoys, remote sensing devices (e.g., light detection and ranging – LiDAR – and sonic detection and ranging – SODAR), and observation platforms, for assessing potential offshore wind project sites and establishing zones of prioritized activity. Furthermore, the 'Wind Atlas Analysis and Application Program' (WAsP) [53, 54] can be used for predicting wind statistics on the basis of conventional weather observations and orographic and topographic information [55]. In addition, mesoscale modeling (validated in conjunction with accurate long-term measurements) and earth satellite imagery data may be used in case of a preliminary assessment of the long-term wind regime at the area under investigation [56, 57]. However, most of the above methods are associated with a notable degree of uncertainly in wind and energy production estimations that should be considered.

Offshore measurements with meteorological masts are taken in an advanced phase of the project development as they comprise the most accurate and effective methodology for obtaining wind resource information although they are very costly (varying between €1 and 5 million). This high cost depends largely on the construction of the support structure for the meteorological mast and is almost 100 times more than it would be on-land [58]. So, unlike the typical onshore methods applied for obtaining wind data, offshore measurements are rather difficult for a large number of sites due to their high cost. However, at great distances from the shore where there is normally absence of topography (e.g., obstacles and mountains), recordings from one meteorological mast may be used for a much wider offshore area than onshore.

Once adequate wind speed data are available (~3–5 years), the estimation of the electricity generation of a wind power plant in an offshore site is the same as for onshore projects determined by the specific power curve of the employed wind turbine type (*see* Chapter 2.06).

In general, offshore winds are less turbulent than onshore and the wind shear is less. In this context, it should be noted that, in offshore sites, wake losses may be higher than onshore, due to lower ambient turbulence levels, so the careful layout design of a project is essential. On the other hand, offshore winds blow stronger and more uniformly than on-land, resulting in a higher annual energy production, with capacity factors (i.e., ratio between the real and the potential electricity production if the wind turbine had operated at rated capacity) exceeding 40% in many cases [59]. At this point, it should be mentioned, however, that there is a remarkable possibility for a wind turbine to be out of order for a quite long period of time and the required maintenance work to be delayed due to difficult access in bad weather conditions (e.g., ice formation in the sea water and waves with great height), a fact which results in lower capacity factor values than the above mentioned. In this context, improved accessibility (e.g., employing a helicopter landing station to facilitate access to major wind turbine components during these extreme weather events) comprises a critical factor to the design of an offshore wind farm.

2.14.4.1.2 Wave and current evaluation

The design of offshore wind farms requires also the evaluation of long-term wave and current conditions, primarily not only due to their effect on the turbines' support structures and towers but also due to accessibility considerations of vessels during construction and maintenance facilities.

In general, the creation of waves at open sea occurs when wind is blowing across the water surface. As wind speed increases, wave heights increase too, although there may be a time lag, so that extreme winds and waves do not absolutely coincide. Analytical measurements of offshore wave conditions include the following [60, 61]:

- *Significant wave height (SWH) and period.* SWH is the average height (trough to crest) of one-third of the largest waves (see **Figure 35**).
- *Wind-wave direction, height, and period.* Wind-waves are produced by local wind. If a swell is present, these waves arrive at a lower period (more frequently) than do the swells. Wind-wave height is the average height of the highest one-third of the wind-waves. Wind-wave period is the peak period in seconds of the wind-waves.
- *Swell direction, height, and period.* Swells are waves not produced by the local wind and come in at a higher period (longer wave length) than waves produced by the local wind. Swell height is the estimated average height of the highest one-third of the swells. Swell period is the peak period in seconds of the swells. If more than one swell is present, this is the period of the swell containing the maximum energy.
- *Steepness.* For a given wave height, steep waves represent a more serious threat to capsizing vessels or damaging marine structures than broad swell. Steepness is determined by examining the SWH and the dominant wave period when compared with climatology.

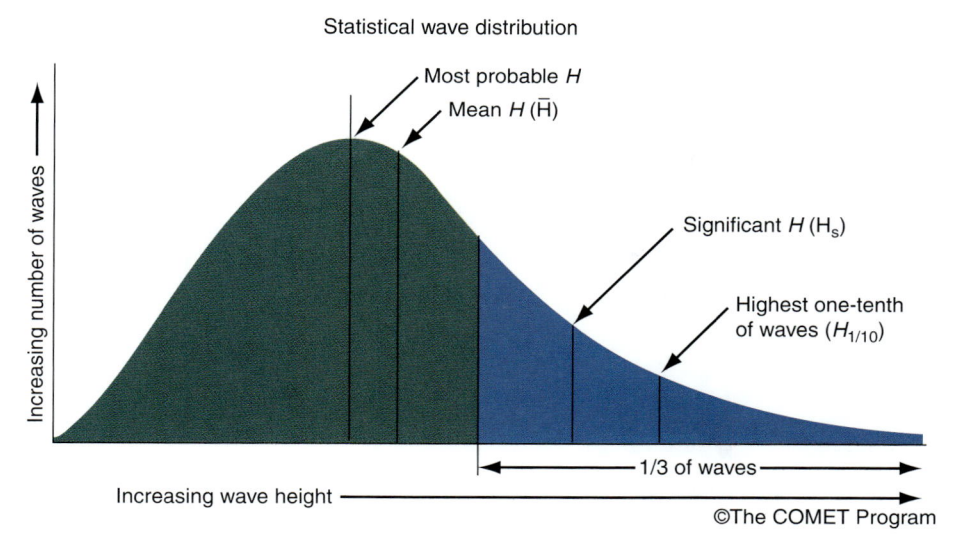

Figure 35 Statistical distribution of ocean wave heights [62].

Currents are generally produced by tides, differences in temperature, rain, runoffs, ocean bottom topography, and the wind (near-surface currents). Currents can cause sand wave transport and foundation scouring and affect seabed characteristics and vessel motion during construction or maintenance activities of the offshore wind farm.

Measurements of waves and currents are carried out using different techniques and equipment, depending much on the special needs of a project (cost, accuracy required, duration, etc.). Measuring methods are [61, 63] (see also **Figure 36**) as follows:

A. *Acoustic Doppler current profiler (ADCP)*. It provides a robust means of estimating wave direction and height in both shallow and deep waters.
B. *A directional buoy*. It measures near-surface waves and currents.
C. *An array of pressure sensors*. It measures near-surface waves.
D. *An ultrasonic device*. It measures near-surface waves upward.
E. *An echo sounder*. It measures near-surface waves from above.
F. *Wave radar*. It measures ocean waves and currents.
G. *Remote sensing synthetic aperture radar*. It comprises a microwave instrument producing high-resolution imagery regardless of clouds, dusty conditions, and solar illumination. It measures near-surface currents and wave fields.

2.14.4.2 Other Wind Farm Design Considerations

Offshore wind farm micrositing (i.e., the exact determination of the turbines' installation positions inside a wind farm's site) if not designed properly can have a significant effect on the project's energy and economic performance. On top of the above-described issues (access, wind, and wave loading on wind turbines and support structures), there are many more that should be considered

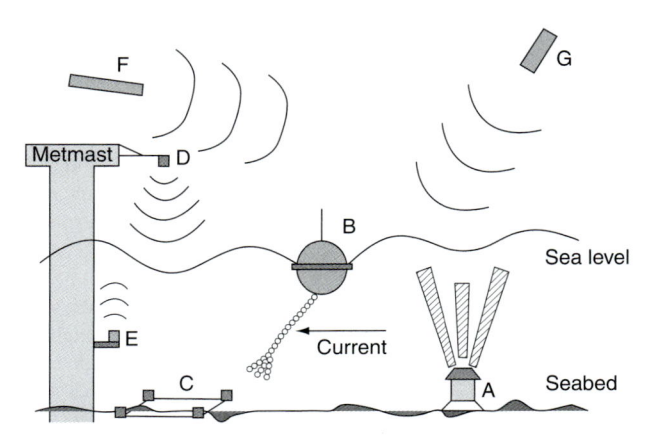

Figure 36 Different measurement methods [61].

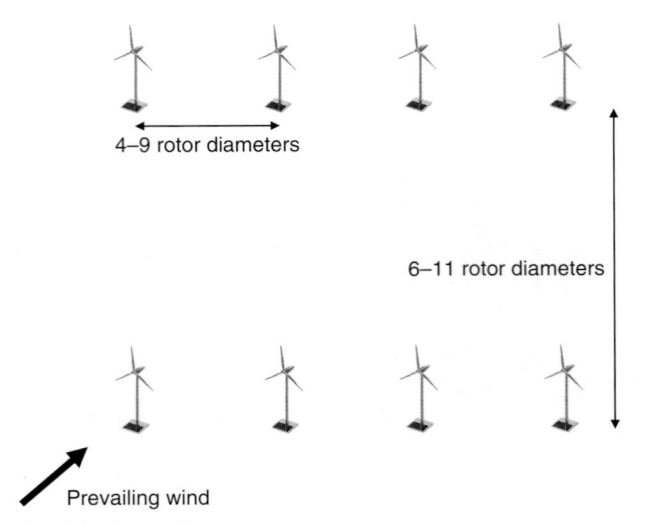

Figure 37 Schematic representation of wind turbine spacing.

during the micrositing process of a wind farm. These may include legal, regulatory, and environmental parameters such as permitting requirements, shipping lanes, aesthetics, visual and noise concerns (for near-shore projects), underwater archaeological sites, shipping lanes, existing underwater cabling, fishing areas, and so on.

Another important issue that should be taken into account is the wind turbine distance (between turbine rows and between turbines within a row) and arrangement relative to the prevailing wind direction. Specifically, in offshore locations as usual practice, the distance between wind turbines aligned in a row is kept in the order of 4–9 rotor diameters and distance between rows 6–11 rotor diameters. Accordingly, the rows are set perpendicular to the prevailing wind direction (**Figure 37**). If the above spacing is not satisfied and the wind turbines are placed quite close, wake effects will affect negatively the energy production of individual wind generators (impacted machines) and thus the performance of the wind farm as a whole. However, minimizing wake losses means greater distances between turbines, which lead in turn to higher costs due to longer underwater cabling requirements. Thus, for each specific project, counterbalancing between the cost of cabling and wake losses is a matter of great importance. A more detailed analysis of offshore wind farm micrositing is out of the scope of this chapter, however. More information on the subject may be found in the corresponding chapter of this volume (i.e., see Chapter 2.07).

2.14.4.3 Installation and Transportation Facilities

The installation, transportation, and assembly processes of offshore wind farm components possess significant portion of the capital cost. The associated problems are more complex and require different approaches than for land-based projects, mainly due to the harsh environmental conditions that are usually met in offshore sites. Weather is a risky parameter for works in the sea and should be carefully considered during logistics calculations. Wave heights of more than 1 m and strong winds can delay the installation of a wind farm for many days since all currently known methods can be carried out only under calm sea conditions.

On top of the environmental conditions, the extent of the installation complexity depends also on many other things, with the type of foundation used, however, being one the most important, as it determines the assembly works at sea and the equipment required for its transportation and erection (e.g., hydraulic hammers). The transportation to the site of support structures is generally carried out with a floating assembly platform (see, e.g., **Figure 38**). Once the foundation arrives at the site, its complete installation may take more than 2 days. For example, a jacket or a tripod foundation requires a minimum of about 2–3 days to be fully erected.

Offshore, the installation process has normally two main phases. First, the foundations are placed into the seabed and then the tower and the wind turbine are installed on top of the support structure (see **Figure 39**). What has been done up to now in most cases is to transport components to the site one by one and then erect the turbines as on land (a procedure which takes ~24 h), that is, first the tower in segments and then the nacelle and the rotor. However, due to economic reasons, efforts are currently made to preassemble most of the wind turbines and components on-land in order to minimize the expensive assembly process at sea with its uncertainties in respect to weather delays [22]. But this, in turn, requires heavy investment in port infrastructure with adequate space for storage and preassembly facilities of foundations and wind turbine components.

The installation generally takes place with either a jack-up barge or a floating crane vessel, which ideally needs to have sufficient height, storage capacity, and ability to operate in a wide range of water depths, wave heights, and currents. The crane must be capable of lifting the structures, with hook heights being greater than the level of the nacelle to enable the tower and wind turbine assembly. Nevertheless, the world market for offshore installation vessels is still tight, with a very limited number of suitable ships available worldwide so far. In **Figure 40**, one may see the basic characteristics for three types of vessels used for the installation of offshore wind turbine projects.

Figure 38 Gravity-based (left) [16] and tripod (right) support structures shipped to the site of installation [64].

Figure 39 General sequence of a wind turbine installation offshore [65].

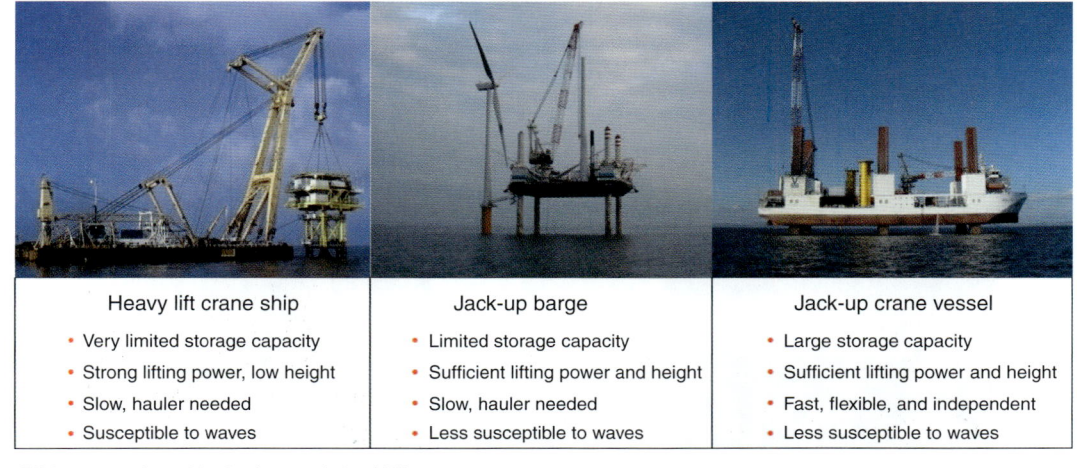

Heavy lift crane ship	Jack-up barge	Jack-up crane vessel
• Very limited storage capacity	• Limited storage capacity	• Large storage capacity
• Strong lifting power, low height	• Sufficient lifting power and height	• Sufficient lifting power and height
• Slow, hauler needed	• Slow, hauler needed	• Fast, flexible, and independent
• Susceptible to waves	• Less susceptible to waves	• Less susceptible to waves

Figure 40 Offshore vessels and basic characteristics [16].

As far as the substation installation is concerned, it is generally much more conventional for the offshore industry. Usually, a large crane vessel is employed, which is either a shear-leg crane or another heavy lift unit.

The total duration of the installation of a multiunit offshore wind farm may take several months due to, as mentioned above, weather constraints. The result of such installation delays is that costs are inevitably driven upward. However, this can be eliminated by scheduling building operations of the wind farm during calm periods (e.g., summer), when both wind speed and wave heights are most likely to be within acceptable limits.

2.14.4.4 O&M Facilities

As offshore wind turbines operate far from shores in harsh environments, the need for high reliability and low O&M costs is higher than for on-land applications. As aforementioned, O&M costs are generally too high in offshore sites, comprising more than 20% of the total life cycle cost of a wind power plant. One of the main causes for these high O&M costs is the rather frequent need for employing expensive transportation means (e.g., crane vessel) in order for the personnel to reach the wind farm and make the required service work [66].

In this context, high operational reliability and adequate maintenance capability are two critical issues for the long-term operation of an offshore wind farm, in both technical and economic terms. For that reason, parameters such as minimization of maintenance requirements and maximization of access capability are of great importance during the design procedure of a project. Thus, in order to avoid fatal economic consequences due to a potential system fault, careful decisions should be taken from the beginning of the project through the optimal planning of O&M strategies.

In general, maintenance activities of offshore wind farms are divided into corrective, which are applied in case of a component failure, and preventive, which are performed to avoid failure [67]. Nevertheless, despite the simpler nature of corrective maintenance, it should be noted that it is strongly associated with much larger uncertainty than preventive maintenance [68]. This is because major failures are most likely to occur during a period with harsh wind and wave conditions (e.g., winter), that is, when the accessibility to the wind farm is almost impossible, leading to high levels of energy production loss.

Accordingly, preventive maintenance splits up into scheduled service visits and condition-based activities in terms of a continuous monitoring of the system's state. Particularly, in an attempt to minimize maintenance costs, obtain better diagnostic data, prevent major component failures, and maximize productivity, offshore wind turbines may incorporate advanced condition monitoring systems [69, 70], automatic bearing lubrication systems, and preheating/cooling systems (to maintain gear oil temperature within a narrow range), all of which are beyond the standard equipment used for onshore machines [8, 71].

The on-site inspection of an offshore wind farm is normally made once or twice per year. Condition monitoring systems can provide a continuous inspection of the state of the plant and detect a sudden or gradual failure, which occurs faster than the time interval between two inspections. For example, if a major element of a wind turbine, such as rotor blades and gearbox, fails due to extreme wind and wave loading conditions, problematic installation, or an unforeseeable event (e.g., lightning), condition monitoring systems can detect the failure in an early stage and thus prevent a major component damage [72–74].

Generally, scheduled service visits and corrective maintenance of offshore wind farms are performed by highly skilled technical experts who reach the site in special workboats or vessels (**Figure 41**) with the aid of experienced sailors. However, maintenance activities cannot be accomplished all year round due to wave height and wind speed restrictions. Specifically, most workboat transfers cannot be performed in sea states where the SWH is higher than 1.5 m and wind speed is greater than $12\,\mathrm{m\,s^{-1}}$ [58]. As a result, 100% accessibility rate to an offshore wind power plant is not achievable with the use of the current technology.

A relation between accessibility and availability is shown in **Figure 42**. The data depicted are based on results described in References 75 and 76 for a 100 unit offshore wind farm with 'adapted from onshore technology' and 'integrated design with increased reliability' wind turbines, for a given maintenance strategy, that is, vessels for personnel transport to the site. Nowadays,

Figure 41 Left: O&M vessel arriving at site. Right: Accessing a wind turbine for maintenance [16].

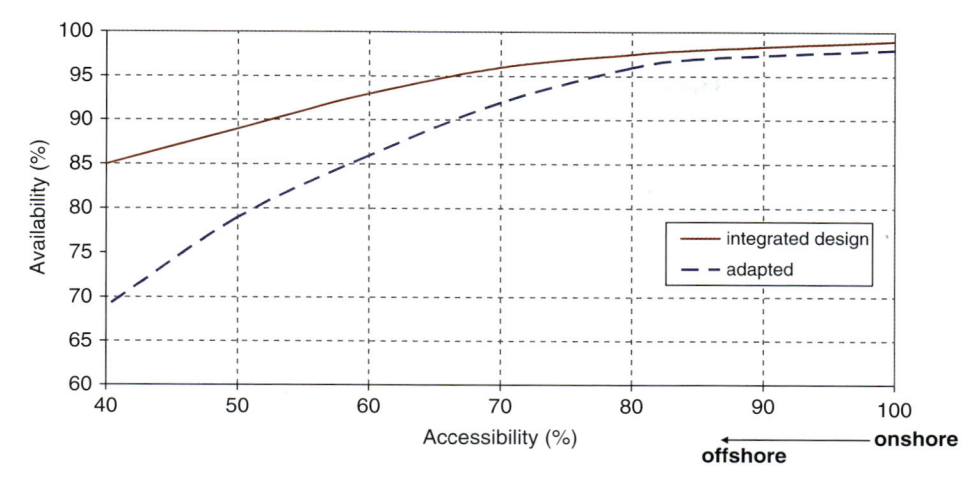

Figure 42 Availability of a 100-unit offshore wind farm as function of vessel accessibility to the site. Based on data from van Bussel [75, 76].

contemporary land-based wind turbines and wind farms reach availability levels of 98% or even more [77, 78], but as seen on the graph, once these wind turbines are placed offshore, the accessibility is significantly restricted due to wind and wave conditions. In offshore sites, the accessibility with a standard vessel may drop to 60% or even lower, thus causing a considerable impact to the availability of the wind farm and in turn to the energy and economic performance of the project.

So far, a variety of concepts are being developed to increase as much as possible the accessibility figure of offshore commercial wind power plants. For instance, with the aid of submarine vehicles, properly equipped – with diver suits – personnel, entering the tower underwater, comprises one of the solutions [79]. An alternative solution could be to reach the wind turbines by air, by means of a service helicopter. Nevertheless, this requires either a platform located on the nacelle of each wind turbine for the personnel to land on (see **Figure 43**) or even, at very large machines, a helicopter landing pad. It is doubtful, however, if the above solutions are economically viable and can guarantee 100% accessibility rates regardless of sea conditions. The option of helicopter access has already been adopted in the Horns Rev offshore wind farm in Denmark. As it seems with the up to now experience, this solution is quite expensive as a routine method for service visits to offshore wind turbines, assuming current project sizes and distances from shore [58]. However, in the future, as projects grow in size and go in deeper waters, this may be a possible option.

2.14.5 Offshore Wind Energy Economic Considerations

During the last 20 years, many countries all over the world have invested in the wind power sector in view of the rapidly increasing population and the limited resources for conventional power generation with its adverse consequences on climate and human health. To date, most existing wind farms have been built on-land, but during the last years many countries, especially in northwest

Figure 43 Wind turbine with helicopter supply platform in Denmark's Horns Rev offshore wind farm [80].

Europe, have also invested in offshore applications. As stated earlier, in offshore sites the winds are stronger and steadier than on-land, making wind farms more productive with higher capacity factors. On the other hand, however, as offshore wind energy is a new concept, most of the costs associated with its development are still much higher than from onshore counterparts, but some recent technological progress in terms of more efficient production patterns (increase of the size of wind turbines and improvements in the design of the projects) may have the potential to narrow this gap in the future. This section uses two approaches for analyzing offshore wind energy economics, that is, in terms of capital cost of investment and the cost of generating energy.

In general, for most of the existing projects, current turnkey (or capital) offshore wind power costs are estimated to be within the wide range of €1.3–2.5 million MW^{-1} while for onshore installations they are significantly lower, that is, approximately €1.1–1.4 million MW^{-1} for newly established projects in Europe. In some emerging markets, these costs may be lower due to cheaper labor works, grid connection, upgrades issues, and so on [81].

Capital costs of offshore wind power projects can be divided into the following main categories:

- cost of wind turbines (e.g., blades, rotor, tower, and condition monitoring)
- cost of electrical infrastructure (underwater cables for collection of power and transmission to the grid, substations, transformers, etc.)
- cost of support structures
- cost of logistics and installation
- development and engineering costs (e.g., licensing procedures, permits, and environmental impact assessment studies)
- other miscellaneous costs which are not included in the above categories.

As one may easily obtain from **Table 5**, capital costs are not standard and depend on a variety of factors such as distance from the shore, water depth, foundation technology employed, and so on; thus, they can exceed the above €2.5 million MW^{-1} threshold for a distinct case. For example, for Alpha Ventus wind farm, the capital cost per MW exceeds €4 million (see **Figure 44**) due to the demonstrative nature of the project (being the first large-scale offshore wind farm located in transitional waters). Nevertheless, increased offshore wind power costs, on top of complex engineering due to site-specific conditions, may be also attributed to high material prices and partly to a rapidly increasing demand relative to supply chain capacity [82].

Figure 45 presents data concerning main capital cost estimates for offshore wind power projects located in shallow waters. The estimates for the turbine's contribution to total capital cost range from 36% to 49%, with a mean value of 43%. At this point, it should be noted that the initial cost of a project on-land is dominated by the cost of the turbine itself, varying between 74% and 82% [84]. These cost differences are mainly attributed to the support structure, installation process, and grid connection issues that are more expensive in case of offshore wind power projects. Specifically, the above discrepancies are related with the following key issues:

- Foundations in offshore sites are much more expensive than on-land. For a conventional wind turbine installed on-land, the share of the foundation is approximately 5–9% [58], while in an offshore site it may be up to 30% of the initial capital invested and even higher in case of very deep waters and unfavorable soil conditions.
- Construction and installation techniques adopted for offshore projects are still immature.
- Electrical connection issues generate substantial additional costs compared with onshore installations.
- Higher technical risks and siting complexity drive cost up.

Table 5 Capital costs of several offshore wind farms. Based on data from [29]

Project	Rated capacity (MW)	Average water depth (m)	Average distance from shore (km)	Support structure	Turbine capacity (MW)	Investment costs (million €)	Year online
Donghai Bridge	102	10	10.5	Gravity based	3	258	2010
Alpha Ventus	60	30	53	(6) tripods (6) Jackets	5	250	2009
Horns Rev II	209	13	30	Monopiles	2.3	470	2009
Princess Amalia	120	22	23	Monopiles	2	380	2008
Lynn/Inner Dowsing	194.4	10	5	Monopiles	3.6	349	2009
Rhyl Flats	90	8	8	Monopiles	3.6	216	2009
Robin Rigg	180	5	9.5	Monopiles	3	500	2009
Thanet	300	22.5	11.5	Monopiles	3	912	2010
Middelgrunden	40	8	3	Gravity based	2	50	2000
Horns Rev I	160	10	16	Monopiles	2	270	2002
Nysted	165.2	8	8	Gravity based	2.3	268	2003
Egmond aan Zee	108	20	10	Monopiles	3	200	2006

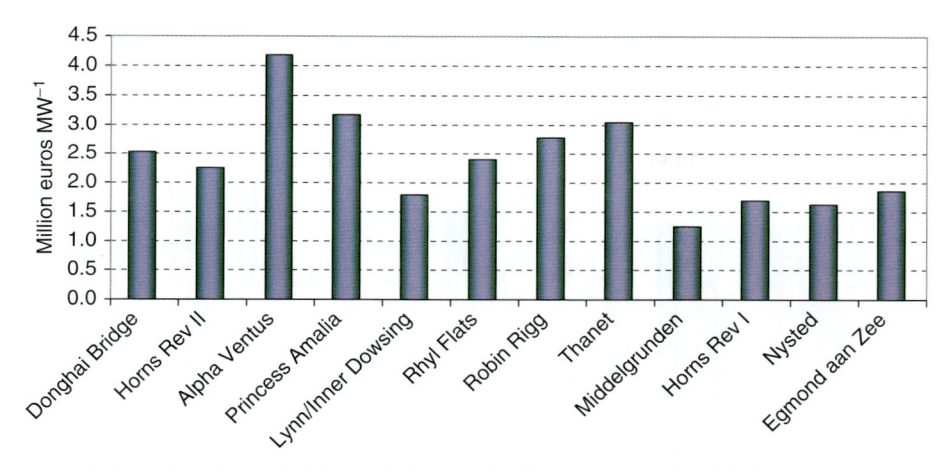

Figure 44 Indicative historical capital costs per MW of several offshore wind farms. Based on data from Lindoe Offshore Renewables Center (LORC) [29].

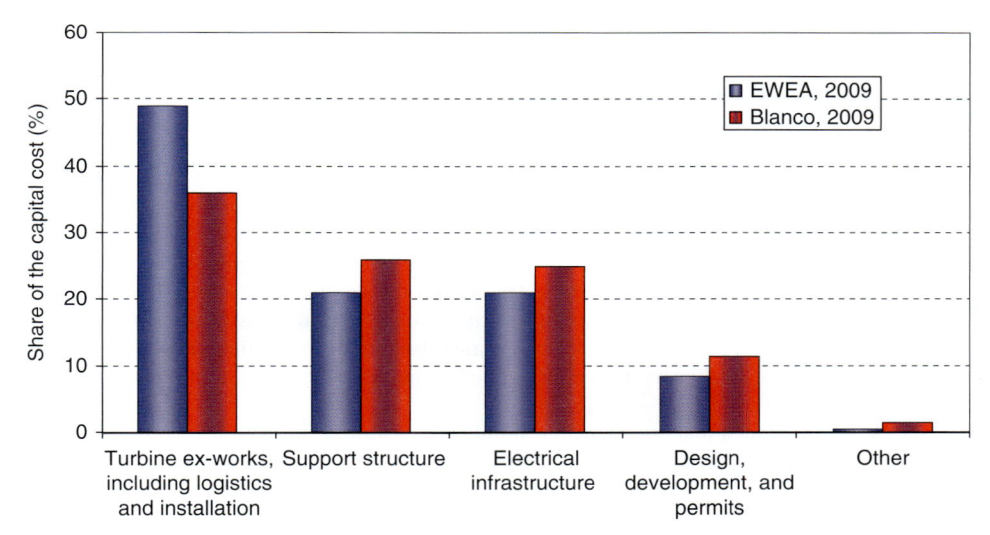

Figure 45 Capital cost breakdown for offshore wind power projects in shallow water. Based on data from Blanco M (2009) The economics of wind energy. *Renewable and Sustainable Energy Reviews* 13: 1372–1382 [81] and European Wind Energy Association (EWEA) [83].

As the distance of wind turbines from shore increases, installation and electrical infrastructure costs are driven upward. The construction of wind farms further from shore normally involves higher depths, which may require more complex installation procedures (e.g., vessels capable of carrying larger wind turbines and components) and more expensive equipment (e.g., support structures). Furthermore, greater distances result in an increase of the traveling time of the construction vessels in the sea. In addition to that, one should take into account a possible time delay of the installation due to harsher wind and wave conditions when moving deeper in the sea. In this context, the additional time required for completing the installation due to 'weather downtime' may reach 20–30% [84]. Also, moving deeper implies a larger undersea cabling system for connecting the wind farm with the electrical grid and possibly the employment of an offshore substation, thus affecting significantly the electrical infrastructure costs. Based on official data, costs for offshore cables are between €500 000 and 1 million per km [85].

Figure 46 depicts the scale factor by which capital costs increase as a function of both water depth and distance from shore. Note that the results have been estimated by assuming 'weather downtime' of 25%, export cable costs equal to €1 million per km, installation and grid connection costs to be linear, and the relationship for foundation supply cost to be exponential according to Reference 86. Thus, if the capital cost in shallow waters (0–10 km distance from shore and 10–20 m depth) is, for example, €1800 kW^{-1} (reference case), in a transitional depth (40–50 m) at 100–200 km distance, the respective current cost would be €3500 kW^{-1}. It should be mentioned, however, that this is only a qualitative approach, since for specific cases, as aforementioned, the costs may be considerably higher (e.g., Alpha Ventus demonstration project).

In addition to the higher investment costs, offshore projects have higher generation costs (or life cycle costs) from onshore wind farms. Broadly speaking, the cost of generating energy of a wind power project is the sum of initial investment, O&M costs (split into

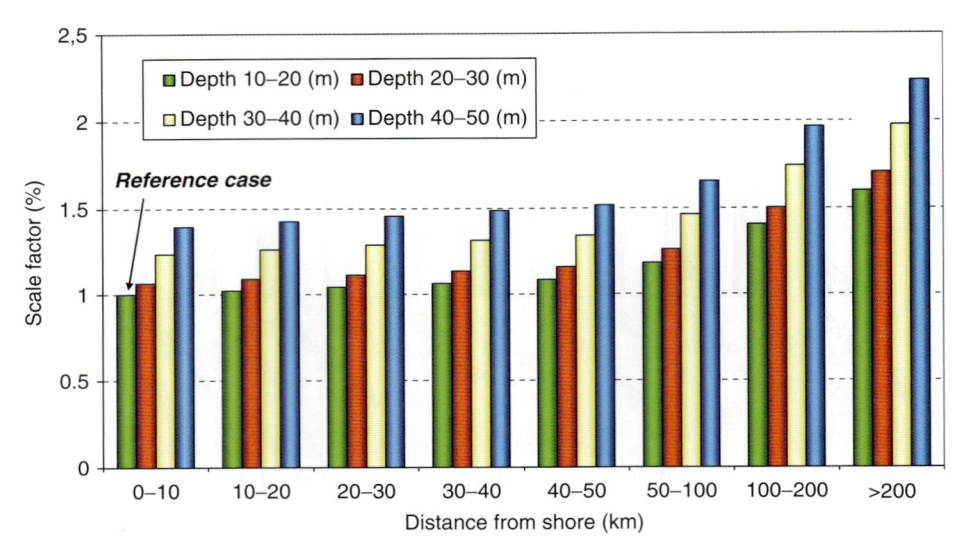

Figure 46 Scale factors for cost increase as a function of water depth and distance from shore. Based on data from European Environment Agency (EEA) [84].

the fixed maintenance cost and the variable one) over the life of the project (e.g., 20 years), and cost of capital, divided by the total energy output of the project. Subsequently, the generation cost is estimated as a unit of currency per unit of energy produced (e.g., in ¢ kWh^{-1} or €cent kWh^{-1}). Current costs of land-based projects vary within the range of 5–8 ¢ kWh^{-1} [8] (or ~4–6 €cent kWh^{-1} based on present day currency conversion prices, i.e., €1 = $1.43) while for offshore installations, generation costs are almost double, that is, 6–11.1 €cent kWh^{-1} [81]. However, life cycle costs are related with a quite high degree of uncertainty, mainly due to different policy measures and support mechanisms adopted in several countries.

Estimated life cycle costs for a typical offshore wind power project are presented in **Figure 47**. As seen in the figure, costs are largely determined by a range of parameters, which extend far beyond the wind turbine itself. Particularly, life cycle costs are dominated by O&M costs while logistics, installation, support structures, and electrical infrastructure obtain also a considerable part (almost one-third of the total). It should be noted that O&M costs are substantially higher than those of land-based systems (2 or 3 times greater [48]), exceeding 20% of total generation costs, while in some cases they can even reach up to 30%, mainly due to difficult and expensive site access [81].

In conclusion, it should be mentioned that due to the few number of offshore wind power projects currently installed, accurate statistical trends of associated costs of development and operation, as is the case with onshore counterparts, are difficult to be extracted yet. Water depth, distance from the shore, foundations, grid connection issues, infrastructure required, and O&M are apparently determinant factors for the total life cycle costs. Nevertheless, offshore wind energy is still under evolution and requires special R&D efforts in terms of developing cost-efficient O&M strategies, high reliability, site access solutions, innovative components, and improved and fully integrated 'wind turbine support structure' concepts. In this context, significant cost reduction is possible with the experience that will be gained through the years. Future offshore wind energy is expected to go deeper, employing larger projects in terms of capacity. At that point, offshore wind farms will likely benefit from economies of scale, which may drive capital and accordingly generation costs downward. Furthermore, going deeper means higher energy production, which may compensate for the higher costs currently associated with offshore wind power development.

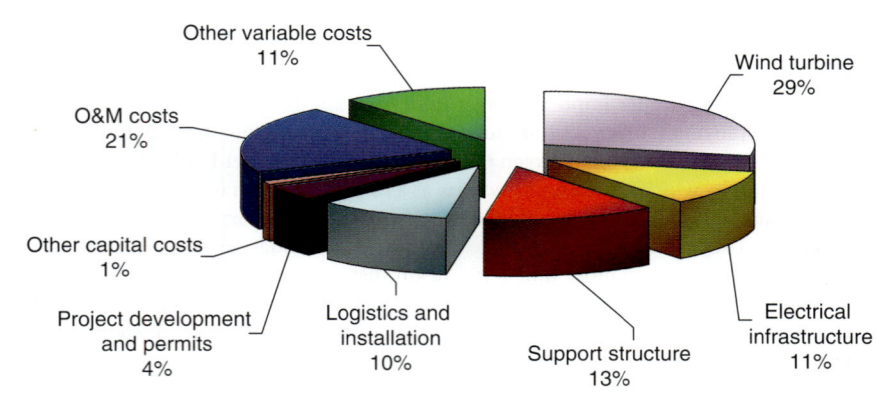

Figure 47 Life cycle cost breakdown for a typical offshore wind farm. Based on data from Musial *et al.* [8] and U.S. Department of Energy [87].

Table 6 Main conceivable environmental impacts (negative) of offshore wind energy in comparison with onshore

Impact	Comparison with onshore
Airborne noise	Minimal or null due to greater distances from receptors
Underwater noise	Exists only in case of offshore wind farms
Space use	Largely reduced but identification of shipping routes and fishing areas is necessary
Electromagnetic interference	Reduced
Visual impact	Minimal or null due to greater distances from receptors
Shadow flicker	Null
Bird collision	Still site specific

2.14.6 Environmental and Social Issues

As has been described in detail in the previous sections, the development of wind projects is more complex offshore than onshore. A short presentation of the offshore wind energy environmental impacts is included here for the completeness of the chapter. A detailed description may be found in Chapter 2.19, where the environmental impacts of the wind energy in general are presented.

By comparison to other forms of electric power generation, offshore wind energy is considered to have relatively benign effects on the marine environment and considerably lower compared with those onshore (see, e.g., **Table 6**). However, offshore projects include platforms, turbines, cables, substations, grids, interconnection and shipping, dredging, and associated construction activity. The O&M activities include the transport of employees by vessel or helicopter and occasional hardware retrofits. Therefore, various impacts incur in the construction, operation, and decommissioning phases: mainly the noise, the visual impacts, and the impacts on the fauna. What should be mentioned is that in many of these issues, there are still serious environmental uncertainties, contradictive views, and ongoing research, especially when the impacts on birds and animals (sea mammals/fish) are concerned.

2.14.6.1 Noise Impacts

Offshore wind farms are located far away from human populations. Therefore, it is most likely that people are not affected by the noise generated by the offshore wind turbines. However, marine animals could be affected by the underwater noise generated during the construction of the wind farm and operation of the wind turbines. For example, during the installation of the foundations, the perceived noise can have lethal effects or cause permanent damage to their hearing and thus disturb sea life. Any effects of the noise, however, will depend on the acoustic sensitivity of the species and their ability to adjust to it.

2.14.6.2 Visual Impacts

Both land-based [88, 89] and offshore wind [90, 91] projects face issues associated with aesthetic concerns. However, offshore wind power projects usually have the advantage of being located quite far from the coastline and from inhabited areas than most land-based projects. Besides that, with the ongoing development of new technology for greater water depths, offshore wind turbines could be sited far enough from shore and thus entirely eliminate any aesthetic concerns [92]. In any case, however, special attention could be required since the coastal landscape is unique and provides some of the most valued areas.

The potential offshore visibility depends on topography, vegetation, and artificial structures which exist in the landscapes. The visibility assessment of offshore developments includes the extent of visibility over the main marine, coastline, and land activities (recreational activities, coastal populations, and main road, rail, and footpath). Research in visual assessment showed that distance, number of turbines, their orientation, and distribution largely determine the visual impact [93]. Furthermore, the magnitude of change in the seascape with the construction of a new offshore wind farm depends on weather conditions and the navigational lighting of turbines. Thus, any changes in navigational lighting and weather conditions may vary considerably the visual esthetics at the same distance. The distance between an observer and a wind farm usually has the strongest influence on the visual impact perception.

2.14.6.3 Impacts on Wild Life

Offshore wind parks mainly affect the seabirds, the mammals, and the fish. From an ecological point of view, shallow waters are usually places with high ecological value and are important habitats for breeding, resting, and migratory seabirds.

Underwater noise generated by the construction and operation of the offshore wind farms represents an increasing threat to marine mammals. While the acoustic emissions only occur occasionally and temporarily during the construction phase, noise and vibration are permanent during the regular operation of the plants. At present, the question as to whether these disturbing noises impair or permanently damage marine mammals is still largely unresolved. It is, however, undisputed that marine mammals are extraordinarily dependent on their hearing systems, for example, for intraspecies communication, for search for food, and for orientation, and are thus particularly sensitive to noise emissions.

On the other side of the coin, the introduction of heavy bottom structures such as wind turbine foundations provides a new artificial substrate which helps the development of a new habitat for marine epifaunal organisms. The most susceptible groups are nonmobile (e.g., mussels, barnacles, and sponges) or hardly mobile species (snail and starfish) or sand-filtering species (oysters). Small fish species depredating over benthic animals and plants may also appear in the new area. Furthermore, larger benthic or pelagic fish as well as sea birds may be attracted from the surroundings areas.

Therefore, the construction of offshore wind farms will modify the relationships of benthic communities, changing the existing biodiversity in the area and creating a new local ecosystem.

2.14.7 Future Trends and Prospects

Offshore wind energy development has shown a quite unsteady progress since the beginning of its appearance, but there are strong indications and motives that it will certainly lead to a more optimistic future. Among the main reasons which will drive this growth are that the opportunities for wind development on-land become increasingly limited, the existence of more consistent and higher winds in offshore sites, the absence of obstacles such as mountains, buildings, and trees in marine environments, the low or even null impact on humans, the pressure to achieve renewable energy targets, and finally the enabling of building offshore wind farms in coastal areas close to many population centers.

With 290 new offshore wind turbines of a total capacity of 826 MW (as of September), offshore wind power experienced a record growth in 2010. Currently, the total offshore capacity is nearly 3 GW, normally supplying in a year's time around 11 TWh of electricity to 2.5 million households. Europe has been the leader in offshore wind energy applications since their introduction, with more than 95% of the global offshore wind farms being located in European waters. Nevertheless, several other countries, including the United States, Canada, and China, have already begun to invest in offshore wind.

For the EU, the challenging targets of 230 and 400 GW of wind power capacity in 2020 and 2030 have been set by the European Wind Energy Association, including 40 and 150 GW of offshore wind, respectively (**Figure 48**). In this context, in order for the EU to reach 40 GW of offshore wind capacity by 2020, about 30% average growth in annual installations is required, that is, rates already proven feasible in the past in onshore wind energy development (between 1992 and 2004 the market for land-based wind capacity grew by an average of 32% annually). The determinant factor for this accomplishment will be the enormous offshore wind potential met in European waters, mainly in the North Sea, the Baltic Sea, the Atlantic Ocean, the Mediterranean, and the Black Sea. Based on results included in the European Environmental Agency report [84] concerning the technical (technically available wind resource potential), constrained (environmental (Natura 2000 and other protected areas) and social constraints are taken into account. For offshore installations, limitations such as shipping routes, military areas, oil and gas exploration, and tourist zones are also considered), and economically competitive (the wind resource potential that is considered as cost competitive in the light of projected average energy costs in the future based on European Commission's baseline scenario [94]) wind potential (**Figure 49**), wind energy could contribute 70 000 TWh by 2020, from which 40% is attributed to offshore installations. It should be mentioned that the above offshore wind potential amount is about 7 times greater than the projected electricity demand over that year (i.e., ~4000 TWh in 2020 based on the 'business as usual' and 'EC Proposal with RES trading' scenarios [95, 96]). However, by taking into account projected average energy generation costs for 2020, the economically competitive offshore wind resource potential could be eventually 2600 TWh, covering almost two-thirds of the projected electricity demand. Accordingly, based on the results of

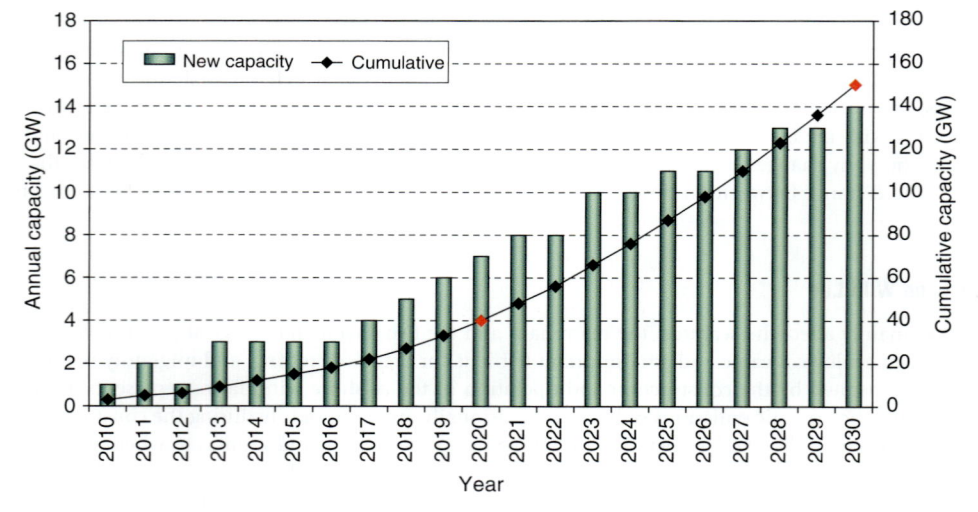

Figure 48 European targets for 2020 and 2030 concerning offshore wind energy installations.

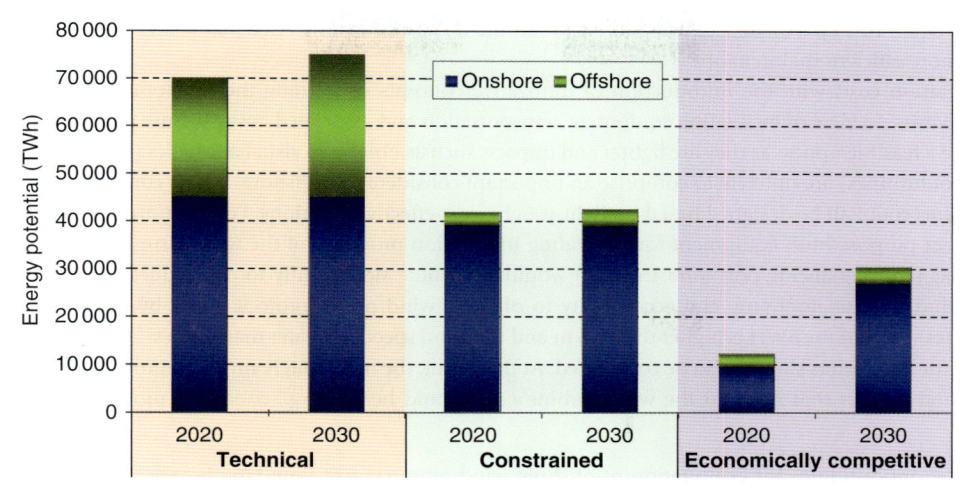

Figure 49 Projected technical, constrained, and economically competitive potential for wind energy development in 2020 and 2030. Based on data from European Environment Agency (EEA) [84].

the same report for 2030, the economically competitive wind resource potential could cover more than 80% of the expected EU electricity demand during that year (i.e., ~4400 TWh [95, 96]).

The enormous interest among Europe's industrial entrepreneurs, developers, and investors is highly depicted by the fact that over 17 GW of offshore wind energy projects are already fully consented or being under construction, while another 45 GW is in the planning stage [10]. These figures clearly demonstrate a positive trend toward offshore wind development among the EU and indicate that the targets of 2020 and 2030 are realistic and can be achieved.

Similarly, as indicated by certain studies [8], the United States also possesses a large and accessible offshore wind energy resource, which extends beyond 4000 MW (not including, though, environmental and socioeconomic constraints) in an area of less than 50 nautical miles from shore. Thus, the interest to develop such projects has already begun with the approval – 10 years after it was first put forward – of the first offshore wind farm 'Cape Wind' (420 MW) off the coast of Massachusetts. The construction of the project will begin by autumn, 2011.

Apart from the excellent potential of the wind energy resource in many maritime locations all around the world, offshore wind energy is still faced with many unique technological challenges. Despite the fact that the first project was built 20 years ago, the offshore wind energy sector still remains under development, and thus many issues concerning its future progress must be addressed through R&D efforts. Although the technology has developed rapidly during the last years, there is a general view that further improvements can be expected in terms of both energy performance and cost. Specifically, the areas of particular challenges are briefly analyzed in the following:

- Developing larger rotors and machines with greater rated power to exploit the enormous wind potential in offshore sites. With stronger winds and fewer conflicting issues than on-land, multimegawatt turbines are likely to dominate the offshore sector in the years to come in order to maximize energy production, capturing economies of scale. The most recently installed offshore wind turbines are on the order of 3.6 or even 5 MW (e.g., Alpha Ventus and Thornton Bank), while many manufacturers are currently developing prototypes between 6 and 7 MW (see, e.g., **Table 4**). These wind turbines will certainty give developers more options, representing a shift away from land-based adaptations. Several manufacturers are currently looking toward the design of tens of MW wind turbines, floating or fixed bottom [97, 98], and projects, such as UpWind [99] and HIPRWIND [100], funded by the EU 6th and 7th framework program, respectively, are developing accurate tools and component concepts to allow this new breed of machines to emerge.
- Improving manufacturing processes and design standards of both the wind turbines and support structures (e.g., durable innovating foundations and successful floating turbine concepts) in a cost-effective manner to meet the needs of the harsh sea environment and deploy wind farms in a wide range of water depths across various geographical areas. Up to now, offshore installations have been predominantly limited to fixed bottom support structures such as monopiles, gravity based, jackets, and tripods. However, as the technology advances into deeper waters, investing on floating wind turbine concepts is thought to be imperative. For that reason, challenges such as the development of low-cost mooring systems and anchors, reduction of turbine weight, and achievement of static and dynamic stability are all of great importance.
- Increasing operational reliability of offshore wind turbines. Higher reliability means higher availability, which may lead in turn to lower O&M costs. Indicative example in this field comprises the adoption of advanced techniques and materials through an integrated design of wind turbines to withstand the demanding sea conditions. Another example is the adoption of more efficient

and newer drivetrain concepts in view of bringing wind turbine reliability up to an acceptable level along with providing faster, cheaper, and more efficient maintenance.

- Reducing generation costs with the introduction of innovative concepts concerning the development and O&M strategies of offshore wind farms. In view of facilitating equipment transportation and associated costs, the use of two-blade machines [101] could comprise a feasible option as they are lighter and impacts such as noise and visual aesthetics (which are strongly correlated with this type of turbines) are unlikely to comprise an important consideration offshore. In this context, towers, drivetrains, and support structures could all be designed based on light-weight, cost-effective solutions. Furthermore, the construction of reliable and cost-efficient purpose-built equipment for facilitating installation processes of the wind farms and adoption of innovative logistic concepts (e.g., enhancing port infrastructure) would contribute significantly to cost reductions. Furthermore, improvement of the wind turbine ergonomy and accessibility to offshore wind power projects either by means of vessels capable of reaching the sites – even if the SWH is higher than 1.5 m and the wind speed is greater than 12 m s^{-1} – or by incorporating special landing stages for helicopters should also be considered. At this point, the increasingly important role of preventive maintenance with systems and sensors that monitor the wind turbine's status and health (e.g., condition monitoring systems) should be underlined.

Recapitulating, the opportunities for exploitation of offshore wind resources are abundant; however, the barriers and challenges are also significant. The ongoing R&D activities are many in the field, and a variety of concepts are currently under investigation (*see* Chapter 2.21). Even if only few of these expectations are realized, then the future of offshore wind energy development will become very bright. The forthcoming years will determine whether offshore wind will be able to gain a place among other large-scale sources of energy generation. Only time will tell.

References

[1] Doerner H (2010) Milestones of wind energy utilization 1. http://www.ifb.uni-stuttgart.de/~doerner/ewindenergie1.html (accessed May 2011).
[2] Heronemus WE (1972) Pollution-free energy from offshore winds. In: *Proceedings of the 8th Annual Conference and Exposition Marine Technology Society*, Washington, DC, USA, September 11–13.
[3] Energy saving (2010) http://energy.saving.nu/windenergy/large.shtml (accessed December 2010).
[4] Dyre K (1992) Vindeby offshore wind farm – The first experiences. In: *Proceedings of the EWEA Conference*. Herning, Denmark, 8–11 September.
[5] http://www.martinbondphotos.co.uk/renewable_energy/image5.html (accessed May 2011).
[6] http://www.udafdetblaa.dk/uk/uk_foto_frame.html (accessed May 2011).
[7] Middelgrunden Wind Farm official website. http://www.middelgrunden.dk/middelgrunden/?q=en#10 (accessed May 2011).
[8] Musial W, Thresher R, and Ram B (2010) *Large-Scale Offshore Wind Energy for the United States: Assessment of Opportunities and Barriers*. Golden, CO: National Renewable Energy Laboratory. http://www.nrel.gov/wind/pdfs/40745.pdf (accessed May 2011).
[9] European Wind Energy Association (EWEA) (2010) The European Offshore Wind Industry Key Trends and Statistics. http://www.ewea.org/ (accessed May 2011).
[10] The Wind Power Database. http://www.thewindpower.net/offshore_wind_farms_list.php (accessed May 2011).
[11] BTM Consult (2010) Offshore Wind Power 2010. http://www.btm.dk/news/offshore+wind+power+2010/?s=9&p=&n=39 (accessed May 2011).
[12] European Wind Energy Association (EWEA) (2007) Delivering Offshore Wind Power in Europe. http://www.ewea.org (accessed March 2011).
[13] GE Energy official website. http://www.ge-energy.com/ (accessed March 2011).
[14] Vattenfall official website. Thanet Offshore Wind Farm. http://www.vattenfall.co.uk/en/thanet-offshore-wind-farm.htm (accessed May 2011).
[15] http://en.wikipedia.org/wiki/File:Thanet_wind_farm.JPG (accessed May 2011).
[16] E.ON Offshore Wind Energy Factbook (2011). http://www.eon.com/de/downloads/2011_01_07_EON_Offshore_Factbook_en_Jan_final.pdf (accessed May 2011).
[17] Lange B, Aagaard E, Andersen P-E, *et al.* (1999) Offshore wind farm Bockstigen. Installation and operation experience. In: *Proceedings of the European Wind Energy Conference*. Nice, France.
[18] http://ecoagile.net/SecurityTopstheEnvironmentinChinasEnergyPlanNYT20100617.aspx (accessed May 2011).
[19] Chinese Renewable Energy Industries Association (CREIA). http://www.creia.net (accessed May 2011).
[20] Alpha Ventus Wind Farm Official Site. http://www.alpha-ventus.de/index.php?id=80 (accessed May 2011).
[21] Schwartz M, Heimiller D, Haymes S, and Musial W (2010) Assessment of offshore wind energy resources for the United States. *Technical Report NREL* (http//www.nrel.gov/docs/fy10osti/45889.pdf).
[22] Breton S-P and Moe G (2009) Status, plans and technologies for offshore wind turbines in Europe and North America. *Renewable Energy* 34: 646–654.
[23] A Framework for Offshore Wind Energy Development in the United States, 2005. http://www.masstech.org/offshore/final_09_20.pdf (accessed May 2011).
[24] CAPE WIND official website. http://www.capewind.org/article19.htm (accessed June 2011).
[25] Horns Rev Wind Farm official website. http://www.hornsrev.dk/Engelsk/default_ie.htm (accessed March 2011).
[26] 4C Global Wind Farms Database. http://www.4coffshore.com/ (accessed May 2011).
[27] Wind Energy the Facts. http://www.wind-energy-the-facts.org/images/fig/chap1/5-4.jpg (accessed May 2011).
[28] Leirgulen SI (2011) New design practices for offshore wind turbine structures. *Det Norske Veritas*. http://www.dnv.com/press_area/press_releases/2011/new_design_practices_offshore_wind_turbine_structures.asp (accessed June 2011).
[29] Lindoe Offshore Renewables Center (LORC). http://www.lorc.dk/ (accessed May 2011).
[30] Houlsby GT, Kelly RB, Huxtable J, and Byrne BW (2005) Field trials of suction caissons in sand for offshore wind turbine foundations. *Geotechnique* 55(4): 287–296.
[31] Ibsen LB, Liingaard M, and Nielsen SA (2005) Bucket Foundation, a Status. http://wind.nrel.gov/public/SeaCon/Proceedings/Copenhagen.Offshore.Wind.2005/documents/papers/Future_innovative_solutions/L.B.Ibsen_Bucket_Foundation_a_status.pdf (accessed February 2011).
[32] Zhan Y-G and Liu F-C (2010) Numerical analysis of bearing capacity of suction bucket foundation for offshore wind turbines. *Electronic Journal of Geotechnical Engineering*. http://www.ejge.com/2010/Ppr10.051/Ppr10.051.pdf (accessed March 2011).
[33] Areva/Multibrid official website. http://www.areva-wind.com/index.php?id=69&highlight=110&L=1 (accessed March 2011).
[34] http://flickriver.com/photos/cuxclipper1/4872991482/ (accessed June 2011).
[35] BARD official website. http://www.bard-offshore.de/en (accessed June 2011).

[36] Karimirad M and Moan T (2010) Effect of aerodynamic and hydrodynamic damping on dynamic response of a spar type floating wind turbine. In: *Proceedings of the European Wind Energy Conference (EWEC)*. Warsaw, Poland.
[37] Lackner MA and Rotea MA (2011) Structural control of floating wind turbines. *Mechatronics* 21(4): 704–719.
[38] Musial W, Butterfield S, and Ram B (2006) Energy from Offshore Wind. In: *Proceedings of the Offshore Technology Conference*. Houston, TX, USA, 1–4 May.
[39] Butterfield S, Musial W, Jonkman J, and Sclavounos P (2007) *Engineering Challenges for Floating Offshore Wind Turbines. NREL/CP-500-38776*. Golden, CO: National Renewable Energy Laboratory (NREL). http://gisceu.net/PDF/U444.pdf (accessed June 2011).
[40] Skaare B, Hanson TD, and Nielsen FG (2007) Importance of control strategies on fatigue life of floating wind turbines. In: *Proceedings of the 26th International Conference on Offshore Mechanics and Arctic Engineering (OMAE)*. San Diego, CA, USA, June.
[41] Nielsen FG, Hanson TD, and Skaare B (2006) Integrated dynamic analysis of floating offshore wind turbines. In: *Proceedings of the 25th International Conference on Offshore Mechanics and Arctic Engineering (OMAE)*. Hamburg, Germany, June.
[42] Wayman EN, Sclavounos PD, Butterfield S, *et al.* (2006) Coupled dynamic modeling of floating wind turbine systems. In: *Proceedings of the Offshore Technology Conference*. Houston, TX, USA, May.
[43] Jonkman JM and Buhl ML, Jr. (2007) Loads analysis of a floating offshore wind turbine using fully coupled simulation. In: *Proceedings of the WindPower Conference and Exhibition*. Los Angeles, CA, USA.
[44] Mywindpowersystem website. http://www.mywindpowersystem.com/2009/09/the-worlds-first-floating-windturbine-launched-in-norway/ (accessed June 2011).
[45] Statoil official website. http://www.statoil.com/ (accessed June 2011).
[46] Finn J (2008) Designing substations for offshore wind farm connections. Siemens Transmission and Distribution Ltd. *CIGRE NGN NAREC 22nd*. http://www.cigre-ngn-uk.org/resources/documents/NGN%20TE2%20(08)%20-%20Presentation%20-%20JohnFinn.pdf (accessed July 2011).
[47] ABB. Cables for Offshore Wind Farms. http://www05.abb.com/global/scot/scot245.nsf/veritydisplay/d983a80ac3404eb4c1256e83003d3f25/$File/Cables%20for%20Offshore%20Wind%20Farms.pdf (accessed July 2011).
[48] Rademakers LWMM, Braam H, Zaaijer MB, and van Bussel GJW (2003) Assessment and optimisation of operation and maintenance of offshore wind turbines. ECN Wind Energy, Delft University of Technology, June. http://www.ecn.nl/docs/dowec/2003-EWEC-O_M.pdf (accessed June 2010).
[49] Junginger M and Faaij A (2004) Cost reduction prospects for the offshore wind energy sector. *Wind Engineering* 28: 97–118.
[50] Germanischer Lloyd WindEnergie (GL) (2005) Rules and guidelines industrial services – Guideline for the certification of offshore wind turbines. http://onlinepubs.trb.org/onlinepubs/mb/Offshore%20Wind/Guideline.pdf (accessed May 2011).
[51] BSH (2007) Standard-design of offshore wind turbines. http://onlinepubs.trb.org/onlinepubs/mb/Offshore%20Wind/Standard.pdf (accessed May 2011).
[52] Det Norske Veritas (DNV) (2010) Design of offshore wind turbines structures – Offshore standard, DNV-OS-J101. http://exchange.dnv.com/ (accessed July 2011).
[53] Mortensen NG, Heathfield DN, Myllerup L, *et al.* (2005) *Wind Atlas Analysis and Application Program: WAsP 8 Help Facility, 335 Topics*. Roskilde, Denmark: Risø National Laboratory. ISBN 87-550-3457-8.
[54] Troen I and Petersen EL (1989) *European Wind Atlas*. Roskilde, Denmark: Risø National Laboratory. ISBN 87-550-1482-8.
[55] Sempreviva AM, Barthelmie RJ, and Pryor SC (2008) Review of methodologies for offshore wind resource assessment in European seas. *Surveys in Geophysics* 29: 471–497.
[56] Coelingh J and Crockford A (2010) Best practice for use of mesoscale models in wind resource assessments. In: *Proceedings of the European Wind Energy Conference and Exhibition (EWEC)*. Warsaw, Poland.
[57] Badger J, Barthelmie R, Frandsen S, and Christiansen MB (2006) Mesoscale modeling for an offshore wind farm. In: *Proceedings of the European Wind Energy Conference and Exhibition (EWEC)*. Athens, Greece.
[58] European Wind Energy Association (EWEA) (2009) *Wind Energy – The Facts* (http://www.wind-energy-the-facts.org/.
[59] Barthelmie RJ (2007) Wind energy: Status and trends. *Geography Compass* 1(3): 275–301.
[60] National Data Buoy Center (NDBC). http://www.ndbc.noaa.gov/waveobs.shtml (accessed June 2011).
[61] Bendfeld J, Krieger J, and Splett M (2010) Wave and current measurements for offshore windfarms. *Proceedings of the EWEC*. http://www.ewec2010proceedings.info/allfiles2/285_EWEC2010presentation.pdf (accessed May 2011).
[62] Cooperative Program for Operational Meteorology, Education and Training (COMET). http://www.comet.ucar.edu/ (accessed July 2011).
[63] Pandian PK, Emmanuel O, Ruscoe J, *et al.* (2010) An overview of recent technologies on wave and current measurement in coastal and marine applications. *Journal of Oceanography and Marine Science* 1(1): 1–10.
[64] Offshore Wind Technologie (OWT). http://www.owt.de/en/03_references/03_references_2008.php (accessed June 2011).
[65] CRESP. Offshore wind farm construction, installation methods and plant. Beijing, Garrad Hassan & Partners Ltd., January 2009. http://www.cresp.org.cn/uploadfiles/73/1036/4/andrew_EN.pdf (accessed June 2011).
[66] van Bussel GJW and Zaaijer MB (2001) Reliability, availability and maintenance aspects of largescale offshore wind farms, a concept study. In: *Proceedings of the MAREC*. Newcastle, UK, March.
[67] Nielsen JJ and Sørensen JD (2011) On risk-based operation and maintenance of offshore wind turbine components. *Reliability Engineering & System Safety* 96(1): 218–229.
[68] Rademakers L, Braam H, and Obdan T (2008) Estimating costs of operation & maintenance for offshore wind farms. In: *Proceedings of the EWEC*, Belgium, 31 March–3 April 2008.
[69] Amirat Y, Benbouzid MEH, Al-Ahmar E, *et al.* (2009) A brief status on condition monitoring and fault diagnosis in wind energy conversion systems. *Renewable and Sustainable Energy Reviews* 3(9): 2629–2636.
[70] OSMR Consortium (2004) Predictive condition monitoring for offshore wind energy converters with respect to the IEC61400-25 standard. In: *Proceedings of the German Wind Energy Conference (DEWEK)*. Wilhelmshaven, Germany.
[71] Caselitz P and Giebhardt J (2005) Rotor condition monitoring for improved operational safety of offshore wind energy converters. *Solar Energy Engineering* 127: 253–261.
[72] Wiggelinkhuizen EJ, Verbruggen TW, Braam H, *et al.* (2008) Assessment of condition monitoring techniques for offshore wind farms. *Transactions of the ASME: Journal of Solar Energy Engineering* 130: 1004-1–1004-9.
[73] Wiggelinkhuizen EJ, Rademakers LWMM, Verbruggen TW, *et al.* (2007) *Conmow Final Report, ECN-E--07-044*. June. http://www.ecn.nl/docs/library/report/2007/e07044.pdf.
[74] Braam H, Rademakers LWMM, and Verbruggen TW (2003) CONMOW: Condition monitoring for offshore wind farms. In: *Proceedings of the European Wind Energy Conference, ECN-RX--03-036*. Madrid, Spain, 16–19 June.
[75] van Bussel GJW (1999) The development of an expert system for the determination of availability and O&M costs for offshore wind farms. In: *Proceedings of the European Wind Energy Conference*, pp. 402–405. Nice, France, March.
[76] van Bussel GJW (2002) Offshore wind energy, the reliability dilemma. In: *Proceedings of the World Wind Energy Conference*. Berlin, Germany, 2–6 July.
[77] Kaldellis JK (2004) Investigation of Greek wind energy market time-evolution. *Energy Policy* 32: 865–879.
[78] Kaldellis JK (2002) An integrated time-depending feasibility analysis model of wind energy applications in Greece. *Energy Policy* 30: 267–280.
[79] Hau E (2006) *Wind Turbines, Fundamentals, Technologies, Application, Economics*, 2nd edn. New York: Springer.
[80] Horns Rev official website. http://www.hornsrev.dk/Engelsk/nyheder/nyh_mar_02/uk-marts.htm (accessed June 2011).
[81] Blanco M (2009) The economics of wind energy. *Renewable and Sustainable Energy Reviews* 13: 1372–1382.
[82] Greenacre P, Gross R, and Heptonstall P (2010) *Great Expectations: The Cost of Offshore Wind in UK Waters – Understanding the Past and Projecting the Future*. London: UK Energy Research Centre.
[83] European Wind Energy Association (EWEA) (2009) The economics of wind energy. http://www.ewea.org/fileadmin/ewea_documents/documents/00_POLICY_document/Economics_of_Wind_Energy__March_2009_.pdf (accessed May 2011).

[84] European Environment Agency (EEA) (2009) Europe's onshore and offshore wind energy potential. An assessment of environmental and economic constraints. *Technical Report*. http://www.energy.eu/publications/a07.pdf (accessed June 2011).
[85] International Association of Engineering Insurance (2006) Engineering Insurance of Offshore Wind Turbines. http://www.imia.com/downloads/imia_papers/wgp45_2006.pdf (accessed June 2011).
[86] Papalexandrou (2008) *Economic Analysis of Offshore Wind Farms*. Utrecht: Ecofys International.
[87] US Department of Energy (2011) A national offshore wind strategy: Creating an offshore wind energy industry in the United States. http://www1.eere.energy.gov/windandhydro/pdfs/national_offshore_wind_strategy.pdf (accessed June 2011).
[88] Kaldellis JK (2006) Evaluation of Greek wind parks visual impact: Public attitude and experts' opinion. *Fresenius Environmental Bulletin* 15(11): 1419–1426.
[89] Kaldellis JK, Kavadias KA, and Paliatsos AG (2003) Environmental impacts of wind energy applications: Myth or reality? *Fresenius Environmental Bulletin* 12(4): 326–337.
[90] Firestone J and Kempton W (2007) Public opinion about large offshore wind power: Underlying factors. *Energy Policy* 35: 1584–1598.
[91] Haggett C (2011) Understanding public responses to offshore wind power. *Energy Policy* 39: 503–510.
[92] Ladenburg J (2008) Attitudes towards on-land and offshore wind power development in Denmark; choice of development strategy. *Renewable Energy* 33: 111–118.
[93] Bishop ID and Miller DR (2007) Visual assessment of off-shore wind turbines: The influence of distance, contrast, movement and social variables. *Renewable Energy* 32: 814–831.
[94] European Wind Energy Association (EWEA) (2008) Pure Power – Wind Energy Scenarios up to 2030. http://www.ewea.org/fileadmin/ewea_documents/documents/publications/reports/purepower.pdf (accessed March 2011).
[95] EC (2008) European energy and transport-trends to 2030 (update 2007). http://bookshop.europa.eu/eubookshop/download.action?fileName=KOAC07001ENC_002.pdf&eubphfUid=586483&cata logNbr=KO-AC-07-001-EN-C (accessed March 2011).
[96] Capros P, Mantzos L, Papandreou V, and Tasios N (2008) Model-based analysis of the 2008 EU policy package on climate change and renewables. *Report to DG ENV*. http://ec.europa.cu/clima/policies/package/docs/analysis_en.pdf (accessed May 2011).
[97] de Vries E (2009) Wind turbine technology gets bigger and better. *Renewable Energy World*, May. http://www.renewableenergyworld.com/rea/news/article/2009/05/wind-turbine-technology-gets-bigger-and-better (accessed June 2011).
[98] Renewable Energy Focus (2010) Sway to erect 10 MW offshore wind turbine. February. http://www.renewableenergyfocus.com/view/7279/sway-to-erect-10-mw-offshore-wind-turbine/ (accessed June 2011).
[99] Upwind. Finding solutions for very large wind turbines. http://www.upwind.eu/ (accessed June 2011).
[100] HIPRWIND. http://www.hyperwind.eu/ (accessed June 2011).
[101] Butterfield S, Musial W, Jonkman J, and Sclavounos P (2005) Engineering challenges for floating offshore wind turbines. In: *Proceedings of the Copenhagen Offshore Wind Conference*. Copenhagen, Denmark.

Further Reading

Committee on Offshore Wind Energy Turbine Structural and Operating Safety; Transportation Research Board (2011) *Structural Integrity of Offshore Wind Turbines: Oversight of Design, Fabrication, and Installation – Special Report 305*. The National Academies Press.
Köller J, Köppel J, and Peters W (eds.) (2006) *Offshore Wind Energy: Research on Environmental Impacts*. Berlin: Springer.
Lesny K (2010) *Foundations for Offshore Wind Turbines Tools for Planning and Design*. Essen: VGE GmbH.
Sørensen D and Sørensen JN (eds.) (2011) *Wind Energy Systems – Optimising Design and Construction for Safe and Reliable Operation*. Oxford: Woodhead Publishing Series in Energy.
Twidell J and Gaudiosi G (eds.) (2009) *Offshore Wind Power*. Brentwood, UK: Multi-Science Publishing. ISBN 978-0906522-6392009.

Relevant Websites

http://www.awea.org – American Wind Energy Association.
http://europa.eu – EUROPA – EU Website.
http://www.ewea.org – EWEA: The European Wind Energy Association.
http://fee.asso.fr – France Energie Eolienne.
http://www.gwec.net – GWEC: Global Wind Energy Council.
http://www.iea.org – International Energy Agency (IEA).
http://www.offshorewindenergy.org – Offshore Windenergy Europe.
http://www.risoe.dk – Risø DTU: National Laboratory for Sustainable Energy.
http://www.sealab.gr – Lab of Soft Energy Applications and Environment Protection, Technological Education Institute of Piraeus.
http://www.eia.doe.gov – U.S. Energy Information Administration.
http://www.windpower.org – Vindmølleindustrien: Danish Wind Industry Association.
http://www.windstats.com – Windstats: Windstats Newsletter.
http://www.wwindea.org – World Wind Energy Association.

2.15 Wind Energy Economics

D Milborrow, Lewes, East Sussex, UK

© 2012 Elsevier Ltd. All rights reserved.

2.15.1	Introduction	470
2.15.2	**Basic Financial Issues**	471
2.15.2.1	Definitions	471
2.15.2.1.1	Cost inputs	471
2.15.2.1.2	Energy prices	471
2.15.2.1.3	Net present value	471
2.15.2.1.4	Payback period	471
2.15.2.1.5	Internal rate of return	472
2.15.2.2	Price Calculation Methods	472
2.15.2.3	Recommended Practices	472
2.15.2.4	Interest Rates	472
2.15.2.5	Amortization Periods	472
2.15.2.5.1	Influence of interest rates and repayment periods	473
2.15.3	**Cost and Performance Issues**	474
2.15.3.1	Balance of Plant Costs	474
2.15.3.2	Operational Costs	474
2.15.3.3	Size of Wind Farm	475
2.15.3.4	Installed Costs and Wind Speeds	475
2.15.4	**Onshore Wind**	475
2.15.4.1	Historical Cost and Performance Trends	475
2.15.4.2	Current Plant Costs	476
2.15.4.3	Current Electricity Generation Costs	477
2.15.4.4	Small Wind Turbines	477
2.15.4.4.1	Offshore wind	478
2.15.4.5	Historical Price Trends	478
2.15.4.6	Current Installed Costs	479
2.15.5	**Analysis of Offshore Costs**	480
2.15.5.1	Operation and Maintenance Costs	480
2.15.5.2	Water Depth and Distance from Shore	481
2.15.6	**Electricity-Generating Costs**	481
2.15.6.1	Generation Cost Comparisons	482
2.15.6.1.1	Key issues	482
2.15.6.2	Cost Comparisons – Wind and Other Plant	483
2.15.6.3	Cost Comparisons on a Level Playing Field	483
2.15.7	**External Costs**	484
2.15.7.1	Types of External Cost	484
2.15.7.2	Costing Pollution	485
2.15.7.3	Market Solutions	485
2.15.7.4	The UK Climate Change Levy	486
2.15.7.4.1	External costs of renewable energies	486
2.15.7.5	Renewable Energy Support Mechanisms	486
2.15.7.6	Embedded Generation Benefits	486
2.15.8	**Variability Costs**	487
2.15.8.1	Electricity Networks	488
2.15.8.1.1	Economies of scale	488
2.15.8.2	Characteristics of Wind Energy	489
2.15.8.3	Assimilating Wind	489
2.15.8.4	Extra Short-Term Reserve Needs and Costs	490
2.15.8.5	Carbon Dioxide Savings	491
2.15.8.6	Extra Backup and Its Costs	491
2.15.8.7	Capacity Credit	491
2.15.8.8	The Cost of Backup	492
2.15.8.9	Transmission Constraints	492

2.15.8.10	Wind Surpluses at High Penetration Levels	492
2.15.8.11	Total Costs of Variability	493
2.15.8.12	Mitigating the Effects and Costs of Variability	494
2.15.8.12.1	Wind forecasting	494
2.15.8.12.2	Demand management	494
2.15.8.12.3	Energy storage	495
2.15.8.12.4	System storage	495
2.15.8.12.5	European supergrids	496
2.15.8.12.6	Electric cars	496
2.15.8.12.7	'Smart grids' and the growth of decentralized generation	496
2.15.8.12.8	Electric spaces and water heating	497
2.15.8.12.9	Overall effects	497
2.15.9	**Total Cost Estimates**	497
2.15.10	**Future Price Trends**	497
2.15.10.1	Future Fuel Prices	498
2.15.10.2	Price Comparisons in 2020	499
2.15.11	**Conclusions**	499
References		500

2.15.1 Introduction

The aims of this chapter are:

- To review the generation costs for onshore and offshore wind energy; determine the relative importance of turbine prices, slight costs, and other factors; and indicate how generation costs are influenced by test discount rates and depreciation periods.
- To discuss the key factors that need to be taken into account when comparing renewable energy generation costs with those from the thermal sources, principally:
- External costs
- The 'embedded benefits' of renewable sources (which can be positive or negative)
- The extra balancing costs incurred by the variable sources such as wind, wave, and solar.

There are no absolutes in energy prices. No single number can be assigned to the price of wind energy. The same is true of energy prices for thermal plant. Unless the relevant assumptions are clearly set out, single numbers are virtually meaningless.

It is important to distinguish between the cost of plant (such as wind turbines and wind farms) and the price of the electrical energy they produce. Capital costs are primarily a function of the size of the installation (due to economies of scale). This chapter focuses principally on large-scale wind farms as these deliver the cheapest electricity costs, but there is a brief review of the costs of smaller installations.

Wind energy prices depend on wind speeds and institutional factors, and have two components:

- Capital charges, including depreciation and interest charges.
- Operating costs.

The calculation of wind energy generation prices follows procedures that are reasonably standardized across the power industry. 'Real', that is, net of inflation, interest rates (test discount rates) are used to determine the capital charges. The term weighted average cost of capital is also used. National interest rates and repayment periods vary widely, but comparisons can be made provided the levels are quoted.

Institutional factors account for most of the apparent variations in quoted wind energy prices. In Denmark, for example, the costs of grid reinforcement for wind installations are not always charged to the developer and the utilities tend to use relatively low interest rates (5–6%). In Britain and the United States, however, investor-owned utilities tend to use interest rates around 10%. In this chapter, for the sake of uniformity, an interest rate of 8% is used, except where stated.

Comparisons of generation costs are not necessarily the most equitable way of assessing the competitive position of renewables and so there is a brief description of the 'external costs' of electricity-generating sources, drawing on the European Union's (EU's) 'ExternE' project plus other material.

A complete and fair comparison between wind energy generation costs and those of the fossil fuel sources demands that the additional costs associated with the variability of wind is also taken into account and that the relevant issues are discussed.

The chapter also discusses methods of valuing renewable energy. One of the distinctive features of renewable energy is that most plants are 'embedded' in distribution networks – rather than connected to transmission networks. They therefore accrue additional value, beyond simple 'fuel saving' levels. The relevant issues are discussed, but it is also noted that the 'embedded value' may be negative if exploitation of renewables demands major transmission reinforcement. Finally, examples of 'total cost estimates' are discussed, which take into account all the debits and credits associated with renewable energy costs. The chapter concludes with a discussion of published forecasts of future price trends.

Note on currency conversions: Present-day (2010) prices have been converted on the basis that £1 = $1.60 and €1 = $1.36. Historical data have been converted at the exchange rates prevailing at the time, but where the data are intended to show trends, rather than absolute values, some have been left in the original units.

2.15.2 Basic Financial Issues

2.15.2.1 Definitions

To the layman, costs are paid to acquire items and prices are the amount for which items are sold or offered. Value is the worth of an item to the recipient. The context must therefore be clear. Manufacturers incur costs when building wind turbines and sell them at a price that includes their profit. A wind energy developer, however, will incur costs throughout the lifetime of the project, which include the turbines, the 'balance of plant' costs plus operation and maintenance costs. Developers sell the energy at a price that includes profit. Inputs are therefore costs and the output is a price. However, conventional terminology sometimes means that rigorous definitions cannot be used without causing confusion. The term 'generation cost', for example, is very widely used, even though it usually includes an element of profit. It has been retained here, even though, strictly speaking, the term should be 'generation price'.

2.15.2.1.1 Cost inputs

There are two cost inputs to a wind developer or owner. The capital, or installed, costs of the plant are most frequently quoted in terms of investment cost per installed kilowatt, or $ kW^{-1}, and, broadly speaking, are primarily a function of the size of the installation (due to economies of scale). Operating costs are the second input, and, similarly, depend on size, but may be dependent, also, on energy yield.

2.15.2.1.2 Energy prices

These depend on installed costs, wind speeds, test discount rates, and capital repayment periods, and are simply the sum of the capital cost element and the operating costs, and are expressed in various ways although $ MWh^{-1} is used in this chapter.

In general, there are three principal components of electricity generation costs:

1. Those associated with repayments of capital (plus interest). Quantifying the total capital costs that need to be included when putting a price on electricity-generating plant is relatively straightforward. The capital cost includes the cost of the plant, land acquisition (unless a rent is paid, in which case this is a running cost), grid connection (although in some European states, the utility has borne the cost), and initial financing costs (not repayment costs).
2. Operating costs include insurance, rent, and local authority rates, as well as the costs of labor and materials used for operations and maintenance.
3. Fuel costs.

Fuel costs for wind, wave, geothermal, and solar installations are zero. The term 'reference price' is used in this chapter to denote energy prices calculated using standard procedures, with defined interest rates. These must be distinguished from prices relevant to particular states, which use appropriate levels of interest rate and repayment period; these are given the generic name 'national prices'.

2.15.2.1.3 Net present value

A number of financial parameters are used when evaluating the viability of wind energy projects. The net present value (NPV) is [1]

> the net present worth of a time series of cash flows, both incoming and outgoing. NPV is a central tool in discounted cash flow (DCF) analysis, and is a standard method for using the time value of money to appraise long-term projects. Used for capital budgeting, and widely throughout economics, finance, and accounting, it measures the excess or shortfall of cash flows, in present value terms, once financing charges are met.

The NPV is calculated by summing the yearly cash flows that have been discounted by an appropriate discount rate. That rate may be set by government – if a wind project is a public sector initiative – or by the individual developer. Public sector projects tend to use lower rates – 5% or 6%, say – and private sector developments usually use rates in the range 8–10%.

2.15.2.1.4 Payback period

When calculating NPVs, the first term in the time series – in the case of a wind project – is the outlay for the capital cost of the plant. That has a negative value and the remuneration from the electricity sales minus the provisions for operation and maintenance charges and other outgoings generally has a positive value. When the sum of these positive monies equals the initial capital outlay, this defines the 'payback period'. 'Simple payback' is calculated in a similar way, but no discount rate is applied to the summation of the yearly cash flows and so it is invariably less.

2.15.2.1.5 Internal rate of return
The internal rate of return (IRR) of an investment is the interest rate at which the NPV of costs (negative cash flows) of the investment equals the NPV of the benefits (positive cash flows) of the investment.

IRRs are commonly used to evaluate the desirability of investments or projects. The higher a project's IRR, the more desirable it is to undertake the project. Assuming all other factors are equal among the various projects, the project with the highest IRR would probably be considered the best and undertaken first [2].

2.15.2.2 Price Calculation Methods

The basic procedures for setting selling prices for electricity are set out in standard texts [3]. The first step is to calculate the annual capital charge, which depends on the project interest rate, or 'test discount rate' and repayment period. An 'annual charge rate' is used, which expresses the fraction of capital cost that needs to be charged each year in order to yield the required rate of return over the specified period.

The annual capital charge includes capital depreciation and interest charges and is divided by the annual energy output to yield the capital element of energy price. The energy output of wind plant is primarily dependent on the wind regime, that is, on its geographical location, and on the performance of the wind turbines.

Institutional factors arguably account for most of the apparent variations in quoted wind energy generation costs. These factors may also influence the exact makeup of capital and operating costs. In Denmark, for example, the costs of grid reinforcement for wind installations have not always been charged to developers. Similarly, utilities in Denmark and elsewhere may not always charge their overheads to 'operating costs', whereas in Britain, by contrast – where private developers undertake all wind developments – all costs are included.

2.15.2.3 Recommended Practices

The calculation of wind energy generation costs follows procedures, which are reasonably standardized across the power industry. The International Energy Agency (IEA) has published guidelines in the form of a 'Recommend Practice' [4] for wind energy, and these are similar to those used for other renewables and for thermal plants. The IEA document advocates the use of 'real', that is, net of inflation, interest rates – more accurately, test discount rates – for the calculations, which is also common practice.

The following items are included in energy price calculations:

- Planning costs
- Capital cost of plant
- Construction costs
- Interest during construction
- Land costs (either as part of the capital or as annual leasing payments)
- Fuel costs – zero for renewable energy plants
- Operating costs (O&M), including labor, materials, rents, taxes, and insurance
- Decommissioning.

The IEA document recommends that capital costs are amortized over the technical life of the plant and that standard test discount rates are used. While this may produce useful data for comparative purposes, actual interest rates and regulatory or institutional frameworks, as noted above, control amortization periods. Each of these parameters needs, therefore, to be considered in more detail.

2.15.2.4 Interest Rates

Public sector companies use test discount rates set by government. These vary, generally between 5% and 8%. Private companies set their own rates. In practice, many projects are financed using a mixture of loan and equity funding. A typical ratio is 80/20. If the loan interest rate is 6% and the equity return is 25%, the equivalent test discount rate for the project as a whole is 10%. This is a fairly typical value for the private sector. Irrespective of the sources of finance, a 'cost of capital' can be derived that expresses the interest rate that can be applied to the total cost of the project to determine generation costs. Alternative nomenclature for this parameter is the 'test discount rate', 'project interest rate', or 'weighted average cost of capital'.

2.15.2.5 Amortization Periods

Amortization and depreciation periods also vary, and are not necessarily as long as the life of the plant. This is rarely used outside the public sector. The IEA Recommended Practice notes that "20 years is commonly used for proven grid connected wind turbines" and is used in this chapter as a default value.

2.15.2.5.1 Influence of interest rates and repayment periods

National institutional factors have a major influence on the financing terms for borrowing money and on investors' expectations for the return on the equity they put into a project. In some places, all the investment is provided by the state, or by nationalized industries, and so the equity contribution is zero. Before privatization of the electricity industry in the United Kingdom, the test discount rate was set by the Treasury and was 8% in 1990. In Denmark today, utilities almost invariably use 'public sector' test discount rates, typically 5% or 6%. In Britain and the United States today there are no fixed criteria and project developers use criteria that tend to be strongly influenced by the financiers. The overall interest rate is dependent on the relative proportions of debt and equity and the appropriate interest rates; most tend to be in the range 8–11%.

The other parameter that strongly influences generation costs is the repayment period. The longer this is, the lower the annual payment to cover depreciation and interest and hence the lower the generation cost. In Denmark, this period often corresponds to the expected life of the project – 20–25 years is common. In the private sector, depreciation periods also vary, they were generally in the region of 12–15 years in the early years of wind energy development, but increasing investor confidence means that finance can now be secured for up to 20 years in some instances.

The 'annual charge rate' is the fraction of capital payable each year to cover repayments of the original investment plus interest, and depends on both interest rate and repayment period. Typical values are shown in **Table 1**. Once the annual cost has been determined, the corresponding generating cost component is simply the annual cost divided by the annual energy generation.

Financing terms can have a significant impact on the 'capital cost' element of electricity-generating costs. The most stringent criteria (bottom line of **Table 1**) mean that annual charges will be double those associated with more relaxed criteria (top line of table). If the capital cost element of the total generation cost is small (as in the case of gas-fired generation), changes in the financing terms will have very little impact on generating costs. In the case of renewable energy technologies such as wind, wave, photovoltaics (PVs), and tidal, where capital costs form the largest element of generation cost, the impact will be much greater.

The data shown in **Figure 1** illustrate just how important interest rates are to capital-intensive electricity-generating technologies such as wind. The estimates of electricity generation costs have been derived using the cost data listed in **Table 2**. Note that these

Table 1 Typical annual charge rates

Interest rate (%)	Repayment period (yr)	Annual charge rate	Comments
5	20	0.0802	Used in Denmark and in some American States
8	20	0.1019	Old 'nationalized industry' UK figure
8	15	0.1168	Typical UK Non-Fossil Fuel Obligation criteria
10	20	0.1175	Widely used now that wind is well established
12	12	0.1614	For investments seen as more risky, for example, offshore wind

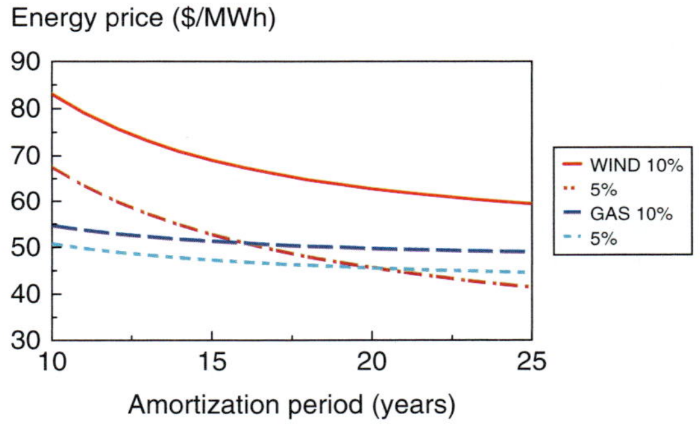

Figure 1 Gas and wind energy prices – influence of interest rates and repayment periods.

Table 2 Data used to illustrate effects of interest rates and repayment periods

Technology	Wind	Gas
Capital cost, $ kW^{-1}	1000	724
Build time, yr	0.5	1
Load factor, %	0.26	0.8
Fuel cost, $ MWh^{-1}	0	33
O&M cost, ECU MWh^{-1}	10	6

Table 3 UK Renewable energy prices

Technology	NFFO5 price (£ MWh^{-1})	August 2006 price (£ MWh^{-1})
Landfill gas	27.3	108.3
Energy from waste	24.3	54.8
Hydro	40.8	98.0
Wind projects > 2.3 MW	28.8	102.3

data are purely for illustrative purposes. Whereas the spread of prices from gas-fired generation is only about $10 MWh^{-1} (from a 10-year amortization period and 10% interest rate to 25 years amortization and 5% interest rate), the corresponding spread for wind energy is about $42 MWh^{-1}. With a 20-year amortization period and 10% interest rate, wind is dearer than gas, but a change in the interest rate to 5% brings the prices into line. Extending the amortization period to 25 years brings wind prices below gas prices. It is assumed that gas prices remain constant in real terms over the period.

Changes in national institutional frameworks illustrate the maxim "Prices are what you want them to be," and price variations in recent years for renewable energy in the United Kingdom bear this out. In the last round of contracts under the Non-Fossil Fuel Obligation in 1998, the average price for 'large' wind energy projects was £28.8 MWh^{-1}, whereas the prices realized in the auction by the Non-Fossil Purchasing Agency in August 2006 was £102.3 MWh^{-1}. Table 3 illustrates how dramatically headline prices for four technologies have changed; the 1998 prices have not been corrected for inflation but this would make little difference to the comparison.

Under the previous arrangements – the Non-Fossil Fuel Obligation – the prices bid by renewable generators were (assuming they were successful) the prices they were paid. Under the new arrangements, prices are subject to negotiation between generators and suppliers and are a function of 'supply and demand'. While the plant costs of renewable generation have not changed dramatically, the price paid, under the new arrangements, is now a complex amalgam of numerous different components. The generators are paid less than the price in Table 3, but the supplier takes the risk that prices into the future may be less than the prices quoted here.

Further details of wind energy support mechanisms are discussed later. It may be noted that national institutional factors are responsible for most of the apparent variations in renewable energy generation prices. These influence the 'cost of capital' and depreciation periods – the latter are not necessarily the same as project lifetimes.

2.15.3 Cost and Performance Issues

Wind turbine and wind farm costs are often quoted on the basis of a price per unit of installed capacity ($ kW^{-1}), but such data can be misleading as manufacturers have differing design philosophies – there is no fixed relationship between rotor size and rating. A 40 m machine, for example, may have a rating anywhere between 350 and 500 kW. The price of a machine with a high rating, relative to its size, will therefore tend to appear low when compared with one that has a low rating for its size. More reliable comparisons may be made by comparing prices on the basis of price per unit swept area ($ m^{-2}). However, although this may be more rigorous, it is probably less readily understood and is used less often.

2.15.3.1 Balance of Plant Costs

Balance of plant costs – the extra costs, additional to those of the wind turbines – add between 15% (onshore) and 100% (offshore) to wind turbine costs, depending on the number and size of machines in the wind farm, and the location. The windiest onshore sites – on hilltop sites, often remote from a grid connection, or coastal locations where deep piling into silt is needed, tend to incur costs above average. Similar considerations apply offshore, where sites in deep water and far from shore are the most expensive.

Although wind turbine prices (in $ kW^{-1}) may increase at the large size ranges, there are nevertheless sound reasons for pursuing the development of such machines. A number of items in the 'balance of plant' costs decrease with size (in $ kW^{-1} terms) of machine and/or machine numbers such as:

- Foundation costs
- Electrical interconnection costs
- Access tracks.

The way in which foundation costs decrease with increasing size has been examined in a study carried out by the author [5]. It was found that foundation costs for 800 kW machines were around one-third less than those of 200 kW machines.

2.15.3.2 Operational Costs

Operational costs also fall with increase of turbine size. Analysis of data from German wind installations has shown that the price of insurance and guarantees both halved, approximately, as ratings increase from 200 to 600 kW. Total costs, which are similar across

Table 4 Operational costs

Item	Cost basis
Service contract	$ kW^{-1} and $ MWh^{-1} both used
Administration	Cost basis varies, $ kW^{-1} common
Insurance	$ kW^{-1} more usual
Land rent	1–2% of revenue, if land not bought
Local rates	$ kW^{-1} more usual
Electricity usage	Standard tariffs
Reactive power	Up to 0.4 kVArh

most of Europe, fell from around 38 electronic control unit (ECU) kW^{-1} yr^{-1} at the 200 kW size to around 15 ECU kW^{-1} yr^{-1} at 600 kW [5] (the ECU was slightly above parity with the US$ during this period).

Operational costs vary between countries and wind farms. Some elements are fixed annual sums, so wind farms on high wind speed sites may have lower costs per unit of electricity generated. **Table 4** shows the main components and the usual basis of charging is denoted. Several costs are size-dependent. Total costs are in the range $32–60 kW^{-1} yr^{-1} onshore and $90–150 kW^{-1} offshore.

Not all utilities charge for reactive power – and not all machines need it. Land rent may be an explicit cost if a developer builds on land he does not own, but may not appear if the wind farm operator owns the land. In the latter case, the cost of the land may be included in the overall capital cost, or the owner may simply receive remuneration from the overall profit.

2.15.3.3 Size of Wind Farm

The size of a wind farm influences its cost, as large developments

- often attract discounts from wind turbine manufacturers
- enable site infrastructure costs to be spread over a number of machines, reducing the unit cost
- enable more effective use of maintenance staff.

2.15.3.4 Installed Costs and Wind Speeds

The attraction of hilly sites onshore and remote sites offshore is the higher wind speeds. Developers can afford higher costs, if they get a higher yield. Increasing the wind speed, for example, from 8 to 9 m s^{-1} at hub height will typically increase output from a wind turbine by 10%. However, remote hilltop sites generally cost more to develop than flat, low sites. The link between onshore installed costs and winds has been examined [5, 6] and it was found that installed costs in Britain increased by between 16% and 25% as the site wind speed increased from 7.5 to 9 m s^{-1}. Another factor that influences this correlation is that tall towers are often used in places such as Germany to obtain higher wind speeds, but at increased turbine cost.

2.15.4 Onshore Wind

2.15.4.1 Historical Cost and Performance Trends

The cost of wind energy plant fell substantially during the period from 1980 to 2004. **Figure 2** shows the average worldwide selling price of wind turbines from the early days (1980) in California to around 1998 (when worldwide capacity was around 10 GW) [5].

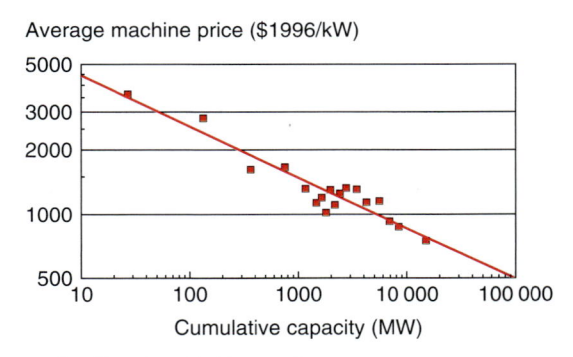

Figure 2 Average price of wind turbines, as a function of worldwide capacity.

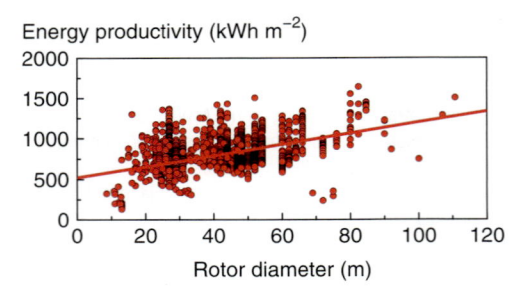

Figure 3 Productivity of wind turbines in Denmark, 2005. Source of data: Danish Energy Agency (1999).

Presentation of the data in this way enables the 'learning curve' reduction to be derived (this is the reduction in cost that is achieved for every doubling of capacity). The data that are plotted suggest this ratio is about 15%, which is consistent with estimates derived by other analyses.

Prices in the 1980s were around $3000 kW^{-1}, or more, and by 1998 they had come down by a factor of 3. During that period, the size of machines increased significantly – from around 55 kW to 1 MW or more – and manufacturers increased productivity substantially. In 1992, for example, one of the major manufacturers employed over seven people per megawatt of capacity sold, but by 2001, only two people per megawatt were needed. The energy productivity of wind turbines also increased during this period. This was partly due to improved efficiency and availability, but also due to the fact that the larger machines were taller and so intercepted higher wind speeds. This is illustrated in **Figure 3**, using data from the Danish Environment Ministry. The small machines in 2005 delivered around 500 kWh m^{-2} of rotor area, or less, whereas the largest machines delivered over twice that amount. A further factor that led to a rapid decline in electricity production costs was the lower operation and maintenance costs.

With capital costs halving between 1985 and the end of the century, and productivity doubling, it may be expected that electricity production costs might fall by a factor of 4. This general trend has been confirmed by the Danish Energy Agency; they suggest that generation costs fell from 1.2 DKK kWh^{-1} in 1982 to around 0.3 DKK kWh^{-1} in 1998 (1 DKK1998 = $0.144) [7].

Shortly after the turn of the century, the downward trend in wind turbine and wind farm prices halted and prices moved upward, as shown in **Figure 4**. This was partly due to significant increases in commodity prices and partly due to shortages of wind turbines. Prices appear to have peaked in 2008, with wind farms averaging just under $2200 kW^{-1} and wind turbines at just under $1600 kW^{-1}. Although the prices may now be falling, based on data available to the autumn of 2009, it should be noted that a complete data set was not available for 2009 at the time the graph was compiled.

2.15.4.2 Current Plant Costs

The price of modern turbines around 55–65 m in diameter, for onshore installations, is around $1500 kW^{-1}. The 'most economic size' of machine has changed over the years and is still moving upward. The larger the machines, the fewer are required for a given capacity. This brings savings in site costs and in operation and maintenance costs, as noted earlier. Overall, site costs add between 15% and 40% to wind turbine costs, depending on the number and size of machines in the wind farm, and the location. **Figure 5** shows a typical cost breakdown for a complete wind farm [8], which now (late 2009) costs around $2150 kW^{-1}.

An analysis of published data from about 30 wind farms around the world, which were completed between January and October 2009 with a total capacity of over 3000 MW, suggests that the average installed cost was $2150 kW^{-1}, with a standard deviation of $466 kW^{-1} [9]. An analysis by the Lawrence Berkeley Laboratory in the United States reached a very similar result – $2120 kW^{-1} [10].

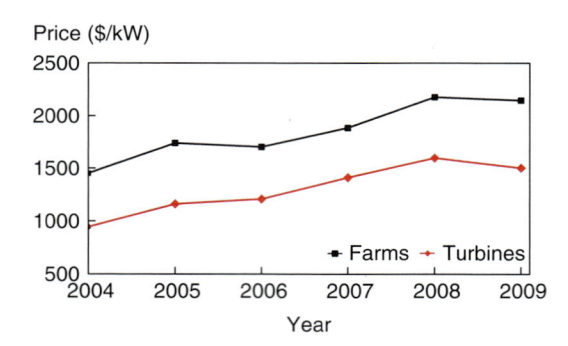

Figure 4 Wind farm and turbine prices, 2004–09.

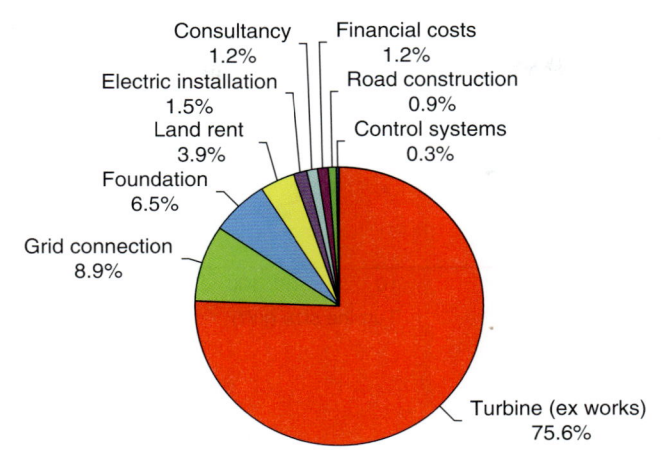

Figure 5 Cost breakdown for an onshore wind farm.

2.15.4.3 Current Electricity Generation Costs

Using estimates ±1 standard deviation from the average installed cost, quoted in the previous paragraph, and rounding slightly, suggests that generation costs based on installed costs between $1700 and $2600 kW^{-1} should have a wide relevance.

These estimates, which are shown in **Figure 6**, were derived using an 8% discount rate and a 20-year amortization period; operating costs have been set at $32 kW^{-1} yr^{-1} for the lower capital cost and $60 kW^{-1} yr^{-1} for the higher capital cost. The link between wind speed and energy productivity has been established by examining the performance characteristics of a number of large wind turbines that are currently available. Although there is not a unique link between wind speed and capacity factor, the spread is quite small. All wind speeds refer to hub height. The estimates suggest that generation costs at $2600 kW^{-1} range from just under $200 MWh^{-1} at 6 m s^{-1}, falling to $87 MWh^{-1} at 9.5 m s^{-1}. At $1700 kW^{-1}, the corresponding range is $125 to $55 MWh^{-1}, respectively.

2.15.4.4 Small Wind Turbines

The discussion and analysis so far has related to wind turbines of 1 MW size and above, and to wind farms of greater capacity. As with most technologies, economies of scale yield significant savings of installed costs, but these effects become progressively smaller at the larger scales. Conversely, below 1 MW (roughly), installed costs rise. Although these higher costs (and lower energy yields) translate to higher electricity-generating costs, that is not necessarily a drawback as the price comparator is likely to be different. Large wind farms compete with gas and coal-fired power stations, but small- and medium-sized wind turbines may be competing with expensive electricity from diesel generators on remote islands or perhaps on remote farms in the developed world. There is such a wide variety of applications for small wind systems that it is difficult to lay down guidelines as to what are the target electricity-generating costs.

Figure 7 suggests that fully installed costs for small wind turbines range from around $8000 kW^{-1}, for machines with a rating of around 1 kW, around $5500 kW^{-1} for a 10 kW machine, down to around $4000 kW^{-1} for a 100 kW machine [11]. These data come from a recent generalized analysis, but the trends are similar to those from an earlier analysis for turbines, only, rather than installed costs shown in **Figure 8**. A very similar trend is evident in the earlier data, with prices for very small machines straddling around $8000 kW^{-1}, falling to around $2050 kW^{-1} at 10 kW size and $1560 kW^{-1} at 100 kW rating [12]. At that time (1999), much more information on selling prices was available than at the present time; there are not enough data at the present time to enable the

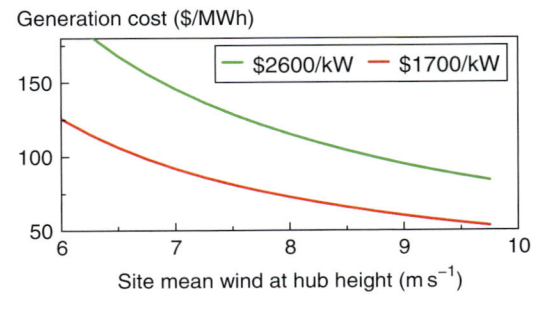

Figure 6 Estimates of electricity generation costs from onshore wind turbines.

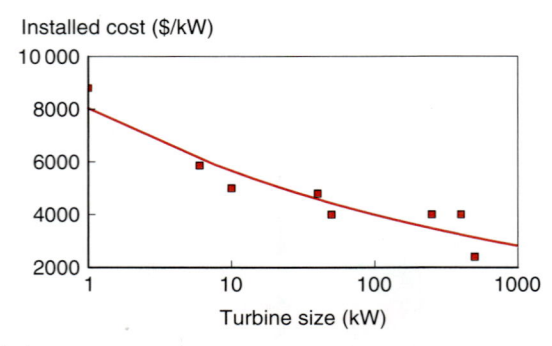

Figure 7 Small wind turbines: fully installed costs.

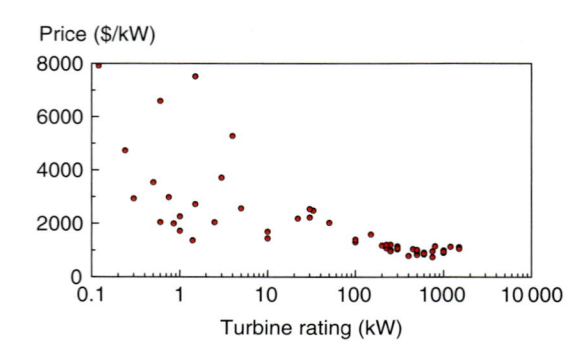

Figure 8 Wind turbine prices, 1999.

information to be updated. The original turbine prices were in ECU, and in 1999, 1 ECU was roughly equal to $1.04. **Figure 7** – for installed costs – and **Figure 8** – for turbine prices only – both clearly illustrate that economies of scale are significant.

2.15.4.4.1 Offshore wind

Offshore wind has the potential to deliver substantial quantities of energy, but it is more expensive than onshore wind. Cost reductions may be expected as the technology is further developed.

A number of factors combine to increase the cost of offshore wind farms above onshore costs:

- The need to 'marinize' the wind turbines, to protect them from the corrosive influence of salt spray. These measures may add up to 20% to turbine costs.
- The cost of the cable connection from the wind farm to the shore; this increases with the distance from the shore, and accounts for between 17% and 34% of the total cost.
- More expensive foundations. The cost increases with water depth and can account for up to 30% of the total cost.
- Increased operation and maintenance costs, with a risk of lower availability due to reduced access to the wind turbines during bad weather.

Foundation and grid connection costs are substantially more expensive when compared with onshore wind energy. In the budgets for the first batch of large Danish offshore wind farms, from which **Figure 9** is drawn, these items together account for around a third of the total cost. (Onshore foundations are typically less than half this amount, whilst grid connection costs are frequently even lower.) This observation underscores the reasons for the interest in larger wind turbines and also for the enthusiasm for larger numbers of machines.

2.15.4.5 Historical Price Trends

Table 5 summarizes the principal operational data for the early Danish wind farms at Vindeby and Tuno Knob [13], together with the pilot Dutch farm in the Ijsselmeer [14], and a later Swedish wind farm.

Although the cost of the Vindeby wind farm was 85% higher than the cost of an onshore installation, the anticipated energy yield was 20% higher. Concerns about low availability offshore – due to problems of access – have not generally been realized. The costs of the early wind farms were significantly higher than those of the later installation, at Bockstigen in Sweden. Just as with onshore wind farms, prices vary depending on the exact location, with distance from shore, seabed conditions, and water depth being key factors.

Another key determinant in offshore wind farm costs is likely to be the number of machines. There is a trend toward larger wind farms than onshore, to spread the cost of offshore transport, cable connection, and operation and maintenance costs.

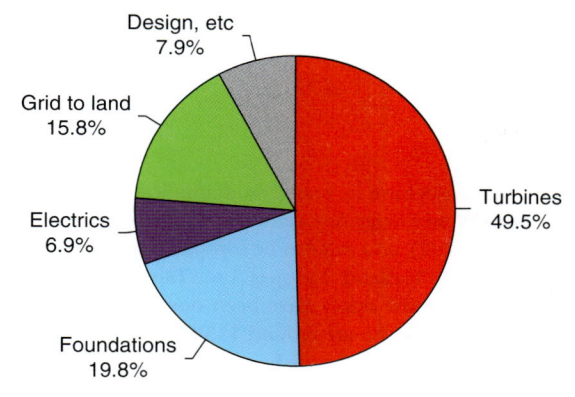

Figure 9 Analysis of offshore wind farm costs.

Table 5 Early offshore wind farms: performance and costs

Location	Date	Turbines No./kW	Capacity MW	Wind $m\,s^{-1}$	Output GWh	Cost MECU	ECU kW^{-1}
Vindeby, DK	1991	11/450	4.95	7.9[a]	11.2	9.6	1939
Comparable onshore farm at that time				7.2[a]	10	5.3	1071
Ijsselmeer, NL	1994	4/500	2	7.7	3.8	5.2	2600
Tuno, DK	1995	10/500	5	7.4[a]	12.5	10.2	2040
Bockstigen, SW	1998	5/550	2.75		8	4	1455

[a]Author's estimate.

2.15.4.6 Current Installed Costs

The energy costs from offshore wind farms cannot be established with the same precision as those of onshore installations; fewer wind farms are being commissioned, and there is a wide spread of costs. Whereas the installed costs for onshore wind farms fell steadily for many years as the industry matured, precisely the opposite has happened offshore. The early offshore wind farms were built for around $1800–2250 kW^{-1}, but some of the latest developments – under construction or planned – will cost over $5000 kW^{-1}, which is over twice the current price of onshore wind farms. The higher cost is partially offset by higher energy yields, as offshore winds are generally higher than those onshore, but generating costs are about twice those of onshore wind farms. Generating costs are very sensitive to interest rates and capital repayment periods, however, and the high capital costs offshore mean that offshore wind farms are more 'capital intensive' than onshore wind farms. Capital repayments offshore account for around 80% of generating costs.

The costs of offshore wind farms rose sharply after the turn of the century, partly due to increases in commodity prices. **Figure 10** shows how prices have risen from $1600 kW^{-1} in 2000 to around $4000 kW^{-1} in 2009. The same graph also shows that the gap between offshore and onshore installed costs has widened in absolute terms; in relative terms, the ratio is still between 1.5 and 1.75,

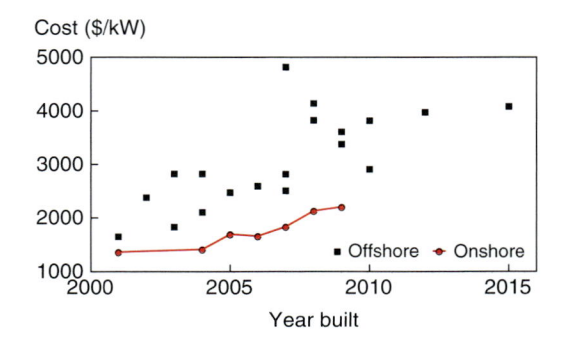

Figure 10 Development of installed costs for offshore wind farms. Note that it is not always clear exactly what is included in the cost figures. The lowest cost for 2010, for example, is for the Danish 'Rodsand II' wind farm but this does not include the grid connection cost. Offshore costs increase with distance from the shore and with water depth and the highest figure for 2009 comes from the German 'Alpha Ventus' wind farm which is 45 km from the shore, in waters that are 30 m deep.

although there are wide variations in current estimates of offshore installed costs. **Figure 10** also shows projected prices up to 2015, with prices remaining at roughly the same level.

2.15.5 Analysis of Offshore Costs

In order to examine the reasons why offshore costs have increased so dramatically, it is instructive to compare current costs with those of the earlier wind farms. The European Wind Energy Association's 'Wind Energy, the Facts' includes a cost breakdown for the Danish wind farm at Horns Rev (completed in 2002), and this can be compared with the figures quoted in a recent British study by Ernst and Young (E&Y) [15] and with data for the Rodsand II project – see **Table 6**.

The table shows that the increases in wind turbine prices have been one of the major influences that have pushed up total installed costs. Current prices of turbines for onshore use are around $1500 kW^{-1} and the figure for Rodsand II (and other data) suggests that the additional costs of the adaptations needed for offshore use add around 30% or more to this figure. There has been a modest increase in foundation costs since 2002, which suggests that more efficient methods of construction have been found that offset the increases in commodity costs. It is not clear why the British estimates for machines and foundations, from Ernst and Young (E&Y), are higher than the Danish figure for Rodsand II. The total cost of the latter does not include a grid connection cost, but even if an allowance is made for this ($750 kW^{-1}, say), there is still a significant difference between the total installed costs.

2.15.5.1 Operation and Maintenance Costs

Offshore operation and maintenance costs are, unsurprisingly, higher than onshore costs, but, as with capital costs, the exact scope of published figures is not always clear. There is less information available on offshore operation and maintenance costs, but **Table 7** summarizes recent estimates and data. The data include actual costs from the third year of operation at one of the early UK wind farms.

With the exception of the last entry in **Table 7**, all the figures suggest that offshore operation and maintenance costs are in the range €10–21 MWh^{-1} ($15–31 MWh^{-1}). The European Wind Energy Association's Analysis includes data from 10 wind farms and all the costs lie within this range. The costs are not substantially higher than those for onshore wind, probably due to the fact that offshore wind farms tend to be much larger and can therefore benefit from economies of scale. Wind speeds also tend to be higher, which means that the fixed costs are spread over a greater number of electricity units.

The report compiled by Ernst and Young for the British government, cited above, contains a detailed breakdown, and is shown in **Table 8**. It is possible that the discrepancy between these figures and the remainder is due to the fact that some of the other estimates do not include all the items listed in this table. A distinction must be drawn between costs associated with maintenance of the turbines and other costs, such as grid charges, insurance, lease, and decommissioning charges. This latter group of costs can, in total, equate to a similar sum as the turbine maintenance costs.

Table 6 Cost breakdown data for offshore wind farms

Source	EWEA	Rodsand II	E&Y
Component			
Turbines	1182	1927	2501
Electrical	515	0	1001
Foundations	508	580	1167
Other	232	0	58
Total	2436	3012	5336

Not all the costs for Rodsand II have been published, hence the gaps. All figures are in $ kW^{-1}.

Table 7 Offshore operation and maintenance costs

Source	€MWh^{-1}	€kW^{-1}
Nysted (DK) 165 MW wind farm budget	13	
UK, Carbon Trust [16]	21	44
European Wind Energy Association [8]	16	
UK, Scroby Sands [17]	13	31
UK, Generic (Ernst and Young) [15]	30	100

Table 8 Operation and maintenance cost estimates for UK offshore wind farms

Component	Cost (€ kW^{-1})	$ MWh^{-1}
Turbine	73	35
Grid charges	8.2	4
Insurance	13	6.3
Lease charges	5.5	2.6
Decommissioning	20	9.6
Total	119.7	57.5

The tentative nature of the estimates should be noted. Offshore failure rates are still a somewhat uncertain quantity and the consultant Garrad Hassan [18] has produced data showing that the operating cost estimates are critically sensitive to failure rates. If these rise from 5 failures per turbine per year to 10, then operating costs would more than double.

The first two British wind farms achieved almost identical availability figures during their first year of operation –84%. Of the downtime at North Hoyle, 67% was due to the turbines, 12% due to construction activities, 5% due to scheduled maintenance, and 17% due to accessibility problems. The chief sources of downtime were problems with the cable termination, a high voltage fault at the onshore end of the cable, generator faults, and instrumentation and other electrical faults.

2.15.5.2 Water Depth and Distance from Shore

Ideally, offshore wind farms should be sited close to the shore and in fairly shallow waters. However, this may not always be possible and attractions of going further offshore are usually that the wind speeds are higher. However, the expense of building further offshore will inevitably be higher – due to the higher costs of the cable connection to the shore and to the higher transport costs. Water depth usually increases with distance from the shore and this also pushes up costs, mainly due to the higher costs of the foundations.

The way in which water depth and distance from the shore increases construction costs is illustrated in **Figure 11**. The reference wind farm is cited in water depths between 10 and 20 m, and not further than 10 km from the shore. With the same water depth, the wind farm 'scale factor' is 1.18 at distances from the shore between 50 and 100 km – in other words, it will be 18% more expensive. If the distance from the coast does not exceed 10 km, then the scale factor with water depths between 40 and 50 m is 1.396 – in other words, it will be 39.6% more expensive. At the extreme limits of the data that are plotted, a wind farm between 50 and 100 km from the shore, in water 40–50 m deep will be 65% more expensive than the reference installation.

The ratios quoted come from a study by the European Environment Agency [19] and the UK Carbon Trust [20] has produced similar estimates, although the scale factors are slightly lower.

2.15.6 Electricity-Generating Costs

The price range selected for the generation cost estimates shown in **Figure 12** is $3800–4600 kW^{-1}. As is the case onshore, the lower price level is likely to apply nearer to the shore, where wind speeds are comparatively modest. The electricity price estimates have not been extended beyond 8 m s^{-1} for that reason and operation and maintenance costs have been set at $90 kW^{-1}. The higher priced wind farms, by contrast, are less likely to be sited in regions with low wind speeds and so the starting point has been set at 7.5 m s^{-1}. The corresponding operation and maintenance costs have been set at $150 kW^{-1}. Based on these assumptions and assuming, as in

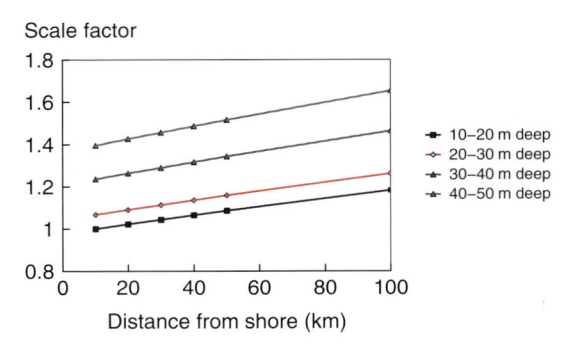

Figure 11 'Scale factors' for wind farms at distances up to 100 km from the shore and water depths up to 50 m. The scale factor is the ratio of the wind farm cost to the cost of a wind farm no further than 10 km from the shore and water no deeper than 10 m. Source: European Environment Agency (2009) Europe's onshore and offshore wind energy potential. *EEA Technical Report No. 6/2009.* http://www.eea.europa.eu/.

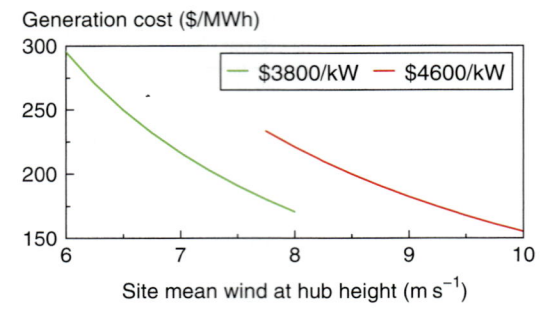

Figure 12 Estimates of offshore electricity-generating costs.

the case of onshore wind, an 8% test discount rate and amortization over 20 years, generation costs, at $3800 kW^{-1} fall from $296 MWh^{-1} at 6 m s^{-1} to $171 MWh^{-1} at 8 m s^{-1}. With installed costs set at $4600 kW^{-1}, generation costs at 8 m s^{-1} are around $221 MWh^{-1} at 8 m s^{-1}, falling to $156 MWh^{-1} at 10 m s^{-1}.

At the low end of the current range of generation costs, The Danish 'Rodsand II' wind farm will receive remuneration at around $125 MWh^{-1}, but in this case, the developer did not have to pay for the costs of the grid connection and the installed cost was just under $3150 kW^{-1}. A levelized offshore electricity cost of $240 MWh^{-1} – almost double the Danish figure – was quoted in a study by Ernst and Young for the UK government. This assumed a construction cost of $5336 kW^{-1} and a rate of return on the project of 10%.

> Most offshore wind tariffs pay for electricity at prices within the range of costs that have been discussed above, although there is a wide range of structures. Some tariff payments 'step down' after an initial period, others are linked to capital subsidies and others are linked to be market price of electricity and/or 'green certificates'.

2.15.6.1 Generation Cost Comparisons

2.15.6.1.1 Key issues

It is unrealistic to discuss the price of electricity from wind energy in isolation – it needs to be set in context alongside prices for the conventional thermal sources and for other types of renewable energy. This section examines typical performance and cost data for a number of electricity-generating technologies.

The electricity generation prices from thermal plants vary widely, and, as with wind, no single figure can quantify the exact costs and performance of any technology. There are national differences in the installed costs and, particularly, the case of renewable energy, in the availability of the energy sources. There are, for example, no sources of geothermal heat that are sufficiently attractive for commercial electricity generation in the United Kingdom (although there are locations where the heat is used), so no installed costs are relevant. In the case of wind and solar energy, the energy productivity – kWh kW^{-1} of plant – varies significantly. Solar installations near to the equator may be expected to be more productive than those in, say, Sweden or New Zealand. Wind energy variations are more diverse; the windiest regions of the world are in New Zealand, the British Isles, and Antarctica, while central Europe and many equatorial regions have low wind speeds.

Table 9 summarizes the key parameters associated with fossil and renewable energy technologies and includes notes as to how these vary. 'Fuel cost' is zero for most types of renewable energy but not for energy crops (where it is positive), nor for the waste-burning technologies (where it is negative). 'Capacity factor' has the usual definition of the ratio between the average output

Table 9 Indicative cost and performance data for large-scale renewable energy and thermal plant [21–24]

Technology	Capital cost ($ kW^{-1})	O&M costs ($ kW^{-1} yr^{-1})	O&M ($MWh)	Load factor (%)	Fuel price ($ MWh^{-1})
Wind, onshore	1900–2600	32–60		20–50	
Wind, offshore	3800–4600	90–150		30–50	
Hydro, large	1800–5400	13–80		50–90	
Solar thermal	3400–3900	57–175		31–73	
Solar PV	4100–5000	12–100		9–21	
Geothermal	1700–3400 [25]	165		90	
Coal with FGD[a]	1900–2100	28–85	4.6	85	7–14
CCGT[a]	960	13	2	90	22–32
Nuclear [26]	3200–4000	90	0.5	90	3

[a]FGD, flue gas desulfurization; CCGT, combined cycle gas turbine.

of the plant and the rated power (both in kW or MW). It must be emphasized that the costs quoted are intended to give an appreciation of possible range of levels, but do not attempt to encompass all possible projects. Fuel prices in the table are based on average levels in the United States and the United Kingdom during 2008.

With the renewable technologies listed (with the possible exception of geothermal), there is also a wide range of load factors and this means that there is a wide spread of electricity-generating costs. In the particular case of wind energy, high installed costs, as noted earlier, tend to be linked with high load factors. The windiest sites tend to be located in hilly, often remote, regions and this means that access can be difficult, which pushes up costs.

2.15.6.2 Cost Comparisons – Wind and Other Plant

The data in **Table 9** have been used as a guide to derive estimates of electricity-generating costs using common financing parameters (20-year life and 8% discount rate). Other sources, particularly Reference 24, have also been used and the data are compared in **Figure 13**. Appropriate allowances have been made for interest charges incurred during the construction period. This varies from a low of 1 year for onshore wind to 6 years for nuclear.

The cost comparisons suggest that large hydro and geothermal plants offer the cheapest renewable energy generation costs – about \$50 MWh^{-1} – although there is a wide range of estimates in each case, taking the upper end of the range to \$72 MWh^{-1} in the case of geothermal and \$92 MWh^{-1} in the case of hydro. The available resources in each case, however, are very site-specific and there are many regions of the world where neither can be exploited to any great extent. Onshore wind energy, with a price range of \$60–110 MWh^{-1}, can compete with both coal and gas at the upper end of their price ranges (around \$100 MWh^{-1}). This assumes a modest carbon cost of €30 tonne^{-1} of carbon dioxide; the competitive position of wind would clearly improve with higher carbon prices, even at the lower end of the price range.

The solar technologies are both considerably more expensive than wind. Solar thermal has an estimated price range of \$200 MWh^{-1} (±\$25 MWh^{-1}) and for solar PV there is a very wide range of prices. The California Energy Commission suggests a range of \$138–639 MWh^{-1} [24] with an average of \$262 MWh^{-1}. Both these technologies are likely to be more attractive in remote off-grid areas where there is no competition from cheap fossil fuels and/or where the delivered costs of these fuels are much higher than the levels quoted here.

Nuclear generation costs are still somewhat uncertain, but a number of analyses have appeared recently, suggesting generation costs in the range \$79–99 MWh^{-1}. This encompasses the range of estimates for wind but it can be argued that the latter technology involves less risk.

2.15.6.3 Cost Comparisons on a Level Playing Field

Although generation costs are used to compare renewable energy and fossil generation, that process is not precise. A 'level playing field' demands that allowances are made for various factors, some of which add value to renewables, some add cost to the fossil sources of generation, or to variable renewables. The key issues that add or reduce the value of renewable energy, relative to the fossil sources of generation are:

- *External costs.* These are costs attributable to an activity that are not borne by the party involved in that activity. All electricity-generating technologies come with external costs, and those of the fossil sources of generation are due to the pollution that arises from their use, and from the impacts of global warming due to their CO_2 emissions. Economists argue that these costs should be added to the generating costs, and this is the thinking behind the proposals for carbon taxes. The early thinking on this issue was that carbon taxes would add unacceptable increases to the price of electricity and so most governments give renewable energy sources a 'bonus' instead. More recently, however, Emissions Trading Schemes have had a similar effect to a carbon tax although the 'cost of carbon' is generally less than the estimates that have come from detailed analyses of the external costs of the fossil sources of generation.

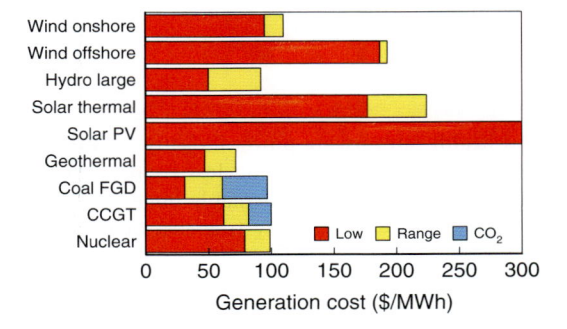

Figure 13 Generation cost comparisons.

- *Embedded generation benefits* acknowledge that many renewable energy sources are small-scale and connect into low-voltage distribution networks. This means that losses in the electricity network may be reduced and, possibly, transmission and/or distribution network reinforcements deferred. The calculation of these benefits is a complex issue and they vary both regionally and locally. It is important to recognize, however, that concentrations of embedded generation can increase distribution losses in rural areas where demand is low and so should be avoided.
- *Extra balancing costs* for variable generation apply especially to wind and wave energy and account needs to be taken of these.

2.15.7 External Costs

Although there is general agreement as to the broad definition of external costs – costs attributable to an activity that are not borne by the party involved in that activity – there are widespread variations in defining the boundaries. There is an argument, for example, that a substantial proportion of Western defense budgets should be regarded as an 'external cost' of oil – for fairly obvious reasons.

External costs – or at least some elements – may be difficult to quantify, but they are real. If the enormous costs of the cleanup operation after the Chernobyl nuclear disaster had been taken into account when the plant was constructed, it is unlikely it would have been built. External costs – in the form of carbon prices under Emission Trading Schemes – seem set to play an increasing role in shaping future energy policy. Governments around the world are recognizing the high costs to society of pollution and of global warming – and the electricity industry is a major contributor to these costs. The task facing energy policy makers is how best to go about the job of reducing pollution in electricity generation when in most countries external costs are not reflected in the market price of the end product. If they were, fossil fuel technology and nuclear prices would rise, making renewable energy sources more competitive.

2.15.7.1 Types of External Cost

Before looking more closely at the procedures available, a brief analysis of the makeup of external costs illustrates why there is such controversy about how to quantify them. For simplification, they can be divided into three broad categories:

- Hidden costs borne by governments
- Costs of damage caused to health and the environment by emissions other than CO_2
- The costs of global warming attributable to CO_2 emissions.

The first category includes the cost of regulatory bodies and pollution inspectorates (generally small) and the cost of energy industry subsidies and research and development programs. These are larger. In one of the first analyses of external costs, published by the European Commission in 1988, Hohmeyer [27] calculated that support to the German coal industry added DEM $0.002\,\text{kWh}^{-1}$ ($\$0.0012\,\text{kWh}^{-1}$) to the price of electricity. He also assigned a cost of DEM $0.0235\,\text{kWh}^{-1}$ ($\$0.014\,\text{kWh}^{-1}$) for nuclear R&D, compared to around DEM $0.004\,\text{kWh}^{-1}$ ($\$0.0024\,\text{kWh}^{-1}$) for wind.

The second category is costs due to emissions that cause damage to the environment or to people. These make up a significant proportion of the external costs of power generation and include a wide variety of effects, including damage from acid rain and health damage from oxides of sulfide and nitrogen emitted from coal-fired power stations. In a European Commission-funded study, ExterneE [28], the costs of damage to health were estimated by calculating the loss of earnings and costs of hospitalization of people susceptible to respiratory diseases. That study considered the following issues:

- Smut deposition (local), acid rain damage (national).
- Obscuration of the sun by plumes, causing local nuisance and harm to trees and crops.
- Noise – due to plant, coal handling, and so on.
- Noise due to fuel delivery effects on human health.
- Discharges into watercourses and to fisheries.
- Plant accidents and their human cost.
- Smells, oil spillages – cleanup costs.
- Dust and fumes, ash disposal accidents.
- Heavy metal depositions.
- Upkeep of emergency evacuation measures (nuclear).
- Leakage from waste (nuclear).

Other costs included in the damage and health category are power industry accidents, whether they occur in coal mines, on offshore oil or gas rigs, or in nuclear plant. The probability of a nuclear accident in Western Europe might be extremely low, but should a catastrophic failure occur, the costs would be undeniably huge. Multiplication of a number close to zero (the probability of a nuclear accident) by a number close to infinity (the cost of such an accident) does not necessarily give a meaningful result.

The third category is by far the largest: external costs due to greenhouse gas emissions that cause global warming – with all its associated effects. This category accounts for some 40–90% of the hidden costs of electricity generation. It is also the most contentious area of the external costs debate. The range of estimates for the possible economic implications of global warming is huge. Costs associated with climate changes, flooding, changes in agricultural patterns and other effects all need to be taken into account. The UK government published a very detailed assessment of these costs in 2006 [29]. This review took an international perspective and suggested that the 'social cost of carbon' (the external cost) is of the order $85 tonne^{-1} of CO_2. This provided a basis for discussion of the appropriate additions to fossil fuel generation costs that might be considered in due course.

2.15.7.2 Costing Pollution

The analyses of external costs have looked at overall damage potentials on health and the environment, assigning a cost penalty to each generating technology, depending on the fuel. This approach enables the difference in external costs between, say, coal and wind, to be easily compared. Another approach calculates costs per pollutant, noting that different fuels generate different amounts of pollutant. Typically these penalties, as proposed by some states in the United States [30], are around $10 tonne^{-1} for CO_2, and up to $25 000 tonne^{-1} for SO_2. Since the quantities of each pollutant, per unit of electricity generated, are well known for the differing fuels, these costs enable calculation of the external cost of each unit of electricity. Coal-fired generation produces the most pollutants – about 1 tonne of CO_2 MWh^{-1} plus SO_2 and other pollutants. It therefore attracts the highest penalties, ranging from about $10 MWh^{-1} upward. Gas, on the other hand, attracts a lower penalty – around half this figure. Table 10 summarizes data from the studies already cited, and others.

2.15.7.3 Market Solutions

Devising market mechanisms that take 'external costs' into account is difficult. The solution favored by economists is 'carbon taxes'. These would simply be added to the cost of electricity generated from particular sources so as to reflect the relevant external cost. The EU's early proposals for carbon tax, for example, would have added about €18 MWh^{-1} to the generation cost of coal and about €10 MWh^{-1} to the generation cost of gas. Apart from the problems of administering such tax, the impact on electricity prices was reckoned to be too severe by most of the member states. The Netherlands and Denmark, among others, nevertheless, acted and introduced the so-called carbon taxes.

Carbon trading in the EU commenced in 2005. The EU sets limits on emissions from fossil-fuelled plant and those who exceed their allowances must purchase 'credits' from generators or others who have not exceeded their allowances. In February 2005, allowances were trading at just under €10 tonne^{-1} of CO_2, which corresponds to a premium of about €10 MWh^{-1} on the price of coal-fired generation, and about half that amount on gas-fired generation. Trading in anticipation of the second phase of the Trading Scheme assigned a cost of about €15 tonne^{-1} late in 2006. The world financial crisis that started in 2008/09 means that future projections are uncertain, but a level of €30 tonne^{-1} appears to be a target. This adds about $40 MWh^{-1} to the price of coal-fired generation and $20 MWh^{-1} to the price of gas-fired generation.

Another approach to external costs – favored by some American states – is to use 'integrated resource planning' (IRP) to assess future generating plant needs. One definition [31] is:

> IRP is a planning methodology that integrates supply and demand-side options for providing energy services at a cost that appropriately balances the interests of all stakeholders. It incorporates into electricity planning the environmental and social aspects of electricity production, as well as the potential for reducing or shaping electricity demand. The objective of IRP is to determine the least-cost solution to a capacity shortage or reliability problem by evaluating the cost-effectiveness of distributed resources, such as small-scale distributed generation (DG) and demand-side management (DSM) technologies, as well as proposed Transmission and Distribution capacity expansion projects.

The beauty of IRP is that, in complying with government mandates to consider all energy supply options, the regulatory body assumes that external costs are to be applied, without actually imposing any. The precise monetary value of pollution damage, or the calculation of cost penalties on polluting fuels, becomes less critical. This straightforward approach does away with much of the bureaucratic agonizing over how to calculate the monetary value of pollution in electricity generation. It also helps to ensure that power plants are built in the right place and that the electricity network operates efficiently. The result is a competitive market operating under guidelines aimed at long-term economic responsibility.

Table 10 Estimates of external costs, in € MWh^{-1}

Category	Coal	Oil	CCGT	Nuclear	Wind
Human health and accidents	7–40	7–48	1–2	0.3	0.4
Crops/forestry	0.7–15	16	0.80	Small	0.8
Buildings	1.5–50	2–50	0.5–1.8	Small	1–3
Disasters				1.1–25	
TOTAL, damage	7–60	7–60	3–7	2–25	2–5
Global warming estimates	0.5–240	5–13	3–7	0.20	0.18
Indicative totals	17–400	37–187	8.3–19	3.6–50	4–10

Note: During the period these studies were carried out €1 = $1.3, approximately.

There are drawbacks to this approach, however. Studies in California and elsewhere indicated that the net result of this approach was simply to shift the utility plant mixes in favor of gas, which was cheap at the time and which has lower external costs than coal. Renewables profit, but the additional market share assigned to them may be relatively small.

2.15.7.4 The UK Climate Change Levy

The UK government introduced the climate change levy on business use of energy, from April 2001. It is not a true 'carbon tax'. A small proportion of the revenue (£50 million per annum) may be recycled into renewables and energy efficiency schemes. At the levels finally imposed, the tax will raise around £1.75 billion.

Rates for the climate change levy were initially set at £2.1 MWh^{-1} for coal and gas and 4.3 MWh^{-1} for electricity.

The energy-intensive industries, renewable energy, and CHP industries sought abatement or exemption from the tax. They argued that the tax will fall unevenly; the service industries will benefit from a tax rebate (as they are labor-intensive), but industry (which is 'electricity intensive') would suffer. Following a vigorous campaign, renewables were exempted.

2.15.7.4.1 External costs of renewable energies

It is not suggested that renewable energies have zero external costs. The ExternE study, for example, examined the external costs of wind energy under nine headings (nv: not valued):

1. Noise.
2. Visual intrusion.
3. Accidents during manufacture and operation.
4. Accidents to public.
5. Impacts of wind turbines on birds (nv).
6. Impacts on local ecosystems (nv).
7. Electromagnetic interference (nv).
8. Acid rain damage – from energy used in construction in case of wind.
9. Global warming effects.

The range of cost estimates – for two specific British sites – lay in the range 2–4 ECU MWh^{-1}. This is consistent with other studies, which generally show lower external costs for wind than either PV or biomass, although all are small. The analysis was very thorough and included estimates of external costs incurred during the manufacturing processes, as well as operation of the plant. Nevertheless, the overall conclusion from the EU study was that the highest estimate of external costs for wind was below the minimum estimate of the external costs for coal. Excluding global warming, the latter were between 5 and 15 ECU MWh^{-1}.

2.15.7.5 Renewable Energy Support Mechanisms

In order to fully internalize the external costs of the sources of fossil fuel generation, the price of electricity from fossil sources would need to rise. The Stern report, cited earlier, suggested costs attributable to global warming, alone, were $85 tonne^{-1} of carbon dioxide. That would increase the price of electricity sourced from coal by around $80 MWh^{-1} and gas-fired generation costs would increase by about $40 MWh^{-1}. These figures correspond to a 100% increase in the price of coal-fired generation and a 40% increase for gas. Rather than penalize coal and gas – which would raise electricity prices significantly in many industrialized nations – the most common method of 'leveling the playing field' has been to give renewables a subsidy, instead. This has less effect on electricity prices. There are various ways of doing this and **Table 11** is a brief summary. It should be noted that these support mechanisms tend to change fairly frequently.

An analysis of prices paid for renewable energy in Europe suggests that the average price for onshore wind is €102 MWh^{-1} and the average price for offshore is €129 MWh^{-1} [35].

2.15.7.6 Embedded Generation Benefits

The value of a new variable renewable source of energy for an electricity network may be specified as:

$$(\text{Fuel saving value}) + (\text{Capacity saving value}) - (\text{Costs associated with variability})$$

The fuel saving value is simply the value of each MWh of fuel saved. In the United Kingdom, in late 2009, that amounted to about $45–75 MWh^{-1} (it varies on an hourly basis, but this is a rough estimate of the annual average, bearing in mind that the price of gas has fluctuated markedly from 2005 onward). Capacity saving value, as its name suggests, is simply the value corresponding to the thermal capacity saved. In the case of the intermittent sources of renewable energy that needs to take into account the 'capacity credit' of the variable source. This concept is explained later, together with the third term above – the costs associated with variability.

In the case of small-scale renewables, however, there is an additional term in the value equation and that is the 'embedded generation benefit'. A simple example may be used to illustrate the point. If a householder were to install a PV panel on the roof of

Table 11 Summary of support mechanisms for renewable energy

Location	Initial tariff ($ MWh^{-1})	Periods, initial/total (yrs)	Second stage tariff ($ MWh^{-1})	Notes, source
Onshore				
China	80–95			Depends on wind speed
Denmark	+54			For 22 000 full-load hours
France	120	10/20	40–120	Second stage tariff depends on wind speed [32]
Germany	92	5/20	73	Initial period depends on site wind
Ireland	94	15		IEA
Netherlands	+$100 kW^{-1}	15		Rate MWh^{-1} depends on wind speed. Target is ~$145 MWh^{-1}
Ontario	125	20		Ontario Power Authority
South Africa	158	20		Reference [33]
United Kingdom	+90 (variable)	20	Market price	Average total price ~ $155 MWh^{-1} in 2008/09
United States	+21	10		
Offshore				
Denmark	100–125			For 50 000 full-load hours
France	195	10/20	45–195	Second stage tariff depends on wind speed [34]
Germany	220	12/20	51	Initial period depends on water depth/distance to shore
Ireland	208	15		IEA
Ontario	175	20		Ontario Power Authority

his/her house and export the surplus electricity to the local electricity company, they would resell it at around $100 MWh^{-1} (depending on the tariff) to neighbors. There would be no backflow through the local 33/11 kV transformer and, as a bonus, the locality might suffer fewer power cuts.

This reasoning may be simplistic, but it is, nevertheless, the principle of 'net metering', which is used by several American utilities to remunerate renewable energy generators. A modified version of the approach has been used in Denmark and Germany, for example, used to pay renewable generators 80–90% of the domestic tariff.

Although studies in America and elsewhere point to the fact that renewable energy may have a high value in certain locations, this point is not widely accepted by utilities, many of whom continue to assign renewable energy a value based on its fuel saving capability. In many instances, renewable electricity-generating technologies deliver energy closer to consumer demand than centralized generation. It substitutes for electricity that has accrued a higher selling price than the generation costs of large thermal plant, due to its passage through the network. This rising level of 'value' with reducing voltage is reflected in higher charges for customers connected at lower voltage levels.

In view of complexity of the issues involved and the fact that 'embedded generation benefits' are dependent on location, it is difficult to quote definitive values. Broadly speaking, however, the embedded benefits rarely exceed about $24 MWh^{-1} in the United Kingdom and are often much lower. The converse problem, where substantial quantities of renewable generation may trigger reinforcements, result in a negative benefit. In the United Kingdom, for example, the need for significant (and costly) transmission reinforcements has been addressed by a Transmission Issues Working Group. Their report examined the implications of installing up to 6000 MW of renewable generation in Scotland and concluded that reinforcement costs would be roughly $800 million per 2000 MW of generation.

2.15.8 Variability Costs

Variability costs acknowledge the fact that wind energy has a variable output that is not totally predictable. System Operators, as a result, incur extra costs as they need to deal with the extra uncertainty when balancing supply and demand. Those extra costs are, however, modest. They need to be considered carefully, as some critics suggest that the addition of these costs destroys the economic viability of wind energy. This analysis draws on material that examines the issues in some detail [36].

The variations from distributed wind are generally less than the demand fluctuations regularly encountered on electricity networks. To cope with these, every network has reserves scheduled at all times and the key issue is the additional reserve that is needed to cope with the variability of wind. That is only a few percent of the rated power of wind plant.

There are also concerns that a system with a high proportion of variable renewables would risk power cuts at times of peak demand. The ability of wind energy to contribute to these peak demands needs to be examined. This introduces the concept of 'capacity credit' – how much thermal plant can be retired with the introduction of wind energy?

The aim of this section is to clarify the issues in more detail, drawing upon the analysis that has been carried out during the past 30 years (one recent review identified over 150 references [37]).

This section is structured as follows:

- A brief description of electricity network issues comes first as this is essential background to discussions of issues surrounding the integration of variable renewable energy sources.
- Next comes an examination of exactly what is meant by 'wind variability'. ('Variable' is a better description of the power fluctuations from wind, wave, etc., than 'intermittent'.)
- The next section deals with the integration of the variable sources into power systems, the costs, and other issues.

2.15.8.1 Electricity Networks

2.15.8.1.1 *Economies of scale*

Although large integrated electricity systems are efficient, they still require 'operational reserve' to deal with short-term mismatches in supply and demand and a 'plant margin' (additional plant, over and above that required to meet the maximum demand) to deal with plant breakdowns and other outages. The effect of wind energy on the short-term reserves and margins is the subject of much discussion and each issue is discussed in the context of electricity networks and the additional costs that may be incurred.

2.15.8.1.1(i) Demand fluctuations

Although aggregation smooth variations in consumer demand, there are still substantial fluctuations when numbers of consumers together increase power needs – at the morning and evening rush hours, for example. **Figure 14** illustrates the demand variations on the network in Great Britain on 9 January 2009. From a nighttime minimum of just over 40 000 MW at 05.00 h, demand rose rapidly to just under 54 000 MW at 10.00 h. It then fell off slightly until there was another surge in demand at the evening peak of just under 60 000 MW, reached at 17.30 h. Demand then fell off steadily. The intra-half hourly changes in demand are shown in **Figure 15**. During the morning peak, the maximum change between two successive half hours was 2300 MW and during the evening peak was 3100 MW. Negative changes in demand were recorded from 18.00 h onwards, reaching a maximum of 2600 MW at 22.30 h.

2.15.8.1.1(ii) Operational reserve

All power systems, with or without wind energy, need short-term operational reserve, often called 'spinning reserve', to deal with demand fluctuations. The terms cover various types of plant with different characteristics, outlined briefly below. Nomenclature varies between utilities, but the exact details are not central to this discussion.

The principal types of plant are:

- Frequency response: Such plant automatically adjusts its output, increasing it when system frequency is low and vice versa.
- Fast reserve: This plant is able to increase or decrease its output, under instruction from the System Operator on a short timescale (typically 30 min).
- Standing reserve: Similar to fast reserve, but on a longer timescale (typically 1–4 h).

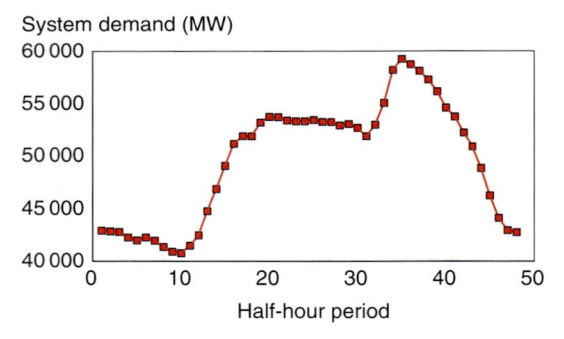

Figure 14 Demand variations on the British electricity network.

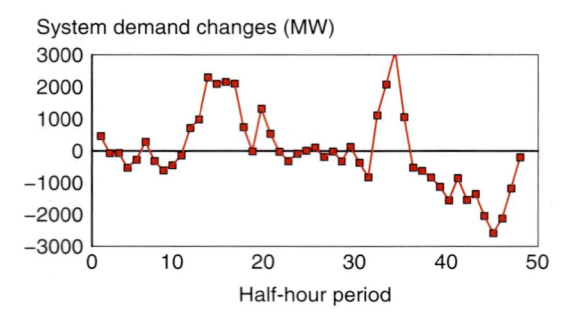

Figure 15 Half-hourly demand changes on the British electricity network.

In most utilities, the operational reserves are generally part-loaded thermal or hydro units. They operate at below maximum capacity, so that the output can be increased or decreased to cater for mismatches between generation and demand. Pumped-storage plant is also used, as it can respond very rapidly to a need for more generation.

2.15.8.1.1(iii)   Costs of reserve

The costs of reserve reflect the fact that they need to operate at part-load (and lower efficiency). Annual costs of frequency response plant in Great Britain are around $230 million and each of the other types was expected to cost around $100 million in 2008/09 [38].

The costs of reserve depend on the precise type and price structure. International values are in the range $6–12 MWh^{-1}, although some fast-response plant, such as pumped storage, secures higher values. These costs compensate the plant owners for the lower efficiency of plant whose output is below its maximum, extra wear and tear, and possibly extra controls; they are additional to payments for the energy actually generated.

2.15.8.1.1(iv)   Plant margin or backup

Reserves ensure minute-by-minute system security, but longer-term security is managed by making sure that there is always enough plant available to meet the highest demands on the electricity network. The 'Plant margin' is a measure of the difference between the total capacity of the plant on the network and the expected maximum demand. The desirable plant margin (plant capacity minus maximum demand) for a large system is around 24% [39]. This does not guarantee that the lights will never go out, but ensures this will happen very rarely. The high level of security and low plant margin stems from the fact that a large system has a number of generating units each with a quantifiable probability of failure, but the combined probability of, say, 3 units failing at the same time, is much less. It may be noted that the plant margin in many regions is higher than the theoretical figure. It is very difficult to design a market that delivers the theoretically desirable optimum, simply because power plant equipment takes a long time to build, and plant closures are not always easy to predict in advance.

2.15.8.2   Characteristics of Wind Energy

An analysis of the wind power fluctuations in Western Denmark in 2007 [40] suggests that for 42% of the year (37.00 h), the intra-hourly fluctuations were within the range ±25 MW (1% of the wind capacity). Extending the range to ±50 MW captures another 18.00 h of fluctuations. At the extremes, fluctuations in excess of ±375 MW (16% of capacity) only occurred 10 times in the year. The complete histogram of power swings is shown in **Figure 16**. The standard deviation of the fluctuations is around 3%. Information of this kind provides a basis for estimating the effects of integrating wind energy into an electricity network.

2.15.8.3   Assimilating Wind

When considering the introduction of the variable renewable energy sources, it is important to preserve the advantages of an integrated electricity network as that minimizes the extra costs to electricity consumers. The UK's National Grid has made this point [41]:

> However, based on recent analysis of the incidence and variation of wind speed we have found that the expected intermittency of wind does not pose such a major problem for stability and we are confident that this can be adequately managed …
> It is a property of the interconnected transmission system that individual and local independent fluctuations in output are diversified and averaged out across the system.

The effects of adding wind to an electricity network may be illustrated by the case of Western Denmark, and examining the changes in demand that need to be managed. If there had been no wind installed there in 2007, the maximum 1 h increase in system demand would have been 675 MW. With 26% wind (the amount on the system that year), sometimes the wind fluctuations

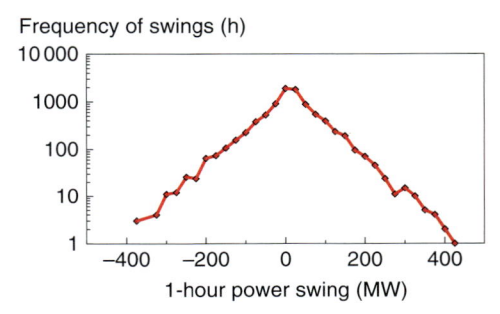

Figure 16   Intra-hourly power swings observed in Western Denmark in the year 2007. The maximum swing never exceeded around 18% of the installed capacity of the wind plant (up or down) and the standard deviation was about 3%.

augmented the demand fluctuations, and sometimes they reduced them. The maximum increase in demand that the System Operator had to deal with went up from 675 to 900 MW. In that hour, there was an increase in demand at the same time as the output from the wind plant fell. However, the number of times that the net demand increased by more than 600 MW in an hour only went up from 55 (consumer demands only) to 63 (consumer demand net of wind production). Even with 39% wind (scaling up 2007 wind outputs by 50%), there would only be about 75 occasions when the net increase in demand exceeded 600 MW.

The impacts of variability and the corresponding possibilities for mitigation can be quantified by examining the three principal 'cost centers':

- the costs of extra operational reserves (balancing costs), which can be reduced by
  - reducing the 'unpredictability' of wind (by better forecasting), or
  - reducing the cost of balancing services.
- 'backup', which can be reduced if the capacity credit can be increased, and,
- 'constraint costs', due to surplus wind, which can be reduced if the surpluses can be reduced.

2.15.8.4 Extra Short-Term Reserve Needs and Costs

Electricity networks with wind energy need extra reserves to deal with the extra uncertainty associated with the presence of wind on the network. It is important to emphasize that this extra uncertainty is not equal to the uncertainty of the wind generation, but to the combined uncertainty of wind, demand, and thermal generation.

The combined uncertainty is determined from a 'sum of squares' calculation that provides the basis for estimates of additional reserve needs:

$$\sigma^2(\text{total}) = \sigma^2(\text{demand}) + \sigma^2(\text{wind})$$

where σ is the standard deviation of the uncertainties.

Although the quantity of operational reserve rises with increasing amounts of wind energy, the UK's National Grid (NGT) is confident that it will be able to procure the necessary amounts, and, moreover, that there is no 'ceiling' on the amount of wind-generated electricity that can be accommodated [42]:

> Based on recent analysis of the incidence and variation of wind speed the expected intermittency of the national wind portfolio would not appear to pose a technical ceiling on the amount of wind generation that may be accommodated and adequately managed.

It may be noted that system operators such as NGT says nothing about the type of plant that may be needed for reserve – that is left for the market to decide, provided it can meet the technical specifications set by operator. In practice, it may be coal-fired plant, combined cycle gas turbines (CCGTs), hydro, or storage. The former tends to be the most economic option, while the latter tends to be the most expensive. However, pumped-storage plant can respond extremely rapidly and so is well suited to a particular type of 'fast reserve'.

The characteristics of most electricity systems are similar, so estimates of the extra reserve needed to cope with wind energy are also similar. With wind supplying 10% of the electricity, estimates of the additional reserve capacity are in the range 3–6% of the rated capacity of wind plant. With 20% wind, the range is 4–8%, approximately.

The UK's National Grid has recently quoted estimates of the extra balancing costs for wind in the United Kingdom for 40% wind [43]. These would increase balancing costs in 2020 by £500–1000 million per annum (£3.5–7 MWh^{-1} of wind, or $5.6–11.2 MWh^{-1}). The uncertainty arises partly because the future trajectory of balancing services costs is uncertain (they are dependent on fuel prices), partly because increased use of the demand-side management (DSM) could reduce the overall costs. The way in which balancing costs are likely to increase with wind penetration level is illustrated in **Figure 17**. This makes use of the National Grid data as 'anchor points' and uses information on demand and wind uncertainty (discussed earlier) to synthesize the rest of the curve. So 10% wind energy is likely to incur extra costs in the range $4–8 MWh^{-1} and 20% wind energy in the range $5–10 MWh^{-1}, approximately.

A recent American review [44] quotes a study that looked at 30% penetration on a peak load basis (probably about 15% on an energy basis) and that suggested an extra balancing cost of $8.84 MWh^{-1} – within the range of the British data.

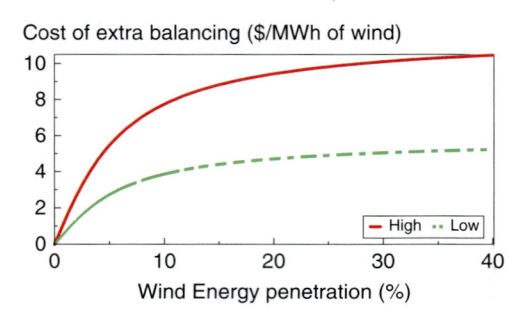

Figure 17 Estimates of additional balancing costs for Great Britain.

2.15.8.5 Carbon Dioxide Savings

As the extra reserve operates at part-load, its lower thermal efficiency means that its emissions increase. The reserve still contributes useful energy to the system, so the extra emissions are those associated with the reduced efficiency of part-loaded plant. Taking a pessimistic estimate of 10% for the reduced efficiency, and taking into account the fact that the load factor of wind plant is just under half that of thermal plant, Dale et al. [45] suggested that this reduces the emission savings from the wind, at the 20% penetration level, by a little over 1%. In other words, if the displaced fuel is coal, for the sake of argument, with CO_2 emissions of 900 kg MWh^{-1}, then the effective CO_2 saving would be around 890 kg MWh^{-1}. If the displaced fuel were gas, with CO_2 emissions of 400 kg MWh^{-1}, the effective saving would be 395 kg MWh^{-1}. At higher penetration levels (40%, say), the nonlinear increase in the necessary reserves brings these figures down to around 875 and 388 kg MWh^{-1}, respectively.

2.15.8.6 Extra Backup and Its Costs

A distinction must be drawn between the extra reserves needed for short-term balancing in an electricity system with wind and the extra backup (if any) needed to guarantee the security of the system at all times. That means making sure that there is always enough power available to meet the peak demands of the system. Although it is suggested that there is a need to provide 'backup for windless days' to ensure that demands are always met [46], this is misleading on two counts:

- When a new thermal power station is built, there is no discussion as to how the electricity system will manage when the station is unexpectedly out of action for emergency repairs during the winter. The 'plant margin' is a common pool of 'extra' plant that ensures peak demands are met. No power stations are 100% reliable, as discussed earlier.
- Not even the most zealous of renewable energy enthusiasts would suggest that System Operators should rely on the full rated capacity of wind power plant. When wind is added to an electricity network, the situation is not fundamentally different from an addition of thermal plant. If the wind plant has some 'capacity credit' (discussed next), then it will be possible to retire some of the older plant, without compromising system security. If the new plant has zero capacity credit, then no plant can be retired, but, either way, no new plant needs to be built for 'backup' – it already exists.

Estimates of capacity credit that are based on wind electricity production during a single winter are unlikely to provide accurate estimates. It is a statistical quantity that requires adequate data – as for nuclear plant. During the winter of 2008/09, for example, at the time of peak demand, the metered wind electricity production in Great Britain was about 18% of its rated output. However, about 5000 MW of nuclear output was not available, for various reasons – nearly 50% of the total [47]. It would be misleading to assign a capacity credit of 18% to wind on the basis of this one instance, and equally misleading to assign a 'firm power' contribution from nuclear as 50% of its rated output.

It is important to emphasize that the capacity credit of wind will never be greater than the plant margin, and even if Britain had 26 000 MW of wind and had been completely becalmed at the time of the peak demand on 6 January 2009, the plant margin would not have been used up, despite the missing 5000 MW of nuclear. It is also worth reiterating that the plant margin is generally greater than the theoretically desirable minimum.

2.15.8.7 Capacity Credit

The term 'capacity credit' for wind, introduced above, tends to be controversial. It may be defined [48] as follows:

> The reduction, due to the introduction of wind energy conversion systems, in the capacity of conventional plant needed to provide reliable supplies of electricity.

Despite the controversy, numerous studies have confirmed that wind can substitute for thermal plant and enable power systems to operate with the same level of reliability. **Figure 18** shows how the capacity credit varies as a function of the installed wind energy penetration level.

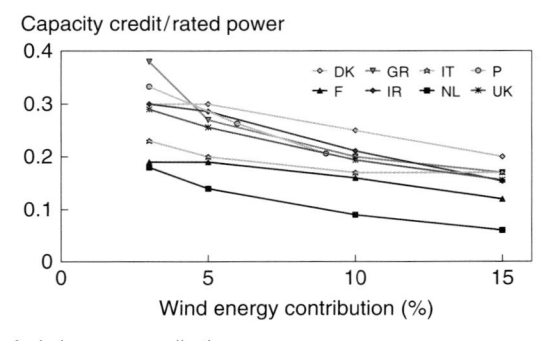

Figure 18 Capacity credits as a function of wind energy contribution.

Comparisons of capacity credits across national boundaries must be made with care. In northern Europe, where peak demands on most electricity systems occur around 18.00 h during the winter months [49], capacity credits for wind energy at low penetrations are mostly close to 'winter quarter' capacity factors. There are differences in the numerical values, however, due to the differing wind speeds. All the results show a similar trend, with capacity credits declining by around 40% between 3% wind energy and 15%. Data from the Irish system operator [50] have yielded similar results to those from British studies, when normalized to take account of differing assumptions about capacity factor [51].

There are a number of references to capacity credits in the American literature. Winds in many inland sites are, however, driven by local thermal effects – particularly in the Californian passes. As a result, wind speeds are more predictable but often have a pronounced diurnal trend. Capacity credits therefore often depend on the coincidence (or lack of it) between the peak winds and peak demands. Some installations claim high capacity credits, whereas others can only claim low values. There are therefore only limited lessons to be drawn from American experience, although the procedures used are similar to those discussed in this chapter.

2.15.8.8 The Cost of Backup

Although the 'extra costs of backup' are not derived by assuming the whole of the wind plant capacity needs to be duplicated by standby thermal plant, there are extra costs associated with the low capacity credit of wind at penetration levels above about 8%. With thermal plant, the average power and the 'capacity credit' are the same, but wind energy is different. In Great Britain, above the 8% penetration level (approximately), the capacity credit of wind is less than its capacity factor. This means that 26 000 MW of wind (roughly 20% energy penetration) delivers electricity that corresponds to around 10 700 MW of thermal plant (assuming a wind capacity factor of 35% and a thermal plant load factor of 85%), but only displaces around 5000 MW of thermal plant. This has the effect of reducing the load factor on the remaining thermal plant. Their generation costs increase, as capital cost repayments are spread over fewer kilowatt-hours. This provides a basis for estimating the 'additional costs of backup', using the methodology used by Dale et al. [45]. Using an up-to-date price for CCGT plant of $960 kW^{-1}, these amount to around $4 MWh^{-1} of wind (at 20% penetration), rising to around $10 MWh^{-1} of wind at 40% penetration.

Even where capacity credits are much lower than has been assumed, the effect on the variability costs would be modest. At 20% wind energy penetration level, for example, the additional variability cost would be about $2.8 MWh^{-1} [47].

2.15.8.9 Transmission Constraints

The foregoing discussion has implicitly assumed that the electricity network can be operated as a single unit, with unrestricted flows of energy. In practice, this is not always the case and there are sometimes occasions when the power production from renewable plant exceeds the transmission capacity that is required to deliver it to the demand centers. This means that there may be occasions when renewable plant may be required to cease generation, or be 'constrained off'. The effect of such constraints will be to increase the costs of the renewable plant, as the capital costs will be spread over fewer units of electricity than was anticipated. Whether or not these costs are borne by the renewable generator depends on the structure of the market as designed by the regulator and government.

In Britain, such constraints are likely to occur due to the large quantities of wind energy – installed or planned – in the north of England and Scotland. For many years, there have been large North to South power flows, as generation capacity exceeds demand in the north, and vice versa. There is increasing concern over the cost of these constraints [52], although these can be alleviated by additional transmission connections at an estimated cost of £4700 million [53].

2.15.8.10 Wind Surpluses at High Penetration Levels

The discussion so far has focused on wind energy penetration levels up to around 40%. In practice, as noted earlier, higher levels are achievable, albeit at increased cost. A detailed analysis by the Danish system operator, Energinet, has examined the implications of operating with 100% wind and quantified the additional costs [54]. The analysis was carried out for Western Denmark, but ignored the existence of the connections to Germany, Sweden, and Norway and did not assume that any storage was available.

Of course, 100% wind is not feasible, but the System Operator assumed that sufficient wind power capacity was installed in order to meet 100% of the electricity requirements. With that level of capacity, around 30% of the wind energy had to be rejected when wind power production exceeded system demand. A similar amount of wind had to be supplied from thermal sources of generation when the system demand exceeded the wind power production.

The possibility that wind power production may occasionally exceed system demand first occurs at penetration levels around 25%. **Figure 19**, which uses actual data from Western Denmark, suggests that it occurred twice during 13/14 January 2007. However, the amounts of 'surplus' wind energy are initially modest and similar estimates come from the Energinet study and from a British study by consultants Sinclair Knight Merz (SKM) [55].

With 30% wind energy, the Danish study suggested that around 1.7% would need to be constrained off or rejected and the SKM study a slightly lower level – although the precise value depended on assumptions about interconnectors and pumped storage. With 40% wind, both studies projected about 4% would need to be rejected and at 50% wind about 7.5%. Data from the two studies are compared in **Figure 20**.

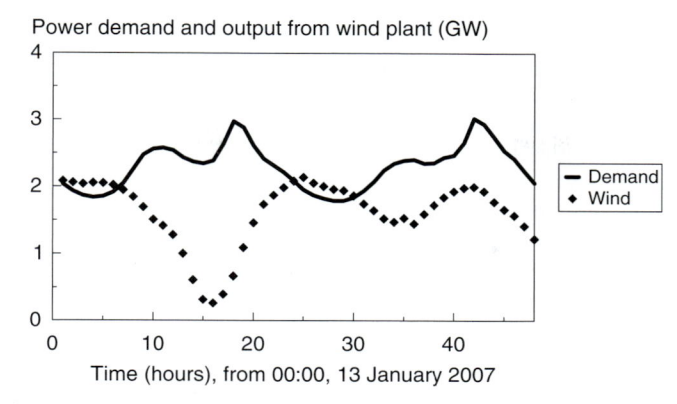

Figure 19 Demand and wind production in Western Denmark, 13/14 January 2007.

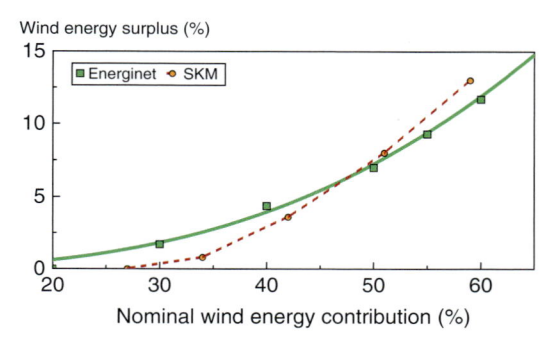

Figure 20 Surplus wind: estimates for Denmark and Britain.

If no market can be found for this 'surplus' wind energy, a small penalty is attached to this 'lost' electricity, as the fixed costs of the wind plant are spread over fewer units of electricity. With 30% wind, this amounts to around $1 MWh^{-1} of wind, rising to around $2.4 MWh^{-1} with 40% wind, based on current installed prices of around $2100 kW^{-1}. Ways in which this 'surplus' may be utilized are discussed later.

2.15.8.11 Total Costs of Variability

The total costs of variability to the electricity consumer – defined as additional balancing costs plus backup costs plus constraint costs – are shown in **Figure 21**. The 'high' estimate uses National Grid's upper balancing cost estimate and an installed cost for CCGT plant of $1000 kW^{-1} in the calculation of backup costs. The 'low' estimate uses National Grid's lower balancing cost and an installed cost of $800 kW^{-1} for a mixture of CCGT and open cycle gas turbine plant. To derive the constraint costs at penetration levels above 30%, it has been assumed that 12 GW of onshore wind costing $2150 kW^{-1} has been installed and 45 GW of offshore wind costing $3200 kW^{-1}. With 10% wind energy, the extra costs are below $2 MWh^{-1} in each case; at the 20% level they rise to a little over $3 MWh^{-1} in the 'high' case ($2.4 MWh^{-1} in the 'low' case) and with 40% wind, the estimates are $12 MWh^{-1} and $8.6 MWh^{-1}, respectively. A 'central' figure would add about 5.5% to domestic electricity bills.

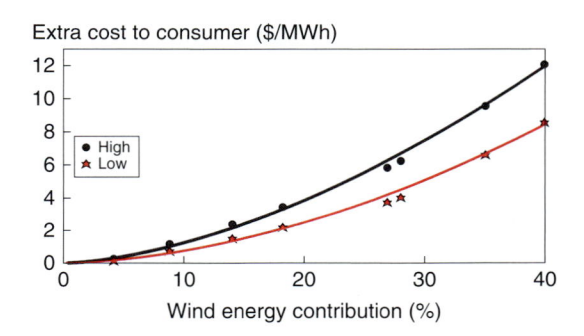

Figure 21 Variability costs estimates.

2.15.8.12 Mitigating the Effects and Costs of Variability

Progress toward high levels of wind penetration will inevitably be gradual and so it is likely that technologies and strategies will develop that will mitigate the impacts of variability.

Some of these are already in use, such as improved methods of wind forecasting and this is likely to have a significant impact. Numerous other ideas are under development or discussion and it is likely that increased use of DSM (possibly aided by the installation of 'smart meters') will also play a key role in reducing variability costs. The use of storage is often advocated, but its use for 'levelling the output' of wind power may be difficult to realize. However, it may have a role to play – for the benefit of the electricity network as a whole – in systems with a high penetration of variable renewables. The construction of more international transmission links should aid the assimilation of variable renewables – and will also work to the benefit of the system as a whole. Further ahead, the widespread introduction of electric cars or a switch to electric heating would be beneficial to wind energy, as it would facilitate the absorption of 'surplus' wind at times of high wind and low demand.

2.15.8.12.1 *Wind forecasting*

There is considerable work in progress on improvements in wind forecasting and the emergence of forecasting services, in both Europe and America, testifies to the fact that it is worthwhile improving the accuracy of projected power outputs. A large EU-funded R&D project involved a large number of contributors [56], and a utility-funded project has been completed in the United States, managed by the Electric Power Research Institute [57]. Commercial forecasting services are also available, with software that improves forecasts up to 24 h ahead. One company claims, for example, that the error in 1 h ahead forecasts is typically 15–25% lower than that of persistence forecasts [58].

Much of this forecasting work is focused on providing services to operators of wind farms, rather than system operators, but estimates are available of countrywide improvements that might be expected [59]. The analysis, for Germany, suggests that the standard deviation of the uncertainty 1 h ahead might be reduced from 3% to below 2% and, similarly, the 4 h uncertainty can be reduced from 6% to around 4%. This would reduce the estimates of balancing costs that were quoted earlier by about 30%, provided the system operator felt that the forecasting accuracy was sufficiently robust.

2.15.8.12.2 *Demand management*

DSM has been an integral part of the load management strategies of system operators for many years. It has the potential both to reduce peak loads and lower the costs of reserve. The variable sources of renewable energy, such as wind, are likely to benefit from the wider adoption of load management in the future, although there are potential benefits for the electricity system as a whole.

There are various types of DSM, although the boundaries are not sharp:

- Provision of reserve and frequency response under contract to the system operator. In the United Kingdom, in 2005/06, users, rather than generators provided about one-third of the 'standing reserve' and 'frequency response' balancing service requirements of National Grid [60].
- *Teleswitching*. This technology has been slowly developing for around 40 years. It enables demands to be modulated in response to radio signals sent by the System Operator. The signals are sent to a special meter and the technology has the potential to control or modulate interruptible demands.
- *Dynamic demand*. While teleswitching is actively (and remotely) controlled, dynamic demand is a passive system that relies on sensors in equipment used by consumers to modulate demands. If all domestic refrigerators in the United Kingdom, for example, included a frequency-sensitive device that inhibited its operation when the frequency fell below (say) 49.8 Hz and switched the fridge on (provided it was not already too cold) at, say 50.2 Hz, then this could substitute for between 728 and 1174 MW of frequency-response plant [61].
- *Smart meters*. These give electricity consumers access to information about the price of their electricity on a continuous basis. The most common perception of such meters at present is to provide information to consumers, rather than intervene to restrict demand on a selective basis.
- 'Time of use' tariffs have been in existence for many years in the industrial and commercial sectors, and, in simplified form, in the domestic sector. The tariffs aim to discourage use at peak demand times – that normally coincide with peak prices – and so iron out, to some extent, demand fluctuations. If that enables the quantity of rarely used (and expensive) 'peaking plant' to be reduced, that reduces both costs and emissions. The most sophisticated development of 'time of use' pricing responds continuously to changes in market prices. Whether or not consumers can react to high or low prices depends on the type of electrical equipment they are using. 'Time of use' tariffs are common in France and their effectiveness appears to be reflected in a lower ratio between maximum and minimum demands. On 21 May 2009, for example, the French ratio was 1.39, whereas in Britain it was about 1.6.

All these concepts act to improve the efficiency of the electricity system as a whole. Any benefits to wind would come through reductions in the costs of balancing services. Some benefits are already being realized (first bullet point) but it is difficult to estimate the magnitude of any additional benefits.

One possible downside (from the point of view of wind) is that a reduction in the uncertainties in the supply/demand balance might mean that the uncertainties in wind power production would become more significant, thus increasing additional balancing costs.

2.15.8.12.3 Energy storage
2.15.8.12.3(i) Dedicated storage
Energy storage is often seen as a means of 'levelling the output' variable renewables, possibly increasing its capacity credit and so increasing its value. Such 'dedicated storage' faces a number of challenges as it adds to the generation cost of the variable renewable. That additional cost needs to be less than the additional value of 'firm power' over variable power. There are additional challenges with dedicated storage, as the store needs to be large to ensure that the 'leveling' continues during long periods of low wind.

An early integration study concluded [62]:

> There is no operational necessity in associating storage plant with wind-power generation, up to a wind output capacity of at least 20% of system peak demand.

This does not imply that 20% is a ceiling, or threshold. It was simply the upper limit that was investigated in the study.

A later American study made the same point [63]:

> Storage may increase the value of intermittent generation. However, studies generally show that dedicated storage systems for renewables are not viable options for utilities because of added capital costs of current storage technologies. Storage can add flexibility and value to utility operations, but it should generally be a system-wide consideration, based on the merit of the storage system.

More recently, the American Electric Power Institute suggested [64]:

> Installing energy storage ... practically eliminates wind integration issues .... Unfortunately the high cost of storage systems limits the situations in which they are useful.

In Britain, the cost threshold that storage would need to meet for viability in the market can be gauged from the difference between 'continuous' and 'variable' power sources. The difference in the prices realized for landfill gas (firm power) and for wind energy (variable power) in the auctions conducted by the Non-Fossil Purchasing Agency is a guide. Between the summer of 2006 and the end of 2008, the minimum price difference was $1.8 MWh^{-1}, the maximum $18.5 MWh^{-1}, and the average $8 MWh^{-1}. The average roughly corresponds to the theoretical 'capacity value', based on the replacement cost of CCGT plant.

2.15.8.12.4 System storage
There is a difference between 'dedicated storage' for variable renewables and storage for an electricity system – with or without variable renewables. Storage has the potential to enable power systems to operate more efficiently – absorbing power at periods of low demand and releasing it at periods of high demand that otherwise needs to be met by expensive generating plant. This is generally a less challenging role than 'dedicated storage'. However, storage has a generation cost, just like any other generation technology, and will only be economic if the differential between the energy prices paid to the storage operator at times of high demand, and by the operator for electricity at times of low demand, is sufficient to cover its costs.

A recent UK Select Committee observed [65]:

> No evidence we received persuaded us that advances in storage technology would become available in time materially to affect the UK's generating requirements up to 2020.

A recent analysis that examined the prospects for Western Denmark concluded [66]:

> The conclusion is that energy storage systems are for most cases uneconomical for day-to-day trading in Western Denmark.

If the introduction of large quantities of wind energy into electricity networks widens the difference between 'high' and 'low' spot prices in the electricity market, that may enable the construction of cost-effective storage. Most of the technologies are able to provide system services (short-term operating reserve, reactive power, and 'black start' capability) and these can provide additional revenue. There are a number of technologies in existence and under development, with a wide range of applications, apart from those discussed here [67].

2.15.8.12.4(i) Additional international connections

Additional international connections give system operators access to more sources of power, effectively increasing the size of the system. The advantages of large systems were discussed earlier and perhaps the simplest way of looking at the effects of additional connections is to view them as additional plant. The 'effective' renewable energy penetration level then drops.

The next stage in the argument for additional interconnections is that, with the two interconnected systems operated as one, the wind variability comes down. However, the evidence on this point is not clear. On the one hand, the standard deviation of hourly wind fluctuations in Britain is similar to that in (smaller) Western Denmark. On the other hand, Foley *et al.* [68] combined British and Irish wind records and showed that the joint occurrence of wind speeds below 5 m s^{-1} was reduced to 16% of the time, whereas the individual occurrences were 22% (Britain) and 28% (Ireland).

2.15.8.12.5 European supergrids

A number of proposals for more extensive international grid connections – mostly using high voltage direct current (HVDC) – have been put forward in recent years, mostly with some or all of the following objectives:

- Facilitating the connection of offshore wind farms.
- Smoothing wind fluctuations on a continental (rather than national) scale.
- Facilitating progress toward very high proportions of renewable energy in the European network including, for example, concentrated solar power plant in Africa.

Hurley *et al.* [69] provided data that illustrated the smoothing effects. They took data from 60 well-distributed sites over a 34-year period and showed, for example, that there were very few occasions when wind power production fell below 12% of rated output in the winter. This suggests that the capacity credit of this widely distributed wind might be higher than the values calculated from individual national studies. Similarly, their analysis of power swings also suggests that there would be a lower uncertainty, probably leading to lower additional balancing costs.

Decker *et al.* [70] have recently summarized most of the proposals that are currently being discussed. Some cater, in the longer term, for up to 100 GW of offshore wind. They note that increased interconnections would be beneficial to European electricity networks as a whole, quite apart from their role in facilitating the connection and smoothing of renewable energy. They also provide data on the smoothing effects, suggesting that hourly variations in excess of plus or minus 10% appear to be negligible. (This may be compared with the maximum hourly swings around 14–18% observed in Western Denmark and estimated for Britain.)

There are, nevertheless, difficulties on the way to the construction of a European Supergrid. Several witnesses who appeared before the UK's Energy and Climate Change Select Committee in April/May 2009 drew attention to technical and regulatory difficulties, although there was support for further analysis of the concept. Another possible difficulty is that national plans for the connection of offshore wind farms are already well advanced and so the possibility of looking at 'the big picture' may already have passed. Nevertheless, the broad concept has support at the European level, through the 'Ten E' programme of support for improved interconnections [71].

2.15.8.12.6 Electric cars

The prospects for electric cars are being studied with a view to reducing greenhouse gas emissions. There is a double benefit as air quality in cities will be improved and national emissions will be reduced, even though the electricity used to charge them at present comes from a mixture that includes lots of coal and gas-fired plant. The attraction from the standpoint of the electricity industry is that it may enable the more efficient use of generating plant, provided most of the charging takes place during the night. In the United Kingdom, between 22.30 and 06.30 h in the winter, the demand drops below 45 000 MW, whereas during the rest of the day, it is above this level, peaking at just under 60 000 MW. Inspection of data for later in the year (21 May 2009) suggests that there was a similar difference between the nighttime demand and the peak.

A margin of around 15 000 MW would be sufficient to charge the entire fleet of British cars if all were to be powered electrically [36]. The additional attraction, from the standpoint of integrating wind, is that this would enable surplus wind power to be utilized at times when wind power generation exceeded demand. There would be no guarantee, of course, that surplus wind would always be generated during the night, but that is a realistic scenario, given the lower demand. Daytime charging would be possible, provided it could be controlled by some form of 'smart meter', or by teleswitching.

Although much of the discussion surrounding electric cars has focused on their use in high-wind scenarios, it is likely that they might be to provide reserve services at modest cost. As noted in the previous paragraph, control of the magnitude of the charging load is a strong possibility, and at modest cost.

2.15.8.12.7 'Smart grids' and the growth of decentralized generation

The term 'Smart Grids' is used to describe various technologies that may need to be developed in the future to enable electricity networks to function more efficiently – especially with large amounts of wind energy. A paper [72] that was commissioned by the UK Government Office for Science has discussed the issues surrounding the concept. The paper suggests that "Fully decentralised energy supply is not currently possible or even truly desirable," but that

> current evidence points towards the deployment of an increasingly decentralised energy supply infrastructure, which will still rely on and benefit from common centralised infrastructures.

The rate at which decentralized generation will grow is somewhat uncertain [73], although both PB Power [74] and National Grid UK [75] appear to be in broad agreement that the additional plant capacity in the United Kingdom will be in the range 3–5 GW by 2020. The present capacity of embedded generation is around 7500 MW.

2.15.8.12.8 Electric spaces and water heating

At present, electric space and water heating is significantly more expensive than gas or oil-fired heating. If, however, there were a move toward more electric heating, this potentially would provide system operators with a large source of inexpensive DSM. This would enable wind surpluses to be utilized and avoid the necessity for wind turbine outputs to be constrained. Such a shift in emphasis might be the result of high fossil fuel prices, government incentives, or both. Electric water heating, and, to a lesser extent, space heating can be modulated without significantly affecting the comfort of the consumer, although wider dead bands may be necessary for central heating systems. The signals that would enable system operators to influence demand levels could be transmitted through 'smart controls' or one of the other technologies discussed earlier. The concept is actively being considered in Denmark [76].

2.15.8.12.9 Overall effects

Precise estimates for impacts of the mitigation measures cannot easily be made in every instance. The prospects for improved methods of wind forecasting are good and the most significant impacts would be at the higher levels of wind energy penetration, where it may be possible to reduce the extra costs of variability by about 20–25%.

2.15.9 Total Cost Estimates

A number of governments have set targets for renewables, or for wind energy of achieving 20% renewable energy (or more) in electricity supply by 2020. This provides a reference point for estimating the total additional cost to the electricity consumer, taking into account all the factors discussed in this chapter. An analysis completed in 2003 [45] suggested that the extra cost would increase domestic electricity bills in the United Kingdom by about 5%. As wind energy is expected to contribute the majority of the renewable energy target, the analysis assumed that all the renewable energy would come from wind and made projections about future trends in wind energy costs. Similar analyses were later made elsewhere, such as the Republic of Ireland, with broadly similar conclusions [77]. The Irish study suggested that electricity consumers might realize savings from about 2010 onward when the additional costs associated with extra balancing were outweighed by the lower costs of wind compared to gas. In all such studies, however, it is essential to examine the assumptions carefully. As the assumptions about gas prices made in the 2003 UK study were too low, a later analysis quantified 'break-even' criteria, when the addition of wind would bring about no increase in electricity prices [78]. If the price of gas is €1 per therm, wind can cost up to €1350 kW^{-1}, but if gas falls back to €0.5 per therm, wind needs to cost less than €820 kW^{-1}.

The extra costs of switching from fossil fuels to renewables have also been quantified elsewhere – in Europe and in America – and they are also extremely modest. In the United States, the effect of a 15% 'Renewables Portfolio Standard' was projected to increase the national average electricity price by 2%, compared with the reference case ($82 MWh^{-1} with the RPS compared to $81 MWh^{-1} in the reference case) [79]. By 2030, prices for natural gas and coal, two key fuels for the electric power sector, are lower with the RPS than in the reference case. These reductions come about because of the reduced demand for the fossil fuels.

In a more ambitious American scenario, it was suggested that 300 GW of wind could generate 1200 TWh of electricity at a cost of $61 MWh^{-1}, or less [80], and made allowances for transmission constraints. The study concluded that the extra cost on consumer electricity bills would be around $0.6 MWh^{-1}, or around 1%.

The extra costs that are coming out of these American studies are very similar to those emerging from Europe. One recent European study [81] suggested that the costs of meeting the 20% renewable energy target (this covers all energy, not just electricity) are estimated to be €18 800 million, which is an additional 1.25% on the EU's total energy bill.

2.15.10 Future Price Trends

The prices of oil and gas have fallen back from the peak levels reached in 2008, and so the competitive position of wind weakened. When the oil price was $140 per barrel, and gas and coal prices were also rising, wind needed little in the way of support. With oil at $70 per barrel however, that picture changes.

Although the downward trend in turbine prices halted around 2004, this was largely due to substantial increases in commodity prices – including fuels. However, there are a number of factors that are still likely to lead to lower costs for both wind turbines and wind farms in the future, including:

- The continuing trend toward larger wind turbines
- More efficient methods of manufacture

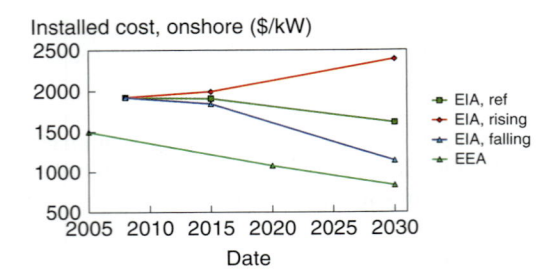

Figure 22 Estimates of future onshore costs. EIA, Energy Information Administration, US DoE; EEA, European Environment Agency.

- A better understanding of wind loads and materials properties
- Larger wind farms.

As the demand for wind turbines in 2009 is still high, there is little incentive for manufacturers to reduce profit margins for sake of competition. On the other hand, high production levels generally foster more productive methods of working – the so-called 'learning curve effect'. Manufactured items that are produced in quantity benefit from increased production, due to improved manufacturing and assembly techniques. The way in which costs fall depends on the product, and is a function of the relative inputs of material and labor. For wind turbines, it has been estimated that the price is likely to fall by 8–15% for each doubling of production. The major manufacturers mostly require between 2.4 and 3 employees to produce 1 MW of wind turbine and there may be some modest scope for this figure to be reduced. Weight reductions may also be a route to cheaper wind turbines. Although wind turbine weights, per megawatt of rated power, fell steadily as machine sizes increased, they now appear to have stabilized at around 100 kg kW^{-1}. However, weight is not the only criterion that governs the price of a wind turbine and the recent move toward concrete towers for very large machines may enable cost savings to be made.

The future trajectory of wind turbine costs, both onshore and offshore, is uncertain. Onshore, the US Department of Energy suggests three scenarios, reference, rising costs, and falling costs [21] and the progression of installed costs up to 2030 is shown in **Figure 22**. With a baseline cost in 2008 of $1923 kW^{-1}, the range in 2030 lies between $1143 kW^{-1} and $2389 kW^{-1}.

The European Environment Agency suggests lower costs. From a baseline in 2005 of $1500 kW^{-1}, they suggest costs will fall to $835 kW^{-1} by 2030.

Future offshore wind costs are equally uncertain. One recent study has identified a range of factors that are likely to influence costs and suggested that installed costs could rise or fall by 20% by 2015 from the current British value of €3570 kW^{-1} [82]. The corresponding cost range by that date lies between $3760 kW^{-1} and $6000 kW^{-1}. However, some of the cost drivers are particularly related to the British market – particularly the link between the British pound and the euro. Other factors would, however, put an upward pressure on prices internationally, particularly high commodity prices, supply chain difficulties in the offshore market, and competition for turbines with the onshore market. Given that the offshore market is still relatively new and that manufacturers and installers are still innovating, the prospects for 'learning by doing' in the medium to long term are good and so, given stable commodity prices, the prospects for cost reductions are also good.

The US Department of Energy suggests a wide range of cost estimates for 2030, ranging from $4230 kW^{-1} to $2023 kW^{-1}, while the European Environment Agency again suggests the lowest cost – at $1475 kW^{-1}. A selection of these estimates is shown in **Figure 23**.

2.15.10.1 Future Fuel Prices

There is a wide range of projections for future fuel prices. There is, however, a good measure of agreement between the reference scenario from the US Department of Energy and one of the scenarios suggested by the UK Department of Energy and Climate

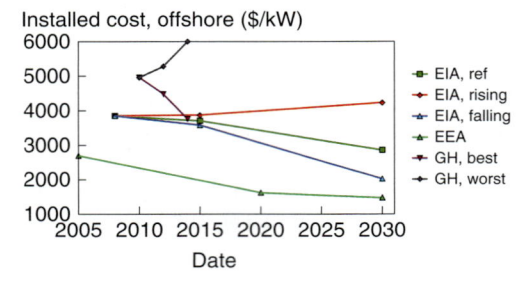

Figure 23 Projections of future offshore wind energy costs. EIA, Energy Information Administration, US DoE; EEA, European Environment Agency; GH, Garrad Hassan.

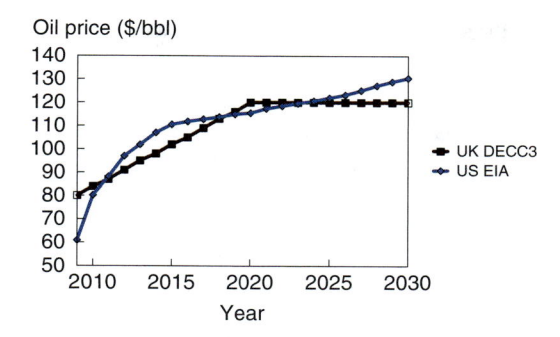

Figure 24 Future oil price estimates.

Change, as shown in **Figure 24**. The latter's High Demand, Producers' Market Power scenario matches the most recent price changes well and suggests $84 per barrel in 2010, $102 per barrel in 2015, and $120 per barrel in 2020 – very similar to the American figures.

The various other scenarios suggested by the UK government put the oil price between $60 per barrel and $150 per barrel in 2020. The American projections have an even wider price range – up to $180 per barrel by 2020.

2.15.10.2 Price Comparisons in 2020

Despite the uncertainty in future wind energy costs, there is an equal uncertainty in future fuel costs. However, once a wind farm has been built, its generation costs are virtually fixed. The same is not true for the fossil sources of generation. Their generation costs are subject to fuel price uncertainty, and this gives wind energy a competitive advantage. The implications of this uncertainty have been examined in some detail by the European Wind Energy Association and it is argued that this gives wind energy a competitive advantage [8].

As there are so many uncertainties in price projections, it is hazardous to make generation cost comparisons into the future. However, if oil, by 2020 is at $120 bbl^{-1} and if, for the sake of argument, gas prices match oil prices (as they have done in the past), that would suggest that the fuel price would be about $74 MWh^{-1}. The corresponding electricity generation price – with no allowance for any carbon price – would be about $168 MWh^{-1}. With no change at all in the installed cost of onshore wind up to that time, that generation cost would ensure onshore wind was competitive at a wide range of sites. For offshore wind to be competitive, the installed costs would need to be about $4100 kW^{-1}. Even a modest adder for the price of carbon would ensure that both onshore and offshore wind were comfortably competitive.

The American Electric Power Institute has examined the issue of competitiveness in 2015 and 2025. In 2015, they found that wind could compete with gas (costing $34 MWh^{-1} approximately) with the carbon price of around $12 tonne^{-1} of CO_2. In 2025, they suggested wind (with a higher productivity) would compete with gas at a similar carbon price.

2.15.11 Conclusions

After falling steadily for about 20 years wind turbine and wind farm costs eased upward from around 2004 – largely due to increased commodity costs – but it seems likely that wind turbine prices have now (late 2009) stabilized at around $1500 kW^{-1}. As more manufacturers enter the market, competing for nearly 30 GW of installations annually, prices are likely to resume their downward trend, provided commodity prices remain stable.

Currently, an average installed cost of $2150 kW^{-1} may be taken as a typical onshore value. There is a very large variation of wind speeds, plant costs, test discount rates, and other factors that influence wind energy prices around the world. With this caveat, the corresponding generation costs (8% interest rate, 20-year amortization) range from about $140 MWh^{-1} on a low wind speed site, falling to about $90 MWh^{-1} on a high wind speed site. Offshore installed costs on average are around $ 4200 kW^{-1}, but generation costs are less than double the onshore values on account of the higher wind speeds. A direct comparison between wind energy prices and those of thermal plant is misleading, as wind has lower external costs and often has a higher value. At the present time (late 2009), wind is slightly more expensive than coal or gas-fired generation if there is no carbon price in lieu of the extra costs.

Variability costs need to be taken into account once wind energy penetration levels exceed about 10% but, even at the 40% level, the additional balancing costs add less than 10% to the price of wind energy. Other factors, such as the cost of backup, also need to be taken into account, but the impact on consumer prices is modest (around 7% at 40% penetration level).

Although there is some uncertainty about the competitive position of wind in the future, it is likely that oil prices continue to rise. If they reach $120 bbl^{-1} – as projections in America and Britain suggest – wind becomes competitive with gas, onshore. A modest carbon price (about $12 tonne^{-1} of CO_2), or a 10% reduction in offshore costs from the present levels, would enable offshore wind to become competitive as well.

References

[1] http://en.wikipedia.org/wiki/Payback-period (accessed 15 November 2010).
[2] http://en.wikipedia.org/wiki/Internal_rate_of_return (accessed 4 January 2011).
[3] Wood A and Woollenberg B (1996) *Power Generation, Operation and Control*. New York, NY: Wiley.
[4] Tande JO and Hunter R (1994) Estimation of cost of energy from wind energy conversion systems. Submitted to *Executive Committee of IEA Wind Programme*.
[5] Milborrow DJ (1995) An analysis of UK wind farm statistics. *British Wind Energy Association, 17th Conference*. Warwick, UK, 19–21 July. London, UK: MEP.
[6] Brocklehurst F (1997) A review of the UK onshore wind energy resource. *ETSU Report ETSU-R-99*. ETSU, Harwell, UK.
[7] Danish Energy Agency (1999) Wind power in Denmark: Technology, policies and results. Danish Energy Agency, Copenhagen. http://193.88.185.141/Graphics/Publikationer/Forsyning_UK/Wind_Power99.pdf (accessed 6 November 2009).
[8] Krohn S (ed.) (2009) *The Economics of Wind Energy*. European Wind Energy Association, Brussels. http://www.ewea.org.
[9] Milborrow DJ (2010) What a difference a year can make. *Windpower Monthly* 26(1): 41–47. These and later data were reported in:
[10] Wiser R and Bolinger B (2010) *2009 Wind technologies market report. LBNL–3716. E.* Lawrence Berkeley Laboratory, California.
[11] Element Energy Limited (2009) Design of feed-in tariffs for sub-5. MW electricity in Great Britain quantitative analysis for DECC. *URN 09. D/704*. Department of Energy and Climate Change, London. http://www.decc.gov.uk.
[12] European Commission (1999) *Wind Energy: The Facts*. Luxembourg: Office for Official Publications of the European Communities.
[13] Madsen PS (1996) Tuno Knob offshore wind farm. *EU Wind Energy Conference*. Göteborg, Sweden, 20–24 May. H. S. Stephens and Associates, Bedford.
[14] Van Zanten W (1996) Lely wind farm. *Caddet Newsletter*. September.
[15] Ernst and Young for the Department of Energy and Climate Change (UK) (2009) Cost of and financial support for offshore wind. URN 09. D/534, London.
[16] L.E.K. Consulting (2003) *Perspectives on Renewable Power in the UK*. London, UK: The Carbon Trust.
[17] Department for Business Enterprise and Regulatory Reform (2008) Scoby sands offshore wind farm. *3rd Annual Report. URN 08/P48*. Department of Energy and Climate Change, London. http://www.decc.gov.uk/.
[18] Morgan C (2006) Optimisation of operations for onshore and offshore wind farms. *EWEC Conference*. Athens, Greece.
[19] European Environment Agency (2009) Europe's onshore and offshore wind energy potential. *EEA Technical Report No. 6/2009*. European Environment Agency, Copenhagen. http://www.eea.europa.eu/.
[20] Carbon Trust (2008) Offshore wind power: Big challenge, big opportunity. The Carbon Trust, London. http://www.carbontrust.co.uk
[21] Energy Information Administration, US Department of Energy (2009) Annual energy outlook. http://www.eia.doe.gov/.
[22] Ofgem (2009) Project discovery. Energy market scenarios. http://www.ofgem.gov.uk.
[23] Commission of the European Communities (2008) Energy sources, production costs and performance of technologies for power generation, heating and transport. *SEC (2008) 2872*. Commission of the European Communities, Brussels. http://ec.europa.eu/energy/strategies/2008.
[24] California Energy Commission (2010) Comparative costs of California central station electricity generation. *CEC-200-2009-07. SF*. California Energy Commission, Sacramento, California.
[25] Geothermal Energy Association (undated) c.2008. http://www.geo-energy.org/reports.aspx (accessed 16 June 2011).
[26] City Analysts Voice New Nuclear Build Scepticism (2009) *New Power* 10: 54–55.
[27] Hohmeyer O (1988) *Social Costs of Energy Consumption*. Berlin, Germany: Springer.
[28] European Commission (1995–1999) *ExternE. Externalities of Energy*, 10 vols. Luxembourg: Office for Official Publications of the European Communities.
[29] Stern L (2006) *Review on the Economics of Climate Change*. Cambridge, UK: Cambridge University Press.
[30] Energy Information Administration, US Department of Energy (1995) Electricity generation and environmental externalities: Case studies. *DOE/EIA-0598*. US Department of Energy, Washington.
[31] Energy and Environmental Economics, Inc. (E3) (2009) http://www.ethree.com/home.html.
[32] Dodd J (2008) Now vying for third slot in European rankings. *Windpower Monthly News Magazine* March: 55.
[33] *Sun and Wind Energy* 9/09: 43.
[34] *Sun and Wind Energy* 2/2006: 74.
[35] Fouquet D (2009) *Prices for Renewable Energies in Europe*. European Renewable Energies Federation, Brussels. http://www.eref-europe.org/.
[36] Milborrow DJ (2009) Managing variability. World Wildlife Fund, Godalming, Surrey. http://www.wwf.org.uk/.
[37] Gross R, Heptonstall P, Anderson D, *et al.* (2006) *The Costs and Impacts of Intermittency*. London, UK: UK Energy Research Centre.
[38] Ofgem (2008) National Grid Electricity Transmission System Operator Incentives from 1 April 2008 (accessed 14 June 2011).
[39] Davies E (ed.) (1991) Modern power station practice. In: *System Operation*, vol. L. Oxford, UK: Pergamon Press.
[40] Milborrow DJ (2009) Quantifying the impacts of wind variability. *Proceedings of the Institution of Civil Engineers* 162: 105–111.
[41] National Grid UK (2004) Seven year statement. http://www.nationalgrid.com/uk/.
[42] National Grid UK (2008) Seven year statement. http://www.nationalgrid.com/uk/.
[43] National Grid plc (2008) Evidence to house of Lords European Union Committee. *27th Report, Session 2007–08*. The EU's target for renewable energy: 20% by 2020. *Report HL 175-II*. London, UK: The Stationery Office.
[44] DeMeo E, Jordan G, Kalich C, *et al.* (2007) Accommodating wind's natural behaviour. *IEEE Power and Energy Magazine* November/December, pp 59–67.
[45] Dale L, Milborrow D, Slark R, and Strbac G (2004) Total cost estimates for large-scale wind scenarios in UK. *Energy Policy* 32: 1949–1956.
[46] EoN UK (2008) Requirement for thermal generation to back-up wind capacity. Evidence submitted to House of Lords Economic Affairs Committee into the Economics of Renewables. HL Paper 195. London, UK: The Stationery Office.
[47] Milborrow D (2009) Is wind reliable? *New Power UK* 1, pp. 59–67.
[48] British Wind Energy Association (1982) *Wind Energy for the Eighties*. Stevenage, UK: Peter Peregrinus Ltd.
[49] Union for the Co-ordination of Production and Transmission of Electricity (UCPTE) (1995) *Annual Report*. Paris.
[50] ESB National Grid (2004) Impact of wind power generation in Ireland on the operation of conventional plant and the economic implications. www.eirgrid.com/.../2004%20wind%20impact%20report%20.
[51] Milborrow D Assimilation of wind energy into the Irish electricity network. Report for Sustainable Energy Ireland. www.seai.ie/Archive1/Files_Misc/DavidMilborrowIreland.ppt.
[52] Ofgem (2009) Managing constraints on the GB transmission system. Open letter from Ofgem to National Grid, 17 February. http://www.ofgem.gov.uk/Pages/MoreInformation.aspx?docid=119&refer=Networks/Trans/ElecTransPolicy/tar.
[53] Electricity Networks Strategy Group (2009) Our electricity transmission network: A vision for 2020. webarchiv.nationalarchives.gov.uk/.../ensg.gov.uk/.../ensg_transmission_pwg_full_report_final_issue_1.pdf.
[54] Pedersen J, Eriksen P, and Orths A (2006) Market impacts of large-scale system integration of wind power. *European Wind Energy Association Conference*. Athens, Greece. European Wind Energy Association.
[55] Sinclair Knight Merz (2008) Growth scenarios for UK renewables generation and implications for future developments and operation of electricity networks. *BERR Publication URN 08/121*, London.

[56] Kariniotakis G, Moussafir, J, Usaola, J, et al. (2003) ANEMOS: Development of a next generation wind power forecasting system for the large-scale integration of onshore and offshore wind farms. *European Wind Energy Conference*, Madrid, Spain.
[57] (2003) Wind generation forecasting for power dispatching. *EPRI Journal Online* May. http://www.epri.com.
[58] Gow G (2003) An adaptable approach to short term wind forecasting. *American Wind Energy Association (AWEA) Conference*, Austin, Texas, AWEA.
[59] Wessel A, Jiang J, and Dobschinski J (2009) Improving short-term forecasting with online wind measurements. *European Wind Energy Conference*. Marseille, France. European Wind Energy Association.
[60] Perkins J (2006) Demand side participation in balancing services. UK: National Grid, London. http://www.nationalgrid.com/NR/rdonlyres/.
[61] Department of Energy and Climate Change (2008). The potential for dynamic demand. *URN 08/1453*. UK Department of Energy and Climate Change, London.
[62] Farmer ED, Newman VG, and Ashmole PH (1980) Economic and operational implications of a complex of wind-driven power generators on a power system. *IEE Proceedings A* 127: 5.
[63] Wan Y and Parsons B (1993) Factors relevant to utility integration of intermittent renewable technologies. *NREL/TP–463–4953*. National Renewable Energy Laboratory, Golden, Colorado.
[64] Douglas J (2006) Putting wind on the grid. *EPRI Journal* Spring.
[65] House of Lords, Select Committee on Economic Affairs (2008) The economics of renewable energy. *4th Report of Session 2007–08, HL Paper 195–I*. London, UK: The Stationery Office Limited.
[66] Greiner C, Korpas M, and Gjengedal T (2009) Optimal operation of energy storage systems combined with wind power in short-term power markets. *European Wind Energy Conference*. Marseille, France. European Wind Energy Association.
[67] Electric Power Research Institute (2008) Emerging technologies to increase the penetration and availability of renewables. EPRI, Palo Alto, California. http://www.epri.com.
[68] Foley A, Leahy P, and McKeogh E (2009) Wind energy variability, the Wales-Ireland interconnector and storage. *The Proceedings of the IEEE PES/IAS Conference on Sustainable Alternative Energy at Instituto de Ingeniería Energética*. Spain, Universidad Politécnica de Valencia, 28–30 September.
[69] Hurley B, Hughes P, and Giebel G (2007) Reliable power, wind variability and offshore groups in Europe. In: Boyle G (ed.) *Renewable Electricity and the Grid: The Challenge of Variability*. London, UK: Earthscan.
[70] De Decker J, Vu Van T, and Woyte A (2009) The Greenpeace offshore grid report: Development drivers and benefits. *European Wind Energy Conference*. Marseille, France. European Wind Energy Association.
[71] 2nd TEN-E Information Day, Brussels. http://ec.europa.eu/energy/.../2008_05_20_ten_e_infoday_slide_presentation.pdf (accessed 20 May 2008).
[72] Bouffard F and Kirschen D (2008) Centralised and distributed electricity systems. *Energy Policy* 36: 4504–4508.
[73] Ofgem (2009) Electricity distribution price control review: Methodology and initial results paper. *Ofgem 47/09*. Office of Gas and Electricity Markets, London.
[74] PB Power (2008) The PB Power report on future network architectures. *BERR file 46168*. UK Department of Energy and Climate Change, London.
[75] National Grid Briefing Note. 'Gone Green' a scenario for 2020. http://www.nationalgrid.com/uk/Electricity/Operating+in+2020/2020+Consultation.htm.
[76] Elkraft System (2005) Long-term challenges in the electricity system. [Elkraft was the system operator in Eastern Denmark and is now merged with Energinet].
[77] Milborrow DJ (2004) Wind economics set to beat gas in Ireland. *Windpower Monthly* December: 31.
[78] Milborrow DJ (2006) Nuclear suddenly the competitor to beat. *Windpower Monthly* January: 43.
[79] Energy Information Administration (2007) Impacts of a 15% renewable portfolio standard. *SR/OIAF/2007–03*. US Department of Energy, Washington.
[80] DeMeo E (2007) A picture of 20% US electrical energy from wind. *UWIG Technical Workshop*. Anchorage, Alaska. 24 July.
[81] Poyry Energy Consulting (2008) Compliance costs for meeting the 20% renewable energy target in 2020. *URN 08/757*. Department for Business Energy and Regulatory Reform, London. http://webarchive.nationalarchives.gov.uk/.
[82] Garrad Hassan and Partners, Bristol (2009) UK offshore wind: Charting the right course. British Wind Energy Association. http://www.bwea.com.

2.16 Environmental-Social Benefits/Impacts of Wind Power

E Kondili and JK Kaldellis, Technological Education Institute of Piraeus, Athens, Greece

© 2012 Elsevier Ltd. All rights reserved.

2.16.1	Introduction – Scope and Objectives	504
2.16.2	Main Environmental Benefits of Wind Power	504
2.16.2.1	General Considerations	504
2.16.2.2	Avoided Air Pollution – Reduction of CO_2 Emissions	504
2.16.2.3	Reduction of Water Consumption	505
2.16.3	Main Social Benefits of Wind Power	507
2.16.3.1	Fossil Fuel Saving/Substitution	507
2.16.3.2	Regional Development – New Activities	507
2.16.3.3	Employment Opportunities and Job Positions in the Wind Power Sector	508
2.16.4	Environmental Behavior of Wind Energy	510
2.16.5	Methods and Tools for Environmental Impact Assessment	511
2.16.6	Noise Impact	513
2.16.6.1	Qualitative and Quantitative Consideration of Noise Impact	513
2.16.6.2	Research and Development Relevant to Wind Turbine Noise	518
2.16.7	Wind Turbines' Visual Impact and Aesthetics	518
2.16.7.1	General Considerations on Visual Impact and Aesthetics	518
2.16.7.2	Shadow Flickering	522
2.16.8	Impacts in Fauna and Flora and Microclimate	522
2.16.8.1	Impacts in Flora and Fauna	522
2.16.8.2	Impacts on the Microclimate	523
2.16.9	Other Environmental Impacts	524
2.16.9.1	Interference of a Wind Turbine with Electromagnetic Communication Systems	524
2.16.9.2	Traffic – Transportation and Access	524
2.16.9.3	Archaeology and Cultural Heritage	524
2.16.9.4	Health and Safety	525
2.16.10	Offshore Environmental Impacts	525
2.16.10.1	Offshore Noise Impact	525
2.16.10.2	Construction and Decommissioning Noise	526
2.16.10.3	Operational Noise	526
2.16.10.4	Visual Impacts	527
2.16.10.5	Impacts on Marine Mammals	528
2.16.10.6	Impacts on Fish	528
2.16.10.7	Impacts on Birds	529
2.16.10.8	Effects of Offshore Wind Energy on the Microclimate	530
2.16.11	Mitigation Measures – Conclusions	530
2.16.11.1	The Importance of Wind Farm Siting	530
2.16.11.2	Mitigation through Technology	531
2.16.12	Social Acceptability of Wind Power Projects	531
2.16.12.1	General Considerations	531
2.16.12.2	Case Studies for Public Attitude Analysis	534
2.16.13	The Public Attitude Toward Offshore Wind Parks	535
2.16.14	Future Trends in Wind Parks' Social and Environmental Impacts Assessment	536
2.16.15	Conclusions	537
References		537
Further Reading		538

Glossary

Impact The change in an environmental parameter over time due to the effect of an action.

Carbon footprint The total amount of CO_2 and other greenhouse gases emitted over a full cycle of a process or product. It is expressed as grams of CO_2 equivalent per kilowatt hour of energy produced (gCO_2eq. kWh^{-1}).

Offshore wind parks Wind parks installed in the sea.

Seascape The coastal landscape and adjoining areas of open water, including views from land to sea, from sea to land, and along the coastline.

Social benefits Benefits for the society in terms of development, job positions, environmental behavior, and income increase.

Visual impact Visual impact is defined as a change in the appearance of the landscape as a result of development which can be positive (improvement) or negative (detraction).

2.16.1 Introduction – Scope and Objectives

Wind energy is characterized as a clean and environmentally friendly technology, and this is one of the main benefits that makes it such an attractive and promising energy supply solution. For the completeness of wind energy analysis it is considered very critical to describe concisely other wind energy effects, such as the social and environmental impacts that may incur from the corresponding projects implementation, in parallel to its technological and/or financial implications. To that effect, the present chapter deals with the main social and environmental benefits from the introduction of wind energy in an area, such as CO_2 emissions reduction, fossil fuels imports reduction, creation of new job positions, and regional development.

On the other hand, there are some environmental concerns resulting from wind power plants, such as noise, visual impacts, and a possible disturbance of wildlife. In some cases, these concerns are extensive and affect negatively or even hinder the implementation of the corresponding projects. The environmental impact assessment (EIA) of these projects identifies in detail the environmental impacts and suggests their mitigation measures, facilitating in that way their acceptance by local societies. Another very interesting issue that is of high priority when examining wind power projects is their social acceptance and the public attitude toward them. These issues are also discussed in this chapter.

Nowadays, it is a common belief that wind energy has a key role to play in combating climate change by reducing CO_2 emissions from power generation. Generally, it does not pollute the air-like thermal power plants that rely on combustion of (carbon containing) fossil fuels such as oil, coal, or natural gas. Wind turbines do not produce atmospheric emissions that cause acid rain or greenhouse gases. Wind power plants may be built in villages, in remote areas, thus benefiting the economy in the region, employment, and the development of parallel satellite activities. It is definitely considered as a green power technology.

In the rest of the chapter the main impacts (positive and negative) of wind energy projects on people in surrounding areas are identified and described. Offshore wind power plants are a special interesting category with distinct and, in many cases, different environmental impacts, and, therefore, they are described in a separate section.

2.16.2 Main Environmental Benefits of Wind Power

2.16.2.1 General Considerations

Wind energy is one of the cleanest and most environmentally friendly energy sources. It has a long-term positive impact on the environment by reducing the threat posed by climate change. It emits no greenhouse gases or air pollutants or particles that are carcinogenic and affect human health severely. The development of wind power plants creates employment opportunities and new job positions during equipment construction, installation, and operation of the new power plants. Also, since wind power plants are located in remote areas, new industries and satellite activities are emerging and regional development is enhanced in order to support the construction and the operation of the new plant during its whole life cycle. At the local level, wind energy may also have positive effects on biodiversity and offer an opportunity to practice ecological restoration both onshore and offshore, such as the creation of new vegetation and animal habitats, improved fish stocks, and other marine life.

Table 1 highlights the main environmental and social benefits of wind energy.

2.16.2.2 Avoided Air Pollution – Reduction of CO_2 Emissions

All electricity generation schemes have a carbon footprint. This means that at some points of their construction and operation, CO_2 and other greenhouse gases are emitted. A carbon footprint is the total amount of CO_2 and other greenhouse gases emitted over a full cycle of a process or product. It is expressed as grams of CO_2 equivalent per kilowatt hour of energy produced ($gCO_2eq. \, kWh^{-1}$).

Fossil fuel technologies have the largest carbon footprints since power production is achieved through combustion processes. Nonfossil fuel technologies such as renewable energy sources (RES) are often referred as low carbon or carbon neutral because they do not emit CO_2 during their operation. Certainly they are not completely carbon-free since CO_2

Table 1 Main social and environmental benefits of wind power

Avoided air pollution – reduction of CO_2 emissions
Reduction of water consumption
Fossil fuels saving/substitution
Positive effects on the microclimate of the area
New job positions – employment opportunities
Regional development
Development and support of domestic construction industry and various satellite activities

emissions arise in other phases of their life cycle, for example, during raw materials extraction, equipment construction, plant installation, maintenance, and decommissioning, however originating from the embedded energy. In any case, their very low carbon footprint compared to the conventional energy sources has been the main advantage for their current development and advancement.

Coal burning power plants have the largest footprint of all electricity generation systems. Conventional coal combustion systems result in emissions of the order of $1000\,gCO_2\,kWh^{-1}$. Wind power is already helping to fight climate change, since each wind-produced kWh avoids a kWh created by the energy mix of coal, oil, and gas – on average $600-1000\,gCO_2\,kWh_e^{-1}$ [1]. Tables 2 and 3 present the emissions of relevant pollutants produced by various power production technologies including wind power [2].

Nearly all the emissions related to wind energy refer to the embedded energy of the various wind park components and occur during the manufacturing and construction phase, arising mainly from the production of steel for the tower of the wind turbine, concrete for the foundations, and materials for the rotor blades. These all account for 98% of the total life cycle emissions. The emissions generated during the operation of wind turbines arise from routine maintenance inspection trips. Onshore wind turbines are accessed by vehicles, while offshore turbines are maintained using special vessels and helicopters. The carbon footprint of offshore versus onshore wind energy generation is marginally greater since it requires larger foundations.

Figures 1 and 2 indicate the CO_2 footprint for various different electricity generation sources. As it can be seen from these figures, electricity generated from wind energy has one of the lowest carbon footprints ranging in the area of $4-10\,gCO_2\,kWh^{-1}$ [3–5].

2.16.2.3 Reduction of Water Consumption

In an increasingly water-stressed world, water consumption is a very important issue. Taking into account the imperative sustainability considerations, the minimization of the water consumption in power production could be one of the most significant criteria for a process and technology selection in case there are alternative solutions available.

Conventional power plants use large amounts of water for the condensing portion of the thermodynamic cycle. For coal power plants, water is also used to clean and process fuel. The amount of water used can be millions of liters per day. By reducing the usage of water, it can be preserved and used for other purposes.

Table 2 Emissions of pollutants per kWh of produced electricity – benefits of wind power versus coal and natural gas [2]

	Emissions per kWh of produced electricity						Wind power benefits		
	Onshore wind	Offshore wind	Average wind	Hard coal	Lignite	NGCC	vs. Coal	vs. Lignite	vs. NGCC
Carbon dioxide, fossil (g)	8	8	8	836	1060	400	828	1052	392
Methane, fossil (mg)	8	8	8	2554	244	993	2546	236	985
Nitrogen oxides (mg)	31	31	31	1309	1041	353	1278	1010	322
NMVOC (mg)	6	5	6	71	8	129	65	2	123
Particulates (mg)	13	18	15	147	711	12	132	696	−3
Sulfur dioxide (mg)	32	31	32	1548	3808	149	1516	3776	117

Table 3 Emissions and benefits of pollutants per kWh of electricity produced by wind, nuclear, solar PV, solar thermal, and biomass combined heat and power (CHP) plants [2]

	Emissions					Wind power benefits			
	Average wind	Nuclear	Solar PV	Solar thermal	Biomass CHP	vs. Nuclear	vs. Solar PV	vs. Solar thermal	vs. Biomass CHP
Carbon dioxide, fossil (g)	8	8	53	9	83	0	45	1	75
Methane, fossil (mg)	8	20	100	18	119	12	92	10	111
Nitrogen oxides (mg)	31	32	112	37	814	1	81	6	783
NMVOC (mg)	6	6	20	6	66	0	14	0	60
Particulates (mg)	15	17	107	27	144	2	92	12	129
Sulfur dioxide (mg)	32	46	0	31	250	14	−32	−1	218

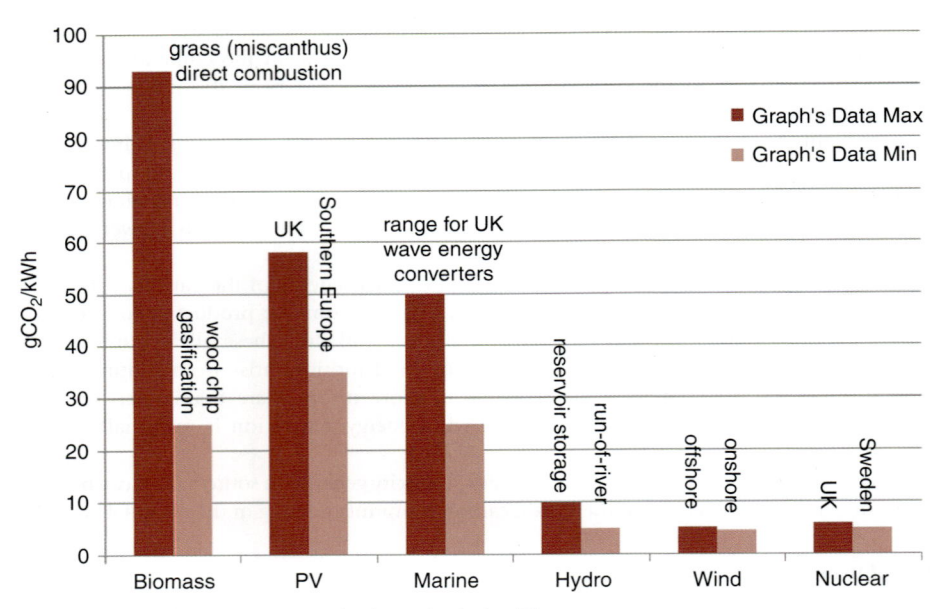

Figure 1 Carbon footprint (bounds) of various power production technologies [2].

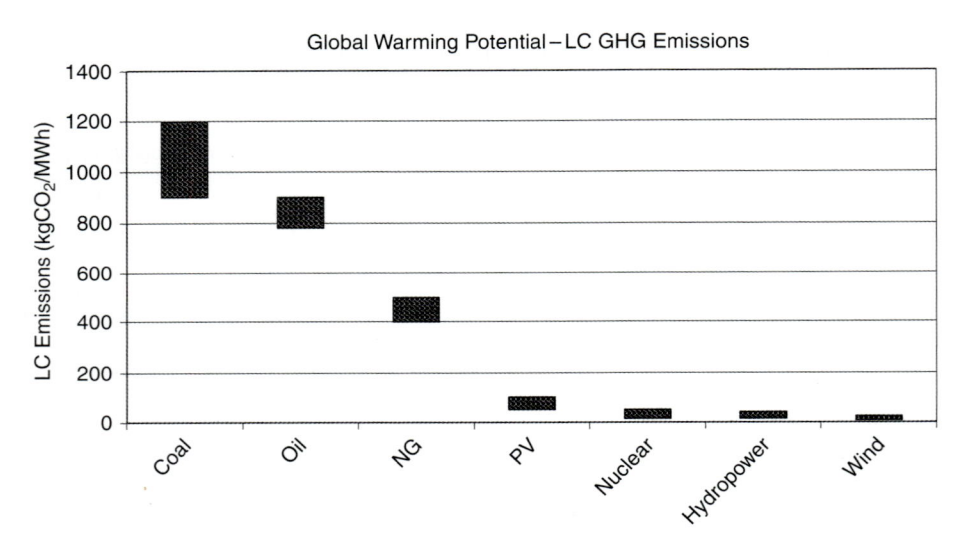

Figure 2 Carbon footprint of various conventional and renewable power production technologies [3].

Figure 3 shows the full-cycle water consumption per unit of electricity for fossil fuels and nuclear power plants, respectively, utilizing once-through (OT), closed-loop (CL), and dry cooling technologies. Combined cycle gas turbines (CCGT) have the lowest consumption rates of the three plant types examined, while nuclear power plants and plants with advanced coal technology and carbon capture and sequestration (CCS) present the highest. Integrated gasification combined cycle (IGCC) is somewhere in between these technologies as far as water consumption is concerned. The averages used are the simple mean of the low and high estimates [6].

Figure 4 shows the corresponding water consumption related to the electricity generation on the basis of RES exploitation.

Renewable sources for electricity have very diverse water consumption issues. Wind and solar photovoltaic (PV) use practically no water, while concentrating solar power (CSP) uses steam turbines and therefore has water consumption patterns comparable to or higher than conventional power plants. The different ones are geothermal and hydropower, as they both use very large quantities of water, but have definitional issues that make it difficult to compare directly with other sources of electricity.

In any case, from all the above it is apparent that wind energy in its life cycle uses very little or no water and it is very advantageous in that respect compared to other power generation technologies.

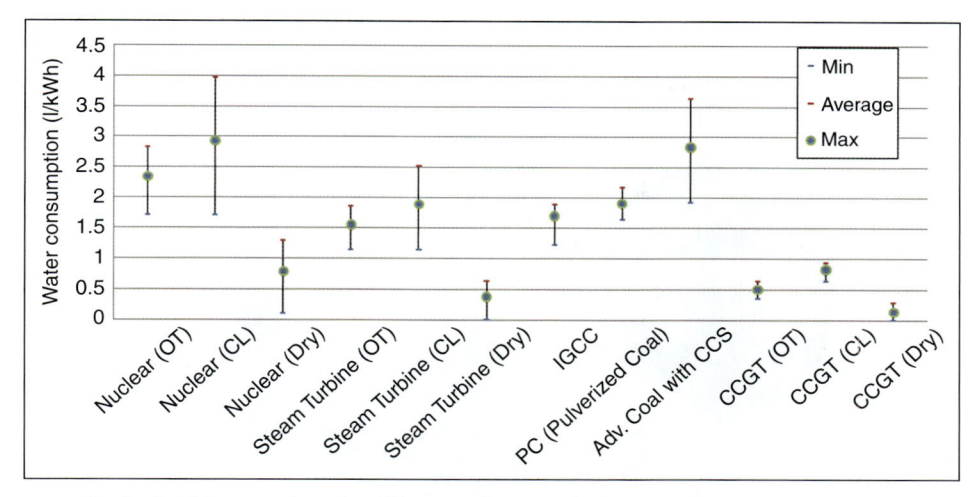

Figure 3 Water consumption in electricity generation using different cooling technologies, including water consumed during fuel extraction and processing [6].

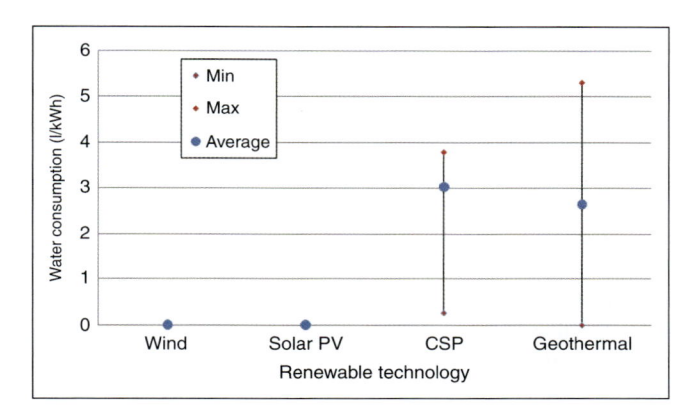

Figure 4 Water consumption from renewable energy sources [6].

2.16.3 Main Social Benefits of Wind Power

2.16.3.1 Fossil Fuel Saving/Substitution

One of the main social benefits of the exploitation of wind energy is its contribution in minimizing the operation of thermal power stations; hence, the operation of wind parks substitutes coal and oil-fired or natural gas-based thermal power stations. More specifically, the fuel saving amount 'M_f' may be estimated by the following relationship:

$$M_f = \frac{E_{wind}}{\eta H_u} \qquad [1]$$

where 'E_{wind}' is the wind energy produced, 'H_u' is the fuel-specific calorific value, and 'η' is the total transformation efficiency of the chemical energy of the fuel to electricity.

More specifically, the operation of wind-based power stations first of all reduces the energy imports (oil, natural gas, coal, etc.) for almost all energy-importing industrialized countries contributing to annual exchange loss reduction. Note that the imported energy exchange loss is strongly dependent on the unstable and continuous increasing prices of oil and natural gas in the international market. In order to avoid any misleading conclusions, the money spent to import the necessary equipment (e.g., wind turbines) is less than the macroeconomic cost resulting from the corresponding fossil fuel imports during two successive years, while the service period of the wind power stations exceeds 20 years.

Besides, the exploitation of wind energy improves energy supply security, since it minimizes the significant hidden cost of fossil fuel utilization, like political dependency, cost of 'controlling' the existing fossil fuel reserves, and so on. On top of these, wind energy contributes in reducing the exploitation of fossil fuel reserves, prolonging, in this way, their operational life.

2.16.3.2 Regional Development – New Activities

As with most business ventures, wind energy projects create jobs and new activities in the specific areas where they are installed and, more widely, in the whole country where they are implemented.

508   Environmental-Social Benefits/Impacts of Wind Power

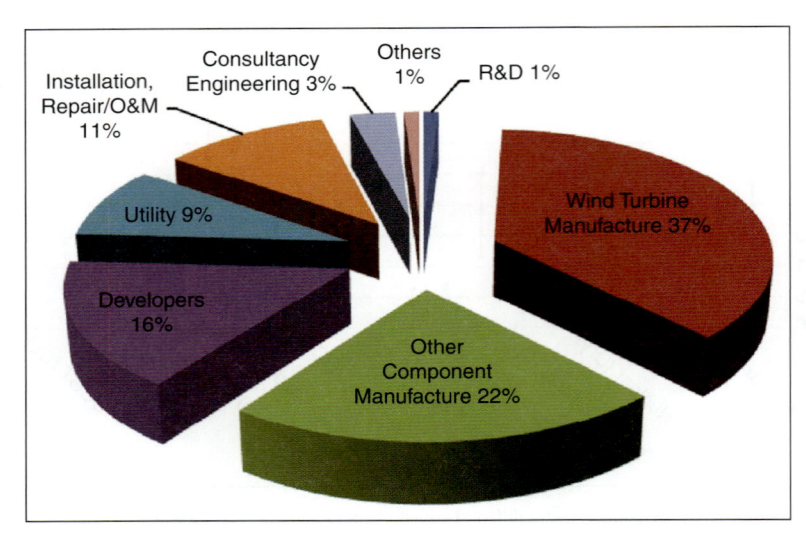

Figure 5   Direct employment by type of company in the wind energy sector [7].

In general, the main activities associated with the wind energy include the manufacturing of the turbine and all the other necessary equipment, the construction and installation of the plant, its operation and maintenance activities, and other parallel activities such as engineering, consultancy, education, distribution network, and utilities.

More specifically, the activities and the relevant employment fields related to wind power plants (**Figure 5**) include the following:

- Raw materials processing (e.g., metallic, synthetic materials)
- Wind turbine manufacturers
- Major subcomponent manufacturers (metallic and electrical machinery)
- Companies generating and distributing electricity (utilities)
- Wind energy promoters (consultancy and engineering)
- Research and development (R&D) activities in aerodynamics, computational fluid dynamics, and materials
- Engineering companies for the design and development of the wind power plants
- Technicians and specialized personnel for the operation and maintenance of the plant
- Wind energy measurement and forecasting (developers)
- Instrumentation manufacturing and trade (manufacturing other components)
- EIA professionals (consultancy and engineering)
- Education and training services (others)
- Land and site development (developers)
- Activities related to the permission acquirement (consultancy and engineering)
- Specialized financial services (others)
- Legal, health, and safety services (others).

All the above create direct or indirect employment. Most of these activities are closely related to the place where the plant is to be installed and this is the reason that regional development is achieved. Nevertheless, for the completeness of the subject, it should be mentioned at this point that some job positions may be lost because of the development of a wind power plant replacing partially or completely a local thermal power station.

2.16.3.3   Employment Opportunities and Job Positions in the Wind Power Sector

Wind energy projects generate many new activities and certainly have positive effects on employment [7]. The implementation of these projects creates a significant number of specialized jobs (over 104 000 in 2008) [8], especially at a time when other energy sectors are shrinking. Wind turbine manufacturers, including major subcontractors (components manufacturers), are responsible for the lion's share of the jobs, and there is a prevalence of males in the workforce. There is also a scarcity of experienced and qualified personnel, such as project managers, engineers, and operation and maintenance technicians. These job positions need a series of educational, mobility, and dissemination measures to be put into practice.

A survey has been carried out to investigate the number of employees working directly in the wind energy sector [8]. The survey has been carried out by means of a questionnaire dispatched to around 1100 organizations from 30 countries (the 27 EU member states plus Croatia, Norway, and Turkey). It went to all European Wind Energy Association members and the members of the EU-27 national wind energy associations. Supplementary information in order to fill the gaps has been provided from the following:

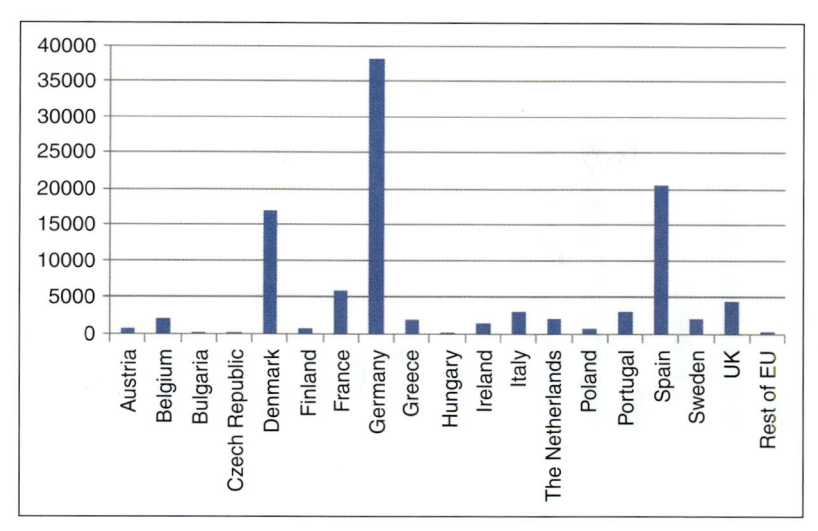

Figure 6 Direct jobs in the wind energy sector in the EU member states [7].

- Reviewing the annual reports and websites of the main wind energy companies, notably large wind turbines manufacturers, component manufacturers, developers, and utilities.
- Using the results of the studies coming from the countries where the main wind turbine manufacturers are based, that is, Denmark, Germany, and Spain.
- Assessing the data compiled by the national wind energy associations.

The results of the survey indicate that wind energy companies in the EU currently employ around 104 000 people. The growth experienced (226%) between 2003 and 2007 is consistent with the evolution of the installed capacity in Europe (276%).

In this context, a significant proportion of direct wind energy employment is based in three countries, Denmark, Germany, and Spain, whose combined installed capacity also adds up to 70% of the total in the EU (**Figure 6**). The situation in the eastern European member states varies, with Poland being in a leading position. Wind energy employment in these countries will probably rise significantly in the next 3–5 years, boosted by a combination of attractive markets, a well-qualified labor force, and lower production costs [7].

Nevertheless, the sector is less concentrated now than it was in 2003 when these three countries (Denmark, Germany, and Spain) accounted for 89% of employment and 84% of EU installed capacity. This is due to the opening of manufacturing and operation centers in emerging markets and to the local nature of many wind-related activities, such as promotion, operations and maintenance, engineering, and legal services [9].

By type of company, wind turbine and component manufacturers (**Figure 5**) account for most of the jobs (59%). Within these categories, companies tend to be bigger and thus employ more people.

Employment from the wind energy sector makes up around 7.3% of the total amount of people working in the electricity-generating sector and it should be noted that wind energy currently meets 3.7% of EU electricity demand. This shows that wind energy is more labor-intensive than the other electricity-generating technologies.

Finally, there is a well-documented trend of energy employment decline in Europe, particularly marked in the coal sector. For instance, British coal production and employment have dropped significantly, from 229 000 workers in 1981 to 5500 in 2006. In Germany, it is estimated that jobs in the sector will drop from 265 000 in 1991 to less than 80 000 in 2020. In EU countries, more than 150 000 utility and gas industry jobs disappeared in the second half of the 1990s and it is estimated that another 200 000 jobs will be lost during the first half of the twenty-first century. The outcomes set out in the previous paragraphs demonstrate that job losses in the European energy sector are independent of renewable energy deployment and that the renewable energy sector is, in fact, helping to mitigate these negative effects in the power sector.

The increase in wind energy installations has led to a multiplication of job offers in all the subsectors, especially in manufacturing and development. Actually, one may state that the average new job creation in the European market is approximately two employees per new MW installed, with values exceeding the seven new jobs per MW installed in some specific countries (see also **Figure 7**). Concerning the qualifications and the profile of the field employees, a shortage in those positions that requires a high degree of expertise and responsibility is identified. The positions that are most difficult to fill in are those related to operations and maintenance, project management, and aerodynamics engineering. The standardization of qualifications and a better information system could help to ease the situation and facilitate the transfer of workers toward the areas where they are needed.

The conclusion is that wind energy represents an attractive source of employment in Europe. Since a number of activities (construction, operation and maintenance, legal, and environmental studies) are best dealt with at local level, there will always be a positive correlation between the location of the wind farm and the number of jobs it creates.

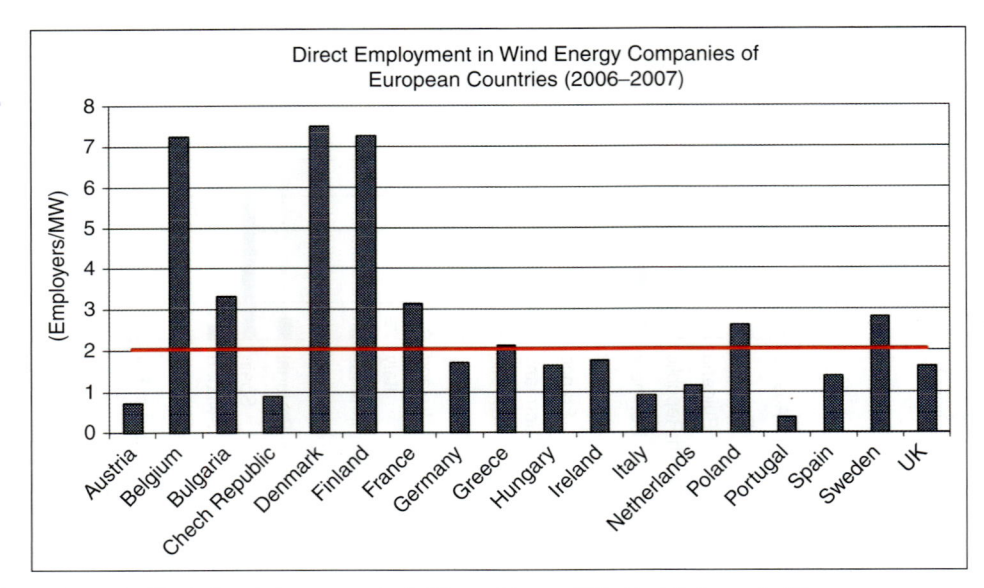

Figure 7 Employment opportunities in the wind energy sector in EU countries per MW of installed capacity [3].

2.16.4 Environmental Behavior of Wind Energy

Although wind energy is possibly the most environmental compatible form of energy, there are some environmental impacts that should be considered when studying the installation of a new wind power plant. Most of the environmental impacts can be avoided or minimized (by careful planning and siting), mitigated, or compensated. In fact, wind farm developers are required to undertake EIA to gauge all potential significant environmental effects before the project's implementation.

The main environmental impacts of a wind farm are shown in **Table 4**. In the general case the most serious environmental impacts of wind power plants are related to noise, aesthetics, and their potential effects in the wildlife of the specific geographical area.

The European legislation associated with the identification and mitigation of environmental impacts of any development activity is the consolidated version of the Council Directive 97/11/EC [10].

When looking at a potentially suitable site, a study analyzing all relevant environmental and ecological factors should be carried out. These form the basis of an EIA that must be submitted alongside a planning application, demonstrating that any potential environmental impact will be mitigated and that the impacts of development are outweighed by the benefits.

The various impacts are classified according to the environmental parameters they refer to. In addition, the impacts are very different for the various stages of a wind park's life cycle. More precisely, the most serious environmental impacts are associated with the equipment manufacturing and the plant construction stages. The operation of a project has no serious environmental impacts. Furthermore, in the general case, the impacts may be characterized as temporary or permanent, reversible or irreversible, and of low or high significance.

A general table of contents of an EIA study as dictated by the current legislation (May 2011) is shown in **Figure 8**.

More specifically, for a wind power plant the EIA must examine the following environmental parameters:

- *Noise*. Noise is considered as one of the most significant environmental impacts of wind power on nearby regions.
- *Visual impacts – aesthetics*. It is also a very significant issue related to wind power plants.
- *Impacts on wildlife*. Effects on local and emigrating bird life, flora, and fauna.
- *Landscape and land use*. The possible need to change the land use and the effects of the wind park on the landscape.
- *Surface and ground water*. To assess any likely impacts on water quantity and quality within both the development area and surrounding countryside and ensure these are minimized.
- *Archaeology – cultural sites*. Both national and local archaeological groups are consulted to establish if proposed sites are likely to have any significant impacts on heritage sites or archaeological remains.

Table 4 Main environmental impacts of wind power plants

Noise	Effect on the electromagnetic waves
Visual impacts – aesthetics	Archaeology and cultural heritage
Landscape and land use	Transportation issues
Impacts on the wildlife, flora, and fauna	Health and safety

Table of Contents of a typical EIA

EXECUTIVE SUMMARY

TABLE OF CONTENTS

CHAPTER 1: PROJECT DESCRIPTION

(Detailed project description including type of the project, project location, technical specifications, size of the project/capacity, infrastructure required, networks, technology to be used, utilities required, project plan, project budget).

CHAPTER 2: PROJECT LOCATION

2.1 Natural Environment (Soil, Topography, Water Resources, Flora, Fauna, Climate)

2.2 Human Environment (Population, Land use, Distances from inhabited areas, Cultural/Historical places, Other characteristics of the area)

CHAPTER 3: EXISTING ENVIRONMENTAL SITUATION

3.1 Existing pollution sources

3.2 Assessment of environmental pollution before the project

CHAPTER 4: ENVIRONMENTAL PARAMETERS OF THE PROJECT – ENVIRONMENTAL IMPACTS

4.1 Environmental Parameters

4.2 Environmental Impacts

4.3 Checklists

4.4 Matrices

CHAPTER 5: ALTERNATIVE SOLUTIONS

- Zero solution
- Other location, other size, other technology/process, etc.

CHAPTER 6: POLLUTION PREVENTION – MITIGATION OF THE ENVIRONMENTAL IMPACTS
How are the impacts going to be controlled and/or eliminated.
(Link the impacts to the pollution prevention measures/techniques)

CHAPTER 7: CONCLUSIONS

REFERENCES – LITERATURE – ANNEXES

Figure 8 Structure and contents of an Environmental Impact Assessment Study according to the Directive 97/11/EC.

2.16.5 Methods and Tools for Environmental Impact Assessment

EIA is a tool for decision-makers to take into account the possible effects of a proposed project on the environment and is also a process for collecting the data related to a project design and project location. Various methods and tools have been developed (**Figure 9**) in order to identify and predict the environmental impacts of a project. In general, the tools may be classified into quantitative and qualitative. The qualitative tools include the following:

- Checklists
- Impacts matrices.

Quantitative methods for EIA include the following:

- Design and development of databases
- Computer analytical models
- Statistical models
- Expert systems.

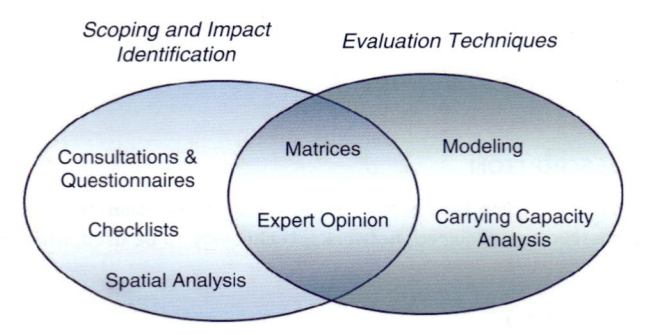

Figure 9 Methods and tools in the environmental impact assessment.

Knowledge-based systems, referred to as expert systems, and different computer-based systems are an emerging technology in information processing and are becoming increasingly useful tools in different applications areas including EIA studies.

The checklists provide a systematic way of ensuring that all likely events resulting from a project are considered. Information is presented in a tabular format. It is a systematic method; therefore, standard checklists for similar projects may be developed. They are very valuable since they present in a simple table all the potential impacts of a project. The main drawback is that cause and effect relationships are not specified.

Matrices are a more complex form a checklist. They link the causes and effects for the specific characteristics of a project and a mark is assigned in each cell indicating how much each project characteristic contributes to a certain impact. Therefore, matrices can be used also quantitatively and can evaluate impacts to some degree. They provide a good visual summary of impacts. In the matrices, since quantitative information is included, the impacts may be ranked to assist in evaluation.

As an example of wind power project checklists, **Table 5** shows the environmental impacts of the construction phase of a wind park, while **Table 6** shows the corresponding impacts of the operational phase [11]. In addition, **Table 7** is an example of

Table 5 Checklist for the environmental impacts of the construction phase of a wind park [11]

Environmental parameter	Environmental impact	Impact characteristics
Earth – soil	Soil compaction	Permanent, medium significance, certain, negative
	Soil fracture, soils admixing	Temporary, medium significance, certain, negative
	Soil erosion	Temporary, medium significance, very likely, negative
	Overlay of soil	Permanent, high significance, certain, negative
	Soil contamination and productivity	Temporary, low significance, likely, negative
	Slope damage	Permanent, medium significance, less likely, negative
	Change of local topography	Permanent, medium significance, certain, negative
Air quality	Air emissions production	Temporary, high significance, certain, negative
	Dust generation	Temporary, low significance, certain, negative
	Odors generation	Temporary, low significance, certain, negative
Water resources	Groundwater contamination	Temporary, low significance, less likely, negative
	Surface waters contamination	Temporary, low significance, likely, negative
	Water consumption	Temporary, low significance, certain, negative
Land use	Change of existing land use	Permanent, medium significance, certain, negative
Flora and fauna	Vegetation disturbance	Temporary, low significance, very likely, negative
	Animals and avian mortality	Temporary, low significance, likely, negative
	Harassment of wildlife and habitats damage	Temporary, low significance, very likely, negative
Energy	Electrical energy consumption	Temporary, low significance, certain, negative
	Fuels consumption increase	Temporary, medium significance, certain, negative
Noise	Mechanical noise	Temporary, high significance, certain, negative
Cultural resources	Damage of significant archaeological resources	Permanent, medium significance, very likely, negative
Visual resources	Landscape aesthetics disruption/improvement	Temporary, low significance, very likely, negative
Natural resources	Increase of local resources' exploitation rate	Temporary, low significance, very likely, negative
Health and safety	Accidents	Temporary, high significance, very likely, negative
	Health issues	Temporary, medium significance, less likely, negative
Transportation	Increase of local traffic	Temporary, low significance, very likely, negative
	Extension (improvement) of existing transportation network	Permanent, medium significance, certain, negative/positive
	Degradation of existing transportation network	Temporary, low significance, likely, negative
Agricultural crops and livestock	Reduction – disturbance of agricultural activities	Temporary, low significance, likely, negative
	Reduction – disturbance of livestock activities	Temporary, low significance, likely, negative
Local society, economy, and services	Arising of objections toward the wind park's installation	Temporary, medium significance, likely, negative
	Employment offer	Temporary, high significance, certain, positive

Table 6 Checklist for the environmental impacts of the operation phase of a wind park [11]

Environmental parameter	Environmental impact	Impact characteristics
Earth – soil	Soil compaction	Permanent, medium significance, certain, negative
	Soil erosion	Permanent, medium significance, likely, negative
Air quality	Air emissions production	Permanent, low significance, certain, negative
	Dust generation	Permanent, low significance, certain, negative
	Odors generation	Permanent, low significance, certain, negative
	Air emissions reduction	Permanent, high significance, certain, positive
Flora and fauna	Harassment of wildlife	Permanent, low significance, less likely, negative
	Avian mortality	Permanent, medium significance, likely, negative
	Animals and birds emigration	Permanent, low significance, likely, negative
Energy	Fuels consumption reduction	Permanent, high significance, certain, positive
	Electricity generation	Permanent, high significance, certain, positive
Noise	Mechanical noise	Permanent, low significance, certain, negative
	Aerodynamic noise	Permanent, high significance, certain, negative
Visual resources	Landscape aesthetics disruption	Permanent, high significance, very likely, negative
	Landscape aesthetics improvement	Permanent, high significance, very likely, positive
	Shadow flickering	Permanent, low significance, very likely, negative
	Flashing	Permanent, medium significance, very likely, negative
Health and safety	Accidents	Permanent, medium significance, very likely, negative
	Health issues (air emissions)	Permanent, high significance, certain, positive
	Health issues (radiation)	Permanent, low significance, less likely, positive
Agricultural crops and livestock	Disturbance of agricultural activities	Permanent, low significance, likely, negative
	Disturbance of livestock activities	Permanent, low significance, likely, negative
Local society, economy, and services	Arising of objections toward the wind park's operation	Permanent, low significance, likely, negative
	Electricity security of supply	Permanent, medium significance, certain, positive
	Local grid power quality issues	Permanent, high significance, certain, negative
	Employment offer	Permanent, low significance, certain, positive
	Reduction of the electricity tariffs	Permanent, medium significance, likely, positive
	Promotion and development of local area	Permanent, medium significance, very likely, positive

an impact matrix of the same wind park, where there is a quantified assessment of the cause–effect relationship in the scale 1 (low) to 5 (high) [11].

2.16.6 Noise Impact

2.16.6.1 Qualitative and Quantitative Consideration of Noise Impact

One of the most noticeable impacts a wind turbine places upon the environment is noise emission. In some cases the impact of noise emission has the potential (mainly in densely populated areas) to lower property values within a varying radius of the plant and is said to be one of the biggest disadvantages of a wind turbine. This one along with the visual impact are the concerns often raised by members of the public, see, for example, Figures 10 and 11 concerning the public attitude toward the noise and visual impact in a Greek region where almost 120 MW of wind power operate since the beginning of the previous decade.

The noise impact depends mainly on the average annual wind speed (i.e., the higher the wind speed, the greater the noise output can be) and the size of the blades. Actually, wind noise is assumed analogous to the fourth to sixth power of the blades (tip) speed relative to the surroundings. In this context, the rotor rotational speed and the corresponding blade's length strongly influence the noise emitted from a wind turbine [13]. On the other hand, it is well known that the energy yield of a wind turbine is directly dependent on the ratio between the wind speed at hub height and the rotor tip speed (λ, tip speed ratio). Hence, specific blade speed is required in order to maximize the energy yield of a wind turbine. Otherwise, the wind turbine would not operate efficiently. In this context, during nights or other socially sensitive time periods, most of the manufacturers include the option of 'night operation', where the machine operates at low rotational speed, reducing the noise emission and the power output as well. On top of that, the energy in sound waves (and thus the sound intensity) in a homogeneous and obstacle-free flow field drops with the square of the distance from the sound source.

In general, wind turbines generate noise as every machine does. The noise from the wind turbine is divided into two major categories depending on the noise source, that is, the mechanical and the aerodynamic noise [14]. Particularly,

Table 7 Example of an environmental impacts matrix of a wind park [11]

Environmental parameter	Impact	Site preparation — Measurements procedure	Construction stage — Roads and paths construction, site demarcation	Delivery of equipment	Setup of temporary facilities	Excavation and foundation works	Towers–turbines assembly and installation	Transformers' housing and substation construction	Interconnection from turbines to substation	Transmission line to high-voltage power network	Site instauration and improvement works	Operation — Wind farm's operation needs	Maintenance needs	Decommissioning — Removal of turbines, ancillary equipment, and power lines	Site remediation
Soil – Earth	Soil erosion		3			4		1	2	2	1	1		2	1
	Overlay of soil		5		1	1		2			1				
	Soil contamination		3	1		2		1	2	2				1	1
	Soil productivity		4	1		2			1						3
	Local topography change		4				2	2	1	1				2	2
Air quality	Air emissions increase/reduction		4	2		2	1	2	2	2		5		3	2
	Dust generation		5	3		4	1	2	4	4	1		1	4	3
	Odors generation		3	2		2		1	1	1	1		1	1	2
	Waters contamination		3	1		3			3	2				1	1
Water resources	Water consumption		3			4		1	2	2				1	1
Land use	Change of land use		4		1		1	1						1	
Noise	Noise emission		5	3	3	5	4	4	2	2	5	5	4	4	3
Visual impacts	Visual annoyance	1	4	3	3	5	4	4	2	2	5	5	2	2	3
Flora and fauna	Vegetation disturbance/growth	1	4		1	4		1	2	3	1			1	2
	Animals and avian mortality		2	1		2			1	1		3		2	
	Wildlife harassment and habitats damage	1	3	1	1	4		1	3	3	1	3		1	
	Animals and birds emigration											2			
Energy	Electrical energy consumption/generation		3		1	3						5		1	1

Noise Impact of Wind Parks in S. Euboea

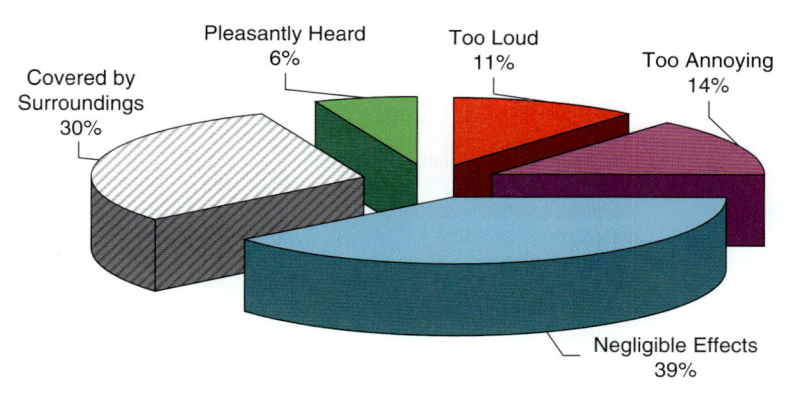

- Pleasantly Heard 6%
- Too Loud 11%
- Too Annoying 14%
- Covered by Surroundings 30%
- Negligible Effects 39%

Figure 10 Social evaluation of noise impact of wind parks in a selected Greek region where more than 120 MW of wind power are operating [12].

Visual Acceptance of Wind Parks in S. Euboea

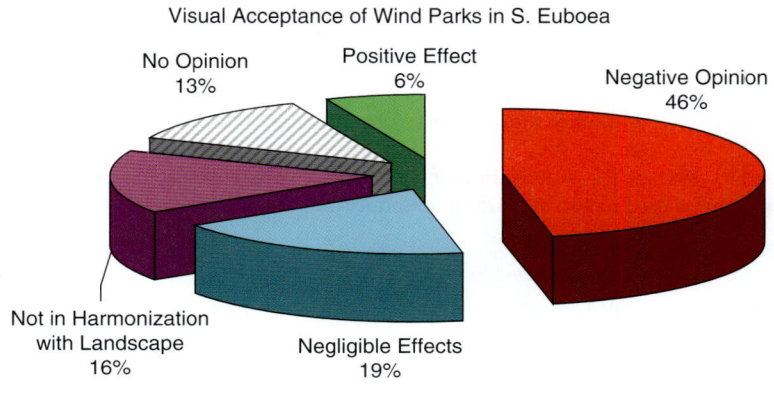

- No Opinion 13%
- Positive Effect 6%
- Negative Opinion 46%
- Not in Harmonization with Landscape 16%
- Negligible Effects 19%

Figure 11 Social evaluation of visual impact of wind parks in a selected Greek region where more than 120 MW of wind power are operating [12].

- Mechanical noise is caused by rotating machinery such as the gearbox, electrical generator, and bearings (tonal sound). Normal wear and tear, poor component designs, or lack of preventative maintenance may all affect the amount of mechanical noise produced.
- Aerodynamic noise is caused by the interaction of the turbine blades with the wind flow field. Such a noise tends to increase significantly with the speed of the rotor as already mentioned. For blade noise, lower blade tip speed results in lower noise levels, for example, 'night operation'. Of particular concern is the interaction of wind turbine blades with atmospheric turbulence.

Modern wind turbines produce little or no noise at all in comparison to their predecessors and to their rated power. This is due to the fact that wind manufacturers realized quickly that the noise problem should be dealt with and started producing quieter machines after serious research efforts. As a result, the noise from the gearbox and the blades has been reduced by careful attention to the design and manufacture of the components and also the generator noise has been minimized with good sound insulation within the turbine's head (nacelle).

Efforts have also been made for the reduction of the aerodynamic noise by:

- Decreasing rotational speed at the tip.
- Using pitch control of upwind turbines in order to permit the rotation of the blades along their long axis, thus remarkably controlling the wind flow field around the airfoils.

At any given location the noise varies considerably depending on the layout of the wind farm, the particular model of the turbines installed, the topography or shape of the land, the speed and the direction of the wind, and the background noise. Wind turbine noise is characterized as very directional.

The unit used to describe the intensity of sound is the decibel (dB). Audible sounds range from 0 dB (threshold of hearing) to about 140 dB (threshold of pain). The normal audible frequency range is approximately 20 Hz–20 kHz. The A-weighted scale, denoted as dB(A), approximates the range of human hearing by filtering out lower frequency noises, which are not as damaging as the higher frequencies. It is used in most noise ordinances and standards.

Table 8 Sound levels of different sources/activities [9, 14]

Source/activity	Noise level dB(A)
Threshold of hearing	0
Whisper	30
Rural nighttime background	20–40
Quiet bedroom	35
Unoccupied air-conditioned office	45–50
Car at 65 km h^{-1} at 100 m	55
Busy general office	60
Conversation	60
Truck at 50 km h^{-1} at 100 m	65
City traffic	90
Pneumatic drill at 7 m	95
Jet aircraft at 250 m	105
Threshold of pain	140

To provide a frame of reference, rustling leaves have a decibel level of 10 dB(A); suburban expressway at 90 m, 60 dB(A); large truck pass-by at 15 m, 90 dB(A); and aircraft takeoff, 120 dB(A). Sound levels from various human activities is given in **Table 8**.

Rationally, wind farms are always located where the wind speed is higher than average, and the background noise of the wind tends to cover any sounds that might be produced by operating wind turbines. Background sound levels depend greatly on the location and presence of roads, trees, and other sound sources. Typical background sound levels range from 35 dB(A) (quiet) to 50 dB(A) (urban setting).

Equation [2] can be used to calculate the contribution of the turbine to the overall sound level at a distance 'R' from the noise emission source and eqn [3] can be used to add the turbine sound level to the background sound level to obtain the overall sound level [15].

$$\text{Turbine sound level} = L_{\text{AWEA}} + 10 \log\left(4\pi 60^2\right) - 10 \log\left(4\pi R^2\right) \quad [2]$$

where L_{AWEA} is the rated sound level in dB(A) at 60 m from the wind turbine and R is the observer distance from the turbine rotor center (m).

$$\text{Overall sound level} = 10 \log\left(10^{\frac{\text{turbine level}}{10}} + 10^{\frac{\text{background level}}{10}}\right) \quad [3]$$

Figure 12 shows noise measurements taken at various distances from the wind turbine for various magnitudes of the background noise, included in the figure. As expected, the background noise becomes prevalent as the distance increases, while the turbine noise is discrete only in distances close to the turbine [15].

Noise impacts can also result from project construction and maintenance. These are generally of relatively short duration and occurrence, but can include equipment operation, blasting, and noise associated with traffic into and out of the facility.

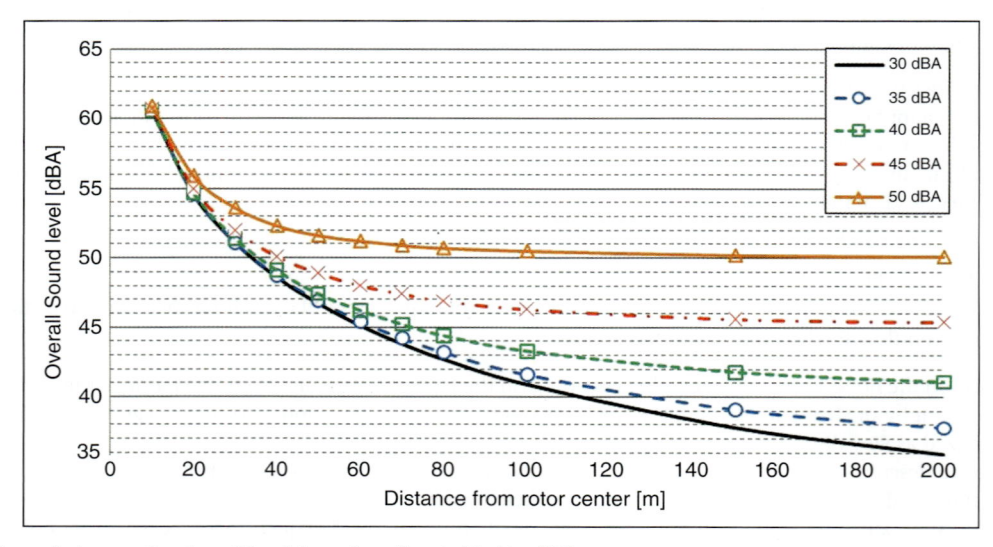

Figure 12 Noise emission as a function of the distance from the wind turbine [15].

Mechanical noise can be minimized at the design stage (e.g., side toothed gear wheels), or by acoustic insulation on the inside of the turbine housing. Mechanical noise can also be reduced during operation by acoustic insulation curtains and anti-vibration support footings. On the other hand, aerodynamic noise can be reduced by careful design of the blades by the manufacturers who can minimize this type of noise by better understanding the flow field pattern around the rotor of the machine.

Wind direction has the tendency to increase noise level relative to the turbine and the receiving point. The highest noise level can be found at the bottom of the wind turbine situated with the wind direction from the plant toward the receiving point. Noise of greatest concern can be generally classified as being of one of these three types:

- Broadband
- Tonal
- Low frequency.

Broadband, tonal, and low-frequency noise have all been examined to some degree in modern upwind horizontal axis wind turbines and turbine technologies continue to improve in this direction. With regard to the design of a wind energy project, one is generally interested in assessing whether the additional noise generated by the wind turbines (relative to the ambient noise) might cause annoyance or a hazard to human health and well-being. Further complicating factors originate from the effects of multiple wind turbines together and the way the noise increases and decreases as the blades rotate – the blade 'swish'.

Wind energy developers are required to meet local standards for acceptable sound levels; for example, in Germany, this level is 35 dB(A) for rural nighttime environments. Generally, noise levels are only computed at medium wind speeds (7–8 m s^{-1}), because at higher speeds, noise produced by turbines can be (but is not always) masked by ambient noise.

Noise emission measurements potentially are subject to serious problems to be overcome. In addition, methods for assessing noise levels produced by wind turbines located in various terrains, such as mountainous regions, need further development.

Figure 13 shows a qualitative comparison of wind turbine and background noise as a function of the wind speed at 10 m height.

Furthermore, there are a limited number of published wind turbines' noise emission measurements, thus deteriorating the opportunity of better investigating the real noise impact of the surroundings. In this context, real-world noise measurements have significant value; for example, in a study by Kaldellis *et al.* [14] measurements have been made and the results are compared with the theoretical (based on analytical methods) ones. As can be shown from **Figure 14**, the experimental results are less than 50 dB(A), while the background noise in this specific area is almost 10 dB(A) lower than the noise emitted when the wind turbines operate. Besides, the experimental measurements are fairly well harmonized with the theoretical ones (see also **Figure 15**).

Different types of wind turbines have different noise characteristics. As mentioned earlier, modern upwind turbines are less noisy than downwind turbines. Variable-speed turbines (where rotor speeds are lower at low wind speeds) create less noise at lower wind speeds when ambient noise is also low compared to constant-speed turbines. Direct-drive machines, which have no gearbox or high-speed mechanical components, are normally quieter. Various measures to reduce noise have been implemented in the design of modern turbines. As wind turbines have become more efficient, more of the wind is converted into rotational torque and less into acoustic noise.

In the design and the planning stage of a wind farm, semi-empirical prediction models and software tools are used to predict noise emissions. Today, noise impact prediction is supported by the use of appropriate software. The performance of a background noise survey around the site will help identify the dwellings that are most sensitive with respect to noise and the wind speed at which the greatest noise impact from the development will occur. Special attention should be paid in analyzing the noise propagation pattern for all the basic wind directions, taking also into consideration the corresponding downwind geomorphology and topography. Appropriate analytical methods can support the relevant surveys and advise on all stages of the process. Acceptability standards for noise vary by nation, state, and locality. They can also vary depending on time of day, since nighttime standards are generally stricter.

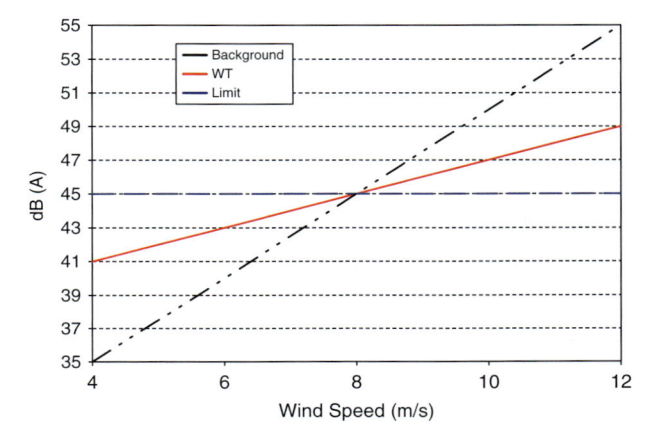

Figure 13 Qualitative comparison of wind turbine noise and background noise as a function of wind speed at 10 m height [16].

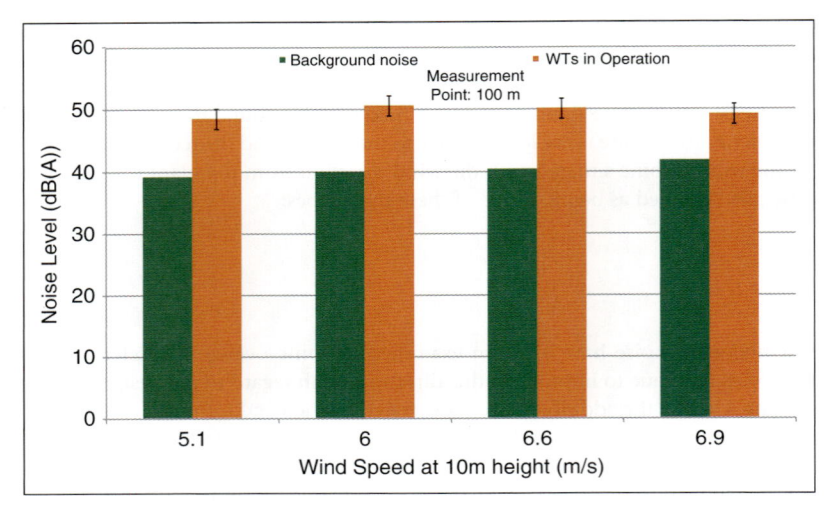

Figure 14 Noise level measurements for different wind speed values [14].

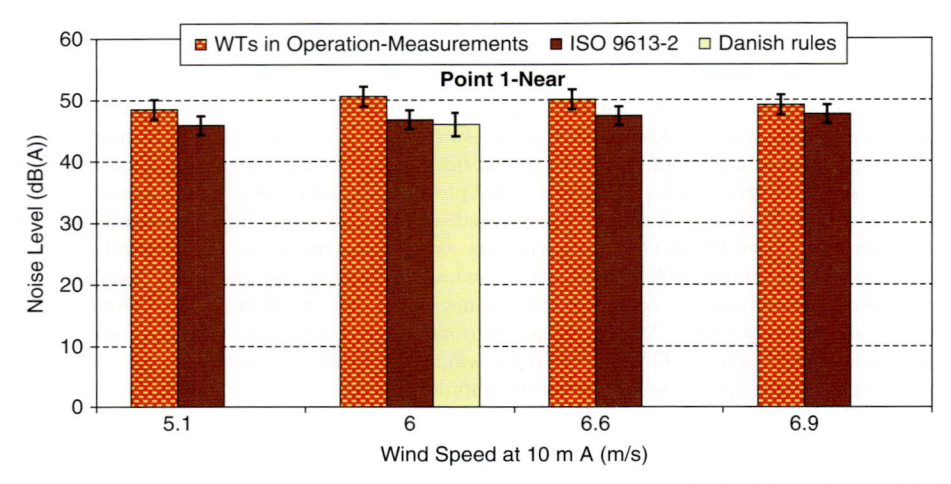

Figure 15 Experimental measurements in comparison with the calculations using ISO-9613-2 and Danish Rules 2007 model [14].

2.16.6.2 Research and Development Relevant to Wind Turbine Noise

Acoustics researchers are investigating the causes of wind turbine noise with the aim of making them quieter. Computer models are developed to predict the noise output from wind farms so that the effectiveness of potential noise-reducing designs and control methods to be accurately and quickly assessed.

In fact, the noise generated from wind turbines is the same sort of noise generated at the edge of aircraft wings and is caused as the turbulent air flows over the sharp edge of the blade. However, it is not known how the flow turbulence and the blade edge, or boundary layer, interact and how that makes the noise louder. When this fundamental mechanism is understood, then ways of controlling and reducing the noise can be looked at, through perhaps changing the shape of the rotor blades (without reducing the machine efficiency) or using active control devices at the blade edges to disrupt the pattern of turbulence [16].

2.16.7 Wind Turbines' Visual Impact and Aesthetics

2.16.7.1 General Considerations on Visual Impact and Aesthetics

Windmills have been in operation during the last 1000 years all over Europe. However, recently, due to the significant number and size of wind turbines installed, the matter of landscape aesthetics has been revived. Actually, wind turbines have been subject to severe criticism because they are 'a new element' and because they are located in highly visible places (e.g., mountains) in order to exploit wind conditions.

In this context, visual impacts are often among the major objections to the development of wind power systems, and a question that should not be ignored when trying to identify their location. It is obvious that the reaction to the sight of a wind farm is highly

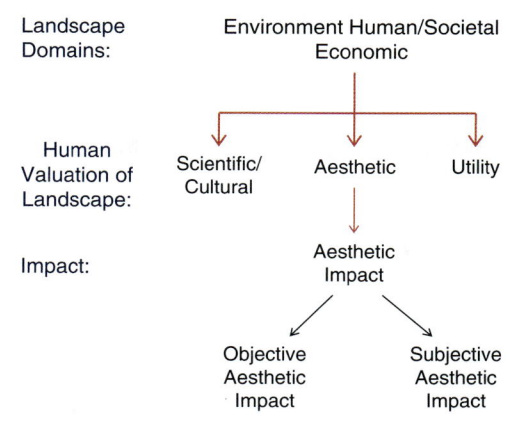

Figure 16 Landscape and aesthetic impact: the three landscape domains.

subjective. Many people believe that they are a welcome symbol of clean energy, whereas others find them disturbing additions to the landscape. Thus, although a wind plant is clearly a man-made structure, what it represents may be seen either as a positive or negative addition to the landscape. More precisely, landscape perceptions and visual impacts are key environmental issues in determining wind farm applications, as landscape and visual impacts are, by nature, subjective and changing over time and location.

The broad term 'visual impact' includes two distinct facets: the landscape impact and the aesthetic impact. The landscape components can be measured more easily as they are related to physical properties. The aesthetic/human appraisal is much more complex since it depends on subjective landscape perception. **Figure 16** shows the major landscape domains.

As far as the landscape components are concerned, in general, the visibility of a particular wind energy system will depend on many factors, including tower height, proximity to neighbors and roadways, local terrain and tree coverage, color or contrast, size, shadow flickering, the time when the turbine is moving or is stationary, the local turbine history, public acceptance, and knowledge of renewable energy technologies. Whatever the surrounding environment is, the developer should try to reduce the visual impact as much as possible.

Table 9 is a synthesis of the various factors affecting seriously the visual impacts of a wind park.

There is no doubt that the visual impacts decrease with the distance. The affected areas are called zones and may be defined as indicated in **Table 10**.

There are various methods for assessing the aesthetic impacts and many research works have been carried out either for the development of a specific methodology or for the analysis of a specific case study [17–23].

The so-called 'Spanish method' attempts to quantify the visual impact of a wind park [17]. It is supported by advanced information technology (IT) tools. More specifically, a 3D analysis of the wind farm and its surrounding area is carried out to

Table 9 Various factors affecting the visual impacts of a wind park

Number of turbines	Local terrain and tree coverage
Size of the turbines	Shadow flickering
Tower height	Time that the turbine is stationery or moving
Color and contrast of the turbines	Access and site tracks
Form and appearance of the turbines	Substation buildings
Surface elevation and topography	Grid connection
Type of landscape	Anemometer masts
Proximity to neighbors and roadways	Transmission lines

Table 10 Definition of zones according to the distance from the wind turbines [9]

Zone	Distance (depending on visibility and weather conditions)	Characteristics – visibility
I	Up to 2 km	Visually dominate
II	1–4.5 km	Visually intrusive
III	2–8 km (in good weather conditions)	Noticeable, turbines clearly visible but not intrusive. Turbines appear small in overall view.
IV	Over 7 km	Element within distant landscape. The apparent size of the turbines is very small, as any other element in the landscape.

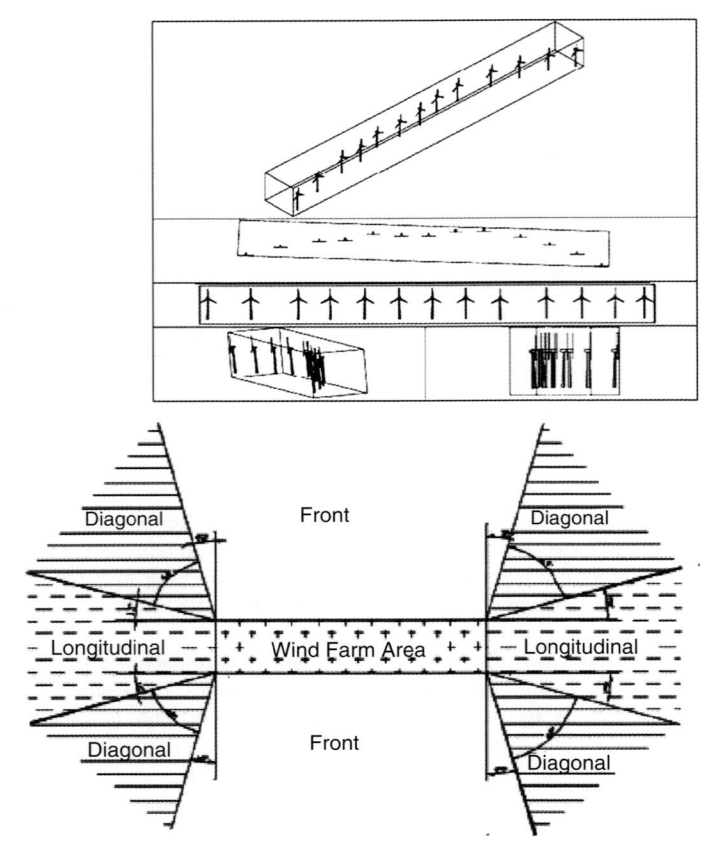

Figure 17 Points of view of a wind park [17].

obtain simulated images describing regions that are potentially affected. Subsequently, a visual impact evaluation matrix applied over the neighboring villages is obtained. The method uses geographical information systems (GIS) and computer-aided design (CAD) systems. **Figure 17** shows various views of a typical wind farm as elaborated for the method [17].

The basic objective of the method is to develop quantitative indexes for the rational evaluation of the visual impacts of a wind park. The method has been applied by Tsoutsos et al. [18] for the visual assessment of a wind park in the Greek island of Crete. The basic steps that have been followed include the recording of the main parameters that affect the visibility of the wind turbines. Also, the visibility of some points of interest around the wind park is investigated. Accordingly, the calculation of properly defined coefficients to be used in the impact estimation is made, and finally, the total evaluation of the installation visual impact is performed.

The process of recording the necessary coefficients for a typical medium-sized wind park located between two remote villages is shown in **Figure 18**.

In Torres et al. [19], the aesthetics aspects in the integration of wind farms into the landscape are emphasized, by using photographs and interviews to develop an objective indicator. The indicator combines measures of visibility, color, fractality, and continuity that can be taken from photographs. Value functions are constructed for each variable and incorporated into the indicator. This indicator has been used to calculate the objective aesthetic impact of five wind farms. Comparison of the indicator results with a population survey shows that the indicator correctly represents the order of impact as perceived by the population sample, and is thus an appropriate objective measure of aesthetic impact of wind farms.

In Ladenburg [20], the focus of the assessment is placed on the observer's prior experience with a technology and public surveys to develop the proposed analysis are used. The importance of parameters such as distance, contrast, and motion in the visual impact assessment with the use of photographs, computer simulations, and interviews is mentioned by Bishop and Miller [21]. According to the results of this work, the visual impacts are reduced as the distance increases from the wind park. These methodologies are useful for the assessment of the visual impact of a single technology (e.g., wind farms) on the local scale (a single project).

Subsequently, in the work of Molina-Ruiz et al. [22] the use of IT tools is examined (Geographical Information Systems and Multi-Criteria Decision Analysis) to facilitate the visual impact evaluation. Accordingly, Rodrigues et al. [23] suggested a method for the global assessment of the visual impact on the landscape of renewable energy. A number of quantitative indexes for the visual impact (objective) and the visual perspective (subjective) estimations are introduced. For the visual impact index estimation, a process for determining whether a location is visually affected by a wind park or not is presented (**Figure 19**).

Figure 18 Process of recording the Spanish method coefficients [18].

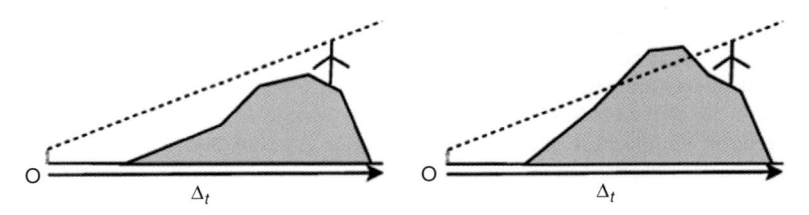

Figure 19 Procedure to establish whether an observation pixel is visually affected [23].

The visual perception index that is introduced relates the visual nuisance with the number of the wind turbines and the distance from the observer (**Figure 20**) [23]. The estimations of the work indicate that for a level of wind energy penetration of 16% of the total electricity generated in 2007, in Spain, 1.7% of the country's territory would be occupied by renewable facilities, but these would be visible from 17% of the territory, and during more than 15% of road-travel time. The proposed methodology for the estimation of the visual impact allows for quantitative comparisons among several scenarios of energy generation with renewable technologies. This is particularly useful when working at regional scales, where impact assessment is more difficult and the proposed indexes can provide an objective and concise basis for comparison. A further strength of the methodology is its reliance on standards, and largely published (public) data as model inputs. With additional work, further refinements can be incorporated into the proposed methodology. For instance, color contrast between the facility and the background can be taken into account; and human subjectivity can be considered by relating the numerical values of the visual perception index to acceptability, with the aid of specifically developed questionnaires to determine the final level of visual impact [12, 24].

It is important to mention at this point that professional designers have been employed by several wind turbine manufacturers to enhance the appearance of their machines. Finally, if turbines remain out of order for a remarkable time period, the public may

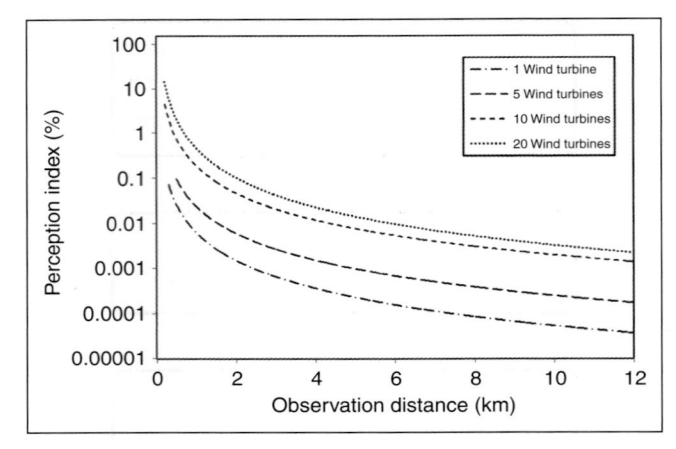

Figure 20 Reference values for the perception index as a function of the number of wind turbines and the observer distance [23].

perceive a wind farm to be unjustified – a waste of visual resources. Thus, when turbines do not operate or are perceived as often broken, the public is far less likely to tolerate the turbines' intrusion on the landscape.

2.16.7.2 Shadow Flickering

Shadow flicker occurs when – at precise latitude, wind direction and height of the sun – rotating wind turbine blades cast shadows upon stationary objects. Shadow flicker only appears under very specific conditions and does not occur simply because the sun is shining and the blades are in motion.

This phenomenon will cause disturbance for residents living in the surrounding area of the turbine. Actually, this moving shadow, at a frequency of three times the rotor speeds (where the turbine has three blades), can lead to a pulsating light level especially in rooms that are naturally lit. For shadow flicker to occur at all, the windows of the nearby residence have to directly face the wind turbine (such rooms with windows are referred to as 'receptors') with no obstructions (trees, hills, other structures) in sight.

If there is no sun, there is no shadow flicker. Reduced visibility situations like haze, fog, and clouds vastly reduce the chance of anyone experiencing shadow flicker.

In addition, the reflection of the sun's ray shining on the turbine is caused by the periodic flashes of light. In most cases, these localized effects may be easily predicted and avoided by careful turbine-siting and appropriate surface finish of the blades as well as by coating the turbine with a material having less reflective properties. Table 11 shows the intensity of the shadow flickering with its occurrence condition.

However, the effect can be precisely calculated to determine whether a flickering shadow will fall on a given location near a wind farm and how many hours in a year it will do so. Potential problems can be easily identified using existing analytical methods, and solutions range from the appropriate setback of the turbines to planting trees disrupt the effect.

The problem of shadows caused by wind turbines is not a serious issue because the turbines are relatively small and therefore do not result in long shadows. More specifically, this is a problem only when turbines are sited very close to workplaces or dwellings and occurs during periods of direct sunlight. These effects may be easily predicted and avoided by carefully considering the machine-site and the surface finish of the blades. A common guideline used in northern Europe is a minimum distance of six to eight rotor diameters between the wind turbine and the closest neighbor. A house, 300 m from a contemporary 600 kW machine with a rotor diameter of 40 m, will be exposed to moving shadows approximately 17–18 h (out of 8760 h) annually.

2.16.8 Impacts in Fauna and Flora and Microclimate

2.16.8.1 Impacts in Flora and Fauna

Wind is the energy source that is considered friendly and most compatible with animals and human beings. Wind energy's ability to generate electricity without many of the environmental impacts associated with other energy sources (air pollution, water pollution, greenhouse gas emissions associated with global climate change) can significantly benefit birds and many other plant and animal species.

Table 11 Intensity of shadow flickering with its occurrence condition [4]

Intensity of shadow flickering	Condition
Higher shadow flickering intensity	Sunrise or sunset where the cast shadows are sufficiently long
	Wind turbine rotor plane is perpendicular to the sun receptor (rotor diameter)
	Larger wind turbine
	Smaller distance with resident
Lower shadow flickering intensity	Wind turbine rotor plane is in plane with the sun (blade thickness)

However, the threat of wind turbines for animals, especially birds, and some occurrences of bird collision with them has been one of the main issues for people reacting against wind turbines. Bird and bat deaths are one of the most controversial biological issues related to wind turbines. The deaths of birds and bats in wind farm sites have raised concerns by wildlife agencies and conservation groups. On the other hand, several large wind energy facilities have operated for years with only minor impacts on these animals.

To try to address this issue, the wind energy industry and government agencies have sponsored research into collisions, relevant bird and bat behavior, mitigation measures, and appropriate study design protocols. In addition, project developers are required to collect data through monitoring efforts at existing and proposed wind energy sites. Careful site selection is needed to minimize fatalities, and in some cases, additional research may be needed to address bird and bat impact issues.

While structures such as smokestacks, lighthouses, tall buildings, radio, and television towers have also been associated with animal kills, their mortality is a serious concern for the wind energy industry.

On the other hand, wind turbines *per se* are responsible only for a small portion of the total number of bird causalities caused by human builds. It is believed that the variable-speed turbine is a more serious threat as there is a correlation between the speed of rotation and the number of birds killed. Birds have much more time to evade the blades of a fixed speed turbine [25].

The wildlife impacts can be categorized into direct and indirect impacts. The direct impact is the mortality from collisions with a wind energy plant, while the indirect impacts are the area avoidance, habitat disruption, and displacement. The potential disturbance to fauna caused by wind turbines, a factor of moderate importance, relates to incidents where birds collide with rotor blades. However, the populations of many bird species are experiencing long-term declines, due not only to the effects of energy use but also to many other human activities. Especially in highways, birds and bats sometimes die as a result of collisions with vehicles.

On the other hand, the number of birds killed by wind turbines can be negligible compared to other human activities [26]. It was found that out of the total number of birds killed in a year, only 20 deaths were due to wind turbines (for an installed capacity of 1000 MW), while 1500 deaths were caused by hunters and 2000 caused by collisions with vehicles and electricity transmission lines. The American Wind Energy Association (AWEA) calculates that if wind energy were used to generate 100% of US electricity needs, it would only cause one bird death for every 250 human-related bird deaths with reference to the current rate of bird kills as described in Table 12.

In some cases, some species under extinction are in threat in the areas that wind farms are planned and this is an issue that causes serious reactions of nongovernmental environmental organizations and the public.

Mitigation measures to minimize impacts may vary by site and species, but some common findings and suggestions are shown in Table 13 [25–27].

2.16.8.2 Impacts on the Microclimate

Wind farms affect the microclimate of the area where they are installed. According to researchers at the United States Department of Energy's Ames Laboratory and the University of Colorado at Boulder, wind turbines not only generate electricity but may also prove to be advantageous to crops. Results of a new study show that wind turbines produce measurable effects on the microclimate near crops. Wind turbine turbulence, in particular, has a positive impact on the crops below through the increased airflow it produces. Wind turbines might reduce temperature extremes and lengthen growing seasons. Also, other benefits of wind turbines could result from their effects on crop moisture levels. Extra turbulence may help dry the dew that settles on plants beginning in late afternoon, minimizing the amount of time fungi and toxins can grow on plant leaves. Additionally, drier crops at harvest help farmers reduce the cost of artificially drying corn or soybeans [28].

In fact, wind turbines have an impact on the temperatures near the ground that affect crop growth. Wind turbine turbulence both warms and cools the nearby ground, depending upon the time of day, with temperature change varying between 0.4 and 1.5 °C.

Table 12 Leading human-related causes of bird kills in the United States

Human-related causes	Number of birds kill per year (million)
Cats	100
Buildings – windows	550
Hunters	100
Vehicles	60–80
Communication towers	10–40
Pesticides	67
Power lines	130
Wind turbines	0.15

Based on data from Saidur *et al.* [4] and Torres *et al.* [9].

Table 13 Mitigation measures for wildlife protection from wind turbines

Important zones of conservation and sensitivity areas should be avoided
Sensitive habitats have to be protected by implementing appropriate working practices
Adequate design of wind farms: siting turbines close together and grouping them to avoid alignment perpendicular to the main flight paths
Provide corridors between clusters of wind turbines when necessary
Underground transmission cables installation, especially in sensitive areas, where possible
Increase the visibility of rotor blades: make overhead cables more visible using deflectors and avoiding use in areas of high bird concentrations, especially of species vulnerable to collision
Relocation of conflictive turbines
Presence of biologist or ecologist during construction in sensitive locations
Stop operation during peak migration periods
Rotor speed reduction in critical periods

Extra air turbulence likely speeds up the heat exchange between crops and the atmosphere, so crops stay slightly cooler during hot days. During evenings, turbulence stirs the lower atmosphere and keeps temperatures around the crops warmer during the night. Therefore, turbines' effects are anticipated to be good in the spring and fall because they would keep the crop a little warmer and help prevent a frost and practically extend the growing season. These early findings need to establish whether wind turbines are in fact beneficial to the health and yield potential of soybean and corn. Still, the researchers believe that this is a realistic possibility.

In one of the first research works to investigate that question, scientists have modeled the impact of a hypothetical large-scale wind farm. Their conclusion, reported in the *Journal of Geophysical Research* [28], is that thousands of turbines concentrated in one area can affect local weather. The impact comes not so much from the turbines' rotor blades slowing down the air but from atmospheric mixing that occurs in the blades' wake. This creates warmer, drier conditions at the surface. The great impact upon local meteorology is caused by the turbulence generated by the rotor.

2.16.9 Other Environmental Impacts

2.16.9.1 Interference of a Wind Turbine with Electromagnetic Communication Systems

Wind turbines in some areas can reflect electromagnetic waves (mainly due to the moving blades), which will be scattered and diffracted. This means that wind turbines can potentially disrupt electromagnetic signals used in telecommunications, navigation, and radar services. The degree and the nature of the interference will depend on the following:

- The location of the wind turbine between transmitter and receiver
- Characteristics of the rotor blades, and characteristics of receiver
- Signal frequency
- The radio wave propagation in the local atmosphere.

Interference can be produced by three elements of a wind turbine: the tower, the rotating blades, and the generator. The tower and blades may obstruct, reflect, or refract the electromagnetic waves. However, modern blades are made of synthetic materials having minimal impact on the transmission of electromagnetic radiation. The electrical system is not usually a problem for telecommunications because interference may be eliminated with proper nacelle insulation and good maintenance. Interference on TV signals can be minimized with the substitution of metal blades with synthetic materials. However, when turbines are installed very close to dwellings, interference has been proven difficult to rule out. It is believed that all these effects can be prevented or corrected by adequate design and location selection using simple technical measures such as the installation of additional transmission masts.

2.16.9.2 Traffic – Transportation and Access

Increased traffic would mainly occur over the construction period of the wind farm. Once operational, the wind farm will have a small number of visits, only for maintenance purposes, and thus minor need for transportation.

2.16.9.3 Archaeology and Cultural Heritage

In the context of an EIA, an archaeological assessment needs also to be carried out. The objectives of this assessment are to gain information about the known or potential archaeological resource within the given area. In general, wind turbines and all associated infrastructure are located in such a way that any archaeological disturbance is minimized or avoided.

2.16.9.4 Health and Safety

Unlike most other generation technologies, wind turbines do not use combustion to generate electricity, and hence do not produce air emissions. The only potentially toxic or hazardous materials are relatively small amounts of lubricating oils and hydraulic and insulating fluids. Therefore, contamination of surface or ground water or soils is highly unlikely. The primary health and safety considerations are related to blade movement and the presence of industrial equipment in areas potentially accessible to the public.

2.16.10 Offshore Environmental Impacts

Offshore wind power gains an increasing contribution as a power source and has very good prospects for the coming years. A detailed description of the offshore wind power plants is provided in the corresponding Chapter 2.17.

The environmental impacts of offshore wind power are similar – at least as far as their categories are concerned – to the already analyzed impacts caused by onshore wind parks. In general, there is no clear indication whether offshore plants are more beneficial, as far as their environmental impacts are concerned, compared to onshore plants. The seascape and marine environment are very different and very special and certainly the inland and the sea environment cannot easily compare to each other.

However the construction and the operation of offshore wind farms have additional environmental impacts that should be described separately. Therefore, the objective of the current section is to provide a short presentation of the environmental benefits and impacts of offshore wind power plants, taking into account that still necessary knowledge improvements need to be acquired in many offshore issues including that of environmental impacts.

European Directives, such as the Strategic Environmental Assessment (SEA), Birds and Habitats Directive require that countries undertake responsibility for assessing the major impacts of offshore plants on the environment. In fact, a set of procedures have been applied for the reliable identification of impacts, including boat-based and aerial surveys and a wide variety of tools such as radars, cameras, and measurement instruments [29].

Research on these issues is carried out mainly in countries that have developed serious offshore wind projects, such as the United Kingdom and Denmark. For example, UK Collaborative Offshore Windfarm Research Into the Environment (COWRIE) is a registered charity set up to advance and improve understanding and knowledge of the potential environmental impacts of offshore wind farm development in UK waters and develops a series of reports dedicated to specific environmental impacts of offshore wind power [29].

The environmental benefits of offshore wind power plants compared to conventional energy sources are the same with onshore wind power plants and more specifically:

- the reduction of carbon dioxide emissions
- the reduction of air pollutants emitted from thermal power stations
- the reduction of the fossil fuels (oil, natural gas, coal) consumption
- the reduction of water consumption.

The identification of offshore environmental benefits compared to the onshore wind power plants is an interesting issue that needs detailed analysis. However, the minimum use of land, the avoided noise, and visual impacts are some of the main driving forces for the development of offshore wind power plants. Nevertheless, from an ecological point of view, the seawater near the coastline has a high ecological value and important habitats for breeding, resting, and migratory seabirds; therefore, special attention should be paid in this direction.

Offshore wind power projects are more complex than onshore ones. In the construction period, offshore developments include the installation of platforms, turbines, cables, substations, grids, interconnection and shipping, dredging, and the associated building works. The operation and maintenance activities include the transport of employees by special vessels and helicopters and occasional hardware retrofits.

The environmental parameters that should be considered for an offshore EIA in the construction and operation phases are presented in **Table 14**.

Up to now, most of the experience gained in the environmental impacts assessment of offshore wind energy available in the open literature comes from several years of monitoring three wind farms in Denmark. Valuable analysis has also been carried out by the Federal Environment Ministry (BMU) of Germany through technical, environmental, and nature conservation research about offshore wind energy foundations.

Furthermore, it is worthwhile mentioning that wind farms may differ significantly in various characteristics, such as construction materials, support structures, distance from the coastline, and layout. All these factors affect significantly their environmental impacts and should be taken into account in detail and distinctively (see, e.g., Reference 30).

2.16.10.1 Offshore Noise Impact

One of the main concerns for onshore wind parks is the noise. Since offshore wind parks are quite far away from human populations, people are not affected by the noise generated by offshore wind turbines and this impact, as far as people are concerned, is eliminated.

Table 14 Main environmental impacts of offshore wind power plants

Noise	Artificial reefs
Visual impacts – aesthetics	Electromagnetic radiation
Impacts on marine mammals	Impacts on the microclimate
Impacts on birds	Water turbidity
Impacts on fish	

However, the noise generated from the wind turbines operation travels underwater and marine animals could be affected. Any effects of the noise will depend on the acoustic sensitivity of the species and their ability to adjust to it. For example, underwater noise can be a serious problem for some marine animals, particularly whales, dolphins, and seals.

The acoustic noise emission from offshore wind turbines as well as its propagation is affected by various parameters, including

- Wind turbine parameters: rated power, rotor diameter
- Type of foundation, material, pile depth
- Effective pile-driving and/or vibration energy
- Period of construction phase and blow or vibrator frequency
- Depth of water at the site.

2.16.10.2 Construction and Decommissioning Noise

Construction and decommissioning noise comes from machines and vessels, pile-driving, explosions, and installation of wind turbines. Indicatively, measurements carried out during construction of a wind farm in the United Kingdom indicated the following [31]:

- The peak noise of pile hammering at 5 m depth was 260 dB and at 10 m depth was 262 dB
- There were no preferential directions for propagation of noise
- The behavior of marine mammals and fish could be influenced several kilometers away from the turbine.

Table 15 shows the expected avoidance reaction of marine species due to pile-driving during the construction of a wind farm [9].

2.16.10.3 Operational Noise

In the operational phase, the sound generated in the gearbox and the generator is transmitted by the tower wall, resulting in sound propagation underwater. Measurements of the noise emitted into the air from wind turbines and transformers have shown a negligible contribution to the underwater noise level. The underwater noise from wind turbines is not higher than the ambient noise level in the frequency range above approximately 1 kHz, but it is higher below approximately 1 kHz. The noise may have an impact on the benthic fauna, fish, and marine mammals in the vicinity of wind turbine foundations.

Operational noise from single turbines of maximum rated power of 1.5 MW in a distance of 110 m at high wind speeds of 12 m s^{-1} has been measured and the one-third octave sound pressure level has been found between 90 and 115 dB [31].

The anthropogenic noise may produce both behavioral and physiological impacts on sea life. Impacts on behavior include the following:

- Attraction to or avoidance of the area
- Panic
- Increases in the intensity of vocal communication.

Table 15 Calculated ranges for avoidance distance for different marine species [9]

Species	Distance (m)	Species	Distance (m)
Salmon	1400	Bottlenose dolphin	4600
Cod	5500	Harbour porpoise	1400
Dab	100	Harbour seal	2000

Reports about noise impact on fish have shown a range of effects, from avoidance behavior to physiological impacts. Changes in behavior could make fish vacate feeding and spawning areas and migration routes. Studies of noise impact on invertebrates and planktonic organisms have a general consensus of very few effects, unless the organisms are very close to the powerful noise source.

Special vessels are involved in the construction of wind parks and also during the operational phase for maintenance of wind turbines and platforms. The noise from vessels depends on their size and speed, although there are variations between similar classes. Vessels of medium size range produce sounds with a frequency mainly between 20 Hz and 10 kHz and levels between 130 and 160 dB at 1 m [31].

Measurements from one 1500 kW wind turbine carried out by the German Federal Ministry of the Environment indicated that operational noise emissions do not damage the hearing systems of marine sea life. Concerning behavior, the same study stated that it is not clear whether noise from turbines has an influence on marine animals [32].

2.16.10.4 Visual Impacts

Experience with onshore wind farm developments has demonstrated that landscape and visual issues are the most usual reasons for public objection. If developers address this issue thoroughly in the EIA and, more importantly, if they mitigate any potential visual impacts, public concerns and any related inquiry will be answered properly and potential reactions will be stopped.

Siting the wind farms out at sea is not proving to be totally out of sight. Largely due to the size of the structures, their color, movement, and their locations being open, the examples erected to date may be clearly visible from land. As great scenic or other landscape value is attached to many parts of the coastline, careful design process is still required.

The everyday meaning of seascape is 'the coastal landscape and adjoining areas of open water, including views from land to sea, from sea to land and along the coastline', and describes 'the effect on landscape at the confluence of sea and land' [33]. Every seascape therefore has three defined components (**Figure 21**):

- An area of sea (the seaward component)
- A length of coastline (the coastline component)
- An area of land (the landward component).

Offshore wind farms involve several elements that have influence on the character of the produced visual impact [33]:

- The site and size of wind farm area
- The wind turbines: size, construction materials, and colors
- The layout and spacing of wind farms and associated structures
- Location, dimension, and form of ancillary onshore (substation, pylons, overhead lines, underground cables) and offshore structures (substation and anemometer masts)
- Navigational visibility, markings, and lights
- The transportation and maintenance vessels
- The pier, slipway, or port to be used by vessels
- Road or track access, and access requirements to the coast.

The tools usually employed to predict the potential effects of new offshore developments, just as in the corresponding onshore ones, are the zones, photomontages, and video montages [9].

Figure 21 The three basic components of the seascape [33].

The potential offshore visibility depends on topography, vegetation, and artificial structures existing on the landscapes. Research in visual assessment by Bishop and Miller [21] showed that distance and contrast affect very much the visual impacts, as well as the number of turbines, their orientation, and distribution. The parameter that has the strongest influence on the visual impact perception is the distance between the observer and the wind. However, potential changes in lighting and weather conditions may change considerably the visual effects at the same distance. The assessment of offshore developments includes the extent of visibility over the main marine, coastline, and land activities (recreational activities, coastal populations and main road, rail, and footpath) [9].

The effects of the curvature of the earth and lighting conditions are relevant in the visibility of offshore wind farms [33]. For instance, rainy and cloudy days result in less visibility. Indicative thresholds established for highly sensitive seascapes are shown in Table 16.

When planning an offshore wind farm project, judgments must be made about the ability of the seascape to accommodate an offshore wind farm(s) and sensitivity is the most appropriate criterion to assess in order to inform the impact evaluation stage.

Understanding the nature of the change comes from describing and understanding the development project. The focus should be on identifying the key aspects of the change that are likely to affect the seascape. Defining the particular features of the character of the seascape that are likely to be affected by a particular type of change requires careful analysis of the potential interactions (**Figure 22**) [33].

Cumulative effects may occur when several wind farms are built in the same area. The degree of cumulative impact is a product of the number of wind farms and the distance between them, the siting and design of the wind farms, the interrelationship between their zones and the overall character of the seascape, and finally, its sensitivity to the various parameters already described.

Finally, **Figure 22** shows the various parameters that should be taken into account when determining the visual impacts of an offshore wind power plant [33].

2.16.10.5 Impacts on Marine Mammals

The main impacts on the mammals originate from the noise, as has been described above. Mammals are very much dependent on their hearing systems, being used for several purposes: communication between individuals of the same species, orientation, and finding prey. The response of marine mammals to noise includes modification of their behavior, displacement, and impossibility to acoustically interpret the environment. The consequences of all the above may be problems of viability and increased vulnerability to diseases. The main reason is that mammals communicate via acoustic signals, or some of them have sensitive hearing which could be damaged by the loud noises associated with wind turbines. In fact, it has been observed that fewer seals and porpoises are using the area of a wind farm and this is an important effect on the viability of the population. On the other hand, however, the foundations of wind farms create new habitats colonized by algae and benthic community. This food availability may attract new species, fish and, subsequently, mammals. In general, it is very difficult to draw long-term conclusions with the current status of knowledge, and further detailed analysis and research are required [34].

2.16.10.6 Impacts on Fish

Wind farms may have positive and negative impacts on fish and, certainly, these effects would cascade up the food chain to have either positive or negative impacts on birds and marine mammals that consume them. Some of the potential effects from offshore wind energy installations may be as follows [9]:

- Noise
- Electromagnetic fields
- Introduction of new artificial habitats.

The response from fish species to the introduction of wind turbine foundations is comparable with artificial reefs. It is expected that fish abundance and species diversity will be increased around the turbine foundations as the new habitat becomes more integrated with the marine environment. However, not many data are available yet and it is expected that more clear and definitive results will be obtained in the coming years, when the colonization process becomes more mature.

Nevertheless, according to the experience already acquired, positive impacts from offshore wind energy are foreseen with the ban of fishing, especially demersal trawling that may result in more local fish. In parallel, the increase of biomass in benthos communities as a result of the construction of new foundations would support this supposition [9].

Table 16 Thresholds for seascapes [33]

Thresholds	
Less than 13 km	possible major visual effects
13–24 km	possible moderate visual effects
More than 24 km	possible minor visual effects

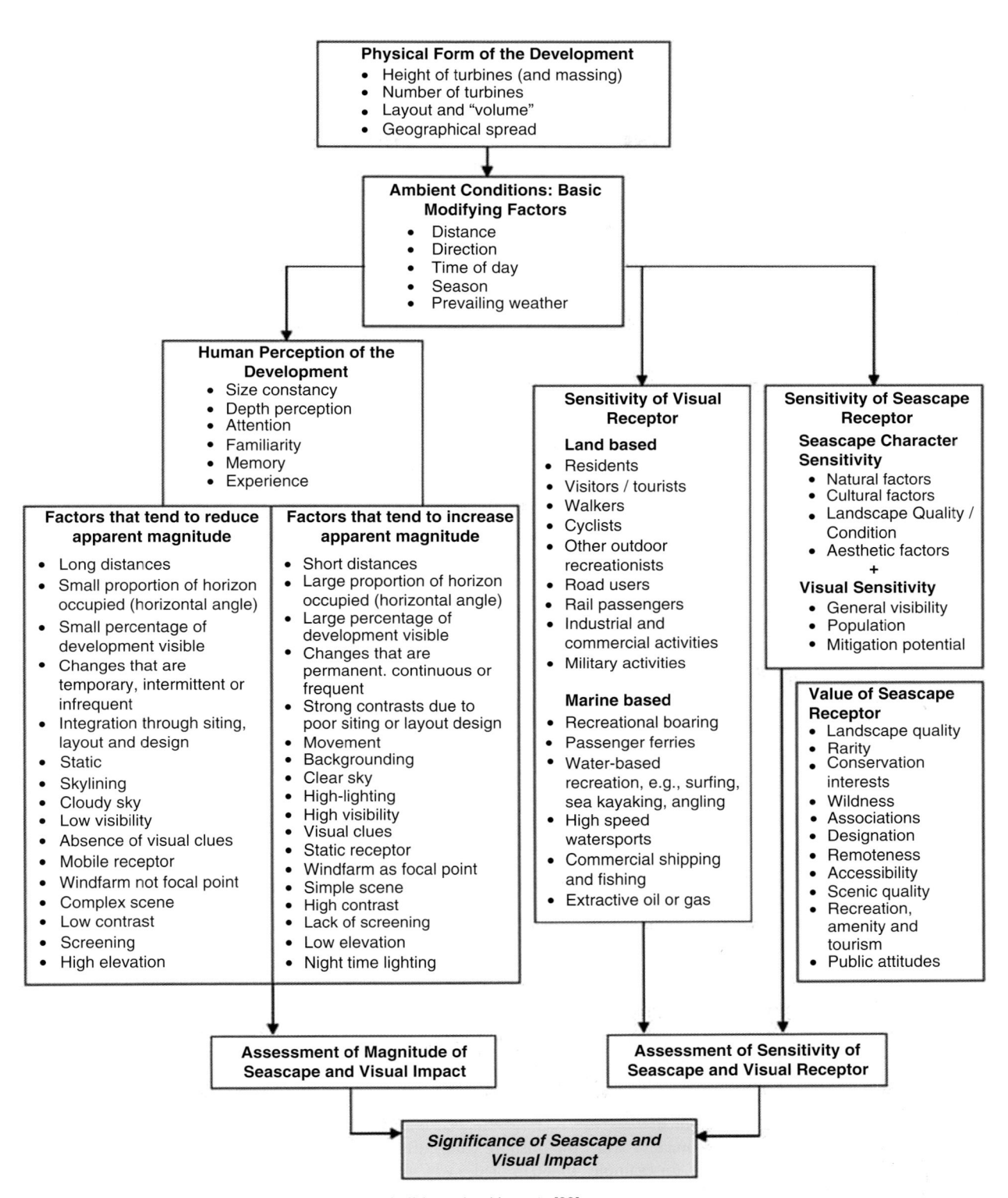

Figure 22 The various parameters for the assessment of offshore visual impacts [33].

2.16.10.7 Impacts on Birds

Birds are potentially endangered by offshore wind farms through collisions, barrier effects, and habitat loss. To evaluate these potential risks, the occurrence and the behavior of birds in space and time in general as well as their behavior at wind farms during construction and operational periods need to be determined. A detailed analysis carried out in the North Sea with regard to offshore wind farms has shown very interesting results concerning the impact of the offshore wind turbines on the bird migration. The tools that have been used to obtain the necessary measurements are a radar, thermal imaging, and visual and acoustic observations.

The identification of these impacts is considered absolutely necessary in order to make decisions on the approval of certain offshore wind power plants or to select their appropriate location. With respect to questions regarding environmental effects and impacts connected with the construction of offshore wind turbines, severe gaps in knowledge have become evident, highlighting the fields of future research and investigation [34–36], that is,

- How many migrants of which species cross the specific place under consideration at which times?
- What is the proportion of birds flying in altitudes up to 200 m (the approximate height of the projected wind turbines)?
- How are migration intensity and flight altitude influenced by weather – namely by wind, precipitation, and visibility?
- How many birds are involved in reverse migration?
- How do migrants react to anthropogenic offshore obstacles?
- Are birds attracted by the illumination of these structures?
- How many birds will collide, why and how?
- Can days of high collision risk be predicted?
- How can collisions be mitigated?
- Which impacts on populations can we expect?

Since roughly two-thirds of all bird species migrate during darkness, when the collision risk with wind turbines is expected to be higher than during daylight, special techniques for studying this 'invisible migration' have to be applied such as two ship radars, a thermal imaging camera, a video camera, and a directional microphone. To allow spatial comparisons, the data collected include also those collected from human observers on islands.

The analysis results show that large numbers of diurnal and nocturnal migrants with considerable variation of migration intensity, time, altitude, and species, depending on season and weather conditions fly at 'dangerous' altitudes, and the considerable reverse migration increases the risk of collision. At poor visibility caused by drizzle and mist, terrestrial birds in particular are attracted by illuminated offshore obstacles. Disoriented birds flew around the platform repeatedly, increasing both their risk of collision and their energy consumption.

On a few nights a year, a large number of avian interactions at offshore plants can be expected, especially in view of the planned number and extent of projected wind farms. Despite the knowledge gaps, several mitigation measures can be recommended:

- Abandonment of plans for wind farms in zones with dense migration, for example, in nearshore areas or along 'migration corridors'
- Alignment of turbines in rows parallel to the main migratory direction
- Several kilometer-wide free migration corridors between wind farms
- No construction of wind farms between, for example, resting and foraging areas
- Shutdown of turbines at nights with bad weather/visibility and high migration intensity
- Refraining from large-scale continuous illumination
- Measures to make wind turbines generally more recognizable to birds.

Perhaps the most effective solution would be lighting adjusted to the weather conditions, for example, flashing lights with long intervals, instead of continuous light in fog and drizzle. During the very few nights in which a high frequency of bird strikes is expected, with predicted poor weather and high migration intensity, a shutdown of turbines and adjustment of rotor blades to minimize their surfaces relative to the main direction of migration could help reduce collisions.

2.16.10.8 Effects of Offshore Wind Energy on the Microclimate

On a global scale wind energy plays an important role on the climate since it saves a very significant amount of carbon dioxide, sulfur, and nitrogen oxides, as it has been described in previous sections. Various climate modeling studies suggest that large-scale use of wind power can alter local and global climate. Wind turbines can change wind patterns which can in turn change the climate by (slightly) altering the amount of heat and moisture transported by the winds. The subject is under investigation. However, there are some results that deserve to be presented.

Ongoing research shows that, on a massive scale, the offshore wind turbines are creating a local climate of their own. The phenomenon is caused by the spinning, for example, 40–60 m blades which churn up the warm air at sea level and mix it with cooler air above. When this happens, the water begins condensing as droplets which become visible [37].

2.16.11 Mitigation Measures – Conclusions

2.16.11.1 The Importance of Wind Farm Siting

The selection of the site for a wind farm is a very critical issue that determines to a great extent its success and its acceptability and approval from the public. This applies equally well for onshore and offshore wind farms. The site selection must take into account a series of parameters in addition to the major issues of

- Wind potential
- Land use
- Grid connection
- Cost
- Power demand patterns.

The parameters under discussion in this section are related to the following:

- Current legislation of the country
- Environmental impacts and constraints
- Land availability
- Allowable land uses of a specific area
- Natural reserves
- Flora and fauna of the location
- Possibility of the area being a route of emigrating birds
- Public acceptability.

For example, concerning the protection of birds, some areas should certainly be avoided since they are known to be bottlenecks to the migratory routes of a large number of birds.

Also, placing offshore wind farms near nesting sites for seabirds may be ecologically hazardous. Even in cases when birds or mammals avoid offshore wind farms, to do that they expend much more energy and this means that there will be population-level impacts.

2.16.11.2 Mitigation through Technology

It seems that the technology used in the construction of offshore power plants greatly affects their environmental impacts. For example, gravity foundations are simple concrete structures that do not require piling operations. Therefore, they have less potential to disturb fish and mammals. In addition, technology advancement is critical for use in deeper water, thus decreasing the possibility of conflicts with local human and animal populations [35]. Deepwater turbines could be placed over the horizon and be invisible from the shore. In addition, deepwater turbines decrease their impact with seabirds that do not migrate over open ocean.

2.16.12 Social Acceptability of Wind Power Projects

2.16.12.1 General Considerations

The term 'social acceptability' deals with the index of acceptance of wind power projects by the local population. This is extremely important since the opinion of the population and pressure groups may heavily affect the amount of time needed to go ahead with a wind power plant project. Therefore, it is very important to assess public opinion at an early stage, and surely earlier than assessing the feasibility of the project.

As already mentioned, the concerns are related to the visual and noise impacts, aesthetics, impacts on the birds and the wildlife, undesirable change of the land use, landscape effects, electromagnetic emissions, and other impacts to natural reserves, especially when the source of the impacts is or will be close to one's home. These matters definitely can vary greatly from one local region or project site to another, and also as a function of population density and local and regional socioeconomic conditions.

As a result, it is difficult to extract general and widely applicable conclusions concerning the public attitude toward wind energy. The project's potential for negative impacts as well as benefits, and the fact that different people have different values as well as different levels of sensitivity, are important aspects of impact assessment.

One of the strongest indicators allowing comparisons of the level of support in different countries is the Eurobarometer (EB) Standard Survey carried out twice yearly and covering the population of the EU. Recent EB data on public opinion confirm the strongly positive overall picture for wind energy for the present and the future [38].

When EU citizens are asked about their preferences in terms of the use of different energy sources, renewable energies, in general, and wind energy, in particular, are rated highly positively (especially when compared with nuclear or fossil fuels). The highest support is for solar energy (80%), closely followed by wind energy, with 71% of EU citizens being firmly in favor of the use of wind power in their countries, 21% expressing a balanced view and only 5% being opposed to it. According to this EB survey, only a marginal number of respondents opposed the use of RES. Focusing on the use of wind energy, on a scale from 1 (strongly opposed) to 7 (strongly in favor), the EU average is 6.3. Even higher rates of support arose in some countries, for example, Denmark (6.7), Greece (6.5), and other three countries, that is, Poland, Hungary, and Malta (6.4). The United Kingdom shows the lowest support figure of the EU (5.7), closely followed by Finland and Germany (5.8) [38]. **Figure 23** shows the attitude of people from various EU countries toward wind energy [38].

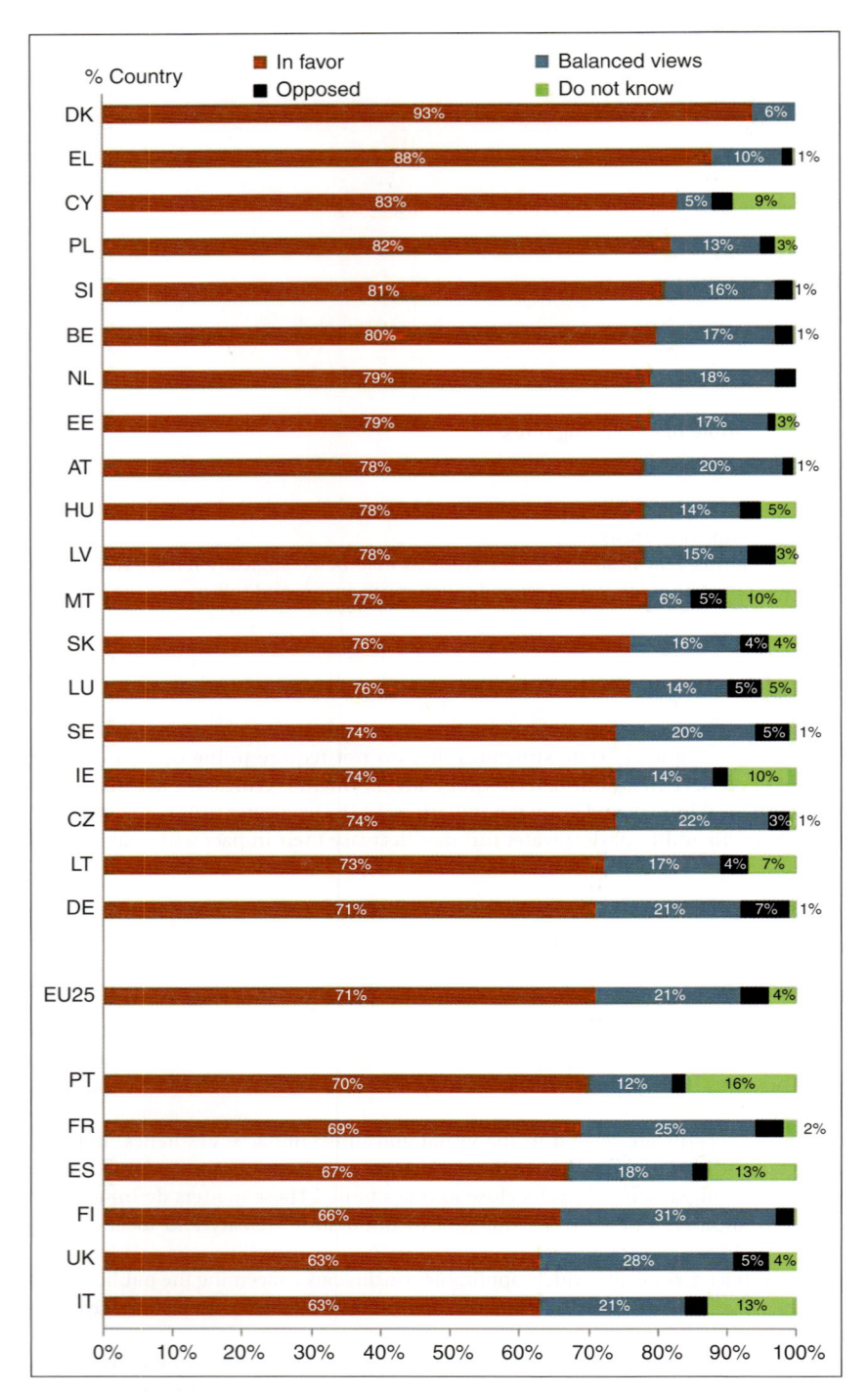

Figure 23 Attitude of EU residents toward wind energy [38].

EU citizens also demonstrate a very positive view of renewable energy, in general, and of wind energy, in particular, when asked about their expectations regarding the three most used energy sources 30 years from now. Results showed that wind energy is expected to be a key energy source in the future – just after solar (**Figure 24**). Respondents in all countries except the Czech Republic, Italy, Slovenia, Slovakia, and Finland mentioned wind energy among the three energy sources most likely to be used in their countries 30 years from now. The expected increase in the use of wind energy from 2007 to 2037 is very important in all countries with an average expected growth of almost 36%.

The factors affecting the public attitude toward wind farms and other energy innovations are shown in **Table 17**.

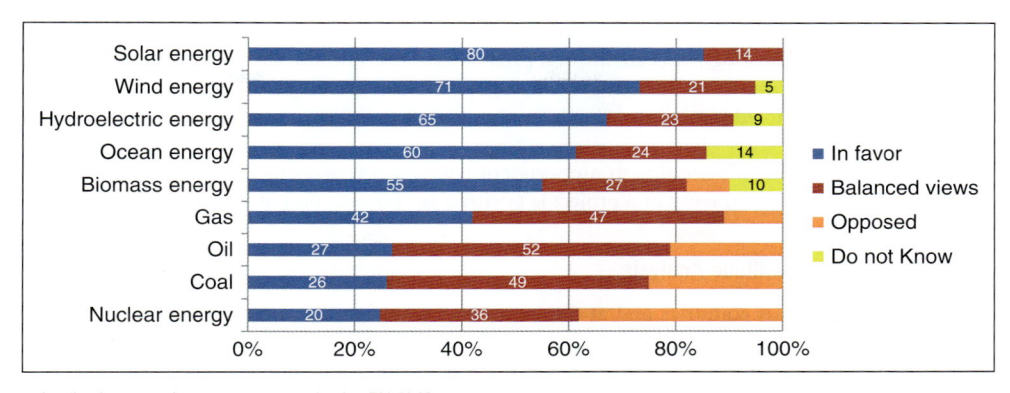

Figure 24 General attitude toward energy sources in the EU [38].

Table 17 Factors affecting the public attitude toward wind farms and other energy innovations

Perceptions of physical and environmental factors	Psychosocial factors
Visual impact	Knowledge
Landscape characteristics	Perceived benefits and costs
Turbine color	Social network and influences
Turbine and farm size	Social and institutional factors
Unity of the environment	Public participation
Wind farm design	
Turbine noise	
Distance to turbines	
Ecological site characteristics (birds and wildlife)	

One interesting question is the association between these high levels of general public support for wind energy and the actual implementation of wind power in each country. This could be analyzed through the correlation of two variables: percentage of people strongly in favor of wind power, from the EB, and wind capacity in kW per 1000 inhabitants. The bivariate analysis shows a low and not significant linear correlation: the highest levels of public enthusiasm about wind power in the sample of countries are not associated with the highest levels of wind capacity per habitant. In line with the most recent formulation of the 'social acceptability' of wind farms, this result may indicate that the generally favorable public support for the technology of wind power does not seem to be directly related to the installed wind capacity.

Various research works have been carried out for the identification and analysis of the key elements involved in the interaction between wind energy developments and the communities hosting them (see Further Reading section). Importantly, these case studies have allowed a better understanding of the factors explaining success and failure of wind energy developments, and this may indeed provide useful insights to more evidence-based decision making in the future. In some cases, the public has serious reactions against these investments, leading even to their cancellation claiming important environmental impacts. In fact, for some time it was believed that there is a public acceptability of wind farms and the people oppose only when the wind farm is very close to their own homes and places. This behavior is called NIMBYism (not-in-my-back-yard). However, it has been proved that public reactions are much more complex and are not only determined by the NIMBY syndrome [39].

One of the key messages from social research points out that how wind farms are developed and how people make sense of the impact of wind farms upon the places in which they live may be more important in shaping public reactions to new projects than the purely physical or technical factors. As is suggested, local opposition is often based on distrust, negative reactions to the actors (developers, authorities, and energy companies) trying to build the turbines, and the way projects are planned and managed, and not to wind turbines themselves [40, 41].

Visual evaluation of the wind power impact on the values of the landscape is by far the dominant factor in explaining why some are opposed to wind power implementation and why others support it. Moreover, on the basis of other research on how people judge scenic value, it is well known that the type of landscape in which the turbine is sited is the most significant factor. Even at a local level, direct environmental annoyance issues, of which noise is the most prominent one, are dominated by the visual/landscape factor. Furthermore, even at the level of the general implementation of wind power – to be distinguished from the attitude toward one particular wind power scheme – the visual/landscape factor that basically represents location characteristics and the identity of the place are the main factors dominating the public reactions.

The aesthetic value of the wind turbines themselves also affects the public attitude. The perceived impact on scenery, visual intrusion of the landscape, and positive judgments are the best predictors of the attitude. This factor is much more decisive for one's standpoint than the perceived environmental benefits of wind power as compared to other forms of conventional electricity generation, such as reduced carbon dioxide emissions. Concerns about noise pollution and hazards to birds have a small impact on attitudes as well.

Therefore, it seems that in most cases the decision to support or oppose a wind energy project will depend primarily on the visual quality of the site. If the perceived visual quality of a project is positive, people will probably support it.

2.16.12.2 Case Studies for Public Attitude Analysis

There are numerous studies in various countries and at different scales investigating public perceptions and the public attitude toward wind energy applications, as well as identifying the factors determining this public attitude. These factors can be classified in various categories such as physical, contextual, political, socioeconomic, social, local, and personal [39].

The research carried out by Kaldellis [42] included public surveys in various selected regions. The results obtained generally showed significant acceptance of existing wind parks, less acceptance for new installations, and a wide differentiation between peoples' attitude in the islands and the mainland. More specifically, in Greek islands the public attitude was clearly supportive for existing and new wind turbines, while on the mainland the public attitude was either divided or definitely against wind power applications. An interesting issue in the survey results has been that there is a minority strongly against wind energy application disregarding any financial benefits of these projects.

Furthermore, the same research team investigated the visual impacts of wind turbines. An extensive public opinion survey has been carried out in Greece in order to investigate the public attitude toward wind parks, while special emphasis was laid on the visual impact [24]. The survey highlights the remarkably negative public attitude of local people against specific wind power stations. Almost all individuals that do not agree with the existing wind turbines find their appearance objectionable, while even the supporters claim serious visual impacts of wind parks (**Figure 25**).

The interesting point in this investigation is that it has been followed by another survey for the same subject addressed to experts in order to examine in depth the above problem. The factors that have been taken into account and seem to affect the visual impacts of wind parks include among others:

- The number of wind turbines consisting the wind park under evaluation
- The rotor diameter
- The general aesthetics of the installation, including the design, and the color of the wind turbines (mainly the tower color)
- The distance of the wind park from the nearest inhabited community
- The adaptation of the wind park with the natural environment
- The engines micro-siting and uniformity
- The houses that are in optical contact with the park
- The relative number of wind turbines that are visible from each house
- The viewing angle
- The area population
- The relative position of the wind park with the daily sun path.

Some indicative results are shown in **Figure 26**. An interesting conclusion is that the experts' evaluation coincides with the results of the opinion of the general public [12, 24].

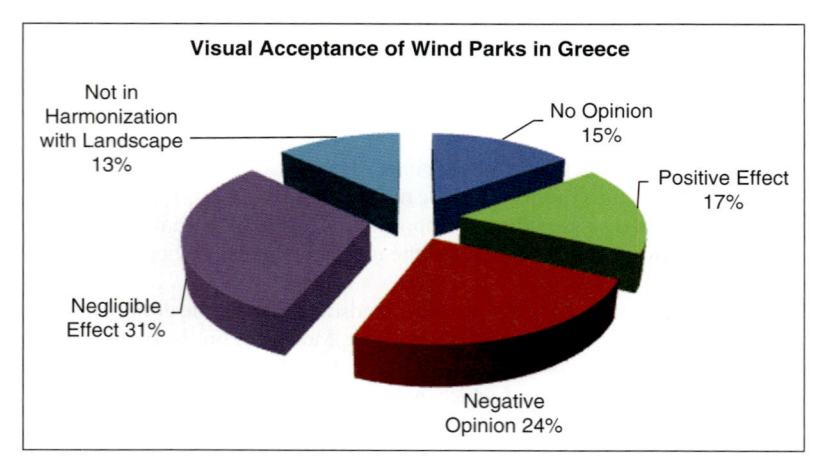

Figure 25 Public opinion survey results in selected areas [24].

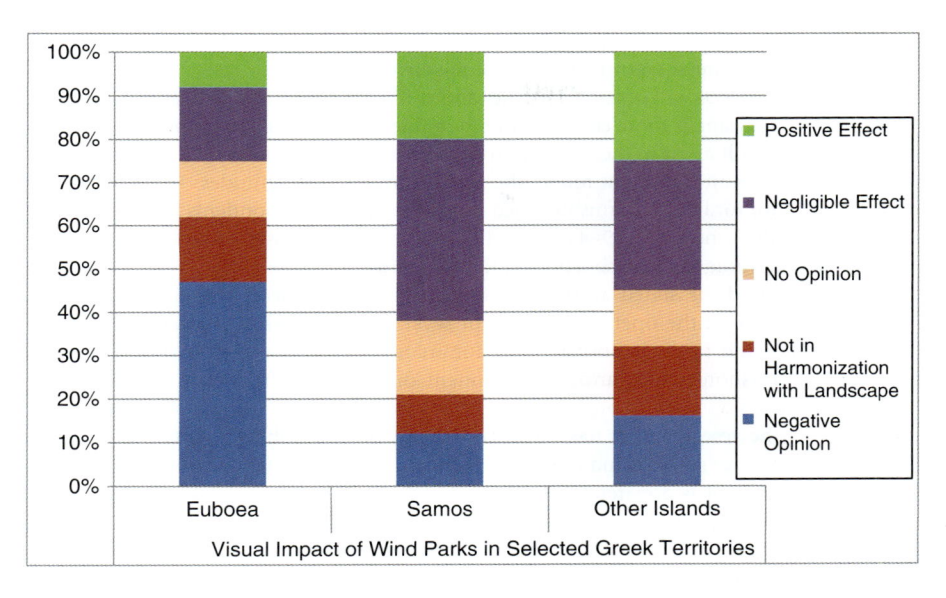

Figure 26 Public opinion survey concerning the visual impact of wind parks in Greek territories [24].

Visual intrusion and noise were the key anticipated problems by respondents in a survey carried out by Warren et al. [43]. However, the same study found that noise pollution and visual impacts were less important to the public than anticipated before a wind power project is implemented, concluding that respondents' fears had not been realized. Case studies of public attitudes toward existing and proposed wind farm developments in Scotland and Ireland are used to test three counterintuitive hypotheses derived from previous attitudinal research. These are: (a) that local people become more favorable toward wind farms after construction; (b) that the degree of acceptance increases with proximity to them; and (c) that the NIMBY syndrome (not-in-my-back-yard) does not adequately explain variations in public attitudes. All three hypotheses are supported by this study. Large majorities favor wind power development in principle and in (local) practice. Although some aspects of NIMBY attitudes exist, the surveys reveal an 'inverse NIMBY' syndrome, whereby those with wind farms in their 'backyard' strongly support the technology. The research endorses the view that aesthetic perceptions, both positive and negative, are the strongest single influence on individuals' attitudes toward wind power projects. Comparison of the current institutional factors driving wind energy development with those during earlier eras of hydropower development and large-scale afforestation emphasizes the need for strategic planning guidance.

2.16.13 The Public Attitude Toward Offshore Wind Parks

The public attitude/response toward the implementation of offshore wind power plants is not very well known yet. In fact, this is an area where further investigation is needed, as the implementation of these projects progresses and the real public reactions/responses are revealed.

It is often assumed that one of the principle objections to onshore turbines – their visual impact – can easily be solved by moving them offshore. But turbines, even several miles offshore, still may have a visual impact – and for many people – this causes negative attitude toward wind energy. While some impacts on people, such as noise, might be mitigated by moving offshore, visual disturbance prevails. In fact, concerning the public attitude, offshore wind farms may be just as controversial as onshore projects, since they affect the seascape and the view of the horizon which is considered as an nonnegotiable value.

Visual impact is important to address because it is still a dominant influence on opinions, even when siting offshore. If people have had negative experience of visual impact onshore, this may be transferred offshore.

Bishop and Miller [21] carried out a survey using simulations of wind farms and found out that offshore wind farms located at relatively short distances generate large levels of visual intrusion compared to offshore wind farms located at larger distances.

Firestone and Kempton [44] carried out a public opinion survey in the United States. With answers from 500 respondents they found that just above half were opposed to the potential of an offshore wind farm and the opponents are much more firmly committed to opposition than supporters are committed to support. The authors developed four types of measures in order to understand the factors that underlie support or opposition, that is, aesthetics, community harmony, local fishing industry, and recreational boating. The opposing attitude has been found to covariate positively with age and negatively with education, income, and perceived likeness of the offshore wind farms.

An interesting issue concerning offshore wind farms is the perceptions of the local seascape and the role of aesthetic seascape qualities in shaping local attitudes [45]. A survey has been carried out and its results showed that attitudes to offshore wind farms are driven by a complex set of values. The aesthetic qualities ascribed to sea appear to be a significant driver of attitudes. Half of all arguments raised against offshore wind parks were shown to be based on the idea that wind farms despoil the open horizon, since 'open horizon' is considered one of the most essential features of the environment.

Therefore, offshore wind power projects will possibly face the same difficulties as far as public attitude is concerned with onshore wind power plants. Certainly, the seascape is more complex and the values assigned to it are more complicated to be identified. A detailed study of the visual impacts will assist in the most appropriate siting of the project.

However, the time parameter plays an important role in the evaluation of public attitudes. The experience from onshore wind parks is that negative perceptions for local wind farms declined over time and the respondents become more supportive after the construction and the operation of the wind farm [39–41]. Therefore, the experience-based attitude appears to have a central role in order to assess if determinants of attitude are representative in the long run.

Recently, Ladenburg [46] analyzed the stated attitude toward offshore wind farms from a sample of Danish respondents who potentially might have experienced the operation of one or several offshore wind farms in Denmark and found that the attitude toward existing offshore wind farms is positive in a dominant share of the sample. Furthermore, it has been found that attitude formation toward offshore wind farms is dependent on type and frequency of the beach and the coastline usage.

Claire Haggette [47] reviews the research that has been carried out on the public response to offshore wind power and highlighted the key factors that influence support and opposition to them. Responses are motivated by visual impact and seascape value. In her work she reveals that what is apparent from this research is that offshore sites are not simply and automatically preferred to onshore, and that moving offshore does not necessarily solve the 'problems' of siting onshore. The work also demonstrates that, just as with on shore wind, 'NIMBY' is a simply an inadequate way to conceptualize and understand opposition.

Higgs *et al.* [48] describe the potential for information technology (IT) in the public participation process and demonstrate the advantages of linkages between the technologies as part of an overall decision support system. In their work they highlight the opportunities offered by IT in the public participation process by drawing on a literature review of participatory techniques in environmental planning. They try to demonstrate how existing techniques can be supplemented with new tools that permit a greater degree of public interaction in the decision-making process. They focus their work in the use of multicriteria evaluation techniques linked to GIS in order to demonstrate the contribution of such tools in the siting of potentially contentious wind farm developments.

2.16.14 Future Trends in Wind Parks' Social and Environmental Impacts Assessment

From the previous analysis, it is obvious that many efforts are made in mitigation of environmental impacts. It is also obvious that the public attitude is mainly dependent on them; therefore, improvement in them will also improve the public attitude toward wind energy.

The future trends of the wind power plants impacts may be seen in various dimensions, such as

- The impacts themselves, whether progress in technology will make them milder or even eliminate them.
- The possibility for more detailed and reliable assessment of the impacts.
- The forecasting of various factors affecting the social attitude toward wind energy.

Discussing the first of the above issues, that is, trends in environmental impacts, it is certain that they will align with the trends in wind turbine technology and the design and implementation of wind power plants projects. Focusing in the most crucial of the impacts, it is certain that they are

- The noise emission level
- The aesthetics and the visual impact
- The influence on the bird habitat and biodiversity in general
- The impacts on natural reserves, land use, and the landscape.

From all the above, it seems that the noise will be mitigated with the development of new wind turbines. Already the new machines create much less noise than the older ones. However, the use of the land, the (subjective) visual impacts, and the aesthetics and the impacts on the wildlife (flora and fauna) will certainly prevail since they are integrated with the nature of wind power plants and cannot be avoided. Furthermore, as the trend is toward larger wind turbines, possibly more severe impacts will be faced, although efficiency will certainly increase and this, by itself, may be beneficial for the environment (i.e., less natural resources will be exploited per unit of power produced).

The future prospect of environmental impact mitigation is related to the following:

- Proper selection of the wind park siting
- Use of the technology in the equipment and the installations
- Use of IT tools
- R&D for knowledge improvement.

Proper siting is a major issue not only for environmental impacts but also for many other technical and financial reasons. However, proper selection of the wind park site will also minimize the visual impacts, eliminate major land use problems, and avoid the impacts on birds and other animals.

Furthermore, considering offshore wind parks and the seascape, again the correct site selection is even more crucial, since there are many values in the marine environment that need to be taken into account.

Noise impacts are mitigated with the development of new wind turbines. Already the new machines create much less noise than the older ones, mechanical noise has been eliminated and aerodynamic noise is controlled with the proper blade design and the use of new materials.

The progress in the development of tools exploiting the new information technologies will affect the detail and reliability of the EIA. Furthermore, the siting and the design of wind power plants will be supported with the use of specific software tools. The GIS will be helpful in the wind turbine site selection. Mathematical and multicriteria optimization, where environmental constraints can be easily embedded, will support the decision-making problem.

The visual impact assessment will be supported with the use of appropriately designed software tools that will be able to simulate various views and evaluate them in the light of public reactions before the project is implemented. When a particular site is proposed, GIS and visibility assessment can help to determine the affected areas and the likely degree of the visual impact. Therefore, the most serious environmental impact, that is, the poor aesthetic integration, could possibly be minimized if the visual impacts are previously evaluated and the GIS could assist very much in this direction.

The identification of the public attitude before the initiation of a project idea may help in the site selection and the whole design which can be supported with the use of planning and simulation tools.

In this context, it is believed that the linkages between the various IT tools in an integrated decision support system framework will help in this direction. While specifically related to siting wind farm developments in this instance, GIS and IT tools could be used in other types of assessment for which a consensus view is needed from a range of interest groups.

Concerning offshore turbines, their impacts are of special interest since the seascape, the marine environment, and the view of the open horizon have their own values. The advancement of the technology will make the installation of wind farms in deeper waters possible. This means that the visual annoyance will be eliminated, the noise will not be heard from the coast line, and the wind farm will be away from animals and out of the migration routes of the birds.

R&D activities in the area of wind energy are analyzed in detail in the corresponding chapter of this volume. What could possibly be highlighted here is the lack of knowledge in some basic environmental issues mainly as far as offshore wind farms are concerned. More specifically, the behavior of many animals and fish and their sensitivity to the underwater sound or even to the existence of wind power parks is not known yet and basic knowledge improvement is required.

2.16.15 Conclusions

Wind energy is nowadays considered as a clean and the most widely applied (among other RES) form for producing electricity. Certainly, wind energy applications for power generation are assumed responsible for some environmental impacts. These impacts are limited and concentrated to the specific location where the wind park has been installed. In contrast, the impacts of thermal or nuclear energy production plants are slow to appear, long term, and certainly they affect a very wide area; in fact, in the case of nuclear energy the impacts are global. Furthermore, the wind power impacts can easily be mitigated through proper design and planning. In the case of thermal or nuclear power plants, even if serious efforts are made, the impacts are almost impossible to be minimized due to their inherent characteristics.

The exploitation of wind energy for power generation has a number of very essential social and environmental benefits such as the reduction of CO_2 emissions, reduction of water consumption, creation of new job positions, regional development, and minimal impacts on the habitat compared to other sources of energy. The most severe negative impacts are the noise caused from the turbines, the so-called visual impacts and the impacts on flora and fauna. However, with the proper siting of the wind park, the detailed design and the implementation of mitigation measures, these impacts can be minimized. Technology helps very much in this direction as far as the noise impact is concerned. The same ideas apply in offshore wind farms, where again the seascape is a valuable human and ecological resource. In general, if wind turbines are designed and planned carefully, many of these negative impacts can be minimized and wind energy will increase its valuable role in the energy supply of our planet.

References

[1] European Wind Energy Association. http://www.ewea.org (accessed May 2011).
[2] Research Center for Energy, Environment and Technology CIEMAT. www.ciemat.es (accessed June 2011).
[3] Kaldellis JK and Zafirakis D (2011) The wind energy (r)evolution: A short review of a long history. *Renewable Energy* 36: 1887–1901.
[4] Saidur R, Rahim NA, Islam MR, and Solangi KH (2011) Environmental impact of wind energy. *Renewable and Sustainable Energy Reviews* 15(5): 2423–2430.
[5] Parliamentary Office of Science and Technology POSTNOTE (2006) Carbon footprint of electricity generation. No. 268: 1–4.
[6] Mielke E, Anadon LD, and Narayanamurti V (2011) Water Consumption of Energy, Resource Extraction, Processing and Conversion. http://belfercenter.ksg.harvard.edu/files/ETIP-DP-2010-15-final-4.pdf (accessed June 2011).

[7] EmployRES (2010) The impact of renewable energy policy on economic growth and employment in the European Union. *Final Report*. http://ec.europa.eu/energy/renewables/studies/doc/renewables/2009_employ_res_report.pdf (accessed May 2010).
[8] Blanco MI and Rodrigues G (2009) Direct employment in the wind energy sector: An EU study. *Energy Policy* 37(8): 2847–2857.
[9] Wind Energy (2009) The facts, Part V: Environmental issues. http://www.wind-energy-the-facts-org (accessed May 2011).
[10] Commission of the European Communities (CEC) (1997) Council Directive 97/11/EC. Council Directive 97/11/EC of 3 March 1997. Amending Directive 85/337/EEC. *Official Journal of the European Communities* 40(L73): 5.
[11] Zafirakis D and Kondili E (2006) Environmental Impacts of a Wind Park in Crete. Assignment in Environmental Impacts Assessment Module. MSc in Energy. Technological Education Institute of Piraeus.
[12] Kaldellis JK and Kavadias KA (2004) Evaluation of Greek wind parks visual impact: "The public attitude". *Fresenius Environmental Bulletin* 13(5): 413–423.
[13] Kaldellis JK, Kavadias KA, and Paliatsos AG (2003) Environmental impacts of wind energy applications: "Myth or reality?" *Fresenius Environmental Bulletin* 12(4): 326–337.
[14] Kaldellis JK, Garakis K, and Kapsali M (2011) Noise impact assessment on the basis of onsite noise emission measurements for a representative wind farm. *Renewable Energy* May. Accepted for application.
[15] American Wind Turbine Performance and Safety Standard. www.awea.org (accessed June 2011).
[16] Klug H (2005) A review of wind turbine noise. *Proccedings of First International Conference on Wind Turbine Noise*, Berlin, Germany, 17–18 October.
[17] Hurtado JP, Fernandez J, Parrondo JL, and Blanco E (2004) Spanish method of visual impact evaluation in wind farms. *Renewable and Sustainable Energy Reviews* 8(5): 483–491.
[18] Tsoutsos T, Tsouchlaraki A, Tsiropoulos M, and Kaldellis JK (2009) Visual impact evaluation methods of wind parks: Application for a Greek island. *Wind Engineering* 33(1): 83–92.
[19] Torres S, Cloquell-Ballester V-A, and Darton R (2009) Development and validation of a multicriteria indicator for the assessment of objective aesthetic impact of wind farms. *Renewable and Sustainable Energy Reviews* 13(1): 40–66.
[20] Ladenburg J (2009) Visual impact assessment of offshore wind farms and prior experience. *Applied Energy* 86(3): 380–387.
[21] Bishop ID and Miller DR (2007) Visual assessment of off-shore wind turbines: The influence of distance, contrast, movement and social variables. *Renewable Energy* 32(5): 814–831.
[22] Molina-Ruiz J, Martínez-Sánchez MJ, Pérez-Sirvent C, *et al.* (2011) Developing and applying a GIS-assisted approach to evaluate visual impact in wind farms. *Renewable Energy* 36(3): 1125–1132.
[23] Rodrigues M, Montañés C, and Fueyo N (2010) A method for the assessment of the visual impact caused by the large-scale deployment of renewable-energy facilities. *Environmental Impact Assessment Review* 30(4): 240–246.
[24] Kaldellis JK (2006) Evaluation of Greek wind parks visual impact "public attitude and experts' opinion". *Fresenius Environmental Bulletin* 15(11): 1419–1426.
[25] Masden EA, Fox AD, Furness RW, *et al.* (2010) Cumulative impact assessments and bird/wind farm interactions: Developing a conceptual framework. *Environmental Impact Assessment Review* 30(1): 1–7.
[26] Toronto Renewable Energy Co-operative (TREC) and Toronto Hydro. www.windshare.ca/documents/EA_draftscreeningdoc.pdf (accessed May 2011).
[27] Sovacool BK (2009) Contextualising avian mortality: A preliminary appraisal of bird and bat fatalities from wind, fossil fuel and nuclear electricity. *Energy Policy* 37: 2241.
[28] Polintan LJ Wind farms' effects on microclimate could be good on crops. http://www.ecoseed.org/wind-energy/article/8-wind-energy (accessed on June 2011).
[29] MacLeen IMD, Wright LJ, Showler DA, and Rehfisch MM (2009) A review of assessment methodologies for offshore windfarms. http://www.offshorewind.co.uk (accessed July 2011).
[30] Lozano-Minguez E, Kolios AJ, and Brennan FP (2011) Multi-criteria assessment of offshore wind turbine support structures. *Renewable Energy* 36(11): 2831–2837.
[31] Thomsen F, Lüdemann K, Kafemann R, and Piper W (2006) Effects of offshore wind farm noise on marine mammals and fish. http://www.offshorewind.co.uk (accessed July 2011).
[32] Koeller J, Koeppel J, and Peters W (eds.) (2006) *Research on Environmental Impacts*. New York: Springer.
[33] Department of Trade and Industry (DTI), Wratten A, Martin S, Welstead J, *et al.* (2005) Guidance on the assessment of the impacts of the offshore wind parks: Seascape and visual impact response. http://www.catpaisatge.net/fitxers/guies/eolics/file22852.pdf (accessed July 2011).
[34] Environmental Impacts of Wind-Energy Projects. www.nap.edu (accessed June 2011).
[35] Hüppop O, Dierschke J, Michael Exo K-M, and Fredrich E (2006) Bird migration and offshore wind turbines. In: Koller J, Koppel J, and Peters W (eds.) *Offshore Wind Energy – Research on Environmental Impacts*, pp. 91–113. Berlin: Springer..
[36] Snyder B and Kaiser MJ (2009) Ecological and economic cost – Benefit analysis of offshore wind energy. *Renewable Energy* 34(6): 1567–1578.
[37] http://trendsupdates.com/wind-turbines-create-their-own-micro-climate (accessed June 2011).
[38] European Commission (2007) Energy technologies, knowledge, perception, measures (Eurobarometer). http://ec.europa.eu/research/energy/pdf/energy_tech_eurobarometer_en.pdf (accessed May 2011).
[39] Devine-Wright P (2005) Beyond. NIMBYism: Towards an integrated framework for understanding public perceptions of wind energy. *Wind Energy* 8(2): 125–139.
[40] Wolsink M (2007) Wind power implementation: The nature of public attitudes: Equity and fairness instead of 'backyard motives'. *Renewable and Sustainable Energy Reviews* 11(6): 1188–1207.
[41] Wolsink M (2000) Wind power and the NIMBY-myth: Institutional capacity and the limited significance of public support. *Renewable Energy* 21(1): 49–64.
[42] Kaldellis JK (2005) Social attitude towards wind energy applications in Greece. *Energy Policy* 33(5): 595–602.
[43] Warren CR, Lumsedn C, O'Dowd S, and Birnie RV (2005) 'Green on Green' perceptions of wind power in Scotland and Ireland. *Journal of Environmental Planning and Management* 48(6): 853–875.
[44] Firestone J and Kempton W (2007) Public opinion about large offshore wind power: Underlying factors. *Energy Policy* 35(3): 1584–1598.
[45] Gee K (2010) Offshore wind power development as affected by seascape values on the German North Sea coast. *Land Use Policy* 27: 185–194.
[46] Ladenburg J (2010) Attitudes towards offshore wind farms – The role of beach visits on attitude and demographic and attitude relations. *Energy Policy* 38: 1297–1304.
[47] Haggette C (2011) Understanding public responses to offshore wind power. *Energy Policy* 39(2): 503–510.
[48] Higgs G, Berry R, Kidner D, and Langford M (2008) Using IT approaches to promote public participation in renewable energy planning: Prospects and challenges. *Land Use Policy* 25: 596–607.

Further Reading

[1] Aitken M (2010) Why we still don't understand the social aspects of wind power: A critique of key assumptions within the literature. *Energy Policy* 38(4): 1834–1841.
[2] Aydin NY, Kentel E, and Duzgun S (2010) GIS-based environmental assessment of wind energy systems for spatial planning: A case study from Western Turkey. *Renewable and Sustainable Energy Reviews* 14(1): 364–373.
[3] Baidya Roy S (2011) Simulating impacts of wind farms on local hydrometeorology. *Journal of Wind Engineering and Industrial Aerodynamics* 99(4): 491–498.

[4] Dimitropoulos A and Kontoleon A (2009) Assessing the determinants of local acceptability of wind-farm investment: A choice experiment in the Greek Aegean islands. *Energy Policy* 37(5): 1842–1854.
[5] Jobert A, Laborgne P, and Mimler S (2007) Local acceptance of wind energy: Factors of success identified in French and German case studies. *Energy Policy* 35(5): 2751–2760.
[6] Josimović B and Pucar M (2010) The strategic environmental impact assessment of electric wind energy plants: Case study 'bavanište' (Serbia). *Renewable Energy* 35(7): 1509–1519.
[7] Jerpåsen GB and Larsen KC (2011) Visual impact of wind farms on cultural heritage: A Norwegian case study. *Environmental Impact Assessment Review* 31(3): 206–215.
[8] Koundouri P, Kountouris Y, and Remoundou K (2009) Valuing a wind farm construction: A contingent valuation study in Greece. *Energy Policy* 37(5): 1939–1944.
[9] Mathur J, Wagner HJ, Bansal NK, and Pick E (2000) Energy and environmental analysis of wind energy systems. In: Sayigh AAM (ed.) *World Renewable Energy Congress VI*, pp. 1209–1212. Oxford: Pergamon.
[10] Meyerhoff J, Ohl C, and Hartje V (2010) Landscape externalities from onshore wind power. *Energy Policy* 38(1): 82–92.
[11] Morrison ML and Sinclair K (2004) Wind energy technology, environmental impacts of. In: Cleveland CJ (editor(s)-in-chief) *Encyclopaedia of Energy*, pp. 435–448. St. Louis, MO: Elsevier.
[12] Punt MJ, Groeneveld RA, van Ierland EC, and Stel JH (2009) Spatial planning of offshore wind farms: A windfall to marine environmental protection? *Ecological Economics* 69(1): 93–103.
[13] Swofford J and Slattery M (2010) Public attitudes of wind energy in Texas: Local communities in close proximity to wind farms and their effect on decision-making. *Energy Policy* 38(5): 2508–2519.
[14] Trivedi MP (1999) Environmental factors affecting wind energy generation in western coastal region of India. *Renewable Energy* 16(1, 4 part 2): 894–898.
[15] Wackernagel M and Monfreda C (2004) Ecological footprints and energy. In: Cleveland CJ (ed.). *Encyclopedia of Energy*, vol. 2, pp. 1–11. Amsterdam: Elsevier.
[16] Wagner H-J, Baack C, Eickelkamp T, *et al.* (2011) Life cycle assessment of the offshore wind farm alpha ventus. *Energy* 36(5): 2459–2464.

2.17 Wind Energy Policy

GC van Kooten, University of Victoria, Victoria, BC, Canada

© 2012 Elsevier Ltd. All rights reserved.

2.17.1	Introduction	541
2.17.2	**Energy and the Economy**	542
2.17.2.1	Global Energy Markets	542
2.17.2.2	Renewable Energy Policy	545
2.17.2.2.1	Scrambling to reduce CO_2 emissions: The renewable target game	546
2.17.2.2.2	Feed-in tariffs: The case of Ontario	546
2.17.3	**Fossil Fuel and Nuclear Options for Reducing CO_2 Emissions**	548
2.17.3.1	Clean Coal	548
2.17.3.2	Natural Gas	549
2.17.3.3	Nuclear Power	549
2.17.4	**Renewable Alternatives to Fossil Fuels**	552
2.17.4.1	Biomass for Generating Electricity	552
2.17.4.2	Hydraulics and Storage	553
2.17.4.3	Geothermal	554
2.17.4.4	Generating Electricity from Intermittent Energy Sources	554
2.17.5	**The Economics of Wind Energy in Electricity Generation**	555
2.17.5.1	Structure of Electricity Grids: Economics	556
2.17.5.1.1	Demand side and demand management	556
2.17.5.1.2	Electricity supply and the wholesale market	557
2.17.5.2	Integration of Wind Power into Electricity Grids	559
2.17.5.2.1	Capacity factors	559
2.17.5.2.2	Reserve requirements	560
2.17.5.2.3	Modeling the management of an electricity grid	561
2.17.5.2.4	Some model results	562
2.17.6	**Discussion**	565
References		567
Further Reading		568

2.17.1 Introduction

In an effort to get serious about climate change, the leaders of the largest eight countries (G8) agreed at their meeting on 8 July 2009 in L'Aquila, Italy, to limit the increase in global average temperature to no more than 2 °C above preindustrial levels. To attain this, they set "the goal of achieving at least a 50% reduction of global emissions by 2050, [with] ... developed countries reducing emissions of greenhouse gases in aggregate by 80% or more by 2050 compared to 1990 or more recent years." (paragraph 65, 'Responsible Leadership for a Sustainable Future' Declaration, G8 Summit, July 2009. Available at http://www.g8italia2009.it/static/G8.../G8_Declaration_08_07_09_final,0.pdf (viewed 22 July 2009)). The US House of Representatives passed the American Clean Energy and Security Act (also known as the Waxman–Markey Bill) by a vote of 219 to 212 on 26 June 2009. The Act identifies certain large emitters of greenhouse gases and these emitters must reduce their aggregate CO_2 and equivalent emissions by 3% below 2005 levels in 2012, 17% below 2005 levels in 2020, 42% in 2030, and 83% in 2050. The Waxman–Markey initiative subsequently stalled in the Senate because of looming midterm elections in November 2010. Nonetheless, the agenda for developing countries is to quickly decarbonize their economies.

To achieve these targets, it is necessary to radically transform the fundamental driver of global economies – the energy system. The main obstacle is the abundance and ubiquity of fossil fuels, which can be expected to power the industrialized nations and the economies of aspiring industrial economies into the foreseeable future. Realistically, global fossil fuel use will continue to grow and remain the primary energy source for much of the next century [1–4].

The extent to which this prognosis will change depends on factors that are impossible to predict in advance. These include primarily the willingness of countries to spend vast sums on programs to reduce reliance on fossil fuels – to forgo cheap fossil fuel energy that emits CO_2 for much more expensive non-carbon energy sources, such as wind, solar, hydro, wave and tidal power, and, of course, nuclear power. They depend on the ability of governments to convince their citizens to accept large increases in energy prices and thereby reduced standards of living. They depend on the prices of fossil fuels relative to other energy options, and on very iffy and uncertain technological breakthroughs. Economists cannot predict technical advances, nor can others, because they depend on the minds and resourcefulness of citizens, and on the educational, cultural, and governance settings of society.

President Obama announced on various occasions that the United States would embark on new research programs that would enable America to retain its technological advantage over other countries, including a research and development program to decarbonize the US economy, especially the electricity sector (see 'Energy and Environment', White House, posted 11 April 2010 (http://www.whitehouse.gov/issues/energy-and-environment, viewed 21 April 2010)). The President is counting on spin-off benefits of the kind that have characterized the US industrial–military complex for the past 50 years and perhaps longer if research related to World War II is taken into account. Government-funded military and space research under the Defense Advanced Research Projects Agency (DARPA) (see http://www.darpa.mil/; "DARPA defines its mission as preventing technological surprise for the United States and to create technological surprise for adversaries" (DARPA: Developing the wild, the wacky and wicked cool for 50 years, by M. Cooney at http://www.networkworld.com/community/node/24814, viewed 20 April 2010)), originally created in 1958 as the Advanced Research Projects Agency (ARPA) in response to the Russian launch of Sputnik, led to technologies – the Internet, microchips, food processing and fast-food technologies currently in use, spandex, cell phones, and others – that are now ubiquitous [5].

This impetus to rid the economy of fossil fuels might indeed change the playing field against fossil fuels. It is a 'put-a-man-on-the-moon' type of R&D program for finding a technological solution that will enable humankind to control the climate. In this chapter, we address questions related to the role of wind power in achieving the desired objective of decarbonizing the energy sector. In order to do so, however, we must briefly consider other energy options. Therefore, we begin our examination with a discussion of the global challenges facing the energy sector in converting global economies from a fossil fuel basis to a nonfossil fuel basis. What are the prospects and the potential costs? Will the new technologies and energy sources reduce the anthropogenic component of global warming?

The chapter is structured as follows. In the next section, we consider the link between energy and economic development, and examine production and trade of various energy resources. In Section 2.17.3, the focus shifts to the important role of fossil fuels and nuclear energy. We argue that fossil fuels are likely to remain important throughout the twenty-first century, although countries will move away from them to the greatest extent possible because of the problem of associated CO_2 emissions. Part of this will lead to greater reliance on natural gas, which emits less CO_2 per unit of energy. Then, in Section 2.17.4, we examine the case of renewable sources of energy besides wind. We argue that, while there is a role for all types of renewable energy, economic feasibility remains a major, if not the only, obstacle. In this regard, wind likely offers the best prospects. Section 2.17.5 is devoted to the economics of wind energy, and we assume that wind will be used solely to generate electricity. Hence, we first discuss the economic structure of electricity grids, and how wind fits into the so-called merit order. Then we examine the costs that wind imposes on the rest of the grid as wind penetration rates increase. We provide some notion as to the potential costs of integrating wind into various generation mixes, in terms of both costs per kilowatt hour and costs per unit of CO_2 emissions saved. The chapter ends with some concluding observations.

2.17.2 Energy and the Economy

While good governance (low corruption, effective rule of law, etc.) is crucial to economic growth, economic development cannot occur without expanding energy use – rich countries are rich because they used and continue to use large amounts of energy to create wealth and satisfy consumption [4]. By 2030, global energy use is expected to increase by nearly 50% compared to the use in 2005; this will require the equivalent of one new 1000 megawatt power generating plant coming onstream every day for the next 20 years just to satisfy growth in electricity demand [2]. Likewise, the International Energy Agency [6] projects that unless governments implement major policies to reduce carbon dioxide emissions, energy consumption will increase by 40% between 2007 and 2030, with three-quarters of this growth coming from fossil fuels. The 40% as opposed to 50% projection is the result of taking into account the impact of the 2008 financial crisis and subsequent recession in North America and Europe.

The majority of the growth in energy consumption will be in developing countries, especially China and India, which together account for about one-third of the world's population. In 2010, China's emissions of greenhouse gases surpassed those of the United States, although its per capita emissions remain glaringly lower. Attempts by rich countries to reign in economic growth in developing countries for the purpose of mitigating climate change are strongly resisted, as indicated by the failure to reach agreement on emission reduction at the 15th Conference of the Parties (COP15) to the 1992 United Nations' Framework Convention on Climate Change (UNFCCC), which was held in Copenhagen in late 2009. Energy policies that lower rates of economic growth in developing countries will simply perpetuate the misery of millions of people who live in poverty. While clean and renewable energy sources can contribute to the energy needs of developing nations, economic growth will depend primarily on traditional sources of energy, such as coal, oil, and natural gas, because they are relatively cheap and ubiquitous, and are a great improvement over heating with wood biomass, agricultural wastes, dung, and other fuels, especially from the standpoint of health. In this section, we consider global energy markets and trade in more detail so that we can better understand the challenges and limitations facing wind energy.

2.17.2.1 Global Energy Markets

Fossil fuels are the most important source of energy in the world. This is clear when we look at the sources of energy used in the global generation of electricity (**Figure 1**) and the world's final consumption of energy (**Figure 2**). Approximately two-thirds of

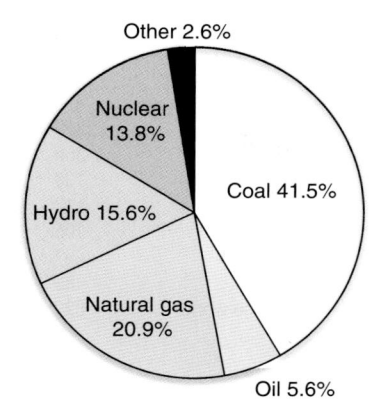

Figure 1 Global electricity production (in %) by energy source in 2007. Total production = 19 771 TWh. Reproduced from International Energy Agency (IEA) (2010) *Key World Energy Statistics 2009*. Paris, France: OECD/IEA [7].

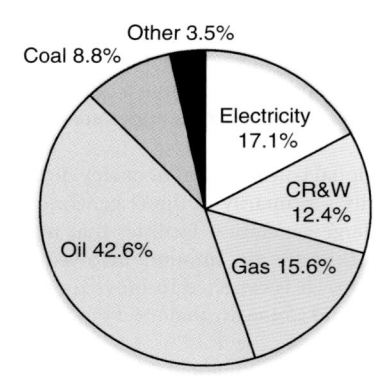

Figure 2 Global energy consumption by source, 2007, percent, total = 8286 Mtoe (million tonnes of oil equivalent). CR&W refers to combustible renewables and waste. Reproduced from International Energy Agency (IEA) (2010) *Key World Energy Statistics 2009*. Paris, France: OECD/IEA [7].

electricity is produced from fossil fuels, while the remainder comes primarily from hydro and nuclear sources. Geothermal, biomass, solar, wind, and other sources contribute a meager 2.6% of the energy required to produce electricity.

To obtain some notion regarding which countries generate the most electricity and the importance of coal in the global electricity generating mix, consider **Table 1**. Nearly 20 000 terawatt hours (TWh) or 20 petawatt hours (PWh) of electricity was generated in 2007, the latest year for which statistics are available from the International Energy Agency [7, 18]. (A watt (W) equals 1 joule (J) per second. A kilowatt (kW) equals 1000 W; megawatt (MW) = 10^6 W; gigawatt (GW) = 10^9 W; terawatt (TW) = 10^{12} W; petawatt (PW) = 10^{15} W. Kilo is abbreviated as k and equals 10^3; mega is abbreviated as M and equals 10^6; giga is abbreviated as G and

Table 1 Largest electricity producers, total and by selected fossil fuel energy source, in 2007 (electricity production in TWh)

Total		Coal/peat		Gas	
United States	4 323	China	2 656	United States	915
China	3 279	United States	2 118	Russia	487
Japan	1 123	India	549	Japan	290
Russia	1 013	Japan	311	Rest of the world	2 435
India	803	Germany	311	Total	4 127
Canada	640	South Africa	247		
Germany	630	Australia	194	*Oil*	
Rest of the world	7 960	Korea	171	Total	1 114
Total	19 771	Russia	170		
		Poland	148		
		Rest of the world	1 353		
		Total	8 228		

Reproduced from International Energy Agency (IEA) (2010) *Key World Energy Statistics 2009*. Paris, France: OECD/IEA [7].

Table 2 Major global producers, exporters, and importers of crude oil in 2007/2008

Producers	Mt	Net exporters	Mt	Net importers	Mt
Saudi Arabia	509	Saudi Arabia	339	United States	573
Russian	485	Russia	256	Japan	206
United States	300	Iran	130	China	159
Iran	214	Nigeria	112	India	122
China	190	UAE	105	Korea	118
Mexico	159	Norway	97	Germany	106
Canada	155	Mexico	89	Italy	94
Rest of the world	1829	Rest of the world	829	France	81
Total	3841			Spain	59
				Netherlands	58
				Rest of the world	515

Production statistics for 2008; exports and imports for 2007.
Reproduced from International Energy Agency (IEA) (2010) *Key World Energy Statistics 2009*. Paris, France: OECD/IEA [7].

equals 10^9; tera is abbreviated as T and equals 10^{12}.) Notice that the United States and China are the largest producers of electricity and also the largest producers of coal-fired power. Other large industrial nations generate large amounts of electricity, with many relying on coal (**Figure 1**). Canada is the sixth largest producer, but much of it comes from hydro sources and a significant amount (≈25 TWh annually) is exported to the United States. Clearly, rich countries are rich because they consume large amounts of energy, especially electricity.

Oil makes the largest contribution to total global consumption of energy, primarily because it is used for transportation and, to a much lesser degree, generation of electricity – primarily in diesel generators in remote communities (as well as much of sub-Sahara Africa), although there are a few large generation facilities that rely on oil. The major producers, exporters, and importers of crude oil are indicated in **Table 2**, as are the amounts involved. Although Canada is not indicated as a major exporter, because the data on exports are for 2007, it is expected to move up the table in the future because of large oil sands development. Notice that both the United States and China are major oil producers, but they are also major importers because of the size of their economies.

Together fossil fuels (coal, oil, and natural gas) account for about 78.5% of total global energy consumption if account is taken of electricity generated from fossil fuels (**Figure 1**). Upon including combustible renewables and waste (CR&W; this includes primarily wood biomass, crop residues, dung, and other fuels that are burned in stoves and used for space heating by those living in developing countries; this is a major source of black carbon (soot) that contributes to global warming; this also includes wastes from sawmilling and pulp making for space heating and generation of electricity), more than 90% of all energy used globally comes from sources that emit CO_2. Of the remainder, 5% comes from hydro and nuclear sources, leaving less than 4% from solar, geothermal, wind, tidal, and biofeedstock sources. Clearly, reducing reliance on fossil fuels in a big way presents a tremendous challenge for the renewable energy sector.

Fossil fuels are ubiquitous and cheap. Therefore, policies to replace them will likely require a combination of large subsidies (e.g., to producers of alternative fuels), regulations forcing firms and individuals to rely more on non-fossil fuel sources (such as renewable energy standard), publicly funded R&D, and taxes or cap-and-trade schemes that drive up fossil fuel prices to the point where it makes economic sense for consumers to switch to alternative energy sources or adopt smaller more fuel-efficient vehicles and smaller houses. However, there are limits on the amounts governments will pay to subsidize development of non-carbon sources of energy and to citizens' willingness to accept huge increases in the price of energy when cheaper fossil fuel alternatives are available. As the French intellectual Christian Gerondeau [8] argues, it is unlikely that cheap fossil fuels will go wanting – someone or some country will use them. But it is morally objectionable to raise energy costs when poor people already need to pay too much for energy [9].

One argument used to justify public spending on alternative energy is that the globe will run out of fossil fuels and that we need to prepare for that eventuality. For example, there are predictions that the world's oil production will soon attain 'Hubbert's peak' and begin to decline [10]. Hubbert's peak is predicated on the notion that prices and technology remain unchanged, because the peak will shift outward with improvements in technology and higher prices. Indeed, from an economic standpoint, the idea that we will run out of oil (or gas or coal) is simply nonsense. We will never run out of oil, gas, or coal. As these resources become increasingly scarcer, supply and demand intersect at increasingly higher prices; the market will always clear – there is always enough of the resource to meet demand. However, the higher prices will, in turn, signal scarcity and thereby induce technological innovations that will increase supply, reduce demand, and/or lead to new sources of energy. Reliance on wind energy will expand without government intervention if it is able to compete as an energy source as prices of fossil fuels rise.

Recent increases in the supply of oil have come from the Alberta oil sands and deepwater drilling. (Deepwater drilling will continue despite the massive oil spill resulting from the British Petroleum disaster in the Gulf of Mexico in 2010. If drilling is prevented in the United States, it does not mean that it will not be pursued by other countries. In Alberta, environmental concerns related to oil sands development are increasingly addressed by new investments in technology and methods for restoring the environment.) As discussed in Section 2.17.3, new natural gas drilling technologies have recently been developed in Texas, which enable gas to be extracted from various types of rocks, most notably shale. This has resulted in massive upgrades in reserves and a surfeit of gas. Shale is globally ubiquitous and the drilling methods developed in Texas can easily be repeated elsewhere. Indeed, recoverable reserves of shale or unconventional gas are now estimated to be about five times as large as recoverable conventional reserves of natural gas (see http://www.dawn.com/wps/wcm/connect/dawn-content-library/dawn/the-newspaper/letters-to-the-editor/breakthrough-in-gas-technology-240, viewed 15 July 2010). In terms of reducing CO_2 output, these developments position natural gas as the most likely alternative to coal for generating electricity because it releases much less CO_2 per heat unit than coal.

At the same time, there have been advances in transportation and other technologies that reduce the amount of energy required to produce the same level of economic services. Vehicles can travel farther using the same amount of fuel, new public transportation infrastructure has been built to reduce demand for fuel, and hybrid and electric vehicles are being brought to market. (Automobiles in the United States require an average of 10 l to drive 100 km, and those in Germany only slightly lower. Automobiles now coming onto the French market have a fuel economy of 5 l per 100 km, despite relying on internal combustion engines, while economy might get down to 3 l per 100 km as a result of better engines, lighter vehicles, and other improvements [8].) Costs of space heating have fallen as buildings have become 'greener'.

Costs of producing electricity from alternative wind and solar sources have fallen dramatically as well, while new geothermal, tidal, wave, and other renewable energy technologies are in various stages of development. Advances in nuclear power generation technology and experience also continue, particularly with regard to performance and safety [11, 12]. However, most of the renewable portfolio standard (RPS) programs implemented by many countries to address concerns about climate change tend to exclude important low-carbon technologies, particularly the substitution of natural gas for coal and greater reliance on nuclear energy. In essence, the objective of reducing carbon emissions is confused with encouraging renewable energy in electricity generation [12].

What has driven these developments? First and foremost, market signals have played an important role. In real terms, oil prices reached an all time high in 1980, peaking again in 2008, but at a slightly lower level; natural gas prices peaked in 2005 and again in 2008, but at a slightly lower level the second time, before plunging as a result of recession and new developments in drilling technology. While oil and gas prices are historically above their levels in the period before the first 'oil crisis' in 1973, which was brought on by the exercise of monopoly power on the part of the Organization of Petroleum Exporting Countries (OPEC) followed by price controls that reduced incentives for bringing new sources of petroleum to market, they have exhibited more erratic movement since then (**Figure 3**). (In **Figure** 3, oil prices are taken from http://inflationdata.com/inflation/inflation_rate/historical_oil_prices_table.asp and gas prices from http://www.eia.doe.gov/oil_gas/natural_gas/data_publications/natural_gas_monthly/ngm.html, viewed 15 July 2010.) More recently, environmental concerns and political factors (much like price controls) have prevented the expansion of drilling activities, while economic growth in developing countries, primarily China, has expanded demand, together resulting in higher real prices of oil. The same was true for natural gas, although the rates of increase in natural gas prices are now limited as a result of the new reserves. Anticipation of continued higher oil prices in the future has spurred on technological changes, greater conservation, and a switch to alternative fuels, including natural gas. The other incentive has been government policies, particularly subsidies.

2.17.2.2 Renewable Energy Policy

Various countries are hoping to wean their economies off fossil fuels and thereby reduce CO_2 emissions. These countries have established renewable energy targets (RPS) and are in the process of implementing policies to meet targets – subsidizing the production of electricity from renewable sources or production of biofuels for transportation, or mandating levels of renewable energy so they can pass costs on to consumers. For example, a jurisdiction can require renewable standards for gasoline and diesel fuel, which will ensure that 20% or 40% (or some other proportion) of the fuel sold at the pump consists of biofuels. Electrical system operators may be required to purchase some minimum proportion of their power from renewable generating sources, or a country may mandate that a minimum proportion of the generating capacity of a particular electricity system must come from renewable sources.

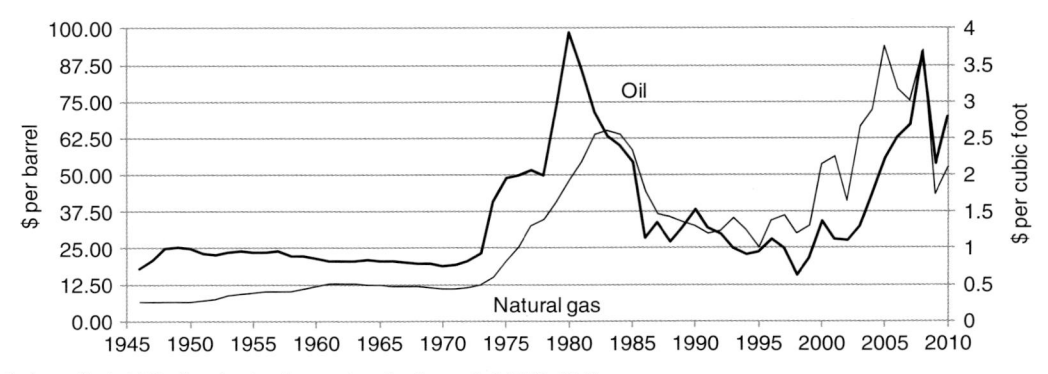

Figure 3 Inflation-adjusted US oil and natural gas prices for the period 1946–2010.

2.17.2.2.1 Scrambling to reduce CO₂ emissions: The renewable target game

Many jurisdictions have now passed laws requiring that renewable targets be met. All the countries of the European Union have agreed that 20% of total energy will be derived from renewable energy sources by 2020, although only some 7% of energy was derived from renewable sources in 2009. To meet these targets, many countries will rely primarily on wind and energy from biomass. However, a wood deficit of 200–260 million m³ is consequently forecast for the European Union by 2020, while, globally, an ECE/FAO report estimates that there will be a wood deficit of 320–450 million m³ annually simply to satisfy planned demand for wood for energy plus a growing wood-based industry (results reported by Don Roberts, CIBC, in presentations given in early 2010). This will certainly cause global wood fiber prices to increase, resulting in potentially detrimental changes in land use. The European Union is also targeting vehicular use of renewables. By 2020, 10% of the fuel used for transportation has to come from biofuels.

As an EU member, the UK's climate change mitigation plan also requires an increase in the share of renewable energy to 20% by 2020 (although 15% was originally targeted) from approximately 1% in 2006. The target requires that 35% of electricity generated in the United Kingdom has to be from renewable sources by 2020, compared to about 5% in 2007. Germany, on the other hand, has more ambitious climate goals than other EU members – a 40% reduction in greenhouse gas emissions from 1990 levels by 2020 (double the EU target). In addition, it aims to have 30% of its electricity generated from renewable sources by 2020, compared with 15.6% in 2009 (see *The Economist*, 4 September 2010, pp. 53–54). The latter target will be difficult to attain given that an earlier government had determined to cease nuclear power generation, which accounted for 22.6% of consumption in 2009, by 2022. Environmentalists will make it difficult to extend this deadline.

The United States has yet to pass comprehensive climate change legislation as noted in the introduction, but its farm legislation requires the production of 36 billion gallons of renewable fuels by 2022, including 21 billion gallons of 'advanced' (non-corn starch) biofuels. Some 50 metric tonnes (Mt) of wood has to be converted to fuel by 2012, with a targeted 70–100 Mt by 2020; the Biomass Crop Assistance Program (announced 8 June 2009) will provide a subsidy of $45 per tonne. This has the potential to result in an annual subsidy of $4.5 billion by 2020.

The Kerry–Lieberman–Graham bill promoted by the Obama administration in early 2010 seeks to cut greenhouse gas emissions by 17% from 2005 levels by 2020 and by 80% from 2005 levels by 2050 (information based on an editorial in *The Washington Times*, 27 April 2010, entitled 'Meltdown of the climate-change bill'; Senator Graham subsequently dropped his sponsorship of the bill out of concerns regarding re-election). Subsequent concerns about midterm elections caused the Senate majority leader Mr. Harry Reid to drop the bill because the public correctly viewed the cap-and-trade provisions in the bill as the equivalent of a tax. Nonetheless, Democratic Senator Jeff Bingham subsequently introduced a bill (S.3813) to create a national 'renewable electricity standard' (RES) (http://www.masterresource.org/2010/10/bingamans-national-res/, viewed 11 October 2010). It requires that by 2021, 15% of the electricity sold by an electric utility be generated from wind or certain 'other' renewable energy sources (presumably solar, wave, geothermal, or tidal, and not hydro), although up to four of the 15% points could be achieved by 'tightly defined' actions that improve energy efficiency. Clearly, wind is the renewable energy source of choice.

Even China hopes to produce 10% of all its energy needs from renewables by 2010, with a target of 15% by 2020. Most of this will come from farm biomass and forest plantations. However, it will be a logistical challenge annually to transport 150 000–200 000 tonnes of bulky straw from thousands of 0.15 ha farms to fuel a large number of 25 MW capacity power plants. The target of planting 13.3 million ha of forests for biofeedstock will be accomplished with help from rich countries through the clean development mechanism (CDM). In effect, these efforts could be counted twice – they enable China to meet its renewable energy targets, while making it possible for developed countries that purchase CDM offset credits to achieve their targets as well (at least until changes are made to the system of crediting offsets).

Other countries have their own targets. Like the United States, Canada is in the process of increasing biofuel production, but it also has a target to eliminate all coal-fired power generation by 2020. Both targets will be extremely difficult to meet, requiring large subsidies that will see electricity prices rise, greater reliance on natural gas, and, most likely, expansion of nuclear generating capacity. Consider the case of Ontario as an example of the direction policy has taken in efforts to increase generation of electricity from renewable energy sources.

2.17.2.2.2 Feed-in tariffs: The case of Ontario

Because electricity grids have their own peculiar dynamics (discussed in Section 2.17.5), feed-in tariffs (FITs) tend to be preferred over mandated levels of renewable use. One of the most ambitious attempts to achieve power generation from renewable sources was launched by the Ontario government when it passed the Green Energy and Green Economy Act on 14 May 2009. Its FIT schedule is provided in **Table 3**. With the exception of solar power, Ontario's FITs are indexed to inflation, which could dramatically increase the strain on the treasury.

The potential size of the subsidies can be determined from information about electricity rates. Ontario has implemented time-of-use billing to shift load from peak to off-peak times, but it costs over $1 billion to install smart meters. Residential customers with smart meters pay 9.9 ¢ kWh^{-1} at peak times (7.00 a.m. to 11.00 a.m., 5.00 p.m. to 9.00 p.m.), 8.0 ¢ kWh^{-1} during midpeak periods (11.00 a.m. to 5.00 p.m.), and 5.3 ¢ kWh^{-1} during off-peak times (9.00 p.m. to 7.00 a.m.). Customers without smart meters pay 6.5 ¢ kWh^{-1} for the first 600 kWh (in summer the first 1000 kWh) and 7.5 ¢ kWh^{-1} thereafter.

Ontario's average electrical load was some 16 000 MW during 2007, although it has fallen somewhat since then as a result of the financial crisis, which caused some major demanders of power to shut down. Coal and gas generating capacities are both about 4000 MW; nuclear generating capacity amounts to some 10 000 MW, while hydro capacity is nearly 6000 MW. To provide some

Table 3 Ontario Power Authority's feed-in tariff (FIT) program for renewable energy projects (base date: 30 September 2009)

Renewable type	Size (capacity of generating plant)[a]	Contract price (¢ kWh^{-1})	Percentage escalated[b]
Biomass			
	≤ 10 MW	13.8	20
	> 10 MW	13.0	20
Landfill gas			
	≤ 10 MW	11.1	20
	> 10 MW	10.3	20
Biogas			
On-farm	≤ 100 kW	19.5	20
On-farm	> 100 kW, ≤ 250 kW	18.5	20
Biogas	≤ 500 kW	16.0	20
Biogas	> 500 kW, ≤ 10 MW	14.7	20
Biogas	> 10 MW	12.2	20
Wind			
Onshore	Any size	13.5	20
Offshore	Any size	19.0	20
Solar			
Roof/ground	≤ 10 kW	80.2	0
Roof top	> 10 kW, ≤ 250 kW	71.3	0
Roof top	> 250 kW, ≤ 500 kW	63.5	0
Roof top	> 500 kW	53.9	0
Ground mount	> 10 kW, ≤ 10 MW	44.3	0
Water power [b]			
	≤ 10 MW	13.1	2
	> 10 MW, ≤ 50 MW	12.2	20

[a] Generally a 20-year contract with 2–3-year lead time; for hydro, a 40-year contract.
[b] Performance factor: 1.35 peak, 0.90 off-peak.
[c] Indexed by the Ontario Consumer Price Index.
Reproduced from http://fit.powerauthority.on.ca/Storage/99/10863_FIT_Pricing_Schedule_for_website.pdf (accessed 21 April 2010).

indication of the costs and benefits of Ontario's FIT program, assume that only 30% of the load is satisfied by fossil fuels, or 4800 MW h^{-1}, and the objective is to eliminate that production. Furthermore, assume that despite the capacities of coal and natural gas generation, coal-generated power accounts for half or more of fossil fuel-generated power. Finally, assume that biomass and wind-generated power substitute for fossil fuel power – biomass accounts for either one-half or one-quarter of the required substitute power with onshore and offshore wind accounting for two-thirds and one-third, respectively, of the remainder.

Approximately 7500 kWh of energy is generated per tonne of coal burned and 2.735 tonnes of CO_2 (tCO_2) is released. Thus, it takes about 320 tonnes of coal to burn half of the 4800 MW of electricity supplied by coal-fired generation each hour, releasing 875 tCO_2 each hour or 7.665 Gt CO_2 per year. At the same time, natural gas plants will release 495.8 tCO_2 each hour or 4.346 Gt CO_2 annually if they generate 2400 MW of electricity each hour (from http://bioenergy.ornl.gov/papers/misc/energy_conv.html (viewed 26 April 2010), coal releases 25.4 Mt of carbon per terajoule (TJ) compared to 14.4 Mt of carbon for natural gas).

The costs to the government of the FIT program depend on the extent to which various renewables substitute for fossil fuel generation and the average amount that final consumers pay for electricity. In **Table 4**, it is assumed that consumers pay an average of 8.5 ¢ kWh^{-1}. Using various biomass and wind combinations and fossil fuel displacement scenarios, and FIT data from **Table 3**, we can calculate carbon fluxes and costs to the public treasury of reducing CO_2 emissions. The results provided in **Table 4** suggest that costs to the treasury could amount to $2.4–$2.6 billion annually, which will put a severe strain on the provincial treasury. In essence, by substituting fossil fuel energy with renewable sources in the generation of electricity, Ontario will pay a subsidy ranging from some $45 per t$CO_2$ to well over $1000 per t$CO_2$, depending primarily on the extent of biomass generation.

Two points are worth mentioning. First, there exist much cheaper ways to reduce CO_2 emissions, including purchase of certified emission reduction credits on carbon markets. As of mid-September 2010, prices on the Chicago Climate Exchange had not exceeded $0.15 per t$CO_2$ since January 2010, while the spot market price of certified emission reduction credits did not exceed €14 per tCO_2 (approximately US$16–$19 per tCO_2) during 2009 and 2010. Second, the analysis in **Table 4** is crude; it focuses only on the costs to the public treasury and excludes any other costs, some of which can be quite high.

Then what are the options being considered by various jurisdictions for reducing carbon dioxide emissions in the generation of electricity? These range from continued reliance on fossil fuels, but then in ways that reduce emissions, to greater reliance on nuclear and a variety of renewable energy alternatives. First we consider options related to coal, natural gas, and nuclear energy, and then renewable energy sources.

Table 4 Costs and benefits of Ontario's feed-in tariff program: hourly CO_2 flux and cost of reducing CO_2 emissions, various scenarios

	Biomass 50%: wind 50%			Biomass 25%: wind 75%		
Coal:NG ratio	1:0	¾:¼	½:½	1:0	¾:¼	½:½
CO_2 flux			tCO_2			
Coal saving	1 749.2	1 311.9	874.6	1 749.2	1 311.9	874.6
NG saving	0	247.9	495.8	0	247.9	495.8
Sequestered[a]	665.8	665.8	665.8	332.9	332.9	332.9
Biomass emission	2 058.2	2 058.2	2 058.2	1 029.1	1 029.1	1 029.1
Net flux	356.9	167.5	−21.9	1 053	863.7	674.3
			US dollars			
Subsidy	272 000	272 000	272 000	300 000	300 000	300 000
Subsidy per tCO_2	762.19	1 624.05	NA	284.89	347.36	44.92

[a] Carbon sequestered in tree growth over 25 years using growth function (9.1), including all aboveground biomass with carbon discounted at 2%. NA indicates not applicable because eliminating fossil fuel generation results in a net release of CO_2 — there is no climate change benefit whatsoever in this scenario; NG, natural gas.

2.17.3 Fossil Fuel and Nuclear Options for Reducing CO_2 Emissions

It is unlikely that cheap and abundant fossil fuel resources can be denied their role in the generation of electricity. (A reviewer suggested that wind energy should be developed because political instability in oil-producing regions leads to erratic and high oil prices. It is true, but oil is not a player in the generation of electricity. As noted earlier, coal and gas are ubiquitous and cheap, and coal (and uranium)-exporting countries, such as Australia and Canada, are politically stable.) It simply makes no economic sense to leave valuable resources in the ground, and it is likely that someone will ultimately exploit the associated rents [8]. When it comes to climate change, therefore, options for their exploitation remain. The same is true of nuclear power. In this section, we examine the 'clean' coal, natural gas, and nuclear options for generating electricity in more detail.

2.17.3.1 Clean Coal

Carbon capture and storage (CCS) is associated with the so-called 'clean coal'. CCS involves removing CO_2 from the flue gas and pumping it into an underground reservoir. As of 2007, there were four industrial CCS projects in operation. Two projects are located off the Norwegian coast, on the Norwegian shelf or Utsira formation in the North Sea. Natural gas from the Sleipner gas field contains 9.5% CO_2 and, to avoid paying carbon taxes, Norway's Statoil pumps the waste CO_2 into a deep underground saline aquifer. Since 1996, it has pumped annually about 1 Mt CO_2 into the aquifer. A similar project at the Snøhvit gas field in the Barents Sea stores 700 000 tCO_2 per year.

The largest CCS project is found at Weyburn in southeastern Saskatchewan, Canada, where the Weyburn–Midale CO_2 Project has since 2000 taken CO_2 from the Dakota Gasification Company plant in Beulah, North Dakota, and injected it underground to enhance oil recovery; approximately 1.5 Mt CO_2 has been injected annually. (A graduate student associated with the Institute for Integrated Energy Systems at the University of Victoria told the author that after working with other engineers on measuring the success of CO_2 storage, it appeared they could not track the eventual destination of CO_2, except for that which actually enhanced oil recovery. There was no guarantee in other words that CO_2 did not leak out of the underground formation at some unknown location.) The North Dakota company had produced methane gas from coal for 30 years while the oil field was discovered in 1954 and thus had also been in operation for quite some time.

The fourth project at In Salah in Algeria is much like the two Norwegian projects. CO_2 is removed from natural gas and reinjected underground, thereby preventing 1.2 Mt CO_2 from entering the atmosphere.

Many other CCS projects are now under consideration or under construction. For example, in Saskatchewan, SaskPower, the electrical system operator, is providing $1.4 billion in subsidies to convert one of its coal-fired generators at the Boundary Dam Power Station to capture CO_2 and pump it underground to enhance oil recovery near Estevan. SaskPower hopes to generate 115–120 MW of base-load electricity from clean coal, thereby avoiding the need to shut down its facility. Although it is only a demonstration project that received the go ahead in early 2010, it is believed that upward of 10 Mt CO_2 can be stored underground. Given that Canada hopes to eliminate coal-fired power plants, CCS projects related to coal are likely to constitute a stopgap measure, especially in Saskatchewan, which had invested heavily in coal-generated power in recent decades. The province of Alberta has announced that it would provide funding of $2 billion for CCS projects. CCS is required to offset emissions related to oil sands development. Germany, Australia, China, and the United States are also looking into 'clean coal', while Norway, the Netherlands, and possibly British Columbia are looking into CCS as they develop natural gas fields that contain high proportions of CO_2.

Although CCS could well be technically feasible on a large scale at some time in the future, it certainly will not be economically feasible. There are two crucial obstacles. First, removing CO_2 from the flue gas, and then compressing, storing, transporting, and finally pumping the carbon dioxide into a permanent underground storage facility is extremely costly. For a coal-fired power plant, output would have to increase by 28% just to cover the costs of removing the CO_2, although some of this can be done in off-peak hours when it is difficult to ramp down power output. Since not all regions have readily available places to store CO_2, it will be necessary to build a large pipeline transmission infrastructure and/or pipeline infrastructure plus storage and ship loading and offloading facilities.

Suppose that the objective is to capture and store just 10% of the world's CO_2 emissions, or about 3 Gt CO_2. Bryce [1] has estimated that if CO_2 is compressed at 1000 pounds per square inch (psi), or 68 atmosphere (atm) (1 atm = 14.696 psi = 101 325 pascal (Pa), where 1 Pa = 1 kg m^{-1} s^{-2} = 1 kg m^{-2}; note that CO_2 reaches a supercritical stage (where it becomes liquid) at about 70 Pa (measured at 31 °C), but to get it there would take a great deal of energy), it would amount to an oil equivalent volume of 81.8 million barrels per day. If all of this CO_2 were to be moved by ship, it would require filling 41 very large crude carriers (each holding about 2 million barrels) each and every day. Of course, much of the CO_2 would simply be transported by pipeline to a suitable underground location, but clearly not all. Even if only a quarter had to be shipped, this would require loading 10 supertankers per day. Clearly, CCS is a very expensive, and probably unrealistic, proposition.

But it is the second issue that is the real obstacle to large-scale CCS. There is always a risk that captured CO_2 is released, which could potentially lead to large loss of life, as when an underwater landslide in 1986 naturally 'burped' a large mass of CO_2 from Lake Nyos in Cameroon, forming a low-lying cloud, it killed over 1700 people before it dispersed. Unless carbon storage occurs in remote regions, which increases its costs, people would need to be compensated to have a storage facility nearby. Research pertaining to the transportation and storage of nuclear wastes indicates that this could be an enormous cost (see Reference 13).

In essence, the only real options appear to be those of conservation (e.g., via smart grids), greater reliance on natural gas and/or nuclear power, or development of alternative renewable sources of energy.

2.17.3.2 Natural Gas

During the 1990s and into the new millennium, a Texas oil and gas well driller, George Mitchell, experimented with various techniques to cause gas to flow from shale deposits. In 1997, he and his crew found that if water under extreme pressure was injected into wells along with sand and certain chemicals, it caused the gas to flow. (Chemicals constitute about 1% of the volume of water. There remains some concern that chemicals could enter the water supply, but this is unlikely because wells are significantly deeper than the porous layers from which water may be taken.) Then, in 2003, they discovered horizontal drilling. Thereby, they could drill down some half to one kilometer and then turn the drills sideways, and drill horizontally (lateral) for several kilometers. At various locations along the lateral (about every 120 m), the rock formation could be 'fractured' by injecting water and sand. The water would force openings in the rock, which were filled with sand, which along with the chemicals facilitated the flow of natural gas.

As a result of horizontal drilling and hydraulic fracturing that opened up the pores to allow gas to flow, the Texas' Barnett Shale vaulted into the top 10 of the globe's natural gas fields. Its recoverable reserves of unconventional or shale gas are estimated to be about 44 trillion cubic feet, or energy equivalent of 8 billion barrels of oil. This compares with the 6 billion barrel East Texas oil field discovered in 1931, which was the largest oil field in the world at that time.

Furthermore, recoverable reserves of unconventional gas in the United States are now estimated at 649.2 trillion cubic feet [1]. This is a huge increase over 1989 estimates of recoverable gas reserves. Furthermore, unconventional gas can be found elsewhere in the world as the technological advance resulting from lateral drilling methods and fracturing formations can be adopted in other locations. Thus, for example, total gas reserves in northeastern British Columbia are approximately equal to total US reserves estimated in 1989. However, some of this gas contains large amounts of CO_2, which will be released as the gas is brought into production.

Given the tremendous increase in global natural gas reserves that the new technology has brought about, many countries will pursue a strategy of substituting highly energy-efficient natural gas for coal in the production of electricity. As shown in **Table 5**, natural gas is generally composed of methane (CH_4), ethane (C_2H_6), and other hydrocarbons. Consequently, compared to coal, it releases much less CO_2 into the atmosphere. Furthermore, natural gas power plants can be simply and quickly built; the up-front construction costs of gas plants is half or less than that of coal plants, and much lower than that of nuclear, solar, wind, or other power generating facilities [14]. Fuel costs tend to be much higher, however. Hence, it is not surprising that countries are opting for natural gas, although in some cases the decision to build natural gas power plants is the result of political indecision concerning the extension of old or construction of new nuclear power plants.

2.17.3.3 Nuclear Power

Together the United States and France produce some 47% of global nuclear energy output, and account for 45% of installed capacity (**Table 6**). More than three-quarters of France's domestic consumption of electricity comes from its nuclear power plants and it exports nuclear power to other countries. It is difficult for a country to expand reliance on nuclear energy much beyond that experienced by France because nuclear plants are base-load power plants, so peaking gas plants or hydro facilities are needed to address short periods of high demand. France avoids some of its need for peaking capacity by selling nuclear power to other European countries, especially ones such as the Netherlands that are looking to reduce their CO_2 emissions and are closing coal and/or gas plants.

Table 5 Comparison of the potential release of greenhouse gases from various fossil fuels

Item	Chemical structure/% of constituents
Natural gas	
75% methane	CH_4
15% ethane	C_2H_6
10% other hydrocarbons	
Hydrocarbons	
Propane	C_3H_8
Butane	C_4H_{10}
Octane	C_8H_{18}
Benzene	C_6H_6
Hexane	C_6H_{14}
Naphthalene	$C_{10}H_8$
Bituminous coal	
Carbon (C)	75–90%
Hydrogen (H)	4.5–5.5%
Nitrogen (N)	1.0–1.5%
Sulfur (S)	1–2%
Oxygen (O)	5–20%
Ash	2–10%
Moisture	1–10%
Coal [a]	C_nH_m ($n > m$, n large, m small)
Glucose	$C_6H_{12}O_6$
Gasoline (average)	C_8H_{18} range: C_6H_{14} to $C_{12}H_{26}$
Diesel	$C_{16}H_{34}$

[a] Macromolecules consisting of clusters of aromatic coal linked by bridges of sulfur, oxygen, or other element(s).
From author's own construction from Internet sources.

Table 6 Nuclear power production and capacity of top 10 producers in 2007

Country	Production (TWh)	Capacity (GW)	Percentage of domestic consumption
United States	837	106	19.4
France	440	63	77.9
Japan	264	49	23.5
Russia	160	22	15.8
Korea	143	18	33.6
Germany	141	20	22.3
Canada	93	13	14.6
Ukraine	93	13	47.2
Sweden	67	9	45.0
United Kingdom	63	11	16.1
Rest of the world	418	48	6.6
World	2719	372	13.8

Reproduced from International Energy Agency (IEA) (2010) *Key World Energy Statistics 2009*. Paris, France: OECD/IEA [7].

The top 10 nuclear power-producing countries are given in **Table 6**. The rest of the world accounts for only 13% of global nuclear generating capacity, and only 6.6% of the consumption in countries outside the top 10 with nuclear capacity is accounted for by nuclear energy. For example, China is not included in the list but, as a nuclear power, has some generating capacity. Nonetheless, the generation of electricity from nuclear energy is confined to a small group of countries. Yet nuclear power is a sensible and realistic (and some would argue only) option for achieving the strict CO_2 emission-reduction targets indicated above. For a country such as Canada, 70% of electricity demand is already met from hydro and nuclear sources, and because it is difficult to expand hydro capacity and given the obstacles posed by biomass energy, Canada might wish to expand its nuclear capacity in order to mitigate climate change.

How realistic is the nuclear option? Despite its promise, there are severe challenges facing expansion of nuclear energy. Nuclear wastes, the potential risk of enriched nuclear material being used by terrorists, high construction costs, cost overruns, and general opposition to nuclear power plants by citizens, and especially environmental groups, militate against nuclear power. Storage of wastes in central facilities such as Nevada's Yucca Mountain makes sense as the amount involved is relatively quite small (no more than the volume of a large room), while the status quo of storing wastes on-site is likely riskier. Given that far less than 5% of the available energy in nuclear fuel is used to generate power, enriching the spent uranium fuel can extend the usefulness of the fuel and, eventually, reduce its radioactive half-life. Because enrichment leads to bomb-grade material, governments have sought to prevent further refinement or recycling of spent fuel, preferring instead to store the more radioactive material. Although recycling adds to the costs of nuclear fuel, it is the fear of nuclear weapons proliferation that makes the future for nuclear power more uncertain.

Despite these obstacles, some countries will necessarily choose to expand reliance on nuclear energy to meet greenhouse gas emission targets and deflect concerns about energy security. As of 2009, there were 44 nuclear power plants under construction globally, with 11 in China, 8 in Russia, 6 in India, 5 in Korea, 2 in each of Ukraine, Bulgaria, Taiwan, and Japan, and 1 in each of Argentina, Finland, France, Iran, Pakistan, and the United States [12]. Estimates provided by Deutch et al. [12] indicate that the life-cycle costs of producing nuclear energy are 8.4 ¢ kWh^{-1}, compared with 6.2 ¢ kWh^{-1} for coal and 6.5 ¢ kWh^{-1} for gas, although the latter costs would rise to 8.3 ¢ kWh^{-1} and 7.4 ¢ kWh^{-1}, respectively, if a carbon charge of $25 per tCO$_2$ emissions was imposed. (These costs are significantly higher than those reported in the earlier MIT study [11], but are probably higher than they would be today given that construction costs have declined since the financial crisis. This needs to be taken into account in the following discussion as well.) Furthermore, if the added risks of capital used in building nuclear reactors were eliminated, so that the carrying costs of capital investments were the same as those of coal and gas plants, nuclear energy would cost 6.6 ¢ kWh^{-1} rather than 8.4 ¢ kWh^{-1}.

It is difficult to compare costs of producing electricity from renewable sources with those from traditional sources. Using data from a survey conducted by the International Energy Agency [15], it is possible to provide some comparison of costs on a per megawatt hour basis. Estimates are provided in Table 7. These indicate that electricity generated from renewable energy sources costs significantly more than that from traditional sources. Waste incineration is only the lowest cost means of generating electricity if there is a payment to dispose of municipal and industrial waste (which explains the negative value in the table, indicating a benefit). Furthermore, the contribution of wastes to total electricity generation will be small, which is also true of combined heat and power (CHP). Coal and nuclear energy are the lowest cost realistic alternatives. Gas is more expensive because of high fuel costs, but gas plants are cheap to build and are needed for fast response to shifts in load.

The argument made by proponents of renewable energy generation is that the costs in Table 7 do not reflect externality costs, in particular the costs associated with CO$_2$ emissions (and other pollutants) from fossil fuel plants and the health and safety risks associated with nuclear power. Assuming that coal emits 0.9–1.0 tCO$_2$ per MWh of electricity [17] – an emission level that is dropping as more efficient plants come online – it would take a carbon tax well above what CO$_2$ emissions have been trading for under the Europe's Emission Trading System or the Chicago Climate Exchange before even wind energy is competitive with coal. But there remains another problem: With the exception of biomass and large-scale hydro, only nuclear and combined-cycle gas turbine (CCGT) plants can replace coal because, without storage, intermittent sources of power cannot serve base-load needs [17].

Table 7 Lifetime generation costs ($ MWh^{-1}) by generating type

Generating type[a]	Midpoint	Low	High
Wind onshore	68.08	36.39	168.71
Wind offshore	78.54	59.09	144.38
Solar thermal	193.64	193.64	315.20
Solar photovoltaic	192.21	141.10	2195.39
Small-scale run-of-river hydro	108.28	46.45	283.02
Large-scale hydro	53.12	53.12	99.33
Nuclear	30.71	24.34	80.26
Coal (lignite)	39.35	34.40	75.35
Coal (high quality)	31.90	30.30	80.85
Coal (integrated coal gas)	44.73	31.94	69.15
Gas (CCGT)	54.62	44.69	73.24
Gas (open)	54.64	54.64	57.33
CHP (using CCGT)	55.12	33.11	94.65
CHP (using coal)	39.09	29.25	54.87
CHP (using other fuels)	40.01	34.40	116.42
Waste incineration	11.39	−4.68	61.19
Biomass	48.74	43.64	117.59

[a] Open-cycle gas turbines lose exhaust heat but can respond quickly to changes in demand; combined-cycle gas turbines (CCGTs) recycle exhaust heat, which makes them suitable as base-load plants but makes it more difficult for them to ramp up and down. Combined heat and power (CHP) occurs when heat is used to generate power instead of being used for space heating; such power is usually available at night and in colder climates. The costs include capital, operation and maintenance, and fuel costs over the lifetime of a power plant, discounted to the present and 'levelized' over the expected output of the generating source over its lifetime. Values are in 2008 US dollars. The midpoint value is based on a 5% discount rate, as is the low value (except in the case of high-quality coal); the high value is derived using a 10% discount rate.
Reproduced from van Kooten GC and Timilsina GR (2009) *Wind Power Development: Economics and Policies*, 32pp. Policy Research Working Paper 4868. Washington, DC: The World Bank, Development Research Group, Environment and Energy Team [16].

2.17.4 Renewable Alternatives to Fossil Fuels

In the electricity sector, fossil fuel sources of energy are primarily coal and natural gas, while renewable sources include large-scale hydro, small-scale run-of-river hydro, geothermal, wind, tidal, solar, wave, municipal solid wastes, and biomass. Some of these sources are severely constrained. Consider biomass. While there has been a great deal of emphasis on the use of terrestrial carbon sinks for reducing atmospheric concentrations of CO_2, and even offsetting fossil fuel emissions, the costs of sequestering carbon in agricultural and forest ecosystems are generally quite a bit higher than emission-reduction options [18, 19]. There are some fundamental problems with the use of terrestrial sinks, which make them a very dubious means of mitigating climate change; these include their ephemeral nature, high monitoring and transaction costs in establishing CO_2 baselines and flux, and potential for corruption [20, 21].

In this section, we want to consider the future prospects of renewable energy sources in generating electricity, especially their near-term prospects given that many developed countries have ambitious greenhouse gas emission targets that are supposed to come into force within a decade. We consider the prospects for biomass, hydropower, and, finally, intermittent resources such as wind, wave, tidal, and solar. In Section 2.17.5, we consider wind power in more detail from an economics standpoint because wind has become the fastest growing renewable energy source. Given the scope of our discussion in this section, however, we provide only a broad-brush analysis of the challenges society faces in turning a fossil fuel-based economy into one that is much less so.

2.17.4.1 Biomass for Generating Electricity

One focus of current policies to mitigate climate change has been on the potential of using biomass to generate electricity. Increasing electrical power production from forest biomass, sawmill residue, and 'black liquor' from pulp mills is constrained by high transportation costs and competition for residual fiber, which makes forest biomass an expensive source of energy. Consider the example of British Columbia, which is a major forest products exporting jurisdiction.

Because of the extent of mountain pine beetle damage to forests in the interior of British Columbia, many commentators felt that an obvious use of beetle-killed trees would be power generation. Studies that examined the costs of producing electricity from dead trees argue that this could be done with little in the way of government subsidies. This analysis is based on average past costs of harvesting and hauling timber from the forest to sawmills. However, when one takes into account the rising costs of hauling timber as more remote timber-damaged sites need to be harvested, marginal costs rise rapidly with truck cycle times (the time required to travel to and from the harvesting site) of 9 h or more [22]. An electrical generating facility turns out to be only a marginally attractive option for reducing CO_2 emissions when feedstock costs are low; however, as feedstock costs alone rise from an equivalent of 4 to 8.5 ¢ kWh^{-1}, biomass power is no longer an economically viable option.

Producing char from biomass through a process known as pyrolysis (a form of incineration that chemically decomposes organic matter by heat but without oxygen) suffers from similar problems, although high transportation costs might be mitigated somewhat by producing char on-site. Nonetheless, the amount of char available for generating electricity will be negligible in comparison to what is needed and there are concerns that the process produces hazardous wastes.

Perhaps the best option for generating electricity from wood biomass is wood pellets. Wood pellet production plants are relatively inexpensive to construct and can, in some instances, be moved quite easily to new locations (although they are not mobile enough to be located at the harvesting site). Wood pellets can be used directly in coal-fired power plants with little or no adjustments to the burners – pellets can be pulverized much like coal and pellets are preferred over wood chips (which are used for pulp). Wood pellet stoves are also popular for space heating in residential homes.

Because of their flexibility, relatively low production costs, and government programs and subsidies, demand for pellets has risen sharply. European demand for wood pellets has risen rapidly since about 2005 because of subsidies. As a result, British Columbia's wood pellet production capacity has risen to about 1 million tonnes by 2010. But, as noted earlier, as demand for pellets, char, and other energy uses of wood biomass increases, prices will rise making them less attractive as an alternative form of energy.

Using a regional fiber allocation and transportation (mathematical programming) model, Stennes et al. [23] demonstrate a major drawback of timber feedstocks. As one of the largest lumber-producing and exporting jurisdictions in the world, British Columbia's forest resources are enormous and one would think that these resources would form a logical foundation for a thriving bioenergy sector. Lumber is far and away the most lucrative product that is produced in the province. Chips from sawmilling operations form the mainstay of the province's pulp industry. Other sawmill residues (bark, sawdust, etc.) are already allocated by mills to on-site space heating and power generation, with some excess chips and residues used in the production of wood pellets, oriented strand board, and other products. Competition for sawmill residuals occurs between pulp mills and other wood product manufacturers as well as heating and electricity sectors. There is some leeway to increase available wood waste by hauling roadside and other waste from harvest operations to electricity generation and other facilities that might be able to use them. The important point to note is that any residuals and other wood waste are available at a reasonable cost only as a result of timber harvests for sawmilling purposes [22, 24].

When account is taken of the supply and demand of wood fiber for all its different purposes, and when costs of transporting various types of fiber from one location in the province to another are considered, there is little wiggle room. Indeed, the government might wish to implement policies, such as direct construction subsidies or FITs, to increase power generation or wood pellet production from a wood biomass feedstock, but this will only lead to increased demand for fiber. This causes prices of wood residuals and wood 'waste' to increase, driving out existing users such as pulp mills, or the bioenergy producers themselves, depending on their ability to compete [23]. For example, pulp prices were less than $500 per tonne several years ago, but reached $1000 per tonne in 2010. Pulp producers can outbid energy producers for wood fiber at high pulp prices but have a harder time competing at lower prices, especially if bioenergy producers are subsidized.

What is often neglected in discussions of biofuels and biomass-fired power generation is the fact that biomass and biofuels are not carbon neutral as is often claimed. The combustion of biofuels and biomass releases carbon dioxide, which is indeed more than what is released from fossils fuels to generate an equivalent amount of energy. It is only when crops and trees grow that carbon dioxide is removed from the atmosphere, and this can take quite a long time in the case of trees. Furthermore, CO_2 and other greenhouse gases are emitted in the harvest and hauling of biomass, and during the conversion of biomass to fuel or power. In the case of ethanol, for example, this could even offset the gains from replacing gasoline. For example, Crutzen et al. [25] found that given current nitrogen-use efficiencies in agriculture, the increase in fertilizers used to grow energy crops has offset the reduction in CO_2 emissions from the gasoline the biofuel replaced. If ethanol came from sugarcane, the contribution of the biofuel to global warming was between 0.5 and 0.9, where a value above 1.0 indicates increased release of greenhouse gases (greater warming rather than cooling); if ethanol came from corn, the warming factor was 0.9–1.5; however, if the biofuel came from canola, it resulted in no benefit as the greenhouse gases released exceeded those associated with the fuel that was replaced (factor of 1.0–1.7).

When wood biomass is burned in lieu of coal, say, more CO_2 is released than with coal. In addition, more CO_2 is released in gathering biomass across a large landscape than is the case with coal as coal deposits are concentrated near a particular location. Thus, there is an increase in the release of carbon dioxide, not a reduction. The reduction comes only as trees grow, which could take as much as 80 years. To mitigate the length of the growing season, fast-growing tree species, such as hybrid poplar, can be grown, or alternative plants such as switchgrass can be used as a biomass fuel. While this tilts the greenhouse gas emissions more favorably toward biomass burning, nitrogen fertilizer is often required to spur growth, and nitrogen oxides are a more potent greenhouse gas than CO_2.

Finally, land is the most important factor in the production of biofuels. Increased demand for energy crops reduces cultivated area devoted to food production as land is diverted into energy crops [26]. It also increases the carbon footprint. Overall, therefore, the process of generating electricity from biomass is hardly carbon neutral.

From a policy perspective, biological methods are not an efficient means of addressing climate change, although promising research into various biological organisms that make this process more efficient is ongoing. These may very well come to fruition, but it could be several decades before such options are commercially viable. However, energy from biological organisms does not appear to be a major component of governments' policy arsenals for combating climate change. Landfill gas generated from solid waste is a potential source of electricity, but even if it is employed on a large scale, its contribution to the globe's electricity needs would necessarily be extremely small. The same holds for the incineration of municipal wastes.

2.17.4.2 Hydraulics and Storage

A number of countries have developed their hydraulic resources to build large-scale hydropower facilities. With the so-called 'Three Gorges Dam' (affecting the upper Mekong, Yangtze, and Salween rivers), China now has the greatest hydro capacity in the world (**Table 8**). In 2007, hydro production accounted for only 14.8% of China's consumption of electricity. This is much less than the proportions accounted for by hydro in Norway (98%), Brazil (84%), Venezuela (72%), and Canada (57%). India relied on hydropower to a greater extent than China, as did Russia despite its relatively abundant fossil fuel resources.

Large-scale hydro remains one of the best options for generating 'clean' electricity, but its main drawbacks relate to inadequate runoff for power generation (especially in regions where water is scarce, intermittent, and/or unreliable) and negative

Table 8 Hydroelectric power production and capacity in 2007

Country	Production (TWh)	Capacity (GW)[a]	Percentage of domestic consumption
China	485	126	14.8
Brazil	374	73	84.0
Canada	369	73	57.6
United States	276	99	6.3
Russia	179	46	17.6
Norway	135	29	98.2
India	124	35	15.4
Japan	84	47	7.4
Venezuela	83	NA	72.3
Sweden	66	NA	44.5
Rest of the world	987	NA	NA
World	3162	889	15.9

[a] Data for 2006.
NA, not available.
Reproduced from International Energy Agency (IEA) (2010). *Key World Energy Statistics 2009*. Paris, France: OECD/IEA [7].

environmental externalities (changes in the aquatic ecosystem, impediments to fish migration, land inundation by reservoirs, etc.). Environmentalists oppose large-scale hydro development, particularly in developing countries, because of the ecological damage it causes, while even small-scale, run-of-river projects have been opposed in rich countries on environmental grounds. Because of strong environmental opposition against hydropower developments, hydropower's future contribution to increases in overall generating capacity will inevitably remain limited in scope. Expansion of water power is not expected to be a large contributor to the mitigation of climate change.

Although unlikely to contribute much in the way of additional clean power, existing large-scale hydro and strategic expansions of reservoir storage capacity (which raise generating capacity) might serve an important purpose when combined with intermittent sources of energy, namely, wind, tidal, and solar sources. For example, wind-generated power is often available at night, when base-load power plants are able to supply all demand. Wind energy would then need to be curtailed (wasted) or, where possible (and it may not always be possible), base-load plants would need to reduce output, causing them to operate inefficiently. If a base-load plant is coal fired, inefficient operation implies that CO_2 emissions are not reduced one-for-one as wind replaces coal. In some cases, the trade-off is so poor that CO_2 emissions are hardly reduced whatsoever. This problem can be overcome if adequate transmission capacity exists so that the excess wind-generated power could be stored behind hydro dams by displacing electricity demand met by hydropower. This is the case in northern Europe, where excess wind power generated at night in Denmark is exported to Norway, with hydropower imported from Norway during peak daytime hours.

Similar relationships are found elsewhere. In Canada, for example, the provinces of Quebec and British Columbia rely almost exclusively on hydropower, while the respective neighboring provinces of Ontario and Alberta generate significant base-load power from coal (or nuclear in Ontario's case). Ontario and Alberta are both expanding their installed wind capacity. During off-peak nighttime hours, excess wind and/or base-load power from Ontario (Alberta) is sold to Quebec (British Columbia), with hydropower sold back during peak periods. Given that the rents from these transactions have accrued to the provinces with hydro assets, Ontario and Alberta have been less than keen to upgrade the transmission interties, preferring to look at other possible solutions to the storage problem.

In all three cases, there are net economic and climate benefits from the development of higher capacity transmission interties; or, in the case of northern Europe, it would be beneficial to simply have more interties between jurisdictions where wind power is generated (northern Germany, other parts of Denmark) and those with hydro resources (Norway and Sweden). The main obstacle is the lack of incentives for the wind-generating region to 'dump' power into the region with storage, as the latter captures all the rents from such an exchange. This is a game theory problem: If institutions can be developed that facilitate the sharing of both the economic rents and the climate benefits (emission-reduction credits), the jurisdictions have the incentive to better integrate the operations of their electricity grids (including construction or upgrading of transmission interties) so that overall CO_2 emissions are minimized.

2.17.4.3 Geothermal

The temperatures are much higher deep in the earth than on the surface. In these places, the magma of volcanoes forms. In some places, heat escapes from underground through vents or geysers and can be captured to generate electricity or used for space heating. The country that relies most on such geothermal energy is Iceland. Proposals to drill deep into the earth and capture heat for power generation suggest that this is a viable source of energy from an engineering standpoint. Economic considerations will prevent the use of geothermal energy on a sufficiently large scale to make a dent in the globe's energy supply in the foreseeable future.

2.17.4.4 Generating Electricity from Intermittent Energy Sources

There exist a number of promising renewable energy sources that could at some time in the future make a significant contribution to global electrical energy needs. However, the likelihood that these will have a major impact in the short or medium term (5–50 years) is small. It is evident from **Figures 1** and **2** that nonconventional sources of energy constitute only about 4% of global consumption. Raising that to 20% or more constitutes an enormous challenge, especially in a world where energy demand is rapidly increasing as a result of economic development in countries such as India and China. Simply expanding the use of renewable energy and then incorporating renewable energy sources into energy systems will prove difficult, not least because an expansion in the use of renewables will lead to increases in their prices (as we noted with regard to wood biomass).

Among alternative energy sources, tidal and wave energy are promising, especially considering the potential energy that might be harnessed. Tidal energy is considered particularly desirable because of its regularity and predictability. While some tidal barrage systems are in place and experiments are under way with tidal turbines (which function much like wind turbines), huge technological and cost obstacles still need to be overcome. This is even more the case for wave energy conversion systems, which simultaneously suffer from unpredictability and intermittency. For both wave and tidal systems, costs of transmission lines can be prohibitive.

Solar energy is another promising energy source. The energy or irradiance from the sun averages some $1.366\,\text{kW}\,\text{m}^{-2}$, or 174 PW for the entire globe, but it is difficult to convert to usable energy. Other than through plant photosynthesis, there are two ways to harness this solar energy: (1) solar photovoltaic (PV) converts the sun's energy directly into electricity, while (2) solar heaters warm water (swimming pools, water tanks, etc.). Solar heaters convert up to 60% of the sun's energy into heat, while PV cells convert only 12–15% of the energy into electricity, although PV laboratory prototypes are reaching 30% efficiency. One problem with solar electricity is its prohibitive capital costs, which amount to some $13 000–$15 000 per kW of installed capacity [15], although costs have subsequently

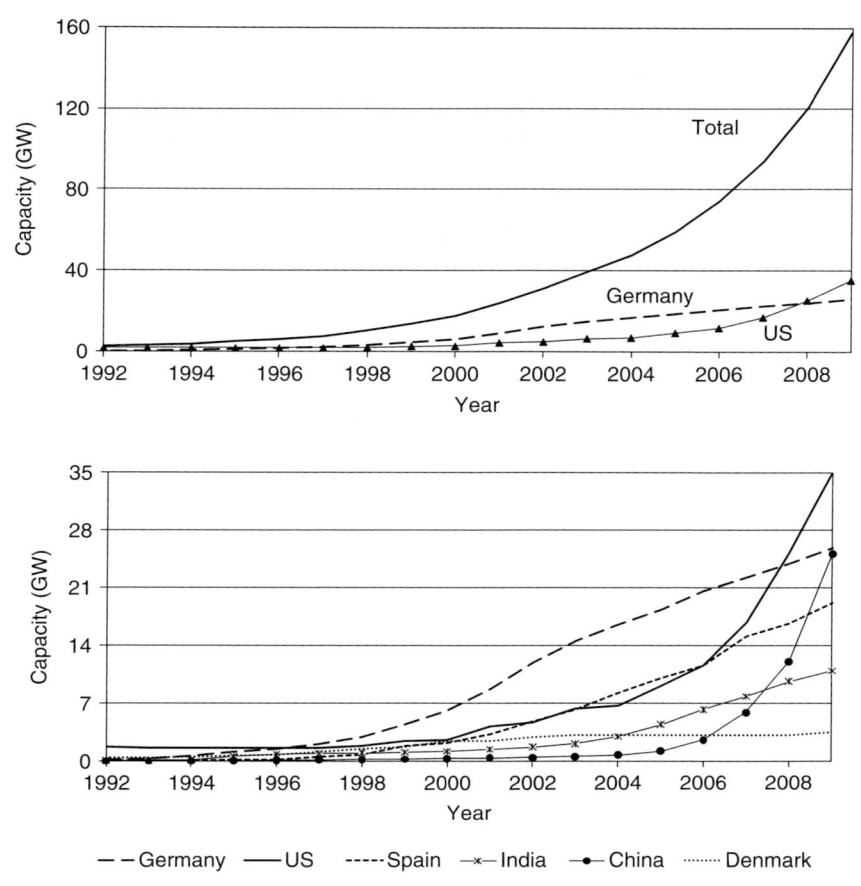

Figure 4 Expansion of global wind generating capacity, total and selected countries.

fallen (almost to one-third) in the past several years. In addition, solar power is intermittent (e.g., output is greatly reduced on cloudy days), unavailable at night, and, in high latitudes, less available in winter when demand is high than in summer (due to shorter days). Nonetheless, for remote locations that receive plenty of sunshine and are not connected to an electrical grid, the costs of constructing transmission lines to bring in outside power might make solar PV and solar heaters a viable option.

Given the current drawbacks of many other renewable sources of energy, wind energy appears to be the renewable alternative of choice when it comes to generation of electricity. As a result, global wind generating capacity has expanded rapidly from only 10 MW of installed capacity in 1980 to 157 899 MW by the end of 2009 (see **Figure 4**), an average annual rate of increase of some 49% [27]. Again, it needs to be emphasized that the euphoria about wind energy needs to be accompanied by a realistic view of its potential contribution to a future energy economy. This is discussed in Section 2.17.5.

Before considering wind energy in more detail, consider one of the main problems facing renewable energy – the problem of energy density. As indicated in **Table 9**, the energy density of most renewable energy sources is simply too low compared to that of fossil fuels and nuclear power to make them sufficiently competitive with fossil fuels and nuclear power, thereby requiring the types of subsidies we find in **Table 3**. While subsidies might help in the short run, they are not sustainable in the long run because they distort production decisions resulting in inefficiencies. This is particularly the case if only some countries employ subsidies as these will lower the costs of fossil fuels causing those countries that continue to rely on fossil fuels to use them less efficiently thereby offsetting the climate benefits of the original subsidies.

2.17.5 The Economics of Wind Energy in Electricity Generation

Installed global wind generating capacity has expanded rapidly over the past three decades. At the end of 2009, it reached nearly 160 GW (**Figure 4**). At the end of 2009, The United States, Germany, Spain, India, and China accounted for 75.5% of global wind power capacity, while developed countries alone accounted for about the same proportion (**Figure 4**). With the exception of China and India, and a few other countries, very little electricity is produced from wind in developing countries, and especially in the least developed countries, although wind is used on a small scale in many developing countries to drive mechanical devices such as water pumps.

Table 9 Energy densities: comparison of the physical area required to produce energy from selected sources

Energy source	Energy density (W m^{-2})	Index
Corn ethanol	0.05	1.0
Biomass-fueled power plant	0.4	8.1
Wind turbines	1.2	24.6
Oil stripper well[a] producing 2 barrels per day	5.5	115.4
Solar photovoltaic	6.7	138.5
Oil stripper well[a] producing 10 barrels per day	27.0	577.0
Gas stripper well[a] producing 60 000 cubic feet (ft^3) per day	28.0	590.4
Average US natural gas well producing 115 000 ft^3 day^{-1}	287.5	1105.8
Nuclear power plant[b]	56.0	1153.8

[a] A stripper well is one that has passed its peak production (or never was a large producer) but continues to pump oil or gas. Stripper wells are defined by their maximum output – 10 barrels per day for oil wells and 60 000 ft^3 day^{-1} for gas wells.
[b] Based on a 4860 ha location in Texas, although the power plant occupies only a very small area within the property.
Reproduced from Bryce R (2010) *Power Hungry: The Myths of 'Green' Energy and the Real Fuels of the Future*, pp. 91–93. New York, NY: Public Affairs.

Over the period 1990–2009, growth in wind generating capacity averaged just over 26% per annum, and was even slightly higher at about 27% over the period since 2000. It is not surprising, therefore, that the growth in capacity is likely to continue at well above 20% until at least 2012. Yet, despite these very high rates of growth over the past several decades, the current role of wind power in meeting global electricity demand is almost negligible as it accounts for much less than 2% of the global electricity supply (**Figures 1** and **2**). What are the prospects for wind energy? What are the obstacles?

Some quick answers to these questions are as follows. First, it is unlikely that even under the most optimistic estimates, wind will account for more than 5% of total global electricity production [16]. Second, wind energy requires storage, is unreliable, costly to install, harmful to some wildlife (e.g., birds), noisy, visually unattractive, and, above all, destabilizing of existing electrical grids. Wind turbines produce only about one-fifth of their rated output because of vagaries in wind, while attempts to reduce intermittency by scattering wind farms across a large geographic area and integrating wind power into a 'supergrid' have not overcome the grid instability that occurs when wind penetration reaches about 30%. Most of these results are based on various modeling exercises (see, e.g., References 17, 28–31, and 54).

In summary, the economics of wind-generated energy restricts its potential, essentially deflating the euphoria that is often brought to this renewable energy source. This is not to deny that wind energy does have a role to play. For example, van Kooten and Wong [32] and others have demonstrated that there are huge savings to be had from investing in wind turbines under certain circumstances (discussed further below). But, in order to understand the limitations of wind energy, we need to first consider the way the electricity grid functions and the challenges that this poses for wind power. We then turn to studies that have examined the integration of wind power into electricity grids. And we end with a discussion regarding wind energy's future.

2.17.5.1 Structure of Electricity Grids: Economics

Electricity is an unusual commodity in that production and consumption occur simultaneously and at every instant in time. That is, unlike a normal market where there is a mechanism that enables consumers and producers to 'discover' the market clearing price over a period of time, the market for electricity must clear continuously. Nonetheless, supply and demand for electricity remain the essential means for describing the underlying process that enables the electricity grid to function.

2.17.5.1.1 Demand side and demand management

Final consumers of electricity have rarely been asked to respond to changes in wholesale prices; with the exception of differences in nighttime and daytime rates, consumers in most jurisdictions face the same price regardless of the time of day. Furthermore, retail prices change only when the regulator permits the system operator to make the change. Prices are regulated because production, transmission, and delivery of electricity are inherently monopolistic activities, at least historically. The generation of electricity and its delivery to the final consumer were considered to be the function of a single firm – a monopolistic activity that then had to be regulated. Recently, many jurisdictions have separated generation, transmission, and delivery to varying degrees.

The first step in this process is to separate ownership of power generation from transmission and delivery, thereby creating a wholesale market for electricity. An independent (private or public) electricity system operator (ESO) will oversee the allocation of power generation from various facilities, and arrange its transmission and delivery to customers. While the wholesale price might fluctuate widely in this case as power generating companies compete to sell electricity, the retail price is set by a regulator or, in a fully deregulated system, fluctuates hourly with the wholesale price, the difference reflecting the cost of transmission and delivery. Without 'smart' controls that receive price signals and adjust electrical use accordingly, consumers are simply unable to respond to real-time price signals – with the exception of large industrial or commercial consumers, it would be too expensive in terms of time and effort for them to do so.

With respect to demand, it is important to distinguish between efforts to shift load from peak periods to off-peak periods and a fully deregulated retail market. Most government policies focus on load shifting because smart controls are not widely available to most customers. Even so, time-or-use billing can simply be used to shift load by distinguishing between daytime and nighttime prices (which small customers can handle), but even this requires that smart meters are installed at each consumer's location. An alternative is to provide incentives only to the largest industrial and commercial customers that cause them to reduce demand during peak times, perhaps shifting it to other times of the day. The purpose of these incentives is to shift load (as with daytime–nighttime pricing) or shed load (reduce demand). If peak load can be 'shaved' (reduced) by shifting demand to off-peak times, substantial cost saving may be found as less overall and reserve generating capacity are required. Shedding load is a different proposition: An ESO will need to shed load in an emergency when the system load exceeds generation. This can be done via built-in incentives or, more often, contracts between the operator and large consumers. However, the purposes here are not to conserve energy as much as reduce system management costs.

If retail prices are fixed, the demand function is essentially a vertical line – load does not respond to changes in wholesale prices. One way to affect consumer demand is to employ a tiered system whereby rates rise (or fall) with increased usage over a specified period. Rather than redistribute some load from peak to off-peak hours, a tiered system of prices can reduce or increase demand, depending on circumstances and prices of alternative energy sources. (An increase in demand can occur if a large consumer of electricity is generally well below the use that would take it to the next, higher price tier. Suppose the consumer heats water using natural gas and currently does not reach the next price level in its use of electricity. If gas prices are sufficiently high, it will pay for the consumer to convert its boilers so that water can be heated by gas or electricity. Electricity will be used for heating water up to the point where the power usage encounters the threshold for the higher price tier of use.)

Time-of-use (real) time pricing at the retail level affects demand directly, but likely requires the implementation of a 'smart grid' – something beyond just smart meters. There is much discussion about smart grids, but there are some obstacles to its implementation. Currently, if there is a power outage, the local system operator is unable to even determine whether there is an outage let alone where it occurs. It relies on customers to provide the information. A smart grid (or just smart meters) enables the system operator to identify outages by placing computer chips on transmission lines, including lines leading to each home (smart meters). The computer chips send and receive signals, usually in conjunction with the Internet. It is also possible to install chips that would enable the system operator (or customer) to control appliances, change thermostat settings, and affect other devices that connect to the electrical grid from a distance. For example, appliances such as dishwashers, washing machines, clothes dryers, and heaters could be turned off or on depending on the price of electricity. At times of excessive load or when a generator fails, the system operator could curtail consumers' use of electricity or signal certain appliances to shut down. While not all electronic devices have smart technology embedded in them, and installing smart devices could be expensive, perhaps the greatest obstacle to smart grids might be concerns about privacy. One solution might be to allow consumers to opt out of the smart grid, but at a cost (e.g., higher overall average electricity rates).

It is fair to conclude, at this point, that prices vary little at the retail level and, further, that the demand for electricity is probably highly inelastic should a form of real-time pricing be implemented. Based on cross-section and time-series analyses, the short-run elasticity of demand is often assumed to be about −0.3 [33], while it is between −1.5 and −0.5 in the long run. (Estimates of both the short- and long-run price elasticities of demand for electricity vary widely. In a meta-regression analysis of studies of US residential demand for electricity, Espey and Espey [34] concluded that the best estimates of short- and long-run elasticities were −0.28 and −0.81. For example, a cointegration study found long-run price elasticity to be −0.5 [35]. However, a more recent Swiss study found long-run price elasticity of demand to range from −1.27 to over −2.0, with demand more elastic during peak than off-peak periods [36].) This implies that a 1% increase in the price of electricity results in a 0.3% reduction in demand in the short run, and a reduction of 0.5–1.5% in the long run.

2.17.5.1.2 Electricity supply and the wholesale market

In electricity systems that are at least somewhat deregulated at the wholesale level, the ESO requires owners of generating facilities to commit to produce electricity at a given hour 1 day (24 h) ahead of actual delivery. Each generator will offer to produce a certain amount of electricity at a particular price, knowing that the final price they will receive is the market-clearing price for that hour (actually, it is the average of the prices that clear the market throughout that hour). In essence, a power plant will offer units of electricity at a single or variety of prices to be produced on a specified hour the next day. This is known as day ahead unit commitment. Of course, as the hour approaches for which an owner of a generating facility has committed power output, more information about the status of generators and the evolution of prices becomes known – some uncertainty is resolved. Therefore, generators are able to make changes to their offers up to 1 h before delivery. The extent of permitted changes is increasingly constrained by penalties as the hour approaches.

What do the offers to supply electricity look like? Base-load nuclear and coal-fired power plants will bid in lowest. Indeed, for base-load facilities that cannot readily change their power output, or can do so only at high cost, the optimal strategy is to provide very low-price bids to ensure that they can deliver power to the grid. Open-cycle, natural gas peaking plants will want to bid in at their true marginal cost of production, which is primarily determined by the price they have to pay for fuel. The facilities to provide the highest bids are those that wish to export electricity to another system, regardless of the energy source used to generate the power; by setting their price high, their output is unlikely to be chosen by the system operator and can thus be exported. (Importers will want to set their prices low to guarantee that the imported power will be chosen.) In between the extreme prices are found a

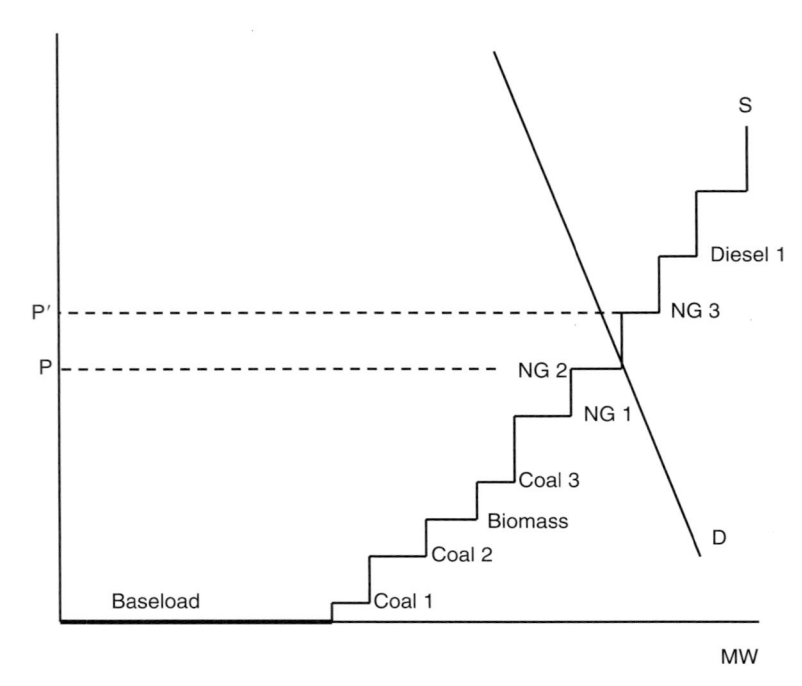

Figure 5 The merit order and intersection of supply and demand for electricity.

variety of generating facilities, such as biomass plants, CCGT plants, different importers, and even various subunits of power plants that might be at different levels of readiness, maintenance, and other matters. Once the ESO has all of the information regarding the amounts of electricity that the various components of the generating system are willing to supply and their associated prices, a merit order is developed to allocate power across the generators depending on demand. An example is illustrated in **Figure 5**.

In **Figure 5**, the market clears at price P, which equals the marginal cost (bid value) of generator NG 2 – a natural gas unit or 'peaker'. All units below the dashed horizontal line P receive the market-clearing price, while NG 3, Diesel 1, and other higher cost units are not asked to deliver power to the grid.

There remains a problem: Transmission constraints have been ignored. Because generators and load centers are found at various locations across the system landscape, they need to be connected by transmission lines. In terms of **Figure 5**, it may be the case that a load center is nearer generator NG 3 than generator NG 1 and that there is insufficient transmission capacity between NG 1 and the rest of the grid. As a result, the ESO is unable to accept power from NG 1 and must, instead, turn to NG 3. The resulting system price is then equal to P′, the marginal cost of NG 3, rather than P. Thus, all of the generators in the merit order that have a lower cost than that of NG 3, with the exception of generator NG 1, receive the system price P′ rather than P.

The higher average system price distorts incentives. As a result, some systems have gone to location-specific pricing, with the prices that generators receive established at a local or regional center within the ESO's operating area rather than averaged over the entire operating area. Knowing this, the bidding in strategy could change, both in the market for power delivery to the grid and in the market for ancillary services (to be discussed next). Furthermore, such location-specific pricing provides incentives to upgrade or build transmission lines connecting regions.

There is also a market for ancillary services. Ancillary services are not homogeneous, and even how they are defined and handled may differ across jurisdictions. Regulatory (fast-response) services are needed to address second-by-second, minute-by-minute fluctuations in demand so that grid reliability is maintained – that the grid delivers 120 V at 60 MHz (in North America). Such short-term fluctuations are generally met by the online generators themselves, as standards require plants to be able to vary their outputs slightly as needed (e.g., slightly more or less gas can be delivered to a turbine, or more or less pulverized coal to the burner). Hence, they are also referred to as 'spinning reserves' as their main function is to ensure that the grid remains synchronized. Storage devices, such as batteries and flywheels, might also be used in a regulatory capacity, as might hydropower.

Load-following reserves are those that are required to follow shifts in load on time frames that usually do not exceed 10 min, and have much in common with regulatory reserves. Contingency (or standby) reserves, on the other hand, are those capable of providing power within about 10 min, but are unlikely to cover shortfalls prior to that time. There is a great deal of overlap between the two types of reserves. For example, a peak gas plant might be operating at only 55% capacity, but can power up to 90% or greater capacity within 1 min, while an open-cycle gas plant or diesel facility might need 5–10 min to power up from a cold start.

In addition to the market for the delivery of electricity to the system (**Figure 5**), there is a market for ancillary services. The merit order in this case is the inverse of what one finds in the former market. The peakers will now want to bid in at the lowest price because they are the ones that can get off the mark the quickest. Peakers such as NG 3 and Diesel 1 (**Figure 5**) will bid in low knowing that when there is a demand for ancillary services, they will receive at least the price determined by the marginal generator (NG 2 in

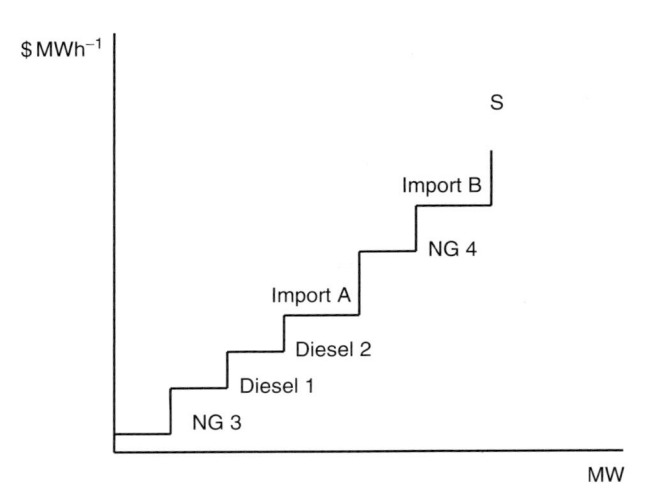

Figure 6 The market for ancillary services: merit order.

Figure 5) plus their own bid in the ancillary market. Base-load plants, on the other hand, will bid in very high, if at all, because they can only ramp up output at great expense. The market for ancillary services will look something like what is shown in **Figure 6**.

Hydroelectricity is a particularly good provider of ancillary services, although it can also provide base-load power. Hydropower can bid in as low-cost provider in the generating services market or as a low-cost provider of ancillary services. It can play either role, although the makeup of the hydroelectric facilities in the system will determine the role it actually plays. For example, in British Columbia, large hydro dams make it ideal for base-load power, with an open-cycle gas facility providing power in the rare instances when load cannot be met from hydro plus imports. In Alberta, on the other hand, there is only a limited ability to store water, with reservoirs tending to be small relative to the needs of the grid. Hence, hydropower is used almost solely for providing ancillary services and meeting peak-load demand.

Although some renewable services can easily be integrated into electricity markets (e.g., biomass in **Figure 5**), it is an altogether different proposition when wind and other intermittent sources of renewable energy are introduced into the system. In the remaining sections, we focus on the integration of wind into existing electricity grids.

2.17.5.2 Integration of Wind Power into Electricity Grids

Unless wind power is readily storable behind large hydro dams, wind requires fast-responding, open-cycle (as opposed to base-load combined-cycle) gas plants as backup. However, since any wind energy will first displace electricity produced by fast-responding gas, it cannibalizes existing peak-load gas capacity and makes investments in such plants less attractive. Even adding a more stable renewable source, such as tidal power, does little to address the problem of intermittency [37].

Intermittency is the greatest obstacle to the seamless integration of wind-generated power into electricity grids. When there is no wind, no power is generated; the wind comes and goes, and does not always blow with the same intensity – it is a whimsical source of power. Wind power enters an electricity grid whenever there is adequate wind; unless provision exists to curtail wind generation, any electricity generated by wind turbines is 'must run' – it is referred to as nondispatchable. Because of this intermittency, the supply of wind power will fluctuate more than that of traditional generating sources.

Producers of wind power are able to forecast with some degree of accuracy, but with large variance, the likely amount of wind power they can deliver to the grid at a given hour the next day. They bid the expected amount of power into the merit order at the lowest price (as base load), and can change the expected quantity up to 1 h prior to delivery. Nonetheless, there is no guarantee that the amount of power bid into the system can actually be delivered, whether it will exceed the stated or bid amount or be below it. As an incentive, some European systems impose a penalty on wind producers if they exceed the stated amount or come in below that amount.

Consider **Figure 5**. The entire merit order will shift to the right if wind is bid into the system. If the wind does not materialize, the entire merit order will shift back to the left. That is, the location of the supply function and the eventual market clearing price in each hour become uncertain as more wind is bid into the market. This uncertainty has a cost. The direct costs of wind power include those associated with the construction of wind turbines, including the cost of purchasing or renting land, the upgrading and construction of transmission lines, and the environmental costs related to bird kills and impact on human health [1, 38]. The indirect costs associated with intermittency are, most notably, (1) the costs of additional system reserves to cover intermittency, and (2) the extra costs associated with balancing or managing generating assets when power from one (or more) generation sources fluctuates.

2.17.5.2.1 Capacity factors

Consider first the so-called 'capacity factor'. If 1 MW of wind generating capacity is installed, the potential amount of power that can be generated annually is given by the number of hours in a year multiplied by the generating capacity. For a 1 MW turbine,

Table 10 Capacity factors for some Western Canada wind sites

Site	Capacity (MW)	Production (GWh)	Capacity factor (%)
Sites in southern Alberta currently in operation			
Castle River #1	40	350.440	28.7
Cowley Ridge	38	332.918	7.4
Kettles Hill	9	78.849	27.4
McBride Lake	75	657.075	34.4
Summerview	68.4	599.252	34.9
Suncor Magrath	30	262.830	36.6
Taylor Wind Farm	3.6	31.540	18.8
Hypothetical sites in northeastern British Columbia[a]			
Aasen	2.3	4.250	21.1
Bessborough	2.3	3.387	16.8
Erbe	2.3	3.603	17.9
Bear Mountain	2.3	7.044	35.0

[a] Values are based on wind data for these sites, converted to power output for a single 2.3 MW turbine as described in the text.

regardless of the energy source, the potential power output is 8760 MWh. For coal and nuclear plants, actual generation will be about 85% to as much as 95% of potential. This is the capacity factor. However, given wind variability, the average capacity factor of a wind farm is usually less than 20%. Thus, rather than generating 8760 MWh of electricity, only an average of some 1750 MWh is generated with actual generation varying greatly from one year to the next. Of course, capacity factors at some wind locations exceed 30% and on occasion even 40%, but that is the exception rather than the rule.

To illustrate the types of capacity factors one might encounter, consider the Great Plains region east of the Rocky Mountains in western Canada. This region is considered to be an area of high wind power potential because of prevailing winds off the mountains. In **Table 10**, we provide data on capacity factors from actual wind farms in southern Alberta and potential capacity factors for several areas in northeastern British Columbia where wind speeds have been measured for a period of one or more years (but development of wind farms has not yet taken place due to lack of transmission connections) (data can be found at http://web.uvic.ca/~kooten/documents/LSRS2009WindData.xls). The two regions are about 1000 km apart and are directly east and near to the Rocky Mountains. Capacity factors vary from 7.4% to 36.6% for the region.

While the information in **Table 10** is based on a single year of data and wind power output can be expected to vary greatly from one year to the next, the results are illustrative nonetheless. First, the results demonstrate that capacity factors can often be quite low, and are usually lower than expected, even for good wind site locations [1]. Second, even when wind sites are spread across a large landscape so that they are as much as 1000 or more km apart, wind power is generally not available every hour of the year.

2.17.5.2.2 Reserve requirements

Next consider reserve requirements. By installing wind generating capacity, greater system balancing reserves are required than would normally be the case if an equivalent amount of thermal or hydro capacity was installed. This is true even after one adjusts for the lower capacity factors associated with wind. The reliability of power from wind farms is lower than that of thermal or hydro sources because of the high variability associated with wind power, and this variability must be compensated for by greater system reserves.

Suppose that σ_s and σ_d are the standard deviations of supply and demand fluctuations, respectively. Then, as a rule of thumb, a system operator requires reserves equal to three standard deviations of all potential fluctuations, or reserves $= \pm 3\sqrt{\sigma_s^2 + \sigma_d^2}$ (see References 39–41). If wind farms are added to an existing grid, required reserves must be increased to $\pm 3\sqrt{\sigma_s^2 + \sigma_d^2 + \sigma_w^2}$, where σ_w is the standard deviation associated with wind intermittency. If $\sigma_w > \sigma_s$ and wind replaces other generation that is more reliable, then reserves must increase; if $\sigma_w < \sigma_s$, reserve capacity would decline. How large must the additional reserves be? According to Gross et al. [40, 41], assuming no correlation between demand and variable supply from wind, additional reserve requirements would be small. Suppose that, as they find, the standard deviations of wind fluctuations amount to 1.4% of installed wind capacity for a 30 min time horizon and 9.3% of installed capacity over a 4 h time period. (These standard deviations would vary from one location or jurisdiction to another.) For the shorter time horizon, regulating or fast-response reserves are affected, while contingency or standing reserves are affected in the case of longer time horizon.

If there is 10 GW of installed wind capacity, then σ_w would equal 140 MW for regulating and 930 MW for contingency reserves. Suppose further that total generating capacity is 24.3 GW and that $\sigma_s + \sigma_d = 340$ MW. Then regulating reserves would need to equal 1020 MW ($= 3 \times \sqrt{340^2}$) without wind and 1181 MW ($= 3 \times \sqrt{340^2 + 140^2}$) with wind, while respective contingency reserves would need to be 6780 and 7332 MW. Thus, wind intermittency requires increases in regulating reserves of 15.8% (161 MW) and contingency reserves of 8.1% (552 MW). (These are the current author's calculations using values from Gross et al. [41]. Although not given, total generating capacity is approximately 24.3 GW. However, there is no discussion in Gross et al. [40, 41] as to whether wind generating capacity simply replaces conventional generating capacity; yet this seems to be the logical assumption based on the discussion found in these sources. The analysis presented here suggests that this is a highly optimistic analysis of wind power.) These are not insignificant requirements. Yet they are likely an underestimate because they are based on the assumption that there is no correlation between wind output and load, which is unlikely as wind blows to a greater extent at night when demand is low (see, e.g., Reference 42).

2.17.5.2.3 Modeling the management of an electricity grid

In addition to the need for greater system reserves, there is a second cost associated with the need to retain system balance, the added cost of managing the grid [28]. How the grid is to be managed depends on the policy implemented by the authority. If the grid operator is required to take any wind power that is offered (wind is 'must run' or nondispatchable), extant generators may need to operate at partial capacity, although they must be ready to dispatch power to the grid in the event of a decline in wind availability. Peak-load diesel and simple (open-cycle) gas plants and, to a much lesser degree, combined-cycle natural gas plants are able to ramp up and down to some extent. (CCGT plants employ heat that escapes out of the stack in an open-cycle system to generate additional electricity. While CCGT plants can be built to ramp more quickly, there is always a trade-off that adds to cost. Even coal-fired generators can be built to better track changes in output from variable generating sources, but again at increased cost in terms of reduced efficiency and greater wear and tear of equipment.) If they are unable to match the ups and downs in wind power availability, there will be excess power in the system that must be sold to another operator, usually at low cost. With nondispatchable wind power entering a grid, there is an economic cost because other generators in the system operate more often below their optimal efficiency ratings (less than their optimal instantaneous capacity factors). In addition, wind variability causes peak-load diesel and open-cycle gas plants to stop and start more frequently, which increases operation and maintenance (O&M) costs.

A suitable constrained optimization or mathematical programming model of an electricity grid can be used to address these issues. Models assume that load and wind power availability are known beforehand (which is referred to as 'rational expectations' in mathematical programming models). A grid optimization model takes explicit account of the need to balance output from existing generators on the grid [29, 31, 43]. Costs of new transmission lines from wind assets to an existing grid are ignored for convenience. Also, the grid management model does not take explicit account of the additional investments in reserve capacity that might be required – the need for additional backup generation should one or more generators in the system fail, given that wind cannot be used for backup generation because of its intermittency. The constrained optimization model that is used to develop outcomes described below is linear, with constant marginal generation costs and simple capacity limits and ramping constraints; it is more fully described in van Kooten [17]. Linear models are often sufficiently robust and useful when the intention is primarily to investigate the effects of government policies.

It is difficult to replace conventional generation capacity with nondispatchable wind power and maintain system reliability [28, 42, 44, 45]. To illustrate the problems and, at the same time, provide estimates of the costs of reducing CO_2 emissions, we examine integration of wind into three grids with different generating mixes. We denote the three generating mixes as 'high hydro', 'typical', and 'high fossil fuel', with details provided in **Table 11**. The high hydro mix contains 60% hydroelectric generation with the other 40% allocated between nuclear and other thermal generating units. Typical is made up of 50% pulverized coal generation and 20% nuclear generation along with hydro and gas-fired units, while high fossil fuel also has 50% coal-fired generation, some gas and hydro but no nuclear units.

We employ hourly load data from the Electric Reliability Council of Texas (ERCOT, Texas) system for 2007, and wind data from sites located in western Canada (ERCOT data are from http://ercot.com/, but all ERCOT and BC data are available at http://web.uvic.ca/~kooten/documents/LSRS2009WindData.xls). The ERCOT load data are standardized to a peak load of 2500 MW (multiplying load data by 2500 MW and dividing by ERCOT peak load of 62 101 MW). Wind power output consists of actual data from wind farms in southern Alberta and wind speed data for British Columbia (**Table 10**), converted to wind energy using a turbine manufacturer's power curves. Net load equals demand minus wind output, assuming wind penetration rates of 0%, 10%, and 30%, where penetration is the ratio of installed wind capacity to peak load.

The costs and benefits of introducing wind power into an electricity grid depend on the generating mix of the particular grid. To provide estimates of the costs and benefits of wind, the model takes into account fuel costs, O&M costs, and investment costs, as

Table 11 Generating mixes as a percent of total installed capacity

Technology	High hydro (%)	Typical (%)	High fossil fuel (%)
Hydroelectric	60	8.4	10
Nuclear	12	20	0
Pulverized coal	18	50	50
Combined-cycle natural gas (CCGT)	6	18	34
Other (biomass)	4	3.6	6
Total	100	100	100

Reproduced from van Kooten GC (2010) Wind power: The economic impact of intermittency. *Letters in Spatial & Resource Sciences* 3: 1–17 [17].

Table 12 Example cost data for generating technologies

Technology	Fuel cost ($ MWh^{-1})	Variable O&M ($ MWh^{-1})	Construction cost ($ 10^6 MW^{-1})	Emissions (kg CO$_2$ MWh^{-1})[a]
Hydroelectric	1.13[b]	0.02	1.55	0.009 (0.028 4)
Nuclear	6.20	0.07	1.70	0.012 (0.014 7)
Pulverized coal	13.70	0.70	1.10	0.980 (1.134 0)
Combined-cycle natural gas (CCGT)	37.00	5.00	0.55	0.450 (0.049 6)
Open-cycle natural gas (peak plant)	41.00	4.50	0.46	0.650 (0.049 6)
Wind	0	0.17	1.30	0.015 (0.020 0)

[a] Emission data vary from one source to another and depend on the methods used to calculate life-cycle emissions, quality of fuel, and other parameters. Data in parentheses are from a second source.
[b] One might expect the fuel cost to be zero, but Natural Resources Canada, in a 2005 report entitled 'Greenhouse gas and cost impacts of electric markets with regional hydrogen production' (Report No. 2007), indicates that there is a fuel cost.
O&M, operation and maintenance.
Reproduced from van Kooten GC (2010) Wind power: The economic impact of intermittency. *Letters in Spatial & Resource Sciences* 3: 1–17 [17].

well as life-cycle CO$_2$ emissions. This information is provided in **Table 12**. Linearity permits optimization over a full year or 8760 h. Operating reserve requirements (regulating and contingency reserves) are ignored.

The simplifying assumptions (including linearity) are for simplicity only (although wind power output can be forecast with a relatively high degree of certainty), and they do not in any way jeopardize the main conclusions that are reached. Indeed, it turns out that the main conclusions from linear models with rational expectations are reinforced if nonlinearities and uncertainty are added. This is confirmed by other researchers (e.g., [28–31, 46]).

Once we have developed a model to simulate management of an electricity grid, we would like to use it to answer some policy questions. The central question of concern is the following: What is the expected cost of reducing CO$_2$ emissions by building and operating wind turbines to generate electricity? To what extent will electricity rates have to increase? What are the impacts of wind turbines on existing generating facilities? What if any are the limits to substituting fossil fuel-generated electricity with wind power?

2.17.5.2.4 Some model results

A linear program similar to that described by van Kooten [17] is employed to simulate the introduction of various levels of wind generating capacity into the electricity grids described in **Table 11**. Simulation results are provided in **Figures 7–9**.

In **Figure 7**, we provide the load (demand) profile facing existing generators when available wind power is subtracted from the original load. This assumes that wind power is must run or nondispatchable. The data are only for two 48-h periods, one in January and one in July, so that the load profile can be better identified. It is important to recall that since the data represent a Texas load, summer demand is higher than it would be in more northern latitudes as power is required for air conditioning as opposed to heating; heating is more prevalent in January. Note that once wind power has been subtracted from the load, the remaining demand profile has greater variability than the non-wind load, although the adjusted series still track the morning (6.00 a.m.–12.00 p.m.) and evening (6.00 p.m.–11.00 p.m.) peaks quite well. The higher the extent of wind penetration, the greater the volatility of the remaining load. If a longer profile was chosen, the volatility would be even sharper.

Clearly, wind penetration will vary according to the extant generating mix. This is shown in **Figure 8**, where output is indicated by generation type for various levels of wind penetration. For the generating mix with high hydro capacity in **Figure 8(a)**, hydropower adjusts instantaneously to changes in wind, enabling nuclear and coal-fired base-load plants to operate at the same capacity as wind penetration increases. This means that the base-load plants do not need to operate below the most efficient operating levels. In a mix with less hydro capacity, namely, the typical mix in **Figure 8(c)**, outputs of base-load nuclear and coal facilities vary and they operate at lower average capacity (lower capacity factor) as wind penetration increases. Finally, in a fossil fuel generating mix (panel c), hydro's capacity factor changes least because almost all hydro capacity is utilized; hydro and gas adjust to short-term fluctuations in net load. Coal generation is affected by increasing wind penetration, leading to excess generation, because it cannot adjust quickly enough to changes in net load.

Despite perfect foresight regarding wind availability, generators cannot adjust their output quickly enough to prevent unnecessary generation, unless there is sufficient hydro generating capacity. Hydroelectric units can be adjusted on extremely short notice. As a result of excess thermal generation, the reduction in CO$_2$ emissions associated with the integration of wind assets is also relatively small, and is largest for the fossil fuel mix. For 30% wind penetration, the largest reduction in emissions amounts to only 14.5% of the zero wind scenario, and then only for the fossil fuel mix; for the typical and high hydro mixes, CO$_2$ emissions are reduced by only 8.1% and 1.3%, respectively. Clearly, the degree to which wind power is able to reduce CO$_2$ emissions depends on the amount of hydroelectric and nuclear generating capacity available in the generating mix, as these emit little CO$_2$.

The average and marginal costs of reducing CO$_2$ emissions are provided in **Table 13** for wind penetrations of 10% and 30%. Average and marginal costs are lowest for the high fossil fuel mix and greatest for the high hydro mix, with marginal costs in the case of the high hydro mix more than $1000 per tCO$_2$ even for wind penetration rates as low as 5%. This is the result of introducing zero emission technology into a generation mix that already produces little in the way of CO$_2$ emissions. Thus any additional CO$_2$

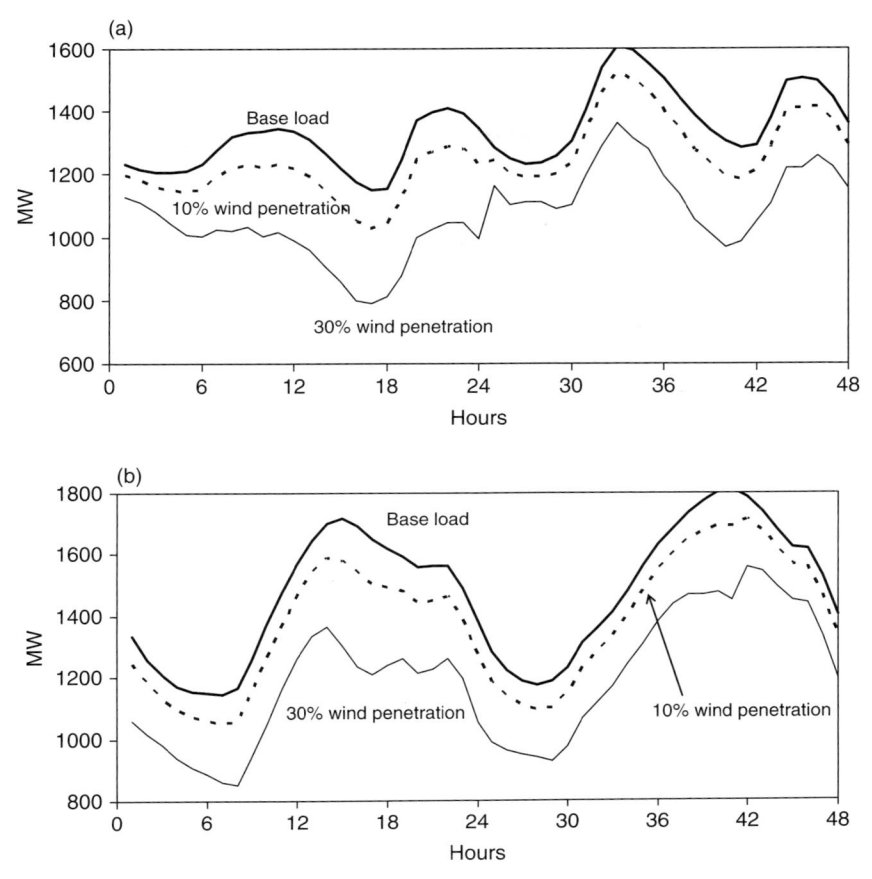

Figure 7 Load or demand to be met by traditional generators for the first 2 days (48 h) in (a) January and (b) July.

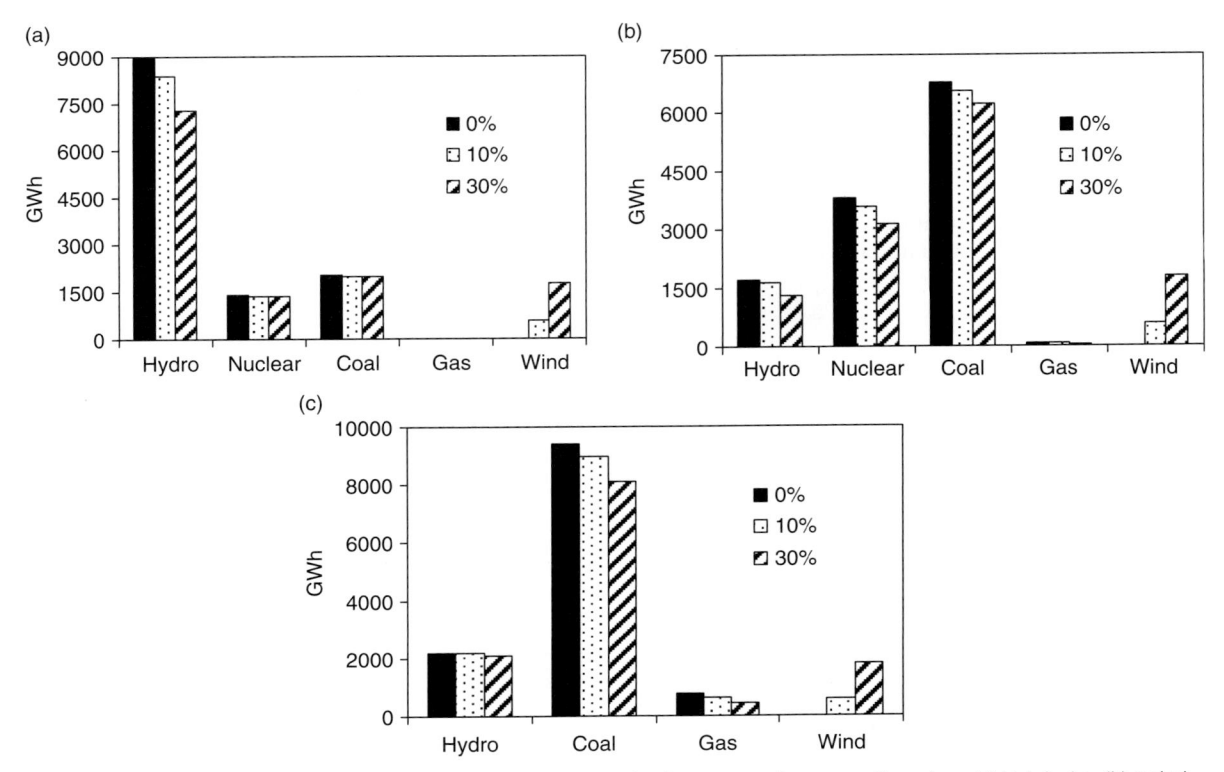

Figure 8 Effect on power production from various sources as wind penetration increases, various generating mixes: (a) high hydro, (b) typical, and (c) high fossil fuel.

Table 13 Marginal costs of reducing CO_2 emissions

	Reducing emissions per tCO_2		Increase in costs per MWh	
Generation mix/wind penetration	10%	30%	10%	30%
High hydro	$1622.29	$2639.25	73%	245%
Typical	$130.68	$229.38	26%	88%
Fossil fuel	$43.79	$57.06	16%	58%

reductions come at great cost. For a grid with mainly fossil fuel units, emission reductions can be produced at much lower marginal cost ($43.79 per tCO_2 vs. $1622.29 per tCO_2 for 10% wind energy penetration).

Finally, the introduction of wind power into most electricity grids does not imply that other generating assets can be replaced. There are times when no wind, or too little wind, is available (for the wind profiles of northeastern British Columbia and southern Alberta there were 18 h without wind), and the number and times when this occurs vary from one year to the next. As a result, extant generators cannot be replaced with wind turbines, and certainly not one-for-one. Therefore, electricity costs will need to increase whenever wind generation is added to the mix. We find that electricity costs rise by 16–73% for 10% wind penetration, and much more for higher penetration levels (**Table 13**). These increases are not balanced by an efficient reduction in the externality as costs for reducing CO_2 emissions exceed the costs of purchasing emission offsets in markets.

The above results were obtained using a linear mathematical programming model. To see how sensitive our results are to the linearity assumption, we consider the results from Maddaloni et al. [30]. While the linear model assumed per unit generating costs did not vary with the level of a generator's output, Maddaloni and his colleagues investigated the integration of wind into an extant grid using a nonlinear constrained optimization model that permitted declining efficiency at below optimal operation of generators. As a result of computational restrictions, they could only run scenarios over 2 weeks (336 h); they used representative winter and summer load and wind profiles. The generation mixes were typical of those found in Canada (closer to 'high hydro' in **Table 13**), the United States ('high fossil fuel'), and the Pacific Northwest Power Pool (NWPP or 'typical'), but normalized to 2054 MW rather than 2500 MW; thus, the generating mixes were not dissimilar from those in **Table 11**.

Average and marginal costs for Maddaloni et al. [30] are provided in **Figure 9** for a range of wind penetration levels. For a grid with mainly fossil fuel units, emission reductions can be produced at much lower average and marginal costs than with the typical or high hydro mixes. Only for the fossil fuel mix are average and marginal costs below some $50 per tCO_2 emission reduction, and then only up to a penetration of about 20%. Nowhere are emission reduction costs below $30 per tCO_2. The results in **Figure 9** suggest that wind can be integrated into a US (high fossil fuel) or NWPP (typical) mix at a 'reasonable' cost of reducing CO_2 emissions (say, lower than $50 per tCO_2), but then only to a penetration of about 15% for the US mix but 50% for the NWPP mix.

Other studies find similar high costs of reducing CO_2 emissions, in contrast to the finding by the U.S. Department of Energy [47] that wind power could reduce CO_2 emissions at a cost of $5.70 per tCO_2. A German study by Rosen et al. [48] found that costs of reducing CO_2 emissions rise from €87.70 per tCO_2 to €125.71 per tCO_2 and then to €171.47 per tCO_2 as wind power production increases from 12.0 TWh (6 GW installed capacity in 2000) to 34.9 TWh (17.3 GW installed capacity in 2005) and 50.4 TWh (22.4 GW installed capacity in 2010) corresponding to respective wind penetrations of about 8%, 23%, and 29%.

The results presented above indicate that several factors must be aligned before wind energy can reduce system-wide CO_2 emissions at reasonable cost. These include the load and wind profiles, and crucially the existing generating mix into which wind power is to be integrated. Operating constraints for coal- and gas-fired base-load generation lead to overproduction of electricity during certain periods, because units cannot ramp up and down quickly enough when wind energy is available. This results in less

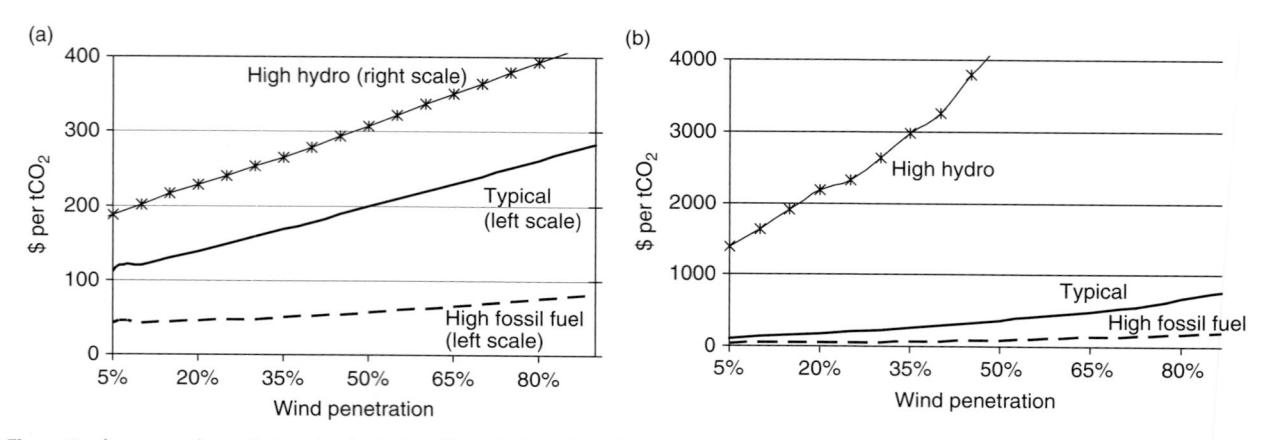

Figure 9 Average and marginal costs of reducing CO_2 emissions for various wind penetrations and three generating mixes: (a) average costs and (b) marginal costs.

emission reductions than anticipated. Wind integration into a system that has high nuclear and/or hydroelectric generating capacity might also see fewer CO_2 benefits than anticipated as wind displaces non-CO_2-emitting sources, despite the ability of some hydro facilities to fluctuate as quickly as wind. Hydro storage is an advantage, but not always. Research indicates that a high degree of wind penetrability is feasible (negative to low costs of reducing CO_2 emissions) for flexible grids such as the NWPP that have sufficient hydro for storage and relatively fast-responding gas plants that track changes in load minus nondispatchable wind, while keeping base-load nuclear and coal power plants operating efficiently (with only minor changes in output).

Rather than allowing extant generators to vary their output, thus increasing system costs, an alternative policy is to make wind power dispatchable by requiring wind operators to reduce output (by 'feathering' wind turbines or simply stopping blades from rotating) whenever the grid operator is unable to absorb the extra electricity. In this case, output from base-load plants is effectively given precedence over wind-generated power because such plants cannot be ramped up and down, the ramping costs are too great, and/or excess power cannot be stored or sold. (In practice, base-load coal and nuclear power plants do not vary output, while CCGT plants have some ability to ramp up and down (although preference is not to do so). Peak gas plants tend not to be turned off and on more than once during a 24 h period. Hence, wind variability creates problems that can only be handled in current grids by selling electricity to other jurisdictions or forcing wind plants to reduce output if necessary.) In Alberta, for example, further expansion of wind farms was initially permitted only after developers agreed to control power output so that wind power was no longer 'must run'. This policy makes investments in wind farms much less attractive and is usually unacceptable to environmental groups.

Another possibility is to permit wind farms only if they come with adequate storage, which generally means that they need to be connected to large-scale hydro facilities that have adequate reservoir capacity, or are bundled with a peaker plant. With respect to the latter, the output of a wind facility would be reliable because any shortfall in wind output would be covered by natural gas. However, as noted earlier, this has a drawback because wind variability tends to increase the costs of a peak gas plant because of the more frequent stops and starts.

Placement of several or many wind farms across a sufficiently large geographic area is also a possibility that has been promoted for mitigating wind's intermittency. To overcome variability, it is argued that wind farms can be located across as large a geographic area as possible, with their combined output integrated into a large grid. By establishing wind farms across the entire country, onshore and offshore, the United Kingdom hopes to minimize the problems associated with intermittency. Furthermore, by connecting all countries of Europe and placing wind farms throughout the continent as well as in Britain and Ireland, the hope is to increase the ability to employ wind-generated power. But as demonstrated by Oswald *et al.* [49], large weather systems can influence the British Isles and the European continent simultaneously. Oswald and his colleagues demonstrated that at 6.00 p.m. on 2 February 2006, electricity demand in the United Kingdom peaked, but wind power was zero (indeed wind farms added to the load at that time). At the same time, wind power output in Germany, Spain, and Ireland was also extremely low – 4.3%, 2.2%, and 10.6% of capacities, respectively. The wind data presented above suggest that something similar occurs with respect to wind farms located some 1000 km apart in the Great Plains of Canada near the Rocky Mountains [17]. Thus, even a supergrid with many wind farms scattered over a large landscape cannot avoid the problems associated with intermittency, including the need to manage delivery of power from various non-wind power generators.

The best strategy for dealing with the issue of integrating intermittent wind and other renewable resources into electricity grids is to provide incentives that cause the intermittent resources to take into account the costs they impose upon the grid. We have already noted that some European jurisdictions penalize wind power providers if they deliver more or less than an agreed upon amount of electricity to the grid – they incur a penalty for variability. This might cause producers to waste renewable energy if they exceed the limit, or pay a fee if they are under it. However, it also provides strong incentives to store electricity or build backup power plants.

It is also possible that special ancillary markets develop to mitigate intermittency. This amounts to the provision of the same incentives as a penalty regime. Payments for backup services provide service providers with incentives to store electricity and/or ensure that sufficient backup services are available at the lowest cost.

Finally, upon examining the potential of wind energy to meet global society's energy needs, Wang and Prinn [50] conclude that if 10% of global energy is to come from wind turbines by 2100, it would require some 13 million turbines that occupy an area on the order of a continent. Wind turbines themselves would cause surface warming exceeding 1 °C over land installations, and alter climate (clouds and precipitation) well beyond the regions where turbines are located – reducing convective precipitation in the Northern Hemisphere and enhancing convective precipitation in the Southern Hemisphere. Wind turbines on such a massive scale would also lead to undesired environmental impacts and increase energy costs because of the need for backup generation, on-site energy storage, and very costly long-distance power transmission lines.

2.17.6 Discussion

Despite an economic crisis, the United States, Canada, Europe, Japan, and Australia, to one degree or another, are implementing climate policies in a major effort to reduce emissions of greenhouse gases. They are using the powers of the state to shift their economies toward ones that are carbon-neutral and even nuclear-free. At the moment, wind energy plays a very important role in this shift. Will this continue or is it a passing fad? What are the prospects for a carbon-neutral world?

In February 2010, a group of climate economists met at Hartwell House, Buckinghamshire, England, under the auspices of Oxford University and the London School of Economics, to examine the next step regarding global climate policy [9]. The background to the meeting was the failure of countries to agree to limit global emissions of CO_2 at the 15th Conference of the Parties to the UNFCCC at Copenhagen in late 2009. The economists recognized that fossil fuels are both too cheap and too expensive. They are too cheap because they impose a global externality by way of CO_2 emissions that lead to climate change, but they are also too expensive because many poor people lack access to sufficient energy to enable them to escape poverty.

As reported in *The Economist* (25 September 2010, p. 117), in 2009, 1440 million people lacked access to electricity, while some 2.7 billion still cook their food on inefficient stoves that use dung, crop residues, and fuel wood. Perhaps 500 000 people die prematurely each year because of health problems associated with biomass-burning, poorly ventilated stoves. Collection of biomass for burning occupies much of women and children's time, robs cropland of important nutrients that can only partly be replaced by artificial fertilizers from off-site, and causes deforestation. One-quarter to one-third of the world's population needs to be provided with electricity and high-density energy, such as can currently be found only in fossil fuels, so that they can raise their standards of living. It would be immoral to deny the poor the ability to develop by curtailing their access to cheap energy.

The result is a *huge dilemma*: We can pursue the rich world's environmental climate objectives only by denying developing countries the cheap energy needed for economic development. Wind energy can help in some cases, particularly in developing countries that have unreliable grids and where diesel generation is the most common source of power or backup generation [32]. However, in most other cases, compared to fossil fuels wind sources of energy simply cannot compete with coal, petroleum, and natural gas as a foundation for economic development. After all, there are sufficient fossil fuels and they can be made available cheaply enough to drive economic development of even the least developed nations.

The problem is not lack of resources; it is the obstacles that both rich and poor countries put in the way of exploration, development, transportation, and distribution of energy. Rich countries block exploitation of all sorts of natural resources on the grounds of their potential adverse environmental impacts, while poor governance, corruption, and failure of rule of law hinder all aspects of the energy supply chain, resulting in huge waste. Sources of low-cost, fossil fuel energy are plentiful enough to drive economic development. The problem is the lack of will to do so.

The dilemma is that rich countries have agreed to pursue policies of economic development in poor countries, so that living standards of the poor converge toward those of the rich. But rich developed countries have also agreed to decarbonize the global economy. These objectives are incompatible. China and India recognize this all too well, which is why they refused to allow rich countries to seduce them into limiting their greenhouse gas emissions. The incompatibility between these goals led to the failure to reach a climate accord at Copenhagen.

What has been the response of the developing countries to the aforementioned dilemma? Surprisingly, rather than focus efforts on helping poor countries access sources of energy to enable the economic growth required to adapt to the negative effects of climate change, rich countries are acting as if there is no dilemma whatsoever. They are ramping up efforts to decarbonize their own economies while continuing to threaten and cajole developing countries into doing the same – the focus is on mitigating climate change and not adapting to it. The developing countries have simply rejected such efforts, continuing to expand their energy consumption and CO_2 emissions as fast as they can. China is in the forefront, with India coming on and others likely to follow in the not-too-distant future.

Consider the evidence. Coal is primarily used by industrial countries to generate electricity and make steel. Coal consumption by the United States, Russia, and Japan has remained relatively flat since 1990, while that of Germany declined slightly, mainly because of unification and the closing of inefficient coal-fired power plants and steel factories in the east. Indian consumption has risen slowly and should overtake US consumption within the next several years. However, China's consumption of coal has increased some threefold since 2000, and fourfold since 1990. The same picture emerges if you consider installed electrical generating capacity, which has remained relatively unchanged in most countries over the period 1990–2007, with the exception of the United States and China. US capacity has increased by some 260 GW (or 36%), while that of China has increased by a whopping 578 GW (519%) and India by 84 GW (210%).

One thing is very clear. No matter what rich western countries are doing about CO_2 emissions, global emissions of CO_2 will continue to rise inexorably. In addition to wind, nuclear, and gas capacity, China is currently adding 1000 MW of installed coal-fired generating capacity every week, and China's consumption of coal in 2009 exceeded the total consumption of Germany, Russia, India, Japan, and the United States combined! Despite this, China's generating capacity lags behind that of the United States by more than 30%, although total generation of electricity lags behind that of the United States by only about 20%. This is partly because the United States is a net importer of electricity from Canada.

The response of the developed nations has been to stick to the ill-advised UN FCCC Kyoto process as the roadmap to follow and to try to impose it upon the rest of the globe. In September 2010, US Senators again introduced a bill requiring an RES that would require 3% of electricity to be generated from renewable sources by 2012 and 15% by 2021. Similar to the generous FITs provided by the province of Ontario, these provide huge subsidies to wind and solar companies. The costs to the Ontario treasury of its FIT program are estimated at $2.4–$2.6 billion per year, although budgetary pressures will cause politicians to pass costs onto electricity consumers in the form of large rate hikes. In terms of climate change, the Ontario program reduces emissions at a cost of hundreds of dollars per tonne of CO_2, but does absolutely nothing to forestall global warming because of what is happening in China, India, and elsewhere. The same can be expected of the US program and similar programs in Europe, where targets require countries to achieve a 20% renewable standard in the production of electricity by 2020.

Despite the fact that none of these programs, even collectively, can impact climate change, why do governments continue to pursue them? One reason is the mistaken notion that these large subsidies will lead to greater employment and the development of a renewable energy sector that is a global leader. Every country believes that it will be the global leader in the development of wind turbines and/or solar panels. However, research indicates that public funds directed at the renewable energy sector actually reduce employment by crowding out private sector investment or public infrastructural investments elsewhere in the economy (e.g., investments in transportation infrastructure that reduce costs of moving goods and people) [51, 55]. Indeed it appears that the main winner from efforts by countries to expand wind and solar output is China. China currently controls the supply of rare earth minerals which are used to make solar panels and parts of wind turbines, among other things. Recently, China restricted exports of these minerals as it desires to export the manufactured products in which they are used [52]. China gains from subsidies to solar and wind producers.

The other reason for pursuing the Kyoto roadmap is associated with environmental groups and the media, which together have convinced politicians to do something about reducing greenhouse gas emissions and reducing the so-called carbon footprint. Doing something, anything, is not always wise. Economists have long known that governments cannot pick winners and, worse, government subsidies can lock-in technologies that become a hindrance to more efficient energy use rather than a solution.

Then what about wind? While a clean source of energy, wind power must be able to compete in the marketplace. It must be able to compete in the production of electricity without subsidies of any form. But other generating sources must also compete without subsidies – the playing field must be level and the role of government is to ensure that this is indeed the case. The government should not be in the business of trying to pick winners. Under these circumstances and because of problems with intermittency, the future role of wind power might be limited. As with any good thing, there comes a point where more may not be in the best interests of society – where the marginal social benefit from installing more wind capacity equals the marginal social cost. A buoyant and optimistic wind sector is of the opinion that that point is still far in the future. This might be true, but it may also be the case that the bubble is about to burst. Only time will tell [53].

References

[1] Bryce R (2010) *Power Hungry: The Myths of 'Green' Energy and the Real Fuels of the Future*, pp. 96–97, 162–165, 241.New York, NY: Public Affairs.
[2] Duderstadt J, Was G, McGrath R, *et al*. (2009) *Energy Discovery – Innovation Institutes: A Step toward America's Energy Sustainability*, p. 9. Washington, DC: Brookings.http://www.brookings.edu/~/media/Files/rc/reports/2009/0209_energy_innovation_muro/0209_energy_innovation_muro_full.pdf.
[3] International Energy Agency (IEA) (2009) *World Energy Outlook 2008*. Paris, France: OECD/IEA.
[4] Smil V (2003) *Energy at the Crossroads. Global Perspectives and Uncertainties*. Cambridge, MA: MIT Press.
[5] Nowak P (2010) *Sex, Bombs and Burgers. How War, Porn and Fast Food Created Technology as We Know It*. Toronto, ON: Viking Canada/Penguin Group.
[6] International Energy Agency (IEA) (2010) *World Energy Outlook 2009. Executive Summary*. Paris, France: OECD/IEA.
[7] International Energy Agency (IEA) (2010) *Key World Energy Statistics 2009*. Paris, France: OECD/IEA.
[8] Gerondeau C (2010) *Climate: The Great Delusion*, pp. 100–106. London, UK: Stacey International.
[9] Prins G, Galiana I, Green C, *et al*. (2010) *The Hartwell Paper. A New Direction for Climate Policy after the Crash of 2009*, 42pp. London, UK: London School of Economics. http://www.lse.ac.uk/collections/mackinderProgramme/theHartwellPaper/Default.htm (accessed May 2010).
[10] Deffeyes KS (2003) *Hubbert's Peak. The Impending World Oil Shortage*. Princeton, NJ: Princeton University Press.
[11] Ansolabehere S, Deutch J, Driscoll M, *et al*. (2003) *The Future of Nuclear Power. An Interdisciplinary MIT Study*. Cambridge, MA: Massachusetts Institute of Technology.
[12] Deutch JM, Forsberg CW, Kadak AC, *et al*. (2009) *Update of MIT 2003 Future of Nuclear Power. An Interdisciplinary MIT Study*, p. 9. Cambridge, MA: Massachusetts Institute of Technology. http://web.mit.edu/nuclearpower/(accessed 7 June 2010).
[13] Riddel M and Shaw WD (2003) Option wealth and bequest values: The value of protecting future generations from the health risks of nuclear waste storage. *Land Economics* 79(4): 537–548.
[14] NEA & IEA (Nuclear Energy Agency and International Energy Agency) (2005) *Projected Costs of Generating Electricity. 2005 Update*. Paris, France: Nuclear Energy Agency, IEA, OECD.
[15] International Energy Agency (IEA) (2005) *Projected Costs of Generating Electricity. 2005 Update*. Paris, France: Nuclear Energy Agency, OECD/IEA.
[16] van Kooten GC and Timilsina GR (2009) *Wind Power Development: Economics and Policies*, 32pp. Policy Research Working Paper 4868. Washington, DC: The World Bank, Development Research Group, Environment and Energy Team.
[17] van Kooten GC (2010) Wind power: The economic impact of intermittency. *Letters in Spatial & Resource Sciences* 3: 1–17.
[18] van Kooten GC, Laaksonen-Craig S, and Wang Y (2009) A meta-regression analysis of forest carbon offset costs. *Canadian Journal of Forest Research* 39(11): 2153–2167.
[19] van Kooten GC and Sohngen B (2007) Economics of forest carbon sinks: A review. *International Review of Environmental & Resource Economics* 1(3): 237–269.
[20] van Kooten GC (2009) Biological carbon sequestration and carbon trading re-visited. *Climatic Change* 95(3–4): 449–463.
[21] van Kooten GC (2009) Biological carbon sinks: Transaction costs and governance. *The Forestry Chronicle* 85(3): 372–376.
[22] Niquidet K., Stennes B., and van Kooten G.C. (2010) Bio-energy from Mountain Pine Beetle timber and forest residuals: The economics story. *Biomass & Bioenergy*. Submitted.
[23] Stennes B, Niquidet K, and van Kooten GC (2010) Implications of expanding bioenergy production from wood in British Columbia: An application of a regional wood fibre allocation model. *Forest Science* 56(4): 366–378.
[24] Bogle T and van Kooten GC (2010) *What Makes Mountain Pine Beetle a Tricky Pest? Optimal Harvest When Facing Beetle Attack in a Mixed Species Forest*. Repa Working Paper. Victoria, Canada: Department of Economics, University of Victoria.
[25] Crutzen PJ, Mosier AR, Smith KA, and Winiwarter W (2008) N_2O release from agro-biofuel production negates global warming reduction by replacing fossil fuels. *Atmospheric Chemistry and Physics* 8: 389–395.
[26] Searchinger T, Heimlich R, Houghton RA, *et al*. (2008) Use of U.S. croplands for biofuels increases greenhouse gases through emissions from land-use change. *Science* 319: 1238–1240.
[27] GWEC (2010) *Global Wind 2009 Report*. April Global Wind Energy Council. http://www.gwec.net/index.php?id=167&L=0%25B4 (accessed 15 July 2010).
[28] Lund H (2005) Large-scale integration of wind power into different energy systems. *Energy* 30(13): 2402–2412.
[29] Maddaloni JD, Rowe AM, and van Kooten GC (2008) Wind integration into various generation mixtures. *Renewable Energy* 34(3): 807–814.
[30] Maddaloni JD, Rowe AM, and van Kooten GC (2008) Network constrained wind integration on Vancouver Island. *Energy Policy* 36(2): 591–602.
[31] Prescott R and van Kooten GC (2009) The economics of wind power: Destabilizing an electricity grid with renewable power. *Climate Policy* 9(2): 155–168.
[32] van Kooten GC and Wong L (2010) Economics of wind power when national grids are unreliable. *Energy Policy* 38(4): 1991–1998, doi:10.1016/j.enpol.2009.11.080.
[33] U.S. Energy Information Administration (2010) Assumptions to the annual energy outlook 2010, p. 26. *Report #DOE/EIA-0554(2010)*. http://www.eia.doe.gov/oiaf/aeo/assumption/pdf/0554%282010%29.pdf (accessed 16 September 2010).
[34] Espey JA and Espey M (2004) Turning on the lights: A meta-analysis of residential electricity demand elasticities. *Journal of Agricultural and Applied Economics* 36(1): 65–81.
[35] Silk JI and Joutz FL (1997) Short and long-run elasticities in US residential electricity demand: A co-integration approach. *Energy Economics* 19: 493–513.

[36] Filippini M (2010). *Short and Long-Run Time-of-Use Price Elasticities in Swiss Residential Electricity Demand*. CEPE Working Paper No. 76, 21pp. Zurich: Center for Energy Policy and Economics, Swiss Federal Institutes of Technology. http://www.cepe.ethz.ch (accessed July 2010).
[37] Monahan K and van Kooten GC (2010) The economics of tidal stream and wind power: An application to generating mixes in Canada. *Environmental Economics* 1(1): 90–99.
[38] Pierpont N (2009) *Wind Turbine Syndrome: A Report on a Natural Experiment*, p. 85, 121–124. Santa Fe, NM: K-Selected Books.
[39] DeCarolis JF and Keith. DW (2005) The costs of wind's variability: Is there a threshold? *The Electricity Journal* 18: 69–77.
[40] Gross R, Heptonstall P, Anderson D, *et al.* (2006) *The Costs and Impacts of Intermittency: An Assessment of the Evidence on the Costs and Impacts of Intermittent Generation on the British Electricity Network*, 96pp. London, UK: Energy Research Centre. http//www.ukerc.ac.uk/Downloads/PDF/06/0604Intermittency/0604IntermittencyReport.pdf (accessed 25 April 2008).
[41] Gross R, Heptonstall P, Leach M, *et al.* (2007) Renewables and the grid: Understanding intermittency. *ICE Proceedings, Energy* 160(1): 31–41.
[42] Pitt L, van Kooten GC, Love M, and Djilali N (2005) Utility-scale wind power: Impacts of increased penetration. Paper No. IGEC-097, *Proceedings of the International Green Energy Conference*. Waterloo, Ontario, Canada, 12–16 June.
[43] Prescott R, van Kooten GC, and Zhu H (2007) The potential for wind energy meeting electricity needs on Vancouver Island. *Energy & Environment* 18(6): 723–746.
[44] ESB National Grid (2004) *Impact of Wind Power Generation in Ireland on the Operation of Conventional Plant and the Economic Implications*, 42pp. Dublin, Ireland. http://www.eirgrid.com/media/2004_wind_impact_report_[for_updated_2007_report,_see_above].pdf (accessed 15 July 2010).
[45] Liik O, Oidram R, and Keel M (2003) Estimation of real emissions reduction caused by wind generators. *Paper presented at the International Energy Workshop*, IIASA, Laxenburg, Austria, 24–26 June.
[46] Weber C (2005) *Uncertainty in the Electric Power Industry. Methods and Models for Decision Support*. New York, NY: Springer.
[47] U.S. Department of Energy (2008) 20% wind energy by 2030. Increasing wind energy's contribution to U.S. electricity supply. *DOE/GO-102008-2567*, July, 248pp. Oak Ridge, TN: U.S. DOE. http://www.nrel.gov/docs/fy08osti/41869.pdf (accessed 21 July 2010).
[48] Rosen J, Tietze-Stöckinger I, and Rentz O (2007) Model-based analysis of effects from large-scale wind power production. *Energy* 32: 575–583.
[49] Oswald J, Raine M, and Ashraf-Ball H (2008) Will British weather provide reliable electricity? *Energy Policy* 36(8): 3202–3215.
[50] Wang C and Prinn RG (2010) Potential climatic impacts and reliability of very large-scale wind farms. *Atmospheric Chemistry & Physics* 10: 2053–2061.
[51] Álvarez GC, Jara RM, Rallo Julián JR, and Bielsa JIG (2009) Study of the effects on employment of public aid to renewable energy sources. Lessons from the Spanish renewables bubble. Borrador draft, March, 43pp. Madrid: Universidad Rey Juan Carlos. http://www.juandemariana.org/pdf/090327-employment-public-aid-renewable.pdf (accessed 9 July 2010).
[52] Humphries M (2010) Rare earth elements: The global supply chain. *CRS Report for Congress, R41347*, 14pp. Washington, DC: Congressional Research Service. http://www.fas.org/sgp/crs/natsec/R41347.pdf (accessed 17 September 2010).
[53] Louck DP, Stedinger JR, and Haith DA (1981) *Water Resource Systems Planning and Analysis*. Englewood Cliffs, NJ: Prentice-Hall.
[54] White DJ (2004) Danish wind: to good to be true? *The Utilities Journal* July: 37–39.
[55] Morriss AP, Bogart WT, Dorchak A, and Meiners RE (2009) *Green Jobs Myth*. University of Illinois Law and Economics Research Paper Series No. LE09-001, 97pp. http://ssrn.com/abstract-1358428 (viewed 11 August 2009).

Further Reading

[1] Bryce R (2010) *Power Hungry: The Myths of 'Green' Energy and the Real Fuels of the Future*. New York, NY: Public Affairs.
[2] Deutch JM, Forsberg CW, Kadak AC, *et al.* (2009) *Update of MIT 2003 Future of Nuclear Power. An Interdisciplinary MIT Study*. Cambridge, MA: Massachusetts Institute of Technology.
[3] Lomborg B (ed.) (2010) *Smart Solutions to Climate Change. Comparing Costs and Benefits*. Cambridge, UK: Cambridge University Press.
[4] Oswald J, Raine M, and Ashraf-Ball H (2008) Will British weather provide reliable electricity? *Energy Policy* 36(8): 3202–3215.
[5] Pierpont N (2009) *Wind Turbine Syndrome: A Report on a Natural Experiment*. Santa Fe, NM: K-Selected Books.
[6] Prins G, Galiana I, Green C, *et al.* (2010) *The Hartwell Paper. A New Direction for Climate Policy after the Crash of 2009*, 42pp. London, UK: London School of Economics.
[7] Smil V (2003) *Energy at the Crossroads. Global Perspectives and Uncertainties*. Cambridge, MA: MIT Press.
[8] Stoft S (2002) *Power System Economics. Designing Markets for Electricity*. Piscataway, NJ: IEEE Press and Wiley-Interscience.
[9] van Kooten GC (2010) Wind power: The economic impact of intermittency. *Letters in Spatial & Resource Sciences* 3: 1–17.
[10] Weber C (2005) *Uncertainty in the Electric Power Industry. Methods and Models for Decision Support*. New York, NY: Springer.

2.18 Wind Power Integration

JA Carta, Universidad de Las Palmas de Gran Canaria, Las Palmas de Gran Canaria, Spain

© 2012 Elsevier Ltd. All rights reserved.

2.18.1	**Introduction**	570
2.18.2	**Overview of Conventional Electrical Power Systems**	571
2.18.2.1	Structure of an Electrical Power System	571
2.18.2.1.1	Generation	571
2.18.2.1.2	Electrical networks	577
2.18.2.1.3	Loads	579
2.18.2.2	Operational Objectives of an Electrical Power System	581
2.18.2.3	Operating States of an Electrical Power System	581
2.18.2.3.1	Active power–frequency control	582
2.18.2.3.2	Voltage control	585
2.18.3	**The Distinctive Characteristics of Wind Energy**	586
2.18.3.1	The Unpredictability and Variability of Wind	586
2.18.3.2	The Variability of Electrical Energy from Wind Sources	588
2.18.3.2.1	Effect of wind turbine aggregation on wind power variability	590
2.18.3.2.2	Effect of the geographical distribution of wind farms on wind power variability	591
2.18.4	**Wind Power and Power System Interaction**	591
2.18.4.1	Comparison between Conventional and Wind Generation Technologies	592
2.18.4.2	Potential Disturbances in the Interaction of Wind Turbines with the Electrical Network	593
2.18.4.2.1	Frequency variations	593
2.18.4.2.2	Voltage variations	594
2.18.4.2.3	Voltage flicker	594
2.18.4.2.4	Phase voltage imbalance	594
2.18.4.2.5	Voltage dips and swells	594
2.18.4.2.6	Harmonics	595
2.18.5	**Planning and Operation of Wind Power Electrical Systems**	596
2.18.5.1	Repercussions of Wind Power for Power System Generation	596
2.18.5.1.1	Repercussions of wind power for generation reserve capacity	598
2.18.5.1.2	Repercussions of wind power for energy storage needs	599
2.18.5.1.3	Repercussions of wind power for generation capacity	601
2.18.5.2	Impact of Wind Power on the Power Transmission and Distribution Networks	602
2.18.5.2.1	Electrical power transmission from remote onshore wind farms	602
2.18.5.2.2	Electrical power transmission from offshore wind farms	603
2.18.5.2.3	Integration of wind power in distribution networks	606
2.18.6	**Integration of Wind Energy into MGs**	607
2.18.6.1	MG Modeling	611
2.18.6.2	Benefits of Wind Energy Integration into MGs	611
2.18.6.3	Problems Associated with Wind Energy Penetration in MGs	612
2.18.7	**Questions Related to the Extra Costs of Wind Power Integration**	612
2.18.8	**Requirements for Wind Energy Integration into Electrical Networks**	613
2.18.9	**Wind Power Forecasting**	614
2.18.9.1	Physical Models	615
2.18.9.2	Statistical and Data Mining Models	615
2.18.9.2.1	Statistical models	616
2.18.9.2.2	Data mining techniques	616
2.18.9.3	Currently Implemented Forecasting Tools	616
2.18.10	**Future Trends**	617
References		618
Further Reading		622
Relevant Websites		622

2.18.1 Introduction

The main application of the first wind turbines that were built at the end of the nineteenth century to convert the wind's kinetic energy into electricity was in stand-alone systems [1–3]. That is, these wind generators were connected to small stand-alone electrical networks and operated in parallel with electrical generators coupled to diesel engines, or incorporated some type of energy storage system which often consisted of a battery bank. The main purpose was to provide electricity in remote areas where the installation of transmission and distribution lines from the power generation stations was prohibitively expensive. Today, on the other hand, most wind installations fundamentally comprise installation, transmission, and distribution at a low cost.

These wind turbine clusters, known as wind parks or wind farms [4], are interconnected to the main network, operating in parallel with it in such a way that they are both feeding power into and consuming power from that network. While the first wind farms were installed in the 1980s in the United States and then in Europe [3, 4], it was not until the final years of the twentieth century that the numbers of wind farms connected to electrical networks began to rise spectacularly throughout the world [5–10].

Wind farms were initially installed onshore (**Figure 1**), and indeed this trend continues. However, in some northern European countries, a combination of the scarcity of suitable onshore sites with exploitable wind resources and certain favorable characteristics presented by the sea has led to the installation of offshore wind farms, as shown in **Figure 2**, which first began to be developed from 1991 onward [3, 8, 11]. The initiative to install offshore wind farms was taken by Denmark, followed by Sweden, Ireland, the United Kingdom, and The Netherlands. By the end of 2010, the 27 member states of the European Union (EU) were benefiting from a total installed wind power capacity of 84 278 MW, of which 2946 MW corresponded to offshore installations [5]. According to the World Wind Energy Association (WWEA), the installed wind power capacity worldwide as of the end of 2009 amounted to 196 630 MW [6].

Figure 1 Whitelee onshore wind farm, Scotland, UK. Courtesy of Iberdrola (http://www.iberdrola.es).

Figure 2 Horns Rev offshore wind farm, Denmark. Courtesy of Vestas Wind Systems A/S (http://www.vestas.com).

However, mean wind energy penetration, that is, the percentage of the demand for electricity that is covered over a long time period (normally 1 year) in a particular region by electrical energy derived from wind resources, can vary considerably from one country to another. In some countries this penetration was less than 1%, while in Denmark a figure of around 21% was obtained [6]. For 2008, the mean penetration throughout the EU was 4.2% [8]. However, according to the European Wind Energy Association (EWEA) and its reference scenario for 2030, 300 GW of wind power will be installed by that year. It is estimated that this power will produce 935 TWh of electricity, half of which will come from offshore installations, and will cover somewhere between 21% and 28% of the electricity demand of the EU [8], depending on the evolution of future power consumption.

Parallel to the growing numbers of onshore and offshore wind farms which are connected to the high-voltage (HV) electrical network, there has been an increasing interest in proposals for the installation of 'embedded' or 'distributed' generation (DG), given the benefits such a system can offer [12–19]. This type of generation refers to small generators that are normally connected to a distribution network at medium (MV) or low voltages (LV) rather than to a transmission network at high voltages, which is the normal situation in centralized generation (CG) systems. The use of DG systems rules out the possibility of including large wind farms or large hydroelectric plants, but does provide the possibility of using generators powered by renewable energy sources, emergency generators, and combined heat and power (CHP) cogeneration systems. Among the various options that have been proposed for DG are the subsystems known as microgrids (MGs) [12, 20].

MGs are small-scale, low-voltage networks which aim to supply energy to small communities. An MG's generation system is normally hybrid. That is, it usually comprises generators powered by a variety of energy sources [21–26], both renewable and conventional, and energy storage devices [27–30]. Such a power system supplies energy to loads that are located in the vicinity through intelligent coordination of the whole system. These MGs can be designed in such a way that they can normally operate interconnected to the main network [31] or can operate in stand-alone mode [32].

There are a number of advantages to the integration of wind energy into already existing networks or into those under development. This chapter will examine these advantages, along with the consequences that the unusual characteristics of this energy source (i.e., its unpredictable nature and the fluctuations in the power generated) can give rise to in the network to which it is connected, as well as the effects such integration has on the network's operational strategies. A presentation is also made of distributed systems together with an explanation of the benefits of the integration of wind energy into normal interconnected MGs and stand-alone MGs.

2.18.2 Overview of Conventional Electrical Power Systems

Most existing electrical energy systems in the world have very similar structures regardless of the country in question. They are basically industrial systems geared toward the generation, transmission, distribution, and supply of electricity [33–38] (**Figure 3**). Historically, the generation of electricity has been undertaken at large power production stations. Often, this type of centralized station is located some distance away from the areas of major consumption, and the energy is supplied to these areas via electrical networks. Large wind farms and renewable DG systems are connected to these networks by feeding energy into and extracting energy from them. The resulting power flow caused by these installations can affect both the installations themselves and the power systems to which they are connected. For a better understanding of the problems associated with wind energy integration, an introduction to a number of questions related to electrical power systems is given below.

2.18.2.1 Structure of an Electrical Power System

Electrical energy systems can basically be structured into three main blocks: generation, energy transmission/distribution networks, and loads. A brief presentation of each of these aspects, as well as of control and protection systems, will be made in the following sections.

2.18.2.1.1 Generation
Power stations traditionally convert the energy stored in a primary energy source like coal, oil, nuclear fuel, gas, or a volume of water at a certain height into electrical energy. The most commonly used technologies are hydro, thermal, and nuclear power plants.

The generation of hydroelectric power (**Figure 4**) entails the conversion of the potential energy of a volume of water located at a certain height into kinetic energy in a hydraulic turbine and the conversion of mechanical energy into electrical energy in an electrical generator. So, hydroelectric power stations require a flow of water and a difference of level in that flow [23, 28, 38–42].

Depending on the method used to control the flow of water, hydroelectric plants can be classified into two basic types: run-of-river power plants and reservoir power plants. Run-of-river power plants take part of the flow of a river and direct it toward the turbines. There are a variety of possible configurations, but this type of plant can only allow small controlled flows of water through the turbines. Reservoir power plants have the capacity to store water by means of a dam and thus control the flow of water through the turbines and, consequently, the production of electricity.

Thanks to the storage capacity of reservoir power stations, these power stations can be combined with pumping stations to make pumped storage plants. The pumping stations are responsible for returning to the dam, or the upper reservoir, the water that has been discharged from the turbines into a reservoir constructed in the lower part of the station. In this way, the surplus energy

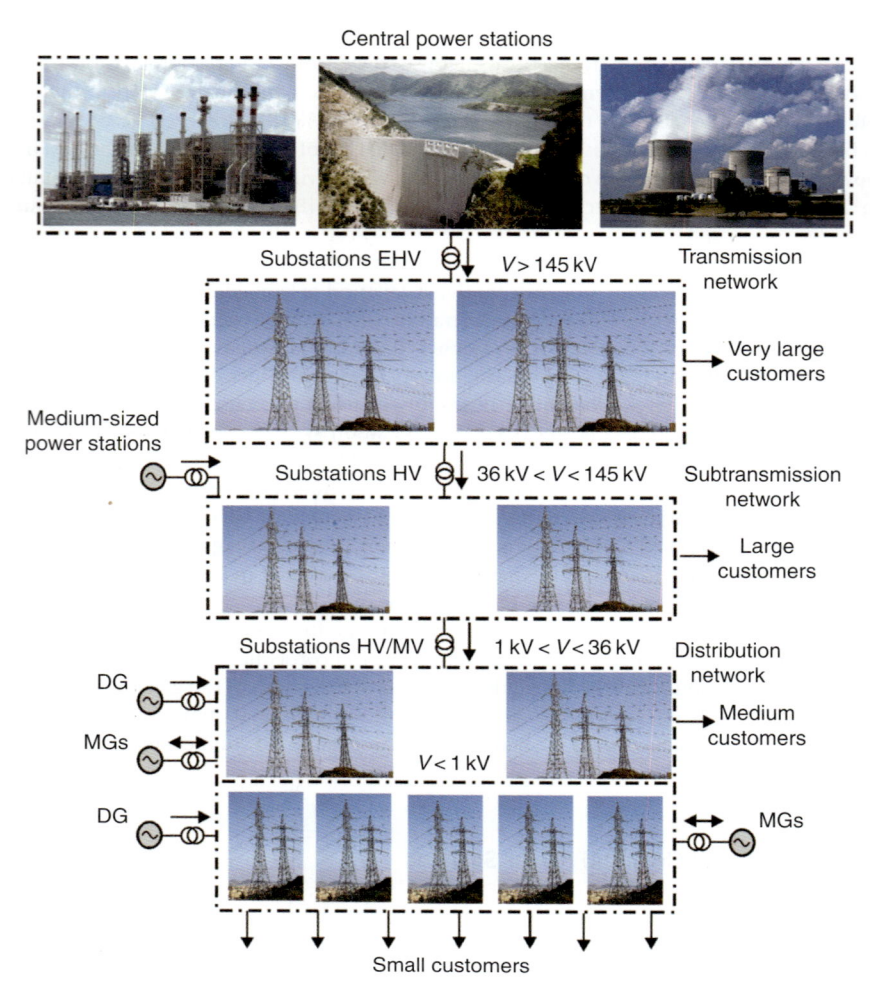

Figure 3 Schematic diagram of the structure of an electrical power system. EHV, extra high voltage.

Figure 4 Cortes de La Muela hydroelectric power station in Cortes de Pallás, Valencia, Spain. Courtesy of Iberdrola (http://www.iberdrola.es).

produced by thermal and nuclear power stations which face certain difficulties in controlling power output can be stored. Likewise, the surplus variable energy generated by wind farms can also be stored.

Hydroelectric power plants employ various systems and devices for their supervision, control, and protection, depending on the type of technology employed and the envisaged operating parameters. Smaller hydroelectric power plants (<5 MVA) tend to use induction generators. However, most hydroelectric power stations operate with synchronous generators. Some of the operating characteristics of hydroelectric power plants are of particular interest. These plants enjoy a fast start-up response, with start-up times of just a few seconds. Moreover, they can maintain a practically constant efficiency throughout the power output range, which can be widely controlled. So, hydroelectric power plants constitute a highly flexible source of electrical generation that can be adapted to variations in demand. Other advantages include the cost of the fuel and the absence of atmospheric contamination. However, drawbacks of such plants include the high investment costs, a degree of randomness and constraints in terms of the amount of primary energy available, and the need to flood extensive areas with its consequent environmental impact.

Conventional thermal power plants convert the primary energy that comes from a fossil fuel (coal, oil, or natural gas) into electrical energy [23, 34–38, 42–46]. In these power stations, the fuel is burned in a steam boiler. Here, the primary energy is converted into the thermal energy contained in the steam and gas emissions which are produced in the combustion process and escape into the atmosphere. A steam turbine (**Figure 5**) converts the thermal energy stored in the water vapor into mechanical energy, namely, the rotational movement of a shaft. This mechanical energy is then turned into electrical energy by means of a generator coupled to the turbine shaft (**Figure 6**).

As a result of the thermal inertia of the boiler, these power stations are somewhat inflexible in terms of connection and disconnection. Moreover, control of conventional units is not possible over the entire power output range. In order to guarantee power generation availability and to improve the system's flexibility, a large number of units need to be permanently connected covering the loads, regardless of the power demand. This means that a number of turbines operate under partial load, which is uneconomical. The use of conventional thermal units to cover demand peaks results in efficiency losses and an important restriction to optimizing the use of the primary energy source.

Figure 5 Steam turbine at Jinámar power station, Gran Canaria Island, Spain. Courtesy of ENDESA.

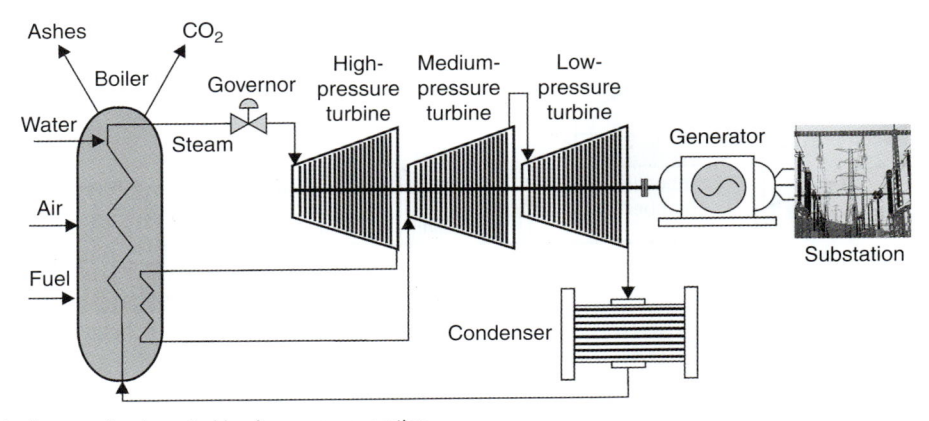

Figure 6 Schematic diagram of a steam turbine for power generation.

One of the advantages of thermal power stations is that, in principle, enough primary energy can be stored to guarantee its availability for continuous use during a reasonably long period of time. Drawbacks of the system, in addition to those outlined above, include the cost of the fuel and its contribution to atmospheric contamination.

Conceptually, the turbines employed in gas-fired thermal power stations (**Figure 7**) are basically the same as steam turbines. The fundamental difference lies in the fact that the stream which strikes the turbine blades is a mixture of the gases that result from the combustion of the fuel used, rather than water vapor (steam). The system uses a compressor which introduces air at high pressure (thereby raising its temperature) into a combustion chamber where it is mixed with the fuel, which ignites without a large increase in pressure, raising the temperature of the air. The gases thus generated are directed toward the blades of a turbine, causing its shaft to rotate. This shaft is coupled to an electrical generator (**Figure 8**). The exhaust gases, usually at a temperature range of 400–600 °C, are emitted into the atmosphere.

Modern gas turbines used for electrical power generation employ axial compressors and multistage turbines in order to achieve high levels of efficiency. A number of strategies aimed at improving efficiency have been proposed.

Gas turbines are a little behind hydroelectric plants in terms of start-up times, interruptions, and operational load range. They are suitable for covering power demand peaks. In just a few minutes, they are able to achieve full output and can respond rapidly to variations in load demand or unforeseen output losses on the part of other generators. Most gas turbines burn natural gas, which is a relatively clean fuel. In addition to the relatively low contamination produced, investment costs are lower than those for coal-fired thermal power plants.

Gas turbines in themselves are not very efficient. This is partly due to the fact that the exhaust gases are still very hot. In other words, the exhaust gases contain a significant amount of energy which is not being exploited. One strategy to combat this is to capture the heat of the exhaust gases in a steam boiler and produce steam to drive a turbine and generate additional electricity (**Figure 9**). This is the principle behind combined cycle power plants (**Figure 10**). These plants are capable of achieving efficiencies of up to 60%. This advantage, along with their modularity and the relatively reasonable investment costs, makes them useful for covering base demand and peaks.

Figure 7 Gas turbine at Jinámar power station, Gran Canaria Island, Spain. Courtesy of ENDESA.

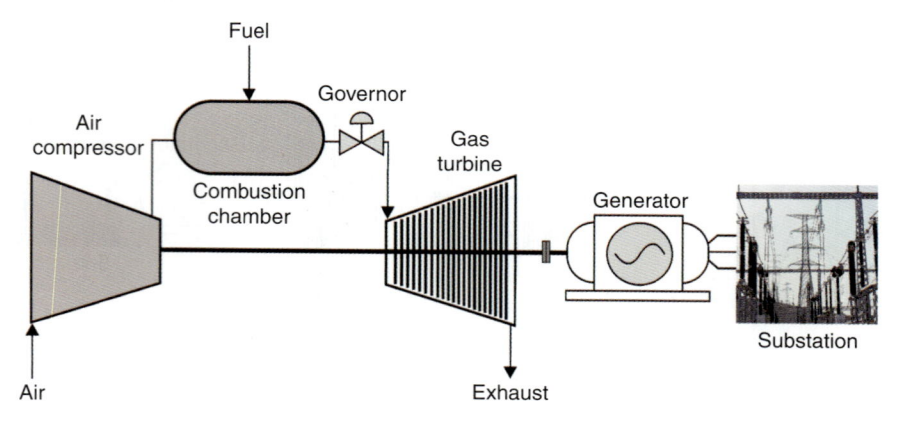

Figure 8 Schematic diagram of a gas turbine for power generation.

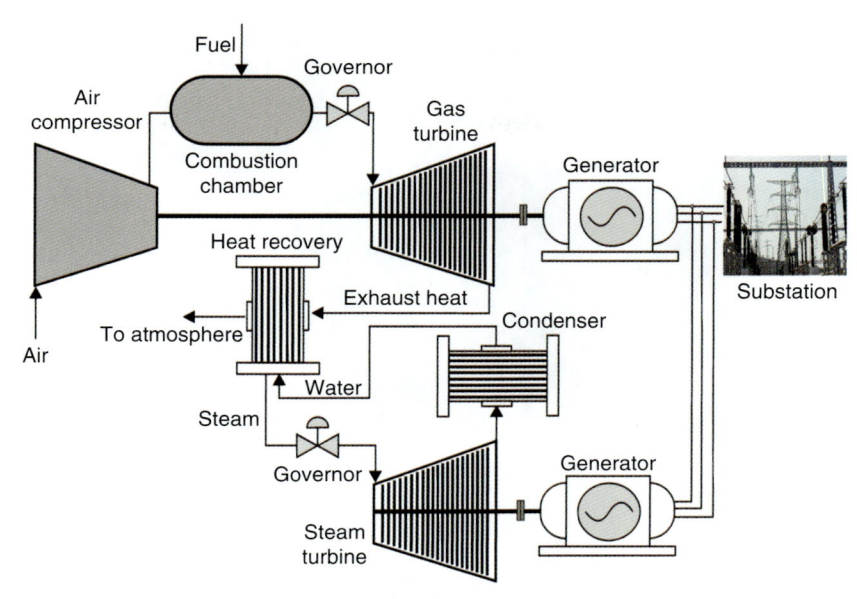

Figure 9 Schematic diagram of a combined cycle plant for power generation.

Figure 10 Combined cycle plant in Tarragona, Spain. Courtesy of Iberdrola (http://www.iberdrola.es).

In conventional power stations, generating units based on reciprocating engines or piston engines are also used. Reciprocating internal combustion engines are devices that convert the chemical energy contained in a hydrocarbon into mechanical energy (rotation of a shaft with a certain speed and torque) and into the thermal energy of the waste gases that escape into the atmosphere. These engines can generate electricity if an electrical generator is coupled to its output shaft, while the waste heat can also be exploited for thermal applications (cogeneration). These piston engines can be classified into three categories: high-, medium-, and low-speed engines. The choice will depend on the application. Large engines of low (**Figure 11**) or medium (**Figure 12**) speed are generally the most suitable when it comes to covering the base load. However, high-speed engines are more effective, economically speaking, for use as a backup service, where there is no requirement to operate over many hours throughout the year. Internal combustion engines can work well under partial-load conditions. Diesel engines in particular work very well when dealing with falls in load from 100% to 50%.

Modern-day nuclear power plants (**Figure 13**), of which there are several types, generate electricity by utilizing the enormous amounts of energy released when the nucleus of certain heavy elements, like uranium, splits after being bombarded by neutrons in a process known as nuclear fission [23, 35, 38, 47–51]. The means of exploiting this type of energy is exclusively through the production of heat, which raises the temperature of a substance such as water, carbon dioxide, or sodium, converting it into steam or a high-pressure gas and driving a turbine with this pressure to transform the thermal energy into mechanical energy. Connection of electrical generators to the turbine shafts enables the production of electricity.

Figure 11 Low-speed diesel generation unit at Jinámar power station, Gran Canaria Island, Spain. Courtesy of ENDESA.

Figure 12 Medium-speed diesel generation unit at Las Salinas power station, Fuerteventura Island, Spain. Courtesy of ENDESA.

Figure 13 Nuclear power station at Cofrentes, Valencia, Spain. Courtesy of Iberdrola (http://www.iberdrola.es).

Nuclear plants are more capital-intensive than plants which use fossil fuels, but the cost of the fuel is much less. As a result of the high investment costs and the problems that can arise when changing the reactor's cooling conditions, it is advisable to use these plants to cover the base demand operating at maximum availability in order to achieve a high utilization factor of the nuclear energy. The main drawbacks of nuclear power arise as a result of the dangers associated with breakdowns and the problems involved in the disposal of radioactive waste. As a consequence, nuclear power plants are the most controversial of all power generating systems.

2.18.2.1.2 Electrical networks

Conventional electrical power generation plants produce power at a voltage between 6 and 25 kV. These relatively low voltages are not suitable for the transmission of power over long distances due to the losses that occur during transmission. Longitudinal losses are proportional to the resistance of the medium and the square of the intensity of the current that is circulating. Therefore, the intensity and/or resistance need to be reduced in order to reduce the losses [34, 35].

The voltage that leaves the power station has to reach the terminals of the consumers. Since voltage drops occur across the impedance of the network, the impedance of the network or the intensity of current needs to be reduced in order to reduce the voltage drop. For this purpose, large transformers are used, which raise the voltage to hundreds of thousands of volts, transmitting the same power but reducing the current [34, 35, 37, 38]. On lowering the intensity and increasing the voltage, losses as a result of the Joule effect are reduced quadratically, while the voltage drop is linear [35].

Extra-high-voltage lines transmit the energy produced by the power generation stations to high-voltage substations – the starting point of the so-called subtransmission networks (**Figure 3**). These networks operate at a lower voltage than the transmission networks and, in turn, supply the local networks, known as distribution networks, via substations that reduce the high voltage to medium voltage. The distribution networks usually have a distinctively radial configuration for the purpose of supplying energy to the medium- and small-sized consumers spread out throughout the area and connected, respectively, to medium and low voltages. Medium-sized consumers are generally the large industries, while the small-sized consumers tend to be represented by domestic loads, businesses, and small factories. In order to cover their particular energy requirements, large-sized consumers are usually connected to the high-voltage network (**Figure 3**).

Electrical networks, fundamentally comprising lines and substations, were initially used to connect the production and consumption centers of a particular region. Gradually, however, from the end of the nineteenth century to the present day, these networks have found themselves hooked up to other networks of nearby areas until the networks have grown to cover the geography of each country [35]. **Figure 14** shows an outline of the transmission network map of the Spanish mainland system. According to Red Eléctrica de España (REE), the Spanish transmission system operator (TSO), Spain's transmission system in 2009 was 34 754 km long, with 3385 substation positions and a transformation capacity of 66 259 MW. Indeed, given the economic advantages presented by network interconnection, some continents now have network interconnections between several countries, with the consequent creation of enormous and complex supranational meshed networks.

Most networks work with alternating current (AC), though there are a few exceptions in high-voltage energy transmission (e.g., direct current (DC) transmission may be more convenient when the aim is to connect production and consumption centers separated by considerable distances) [35]. So, when operating at the same rated frequency and with all the synchronous generators in phase, it is possible for the energy produced in an area of one country to be transmitted beyond its frontiers and shared with other areas of the country or with other countries. One of the advantages offered by a robust and secure meshed network is supply continuity, since the various substations can be fed from a number of directions. The feasibility of reducing the reserve capacity required to cover demand peaks also constitutes an added value. Another advantage lies in the possibility of reducing the spinning reserve, namely, the power that has to be connected, but without a load, to cover unforeseen increases in demand. The way that

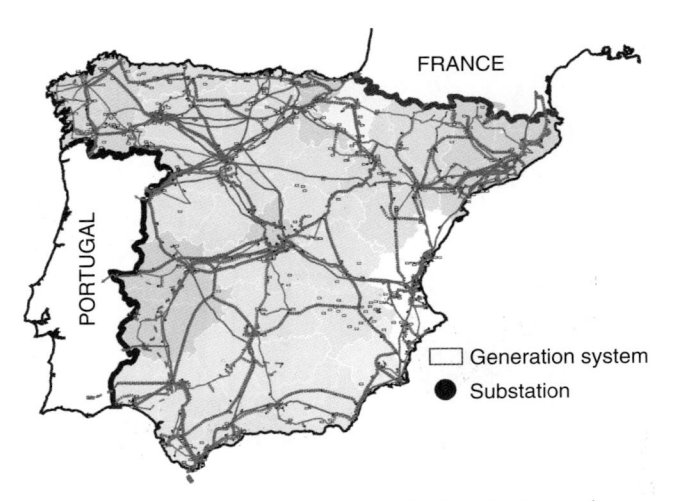

Figure 14 Spanish mainland's electricity transmission network map. Courtesy of REE (http://www.ree.es).

Figure 15 High-voltage tower. Courtesy of Iberdrola (http://www.iberdrola.es).

these interconnected networks function sees the reserve capacity shared out between different generation centers in such a way that there is mutual support against network disturbances. Market systems can decide how the power injected into the network is to be shared out between the different power generation stations at any given moment.

Aerial power lines (**Figure 15**), which generally consist of steel-reinforced, stranded aluminum alloy cables, are sized according to the maximum operating voltage, the power to be transmitted, the distance involved, and the location of the starting/end points and other interconnection nodes [34, 35]. The aim is to achieve a design that, from both an electrical and a mechanical point of view, generates the least longitudinal and transverse losses in the transmission of the energy and minimizes the investment, operating, and maintenance costs. Longitudinal losses are primarily due to the Joule effect, while transverse losses are the result of the corona effect. The Joule effect and the corona effect [37] are related to the operating current and voltage, respectively.

Fiber-optic cables of the telecommunications network can also be housed inside the high-voltage cables. Spain's TSO, responsible for the high-voltage network, currently has a network of more than 21 300 km of fiber-optic cable and around 19 000 devices to provide telecommand, telecontrol, and teleprotection services [52].

The substations [53] act as network nodes and, in their most basic configuration, comprise thick bars to which the electrical lines are interconnected. They can, however, be configured in very different ways, each one of which gives the substation different characteristics in terms of reliability, operational flexibility, cost, and so on.

Substations (**Figure 16**) can be classified according to their use, and they fulfill a variety of functions. One of those functions is to serve as an interconnection point for the power lines, directing the power flow toward different geographical regions in such a way

Figure 16 Substation at La Vall D'Uxió, Castellón, Spain. Courtesy of Iberdrola (http://www.iberdrola.es).

that the flow of power generated in the various power generation stations can be controlled in accordance with the country's energy policy or market conditions. Another function can be as a transformation center which carries out interconnections at different operating voltages. This function also includes raising the outgoing voltage of the transformation centers. A third function is that of housing the various elements of protection, cut-out, and switching.

The equipment of a substation comprises power transformers, devices used to connect and disconnect electrical circuits, measuring and protection transformers, protection relays, and so on, depending on its configuration.

Among the devices used for the connection and disconnection of electrical circuits are automatic switchgear and isolators. Automatic switchgear is designed to open and close a line along which an abnormally high current circulates as a consequence of, for example, a short circuit. The job of the isolators is not to cut off any current, but rather to electrically isolate in a visible way the damaged area once the current along the line has been cut off as a result of the activation of a switch. Measuring and protection transformers, usually of current or voltage, are used to power the measuring instruments, relays, and other equipment, including the communications system. Measuring devices detect faults, and the protection equipment decides what switch needs to be activated to clear the fault. For this reason, protection systems need to be selective, reliable, and sensitive enough to operate under minimum-fault conditions in the system area for which it is responsible and must be able to act with a speed appropriate to the type of fault that needs to be cleared. Selectivity in this case is related to the capacity to clearly recognize the type of fault and to minimize the size and extent of the interruption. Reliability indicates the capacity to operate exclusively when a fault condition arises.

Though the interconnection of networks does present economic advantages, the intensity of the current increases when a short circuit occurs in a system. Disturbances caused by a short circuit can extend to systems that are interconnected to it. So, for a network to fulfill its mission and guarantee its operation in secure and safe conditions, it must be equipped with appropriate measuring, protection, and control equipment.

2.18.2.1.3 Loads

Power systems have to cover the demand for electricity that may come from a number of consumer categories: industrial, domestic, commercial, and so on. Instantaneous power demand is typically a variable parameter that depends on the electricity requirements of the consumer at any given moment [23, 35–37, 54]. The profiles represented by the power demand as a function of time (typically 24 h) are known as load curves. The area enclosed by a load curve and the time axis represents the energy consumed in the period under consideration.

The load curve for each consumer category usually has its own distinctive characteristics [18, 23]. Some may display clearly noticeable demand peaks and troughs, while others may be flat. For example, the maximum domestic sector consumption tends to occur when people are at home and are using their electrical household appliances. This happens usually during mornings and evenings and at weekends. By contrast, the domestic sector's minimum consumption tends to be during the rest of the day and at night. Electricity consumption is also extremely dependent on the weather and climate of a particular region, which affect the amount household appliances consume for cooling or heating purposes. Industrial consumption tends to display a more stable profile than domestic or commercial consumption.

By superimposing the different load curves of the various consumer types, the electrical system's load curve is obtained. These load curves can be represented for different time periods. That is to say, they can be daily, weekly, monthly, or annually. It should be mentioned that fluctuations in total demand are less than those corresponding to an individual load. In other words, demand aggregation gives rise to a smoothing effect of the load curves. This is due to the different load profiles of the various consumption sectors and the random component of demand. As a result, the variance of total consumption is less than that of any one individual consumer type.

Figure 17 shows the total demand curve for 14 and 15 February 2010 (a Sunday and Monday, respectively), in the Spanish mainland system. The variability of demand over time can be observed together with the hourly intervals in which the peaks and troughs took place. **Figure 18** shows the evolution of the peaks and troughs of the daily demand curves recorded during 2009. The influence of weekends and holiday and seasonal periods can be observed.

Meanwhile, each point of the so-called load–duration curves indicates, on the x-axis, the accumulated time in which the system's power demand was higher than the value indicated on the ordinate axis (**Figure 19**). These curves, like the load curves, can be represented for different time periods: weekly, monthly, or yearly.

Though it depends on the nature of the loads, that is, whether they are resistive or inductive, the overall power demand has an active and a reactive component. Active power is the power converted into physical power. Reactive power helps create the magnetic field which certain loads require. So, there is a variation of these components in the daily evolution of power demand. With regard to reactive power, it should be mentioned that aerial power lines, depending on their load, generate or consume reactive power. Transformers, on the other hand, always consume reactive power.

The electrical demand of the loads, unlike the other components of a conventional electrical generation system, cannot be controlled and displays a high degree of randomness. This random behavior can be modified to a certain extent through the use of demand-side management techniques aimed at rationalizing electrical energy consumption [55–57]. Some loads, normally known as deferrable loads or interruptible loads, can postpone their connection to the network within certain time intervals. Loads that can feasibly be temporarily interrupted include those that have thermal inertia (air conditioning, heating, etc.), certain water pumping applications, and sea or brackish water desalination plants [58–60]. Likewise, the establishment of electricity tariffs that depend on

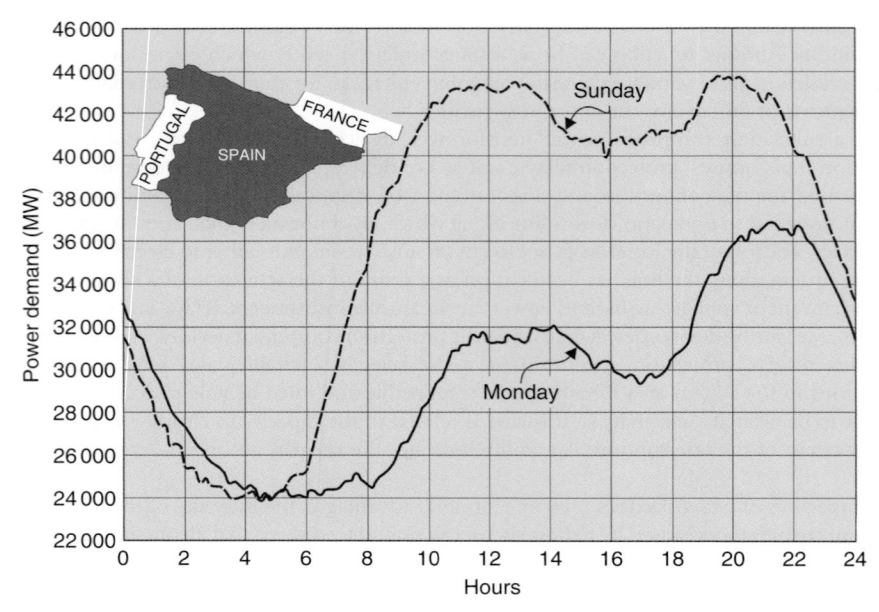

Figure 17 Power demand curves of the Spanish mainland electricity system for 2 days in February 2010. Courtesy of REE (http://www.ree.es).

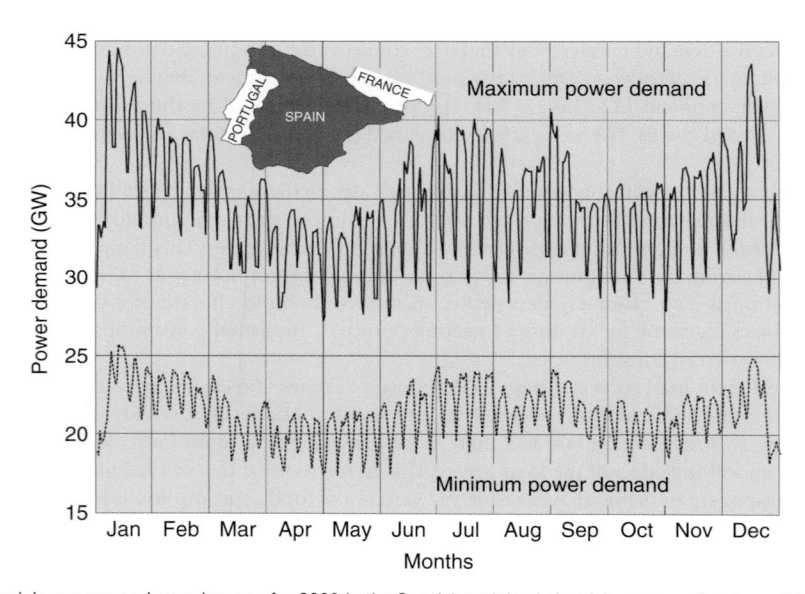

Figure 18 Maximum and minimum power demand curves for 2009 in the Spanish mainland electricity system. Courtesy of REE (http://www.ree.es).

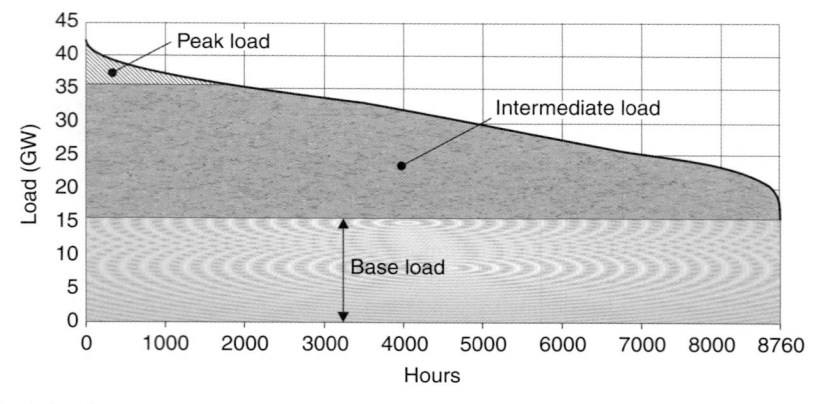

Figure 19 Example of a load–duration curve.

the amount consumed and the time of consumption (via the use of time bands) can have the effect of persuading consumers to react to the price of the energy used and alter their consumption habits accordingly.

In order to be able to carry out both the planning and operational tasks of an electrical system, short-term demand has to be estimated in all situations. The use of predictive models based on time series [61, 62] and models that employ data mining techniques, such as neural networks [63], has been proposed to estimate short-term demand and employ it in electrical system operational tasks. These models take advantage of certain behavioral traits that are observed in the evolution of demand, which have been mentioned above, namely, the relationships that exist between the demand and parameters such as type of day, time of the day, climate and atmospheric conditions, type of user, and geographical location.

Electricity operators have developed expert systems for the forecast of daily and hourly demand to help in their operational decision-making [52].

2.18.2.2 Operational Objectives of an Electrical Power System

The operational objectives of electrical power systems can be synthesized into two fundamental priorities, namely, guaranteeing continuity of supply so that demand is covered with the required quality and, within the restrictions imposed by this objective, ensuring that the system is run in the most economic way possible [62, 64, 65].

Guaranteeing continuity of supply requires the establishment of security criteria in the operation of the electrical system. For this, a series of parameters must be controlled that enable supervision of the status of the electrical system. These parameters are the frequency, the voltages at the network nodes, and the load levels in the various elements of the transmission network that the system operator manages, namely, the lines and substations.

The control centers (**Figure 20**) [9, 52] manage the information they receive in real time from the power generation centers and the network via an extensive telecommunications network. Studies that guarantee security of the electrical system are carried out using this information.

Security depends on the robustness of the system in the face of predefined contingencies. For example, the contingencies that are normally considered are (1) single outage of any element in the system; (2) simultaneous outage of double-circuit lines that share towers over an extensive section of the line path; and (3) in special situations, the outage of the largest generator unit in the area and of one of its interconnection lines with the rest of the system [33].

The system must have the capacity to maintain the control parameters within certain preestablished admissible limits in the face of changes in demand and contingencies that may arise. Given the inherent uncertainty in relation to some contingencies, when the term 'security' is used, it often refers to a measure of short-term operational reliability.

The second objective of electrical power systems is related to what is known as the economic dispatch [33, 62], that is, the method of dispatching the available generation resources to supply the load on the system in such a way that the total generation cost is minimized.

2.18.2.3 Operating States of an Electrical Power System

A balance must be achieved at all times in the operation of electrical systems between generation and demand without overloading the system. The function of the system operator lies in ensuring that this balance is always maintained. For this purpose, the operator needs to be able to forecast demand and supervise the generation and transmission installations in real time. If the system gets out of balance, the operator orders the production centers to adjust generation so that it can be adapted to the variations in demand. However, depending on the conditions in which the power system finds itself, it can be run under different operating states [33, 66, 67].

In the normal operating state, in addition to the prerequisites that there exist a balance between generation and demand and that the restrictions imposed on certain variables be met, a specific security level is also contemplated. That is, the normal operating state is also characterized by reserve margins, in relation to both the transmission system and the power generation system. Typically, a system will find itself under the normal operating state for a high percentage of the time [68] (**Figure 21**).

Figure 20 Electricity Control Center of REE, CECOEL. Courtesy of REE (http://www.ree.es).

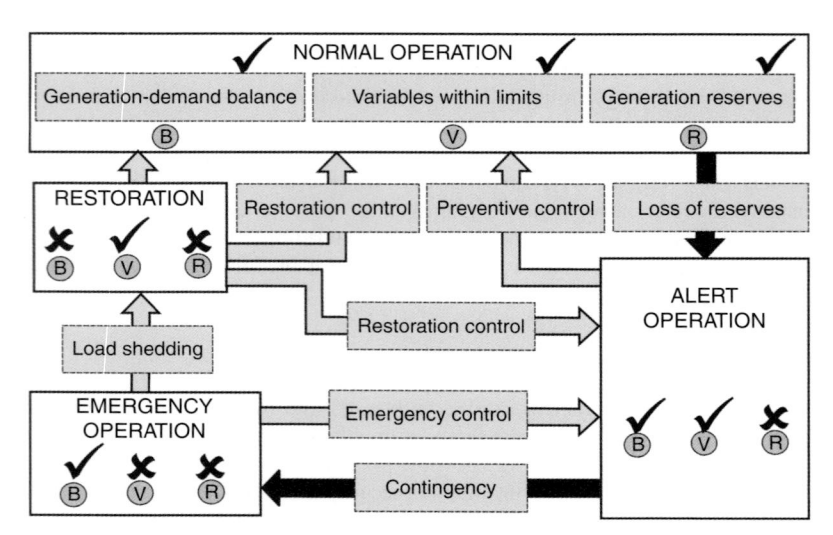

Figure 21 Schematic diagram of the operating states of an electrical power system.

If the levels of security fall, whether as a result of an increase in load or due to the probability that some disturbance will occur, then the system reliability gets reduced. When the level of security falls below a specified limit, even if the demand is covered and the operating limits imposed on the variables are not breached, the system finds itself in the state known as 'alert'.

In alert state, any disturbance caused by the evolution of demand or the presence of a contingency could result in the operating variables being outside their established ranges. If such a situation arises, the system changes to emergency state.

When a system is in emergency state, it has to make urgent use of corrective measures required to avoid the system losing its integrity and collapsing. Among the measures that can be used to ensure that the values of the variables return to admissible operating intervals is the temporary suspension of the supply to the users. That is, a load shedding is performed.

In some countries, automatic load shedding is undertaken following the guidelines of the Union for the Coordination of Transmission of Electricity (UCTE), which has established the load percentages to be disconnected depending on the frequency of the system. However, it must be pointed out that from 1 July 2009 onward, the European Network of Transmission System Operators for Electricity (ENTSOE) [69] took over all operational tasks of the six existing TSO associations in Europe, including the UCTE.

There are also nonautomatic, selective load shedding mechanisms designed to avoid loss of demand in alert or emergency situations. Both types of shedding try to avoid the disconnection of highly sensitive loads, such as hospitals and radio and television services. Likewise, as mentioned in Section 2.18.2.1.3, there can also exist load interruption services. In Spain, this service can be offered by consumers who acquire the energy from the production market [52]. The system operator, depending on the category of the load interruption service, can interrupt the energy supply to the consumers during certain time periods. In practically all the service categories, the consumers must be given prior notification.

Action must be taken to restore the system to the normal or alert status. In problematic situations, operational objectives of a technical nature take priority over economic ones.

From the consumer's point of view, optimum quality of the electricity supply is determined by the uniformity of the voltage, with a pure sinusoidal wave at a constant frequency and effective value. The quality of the supply will be affected by disturbances that modify these characteristics. Sine wave purity is becoming increasingly relevant as a result of the demands of the recipients. The waveform can be distorted by both the generation itself and the actual recipients of the electrical energy. The problems related to waveform quality are usually tackled at a local level. However, supervision of the frequency and effective value of the voltage is usually dealt with by a centralized and hierarchical control structure.

In order to better understand how electrical energy systems function, something which will be useful when it comes to analyzing the impact of wind energy integration into the systems, the following sections will provide a brief description of (1) active power and frequency control and (2) reactive power and voltage control, though to a certain extent both types of control are interrelated.

2.18.2.3.1 Active power–frequency control

The rated frequency used in European and African countries is 50 Hz. This frequency is also used by the vast majority of countries in the Middle East, Asia, Australia, and the Pacific Islands. However, in the United States, Canada, and most Central and South American countries, the frequency used is 60 Hz.

The frequency of an electrical system is closely related to the equilibrium that exists between the power supplied by the generation system, the power consumed by the loads, and power losses. When there occurs a deviation in this power balance, the control system acts to reestablish it following a hierarchical procedure organized into three stages: primary, secondary, and tertiary control [52, 65, 70]. Each of these levels operates over different time margins and involves areas of greater or lesser size of the whole electrical system.

If the power demand increases sharply or a generator fault occurs, the primary control stage must be immediately available to provide the generation power required to reestablish the system's power balance. This additional generation power is provided initially by making use of the kinetic energy stored in the rotating elements of the power generation units, which are able to provide full output power for a few seconds, and following this by intervention of the turbine and engine speed governors.

The kinetic energy depends on the inertia of the rotating masses and the rotational speed. The rotational speed of the synchronous generators of an electrical system is proportional to the frequency of the voltage. So, a deviation from the active power balance leads to changes in the rotational speed of the generators and, consequently, in the frequency of the system.

After a certain delay, while the system responds to the release of the stored kinetic energy, more significant amounts of energy can be supplied to restore the active power balance. This supplementary energy is achieved through the intervention of the systems that regulate the opening of the valves that control engine fuel input, the flow of water in hydroelectric plant turbines or the flow of gas or steam in thermal power plant turbines (**Figure 22**). As the engines and turbines are mechanically coupled to the generators it is possible to regulate the power that the latter generate by controlling the mechanical power output of the former. When a reference power level is either not reached or exceeded, the turbine and engine governors adjust the valves to increase or decrease mechanical power. It should be mentioned that some loads are sensitive to frequency changes and vary their power demand accordingly.

The participation of generators in restoring the power balance depends on their power–frequency characteristic. This characteristic depicts the variation in frequency when the power generated by a machine changes from zero to its rated value. This relationship can be approximated to a straight line whose slope, of negative sign, is the constant of the governor. This constant is what determines the characteristic of the governor in continuous operating conditions (steady state) and is known as the generator speed droop. Speed droop is expressed in hertz per megawatts, and typical values are in the range of 4–6%. The point where the straight line intercepts the frequency axis is known as the set point. The governor allows the system operator to adjust the set point in such a way that the mechanical power output varies without modifying the frequency.

Figure 23 shows the power–frequency characteristic which corresponds to a generator with a specific regulation constant, operating at two different set points. However, the primary control does not modify the set point; rather, the variation in mechanical power is obtained by varying the frequency.

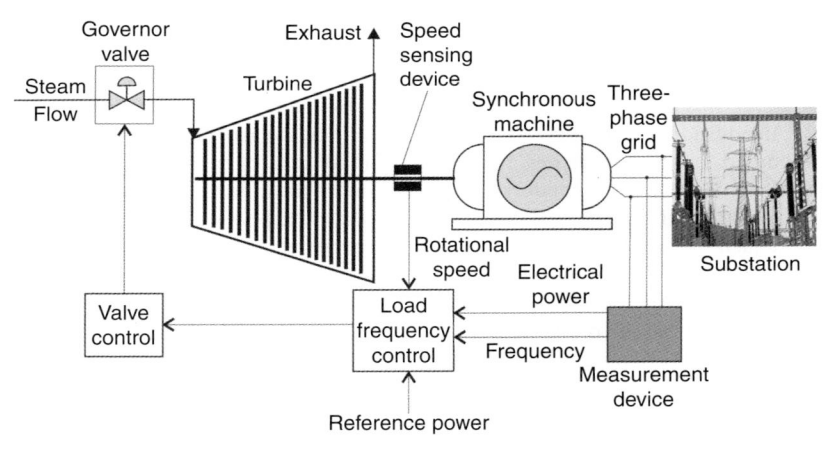

Figure 22 Schematic diagram of the frequency control system of a synchronous generator.

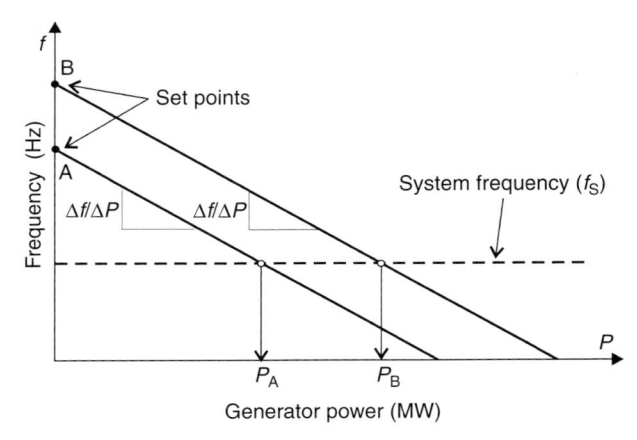

Figure 23 Active power–frequency characteristic of a generator with two set points (A and B). P_A, power supplied by the generator with set point A; P_B, power supplied by the generator with set point B.

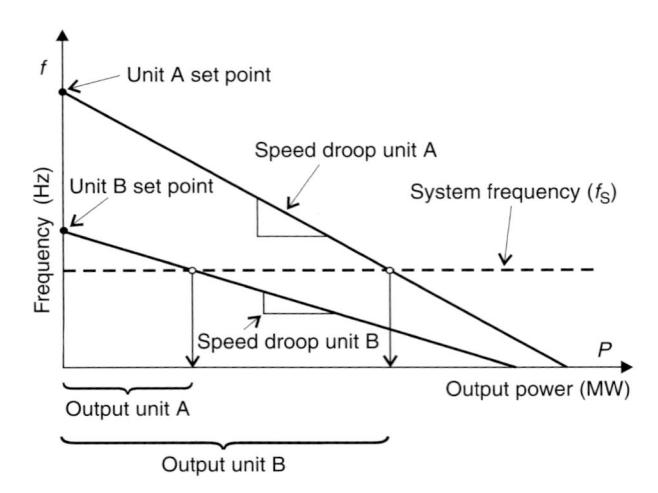

Figure 24 Schematic diagram of load distribution between two generators in parallel with different speed droops.

When there are various generators of different rated powers working in parallel with different speed droops, the contribution each one makes will depend on the value of its speed droop. A unit with a lower speed droop will contribute to the primary regulation a higher percentage of power with respect to its rated power, while a generator with a higher speed droop contributes a lower percentage of power. **Figure 24** shows load allocation between two generators with different speed droops. If several units in parallel have the same speed droop, all of them will contribute to the primary control proportionally to their rated power.

Primary control, which acts at a local level, enables restoration of the balance between power generated plus losses and power demanded. The primary control must complete its intervention within 15–30 s of the instant when the imbalance takes place. This time will depend on the magnitude of the imbalance. The primary control ensures that the frequency is never outside the acceptable range. However, this control is unable to prevent the frequency from remaining deviated from the nominal or rated reference frequency. In addition, the load increase allocation among the generators does not have to maintain the power flows that have been scheduled. In some countries, like Spain, primary control is an obligatory and unpaid complementary service that must be provided by connected generators. In Spain, primary control of generating units must allow a speed droop such that the generators can vary their load by 1.5% of their rated power [52].

The secondary power–frequency control acts on a zonal level, where the frequency in each of the neighboring production zones is uniform. This control level allows the defects of the primary control to be corrected, though it is slower-acting. Commencement of secondary control intervention should not be delayed for longer than 30 s. The automatic generation control (AGC) is responsible for this intervention level, and its actions are centralized.

As has been mentioned, it is possible to modify the reference power of the generators. That is, it is possible to change the set point in the power–frequency characteristics. This action entails vertical movement of the power–frequency characteristic, as can be seen in **Figure 23**.

Through determination of the reference power that has to be produced by each generator which intervenes in the secondary control, the frequency error can be corrected in a stable manner, thereby contributing to maintaining the frequency in that particular zone or area. In addition to covering the demand of the area, secondary control, which is performed by the system operator, must maintain the scheduled energy exchanges. The control strategy defines for each area an error signal known as the area control error (ACE). The reference power variation allocated to each of the generators that participate in the secondary control has to be proportional to the integral of the ACE. That is, the error signal is an input variable of an integrator. Its purpose is that the mechanical power variation of the generators is modified in such a way that the area error tends to zero in steady state. The gains of the integrator are determined with control stability criteria.

In the participation of the different generation systems in frequency control and demand variation control, several strategies can be used based on speed of response, nondiscrimination of generator type, and so on. The intervention time of the secondary control reserve is usually limited and should normally be no greater than 15 min.

The reserve power that must be maintained to undertake secondary control is determined by the system operator. In the Spanish mainland electrical system, the recommendation of the UCTE is normally taken as the point of reference. In Spain, the secondary control service is optional and paid for through market systems [52].

Tertiary control operates over a more extensive range of the electrical system, simultaneously regulating the frequency and voltages following economic and security criteria [33]. The purpose of tertiary control is restoration of the secondary control reserve to make it available again. In general, tertiary control works with generators that may or may not be coupled and must act within a time margin of between 10 and 15 min, and its reserves must be able to be maintained for some hours.

In some countries, tertiary control is a complementary service which is optional and paid for through market systems.

2.18.2.3.2 Voltage control

The purpose of voltage control is maintenance of the effective value of the voltages in the network within acceptable limits [33, 52, 64, 65, 68]. There is a close relationship between the reactive power flow between two network nodes and the difference between the effective voltage values at these nodes. Reactive power variations entail voltage variations. So, the control system has to be constantly working to correct voltage deviations. There must also be reactive power reserves available to resolve any voltage incident that might take place.

A variety of devices can be used to control the voltage. These include static compensators, synchronous compensators, and synchronous generators [71].

Capacitor and/or reactor banks constitute static compensators that inject or consume reactive energy into/from the nodes where they are connected. The voltage is discretely modified via connection and disconnection of these devices. Mechanical connection is performed through relays and electronic connection through thyristors.

Static compensators consisting of fixed-capacity condensers and adjustable coils can be used for continuous regulation of the reactive power injected or consumed into/from the network. This device is known as a thyristor-controlled reactor-fixed capacitor (TCR-FC; **Figure 25**).

Thanks to advances in power electronics, the pulse-width modulation (PWM) technique is being used more and more commonly in power electronic systems [72–76]. Indeed, it can be stated that the PWM technique has opened up a whole new field in reactive energy compensation methods.

Static compensators (STATCOMs) normally use the PWM technique. The STATCOM (**Figure 26**) is a voltage-sourced converter (VSC) system that generally uses gate turn-off thyristors (GTOs) or insulated gate bipolar transistors (IGBTs) combined with diodes enabling application of the PWM technique. The frequency at which the switches operate can vary depending on the power of the system to which the STATCOM is connected. Thus, the STATCOM behaves as if it were a synchronous capacitor, consuming or absorbing reactive power continuously, but without storing energy to compensate.

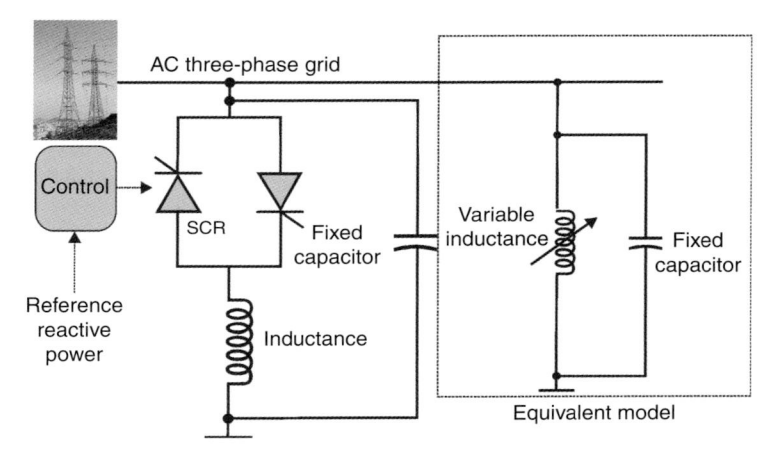

Figure 25 Schematic diagram of a TCR-FC. SCR, silicon-controlled rectifier.

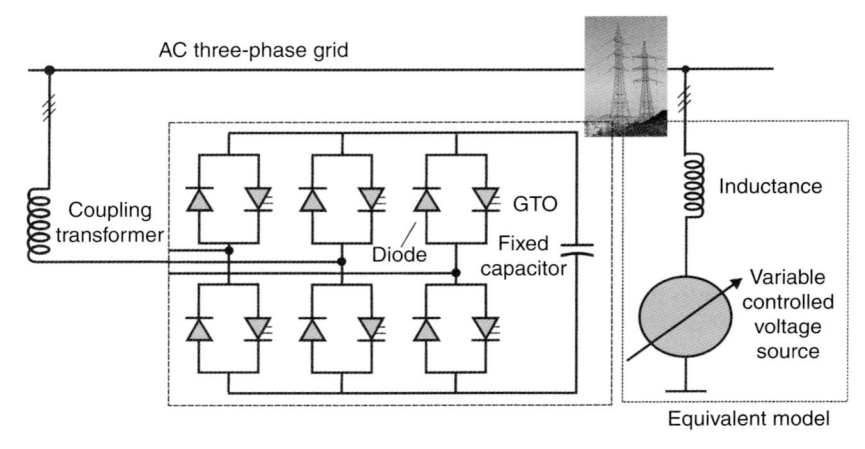

Figure 26 Schematic diagram of a STATCOM.

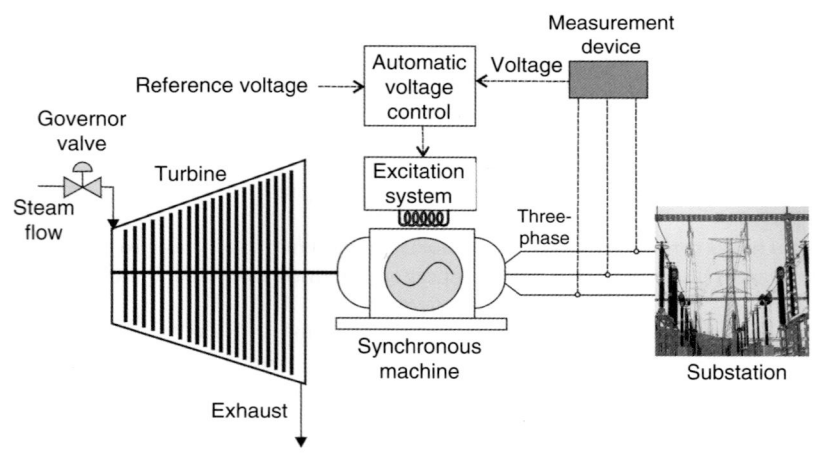

Figure 27 Schematic diagram of the voltage control system of a synchronous generator.

Control of static compensators, in the specific case of voltage regulation in an electrical power system, is carried out by means of a closed loop similar to that of the governors used in synchronous generators. The bar voltage is compared with a reference voltage. The error passes through a proportional–integral governor, which generates the firing angle required to obtain the desired voltage.

A synchronous compensator, also known as a synchronous capacitor, is a synchronous machine whose shaft is not coupled to any mechanical load. It consumes and generates reactive power when underexcited and overexcited, respectively. There are a number of advantages to this device when compared with static compensation devices, including continuous voltage regulation without electromagnetic transients. Another advantage is that they do not introduce harmonics into the network, nor are they affected by them. Likewise, they do not generate problems as a result of electrical resonance.

Like frequency control, voltage control is also undertaken at hierarchical levels [33]. The primary control aims to maintain a voltage set point at a particular system node. The synchronous generator constitutes the most characteristic element in primary control of voltage. Synchronous generators, which can modify their active power as described in Section 2.18.2.3.1, are also capable of modifying their reactive power. Control of the latter is automatic and is achieved via regulation of the generator excitation current (**Figure 27**).

Automatic voltage regulation (AVR) acts within a very few seconds, and its objective is to control the generated reactive power and/or maintain the voltage at the generator terminals. A sensor measures the voltage at the generator terminals, corrects it, and compares it with the desired voltage.

While primary voltage control is local in scope since the information it uses is local, secondary control [33, 70, 77, 78] is responsible for the voltages of a set of representative nodes of an area or region, known as pilot nodes. Secondary control coordinates the voltage governors of the area's generators and, like primary control, functions automatically.

Tertiary control, as has been mentioned, is a combined control of frequency and voltage. It is generally nonautomatic and uses information from the whole system to determine the reference values of the pilot nodes.

2.18.3 The Distinctive Characteristics of Wind Energy

Electrical energy generated using wind as the energy source displays some distinctive characteristics, which distinguish it from the power generated by the conventional energy sources described in Section 2.18.2. In this respect, the most notable features of wind energy are its temporal and spatial unpredictability and variability, the impossibility of directly storing the primary energy, the abundance of the resource in many places in the world, and its renewable and noncontaminating character.

2.18.3.1 The Unpredictability and Variability of Wind

The power of wind on the Earth is a consequence of solar radiation [79–81]. On a planetary scale and due, among other factors, to the shape and position of the Earth with respect to the Sun, there exist insolation differences between different areas of the planet. Broadly speaking, the thermal differences that occur, combined with the rotation of the Earth with respect to its own axis, give rise to the displacement of masses of air. Such displacement or the large-scale movement of air is known as atmospheric circulation.

These global winds are affected by the presence of the continents and water masses that shape the Earth's surface and by the movement of the planet with respect to the Sun. The circulation of these air masses will also be influenced by local thermal and climate effects as well as by the orography of the region. Thus, wind characteristics depend markedly on geographical location. Because of the influence of orographic features, the wind speed in one area can differ substantially from that in another just a few kilometers away.

Figure 28 shows, by way of example, the variation in daily mean wind speeds during the month of August, 2005, at two anemometer stations on the island of Gran Canaria (Canary Island Archipelago, Spain) installed 10 m above ground level and separated by a distance of approximately 34 km. The mean wind speed for that month differs by about 36.6%.

The considerable number of variables that can affect the movement of air masses makes the wind unpredictable and, over a wide range of scales, means that its behavior is both temporally and spatially variable. The wind shows variations from a scale of seconds to interannual timescales. That is, the mean wind speed of a site can vary from one year to another. **Figure 29** shows, by way of example, the mean interannual wind speed variation over a 10-year period at an anemometer station installed 10 m above ground level on an island in the Canary Archipelago.

Significant changes can also be observed from one season to another and, indeed, from one month to another during the same year. **Figure 30** shows the monthly wind variation at an anemometer station on the island of Gran Canaria. It can be seen how, given its geographical location (between latitudes 27°37′ and 29°25′, subtropical, and longitude 13°20′ W of Greenwich), the frequency of the trade wind regime is very high during the summer months, with the highest wind speeds occurring during that season.

Normally, the wind behaves differently in the Northern Hemisphere, with the summer months seeing the lowest wind speeds. Similarly, wind speed can vary from one hour to another over the course of a day.

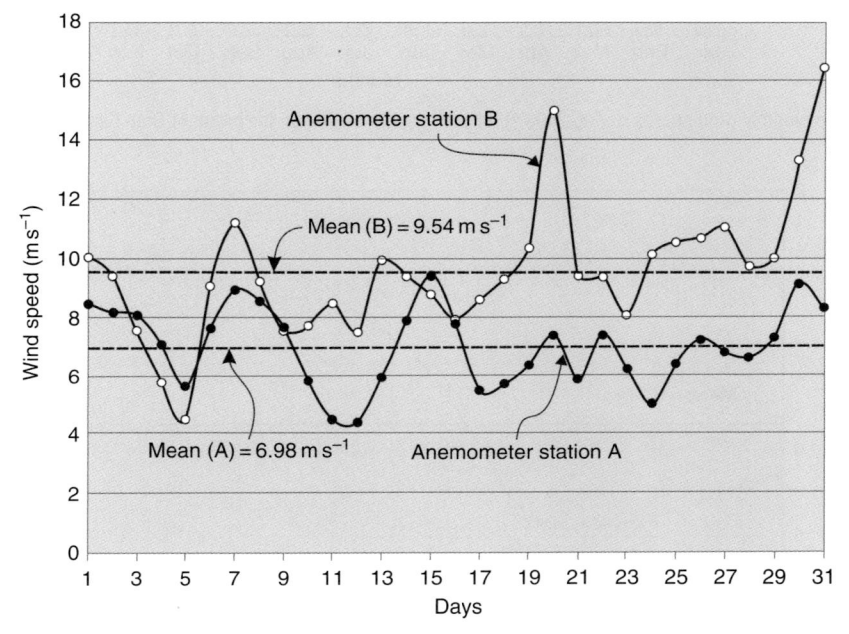

Figure 28 Mean daily wind speed variation during the month of August, 2005, at two anemometer stations on the island of Gran Canaria, Spain.

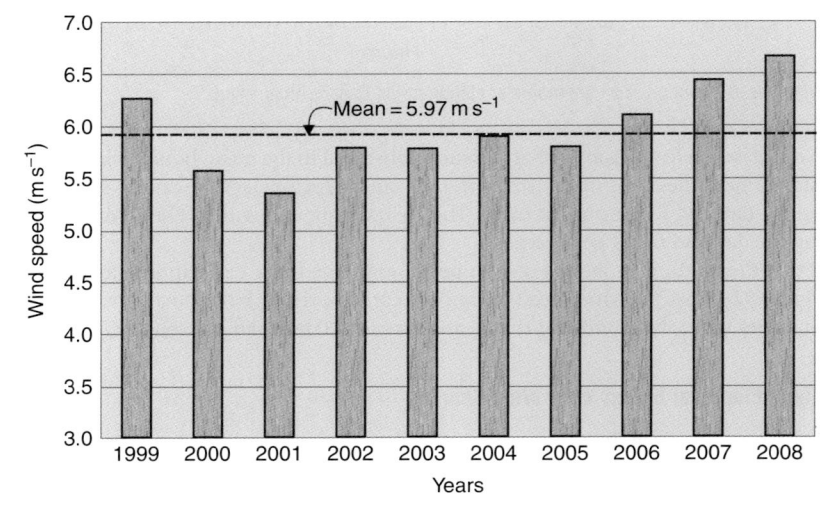

Figure 29 Mean interannual wind speed variation recorded 10 m above ground level at an anemometer station on the island of Gran Canaria, Spain.

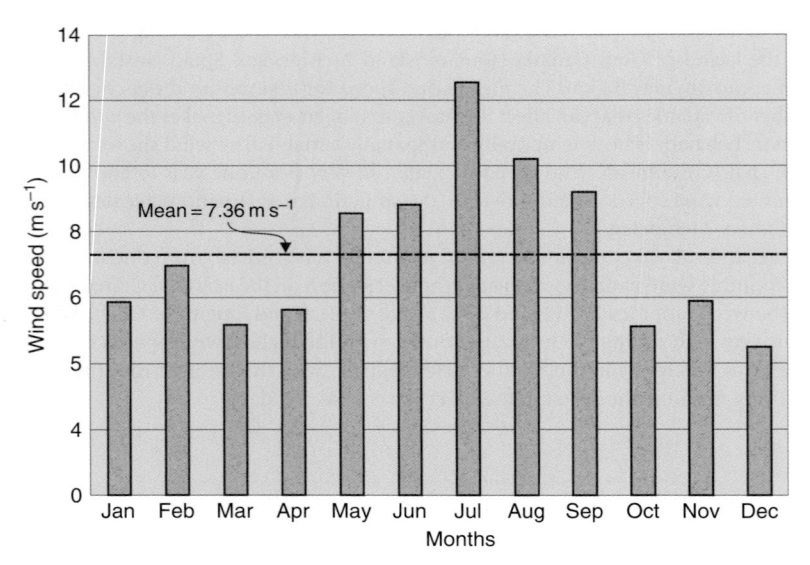

Figure 30 Evolution of the monthly wind speeds during 2003 at an anemometer station on the island of Gran Canaria, Spain.

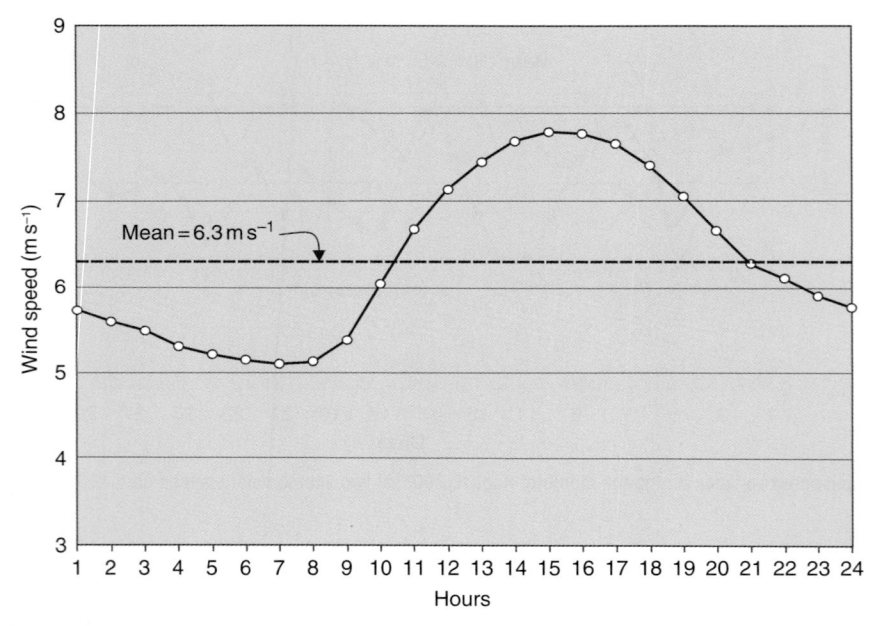

Figure 31 Average daily wind speed evolution at an anemometer station in the Canary Archipelago.

Figure 31 shows, by way of example, the substantial variations observed in the mean hourly wind speed on a day timescale at an anemometer station installed near the coast of an island in the Canary Archipelago. It can be seen how the wind displays very high-speed values during the day and lower ones at night. This behavior is the result of the different effects of the heating of the surface of the land during the day and of the sea breezes.

It is usually accepted that the random variations seen in periods ranging from 1 s to approximately 10 min represent turbulent wind speed variations. **Figure 32** shows the wind speed variation recorded over a 2 h period at an anemometer station located in the Canary Archipelago. The values for each second and the means for each 10 min can be seen.

2.18.3.2 The Variability of Electrical Energy from Wind Sources

The power that a wind turbine extracts from the wind is proportional to the air density, the rotor swept area, the power coefficient, the power transmission system efficiency, and the cube of the wind speed [1, 82–84]. The power coefficient is a function of the tip speed ratio and the pitch angle [82–84]. Air density varies with pressure, temperature, and humidity [85]. However, given the more striking variations in wind speed and its cubic influence, it is wind speed variations that can give rise to the most significant power fluctuations of a turbine.

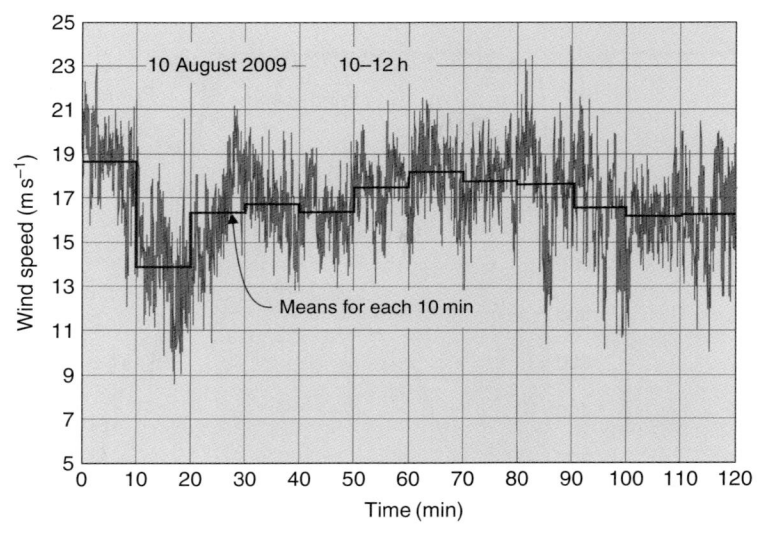

Figure 32 Evolution of wind speed recorded each second, over a 2 h period, 40 m above ground level at an anemometer station on an island in the Canary Archipelago.

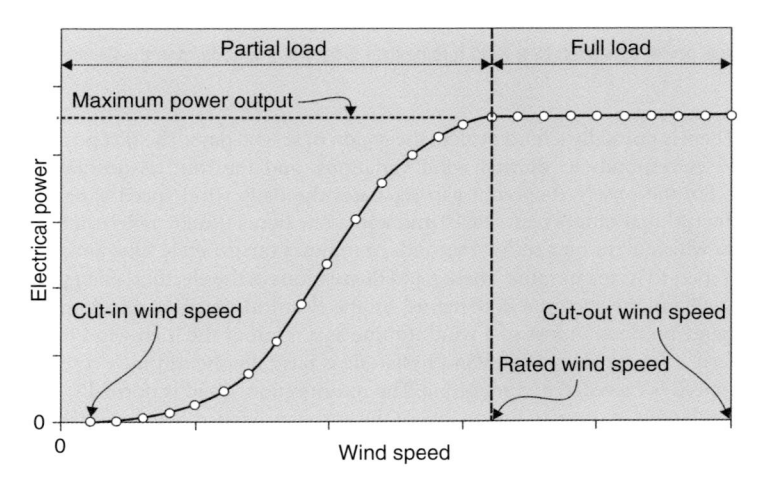

Figure 33 Typical power curve of a wind turbine.

There are different control systems that can be used for wind energy conversion systems (WECSs) [3, 8–10, 82, 86–88]. The intervention of these control systems enables regulation of the electrical power generated by the wind turbine.

Figure 33 shows a typical power curve for a modern pitch-regulated wind turbine. This curve represents the mean performance of the wind turbine. Oscillations and deviations from the mean values will appear in the event of significant turbulence. Likewise, the local orography and wake caused by nearby turbines will distort the power curve provided by the manufacturer. Two clearly differentiated areas can be observed in **Figure 33**. One area lies between the cut-in wind speed and the rated wind speed and the other between the rated wind speed and the cut-out wind speed. At the rated wind speed, the electrical generator of the wind turbine will produce its maximum power output. When the wind turbine is operating in the first section of its power curve, it is said to be working in the partial-load range. However, if the rated wind speed is exceeded, then the machine is said to be operating in the full-load range. If the wind speed exceeds the cut-out wind speed for a few seconds, then the turbine stops and, therefore, no longer produces energy. Likewise, the wind turbine has no output for wind speeds below the cut-in wind speed.

Figure 34 shows the power produced by a wind turbine installed in a wind farm in the Canary Archipelago over a 2-day period. It can be deduced from the figure that wind speed fluctuations in the partial-load range of a single wind turbine can give rise to large fluctuations in its electrical power output. In the full-load range, the power curve displays a constant mean performance and is not affected much by wind speed variations.

The timescale of wind speed variation has a significant effect on the power output fluctuation of the wind turbine. If the spectra of wind fluctuations are analyzed at a particular site from micro- to macrometeorological range, it can be seen how the kinetic energy of the horizontal wind speed is distributed as a function of the variation frequency of that wind [89–93]. Regardless of the site where the spectral analysis is conducted, a valley or spectral gap can typically be observed, which is bounded by one peak at around 1 min and

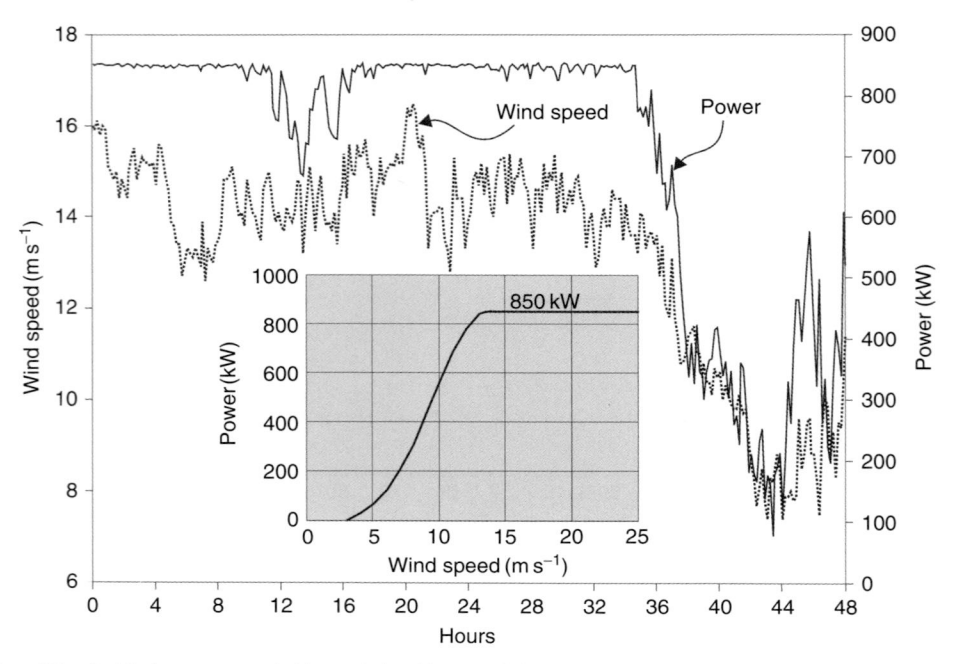

Figure 34 Variation of the electrical power generated by a wind turbine over 2 days at a wind farm in the Canary Archipelago.

another peak at around 12 h. There is normally a third peak in the region of several days. The first peak is the consequence of turbulent wind fluctuations, the second corresponds to diurnal wind variations, and the third is normally attributed to the passage of anticyclones and depressions. So, the observed spectral gap separates the daily wind speed variations from turbulent variations. Within this spectral gap, the interval that ranges between 10 min and a few hours usually reflects a low wind energy content.

Turbulent wind fluctuations which occur on a scale of seconds or minutes can generate substantial deviations in the power output of a single wind turbine with respect to its mean value. These rapid fluctuations in the electrical energy generated by a wind turbine can have a harmful effect on the quality of the energy and, therefore, on the electrical system to which the turbine is connected. It should also be mentioned that the energy production loss of a wind turbine as a result of the high-wind hysteresis effect [87, 93] depends, among other factors, on the level of turbulence. High-wind hysteresis is basically the turbine's control system lag between shutting down when the cut-out wind speed is exceeded and restarting. The reconnection speed is normally 3–4 m s^{-1} lower than the cut-out speed. The harm that wind turbulence can cause to the quality of the energy generated and its impact on losses due to the high-wind hysteresis effect depend to a large degree on the level of the technology installed in the wind turbine.

Knowledge of the short-term behavior of the wind is of vital importance in the operation of electrical systems, whereas monthly, seasonal, and interannual behavior will have an impact on, among other questions, the planning of the electrical system.

2.18.3.2.1 Effect of wind turbine aggregation on wind power variability

The power output fluctuations of a single wind turbine, as described in the previous section, could cause significant problems in terms of the integration of the wind power into an electrical power network if the energy generated by each of the various turbines that make up the wind farm behaved in an identical manner.

The total power output of a wind farm is the summation of the output of each of the wind turbines that compose it. However, since the wind speeds that strike the rotors of the different wind turbines on a wind farm are generally not identical, the power output fluctuations of each wind turbine are different. As happens with demand aggregation [94], the total power output fluctuation of the wind farm is dampened or smoothed out. That is, the overall fluctuation is less than the individual fluctuations [8, 93, 95].

Figure 35 shows the power output of a wind farm installed in the Canary Archipelago over a 2-day period. The wind farm has nine wind turbines, and the power variation over this period was on the order of 31%. Also shown in the figure is the power output of the turbine with the highest variation (39%).

The extent of the dampening effect depends basically on the number of wind turbines that make up the wind farm and the degree of correlation between the wind speeds that strike the corresponding rotors. The number of wind turbines need not be very high. However, the more uncorrelated the power outputs of the wind turbines are, the higher the level of power smoothing will be. The degree of correlation depends, among other factors, on the topography and roughness of the terrain of the wind farm platform as well as on the downwind spacing between wind turbines [96].

As previously mentioned, the highest fluctuations in the power output of a wind turbine are produced when the wind turbine is operating in the partial-load range with high wind variability. So, the beneficial effects of aggregation will be more pronounced under these operating conditions.

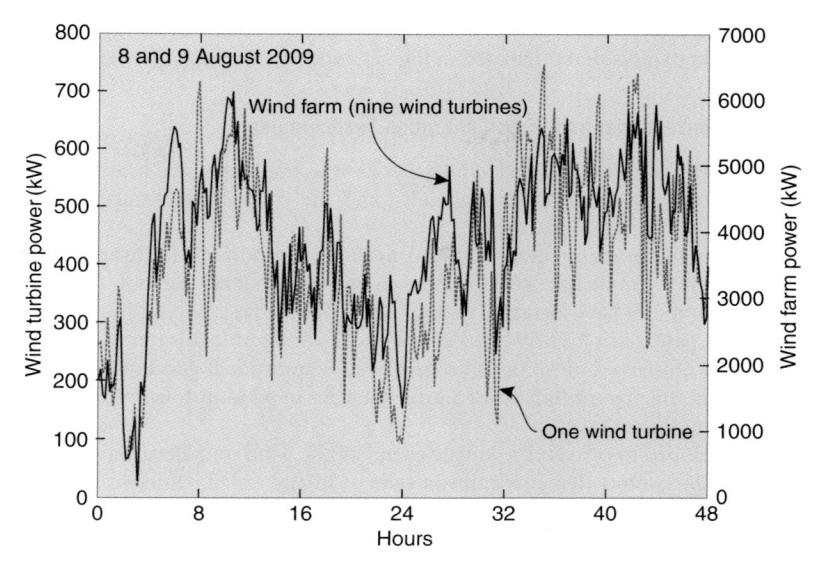

Figure 35 Variation of the electrical power generated over 2 days by a wind farm in the Canary Archipelago and by one of the nine wind turbines that make up the same wind farm.

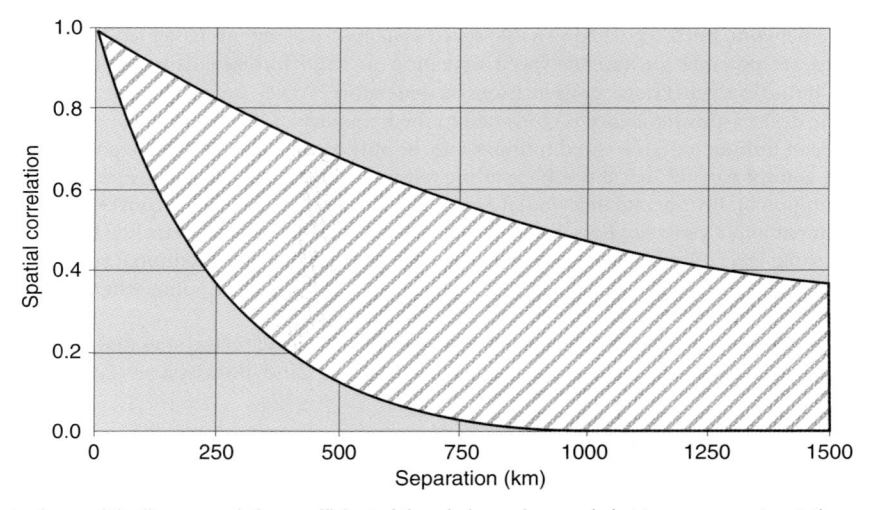

Figure 36 Decreasing tendency of the linear correlation coefficient of the wind speeds recorded at two anemometer stations as the distance between them increases.

2.18.3.2.2 Effect of the geographical distribution of wind farms on wind power variability

Several studies [97–100] have shown that the correlations between wind speeds recorded at different geographical sites decrease with the distance between them (**Figure 36**). When the geographical distance is considerable, the winds can be affected by different microclimatic characteristics. So, at such distances, wind speeds can be practically uncorrelated. Given that wind farm power output fluctuations decrease when the correlation between the wind speeds that strike the various wind turbines is reduced, the geographical dispersion of wind farms over a wide area can entail a notable smoothing of the fluctuation of the total power fed into the interconnected networks [8, 101].

2.18.4 Wind Power and Power System Interaction

As mentioned in previous sections, the primary goal of electrical power systems is quality coverage of the electrical energy demand [102–104]. With this concept of quality in mind, the electrical system has to guarantee the continuity of power supply and ensure that the electrical energy that covers the demand does so with perfect quality of the voltage waveform.

The quality of electricity supply depends not only on the energy source but also on the interaction of that energy source with the network to which it is connected. Wind turbine connection to a network, with the particular operating characteristics the wind turbines possess, can be the cause of a series of disturbances which may affect the quality of energy. At the same time, wind turbines can find themselves affected by disturbances that originated in the network.

2.18.4.1 Comparison between Conventional and Wind Generation Technologies

There are marked differences between conventional and wind generation technologies. The most noteworthy of these include the primary energy source, the rated powers of the individual units, and the control and regulation strategies that the different generation systems use.

As has been mentioned earlier, the primary energy of wind turbines is random and fluctuating and cannot be stored. In comparison, conventional generation technologies use fuels that can be stored and are available at any given moment.

The rated powers of large wind turbines have increased considerably over the past 10 years, but, even so, the rated power of the biggest wind turbine constructed to date is just 7.5 MW [8]. Also the size of wind turbines is much smaller than that of conventional synchronous generators. The main objective of the control strategies of conventional generation systems is to supply the power demanded by the load. However, at the present time, the control strategies of wind turbines aim to maximize the power output, regardless of the load, in order to minimize costs.

Various systems have been developed to convert the kinetic energy of the wind into electrical energy [3, 8–10, 82, 86–88]. The architecture of these systems, like the control elements and strategies, is highly varied. Different wind turbine configurations will depend on the type of generator involved, the variability or constancy of the rotational speed at which the system functions, and the power control devices installed. Specific features of these configurations can have an influence on the characteristics of the electrical energy that is generated and affect to different degrees the response to disturbances caused by the network.

Though variable-speed systems have a higher technological complexity and, perhaps, a lower reliability, they do offer a series of advantages over fixed-speed systems. These include a greater capacity to smooth out wind speed fluctuations. Variable-speed systems are also better able to capture the energy when operating in the partial-load range. Due to the higher quality of the output power they inject into the network, pitch-regulated variable-speed systems are being implemented in most large wind turbines.

Various configurations are possible for variable-speed operation of wind turbines. These configurations can be based on synchronous generators, induction generators, or asynchronous generators. Power is generated at a variable frequency, and, by means of power electronic devices, this frequency is converted to the frequency of the network.

Depending on the type of turbine, variable-speed turbines may be able to regulate the reactive power via the intervention of an electronic converter. This control ensures that the voltage at the terminals of the generator remains within the established limits. That is, a wind turbine can potentially operate in a similar way to synchronous generators at conventional power stations.

Research and development into a variety of power electronic devices is currently being intensified so that wind farms can enjoy a control capability of the same level afforded by the intervention characteristics of a conventional power plant [105, 106]. In the same way as a wide range of strategies can be employed to acquire such characteristics, the points where power electronic devices can be installed on a wind farm can also be diverse.

It should be mentioned that the innovative trends that have followed the larger wind turbines that make up wind farms have not been copied by small wind turbines (**Figure 37**). Small wind turbines used in stand-alone systems, MGs, and DG systems have not

Figure 37 Small wind turbine of 15 kW rated power.

achieved the same technological level, and the costs per installed kilowatt are higher than those for large wind turbines [8]. Evolution of the different systems that comprise small wind turbines has stagnated, and consequently, the differences between the electrical and control systems of small and large wind turbines are enormous.

Conventional synchronous generators, as stated in Section 2.18.2, have control devices that use feedback information provided by the network to regulate the system frequency and voltage. At the present time, however, wind turbine control devices connected to electrical networks do not use feedback information provided by these networks for the purpose of participating in the voltage and frequency control tasks. However, modern variable-speed wind turbines can potentially regulate themselves taking into account the voltage and frequency of the network [3, 8–10, 82, 86–88, 105].

In addition to economic factors, one reason such control mechanisms have not been installed on a widespread scale is the random nature of wind. The use of suitable forecasting tools for the short-term power output of a wind farm could help in this respect, but at the present time it is the network itself that is responsible for maintaining the frequency and voltage within the specified limits.

The lack of feedback mechanisms in wind turbines has a number of different consequences depending on the type of network and the percentage of wind energy injected into it.

2.18.4.2 Potential Disturbances in the Interaction of Wind Turbines with the Electrical Network

The quality of the voltage waveform produced by power generation stations can be disturbed by different faults that might occur in the network [82, 107–109]. These disturbances can affect the correct operation of wind generation systems. Likewise, as a consequence of the type of technology that some wind turbines use or as a result of wind variability and so on, wind farms can be the source of some of the disturbances that occur in the electrical network.

2.18.4.2.1 Frequency variations

As previously stated, frequency variations of an electrical system are essentially caused by alterations to the balance between generation and demand. These imbalances are corrected in conventional electrical systems through the hierarchical intervention of the control systems [33, 65, 70].

Large-scale integration of wind energy into an electrical network introduces new factors in the active power–frequency interaction. Random wind speed fluctuations give rise to variations of the active power generated by wind turbines (**Figure 38**). Hence, the behavior of the active power generated by wind farms differs from the typical behavior of the power generated by conventional synchronous generator sets.

Given the unpredictability and fluctuations of the power generated by wind farms, it can be said that its behavior presents a greater similarity to that of demand than to that of conventional generation.

The variations in the power generated by wind farms will affect the frequency of the system in different ways depending on the size of the electrical system and the level of wind penetration.

Such frequency variations can have a variety of effects on wind systems that use this variable as a reference signal in their operation. In this sense, disturbances can originate from the operation of the power electronic devices, changes to the rotational speed of the wind turbines, and so on. There are several measures that are usually adopted to avoid these frequency variations. These include, among others, an increase of the spinning reserve, the use of energy storage systems, and the establishment of limitations to wind penetration levels.

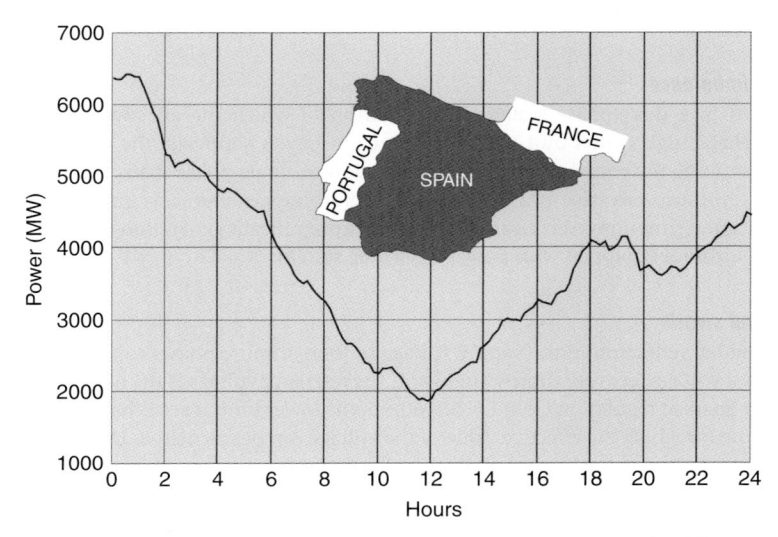

Figure 38 Variation of electrical power obtained from wind resources injected into the Spanish mainland electricity system on 1 April 2010. Courtesy of REE (http://www.ree.es).

2.18.4.2.2 Voltage variations

Voltage variations normally occur when the effective value of the voltage wave finds itself altered. Variations in the power injected into or consumed by wind farms at the connection node to the network can give rise to voltage variations at that node and, eventually, at other nearby nodes [108]. The magnitude of these voltage fluctuations will depend on the technology and operating characteristics of the wind turbines and on the impedance of the network. This last factor depends on the power demand of the loads, which is variable.

Fixed-speed turbines equipped with asynchronous generators connected to a network inject active power into and consume reactive power from that network. Depending on the magnitude of the ratio of the reactance to the resistance, different levels of voltage fluctuation take place. The weaker the network is at the connection node of the wind turbine, the higher the voltage fluctuation levels will be. Wind turbines that have synchronous generators and are connected to electrical networks can control the reactive power through generator excitation.

Wind turbines are usually equipped with specific devices to regulate the power factor, that is, the ratio of active to apparent power. Each country has its own regulations that lay down the minimum power factor values for the installations. The regulations in Spain state that the power factor of installations equipped with asynchronous generators cannot be lower than 0.86 at rated power.

The power factor regulators supply in a controlled manner the reactive power that the turbine needs. Capacitor banks can be used for this purpose, though it is also possible to employ so-called FACTS technology [71, 74], otherwise known as flexible AC transmission systems. Included in this technology are, among others, the static var compensator (SVC) and the STATCOM.

2.18.4.2.3 Voltage flicker

The word 'flicker' comes from the effect the fluctuations in electric voltage have on incandescent lamps and other electrical lighting devices. This effect can be perceived by the human eye, with a maximum sensitivity of between 8 and 10 Hz.

The types of load that commonly give rise to the phenomenon of voltage flicker in power transmission and distribution systems include arc furnaces, high-powered engines with very fast stop-and-start cycles, sawmills, and high-powered welding machines.

Voltage flicker can also be caused by wind turbines [108–115], both during normal operation and during connection and disconnection operations, while the repeated connection and disconnection of capacitor banks can be the cause of so-called fast flicker. Under normal operation, wind turbine power fluctuations are due to wind speed turbulence. As a result of torque fluctuations, the severity of flicker in fixed-speed turbines directly connected to the network is higher than that in variable-speed turbines.

The flicker effect is also influenced by the change of generators in turbines with two generators, as well as by the aerodynamic behavior of wind turbine rotors.

At high wind speeds, fixed-speed pitch-regulated turbines perform worse than the stall-regulated type. This is due to the inertia in the response of the pitch regulation mechanisms.

The shadow that a tower makes when a blade passes in front of it can also be the cause of flicker. For this reason, some wind farms suffer from what is known as the 3P effect [113, 115]. The name of this effect comes from the power and voltage fluctuations caused as a result of the shadow made by the tower each time a blade of a three-bladed wind turbine passes in front of it in a cycle. Fluctuations due to this effect are normally on the order of 1 Hz.

The severity of the flicker caused by a particular wind turbine depends, in addition to the technology employed in its operation, on the wind characteristics at the site and on the characteristics of the network at the connection point. The overall flicker effect of a wind farm is normally dampened as a result of aggregation. However, cases of synchronization phenomenon at wind farms that have resulted in an increase in the flicker effect linear to the number of wind turbines have been known. Wind turbines can be equipped with devices such as static compensators for the purpose of reducing these disturbances.

2.18.4.2.4 Phase voltage imbalance

An imbalance (or mismatch) in a three-phase system is a condition in which the effective values of three voltages differ in amplitude, or their relative phase angles differ by 120°, or both circumstances happen at the same time.

Phase voltage imbalances can be the consequence of the connection of single-phase loads to a low-, medium-, or high-voltage network. These imbalances can cause excessive heating of the wind turbine generators as a result of the abnormal currents that circulate in the windings. In some situations, this heating can result in significant generation losses. Likewise, the imbalances can affect the operation of wind turbines equipped with power electronic systems.

2.18.4.2.5 Voltage dips and swells

A voltage dip (or sag) is a sudden reduction in the supply voltage on one or more phases to a value between 90% and 1% of the reference voltage followed by a voltage recovery shortly afterward. The reference voltage is the nominal voltage, the declared voltage, or the pre-dip voltage. Under Spanish regulation UNE-EN 50160/96, the lower limit is set at half a cycle (10 ms at 50 Hz), since this is the minimum period of time for which the effective value of the voltage can be calculated. Drops in voltage with duration of less than half a cycle cannot be characterized as a change in the effective value of the voltage and are considered transitory. The aforementioned Spanish regulation sets the upper limit at 1 min.

Voltage dips are commonly caused by network faults and load switching. The operating procedures established by various countries require that no wind installation disconnection be undertaken for voltage dips at the network connection point with

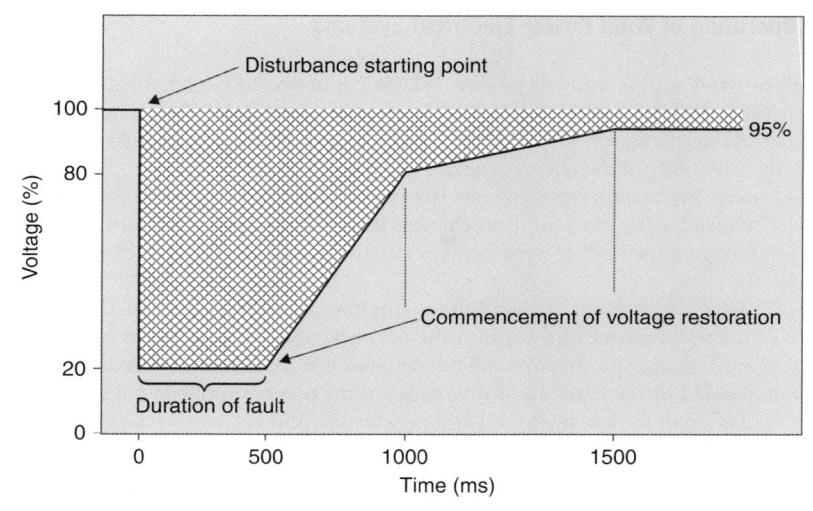

Figure 39 Typical fault-ride-through voltage profile.

certain fault-ride-through profiles (**Figure** 39). There can also be no consumption of active or reactive power on the part of the installation at the network connection point while maintenance work on the fault is being carried out, nor during the period of voltage recovery after clearance of the fault.

The necessary design and/or control measures have to be taken in the installations to avoid wind turbines disconnecting instantaneously during voltage dips associated with correctly cleared short circuits [116, 117].

One measure can consist of installing STATCOM devices at the node where the energy generated by the wind farm is injected into the network. In this way, the probability of the failure of components located between the wind farm and the substation where it is connected is reduced.

Though less common, connection of a turbine working with an induction generator can also cause voltage dips. In this case, the STATCOM device installed in the substation cannot correct the disturbance and the wind turbines connected to the lines where the disturbance has taken place will be disconnected. The installation of a TCR device in each wind turbine will enable it to remain connected to the network during the voltage dip, even if the origin of the disturbance was in the wind farm itself.

Voltage swells are abrupt increases in the instantaneous value of the voltage, which can be several times higher than the nominal value. Voltage swells may or may not be oscillatory and typically last less than a few milliseconds. They can be caused by switchgear opening or closing, atmospheric discharges, the removal of large loads, or the energizing of a capacitor bank. Such voltage swells can also be caused by wind farms themselves, as a result of wind turbine shutdowns and start-ups, capacitor bank connection, and so on.

Depending on the magnitude and duration of the voltage swell, wind turbines that use power electronic systems for their operation can be affected if they are not equipped with overvoltage protection devices.

2.18.4.2.6 Harmonics

Harmonics are distortions of the sinusoidal waves of the voltage and/or current of electrical systems. Distorted waves have frequency components which are whole multiples of the fundamental frequency at which the system has been designed to operate (normally 50 or 60 Hz). Frequency components that are not whole multiples of the fundamental frequency are known as interharmonics.

Harmonic distortions are caused by nonlinear characteristics of certain equipment and loads of the electrical system. That is, such devices do not display a linear relationship between current and voltage.

The parameter used to measure the degree of waveform distortion is called the total harmonic distortion (THD). Regulations, such as the IEC 61000-3-6 of the International Electrotechnical Commission, give the reference levels for voltage harmonics that must not be exceeded.

Appliances that have power converters constitute an important source of high-frequency harmonic currents. The presence of harmonics can cause the incorrect functioning of protective devices, generate interferences with communication circuits, and provoke resonances in wind energy systems.

Since variable-speed wind turbines normally contain electronic converters, harmonic distortions are associated with this type of turbine and must be specified [118–121]. Fixed-speed wind turbines are not prone to causing significant harmonics or interharmonics. However, harmonics can be detected, fundamentally in the brief connection periods when the electronic devices begin operating, though it is also possible to detect harmonics with low THD at other moments probably as a result of resonances between power factor compensation equipment and the generator winding.

In certain situations, the devices that produce harmonic distortion are required to have suitable passive filters for particular harmonic components [122].

2.18.5 Planning and Operation of Wind Power Electrical Systems

Due to the variable nature of wind and its unpredictability, WECSs connected to electrical networks inject into those networks energy that fluctuates over time. This fluctuation can be on a timescale of seconds (short-term variability) to years (long-term variability). These particular characteristics of wind energy mean that the electrical system has to manage, in addition to the variability of the demand, the variability of the energy generated by the WECS [87, 123].

The peculiarities of wind energy production can mean that changes need to be carried out in the power system in order to be able to integrate the wind power efficiently. The need for these changes is related to the power system robustness, the flexibility of the conventional generation technologies, the level of wind penetration, the cost level, the electricity market rules, the network access regulations, and so on [8].

The variance of the net load that conventional generation systems have to cover depends on the variance of the power demand of the loads, the variance of the wind power injected into the network, and the correlation between these two powers. If the correlation between the renewable energy production and the demand is null, then the net load variance is given by the sum of the variance of the power demanded by the loads and the variance of the power supplied by the WECS. Therefore, the impact of the fluctuation of the net load is small for low levels of wind penetration and changes in the electrical system are probably not necessary.

Although there is normally no relation [123] between wind energy supply and load demand, it should be pointed out that in particular locations there may exist a certain specific relationship. For example, in the north of Europe, the strongest winds occur in winter. However, although there is an increase in the energy demand for heating purposes, no strong correlation has been detected between demand and renewable energy production. In the Canary Islands (Spain), the highest wind speed intensity is in summer as a result of the activity of the trade winds, but in summer there is a greater energy demand for water desalination and air-conditioning systems.

Wind penetration levels vary across the world. As mentioned in the introduction, some countries have wind penetration levels lower than 1%, while others have seen levels of around 20% [8]. It is estimated that in not too distant future wind penetration levels will rise considerably.

High wind penetration levels need appropriate planning of the power system design and operation. The planning process will have to take into account, in addition to the short-term effects wind energy integration has on power reserve capacity and the long-term effects on the power system's production capacity, the characteristics of the transmission and distribution network infrastructure so that they do not become congested nor reduce the quality of energy supplied to the consumers.

At the present time, the connection of wind turbines to both transmission and distribution networks, which affects the system in different ways, is undertaken.

2.18.5.1 Repercussions of Wind Power for Power System Generation

In electrical systems, the allocation of the power that each power station has to supply is commonly undertaken on a daily basis. That is, each day allocation of the power that has to be supplied to cover the demand at each moment of the following day is made. The reserve power needed to deal with unforeseen demand variations and the reserve power that has to be available in the event of planned and unplanned shutdowns of the generation systems also have to be allocated [124]. In other words, in addition to covering unforeseen demand variations, the power reserve capacity has to cover the shutdowns of the generation units to carry out scheduled works of maintenance as well as the nonavailability of these units to produce the necessary power in the event of unforeseen faults.

From the point of view of economic load dispatch, generation units can be classified into base-load generators, intermediate-load generators, peak-load generators, and backup or standby generators.

Base-load generators include units whose characteristics recommend that their operation be carried out at continuous rating, such as nuclear power stations and large-sized thermal units.

Intermediate-load generators include generation units which do not necessarily need to operate at full output and whose power output is easily regulated. Among this group are hydroelectric power stations and, in some systems, diesel generation units.

Peak-load generation units are characterized by their rapid start-up and connection to the network. These units typically comprise generators driven by gas turbines, hydraulic turbines, and, in some systems, diesel engines. Their function is to cover scheduled peak-load periods.

When it is sized, an electrical system also has to take into account the demand of a few particularly heavy peak hours a year. In Spain, according to the REE [52], 4000 MW are required – the equivalent of ten 400 MW combined cycle power stations or four 1000 MW nuclear power stations – to deal with the 300 h of highest consumption each year.

The capacity of a backup unit is effectively a power generation capacity margin which exceeds the generation capacity planned to cover the power demand peaks of the loads. In this group are included the so-called spinning generation units and units which can be rapidly put into operation to cover particular contingencies.

Figure 40 shows the generation structure of the Spanish mainland system on 24 February 2010. At 11.20 a.m. on that day, the previous wind energy production record was beaten.

Three types of reserve are used to carry out the primary, secondary, and tertiary controls, described in the general introduction to conventional power systems. These reserves are known as the primary, secondary, and tertiary reserves, respectively.

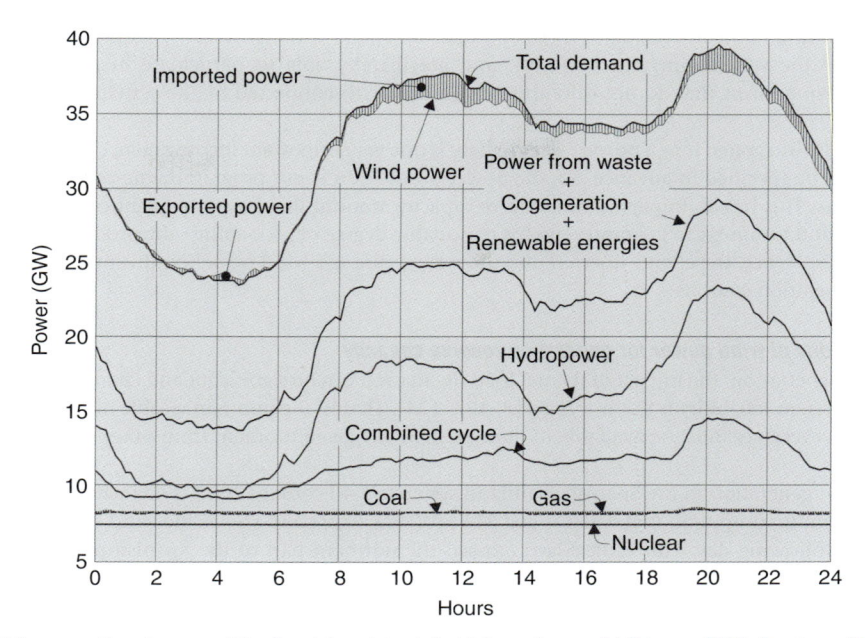

Figure 40 Evolution of the generation structure of the Spanish mainland electricity system on 24 February 2010. Courtesy of REE (http://www.ree.es).

In Spain, the primary control services must obligatorily be provided by generators coupled to the network, with the exception of generators included in the so-called special regime. This special regime is a treatment granted to the production of electrical energy by installations whose installed power is not higher than 50 MW and which use renewable, waste, or cogeneration energy sources. The other two reserve types are paid for according to the supply offered and the use made of the service. This means that expansion of reserve capacities gives rise to an increase in electrical energy costs.

In the Spanish electrical system, and under normal situations, wind farms can inject, regardless of the hourly market price, all their variable production into the network. However, the system operator may inevitably need to reduce wind production when certain critical situations arise. Such situations can arise during off-peak hours because of the need to maintain conventional generation units coupled to the network in order to guarantee coverage of unexpected surges in demand and because of the time these units may need to start up. In addition, the requirements of the complementary services need to be taken into account, as well as the fact that conventional generation units have what is known as a minimum stable generation level, a level below which the unit cannot reduce its generation. For example, nuclear power stations cannot be disconnected, and both thermal and combined cycle power stations have minimum stable generation levels.

Solutions that can be found for this problem include the use of energy storage systems (Section 2.18.5.1.2) and the removal (evacuation) of the surplus energy through interconnected networks (Section 2.18.5.2).

The Spanish system operator (REE) [52] has created a special regime control center called the CECRE (Spanish initials; **Figure 41**), which manages the production of renewable energies in contingency situations. This center coordinates all the regional

Figure 41 Renewable energy control center of REE (Spanish initials: CECRE). The generation of all the renewable energy producers installed in Spain is managed and controlled from CECRE. Courtesy of REE (http://www.ree.es).

control centers as well as wind farms not managed by such centers. In Spain, wind farms can offer prices for the service control and interruption actions that the system operator performs, and are thereby able to participate in power production control in contingency situations. Wind farms that do not offer this service can be disconnected by the system operator as a final option in critical situations.

When wind turbines are integrated into a power system, there is one very important inconvenience: since it depends on the wind, the power output cannot be specified in advance. So, the power production is not programmable as is the case with conventional power generation systems. This has an impact on the reserve capacity amount that has to be planned for.

On the other hand, wind turbines can guarantee, with a reasonable degree of probability, the production of a particular amount of energy on a yearly basis. Hence, the energy injected into the system through wind power on this timescale can be a substitute for other types of power generation stations.

2.18.5.1.1 Repercussions of wind power for generation reserve capacity

For high levels of wind penetration, the impact of the net load fluctuation can be significant and changes in the electrical system are required to ensure that system reliability is not impaired [8, 123, 124]. That is, the nonmanageable nature of wind power can mean that sufficient extra power reserves must be available in the system at any given moment from other energy sources or from energy storage systems.

Figure 42 shows wind generation in the Spanish mainland system on 4 February 2007, a day when little wind was recorded. It can be seen that the maximum output on that day was just 316 MW. The figure also shows the wind energy variation on 23 January 2009. On that and the following day, Hurricane Klaus crossed the northern part of the Spanish peninsula with gusts of winds exceeding 220 km h^{-1}.

Some studies that have been carried out reached the conclusion that the net load fluctuations are dampened and, therefore, wind energy production has only very small or null effects on the amount of primary reserves required – that is, reserves activated automatically with a time lag of less than 30 s – thanks to the effects of wind farm aggregation and the noncorrelation between wind power and the power demanded by the loads [5, 8, 123].

A number of comments have been made about the use of the adjectives 'variable' and 'intermittent' to define the nature of the energy generated by a wind farm [95]. 'Intermittent' can give the impression that wind power may often be available or unavailable over a time period, but not regularly or continuously. Ignoring any breakdowns that might take place, wind energy interruptions occur when the wind speeds are lower than the cut-in wind speed of the turbines or higher than their cut-out wind speed. Wind farms may not be able to produce energy during calm or stormy periods in small-sized areas with small- or medium-sized networks and with no interconnection capacity. Such periods can be planned for to a certain extent, but the circumstances in which a storm develops need to be analyzed to be able to predict its effects on power production with any degree of accuracy.

It is also commonly argued that the adjective 'intermittent' would be better applied to the power generated by conventional technology which, due to the large size of the units, can on occasions suddenly stop producing considerable amounts of power when faults occur. The argument goes that the more appropriate adjective to describe wind energy is 'variable' since, in sufficiently

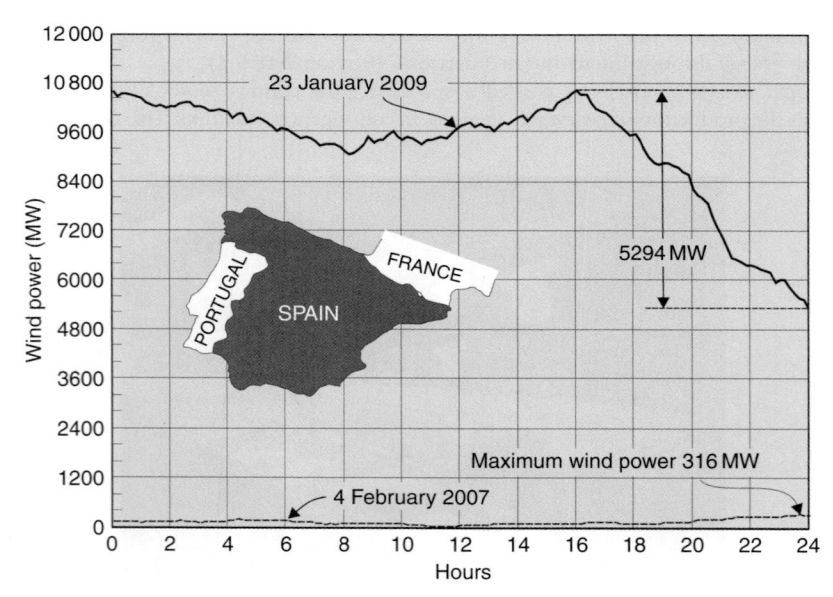

Figure 42 Variation of electrical power obtained from wind resources injected into the Spanish mainland electricity system on 4 February 2007 and 23 January 2009. Courtesy of REE (http://www.ree.es).

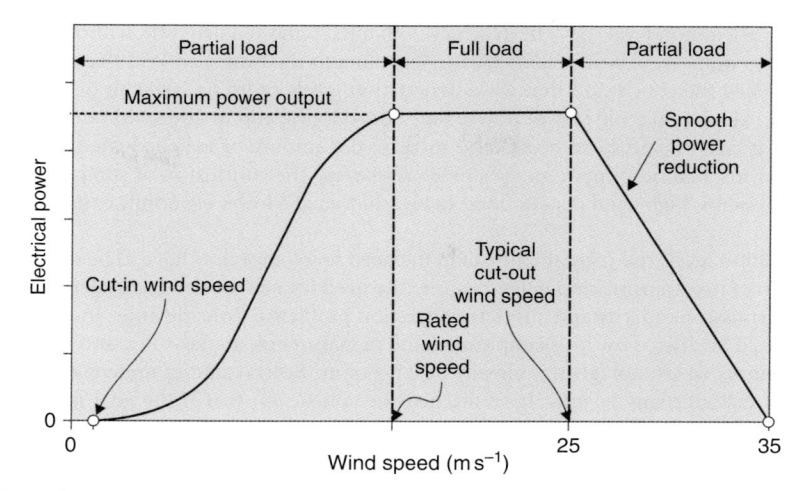

Figure 43 Power curve of a wind turbine modified to dampen the sharp fall in power during periods of very high wind speeds.

large areas where there is a strong interconnection of networks and due to the phenomena of aggregation and geographical dispersion, it is very improbable that all the wind farms would stop producing energy at the same time and instantaneously.

Some wind turbine manufacturers have modified their control strategies so that abrupt shutdowns are avoided in order to lower the hysteresis effects of a wind farm. That is, the shutdown does not happen abruptly when the wind speed exceeds the typical cut-out wind speed at maximum power production. If the wind speed increases drastically, the turbine simply reduces its power output until it stops (**Figure 43**). If the wind speed does not excessively exceed the typical cut-out wind speed, then the turbine operates at lower power, and when the wind speed falls, it immediately begins to operate again at maximum power.

Planning for the reserve capacity amounts required to cover unforeseen faults in conventional power systems generally contemplates coverage of the largest generation unit. At the present time, these reserves are higher than the installed power of a wind farm. There is therefore no need – for the moment – to increase the aforementioned backup or emergency reserves in order to cover wind farm faults [8].

According to the results of some studies that have been undertaken, it is not advisable to allocate to wind turbines the task of supplying the power demanded by unexpected loads [125]. Likewise, these studies state that wind farms should not be entrusted with critical situations due, for example, to the decoupling of conventional generation units from the network.

Secondary reserve requirements are closely related to the wind penetration level [8, 124, 126]. Intervention of these reserves must be implemented within 30 s of the commencement of the contingency, and they must have sufficient capacity to maintain their activity for 15 min in order to return the system to its nominal operating conditions and to free up the primary reserve.

According to various studies that have been made, once penetration levels reach 10% and above, the secondary reserve amounts that need to be used can increase significantly. The results of these studies are very disparate. According to one group of studies, based on penetrations of 10%, it is estimated that the extra reserve capacities required as a consequence of wind energy integration are found to be in an approximate range of 1–5% of the installed wind power capacity. Other studies, however, estimate a range of 2–10% of the installed capacity for the same penetration level. Meanwhile, another group of studies based on 20% penetration claims that the lower and upper range limits are approximately 4% and 7%, respectively.

The extra reserve capacity amount depends on the accuracy of the prediction tools which electrical system operators work with to estimate wind farm power output on timescales of seconds to hours. In addition, the degree of correlation that exists between power demand and wind production will affect the amount of reserves required. The effects of aggregation and dispersion are also important when calculating extra reserve capacities.

The allocation and use of power reserves as a consequence of wind variability entail additional costs [8, 124, 126]. These costs depend, among other factors, on the type of generation unit used to cover the control service. The results of an extensive number of studies carried out in relation to the cost of the reserves per megawatt-hour vary widely. However, there is a clear tendency for the costs of the reserves to rise as the percentage of wind penetration rises [8, 127].

2.18.5.1.2 Repercussions of wind power for energy storage needs

Various studies have analyzed the advantages of adding storage devices for the purpose of matching the wind energy supply to the electrical energy demand [128–132]. One of the main conclusions of these studies is that storage can be an effective and reliable way of providing the system with the balance it requires. However, storage entails additional costs as a result of not only the investment needed but also the losses that occur in the energy transformation process. The use of storage therefore depends fundamentally on economic questions. That is, its use can be an acceptable option if the extra benefits provided by the incorporation of storage technology in the system are greater than the costs incurred [87].

To date, moderate wind penetration levels have been achieved in interconnected networks without the need for storage systems to balance the power output variations of wind plants [5, 8]. According to the American Wind Energy Association (AWEA) [7], a number of studies have reached the conclusion that wind penetration levels of up to 20% can be achieved in the United States without the need for storage. More than 8500 MW of power were added to the grid in 2008 without the need for commercial-scale energy storage. Meanwhile, it has, to date, been possible to increase the amount of installed wind power in various countries in Europe without the need for installation of new energy storage resources. The conclusion of some studies is that with the use of already existing generation systems, high wind penetration can be achieved at a lower economic cost than if storage systems were to be integrated [8].

However, if wind penetration levels rise substantially, then the need for storage may have to be reconsidered. Storage can be an alternative to the installation of new transmission networks or to the need for new work to be undertaken on the existing networks to enable higher power transmission capacity and alleviate congestion problems. Consideration should also be given, however, to the greater flexibility that could be offered by, for example, demand management, market rules, and cross-border energy exchanges. Nevertheless, there are situations where storage may already be a necessity. Several studies undertaken on small- or medium-sized electrical systems, as in the case of many islands, have reached the conclusion that if the goal is to achieve high wind energy penetration levels without affecting power quality, then energy storage systems must be installed [133–140].

Storage systems have fundamentally been proposed for small-scale use with generation systems fully integrated into distribution networks, particularly in MGs. The numerous methods of storing the energy include lead–acid, nickel–cadmium, sodium–sulfur, and flow batteries, as well as flywheels, hydrogen storage, supercapacitors, and magnetic superconductors [23, 27].

However, the use of large-scale storage has also been proposed for use in the transmission networks. Methods proposed here include pumped hydro storage (PHS) [28, 141–145] and compressed air energy storage (CAES) [28, 141, 146–150]. There are other systems, but at the present time PHS and CAES are the ones which can provide more power and store more energy with greater efficiency and at lower cost [131].

PHS systems have been installed in many parts of the world and use the excess electrical energy production, in low-demand periods, to pump water to a reservoir located at a certain height [151]. This water is then recovered at some later moment when it is required by means of a turbine coupled to a generating unit (**Figure 44**). Many of these systems were built to adapt to the substantial increase in nuclear power generation which occurred between the 1960s and the 1980s.

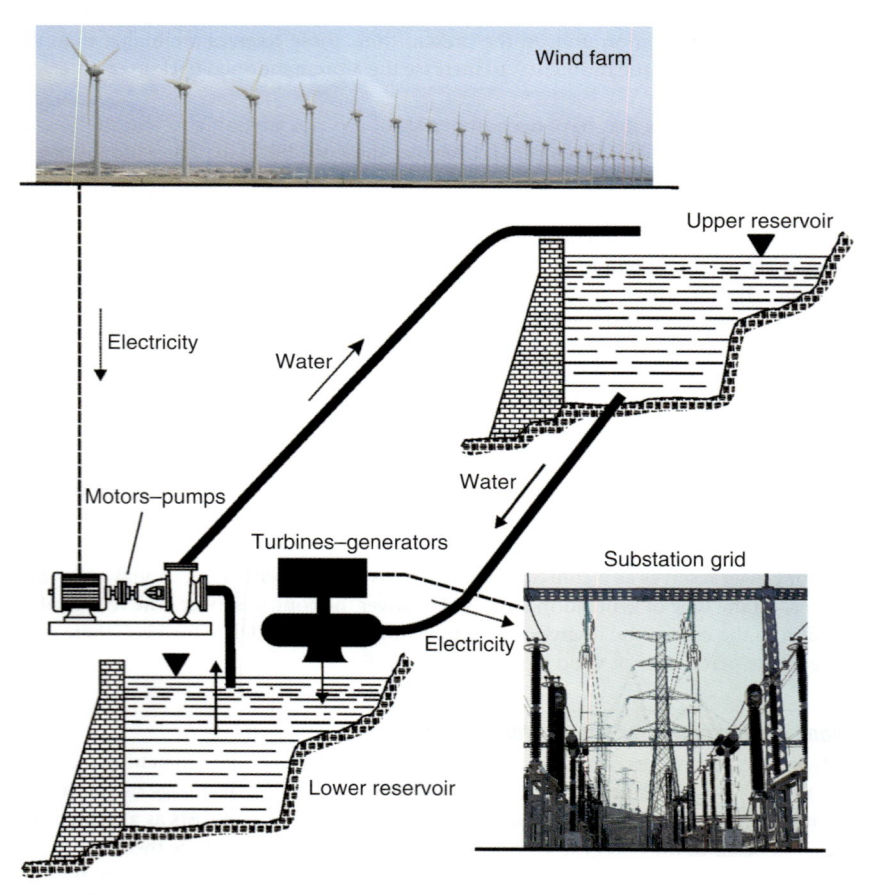

Figure 44 Schematic diagram of a pumped storage hydroelectric power station.

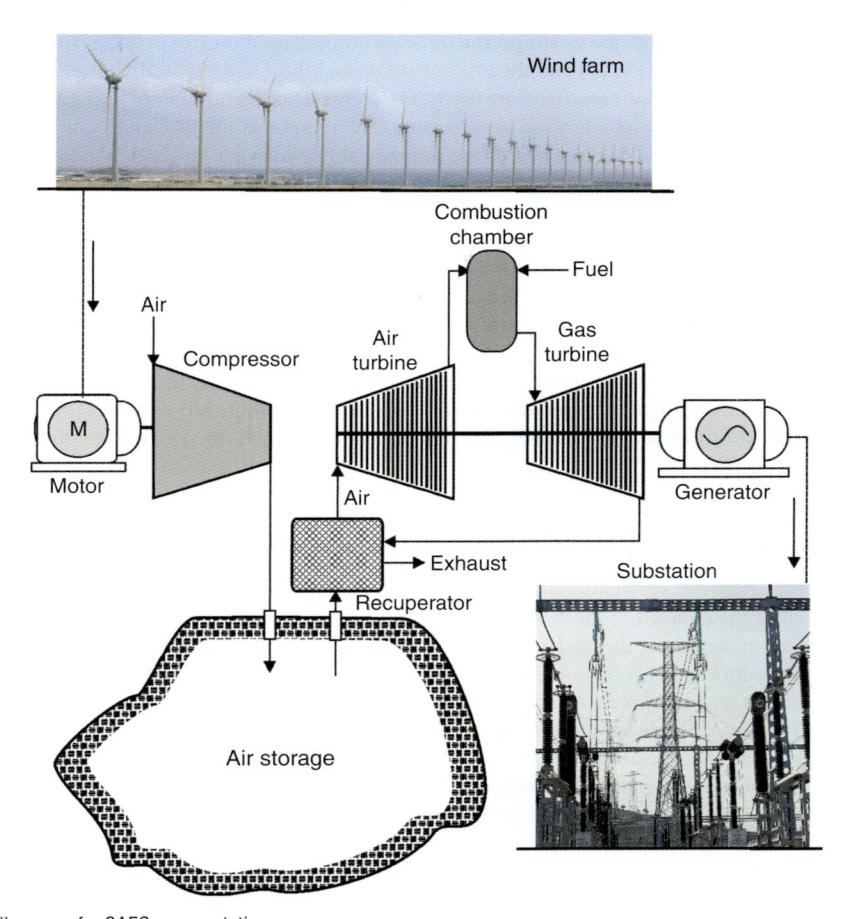

Figure 45 Schematic diagram of a CAES power station.

From the 1970s onward, and probably as a result of the complementary characteristics of PHS systems and wind farms, numerous studies have been carried out in many parts of the world to analyze the feasibility of coupling the two systems [152,153].

The projects that have been proposed can be classified into two basic groups with different goals: on the one hand, large-scale storage and, on the other hand, functionality in small- and medium-sized stand-alone systems. Examples of the latter type of project include the installations built on the island of Foula off the coast of Scotland toward the end of the 1980s [154], a project on the island of Okinawa (Japan) [155], a project on the island of El Hierro in the Canary Islands (Spain) [133], and several proposals for other islands in the same archipelago and for a number of islands in the Greek Archipelago [156–158].

One of the drawbacks of this type of storage is that it is not always easy to find suitable sites for the construction of the reservoirs or tanks. In addition, the investment costs associated with the civil works that have to be carried out are substantial.

CAES systems have been in use in both Germany and the United States [159]. Proposals have been made to use the surplus electrical energy generated by a wind farm to drive compressors which compress and store air in tanks or preadapted caverns (**Figure 45**). When required, the compressed air is recovered to drive a gas turbine coupled to an electrical generator, which produces electricity. These turbines operate with natural gas, but could use gasified biofuels to reduce atmospheric contamination.

2.18.5.1.3 Repercussions of wind power for generation capacity

With the integration of wind power into a power system, it is possible to guarantee, with a reasonable degree of probability, the annual production of a particular amount of energy. It can be said that this integration gives the power system an additional capacity to cover a percentage of the annual energy demand. However, the production of a particular amount of energy cannot be guaranteed at any given moment.

Some studies that have been carried out have reached the conclusion that, despite the peculiar characteristics of wind energy, it can contribute to energy supply security. In other words, wind energy has capacity credit [5, 87, 95, 160]. Capacity credit can be defined as the amount of conventional generation capacity that can be removed and replaced by the integration of wind generation capacity while maintaining the same energy supply security levels. Relative capacity credit is expressed as the ratio of the removed conventional plant capacity to the total installed wind power capacity.

Wind energy capacity credit requires a reliability study. The most commonly used indices in wind energy capacity credit analyses are the loss of load expectation (LOLE) [161–163] and the loss of load probability (LOLP) [163]. In these methods, wind generation and demand are statistically modeled or time series data are used. LOLE represents the number of hours a year in which it is expected that the load power demand will exceed available wind generation. LOLP represents the probability of not satisfying all the power demanded with wind generation. It is usually expressed as the number of hours a year in which wind generation is insufficient to cover the loads.

Various studies have performed calculations of the wind energy capacity credit and obtained a wide range of values. However, there is a clear tendency for the capacity credit to fall as the wind penetration percentage increases [127, 162].

The differences between the values obtained in the studies that have been carried out are the result of the influence a variety of factors have on the capacity credit [5, 8]. These include the installed wind power, the total installed generation capacity, the power demanded and its correlation with the wind power generated, wind turbine aggregation, and the geographical dispersion of wind farms.

The capacity factor of wind installations also affects wind energy capacity credit. Capacity factor is the ratio of the mean annual production to the production that would be obtained if the installation were to operate all year round at its rated power. This factor is related to the so-called availability factor of wind installations or, in other words, the percentage of time the wind installation remains in operation during the year.

2.18.5.2 Impact of Wind Power on the Power Transmission and Distribution Networks

In addition to the differences between conventional and wind technologies that have already been mentioned, there is another important difference related to the concept of location. Wind turbine operation is conditioned by its siting [164]. However, while siting is very important for conventional thermal power plants, it is not an indispensable factor for their operation and the requirements that govern their location display more flexibility. The dependency that wind turbine operation has on its location is a consequence of the fact that its energy source depends on it.

Historically speaking, the most suitable sites to exploit the wind resource are located in areas some distance from conventional power centers and from areas of large consumption. People normally do not want to live in areas with lots of wind, and thermal power stations, which use fossil fuels, tend to be distributed in such a way that they are not very far from the areas of high consumption. The installation of large wind farms in areas, which normally have a low electricity demand, some distance from conventional power centers and from the areas of high consumption means that it may be necessary to export that energy to other places if the objective is to make full use of the electrical energy generated.

There are a number of tasks that need to be performed when it comes to choosing a site for wind energy installations. These include verification of a suitable wind regime [164, 165] and an analysis of any possible constraints such as the capacity of the electrical transmission networks in that area.

A special situation arises in the particular case of exploitation of the electrical energy generated by offshore wind farms. In the past few years, this type of wind farm has undergone spectacular growth in Europe [11] and has begun to arouse considerable interest in other parts of the world [166, 167]. In fact, a number of countries are currently analyzing the feasibility of their implementation and some, for example, China [168, 169], have already begun work on their installation. With offshore wind farms, the construction of new lines to transport the energy to the coast is an indispensable requirement. The particular characteristics of the environment where these wind farms are installed and the considerable amounts of energy to be transported present new challenges when designing the internal electrical systems and power transmission systems to the coast.

As for the distribution networks, given that they are less robust than the transmission networks and that their reliability falls as voltage levels increase, the injection of high wind power levels into distribution networks also means that new challenges have to be faced.

2.18.5.2.1 Electrical power transmission from remote onshore wind farms

The critical drawback of the transmission of electrical power from large wind farms installed in remote areas where the wind resource is exploitable tends to lie in the limited capacity of the existing transmission networks. Lines that might pass close to potential wind farm sites were most probably not designed with future possible connections to large wind plants in mind. In some cases, network constraints impose limits on the energy that can be injected into the power system.

Such restrictions in the transmission of power are related to the thermal limits of the conductors, to voltage stability problems which generally occur while transporting electrical power over large distances, and to the transient stability of the system [170].

The thermal limits of the conductors depend on the characteristics and installation of the conductors as well as on meteorological conditions (wind speed, solar radiation, ambient temperature, etc.). Likewise, other components of the network, such as transformers, can also restrict the power transmission capacity. Hence, optimization of the wind resource in many places may require better network management, reinforcement of the network, and even the installation of new lines [5, 8, 124, 170].

One strategy that can be used to increase the transmission capacity without the need to generate high investment costs is to use so-called soft measures [5, 8, 170]. These measures aim to alleviate congestion problems, with methods being proposed and agreed upon by the TSOs of adjoining countries to undertake optimum energy exchanges across their frontiers.

The reinforcement measures that can be undertaken will depend on the particular circumstances of each case. Possible options include changing the conductor cables for higher capacity ones, which enable the use of the existing towers; increasing the number of transformers in the already existing substations; using FACTS to increase the real capacity of the lines; and leading the flow to the least loaded lines.

The standard transmission systems used to transport the high power generated by large onshore wind farms employ AC. Two transformation levels are required in wind farms with high installed rated power. The first transformation raises the low-voltage output of the wind turbines (generally 690 V) to the voltage of the internal underground network of the wind farm. This internal wind farm voltage depends on the power of the wind turbines. For high-power wind turbines (greater than 1 MW), the range is usually from 30 to 36 kV. The second transformation raises the medium voltage of the internal network of the wind farm to the high voltage of the transmission network, which uses high-voltage alternating current (HVAC) lines.

When large amounts of power need to be transported over very long distances, HVAC lines can cause problems. These problems can be reduced if they are converted to high-voltage direct current (HVDC) lines [171, 172]. With this conversion, transmission losses are lower and power transmission is substantially increased. Changing an HVAC system to an HVDC, one may require considerable investment costs, but lower nevertheless than would be needed for the installation of new transmission lines.

The most effective way of increasing the reduced power transmission capacities from remote areas is the construction of new lines and the use of appropriate soft measures. For environmental reasons, it is not easy in many countries to get the licenses required to undertake expansion work on the transmission system. However, the installation of new lines may be an indispensable requirement to achieve a substantial increase in wind penetration levels.

The rapid development that exploitation of the wind resource has undergone over the past few years in the United States has made it evident that the power transmission infrastructure needs to be extended [170]. It is vital that this be done as soon as possible to deal with the problems caused by the remote location of this resource (typical distances to the centers of consumption are in the hundreds or even thousands of kilometers) and by the imbalance between the relatively short time required to install a wind farm and the longer time needed to plan and build the transmission network. The AWEA [7] recognizes that transmission capacity is the biggest challenge faced as a result of the significant increase in the development of the wind energy resource in the United States. Various international studies carried out by the European Wind Integration Study (EWIS) [173] and TradeWind [174] have made recommendations for the improvement of the European transmission system with a view to favoring the integration of large-scale wind power.

2.18.5.2.2 Electrical power transmission from offshore wind farms

For technical reasons, the distances between wind turbines on offshore wind farms are generally higher than those for onshore farms. The minimum distance from the coast of the offshore wind farms installed to date ranges between approximately 1 and 23 km [5, 8, 11], though it is thought that in some locations there will be a considerable increase in these distances in the future.

Given the characteristics of the surroundings of such offshore wind turbines, new challenges are being faced in terms of the design and installation of the internal electrical systems of offshore wind farms as well as of the network for the transmission of the energy generated to the coast.

The distinctive characteristics of offshore wind farms mean that if they want to be competitive, then economies of scale need to be introduced, which oblige them to have a high installed capacity. Some of the projects that hope to be up and running from 2011 onward could exceed 500 MW [5, 8]. This means that the size of an offshore wind farm will be comparable to that of a conventional power plant.

The considerable power generated by these offshore wind farms has to be transported or transmitted to the large consumption centers. It is clear that the construction of new lines with underwater cables will be necessary to transport the electrical power from the wind farm to the coast.

The electrical power generated by an offshore wind farm must be transported to the coast in such a way that both costs and power losses are minimized. Unlike onshore wind farms, which are normally connected to an already existing network that provides service to several clients, the transmission network of an offshore wind farm to the coast is exclusive to that farm until it reaches the point of common coupling (PCC).

The most efficient way of transporting the power from an offshore wind farm to the coast is by using a high-voltage method. Various transmission systems involving either HVAC or HVDC have been proposed to transport the energy generated to the coast [88, 175–182]. With respect to transmission with HVDC, it should be mentioned that two technologies can be used. One option consists of using a line-commutated converter (LCC)-HVDC and the other a VSC (VSC-HVDC).

Given the possibilities offered by HVDC systems [171, 172, 183], several design and operation proposals have been made for offshore wind farms and their transmission network to the coast [184–188]. Alternative strategies have, however, been proposed to transport the energy generated by these offshore farms to the coast [189].

The existing offshore transmission systems use AC to transport the electrical energy generated in the farms to the coast. The voltage level employed in these systems is related to the distance between the wind farm and the coast, the depth of the water, the characteristics of the terrain, the associated investment costs, transmission losses, and so on.

Thus, for the Middelgrunden offshore wind farm (Øresund, east of Copenhagen harbor, Denmark), which comprises 20 wind turbines of 2 MW rated power anchored at a depth of between 5 and 10 m, a voltage level of 30 kV was chosen for the power transmission between the wind turbine group and the coastal connection (located at a distance of 3 km). The system employed is similar to that presently used for onshore wind turbines which generate around 690 V, with a transformer located at the base of the tower or on the nacelle of the wind turbine, raising the voltage to approximately 30–36 kV.

However, for the Horns Rev I wind farm (Blåvandshuk, Baltic Sea, Denmark), which comprises 80 wind turbines of 2 MW rated power anchored at a depth of between 6 and 14 m, a voltage level of 33 kV is used [190]. This voltage is increased to 150 kV through an offshore transformer substation before its transmission to the coast at a distance of approximately 15 km.

Most underwater power transmission cables are basically made of copper or aluminum wires [191]. These comprise the core of the cable and are electrically insulated. Due to its characteristics, the insulating material most commonly proposed for use in underwater cables is cross-linked polyethylene (XLPE).

AC underwater cables have high capacitive impedance. The capacitance of the underwater lines could give rise to self-excitation of the wind turbine generators if this factor is not taken into account. Such lines can lead to the production of considerable quantities of reactive power, which also needs to be taken into consideration. The capacitive current depends on the frequency and voltage of the system and on the capacitance and length of the cable. So, as cable length increases, so do losses since there is a proportional relationship between the reactive currents and the length of the transmission lines. Consequently, for large offshore installations located at distances from the coast which exceed certain limits and with high transmission system voltages, HVAC systems could significantly restrict the useful power that can be transmitted. The advantages of HVAC transmission systems (i.e., their proven technology, the low amount of space required for the equipment, and their high degree of reliability) do not compensate for their drawbacks. The technical disadvantages and the high cost of the transformers and underwater cables which need to be installed could advise against the use of this technology when large distances to the coast and high installed wind power are involved.

Figure 46 shows the scheme of a possible HVAC configuration for an offshore wind farm, with the wind farm itself, the medium-voltage collection bus, and two substations (one offshore and one onshore). In order to maintain the voltage amplitude of the AC within the established limits, reactive power compensation devices need to be included at both ends of the transmission [192]. It should be mentioned that when the wind farm is comprised of variable-speed wind turbines, these are prepared to provide up to a certain point the reactive power of the network and can participate in the voltage control.

HVDC schemes offer a series of advantages over HVAC schemes. These include, among others, minimum losses in the transport lines, decreased corona effect, elimination of losses due to the nonexistence of capacitive current (since the frequency of the electrical current is null), and low cable costs. So, the length of HVDC transmission systems is not subject to the limitations associated with HVAC systems. There is also the additional possibility of having full control over the active power while the level of faults is relatively low when compared with HVAC schemes. Nevertheless, though HVDC technology is now available for use, there remain a series of technical and economic challenges which must be overcome for it to become an indisputable option in the integration of offshore wind energy.

A DC transmission system can comprise one cable (monopolar) or two cables (bipolar). In monopolar transmission, the cable transports the high-voltage current. The flow of the return current is through the ground or sea. As a result of the drawbacks associated with monopolar transmission systems, the bipolar system is the most commonly proposed design [191].

Due to the dissimilar nature of the DC and AC currents, DC transmission systems require the installation of electronic power converters to carry out the AC-to-DC (rectifiers) and DC-to-AC conversion (inverters) at the ends of the line. Associated with the use of these devices are various drawbacks including the high cost of the conversion equipment, losses caused by the electronic equipment and the large amount of space they require, the generation of harmonics, and the complexity of the controls.

Present-day LCC technology, based on natural commutation with thyristors, has not been used as yet for the transport of power from offshore wind farms. However, it is a technology with a history of use in the transport of electrical energy in several parts of the world, which, to a certain degree, attests to its operational reliability at very high power levels.

Since the moment of activation of the thyristor can be controlled, though not the moment it is switched off, LCC rectifiers can control the active power but not the reactive power. Consequently, a STATCOM (or a synchronous compensator) is required in the AC network to supply the commutation voltage needed for the LCC-HVDC converter to work, and to compensate the reactive power

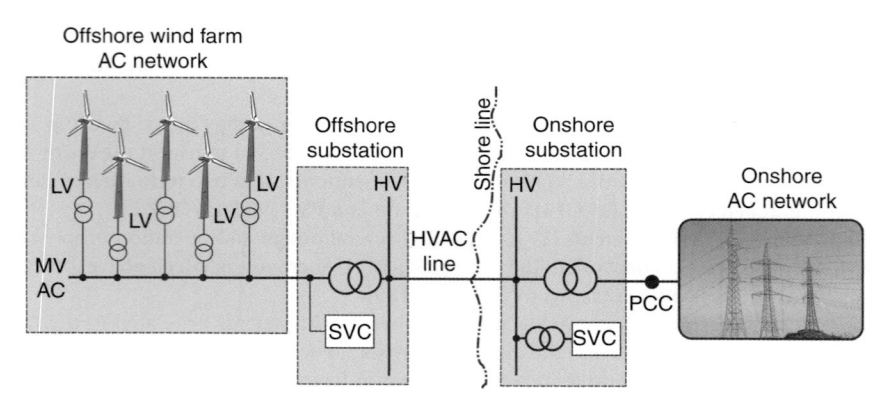

Figure 46 Scheme of a configuration of an HVAC transmission system for an offshore wind farm. Courtesy of REE (http://www.ree.es).

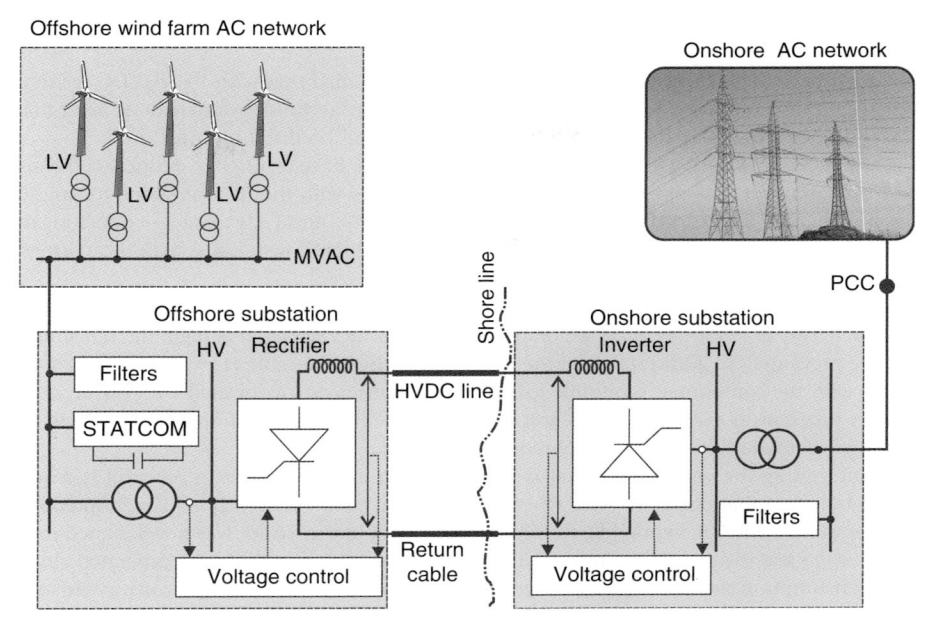

Figure 47 Scheme of a configuration of an LCC-HVDC transmission system for an offshore wind farm.

of the offshore network. Filters also need to be installed to minimize the harmonics in the network, on both the DC and AC sides (**Figure 47**). Control of the HVDC system has to be closely coordinated with that of the wind farm to enable system recovery in the event of an interruption to power transmission as a result of a fault in the AC network close to the onshore terminal.

VSC technology is based on the use of semiconductor devices with forced commutation. Commercially speaking, there are different configurations of converters that have been applied to VSC technology. The most important ones are the HVDC Plus® technology, designed by Siemens [193], and the HVDC Light® technology, developed by ABB [194]. The latter company was the first to undertake the installation of an offshore VSC converter.

The commonly used IGBTs can switch without needing the network, enabling simultaneous and independent control of active and reactive power. So, this technology, which can use PWM, does not require a compensator or a synchronous generator as occurs with LCC-HVDC technology (**Figure 48**). There are many advantages to the VSC technology, particularly in terms of efficiency and controllability. Power has to be decreased in order to maintain the VSC-HVDC voltage below the permitted upper limit when a fault

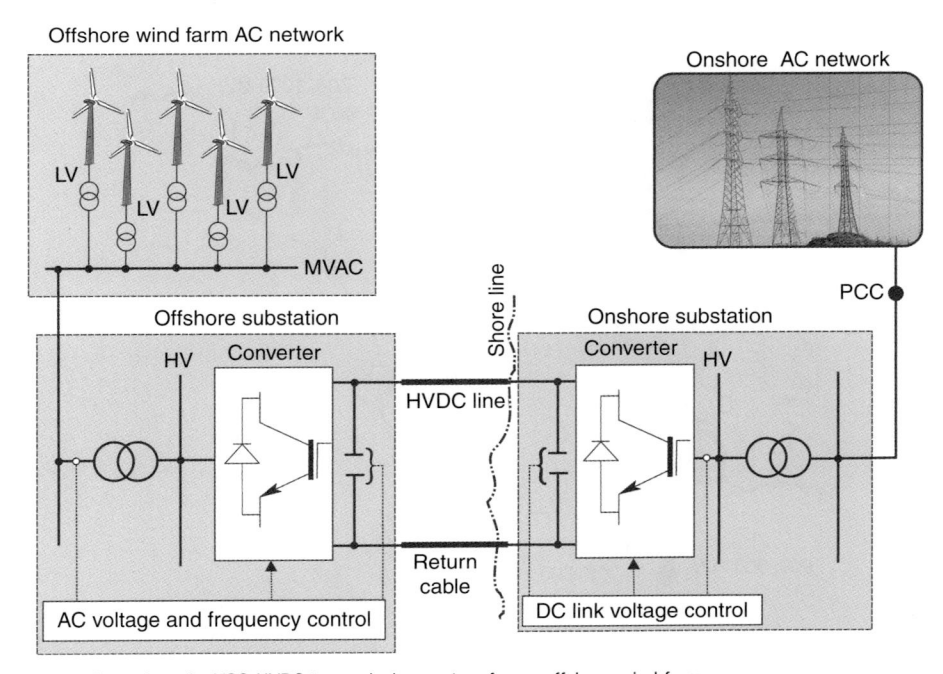

Figure 48 Scheme of a configuration of a VSC-HVDC transmission system for an offshore wind farm.

occurs in the AC network. This can be achieved by dissipating the excess power or by reducing the power output of the wind turbines of the offshore wind farm.

With regard to the total percentage of system losses, it should be mentioned that with VSC-HVDC technology the amount is approximately twice that of LCC-HVDC technology. Defenders of VSC-HVDC technology argue in its favor that a reduction in the cost of electronic power devices will make this technology cheaper in the not too distant future.

The different pros and cons of LCC-HVDC and VSC-HVDC technologies have resulted in proposals for new HVDC concepts. One of these is based on combining the operation of the two technologies with the idea of taking maximum advantage of the benefits offered by each of them in the various system operating modes. The technical advantages of operating the two technologies in parallel include a better voltage quality and the possibility of achieving high power transmission capacity from offshore wind farms with low losses [175].

Generally, in the technological proposals that have been made, no redundancy exists in the transmission of power from the wind farm to the coast, and therefore, if a fault occurs in an underwater cable when the wind is high, the transmission of a substantial amount of power will be prevented. In addition, given the medium in which the cable is located, its repair will probably require some considerable time with the consequent economic losses. However, the costs associated with the laying of a second backup cable and the difficulties inherent in executing a different layout have been the determining factors when it comes to deciding whether or not to employ what would be an effectively redundant system.

For the purpose of integrating the wind power that is concentrated on the shoreline, a network is required with a suitable transmission capacity to transport that energy to areas where it is required (many of which may be in interior regions).

The present-day European electrical network, like those in many places in the world, was not designed for the transmission of large amounts of power over great distances. The future will see large amounts of power being generated along coastlines that are over 1000 km from the consumption centers. This probably means that new lines will have to be constructed to increase wind power penetration in the network. To avoid network congestion and to take advantage of the benefits presented by large interconnected networks, it would be advantageous to have a robust cross-border interconnection network available with accessibility methods and a market organization to facilitate electrical energy exchanges.

Energy exchanges are carried out between some European countries with a reasonable degree of fluidity due to their high interconnection levels. However, in countries like Spain (**Figure 49**), interconnections with other countries are more limited and to date substantial electrical energy exchanges have not been made.

2.18.5.2.3 Integration of wind power in distribution networks

Some consumers connected to the distribution network have traditionally used small-scale generation units as backup reserves. These consumers, comprising principally hospitals, airports, some industries, shopping centers, hotels, university centers, and so on, have installed backup units for the purpose of covering critical loads in emergency situations, that is, in circumstances in which it is of critical importance to have electrical power at their disposal in the event of a distribution network fault.

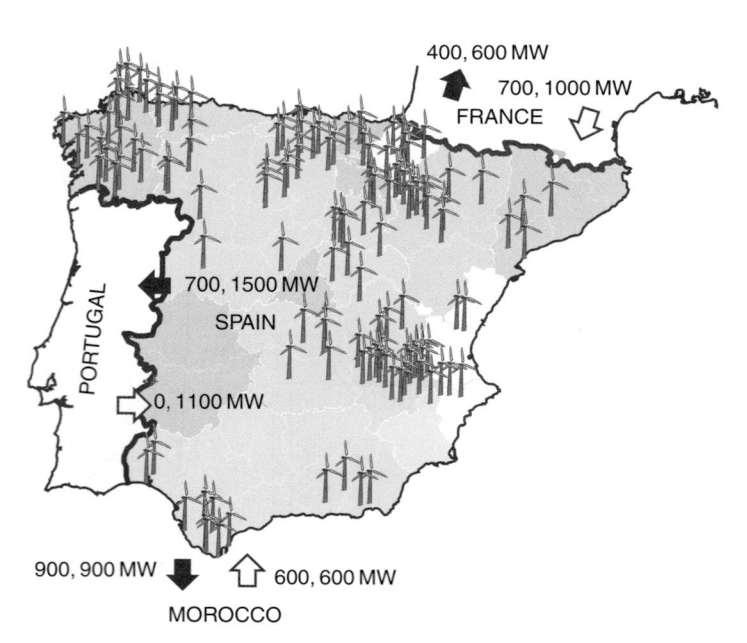

Figure 49 Commercial energy exchange capacity in megawatts, 10–23 April 2010, between the mainland territories of Spain, Portugal, France, and Morocco. Courtesy of REE (http://www.ree.es).

However, the various conventional and renewable generation units, with a power range of a few to hundreds of kilowatts and which are located in areas of consumption, can be connected to the distribution network and inject energy into it. In fact, there is a growing trend toward the use of electrical distribution networks for the injection of wind power.

This type of generation is classified as embedded generation or DG [20, 22]. It is distinguished from CG by, among other reasons, its limited generation of power and by the fact that it is connected to the distribution network at low or medium voltage.

The injection of wind power modifies the typical one-way power flows of power systems which occur from high-voltage to low-voltage networks. These changes to the direction of the active and reactive power flow can interact with the protection and operational systems of the network. The power that a DG system can inject into the network at a PCC must not exceed a specified percentage (in Spain it is 5% and in Germany 2%) of the short-circuit power. So, the generating capacity of a DG system is conditioned by the PCC, which depends on the short-circuit power which, in turn, depends on the impedance of the connection node.

Renewable DG is no more efficient than conventional CG, nor does it enjoy the benefits of economies of scale. Nevertheless, though in particular circumstances it can give rise to some inconveniences, it also enjoys a series of environmental, technical, and economic advantages [14, 16].

One of the main advantages is that the energy is produced near to where it is being demanded. So, if this energy is not exported, then the losses incurred as a result of transportation requirements are reduced. Since voltage control can be undertaken through FACTS or capacitor banks, the wind power can contribute to voltage support at those nodes of the radial networks which commonly present low voltages.

2.18.6 Integration of Wind Energy into MGs

MGs are systems made up of small-scale microsources of generation and energy storage devices that supply electrical energy and/or heat to a set of loads located in the vicinity through a low-voltage electrical micronetwork which interconnects them (**Figure 50**) [12, 20].

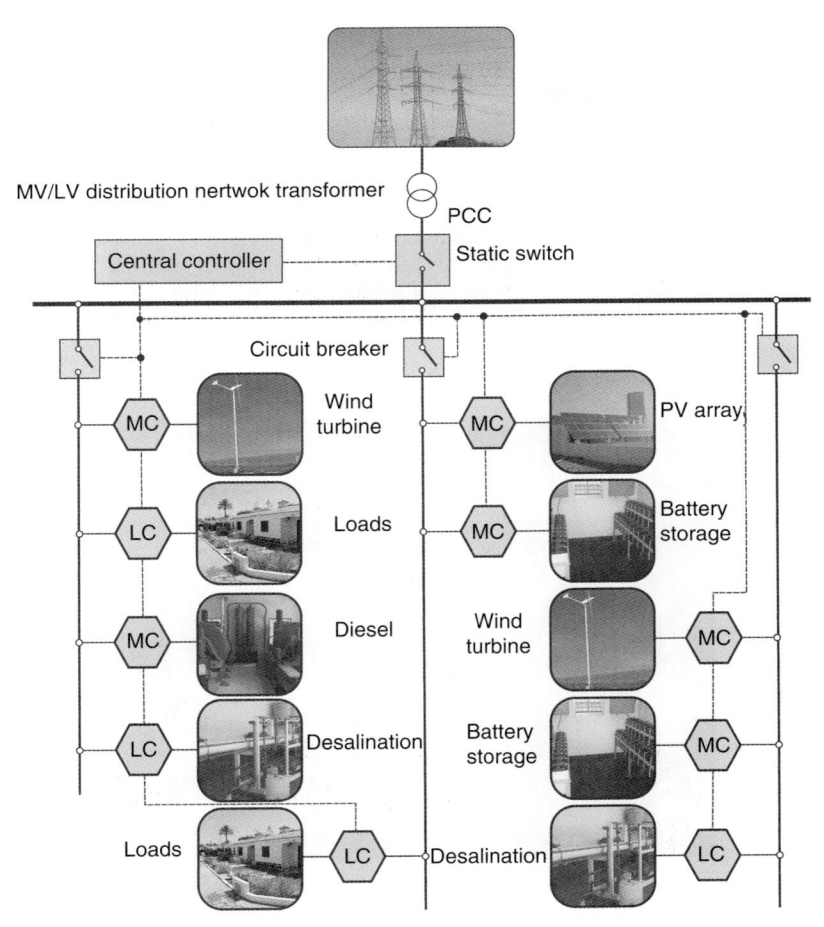

Figure 50 Schematic diagram of an MG. LC, load controller; MC, microsource controller; PV, photovoltaic

The generation devices that compose MGs can be either conventional type or renewable type, though it is generally proposed that the generation system be a hybrid type, in other words, combining both types of generation. The renewable technologies most commonly contemplated for use in MG systems are wind turbines and photovoltaic solar cells, though proposals have been made for the use of fuel cells and hydraulic turbines. With regard to the conventional technologies, the most commonly proposed plans involve reciprocating internal combustion engines, gas microturbines, and micro-combined heat and power (micro-CHP) systems.

The range of storage technologies that can potentially be used, as indicated in Section 2.18.5.1.2, is wide, though at the present time the most commonly used are batteries (**Figure 51**) and flywheels (**Figure 52**).

The architectures of MGs depend fundamentally on the type of current at the buses where the energy generation and storage devices are connected, as well as the loads [20]. Distinction is usually made between modular centralized DC bus architectures, modular centralized AC bus architectures, and hybrid architectures. So that the diverse devices can be integrated into these architectures and work together, the use of power electronic converters is essential. These devices convert one type of current into another and participate in frequency and voltage control.

In DC bus bar architectures, all the microsources and storage systems are connected to the same bus bar. The loads that consume DC as well as those that consume AC are fed from the same bus bar. The connection is direct for DC-consuming loads, but AC-consuming loads require power electronic converters. Power exchange between the MG and the main distribution network is possible and is carried out through the use of a DC–AC inverter (**Figure 53**).

In AC bus bar architectures also, all the microsources, storage systems, and loads are connected to the same bus bar. In this case, the link between the MG and the main distribution network, if desired, can be undertaken through a synchronous AC connection (**Figure 54**).

In hybrid architectures, as in DC architectures, all the microsources and storage systems are connected to one bus bar. However, in this type of architecture, the DC bus bar is connected to an AC bus bar through an inverter. It is at this AC bus bar that the AC loads are connected and from where, if desired, it is proposed that connection be made with the main distribution network (**Figure 55**).

Figure 51 Energy storage battery bank.

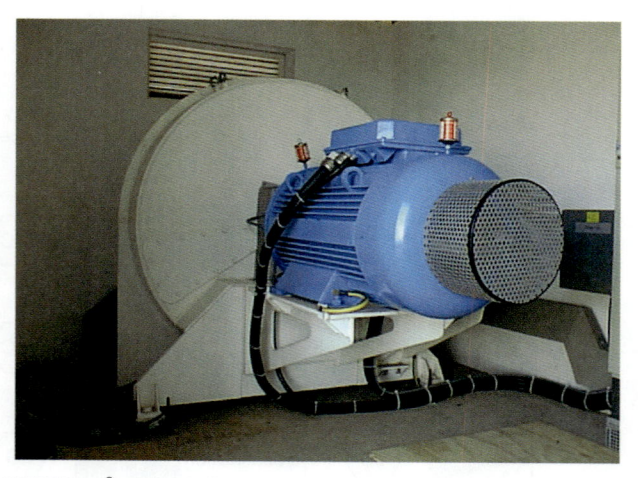

Figure 52 Flywheel with an inertia of 677.5 kg m^2 mechanically coupled to a 100 kW synchronous machine to serve as a network reference frequency and voltage at a stand-alone wind farm on the island of Gran Canaria. This flywheel is used to maintain dynamic stability in the face of disturbances at the moments of connection and disconnection of loads and as a temporary energy storage system.

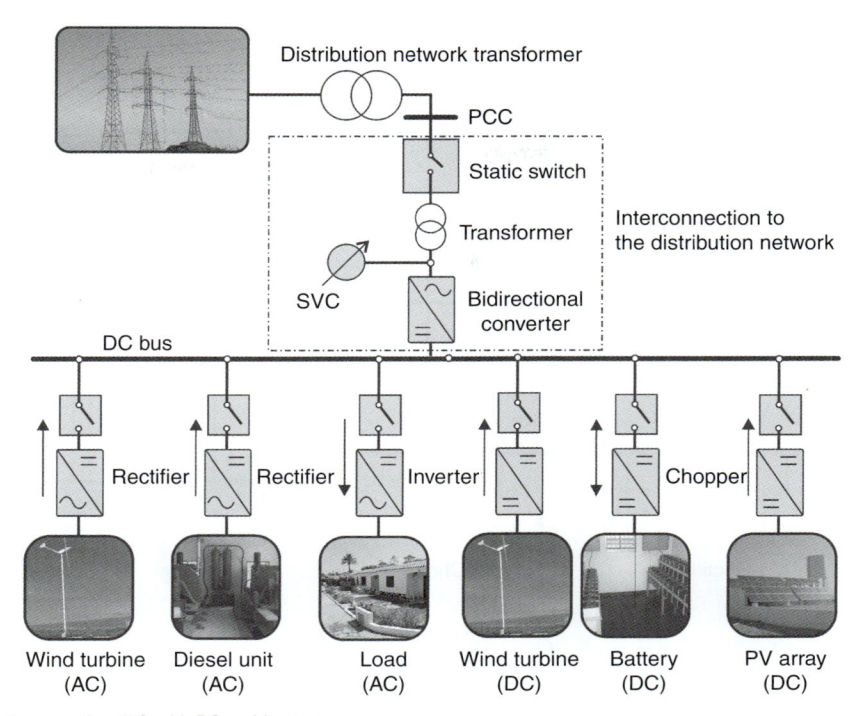

Figure 53 Schematic diagram of an MG with DC architecture.

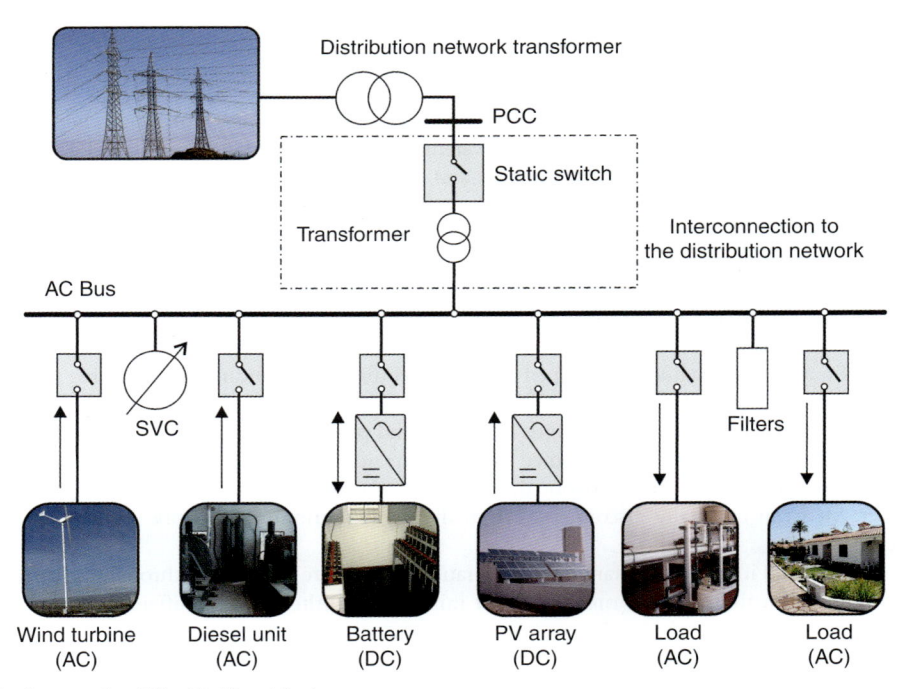

Figure 54 Schematic diagram of an MG with AC architecture.

MGs can be designed to operate either in a normal connection mode to the main distribution network [195, 196] or in a stand-alone mode in remote areas of developing countries which, for technical, economical, or environmental reasons, are not reached by the main power grid [20].

The most commonly used MGs designed for exclusive stand-alone operation have fundamentally consisted of wind–diesel systems [197, 198]. These systems have normally used AC bus bar architectures, with the diesel engine generator units being responsible for the system's frequency and voltage control. Such systems have been in use throughout the world, and the rated

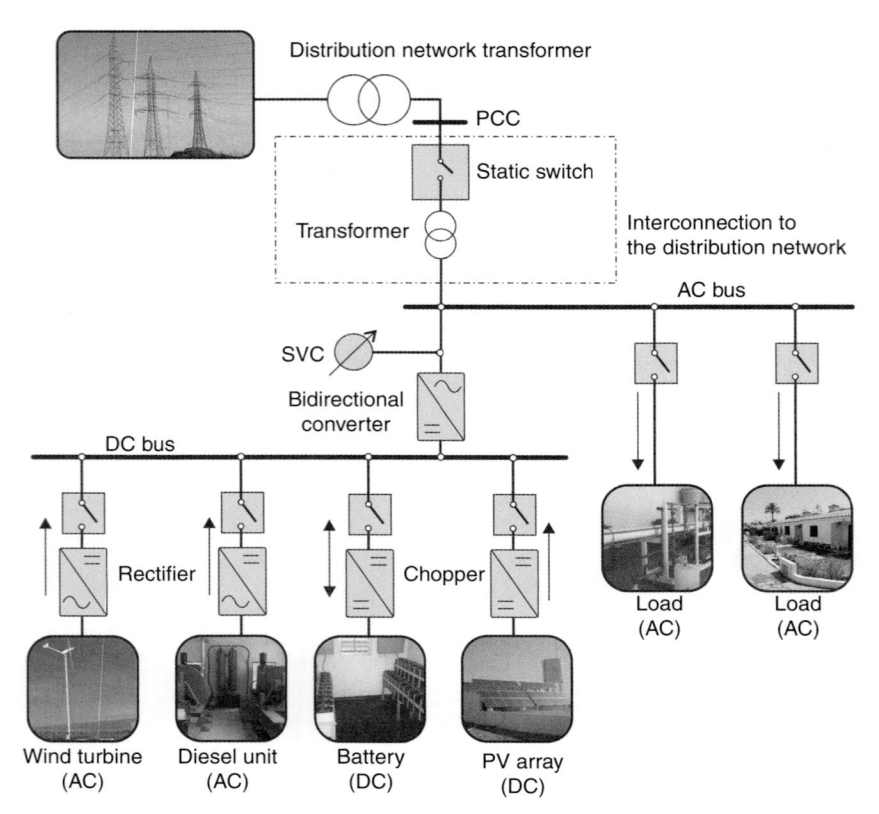

Figure 55 Schematic diagram of an MG with hybrid architecture.

powers of their components vary over a wide range. The rated power of wind turbines, which have been used in these systems, ranges from tens of kilowatts to almost 2 MW, while the equivalent diesel figures are between tens of kilowatts and about 10 MW.

The systems have traditionally used dump loads, batteries, and flywheels to match the energy generated to the demand and to increase wind penetration. In addition to supplying electricity to cover the domestic demand and streetlighting, some systems have also provided other services. A wind–diesel system was installed toward the end of the 1990s on the island of Fuerteventura (Canary Archipelago, Spain) comprising two 60 kW diesel units and a 227 kW rated power wind turbine (**Figure 56**). This system was installed to cover the domestic consumption and streetlighting of a small fishing village with the additional objectives of supplying electrical power to a reverse osmosis desalination plant, a water purification system, the domestic potable water supply equipment, and other services to facilitate the work of the fishermen [199, 200]. These included ice production and freezer installations for the fish that had been caught, as well as engines that helped in the launching and grounding of the fishing vessels. Flywheels, dump loads, and deferrable load management are used to match generation to demand and ensure system stability. Deferrable loads include the desalination plant, which operates in periods of excess wind production and enables storage, rather than of energy, of the potable water produced in tanks specifically designed for that purpose.

MGs connected to the main distribution network through fast semiconductor switches normally operate in parallel to it (**Figure 50**). However, MGs can be totally disconnected from the main distribution network when maintenance tasks or fault repairs need to be carried out.

Disconnection of an MG and its change to stand-alone operational mode are undertaken through the activation of a separating device capable of commutation times on the order of a few milliseconds. Alternatively, different parts of the MG can also be disconnected using circuit breakers.

In stand-alone mode, the generation microsources and the energy storage systems have to supply all the energy demanded by the loads, or at least part of it. In both operating modes, the MG has to operate in steady state. In addition, however, the MG has to remain stable during the two transient states that correspond to the transition period between the two steady states. For this to happen, appropriate devices and strategies need to be used so that unacceptable voltage and frequency disturbances do not occur.

In the operating mode of connection to the main distribution network, the connection can be configured in such a way that it either only allows energy to be injected into the network or allows injection/consumption of power into/from the network.

Whatever be the MG architecture employed, it will require control and coordination devices. These devices have to manage and control the various components (generation, storage, and loads) in the various operating modes of the MG and in the corresponding transient states in such a way that the cluster of devices contributes to the correct operation of the system. These systems are

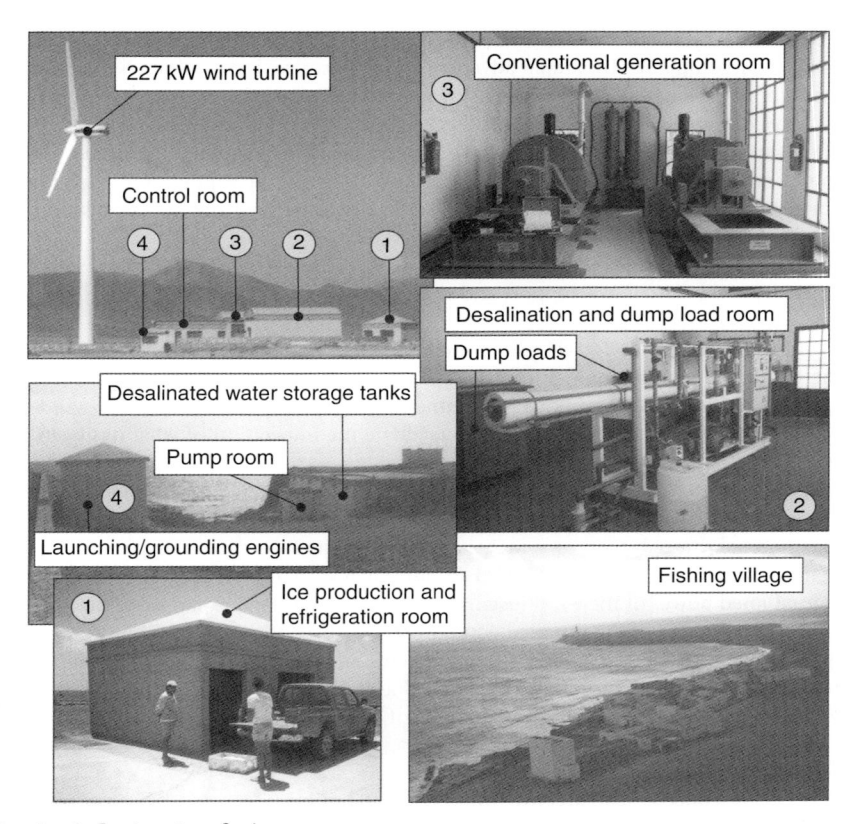

Figure 56 Wind–diesel system in Fuerteventura, Spain.

hierarchical. That is, the MG has local load controllers (LCs) and microsource controllers (MCs), as well as a central controller (CC) which exchanges information with the local controllers and carries out the overall control and protection of the MG.

It should be mentioned that interest in implementing MGs has spread throughout the world. The remarkable number of research projects being undertaken in various continents is testimony to this interest [195]. The design criteria depend on the objectives being pursued. These objectives are usually related to reduction of atmospheric pollution levels, energy diversification and reduction of external energy dependency, cost reductions in high energy price scenarios, supply quality, refusal of permission for new transmission line construction, and so on.

In the following sections, the importance of simulation of MG operation prior to its implementation is explained. Some of the advantages and drawbacks that are commonly associated with the contribution of wind energy to both types of system (stand-alone and integrated into the main distribution network) are also explained.

2.18.6.1 MG Modeling

Before the implementation of an MG, it is important that modeling of the different designs be performed from technical, economic, and environmental points of view for optimum sizing and system operation. Wind turbine integration into MGs requires a detailed study of the wind regimes at the site, the types of load, the temporal evolution of power demand, and the investment and operating costs of its different components.

The models used are normally logistic, employing statistical techniques and/or time series, and dynamic, using the dynamic equations of the movement of the mechanical and electrical components of the system [201, 202].

Logistic models, which generally use time steps of between 10 min and 1 h, enable evaluation of the power flows and the daily, monthly, seasonal, and annual evolution of the energy generated. This information can then be used to evaluate the wind penetration, the economic feasibility of the system, and its contribution to lowering atmospheric contamination.

Dynamic models, which work on a scale of milliseconds, allow analysis of system stability under different operating conditions.

2.18.6.2 Benefits of Wind Energy Integration into MGs

The integration of wind energy into MGs can be used as a strategy to increase the consumption of electrical energy from renewable sources. By increasing the use of wind energy units, optimally managed by the MG's control system, it is possible to achieve a reduction in the emissions of greenhouse gases that conventional generation sources currently produce. Since the wind turbines operate near their loads, an additional benefit is the reduction in losses incurred in transporting the energy.

As mentioned earlier, the remarkable advances that have been made in the development of large-scale wind turbine and wind farm technology have not been accompanied by similar advances for small-scale wind turbines. Nevertheless, an intelligent control system [203] of a cluster comprising small wind turbines using appropriate power electronic devices, energy storage devices, and other generation microsources can together constitute a strategy for integration of those wind turbines.

To achieve optimum integration, the system must also have appropriate management of the loads as well as of the set of cluster components. Wind turbines can collaborate in increasing the security of the energy supply to the MG loads. This contribution to increased security can be achieved if correct sizing of the different components of the MG in relation to demand and energy resources is performed and if detailed operational planning is undertaken.

In regions with small- or medium-sized electrical systems, as is the case of islands, where the networks are weak and interconnection with other networks for control support and energy exchange is not possible, wind energy penetration levels are severely limited.

The integration of wind turbines into MGs, where both load and generation are managed, can facilitate an increase in the utilization factor of wind energy. In the Canary Archipelago (Spain), where each of the seven islands constitutes an independent generation system and where the Canary Autonomous Government has imposed limits on annual wind installation capacities to avoid disturbances in the network, efforts have been made to facilitate the integration of what has been termed 'generation with associated consumption'.

In this type of generation, the wind turbines on an island are connected in parallel to that island's grid, with the energy generated being used mostly for consumption by industrial installations connected to the wind turbines through an MG. The wind turbines have to be permanently connected through their own MG to their loads. The MGs can receive from the main island grid a certain amount of energy and can inject into the main grid its own surplus energy up to a maximum of 50% of the annual mean energy output. In addition, the total rated power of the wind installation must not be greater than twice the amount of contracted power nor twice the amount of the rated power of the installed equipment.

These MGs are unusual in that they have no energy storage systems and have basically been implemented by industries which only work daytime shifts. The regulations that initially established a maximum injection of 50% of the instantaneous generated power have had to be modified because of the significant amounts of 'dumping' or dissipation of wind generation in periods when the industries were idle. In such cases, the installation of energy storage devices could improve the ability to exploit the wind energy and decrease dependency on the main distribution network.

There are many areas where the concept of an MG with integrated wind turbines is particularly interesting. Tourist and residential complexes, for example, which have services with deferrable and/or controllable loads including desalination systems, wastewater purification, air conditioning, heating, and other types of consumption that can be actively managed, could be suitable for the installation of intelligent MGs fed by wind energy and through energy storage devices.

The MG concept, thanks to its implicit control and intelligence capacities, enables a system operator to take into account energy prices, weather conditions, and energy consumption forecasting when planning the operational activities [204] of the generation and storage sources. MGs could also potentially participate in the electricity market, with offers of active power and/or auxiliary services [6, 205, 206]. This would facilitate optimum exploitation of the wind energy from a technical and an economic point of view.

2.18.6.3 Problems Associated with Wind Energy Penetration in MGs

At the present time, the integration of MGs into main electrical distribution networks is hampered by technical and nontechnical constraints.

From a technical point of view, it should be pointed out that MGs are not exempt from generating problems in the operation of the electrical power system. The technical challenges are related to, among other questions, steady-state and transient voltage effects at the PCC, malfunctioning of the protection systems, and the contribution of MG generators to flicker effects, phase voltage imbalance, and power quality. Likewise, stand-alone operation of the MG also presents a series of questions that need to be resolved.

The difficulty in resolving such technical problems is related to the need to control and manage a wide variety of generation microsources, storage systems, and loads. The present lack of standard operational and protection protocols also constitutes an impediment to the implementation of MGs. Despite all the above, there are no technical barriers to the development of MGs which integrate wind generation sources.

In terms of nontechnical constraints, the most significant is the absence of established standards to regulate the concept of MGs. Other barriers to the implementation of MGs are the high investment costs involved and, in many countries, the constraints imposed by the prevailing legislation.

2.18.7 Questions Related to the Extra Costs of Wind Power Integration

In addition to the investment and maintenance costs of wind energy, its integration into electrical networks entails additional associated costs [5, 95, 124, 126, 207]. These extra costs are the consequence of the need to achieve a balance between generation and load in a system into which power that varies over time is injected. Other contributing factors are the costs related to the reliability, the congestions (and losses), and the connection, as well as the costs involved in reinforcement of existing lines and installation of new energy transmission lines [208].

The costs incurred as a result of wind power variability are connected to the costs of the additional reserves required and the extra programming and generation costs incurred by conventional plants operating under partial-load conditions. Studies undertaken show that the costs due to energy variability tend to rise as penetration levels increase [95]. However, there are other factors involved. These include the possibility (or not) of energy exchange with neighboring regions, the aggregation effects of wind turbines and the dispersion effects of wind farms, the cost of conventional fuel, the type of technology employed, and the accuracy of the wind power and short-term demand prediction systems.

Also influential are the time frames of the spot markets [33, 208–210], where energy prices and amounts are flexible and offers made by generators are matched with the system demand forecast, and the time intervals for offer and bid quantities. The spot market is commonly a day-ahead market (the generators offer energy of 1 day for 24 h of the following day) with a time resolution of 1 h, though there are also spot markets with time resolutions of 30 min [33]. If, as some organizations are demanding, the electricity markets were faster, with shorter gate closure times, then the currently existing uncertainty regarding wind production forecasting would be reduced as a result of the shortened forecasting periods. Smaller discrepancies between the energy that it is planned to deliver to the network and the energy that is actually delivered would enable reductions in balancing adjustments, which, in turn, would economically favor wind energy integration into the network.

From analyses undertaken of the additional costs associated with electricity transmission infrastructure as a result of wind energy integration, it can be concluded that though a number of factors are involved, there is a tendency for these costs to rise as wind penetration levels increase.

2.18.8 Requirements for Wind Energy Integration into Electrical Networks

Wind energy producers have to meet a series of technical and administrative conditions before their wind turbines can be connected to electrical networks. However, at the present time, there is no unanimous agreement to the specific conditions that have to be met. The requirements vary considerably from one country to another, and regional legislation within the same country may have specific clauses applicable only to that region.

The authorization procedure for installation of a wind farm in Spain, for example, differs depending on the autonomous community in question. The procedure in the autonomous community of the Canary Islands begins with an official call for tenders published by the autonomous government in which the maximum power that can be installed in the region is specified. Among the various parameters that are assessed when awarding the tender are the technical characteristics of the installation, the envisaged energy efficiency, and the capacity factor of the installation.

Generally speaking, however, in most places, the administrative specifications are related to the information that the wind energy producers and the TSO have to supply. The wind energy producers have to provide, for example, the wind turbine specifications, the maximum power that will be injected into the network, and any additional information required to determine the short-circuit current. Meanwhile, the TSO has to provide information about the PCC and its voltage, the short-circuit power range at that point, and so on.

The technical requirements are generally centered on the devices that have to perform the connection and disconnection operations of the wind turbines to/from the network and on the protection system. Grid codes [211, 212] specify the limits within which certain variables can move when operating normally and after particular contingencies that may take place. For example, it is usually specified that a voltage drop at a coupling point due to wind turbines cannot be lower than 2% of the nominal voltage at that point. Requirements are also established in terms of the power factor limits which wind turbines have to work within. In addition, it is commonly required that the wind installation be able to withstand, without disconnection, voltage disturbances with particular magnitude and duration profiles at the network connection point caused by short circuits. In other words, fault-ride-through capacity is required.

The severity of the control rules is usually conditioned by the robustness of the network and the level of wind penetration. As the wind penetration percentages have risen, so have the demands of the grid codes, requiring greater participation on the part of wind technology in system control.

Requirements have been established in some codes concerning the contribution of wind turbines to frequency and voltage control [87, 106]. That is, the wind turbines are obliged to participate in primary and secondary frequency control, in the same way as it is performed by conventional technology (**Figure 57**). Nevertheless, given wind's variable nature, wind technology is faced with limitations in the pursuit of such an objective. Since wind cannot be controlled, these requirements are easier to meet when dealing with over-frequencies, as wind farms can lower their production by regulating in real time the pitch of the turbine blades or by disconnecting one or more of the turbines.

If the network frequency falls as a result of demand exceeding generation, then wind farms that are producing energy at that moment could still participate in the frequency control. For this to happen, the pitch angle control mechanisms of the wind turbines must have been operating up to that moment capturing less energy from the wind than actually capable of given the wind conditions. In this way, wind farms would be capable of maintaining a 'capture' reserve margin and, hence, a production reserve margin. Wind farms that use this strategy could, via activation of the pitch angle control mechanisms at the moment of the contingency, capture more energy from the available wind and thereby participate in the frequency control process.

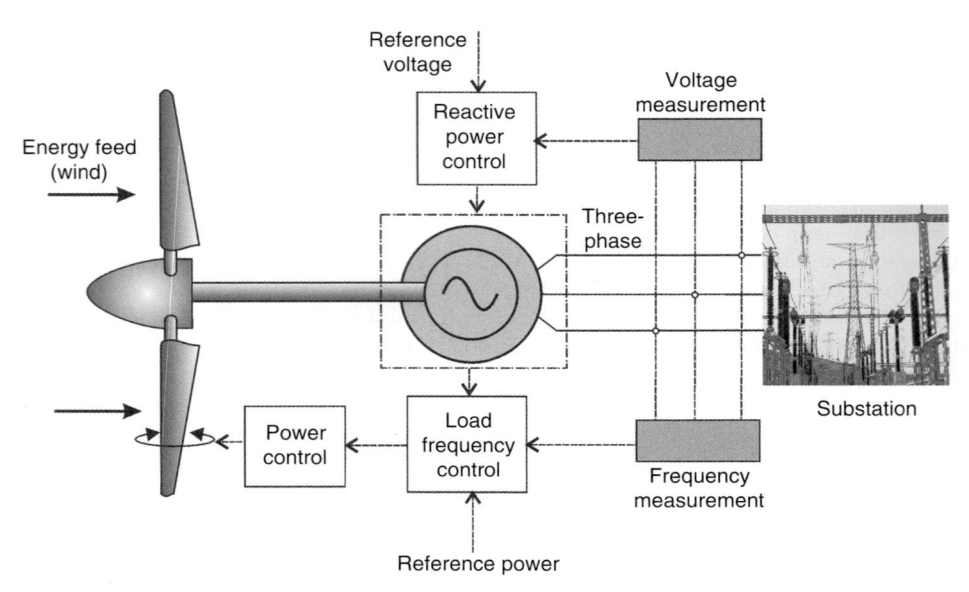

Figure 57 Possible frequency and voltage control functions of wind turbines integrated into the electrical network.

Wind farms are also required to adjust reactive power in order to control voltage by using information received from the network. Wind turbine operation must not be the cause of faults in the electrical network, nor of any lowering of security conditions, nor of disturbances higher than those admitted by the prevailing legislation and which affect other network users.

Finally, maintenance and other staff working on the electrical network cannot have their working conditions endangered by wind turbine operation.

2.18.9 Wind Power Forecasting

As mentioned earlier, the problems caused by the variability of the energy generated by wind turbines could be alleviated to some extent if it were possible to predict the available wind power accurately and some time beforehand.

A priori knowledge of the wind speed at wind installations and, consequently, of the power generated by the turbines is of vital importance for the TSO. Knowing this and other information about expected consumer demand enables better management of the system by the operator. In other words, production scheduling at the different power stations is improved and energy transmission congestion issues can be more accurately resolved.

As well as being of interest to the producers themselves, wind production forecasting is also important for the energy distributors. Accurate forecasting helps the producers when making bids on the electricity markets and in scheduling maintenance work, while the distributors benefit because of a reduction in the number of errors made when purchasing energy to satisfy the needs of the consumers connected to their networks.

Studies related to forecasting have traditionally concentrated on the development of tools that enable long-term wind speed estimation for the purpose of evaluating the energy output of a potential site for the installation of a wind farm. However, as a result of deregulation of the electricity market and increased wind penetration in the electrical networks, there has been a marked intensification of the R&D activities related to wind power forecasting tools with time horizons of up to 48 h. That is, these studies have concentrated on what is commonly known as short-term wind energy forecasting [87, 124, 213–218].

Prediction techniques of the power generated by wind farms initially followed two different paths. One set of techniques was based on time series prediction methods, while the other used weather forecasting methods.

Time series methods use power data series measured at the wind farms to estimate very short-term output power. These methods need to know the variables of the wind farm at the instant prior to issuing their forecast, but their accuracy is considerably reduced when it comes to predicting a few hours ahead. In other words, their forecast horizon is very limited.

Nowadays, however, all methods are usually based on weather forecasting. These methods entail the resolution of equations that describe atmospheric behavior. That is, they use short-term numerical weather prediction (NWP).

Weather forecast-based methods use physical models, statistical models, or a combination or mix of both to predict the wind farm energy output. These methods start with meteorological data provided by physical models which describe the behavior of the atmosphere through a system of different partial equations. These equations cannot be resolved analytically and, therefore, require the use of numerical methods. The initial conditions that are required to resolve this system of equations come from data recorded all over the planet by satellites and weather stations and balloons.

Numerical solution methods, based on finite volumes, finite differences, or finite elements, require the analysis space to be discretized with the configuration of a three-dimensional mesh. The forecast models will give the results at the different mesh nodes as a function of time. Due to the computational load required by global models, the mesh resolution has to be coarse. To increase the resolution, mesoscale models are commonly used with resolutions of a few kilometers. These models use the values obtained from the global models as input data. Various public and private bodies are able to provide such services.

Physical approaches or statistical and data mining approaches are used to forecast the power generated by wind farms.

For various reasons, wind-sourced electrical power forecasting methods are usually applied to a set of wind farms selected as being representative of a region rather than to all the wind farms or turbines of a certain size in that region. Therefore, to estimate the total wind production of a region, techniques that enable extrapolation of the results forecast for the selected wind farms to the remaining wind installations are used. This procedure is known as upscaling.

2.18.9.1 Physical Models

The data derived from the mesoscale NWP models, given their degree of resolution, provide information that can represent the mean behavior of the wind regime at a wind farm site. However, wind speeds at the turbine hub height need to be known to be able to predict the power generated by a wind farm. These speeds are influenced by the local characteristics of the wind farm, for example, the wind farm orography, the wakes of the wind turbines, surface roughness, wind direction, air density, and thermal effects. So, the forecasts obtained with the mesoscale models need to be adjusted in order to obtain a higher resolution that enables observation of the particular effects of the wind at the wind farm site.

Microscale models can be used for this purpose with resolutions that range from a few centimeters to 100 m. The process of interpolating the global results to the local peculiarities of the wind farm in question is commonly called downscaling.

The characteristic wind speed power curve of each of the wind turbines is used to estimate its wind production. **Figure 58** shows a block diagram that summarizes the wind power generation forecasting process through the employment of physical methods.

2.18.9.2 Statistical and Data Mining Models

The starting point for statistical and data mining models is generally the meteorological information provided by the mesoscale NWP models. However, unlike physical models, these models attempt to establish a relationship between the forecasted meteorological data and the power output of the wind farm. The methods commonly employed to tackle this problem include statistical models and models which use data mining techniques.

Figure 59 shows a block diagram that summarizes the wind power generation forecasting process through the employment of statistical and data mining methods.

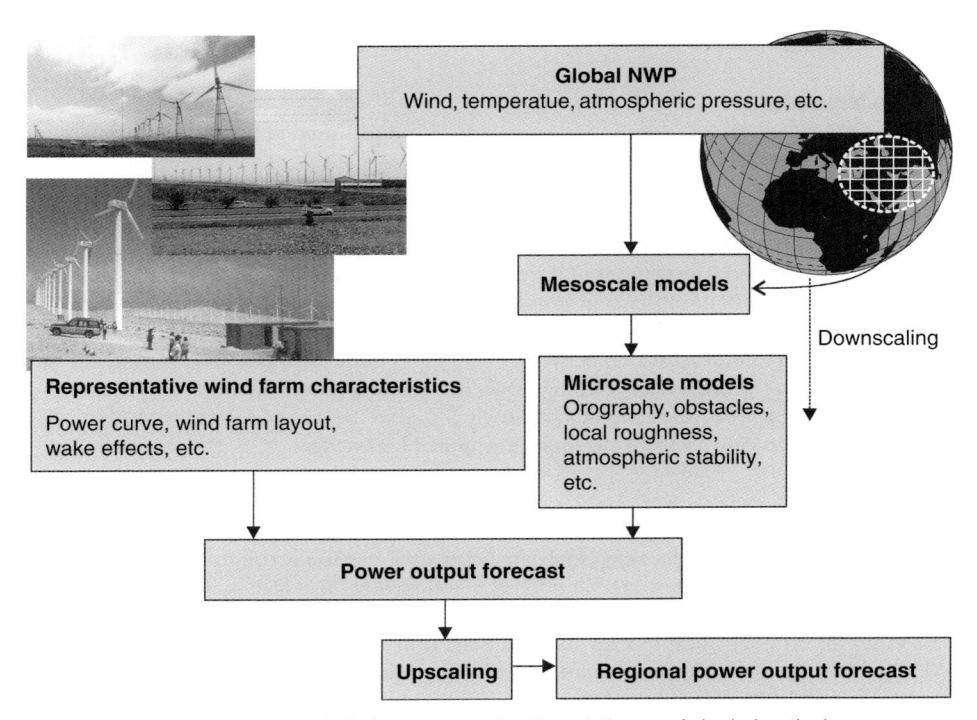

Figure 58 Block diagram of the forecasting process of wind power generation through the use of physical methods.

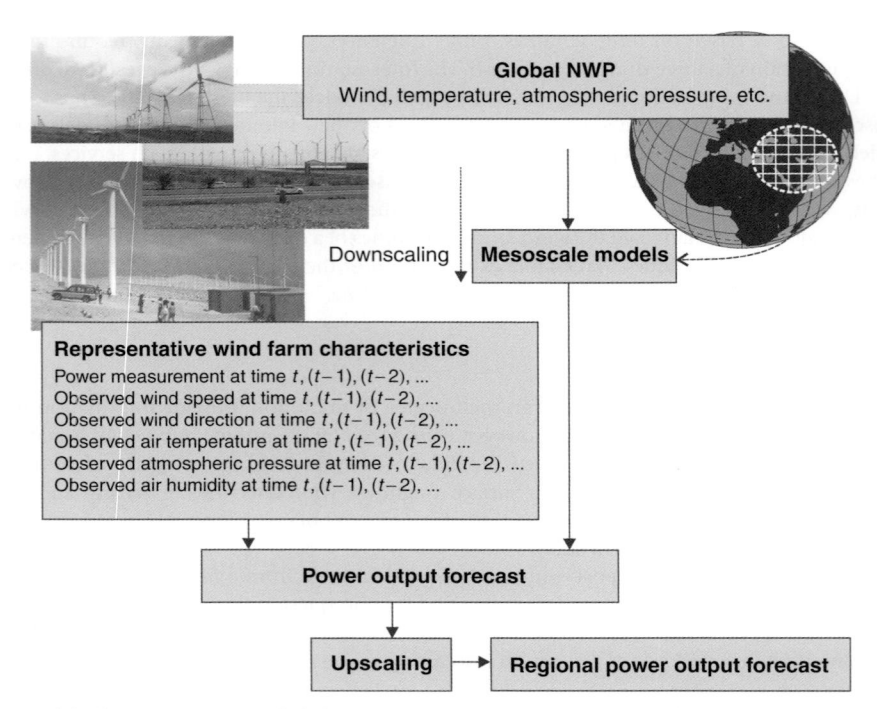

Figure 59 Block diagram of the forecasting process of wind power generation through the use of statistical and data mining methods.

2.18.9.2.1 Statistical models

Among the statistical models used in this field are the ARX time series models, which are autoregressive models with exogenous inputs, and variants of such models.

The ARX techniques used are nonstationary stochastic processes. With these models, the power output of a wind farm is predicted using series of recorded wind speeds and directions and recorded power outputs for periods prior to forecast initiation together with the series of wind speeds and directions as forecast by the NWP models. ARX models depend on trigonometric terms which attempt to model daily wind variations. They also depend on a set of time-varying parameters and a random noise term that need to be estimated.

2.18.9.2.2 Data mining techniques

Artificial neural networks (ANNs) are one of the various data mining techniques used to forecast the power output of a wind farm using meteorological information predicted by NWP models.

ANNs attempt to copy the behavior of biological neural networks. In analogy to the structure of the brain, ANNs consist of single processing units called neurons. In the network structure, the neurons are arranged in layers. Each of the neurons in the input layer receives one of the variables (e.g., wind speed and direction, humidity, temperature, and atmospheric pressure) on which the variables that we wish to forecast depend. The neurons of the output layer return the values of the variables that we wish to forecast (e.g., the power output of the wind farm at subsequent instants). There can also be a series of intermediate layers, called hidden layers. The manner in which the neurons interconnect is known as the connectivity pattern or architecture of the network.

Figure 60 shows an outline of a multilayer neural network. The weights of the connections constitute the network parameters. These parameters are adjusted during the network's 'learning' stage. This learning is undertaken through training with examples. The capacity of the network to resolve the forecasting problem is closely linked to the type of examples which it is given to learn from. The examples enable the network to learn and to generalize the acquired knowledge.

2.18.9.3 Currently Implemented Forecasting Tools

At the present time, a number of different forecasting tools are being used in various countries. Some forecasting tools use only physical methods. These include, among others, Prediktor [219], developed by Risø National Laboratory in Denmark; Previento [220], developed by Oldenburg University in Germany; and eWind®, developed by True Wind Solutions in the United States [221].

Software that makes use of only statistical models has also been developed. These include, among others, the Wind Power Prediction Tool (WPPT) [222], developed by the Department of Informatics and Mathematical Modelling (IMM) of the Danish Technical University (DTU), and SIPREÓLICO [223, 224], currently used by the Spanish TSO (Red Eléctrica). The Advanced Wind Power Prediction Tool (AWPT), developed by ISET (Institut für Solare Energieversorgungstechnik, Kassel) [225], is used by various

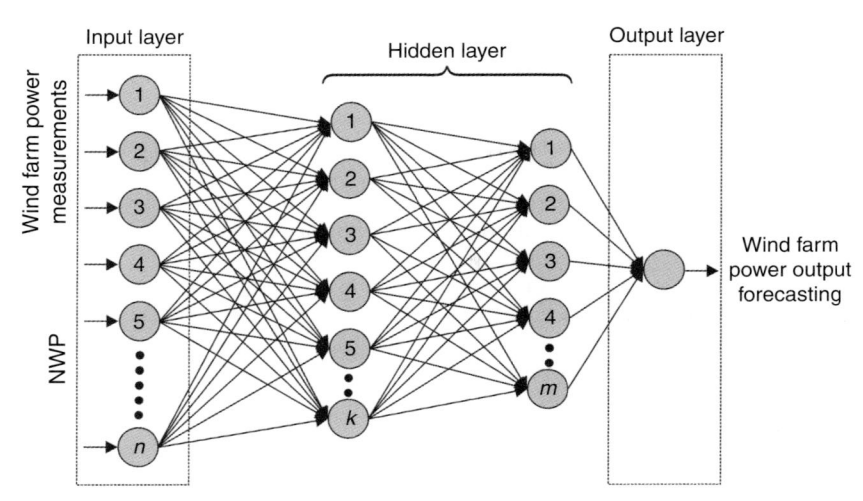

Figure 60 Outline of a multilayer neural network.

German TSOs. AWPT uses ANNs as a prediction model. There is also a prediction system called Zephyr, which combines or mixes physical with statistical models. This model has been developed by Risø National Laboratory and IMM in Denmark [226].

2.18.10 Future Trends

In the past few years, the governing bodies of a number of countries have compiled statistical data on the evolution of the installation of WECSs. The figures that emerge, together with the future scenarios proposed by various associations and official bodies, point clearly to a trend toward greater exploitation of this energy all over the planet. This will entail an onshore expansion in many countries, but for other countries the main source of growth is expected to be offshore.

The installation of wind farms in a marine environment is a relatively recent development, which has given rise to changes in wind technology. Though it has not stood still, technological evolution in offshore wind energy exploitation has not yet reached the same degree of maturity as it has with onshore installations. The coming years will undoubtedly see many innovations in all fields connected with offshore wind energy, including the design of the wind turbines themselves, the structures that support them, and the electrical infrastructure that connects the turbines and transports the energy to the coast.

For several reasons, the electricity production of offshore wind farms will tend more toward aggregation than geographical dispersion. This fact, coupled with the vast quantities of power expected to be installed in these wind farms, may well give rise to major problems of electrical network congestion in EU countries. Such a circumstance will inevitably require, among other measures, an increased interconnection capacity.

Proposals have been made for the creation of a supergrid [8, 94, 227] to take advantage of the high offshore wind energy potential along the European coastlines. It is hoped that this high-voltage underwater transmission supergrid could be an alternative to improving the currently existing onshore transmission network. It is believed that this supergrid would offer greater energy supply security at a lower cost.

The gradual increase in wind energy capacity credit will mean that there will be less conventional generation capacity to cover regulation requirements. It will also mean a greater need for grid code harmonization [94] as the codes begin to impose similar demands on wind technology participation in frequency and voltage control tasks as presently demanded of conventional generation sources.

These demands will lead to the design of wind turbines with more advanced control systems to reduce the mechanical loads of wind turbines and decrease the negative effects that wind energy can have on the operation of the electrical system. This in turn will result in the development of new algorithms and control strategies as well as new power electronic devices and condition-monitoring systems.

A variety of other measures are also being studied with the aim of mitigating the effects of wind energy variability. These include the development of intelligent demand management, improved wind production prediction methods, more efficient energy storage systems, improved and uniform electricity market rules, nondiscrimination in network access, and the installation of intelligent interconnected MGs.

One of the proposals made in the field of intelligent demand management involves network control of certain loads. This refers to the possibility of making changes to the load curves without incurring any negative consequences for the user. Loads with thermal inertia, like refrigerators and freezers, can be dynamically regulated to adapt to the network frequency. This will entail the development and implementation of sophisticated control systems and strategies as well as rules to govern their application.

A key factor to increasing the integration of wind energy with high penetration levels is the degree of accuracy and reliability of wind production forecasting. Tools are presently being developed which improve the prediction results, as in many cases to date the results have not been satisfactory.

The tools must be able to predict rapid changes in global and local meteorological conditions, represent with greater precision the behavior of the wind farms in shutdowns as a result of very high winds, and more accurately represent wind generation for wind farms located on complex terrains.

Given the rapid growth in offshore wind energy exploitation, work will also be needed on developing specific forecasting tools that take into account the peculiarities of the marine environment. Estimation of long-term wind energy availability will also require the development of more sophisticated tools and methods.

Proposals for energy storage are centered around their application in DG systems. However, large-scale hydrogen storage, given its transportability, is a rapidly growing area of research attracting much interest. In the medium term, the electricity sector is taking a close look at the use of the electric vehicle (EV) as a means of energy storage [228, 229]. Fleets of automobiles connected to the electrical network at night could be a way of improving wind energy integration into the system. This would also help in reducing the differences that presently exist between the minimum nighttime demand and the maximum daytime demand.

As for intelligent MGs and the technologies and control and management strategies necessary for their implementation, research is currently under way to resolve these and other pending problems [230]. In this respect, developments have been and continue to be initiated all over the world with the aim of ensuring that MGs, and particularly interconnected MGs, form part of the energy system of the future.

References

[1] Spera DA (1995) *Wind Turbine Technology*, 1st edn. New York: ASME Press.
[2] Golding EW (1980) *The Generation of Electricity by Wind Power*, 5th edn. London: Spon Ltd.
[3] Hau E (2006) *Wind Turbines: Fundamentals, Technologies, Application, Economics*, 2nd edn. New York: Springer.
[4] Gipe P (1995) *Wind Energy Comes of Age*, 1st edn. New York: John Wiley & Sons, Inc.
[5] http://www.ewea.org/fileadmin/ewea_documents/documents/statistics/EWEA_Annual_Statistics_2010.pdf
[6] http://www.wwindea.org/home/images/stories/pdfs/worldwindenergyreport2010_s.pdf
[7] http://www.awea.org/learnabout/publications/upload/Annual_Market_Report_Press_Release_Teaser.pdf
[8] EWEA (2009) *Wind Energy – The Facts*, 1st edn. London: Earthscan.
[9] Ackermann T and Söder L (2000) Wind energy technology and current status: A review. *Renewable and Sustainable Energy Reviews* 4: 315–374.
[10] Herbert GMJ, Iniyan S, Sreevalsan E, and Rajapandian S (2007) A review of wind energy technologies. *Renewable and Sustainable Energy Reviews* 11: 1117–1145.
[11] Bilgili M, Yasar A, and Simsek E (2011) Offshore wind power development in Europe and its comparison with onshore counterpart. *Renewable and Sustainable Energy Reviews* 15: 905–915.
[12] Chowdhury S, Chowdhury SP, and Crossley P (2009) *Microgrids and Active Distribution Networks*, 1st edn. London: IET.
[13] Akorede MF, Hizam HH, and Pouresmaeil E (2010) Distributed energy resources and benefits to the environment. *Renewable and Sustainable Energy Reviews* 14: 724–734.
[14] Karger CR and Hennings W (2009) Sustainability evaluation of decentralized electricity generation. *Renewable and Sustainable Energy Reviews* 13: 583–593.
[15] Amor MB, Lesage P, Pineau PO, and Samson R (2010) Can distributed generation offer substantial benefits in a Northeastern American context? A case study of small-scale renewable technologies using a life cycle methodology. *Renewable and Sustainable Energy Reviews* 14: 2885–2895.
[16] Chicco G and Mancarella P (2009) Distributed multi-generation: A comprehensive view. *Renewable and Sustainable Energy Reviews* 13: 535–551.
[17] Borbely A and Kreider JF (2001) *Distributed Generation: The Power Paradigm for the New Millennium*, 1st edn. Boca Raton, FL: CRC Press.
[18] Willis HL and Scott WG (2000) *Distributed Power Generation: Planning and Evaluation*, 1st edn. New York: CRC Press.
[19] Nigim K (2008) Integration of distributed generation with electrical power system. In: Strzelecki R and Benysek G (eds.) *Power Electronics in Smart Electrical Energy Networks*, pp. 203–228. London: Springer.
[20] Carta JA (2010) Integration of hybrid energy systems into remote micro-grids. In: Kaldellis JK (ed.) *Stand-Alone and Hybrid Wind Energy Systems: Technology, Energy Storage and Applications*, pp. 425–474. Cambridge: Woodhead Publishing Limited.
[21] Jiayi H, Chuannwen J, and Rong X (2008) A review on distributed energy resources and microgrid. *Renewable and Sustainable Energy Reviews* 12: 2472–2483.
[22] Poullikkas A (2007) Implementation of distributed generation technologies in isolated power systems. *Renewable and Sustainable Energy Reviews* 11: 30–56.
[23] Breeze P (2005) *Power Generation Technologies*, 1st edn. Oxford: Newnes.
[24] Katiraei F, Iravani R, Hatziavgyriou N, and Dimeas A (2008) Microgrids management. *IEEE Power & Energy Magazine* 6: 54–65.
[25] Alanne K and Saari A (2004) Sustainable small-scale CHP technologies for buildings: The basis for multi-perspective decision-making. *Renewable and Sustainable Energy Reviews* 8: 401–431.
[26] Kavadias KA (2010) Integration of stand-alone and hybrid wind energy systems into buildings. In: Kaldellis JK (ed.) *Stand-Alone and Hybrid Wind Energy Systems: Technology, Energy Storage and Applications*, pp. 475–505. Cambridge: Woodhead Publishing Limited.
[27] Zafirakis DP (2010) Overview of energy storage technologies for renewable energy systems. In: Kaldellis JK (ed.) *Stand-Alone and Hybrid Wind Energy Systems: Technology, Energy Storage and Applications*, pp. 29–80. Cambridge: Woodhead Publishing Limited.
[28] Ter-Gazarian A (1994) *Energy Storage for Power Systems*, 1st edn. London: Peter Peregrinus Ltd.
[29] Ibrahim H, Ilinca A, and Perron J (2008) Energy storage systems – Characteristics and comparisons. *Renewable and Sustainable Energy Reviews* 12: 1221–1250.
[30] Huggins RA (2010) *Energy Storage*, 1st edn. London: Springer.
[31] Pudjianto D and Strbac G (2006) Investigation of regulatory, commercial, economic and environmental issues in microgrids. *International Journal of Distributed Energy Resources* 2: 245–259.
[32] Kaundinya DP, Balachandra P, and Ravindranath NH (2009) Grid-connected versus stand-alone energy systems for decentralized power – A review of literature. *Renewable and Sustainable Energy Reviews* 13: 2041–2050.
[33] Gómez-Expósito A, Conejo AJ, and Cañizares C (2009) *Electric Energy Systems*, 1st edn. Boca Raton, FL: CRC Press.
[34] Grigsby LL (2007) *Electric Power Generation, Transmission, and Distribution*, 2nd edn. Boca Raton, FL: CRC Press.
[35] Casazza J and Delea F (2010) *Understanding Electric Power Systems: An Overview of Technology, the Marketplace, and Government Regulation*, 2nd edn. New Jersey: Wiley-Blackwell.

[36] Zhang XP (2010) Fundamentals of electric power systems. In: Zhang XP (ed.) *Restructured Electric Power Systems*, pp. 1–52. New Jersey: Wiley.
[37] von Meier A (2006) *Electric Power System: A Conceptual Introduction*, 1st edn. New Jersey: Wiley.
[38] Elgerd OI and van der Puije PD (1998) *Electric Power Engineering*, 2nd edn. New York: Chapman & Hall.
[39] Kaltschmitt M, Streicher W, and Wiese A (2007) *Renewable Energy: Technology, Economics and Environment*, 1st edn. New York: Springer.
[40] Sorensen B (2004) *Renewable Energy*, 3rd edn. Burlington, VT: Elsevier.
[41] Boyle G (2004) *Renewable Energy: Power for a Sustainable Future*, 2nd edn. Oxford: Oxford University Press.
[42] Kiameh P (2003) *Power Generation Handbook*, 1st edn. New York: McGraw-Hill.
[43] Sangster AJ (2010) *Energy for a Warming World*, 1st edn. London: Springer.
[44] Woodruff EB, Lammers HB, and Lammers TF (2005) *Steam Plant Operation*, 8th edn. New York: McGraw-Hill.
[45] Bathie WW (1996) *Fundamentals of Gas Turbines*, 2nd edn. New York: Wiley.
[46] Mahon LLJ (2000) *Diesel Generator Handbook*, 6th edn. Oxford: Butterworth-Heinemann.
[47] Heinloth K (2005) *Energy Technologies: Nuclear Energy*, 1st edn. New York: Springer.
[48] Nuttall WJ (2005) *Nuclear Renaissance: Technologies and Policies for the Future of Nuclear Power*, 1st edn. New York: Taylor & Francis.
[49] Wood J (2006) *Nuclear Power*, 1st edn. London: IET.
[50] Hewitt GF and Collier JG (2000) *Introduction to Nuclear Power*, 2nd edn. New York: Taylor & Francis.
[51] Hore-Lacy I (2006) *Nuclear Energy in the 21st Century*, 8th edn. London: Academic Press.
[52] http://www.ree.es
[53] McDonald JD (2007) *Electric Power Substations Engineering*, 2nd edn. New York: CRC Press.
[54] Eto J and Moezzi M (1997) Metered residential cooling loads: Comparison of three models. *IEEE Transactions on Power Systems* 12: 858–868.
[55] Affonso CM and da Silva LCP (2010) Potential benefits of implementing load management to improve power system security. *International Journal of Electrical Power & Energy Systems* 32: 704–710.
[56] Moura PS and de Almeida AT (2010) The role of demand-side management in the grid integration of wind power. *Applied Energy* 87: 2581–2588.
[57] Strbac G (2008) Demand side management: Benefits and challenges. *Energy Policy* 36: 4419–4426.
[58] Rozakis S, Sldatos PG, Papadakis G, and Kyritsis S (1997) Evaluation of an integral renewable energy system for electricity generation in rural areas. *Energy Policy* 25: 337–347.
[59] Veza JM, Peñate B, and Castellano F (2004) Electrodialysis desalination designed for off-grid wind energy. *Desalination* 160: 211–221.
[60] Carta JA, González J, and Subiela V (2003) Operational analysis of an innovative wind powered reverse osmosis system installed in the Canary Islands. *Solar Energy* 75: 153–168.
[61] Yang HT, Huang CM, and Huang CL (1996) Identification of ARMAX model for short load forecasting: An evolutionary programming approach. *IEEE Transactions on Power Systems* 11: 403–408.
[62] Song YH and Wang XF (2003) *Operation of Market-Oriented Power Systems*, 1st edn. London: Springer.
[63] Steinherz H, Pedreira CE, and Castro R (2001) Neural networks for short-term loads forecasting: A review and evaluation. *IEEE Transactions on Power Systems* 16: 44–45.
[64] Wood AJ and Wollenberg BF (1996) *Power Generation, Operation and Control*, 2nd edn. New York: Wiley.
[65] Bergen AR and Vittal V (2000) *Power Systems Analysis*, 2nd edn. New Jersey: Prentice Hall.
[66] Fink LH and Carlsen K (1978) Operating under stress and strain. *IEEE Spectrum* 15: 48–53.
[67] Dy Liacco TE (1974) Real-time computer control of power systems. *Proceedings of the IEEE* 62: 884–891.
[68] Elgerd OI (1985) *Electric Energy Systems Theory: An Introduction*, 2nd edn. New York: McGraw-Hill.
[69] https://www.entsoe.eu/the-association/history/ucte/
[70] Ili M and Zaborszky J (2000) *Dynamics and Control of Large Electric Power Systems*, 1st edn. New York: Wiley.
[71] Kundur P (1994) *Power System Stability*, 1st edn. New York: McGraw-Hill.
[72] Song YH and Johns AT (1999) *Flexible A.C. Transmission Systems (FACTS)*, 1st edn. London: IET.
[73] Hingorani NG and Gyugyi L (2000) *Understanding FACTS: Concepts and Technology of Flexible AC Transmission Systems*, 1st edn. New York: IEEE Press.
[74] Zhang XP, Rehtanz C, and Pal B (2006) *Flexible AC Transmission Systems: Modelling and Control*, 1st edn. New York: Springer.
[75] Acha E, Fuerte-Esquivel CR, Ambriz-Pérez H, and Ángeles-Camacho C (2004) *FACTS: Modelling and Simulation in Power Networks*, 1st edn. Chichester, UK: Wiley.
[76] Mathur RM and Varma RK (2002) *Thyristor-Based FACTS Controllers for Electrical Transmission Systems*, 1st edn. New York: IEEE Press.
[77] Lagonotte P, Sabonnadière J, Léost J, and Paul J (1989) Structural analysis of the electrical system: Application to the secondary control in France. *IEEE Transactions on Power Systems* 4: 479–484.
[78] Conejo AJ and Aguilar MJ (1998) Secondary voltage control: Nonlinear selection of pilot buses, design of an optimal control law, and simulation results. *Generation, Transmission and Distribution, IEE Proceedings* 145: 77–81.
[79] Hidy GM (1967) *The Winds*, 1st edn. New York: Van Nostrand Company, Inc.
[80] Aspliden CI, Elliot DL, and Wendell LL (1986) Resource assessment methods, siting, and performance evaluation. In: Guzzi R and Justus CG (eds.) *Physical Climatology for Solar and Wind Energy*, pp. 321–376. Singapore: World Scientific.
[81] Barry RG and Chorley RJ (2009) *Atmosphere, Weather and Climate*, 9th edn. New York: Routledge.
[82] Heier S (2006) *Grid Integration of Wind Energy Conversion Systems*, 2nd edn. Chichester, UK: Wiley.
[83] Knudsen H and Nielsen N (2009) Introduction to the modeling of wind turbines. In: Ackermann T (ed.) *Wind Power in Power Systems*, pp. 525–554. Chichester, UK: Wiley.
[84] Slootweg JG, Polinder H, and Kling WL (2009) Reduced-order modeling of wind turbines. In: Ackermann T (ed.) *Wind Power in Power Systems*, pp. 555–584. Chichester, UK: Wiley.
[85] Carta JA and Mentado D (2007) A continuous bivariate model for wind power density and wind turbine energy output estimations. *Energy Conversion and Management* 48: 420–432.
[86] Hansen AD (2009) Generators and power electronics for wind turbines. In: Ackermann T (ed.) *Wind Power in Power Systems*, pp. 53–78. Chichester, UK: Wiley.
[87] Fox B, Flynn D, Bryans L, et al. (2007) *Wind Power Integration*, 1st edn. London: IET.
[88] Naya-Lara O, Jenkins N, Ekanayake J, et al. (2009) *Wind Energy Generation*, 1st edn. Chichester, UK: Wiley.
[89] van der Hoven I (1957) Power spectrum of horizontal wind speed in the frequency range from 0.0007 to 900 cycles per hour. *Journal of Meteorology* 14: 160–164.
[90] Burton T, Sharpe D, Jenkins N, and Bossanyi E (2001) *Wind Energy Handbook*, 1st edn. Chichester, UK: Wiley.
[91] Freris LL (1990) *Wind Energy Conversion Systems*, 1st edn. Cambridge: Prentice Hall.
[92] Bianchi F, De Battista H, and Mantz RJ (2007) *Wind Turbine Control Systems*, 1st edn. London: Springer.
[93] Söder L and Ackermann T (2009) Wind power in power systems: An introduction. In: Ackermann T (ed.) *Wind Power in Power Systems*, pp. 25–51. Chichester, UK: Wiley.
[94] Freris L and Infield D (2009) *Renewable Energy in Power Systems*, 1st edn. Chichester, UK: Wiley.
[95] Milborrow D (2009) Wind power on the grid. In: Boyle G (ed.) *Renewable Electricity and the Grid*, pp. 31–54. London: Earthscan.
[96] Manwell JF, Mcgowan JG, and Rogers AL (2009) *Wind Energy Explained*, 2nd edn. Chichester, UK: Wiley.
[97] Reid SJ and Turner R (2001) Correlation of real and model wind speeds in different terrains. *Weather and Forecasting* 16: 620–627.
[98] Justus CG, Mani K, and Mikhail AS (1979) Interannual and month-to-month variations of wind speed. *Journal of Applied Meteorology* 18: 913–920.
[99] Justus CG (1978) *Winds and Wind System Performance*, 1st edn. Philadelphia, PA: Franklin Institute Press.
[100] Giebel G (2007) A variance analysis of the capacity displaced by wind energy in Europe. *Wind Energy* 10: 69–79.
[101] Hasche B (2010) General statistics of geographically dispersed wind power. *Wind Energy* 13: 773–784.

[102] Dugan R, McGranaghan M, and Beaty H (1996) *Electrical Power Systems Quality*, 1st edn. New York: McGraw-Hill.
[103] Vedam RS and Sarma MS (2009) *Power Quality: Var Compensation in Power Systems*, 1st edn. Boca Raton, FL: CRC Press.
[104] Schalabbach J, Blime D, and Stephanblome T (2000) *Voltage Quality in Electrical Power Systems*, 2nd edn. London: IET.
[105] Rose JD and Hiskens IA (2007) Challenges of integrating large amounts of wind power. In: IEEE (ed.) *Proceedings of the 1st Annual 2007 IEEE Systems Conference*, pp. 1–7. Honolulu, HI: IEEE.
[106] Eriksen P, Ackermann T, Abildgaard H, et al. (2005) System operation with high wind penetration. *IEEE Power & Energy Magazine* 3: 65–74.
[107] Larsson Å (2009) Practical experience with wind power quality and wind power. In: Ackermann T (ed.) *Wind Power in Power Systems*, pp. 349–364. Chichester, UK: Wiley.
[108] Lubosny Z (2003) *Wind Turbine Operation in Electric Power Systems*, 1st edn. Berlin: Springer.
[109] Hanzelka Z, Kempski A, and Smolenski R (2008) Quality problems in smart networks. In: Strzelecki R and Benysek G (eds.) *Power Electronics in Smart Electrical Energy Networks*, pp. 107–146. London: Springer.
[110] Larsson A (2002) Flicker emission of wind turbines during continuous operation. *IEEE Transactions on Energy Conversion* 17: 114–118.
[111] Larsson A (2002) Flicker emission of wind turbines caused by switching operations. *IEEE Transactions on Energy Conversion* 17: 119–123.
[112] Sun T, Chen Z, and Blaabjerg F (2005) Flicker study on variable speed wind turbines with doubly fed induction generators. *IEEE Transactions on Energy Conversion* 20: 896–905.
[113] Hu W, Chen Z, Wang Y, and Wang Z (2009) Flicker mitigation by active power control of variable-speed wind turbines with full-scale back-to-back power converters. *IEEE Transactions on Energy Conversion* 24: 640–649.
[114] Thiringer T, Petru T, and Lundberg S (2004) Flicker contribution from wind turbine installations. *IEEE Transactions on Energy Conversion* 19: 157–163.
[115] Wang H, Wang W, and Bin L (2010) Application of individual pitch controller for flicker reduction on variable speed wind turbines. In: IEEE (ed.) *Proceedings of the 2010 Asia-Pacific Power and Energy Engineering Conference*, pp. 1–4. Chengdu, China: IEEE.
[116] Eskander MN and Amer SI (2009) Mitigation of voltage dips and swells in grid-connected wind energy conversion systems. In: IEEE (ed.) *Proceedings of the ICROS-SICE International Joint Conference 2009*, pp. 885–890. Fukuoka, Japan: IEEE.
[117] Choi SS, Li JD, and Vilathgamuwa DM (2005) A generalized voltage compensation strategy for mitigating the impacts of voltage sags/swells. *IEEE Transactions on Power Delivery* 20: 2289–2297.
[118] Herrera JI, Reddoch TW, and Lawler JS (1988) Harmonics generated by two variable speed wind generating systems. *IEEE Transactions on Energy Conversion* 3: 267–273.
[119] Salameh ZM and Kazda LF (1987) Analysis of the double output induction generator using direct three-phase model: Part II – Harmonic analysis. *IEEE Transactions on Energy Conversion* EC-2: 182–188.
[120] Papathanassiou SA and Papadopoulos MP (2006) Harmonic analysis in a power system with wind generation. *IEEE Transactions on Power Delivery* 21: 2006–2016.
[121] Chen Z and Spooner E (2001) Grid power quality with variable speed wind turbines. *IEEE Transactions on Energy Conversion* 16: 148–154.
[122] Todeschini G and Emanuel AE (2010) Wind energy conversion systems as active filters: Design and comparison of three control methods. *IET Renewable Power Generation* 4: 341–353.
[123] Holttinen H and Hirvonen R (2009) Power system requirements for wind power. In: Ackermann T (ed.) *Wind Power in Power Systems*, pp. 143–167. Chichester, UK: Wiley.
[124] Dragoon K (2010) *Valuing Wind Generation on Integrated Power Systems*, 1st edn. Oxford: Elsevier.
[125] Billinton R and Chowdhury AA (1992) Incorporation of wind energy conversion systems in conventional generating capacity adequacy assessment. *Generation, Transmission and Distribution, IEE Proceedings* 139: 47–57.
[126] Ackermann T and Morthorst PE (2009) Economic aspects of wind power in power systems. In: Ackermann T (ed.) *Wind Power in Power Systems*, pp. 382–410. Chichester, UK: Wiley.
[127] Gross R, Heptonstall P, Leach M, et al. (2009) The UK energy research centre review of the costs and impacts of intermittency. In: Boyle G (ed.) *Renewable Electricity and the Grid*, pp. 73–93. London: Earthscan.
[128] Black M and Strbac G (2006) Value of storage in providing balancing services for electricity generation systems with high wind penetration. *Journal of Power Sources* 162: 949–953.
[129] Black M and Strbac G (2007) Value of bulk energy storage for managing wind power fluctuations. *IEEE Transactions on Energy Conversion* 22: 197–205.
[130] Barton JP and Infield DG (2004) Energy storage and its use with intermittent renewable energy. *IEEE Transactions on Energy Conversion* 19: 441–448.
[131] Loisel R, Mercier A, Gatzen C, et al. (2010) Valuation framework for large scale electricity storage in a case with wind curtailment. *Energy Policy* 38: 7323–7337.
[132] Lu MS and Lee WJ (2009) Combining the wind power generation system with energy storage equipment. *IEEE Transactions on Industry Applications* 45: 2109–2115.
[133] Bueno C and Carta JA (2005) Technical–economic analysis of wind-powered pumped hydrostorage systems: Part II – Model application to the island of El Hierro. *Solar Energy* 78: 396–405.
[134] Bueno C and Carta JA (2006) Wind powered pumped hydro storage systems, a means of increasing the penetration of renewable energy in the Canary Islands. *Renewable and Sustainable Energy Reviews* 10: 312–340.
[135] Kaldellis JK, Zafirakis D, and Kondili E (2010) Optimum sizing of photovoltaic-energy storage systems for autonomous small islands. *International Journal of Electrical Power & Energy Systems* 32: 24–36.
[136] Kaldellis JK, Zafirakis D, Kaldelli EL, and Kavadias K (2009) Cost benefit analysis of a photovoltaic-energy storage electrification solution for remote islands. *Renewable Energy* 34: 1299–1311.
[137] Kaldellis JK and Zafirakis D (2007) Optimum energy storage techniques for the improvement of renewable energy sources-based electricity generation economic efficiency. *Energy* 32: 2295–2305.
[138] Molina MG and Mercado PE (2010) Stabilization and control of tie-line power flow of microgrid including wind generation by distributed energy storage. *International Journal of Hydrogen Energy* 35: 5827–5833.
[139] McDowall J (2006) Integrating energy storage with wind power in weak electricity grids. *Journal of Power Sources* 162: 959–964.
[140] Swift-Hook DT and Ter-Gazarian AG (1994) The value of storage on power systems with intermittent energy sources. *Renewable Energy* 5: 1479–1482.
[141] Sørensen B (2007) *Renewable Energy Conversion, Transmission, and Storage*, 1st edn. Oxford: Academic Press.
[142] Boucher R and Rodzianko P (1994) Advanced pumped storage: The new competitive edge. *The Electricity Journal* 7: 48–53.
[143] Kapsali M and Kaldellis JK (2010) Combining hydro and variable wind power generation by means of pumped-storage under economically viable terms. *Applied Energy* 87: 3475–3485.
[144] Crampes C and Moreaux M (2010) Pumped storage and cost saving. *Energy Economics* 32: 325–333.
[145] Kanakasabapathy P and Swarup KS (2010) Bidding strategy for pumped-storage plant in pool-based electricity market. *Energy Conversion and Management* 51: 572–579.
[146] Lund H and Salgi G (2009) The role of compressed air energy storage (CAES) in future sustainable energy systems. *Energy Conversion and Management* 50: 1172–1179.
[147] Cavallo A (2007) Controllable and affordable utility-scale electricity from intermittent wind resources and compressed air energy storage (CAES). *Energy* 32: 120–127.
[148] Pickard WF, Hansing NJ, and Shen AQ (2009) Can large-scale advanced-adiabatic compressed air energy storage be justified economically in an age of sustainable energy? *Journal of Renewable and Sustainable Energy* 1: 1–10.
[149] Denholm P and Sioshansi R (2009) The value of compressed air energy storage with wind in transmission-constrained electric power systems. *Energy Policy* 37: 3149–3158.
[150] Salgi G and Lund H (2008) System behaviour of compressed-air energy-storage in Denmark with a high penetration of renewable energy sources. *Applied Energy* 85: 182–189.
[151] Deane JP, O'Gallacho BP, and McKeogh EJ (2010) Techno-economic review of existing and new pumped hydro energy storage plant. *Renewable and Sustainable Energy Reviews* 14: 1293–1302.

[152] Chabot B (2000) A long term wind power prospect from hydropower retrospect and prospect: Scenarios and lessons. In: WIP (ed.) *Proceedings of Wind Power for the 21st Century*, pp. 19–22. Kassel, Germany: EUWEC.
[153] Eldridge FR (1980) *Wind Machines*, 2nd edn. New York: Van Nostrand Reinhold.
[154] Somerville WM (1989) Wind turbine and pumped hydro generation on Foula. In: EWEC (ed.) *Proceedings of the European Wind Energy Conference*, pp. 713–171. Glasgow, UK: Peregrinus on behalf of the Institution of Electrical Engineers.
[155] Hiratsuka A, Arai T, and Yoshimura T (1993) Seawater pumped-storage power plant in Okinawa island, Japan. *Engineering Geology* 35: 237–246.
[156] Caralis G, Rados K, and Zervos A (2010) On the market of wind with hydro-pumped storage systems in autonomous Greek islands. *Renewable and Sustainable Energy Reviews* 14: 2221–2226.
[157] Katsaprakakis DA, Christakis DG, Papantonis AD, and Voutsinas S (2008) Pumped storage systems introduction in isolated power production systems. *Renewable Energy* 33: 467–490.
[158] Kaldellis JK, Kapsali M, and Kavadias KA (2010) Energy balance analysis of wind-based pumped hydro storage systems in remote island electrical networks. *Applied Energy* 87: 2427–2437.
[159] Biczel P (2008) Energy storage systems. In: Strzelecki R and Benysek G (eds.) *Power Electronics in Smart Electrical Energy Networks*, pp. 269–302. London: Springer.
[160] Farmer ED, Newman VG, and Ashmole PH (1980) Economic and operational implications of a complex of wind-driven power generators on a power system. *IEE Proceedings A* 127: 289–295.
[161] Karki R (2007) Renewable energy credit driven wind power growth for system reliability. *Electric Power Systems Research* 77: 797–803.
[162] van Wijk AJM, Halberg N, and Turkenburg WC (1992) Capacity credit of wind power in the Netherlands. *Electric Power Systems Research* 23: 189–200.
[163] Milligan M and Porter K (2006) The capacity value of wind in the United States: Methods and implementation. *The Electricity Journal* 19: 91–99.
[164] Hiester TR and Pennell WT (1981) *The Siting Handbook for Large Wind Energy Systems*, 1st edn. New York: Windbooks.
[165] Jain P (2010) *Wind Energy Engineering*, 1st edn. New York: McGraw-Hill.
[166] Manwell JF, Elkintona CN, Rogers AL, and McGowan JG (2007) Review of design conditions applicable to offshore wind energy systems in the United States. *Renewable and Sustainable Energy Reviews* 11: 210–234.
[167] Mostafaeipour A (2010) Feasibility study of offshore wind turbine installation in Iran compared with the world. *Renewable and Sustainable Energy Reviews* 14: 1722–1743.
[168] Zhixin W, Chuanwen J, Qian A, and Chengmin W (2009) The key technology of offshore wind farm and its new development in China. *Renewable and Sustainable Energy Reviews* 13: 216–222.
[169] Rajgor G (2010) China gets serious on offshore wind. *Renewable Energy Focus* 11: 16–19.
[170] Matevosyan J (2009) Wind power in areas with limited transmission capacity. In: Ackermann T (ed.) *Wind Power in Power Systems*, pp. 433–459. Chichester, UK: Wiley.
[171] Arrillaga J, Liu YH, and Watson NR (2007) *Flexible Power Transmission*, 1st edn. Chichester, UK: Wiley.
[172] Kim CK, Sood VK, Jang GS, et al. (2009) *HVDC Transmission: Power Conversion Applications in Power Systems*, 1st edn. Singapore: Wiley.
[173] http://www.wind-integration.eu/downloads/library/EWIS_Standalone_Executive_Summary.pdf
[174] http://www.trade-wind.eu/fileadmin/documents/publications/Final_Report.pdf
[175] Volker T, Mehler C, Raffel H, and Orlik B (2008) New HVDC-Concept for power transmission from offshore wind farms. In: *Wind Power to the Grid – EPE Wind Energy Chapter, 1st Seminar. EPE-WECS 2008*. Delft, The Netherlands, 25 April.
[176] Martinez de Alegría I, Martín JL, Kortabarria I, et al. (2009) Transmission alternatives for offshore electrical power. *Renewable and Sustainable Energy Reviews* 13: 1027–1038.
[177] Gomis-Bellmunt O, Liang J, Ekanayake J, et al. (2011) Topologies of multiterminal HVDC-VSC transmission for large offshore wind farms. *Electric Power Systems Research* 81: 271–281.
[178] Gomis-Bellmunt O, Liang J, Ekanayake J, and Jenkins N (2011) Voltage–current characteristics of multiterminal HVDC-VSC for offshore wind farms. *Electric Power Systems Research* 81: 440–450.
[179] Negra NB, Todorovic J, and Ackermann T (2006) Loss evaluation of HVAC and HVDC transmission solutions for large offshore wind farms. *Electric Power Systems Research* 76: 916–927.
[180] Jovcic D and Strachan N (2009) Offshore wind farm with centralised power conversion and DC interconnection. *Generation, Transmission and Distribution, IET* 3: 586–595.
[181] Kirby NM, Lie X, Luckett M, and Siepmann W (2002) HVDC transmission for a large offshore wind farms. *Power Engineering Journal* 16: 135–141.
[182] Ackermann T (2009) Transmission systems for offshore wind farms. In: Ackermann T (ed.) *Wind Power in Power Systems*, pp. 479–503. Chichester, UK: Wiley.
[183] Hammons TJ, Woodford D, Loughtan J, et al. (2000) Role of HVDC transmission in future energy development. *IEEE Power Engineering Review* 20: 10–25.
[184] Qin N, You S, Xu Z, and Akhmatov V (2009) Offshore wind farm connection with low frequency AC transmission technology. In: IEEE (ed.) *IEEE Power & Energy Society General Meeting*, pp. 1–8. Calgary, Canada: IEEE.
[185] Macken KJP, Driesen JLJ, and Belmans RJM (2001) A DC bus system for connecting offshore wind turbines with the utility system. In: Helm P and Zervos A (eds.) *2001 European Wind Energy Conference*, pp. 1030–1035. Copenhagen, Denmark: WIP – Renewable Energies.
[186] Weixing L and Boon-Teck O (2003) Optimal acquisition and aggregation of offshore wind power by multiterminal voltage-source HVDC. *IEEE Transactions on Power Delivery* 18: 201–206.
[187] Jovcic D (2008) Offshore wind farm with a series multiterminal CSI HVDC. *Electric Power Systems Research* 78: 747–755.
[188] Xu L and Andersen BR (2006) Grid connection of large offshore wind farms using HVDC. *Wind Energy* 9: 371–382.
[189] Mathur J, Agarwal N, Swaroop R, and Shah N (2008) Economics of producing hydrogen as transportation fuel using offshore wind energy systems. *Energy Policy* 36: 1212–1222.
[190] http://powerplants.vattenfall.com/powerplant/horns-rev
[191] Worzyk T (2009) *Submarine Power Cables*, 1st edn. New York: Springer.
[192] Eriksson E, Halvarsson P, Wensky D, and Hausler M (2003) System approach on designing an offshore windpower grid connection. http://library.abb.com
[193] http://www.energy.siemans.com/hq/pool/hq/power-transmission/HVDC/HVDC_Plus_Basic%20and%20Principals.pdf
[194] http://www.abb.com/hvdc.
[195] Lidula NWA and Rajapakse AD (2011) Microgrids research: A review of experimental microgrids and test systems. *Renewable and Sustainable Energy Reviews* 15: 186–202.
[196] Chowdhury SP, Chowdhury S, and Crossley PA (2009) Islanding protection of active distribution networks with renewable distributed generators: A comprehensive survey. *Electric Power Systems Research* 79: 984–992.
[197] McGowan JG, Manwell JF, and Connors SR (1988) Wind/diesel energy systems: Review of design options and recent developments. *Solar Energy* 41: 561–575.
[198] Hunter R and Elliot G (1994) *Wind–Diesel Systems*, 1st edn. New York: Cambridge University Press.
[199] Carta JA and González J (2001) Self-sufficient energy supply for isolated communities: Wind–diesel systems in the Canary Islands. *The Energy Journal* 22: 115–139.
[200] Carta JA, González J, and Gómez C (2003) Operating results of a wind–diesel system which supplies the full energy needs of an isolated village community in the Canary Islands. *Solar Energy* 74: 53–63.
[201] Agrawal A, Wies R, and Johnson R (2007) *Hybrid Electric Power Systems: Modeling, Optimization and Control*, 1st edn. Saarbrücken: VMD.
[202] Mohamed YAI (2009) *New Control Algorithms for the Distributed Generation Interface: Plug-and-Play Integration and Robust Operation in Grid-Connected and Microgrid Modes*, 1st edn. Saarbrücken: VMD.
[203] Zamora R and Srivastava AK (2010) Controls for microgrids with storage: Review, challenges, and research needs. *Renewable and Sustainable Energy Reviews* 14: 2009–2018.
[204] Logenthiran T, Srinivasan D, and Khambadkone AM (2011) Multi-agent system for energy resource scheduling of integrated microgrids in a distributed system. *Electric Power Systems Research* 81: 138–148.

[205] Asmus P (2010) Microgrids, virtual power plants and our distributed energy future. *The Electricity Journal* 10: 72–82.
[206] Mashhour E and Moghaddas-Tafreshi SM (2010) Integration of distributed energy resources into low voltage grid: A market-based multiperiod optimization model. *Electric Power Systems Research* 80: 473–480.
[207] Porter K, Yen-Nakafuji D, and Morgenstern BA (2007) Review of the international experience with integrating wind energy generation. *The Electricity Journal* 20: 48–59.
[208] Hiroux C and Saguan M (2010) Large-scale wind power in European electricity markets: Time for revisiting support schemes and market designs? *Energy Policy* 38: 3135–3145.
[209] Weber C (2010) Adequate intraday market design to enable the integration of wind energy into the European power systems. *Energy Policy* 38: 3155–3163.
[210] Vandezande L, Meeus L, Belmans R, et al. (2010) Well-functioning balancing markets: A prerequisite for wind power integration. *Energy Policy* 38: 3146–3154.
[211] Singh B and Singh SN (2009) Wind power interconnection into the power system: A review of grid code requirements. *The Electricity Journal* 22: 54–63.
[212] Martinez de Alegría I, Andreu J, Martín JL, et al. (2007) Connection requirements for wind farms: A survey on technical requirements and regulation. *Renewable and Sustainable Energy Reviews* 11: 1858–1872.
[213] Lange B, Robrig K, Schlögl F, et al. (2009) Wind power forecasting. In: Boyle G (ed.) *Renewable Electricity and the Grid*, pp. 95–120. London: Earthscan.
[214] Ernst B (2009) Wind power forecast for the German and Danish networks. In: Ackermann T (ed.) *Wind Power in Power Systems*, pp. 365–381. Chichester, UK: Wiley.
[215] Lange M and Focken U (2005) *Physical Approach to Short-Term Wind Power Prediction*, 1st edn. New York: Springer.
[216] Costa A, Crespo A, Navarro J, et al. (2008) A review on the young history of the wind power short-term prediction. *Renewable and Sustainable Energy Reviews* 12: 1725–1744.
[217] Lei M, Shiyan L, Chuanwen J, et al. (2009) A review on the forecasting of wind speed and generated power. *Renewable and Sustainable Energy Reviews* 13: 915–920.
[218] Marciukaitis M, Katinas V, and Kavaliauskas A (2008) Wind power usage and prediction prospects in Lithuania. *Renewable and Sustainable Energy Reviews* 12: 265–277.
[219] http://www.prediktor.dk.
[220] http://energymeteo.com/media/PrevientoENG.pdf
[221] http://www.awstruepower.com/solutions/products/forecasting-grid-integration/ewind-forecasting-service/
[222] http://www.enfor.dk/wind_power_prediction_tool_wppt.php
[223] Sánchez I (2006) Short-term prediction of wind energy production. *International Journal of Forecasting* 22: 43–56.
[224] Usaola J and Castronuovo ED (2009) *Wind Energy in Electricity Markets with High Wind Penetration*, 1st edn. New York: Nova Science Publishers.
[225] http://www.iset.uni-kassel.de/dispower_static/documents/del53.pdf
[226] http://www.risoe.dtu.dk/job_career/student_projects/vea-5.aspx?sc_lang=en
[227] Hertem DV and Ghandhari M (2010) Multi-terminal VSC HVDC for the European supergrid: Obstacles. *Renewable and Sustainable Energy Reviews* 14: 3156–3163.
[228] Andersen PH, Mathews JA, and Rask M (2009) Integrating private transport into renewable energy policy: The strategy of creating intelligent recharging grids for electric vehicles. *Energy Policy* 37: 2481–2486.
[229] Kiviluoma J and Meibom P (2010) Influence of wind power, plug-in electric vehicles, and heat storages on power system investments. *Energy* 35: 1244–1255.
[230] Coll-Mayor D, Paget M, and Lightner E (2007) Future intelligent power grids: Analysis of the vision in the European Union and the United States. *Energy Policy* 35: 2453–2465.

Further Reading

[1] Ackermann T (2005) *Wind Power in Power Systems*, 1st edn. Chichester, UK: Wiley.
[2] Kaldellis JK (2010) *Stand-Alone and Hybrid Wind Energy Systems*, 1st edn. Oxford: Woodhead Publishing Limited.
[3] Boyle G (2009) *Renewable Electricity and the Grid*, 1st edn. London: Earthscan.
[4] Leão RPS, Antunes FLM, Lourenço TGM, and Andrade KRA, Jr. (2009) Comprehensive overview on wind power integration to the power grid. *IEEE Latin America Transactions* 7: 620–629.
[5] Belyaev LS (2010) *Electricity Market Reforms: Economics and Policy Challenges*, 1st edn. New York: Springer.

Relevant Websites

http://www.nrel.gov – National Renewable Energy Laboratory.
http://www.windenergy.org.nz – New Zealand Wind Energy Association.
http://www.norsewind.eu – NORSEWInD.
http://www.offshoregrid.eu – OffshoreGrid.
http://www.wind-energy-the-facts.org – Wind Energy: The Facts.
http://www.windspeed.eu – Windspeed.

2.19 Stand-Alone, Hybrid Systems

KA Kavadias, Technological Education Institute of Piraeus, Athens, Greece

© 2012 Elsevier Ltd. All rights reserved.

2.19.1	Introduction	623
2.19.2	Historical Development of Wind Stand-Alone Energy Systems	624
2.19.3	Contribution of Wind in Stand-Alone Energy Systems	626
2.19.4	System Configuration	629
2.19.4.1	Wind Turbine Generator	631
2.19.4.2	Storage System Unit	632
2.19.4.3	Complementary Electric Generator Unit	632
2.19.4.4	Auxiliary Electronic Equipment	632
2.19.5	Stand-Alone Hybrid Systems Configurations	632
2.19.5.1	Stand-Alone Wind Power Systems	633
2.19.5.2	Stand-Alone Wind–Diesel Power Systems	636
2.19.5.3	Stand-Alone Wind–Photovoltaic Power Systems	638
2.19.5.4	Stand-Alone Wind–Hydro Power Systems	643
2.19.5.5	Stand-Alone Wind–Hydrogen Power Systems	645
2.19.6	Energy Storage in Wind Stand-Alone Energy Systems	647
2.19.6.1	Design Parameters of Energy Storage Systems	649
2.19.6.2	Short Description of Energy Storage Technologies	649
2.19.7	Design, Simulation, and Evaluation Software Tools for Wind-Based Hybrid Energy Systems	651
References		653
Further Reading		655

Glossary

Hybrid power system A power system which uses multiple generation sources by incorporating different components such as generators, storage medium, power conditioning and system control in order to supply power to a remote consumer.

Loss of load hours (LOLH) Power reliability factor indicating the number of load failures in which the load demand exceeds the power supply on hourly based simulations.

Loss of load probability (LOLP) Power reliability factor indicating the probability that instantaneous power demand will exceed the respective power supply for the time period analyzed.

Loss of power supply probability (LOPSP) Power reliability factor indicating the probability of insufficient power supply for a given period of time.

Stand alone energy system An electricity system which operates independently of the electricity transmission and distribution network or is not connected to it at all.

2.19.1 Introduction

Energy is indispensable for sustainable development and poverty reduction. At present, there are 1.6 billion people in the world, mostly in rural areas, who have no access to electricity. Another 2.5 billion people still rely on traditional fuels such as wood, dung, and agricultural residues to meet their daily heating and cooking needs, this, however, having serious impacts on the local environment and on people's health [1, 2]. Apart from the Third World and many of the developing countries that face serious problems of insufficient electrical network infrastructure, isolated electricity consumers who lack direct access to electrical networks and have limited political influence may be encountered in many regions of the developed countries as well. In this context, stand-alone wind power systems, which have already been in use for hundreds of years, have proven to be a reliable and environmentally friendly technological solution for the electrification of remote consumers in areas with moderate or high wind potential.

Stand-alone electrical energy systems constitute the first applications of the implementation of renewable energy sources (RES). The first attempts at generating electricity from wind energy were directed toward providing energy independently in remote areas where there was no connection to the grid [3]. By using a small wind turbine of only a few hundreds of watts and a storage medium, it was possible to cover the modest needs of electrical energy (in most cases lighting). Since then, the term 'stand-alone' has defined an electricity system that operates independently of the electricity transmission and distribution network or is not connected to it at all. The aim of such systems is to meet load demand in a direct way, keeping power generation and consumption as close as possible. In recent years, the term 'stand-alone' has mainly been used to describe power systems of up to tens of kilowatts, which mainly refer to domestic wind systems [4].

Further, hybrid power systems suggest a concept the roots of which can be traced back many years, describing a power system that uses multiple generation sources by incorporating different components such as generators, storage medium, power conditioning, and system control in order to supply power to remote communities [5]. Wind hybrid power systems usually combine two or more forms of energy, resulting in a more efficient system overall. In the basic form of wind hybrid systems, a wind turbine is combined with a small diesel engine (hybrid stand-alone system), or is connected to the local diesel power station as in the case of isolated power stations (autonomous hybrid system) such as in remote islands. Contemporary small-scale wind hybrid energy systems are stand-alone systems which usually comprise a wind turbine, and a photovoltaic (PV) generator and the corresponding energy storage system. In a stand-alone installation that consists only of a wind power energy system, on a short-term basis the wind turbine energy production should meet the power demand of the consumer. Therefore, at any given moment there must be a balance between the energy production of the wind turbine and the respective load demand. In order to attain power balance, either the wind turbine should be controlled accordingly or the power consumption should be adapted to the output of the wind turbine. Hybrid energy systems are used in order to tackle the fundamental technical problems that arise from the dependence of the remote consumer on the stochastic energy yield of a wind turbine [6].

Stand-alone hybrid energy systems are being used in a wide range of applications worldwide. As already made clear, such applications normally concern remote consumers that either do not have the choice of grid connection – as in isolated small islands – or live in entirely remote locations, far away from the nearest electrical grid, resulting in a grid connection cost that is extremely high. In the aforementioned cases, installation of a properly sized wind hybrid energy system may sufficiently fulfill the energy demand. The most common applications of stand-alone hybrid energy systems include winter or summer shelters, isolated farms, grid-isolated communities, telecommunication stations, small desalination systems, water pumping installations, electrification of lighthouses, and even far-off road lighting.

As already mentioned, the most common application of hybrid stand-alone power systems concerns satisfaction of the domestic electrical needs of consumers in remote locations where the available wind potential – either alone or combined with the local solar potential – is exploited. Such installations are always supported by energy storage systems, which are essential to ensure energy autonomy. Another significant parameter that should be taken into consideration is the load demand profile, which in combination with the renewable energy potential of the area constitutes the essential input data for the sizing and cost estimation of wind-based stand-alone systems. In any case, energy security in stand-alone systems is accomplished with the inclusion of a conventional power generator (i.e., diesel generator) which, besides guaranteeing 100% energy demand satisfaction, could also contribute to lowering the size of the renewable energy devices and energy storage system components.

Remote islands can also be considered as application areas of stand-alone hybrid systems, because in most cases their weak microgrid operates on expensive fuel and therefore the exploitation of renewable energy sources is considered as vital for energy cost reduction. In such isolated communities, however, certain problems need to be considered, mainly deriving from the minimum permissible contribution of renewable energy sources in the local microgrid [7]. In order to fulfill such constraints, serious research efforts have been recorded during the last 15 years – and are still ongoing – achieving even 90% RES contribution in small island grids by implementation of RES-based hybrid energy solutions.

Regarding the applications of wind-based hybrid power systems in the telecommunication sector, RES have been identified as an energy solution for minimizing the operating expenses [8]. Windy areas such as coastal locations and hills, where, in many cases, the telecommunication masts are installed, are ideal for wind stand-alone systems that are capable of minimizing the fuel consumption of diesel generators and thereby the operational cost of the installations. Furthermore, RES exploitation can be achieved with the installation of a suitable storage system, which will absorb residual renewable energy and return it back for consumption when lower renewable energy production is encountered. Most telecommunication transmitters require air-conditioning services during the summer periods, which makes the combination of wind energy generation with photovoltaic systems' energy ideal, because during summer the availability of solar energy is quite high.

In combination with covering the electrification needs of remote or isolated consumers, stand-alone renewable energy systems can also contribute to the satisfaction of potable water needs through small desalination systems [9]. Potable water shortage is often encountered in remote island regions, where, in cases where wind conditions in the area are favorable, wind-based stand-alone systems can be used in water desalination plants for the production of potable water. The main constraints on the use of wind energy in such systems is the nonsteady power supply, which forces the desalination plants to operate in suboptimal conditions. In order to overcome this undesirable way of operation, considerable energy storage capacity is necessary to support the installation. Furthermore, the contribution of photovoltaic energy could be essential in many cases for realizing uninterruptible power supply to the desalination plant [10].

Direct utilization of the mechanical energy produced by the wind turbine (shaft power), without converting it to electricity, is possible in water pumping systems [11]. Wind-powered water pumps operate either in a direct manner, that is, directly attached to the turbine's shaft, or through electricity generated by a typical small wind turbine. Wind energy has been in use for centuries for water pumping, and even nowadays there is a large number of installations worldwide. In cases where a high starting torque is necessary, a large number of blades are used similar to the older wind turbines. In cases where the operation of a mechanical drive is used for pumping water, the placement of the wind turbine is restricted to be near the water reservoir, whereas in cases where wind electricity is supplied to the water pump, the wind turbine may be placed far away from the water reservoir for maximizing wind energy exploitation [12]. Potential applications of wind water pumping systems include domestic water supply, community water supply, cattle watering, and irrigation [13].

2.19.2 Historical Development of Wind Stand-Alone Energy Systems

Wind energy has been exploited for grinding grain or pumping water for at least 3000 years [6]. The use of wind turbines for electricity generation can be traced back to the nineteenth century when an experimental wind turbine (**Figure 1**)[14] driving a

Figure 1 The first electricity-producing wind turbine, installed in 1891 [14].

dynamo was built by Poul La Cour in 1891 in Denmark [3]. The remarkable fact is that La Cour at once tackled the problem of energy storage. He used the direct current (DC) generated by his wind turbine for electrolysis and stored the hydrogen gas that was produced, establishing in this way the first wind stand-alone energy system.

Based on La Cour's wind turbine model, by 1908 the Lykkegard company had built 72 electricity-generating wind turbines with power output ranging between 10 and 35 kW, which were used to supply energy to rural settlements. For much of the twentieth century, wind turbines were being used to charge storage batteries which then were used to operate small appliances [15]. The interest in electricity generation by means of wind power during the wind turbine evolution had seen some fluctuations following the diesel fuel cost fluctuations. In periods when the fuel prices were rising, such as during World War I and World War II, the interest in wind power was growing. Back then, the subject of environmental protection had not yet arisen and thus there was no association with energy production. Despite the reduced interest in supplying wind energy to electricity networks, wind turbine manufacturers continued their efforts in building wind turbines for stand-alone applications. In 1922 in the United States, Marcellus and Joseph Jacobs developed small wind turbines which became known as 'wind chargers' which were used for recharging batteries for power supply of rural settlements and remote houses. In Germany until the 1930s, a total of 3600 American wind turbines were built under license, and most of them were used for pumping water but some of them were modified for electricity generation. The first wind turbine feeding a local grid was installed in 1931 in the USSR in Balaklava. The electricity generated was fed into a small grid which was supplied by a 20 MW steam power station. The idea of using wind turbine electricity for supplying a grid network was also supported by Hermann Honneff in 1932, whose vision was a five-rotor wind turbine of 20 MW that was to generate electricity in combination with conventional power plants [16]. Accordingly, in the United States in 1941 the world's first large wind turbine was installed in Vermont [17, 18].

Until the 'oil price shock' of 1973, the extremely low prices of conventional fuels held back the development of the wind energy sector, as the investors were not highly motivated to invest new funds in order to overcome the numerous technical problems and faults that had been encountered during the more practical operation of large wind turbines. Therefore, all these years stand-alone wind power installations continued to be the main application of wind power. After the energy crisis in 1973, the interest in wind turbine technology was rekindled giving a significant boost to the wind technology evolution. Based on the traditional models of three-bladed rotors and grid-connected induction generators that dominated large-scale wind turbine models, Danish companies, which were active in agricultural machinery, began building small turbines to sell them to private owners or agricultural holdings (**Figure 2**). These small

Figure 2 Remote installation of a small wind turbine at a private electricity user's holding in Denmark (1985). Photo by Rüth found in Reference [3].

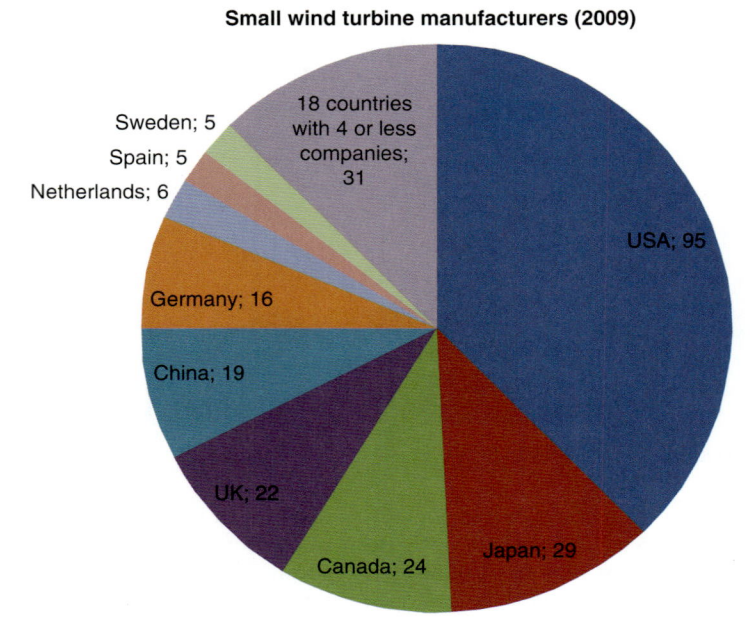

Figure 3 Global distribution of small wind turbine manufacturers (number of companies per country) [20].

wind turbines were also used by consumer associations to cover the electricity needs of small communities. The installation of small wind turbines was supported by the Danish government through financing and legal regulations, and at the same time the pattern of rural Danish settlements with its many single farms generally favored the decentralized installation of wind turbines. By 2001, about 150 000 Danish households were registered as owners of shares in wind turbines [19].

According to the most recent data available, there is a growing interest in the small wind turbine (those of rated capacity < 100 kW) industry. In the United States, the small wind turbine market grew by 15% in 2009 pushing their total installed capacity to 100 MW. It is worth mentioning that almost 50% of the small wind turbines were installed during the last 3 years of the industry's 80 years of history. In this context, the global sales of small wind turbines for the year 2009 were 15 500 units for off-grid connections with a total power of 7600 kW. Another 5200 units were sold for on-grid connection with a total capacity of 34 400 kW. Regarding the different size range of small wind turbines and their use, 100% of the wind turbines with rated power up to 1 kW, 10% of those with rated power 1–10 kW, and < 1% of those with rated power 11–100 kW are used for off-grid applications. According to **Figure 3** [20], about 40% of global small wind turbine manufacturers are located in the United States, 25% in Europe, 10% in Asia, and 25% in the rest of the world, indicating the worldwide interest in small wind turbine installations.

2.19.3 Contribution of Wind in Stand-Alone Energy Systems

Stand-alone power systems are mainly used in cases where there is no grid electricity available or the cost of connection to the local electricity grid is prohibitive. Given that the minimum grid extension cost for low-voltage lines exceeds 10 000 € km^{-1} of grid line – a value which increases in cases of difficult access situations [21–23] – and that the already high cost of fuels increases even more with the remoteness of the location [24], remote consumers should try to exploit all alternative choices that are available in their area. In such cases, renewable energy sources can provide the necessary electricity and thermal energy at a cost competitive to the corresponding electricity cost of the local network.

In the case of grid-connected wind parks, the area in which the park will be installed is selected according to the available wind speed values. In these cases, measurements are taken for quite a long period of time (i.e., at least 12 months) in order to evaluate the wind potential of the area. On the other hand, in the case of wind stand-alone systems, the area of installation is already given, and the owners are not willing to make time-consuming wind speed measurements for the estimation of the wind potential. Therefore, the decision of whether to install a wind stand-alone system is taken in accordance with physical indications such as bending of trees and existence of old windmills in the area, as well as on the basis of the local habitants' experience concerning wind patterns in the area.

In this context, the annual energy yield of a wind turbine depends on the operational characteristics of the wind turbine and the available wind potential in the area. The wind potential of an area could be described to a good approximation by the Weibull function given in eqn [1].

$$f(u_\text{w}) = \frac{k}{C}\left(\frac{u_\text{w}}{C}\right)^{k-1} e^{-\left(\frac{u_\text{w}}{C}\right)^k} \qquad [1]$$

where

$f(u_w)$ is the Weibull distribution function;
k is the shape factor;
C is the scale factor; and
u_w is the wind speed

The quality of the wind potential of the area depends, according to the Weibull distribution, on the scaling factor, C, which is proportional to the mean annual wind speed and the shape factor, k, which depends on how widely wind speeds are spread around the mean wind speed value (inversely proportional to standard deviation).

Accordingly, with respect to the wind frequency distribution, the annual power production of a typical wind turbine for different wind speeds can be calculated as

$$P_w = \frac{1}{2}\rho A u_w^3 \eta_{wt} C_P \qquad [2]$$

where

ρ is the air density ($kg\,m^{-3}$);
A is the swept area of the rotor (m^2);
η_{wt} is the total electromechanical efficiency of the electrical and mechanical components of the wind turbine; and
C_P is the power coefficient of the wind turbine's rotor.

For a wind turbine with a typical (simplified) wind power curve (**Figure 4**), the energy yield for different wind potential areas is presented in **Figure 5**. According to **Figure 5**, the energy production of the wind turbine strongly depends more on the scale factor, C, which is related to the mean annual wind speed and less on the shape factor, k, which is related to the standard deviation of the wind speeds.

Further, if one considers a wind turbine that operates according to a typical power curve, the estimated energy performance per kilowatt of nominal wind turbine power is presented in **Figure 6**. According to **Figure 6**, the energy production potential of a small wind turbine can reach up to $4200\,kWh\,kW^{-1}$ for areas with a mean annual wind speed of $7\,m\,s^{-1}$.

As already mentioned before, the power curve of the wind turbine is of great importance, as it describes the expected power generation for each wind speed at the hub height. Therefore, the annual energy yield of a commercial wind turbine is expected to be different from the one estimated using the typical power curve. **Figure 7** presents the percentage of annual energy yield per kilowatt of rated power of several commercial small wind turbines of different sizes relative to the typical power curve turbine. According to **Figure 7**, the expected deviation between wind turbines with different power curves can be as high as 25%. The data were collected from the official websites of the manufacturers [25-27] and the wind turbine database of Soft Energy Applications and Environmental Protection (SEA&ENVIPRO) Laboratory of TEI of Piraeus [28].

The energy production of the previous figures presented refers to the capability of the wind turbine to produce energy in areas with specific wind potentials. In stand-alone systems, the wind power generation does not always match the power demand of the consumer. Therefore, not all wind energy generated will be absorbed by the demand. The maximum wind energy absorption depends on the wind turbine energy production based on the wind potential of the area and the wind turbine selected, as well as on the corresponding power demand in accordance to the load profile of the consumer. Thus, in order to estimate the wind energy absorption rate of a stand-alone power system the parameters that should be considered are

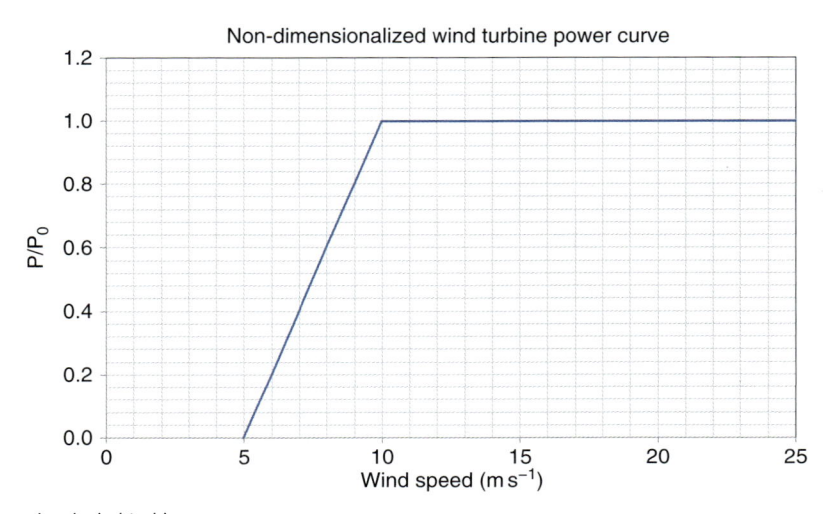

Figure 4 Typical nondimensional wind turbine power curve.

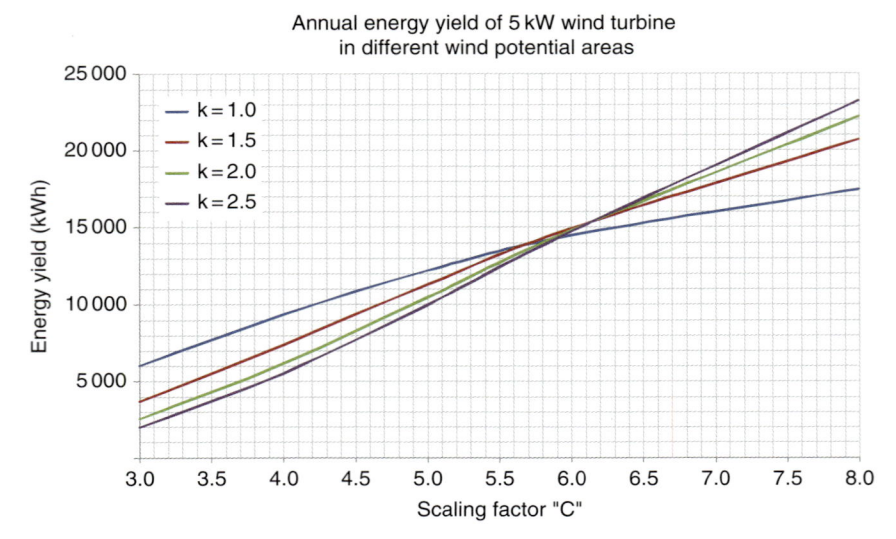

Figure 5 Estimated annual energy yield of a 5 kW wind turbine based on typical power curve, installed in different wind potential areas.

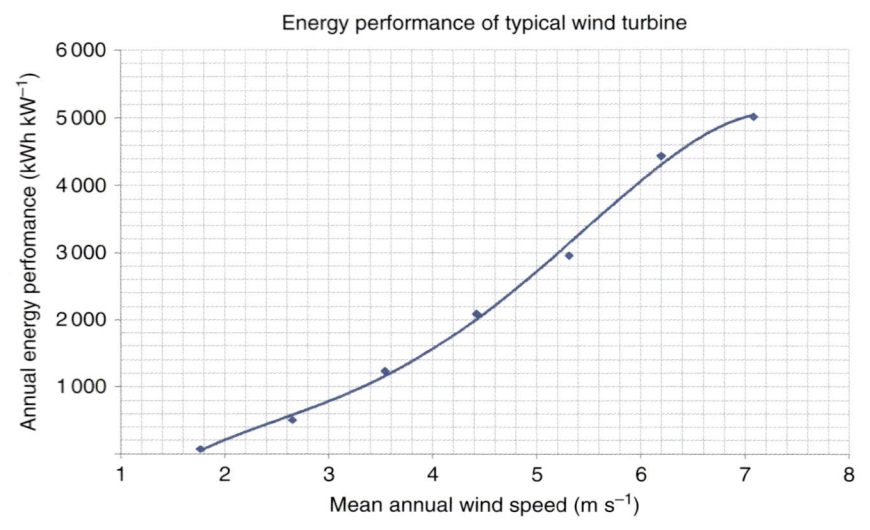

Figure 6 Mean annual expected energy production of a typical wind turbine at different wind potential areas (shape factor $k = 2.0$).

- the wind potential of the area,
- the type and the size of the wind turbine selected,
- the energy demand profile of the consumer, and
- the storage system size.

Kaldellis and Vlachos [29] presented a detailed case study indicating the influence of the above-mentioned parameters. Based on a rural household load profile of a remote consumer [30] with an annual energy consumption of 4750 kWh, they estimated different optimum wind stand-alone configurations in respect of zero load rejections, for an area with a mean annual wind speed of 5.6 m s^{-1} (Kea island in Greece).

According to their results, presented in **Figure 8**, one can clearly see that the wind energy utilized by the consumption is between 35% and 50% of the total wind energy produced during 1 year of operation.

A wind turbine in combination with a PV power station and with the appropriate storage capacity can satisfy the energy demand of stand-alone power systems. The addition of a PV power station to a wind stand-alone system can significantly increase the system's reliability and its ability to cover the electricity needs of a remote consumer setting the diesel fuel generator as an emergency backup unit [31].

In **Figure 9**, the possible combinations of wind turbine, photovoltaic station, and storage medium size are presented [31]. Each proposed configuration is selected based on the zero-load-rejection condition and is capable of covering the annual needs (4750 kWh) of a remote consumer on an hourly-basis calculation. According to **Figure 9**, the storage capacity strongly depends

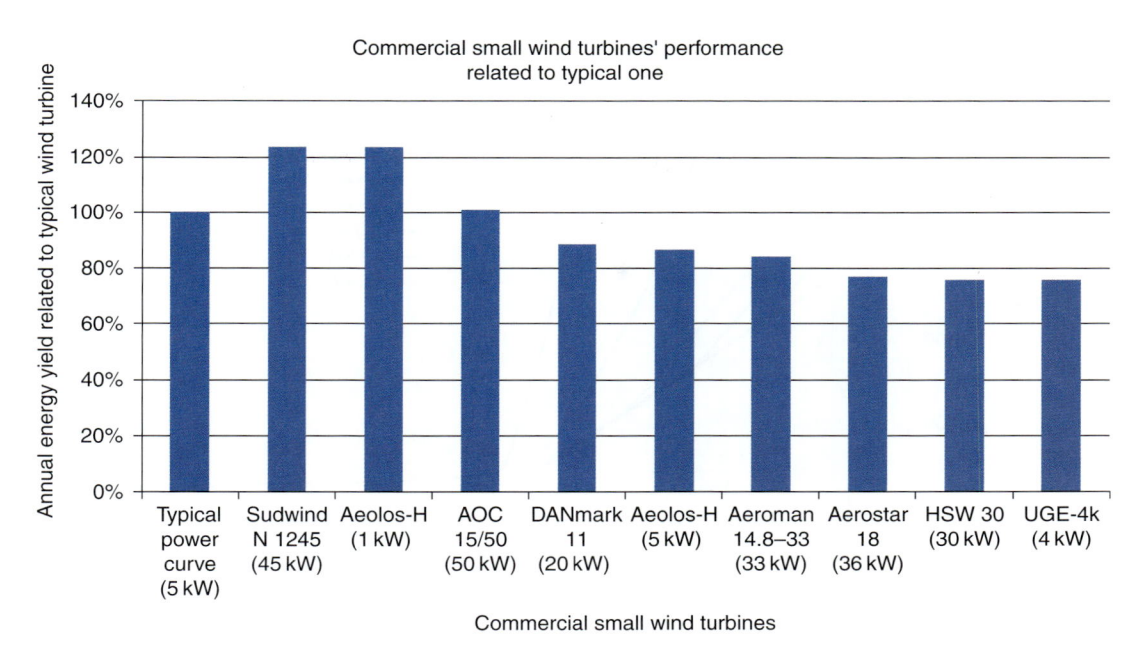

Figure 7 Small commercial wind turbines' annual energy performance relative to the wind turbine with a typical power curve at an area of mean annual wind speed of 5 m s^{-1} and shape factor $k = 2.0$.

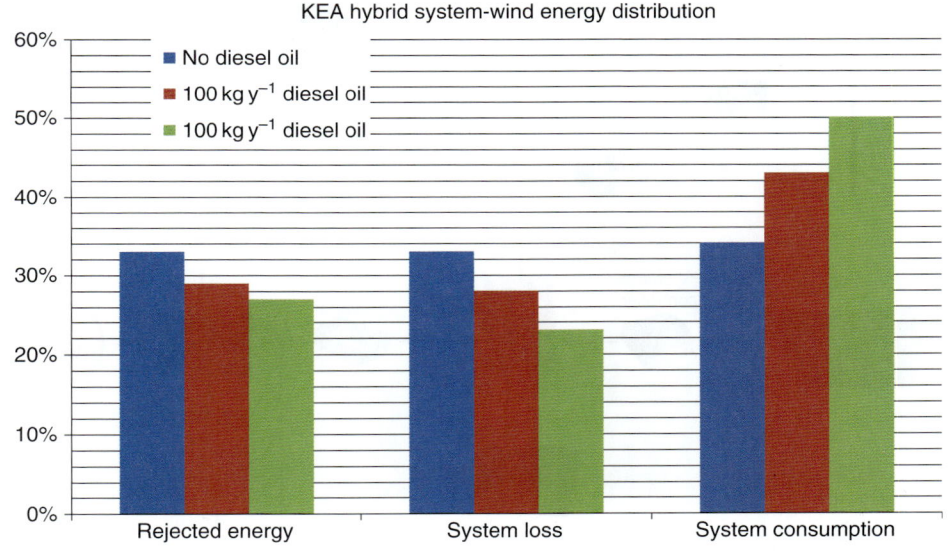

Figure 8 Application results of different wind stand-alone system configurations in the island of Kea in Greece capable of covering the energy demand of a rural consumer.

on the photovoltaic rating and wind turbine size selected. It should be noted that the figure refers to an area with a mean annual wind speed of 5.5 m s^{-1} and an annual solar potential of 1650 kWh m^{-2}.

2.19.4 System Configuration

Stand-alone hybrid energy systems have emerged as one of the most promising ways to handle the electrification requirements of numerous isolated consumers worldwide, including houses in the country, remote farms, shelters, telecommunication stations, small islands, lighthouses, and so on. A typical hybrid energy system combines two or more electricity generation units, which in some cases, where high RES quality exists, can be based purely on RES, along with the appropriate energy storage system and the corresponding auxiliary electronic devices. Typical stand-alone hybrid systems also utilize a small thermal power unit, which is used as a backup power system in cases when the RES power generator units along with the storage system cannot fulfill the energy demand.

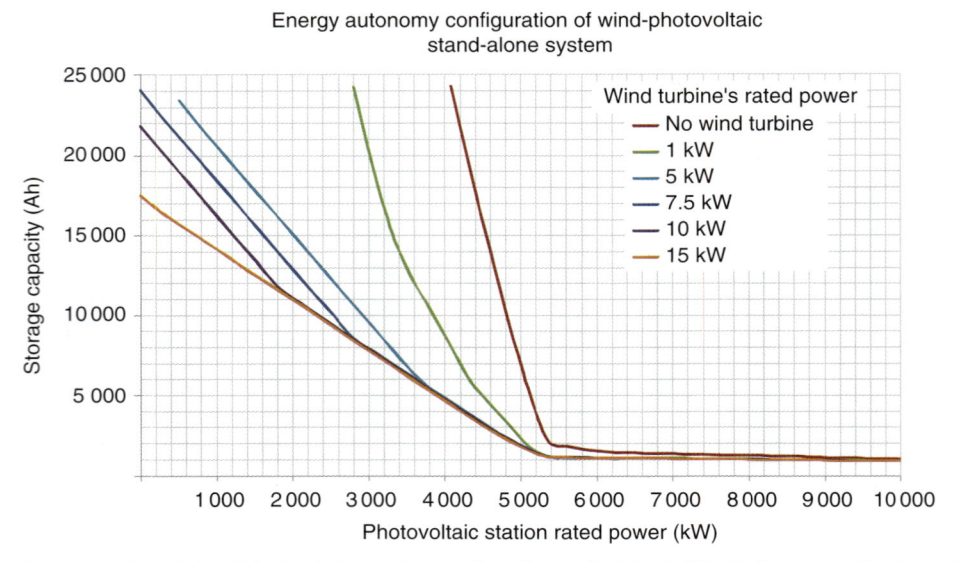

Figure 9 Energy autonomous wind–photovoltaic stand-alone system configurations in the island of Kea in Greece capable of covering the energy demand of a rural consumer.

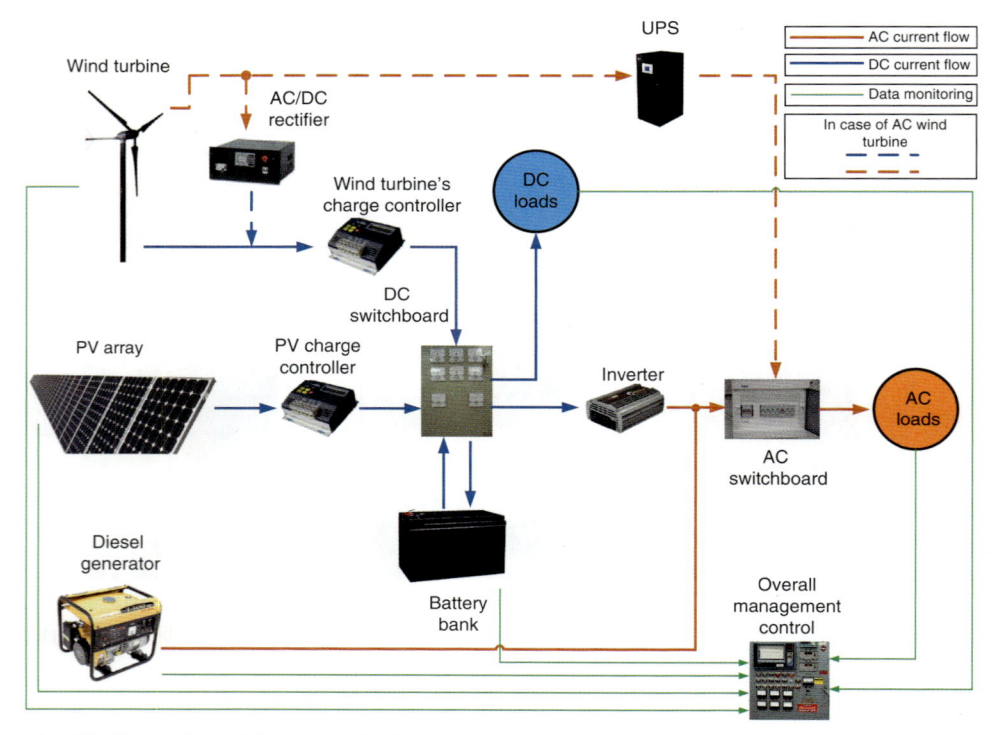

Figure 10 Typical hybrid RES-based stand-alone system [5, 32].

Figure 10 [5, 32] presents the most common configuration of a small-scale RES hybrid stand-alone energy system which comprises a wind energy converter, a photovoltaic power station, a diesel generator used as a backup power provider, a battery bank unit for storing residual energy, and auxiliary electronic equipment which includes charge controllers, an inverter and the corresponding switchboards for alternative current (AC) and DC loads. Contemporary stand-alone systems also include an overall system management unit capable of controlling the power flow according to the instantaneous power generation and power demand.

Several wind-based hybrid energy configurations can be found in the international literature, which incorporate different combinations of renewable energy power production units, conventional electricity generation systems, and storage system configurations. The most well-known systems, apart from the one presented in **Figure 10** are the following (the corresponding indicative references are given in brackets):

- wind–diesel systems [33–35]
- wind–hydro installations [36–39]
- wind–biomass-based installations [40, 41]
- wind–hydrogen/fuel cell hybrid energy systems [42, 43].

Besides, different system configurations exist with regard to the energy storage medium used in each of the above combinations.

2.19.4.1 Wind Turbine Generator

The wind turbines used in stand-alone systems are often in the range of up to 50 kW [4], as the term 'stand-alone system' usually indicates small electricity systems up to the scale of a small community. The amount of power a turbine will produce depends primarily on the diameter of its rotor, as it is the rotor diameter that determines the quantity of wind intercepted by the turbine. Small wind turbines in comparison to large wind turbines operate at a higher rotational speed for the same wind speed; have a tail for the orientation of the nacelle; have significantly smaller tower heights and therefore experience lower average wind speeds; and comprise simpler and cheaper safety systems to withstand high wind speeds. As far as the overspeed protection of small wind turbines is concerned, the most common safety mechanism is the turbine pitch-up or tilt-up and furling. Pitching is more common on very small wind turbines.

Because wind speeds increase with height, the turbines are mounted on a tower. In general, the higher the tower, the more power the wind system can produce. The tower also keeps the turbine above the air turbulence that may exist close to the ground because of obstructions such as hills, buildings, and trees. Note that relatively small investments in increasing the tower height can yield high rates of return in terms of increased power production.

The generator of a small wind turbine is one of the most important parts of the structure and strongly influences the energy performance and the reliability of the wind turbine. Most small wind turbines use permanent-magnet generators, which do not require external excitation. They are simple to use, as they need only a rectifier to produce the DC voltage required for a battery, but, on the other hand, the magnets are easily broken and many are sensitive to temperature changes. Similar to permanent-magnet generators are synchronous generators, which need a field current charge to produce the magnetic field, thus reducing their efficiency. The permanent-magnet generators give satisfactory performance if they are connected through a rectifier to the batteries, whereas in case they are connected directly to an AC load with a constant frequency, the speed of the wind turbine should be constant. The electrical output from the generator is usually three-phase AC with a variable voltage and frequency. The corresponding current is converted to DC using a rectifier and then to a fixed voltage and frequency as required in ordinary electricity-consuming appliances.

Regarding the wind turbine installation, there are two basic types of towers: self-supported (free standing) and guyed. Most home wind power systems use a guyed tower. Guyed towers, which are the least expensive, can consist of lattice sections, pipes, or tubing depending on the design, and are supported by guy wires (see **Figure 11**). They are easier to install than self-supported towers; however, because the guy radius must be between one-half and three-quarters of the tower height, guyed towers require considerable space to install them. Tilt-down towers (which can be either self-supported or guyed) are more expensive, but they offer the consumer an easy way to perform maintenance on smaller, light-weight turbines, usually 5 kW or less. Lattice towers are easier to transport but tend to have a lower service life than pole towers. Tubular towers require smaller foundations but are usually heavier than the other types, thus increasing the purchase and transportation costs. In cases of wind turbines installed near the sea, hot-dipped galvanized tubular towers should be considered. According to Wood [44], the optimum tower height for a small wind turbine is typically 18–33 m depending on the turbine size and wind potential of the area.

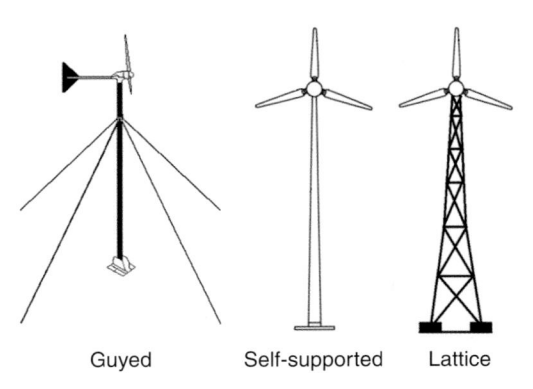

Figure 11 Basic types of wind turbine towers.

2.19.4.2 Storage System Unit

Owing to the stochastic behavior of wind, wind generation cannot always provide a firm capacity to an autonomous electrical power system [45]. In addition, the implied fluctuations can – in some cases – cause problems related to stability, harmonics, or flicker. An energy storage system, when sized appropriately, can match the highly variable wind power production to a generally variable system demand, remarkably limiting the energy production cost (e.g., by generating capacity savings). In this context, the critical parameters concerning the storage systems potentially used in a wind hybrid installation include lifetime expectancy, energy efficiency, depth of discharge, and the initial and operational cost. A short description of the most common storage systems is given in Section 2.19.6.

2.19.4.3 Complementary Electric Generator Unit

The quantity of energy that a wind power generator can produce strongly depends on the available wind potential at the installation area. Although the total annual energy production might seem enough to cover the corresponding electrical energy needs, satisfaction of the load demand by the energy produced should be examined at least on an hour-by-hour basis. The duration of calm spells is an important parameter that influences the decision about the choice of components and the size of a wind hybrid installation for a stand-alone system to provide constant electricity for consumption. There could be situations where, although the calculated annual energy produced seems enough to cover a consumer's power needs, long calm spells could cause a load failure. In order to confront such situations, larger storage systems, which significantly increase the initial cost of the plant, are usually considered.

An interesting option is the installation of an additional, independent electric power generator, which reinforces the electricity production system. Several studies have shown that a wind turbine in combination with a secondary power generator, which could also be based on renewable energy sources (e.g., photovoltaics) or could be conventional fuel-based generators (e.g., diesel or gas), can limit the energy storage system size and in many cases reduces energy production costs.

Another quite interesting option is the combination of the energy storage system with an alternative electric power generator unit. An example of such an installation is the combination of a wind turbine coupled with an appropriate hydrogen production system based on electrolysis, to be used as energy storage, and a fuel cell unit that uses the hydrogen produced and stored during low energy demand to produce electric power during low or very high wind speeds. An additional advantage of the specific installation is the opportunity to use the hydrogen produced as a fuel in appropriate devices (taking advantage of the heat produced by its combustion) or even as a fuel for hydrogen cars. Of course, the currently low energy efficiency of the cycle, that is, from hydrogen production to the final power production by the fuel cell, should also be taken into consideration [43].

Another option is the combination of a wind electric power generator with a small pump-hydro unit in which water is pumped from a lower water reservoir to a higher water reservoir during low energy demand situations, and returned through the hydro turbine to the lower reservoir during low or very high wind speeds [46]. In such installations, the water stored could also be used to cover any water supply needs.

2.19.4.4 Auxiliary Electronic Equipment

The auxiliary electronic equipment needed to support a stand-alone wind hybrid system depends on the application type. For example, the parts required for a wind turbine coupled with a pump-hydro storage system will be very different from those needed for a wind–diesel hybrid system. Most manufacturers provide system packages that include all the necessary parts of the system.

Stand-alone systems, which in most cases are combined with batteries, also need a charge controller to prevent the batteries from overcharging or overdischarging. Small wind turbines generate DC electricity. When using standard appliances that use conventional AC current, an inverter to convert the DC electricity from the batteries to AC is necessary.

The controller of the system ensures that there is a current limit in order to protect the generator and also to monitor the battery condition to avoid overcharged conditions. In addition, it could be used as a primary overspeed protection system by reducing the blade speed. Most wind turbine controllers have a current limit so as to protect the generator by limiting the power output of the wind turbine. In this way, overheating of the generator can be avoided, protecting it from possible insulation and wires melting. Such control is essential as the generator in small wind turbines is usually air-cooled; therefore, the generator's current capability depends on air temperature, wind speed, and the thermal resistance from the wires to the air but also the heat loss of the generator.

The inverter is an essential part of the auxiliary electronic equipment, as it produces the correct voltage and frequency output required by the load. Contemporary inverters also monitor the battery level, thus protecting the battery when the depth of discharge has been reached. Some inverters produce a nearly square output, which is likely to cause more electromagnetic interference.

2.19.5 Stand-Alone Hybrid Systems Configurations

In this section, the most common commercial stand-alone hybrid system configurations are presented. In order for the reader to have a comprehensive view of the opportunities given by the different combinations, scientific research results of the SEA&ENVIPRO Lab are used for the sizing integration of each configuration. Those results refer to case studies in the isolated Aegean Sea islands in Greece, which possess high renewable energy source potential. However, for forming an integrated concept, Section 2.19.7 presents other optimization tools that could also be used for the sizing of stand-alone hybrid power systems.

2.19.5.1 Stand-Alone Wind Power Systems

A stand-alone wind power system is one of the most interesting and environmentally friendly technological solutions for the electrification of remote consumer premises or even entire rural areas. A properly sized wind turbine can exploit the available medium–high wind potential (which is necessary for the implementation of such systems) for producing useful electrical energy. Most wind-only systems are small sized; therefore, the wind turbines used in such systems are up to a few kilowatts in size. An energy storage system is also necessary and should be properly sized in order to be able to match the electricity demand of the consumer with the stochastic behavior of wind.

More precisely, a complete stand-alone wind power system includes a wind turbine, an appropriate energy storage system, and the electronic devices used both to control the battery operation (AC/DC rectifier, battery charge controller) and to guarantee high-quality electricity for the consumer. Besides, an uninterruptible power supply (UPS) and a DC/AC inverter should be used at the outlet of the system if AC output is required (see **Figure 12**).

The reliability of stand-alone wind power systems strongly depends on the wind turbine's generator and control system as both have significant influence on the overall safety and functionality of the system. Of course, the energy reliability of the system's performance also depends on the existence of an energy storage bank, which in most applications refers to a lead–acid battery bank.

More precisely, a stand-alone wind power system is composed of

- a wind converter of rated power P_o and a given power curve $P = P_w(u_w)$ for standard-day conditions;
- an appropriate storage system for h_o hours of autonomy, or, equivalently, with total capacity Q_{max}, operation voltage U, and maximum discharge capacity Q_{min} (or an equivalent maximum depth of discharge DOD_L);
- an AC/DC rectifier of P_r kW and operation voltage values U_{AC}/U_{DC};

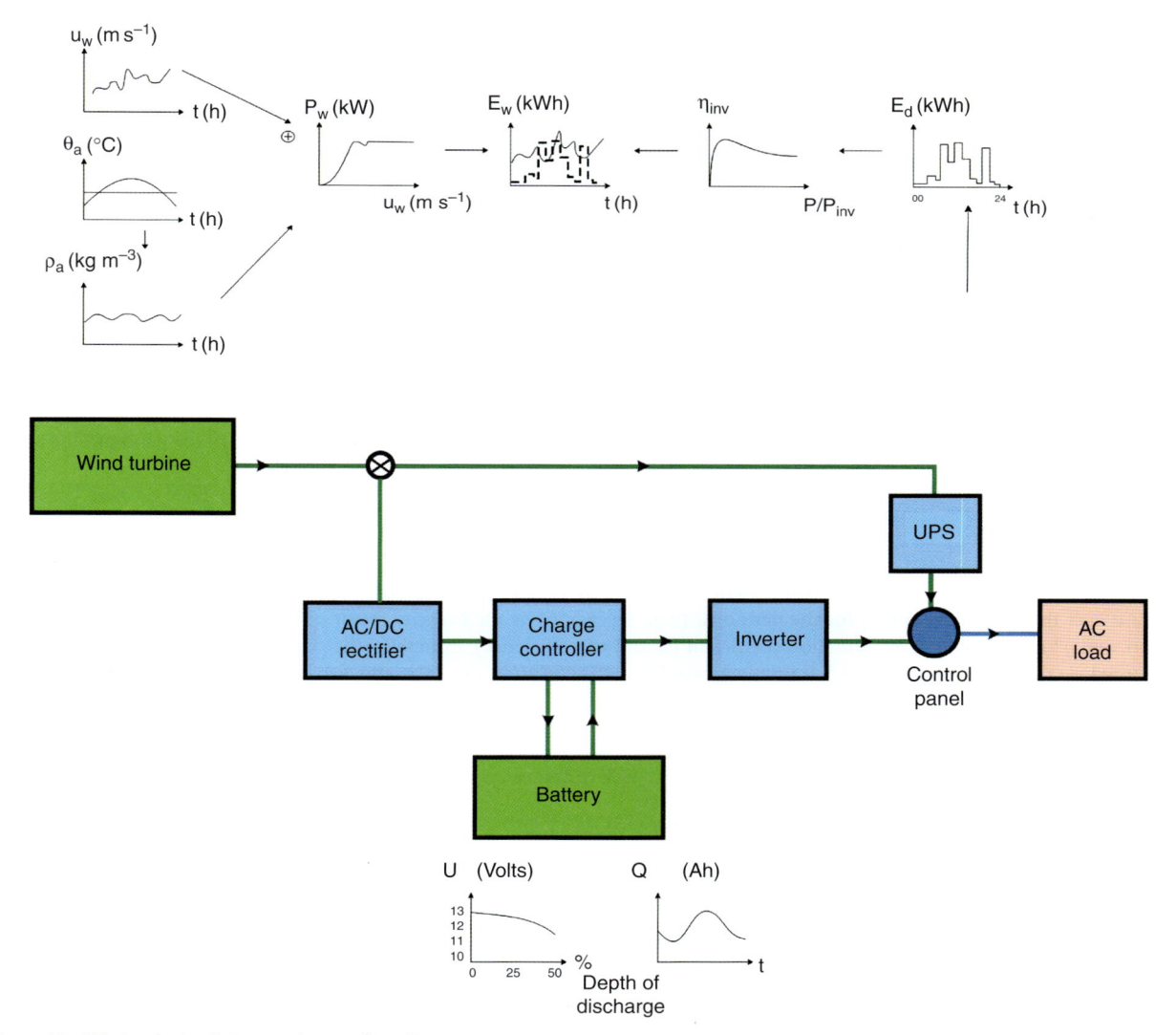

Figure 12 Wind-only stand-alone system configuration.

- a DC/DC charge controller of rated power P_c, charge rate R_{ch}, and charging voltage U_{CC};
- a UPS of P_{UPS} kW, frequency 50 Hz, autonomy time $\Delta t,''$ and operation voltage 230/400 V (or 60 Hz, 120/208 V in the United States); and
- a DC/AC inverter of maximum power P_{inv}, capable of meeting the consumption at peak load demand, frequency 50 Hz, and operational voltage 230/400 V (or 60 Hz, 120/208 V in the United States).

During the long-term operation of the stand-alone wind power system under discussion, the following operating modes may appear:

1. The power demand, P_d, of the consumption is less than the power output, P_w, of the wind turbine including any possible transfer and transformation losses.
    a) In that case, the energy surplus, $\Delta P = P_w - P_d$, is available for being stored in the storage system via the rectifier and the battery charge controller.
    b) The available capacity for charging, $Q_{ch} = Q_{max} \cdot DOD$ (where DOD is the current depth of discharge), of the storage system is compared to the energy surplus (also taking into consideration the corresponding energy losses during charging) and the possible energy surplus is stored.
    c) If the storage system is full, the residual energy is forwarded to low-priority loads.
2. The power demand, P_d, is higher than the power output of the wind turbine, P_w.
    a) In that case, the state of charge, $Q = Q_{max} \cdot (1 - DOD)$, of the storage system is checked. The available storage capacity in the storage system (taking into consideration the energy losses of the discharging process and the energy transformation losses in the inverter) is compared to the energy deficit, ΔP, and is used to cover the load demand.
    b) If the available stored energy is less than the energy deficit or if the storage system is empty, then an energy management plan should be applied, otherwise the load will be rejected.
3. There is no available wind energy either because of low or very high wind speeds or because the machine is not available owing to technical reasons. In that case, the energy demand will absorb the available energy from the storage system. Correspondingly to the previous operating mode, load rejection will take place if the available stored energy is less than the power demand or the batteries are empty and no load management plan is applied.

The sizing procedure is an important task, as the size of the wind turbine and most importantly the size of the storage system – which presents high variable cost owing to the required replacement of the batteries during the service life of the wind turbine – may be significantly lower if an optimization procedure is applied. In order to prove the importance of a wind-based stand-alone system sizing, a representative case study will be presented based on Kaldellis' [33] results. The case study concerns the electricity demand fulfillment of a typical remote consumer (4–6 member families) by the exploitation of the available wind potential of the area. Thus, a small wind turbine with the corresponding battery size and the necessary auxiliary equipment are used. The annual peak load is set at 3.5 kW, whereas the weekly electricity consumption varies between 80 and 100 kWh. Accordingly, the monthly electrical energy consumption varies between 300 and 430 kWh. The area of the installation is a small Aegean Sea island (Kithnos) with an outstanding wind potential, as in several locations in the island the annual mean wind speed approaches 7 m s^{-1} at 10 m height.

In a simplified approach for the sizing of a stand-alone wind-based power system, the rated power, P_o, of the wind turbine ranges as follows:

$$P_{min} = \frac{E_{tot}}{\Delta t \ CF} \leq P_o \leq \frac{E_{tot}}{\Delta t \ CF \ \eta^*} = P_{max} \qquad [3]$$

where E_{tot} is the consumer's electricity requirements (increased by 20% to take into account potential future energy consumption increase over the system's lifetime) for the period Δt (e.g., 1 year), CF is the capacity factor of the installation for the same time period, and η^* is the energy transformation coefficient (round-trip efficiency), expressing the portion of the wind energy produced and stored via the storage system, which is finally forwarded to the consumption. It should also be taken into consideration that the power output of the proposed wind turbine should be high enough to face the maximum (peak) load demand, P_p, of the system. The capacity factor is the product of the installation's technical availability, Δ, and the mean power coefficient, ω, that is,

$$CF = \Delta \omega \qquad [4]$$

with the mean power coefficient, ω, being calculated as

$$\omega = \int_{u_C}^{u_f} \frac{P_w(u_w)}{P_o} f(u_w) du \qquad [5]$$

with u_c and u_f being the corresponding cut-in and cut-out wind speed, respectively, of the wind turbine examined, while $P_w(u_w)$ is the corresponding power versus wind speed, u_w, curve and $f(u_w)$ is the wind speed probability density function at hub height, describing the local wind potential for the time period Δt.

The battery storage capacity is estimated on the basis of the hours of autonomy required for the uninterruptible operation of the system. In wind-based applications, the hours of autonomy are calculated taking into consideration the hours of calm spells that

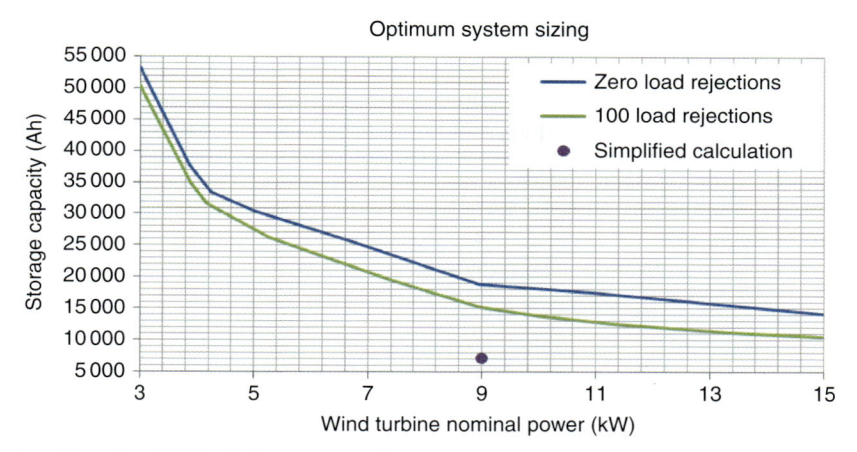

Figure 13 Optimum system sizing of a wind stand-alone power system.

appear, in accordance with the wind potential of the area and the maximum permissible – from the consumer – load rejections. Therefore, the maximum battery capacity in ampere hours is given as

$$Q_{\max} = \frac{E_{\text{tot}}\, h_o}{\Delta t\, \eta_{\text{ss}}\, \text{DOD}_L\, U} \qquad [6]$$

According to eqn [6], the storage system size is determined by the autonomy hours, h_o, of the system; the total energy demand, E_{tot}, for a period Δt; the efficiency of the storage system, η_{ss}; the maximum permitted depth of discharge, DOD_L; and the battery operation voltage, U. In any case, the battery capacity, Q, varies between $Q_{\min}$ and $Q_{\max}$, with

$$Q_{\min} = \text{DOD}_L\, Q_{\max} \qquad [7]$$

where the DOD_L value is strongly related to the life duration (operational cycles, n_c) of the batteries; for example,

$$\text{DOD}_L\, n_c \approx 1500 \text{ to } 1800 \qquad [8]$$

By applying the above calculations to the specific case study, the requested nominal power of the wind turbine is estimated at 9 kW and the maximum battery capacity required is 7200 Ah at 24 V. A more accurate system sizing requires detailed wind speed data along with the ambient conditions data. The numerical algorithm WINDREMOTE was developed by SEA&ENVIPRO Lab in order to confront similar problems by carrying out the necessary parametrical analysis on an hourly energy production–demand basis. The corresponding numerical algorithm is executed for each pair of P_o and $Q_{\max}$ values in the range defined by the user on the basis of the permitted load rejection number. The battery size is increased; the calculation is repeated; and the size combinations of the components of the installation that satisfy the user restrictions are recorded. Calculation results are presented in **Figure 13**, which depicts different size combinations for obtaining different load rejection levels [30].

The results of **Figure 13** denote the significance of an analytical approach to the stand-alone system sizing. The system defined by the simplified calculation is much smaller than the ones required for zero or even 100 h load rejections during 1 year of operation. The choice of the simplified calculation system would result in more than 300 h load rejections. The significance of restricting load rejections is given in **Figure 14**, where the number of load rejections per year (in hours) is given as a function of no-energy fulfillment cost (in Euro/hour) [47]. According to **Figure 14**, high numbers of load rejections are possible only for low no-energy fulfillment cost.

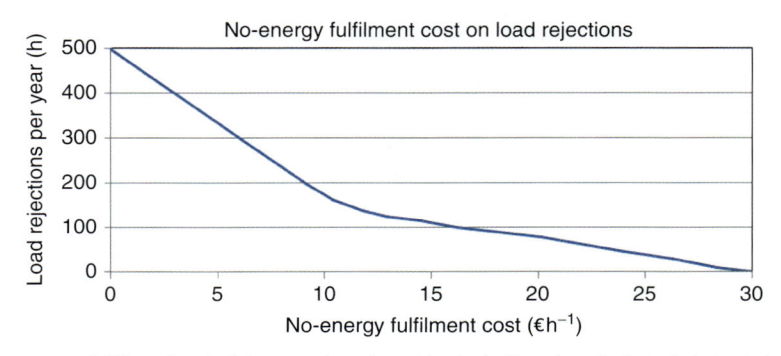

Figure 14 Impact on the non-energy fulfillment cost of the annual number of load rejections for a typical wind stand-alone power system.

2.19.5.2 Stand-Alone Wind–Diesel Power Systems

In medium- or low-wind potential areas, large dimensions of wind-only stand-alone system are required; thus the corresponding initial installation cost in some cases becomes almost prohibitive. For that reason, most remote consumers cover their electricity demand using small oil-fired diesel-electrical generators, with low initial installation cost but very high operational cost. In this context, implementation of the stand-alone wind power system may lead to the respective wind–diesel power system. The addition of a diesel engine can contribute to the reliability and energy security of the system as it guarantees 100% energy demand fulfillment under all circumstances on the condition that sufficient fuel backup exists. The schematic diagram of a typical wind–diesel hybrid power system is presented in **Figure 15**.

More precisely, a typical wind–diesel hybrid system includes

- a wind converter of rated power P_o and a given power curve $P = P_w(u_w)$ for standard-day conditions;
- a small internal combustion engine of P^* kW, capable of meeting the consumption peak load demand P_p (i.e., $P^* \geq P_p$), presenting a typical specific fuel consumption (SFC) curve versus loading of the engine, that is, $SFC = SFC(P/P^*)$;
- a lead–acid battery storage system for h_o hours of autonomy, or, equivalently, with a total capacity of Q_{max}, operation voltage U, and maximum discharge capacity Q_{min} (or equivalent maximum depth of discharge DOD_L);
- an AC/DC rectifier of P_r kW and operation voltage values U_{AC}/U_{DC};
- a DC/DC charge controller of rated power P_c, charge rate R_{ch}, and charging voltage U_{CC};
- a UPS of P_{UPS} kW, frequency 50 Hz, autonomy time Δt and operation voltage 230/400 V (or 60 Hz, 120/208 V in the Unite States); and
- a DC/AC inverter of maximum power P_{inv} capable of meeting the consumption peak load demand, frequency 50 Hz, and operational voltage 230/400 V (or 60 Hz, 120/208 V in the United States).

During the operation of a wind–diesel system, the following energy-production scenarios exist:

1. The power demand, P_d, is less than the power output, P_w, of the wind turbine ($P_w > P_d$). In that case, the energy surplus ($\Delta P = P_w - P_d$) is stored via the rectifier and the battery charge controller. If the battery is fully charged ($Q = Q_{max}$), the residual energy is forwarded to low-priority loads.

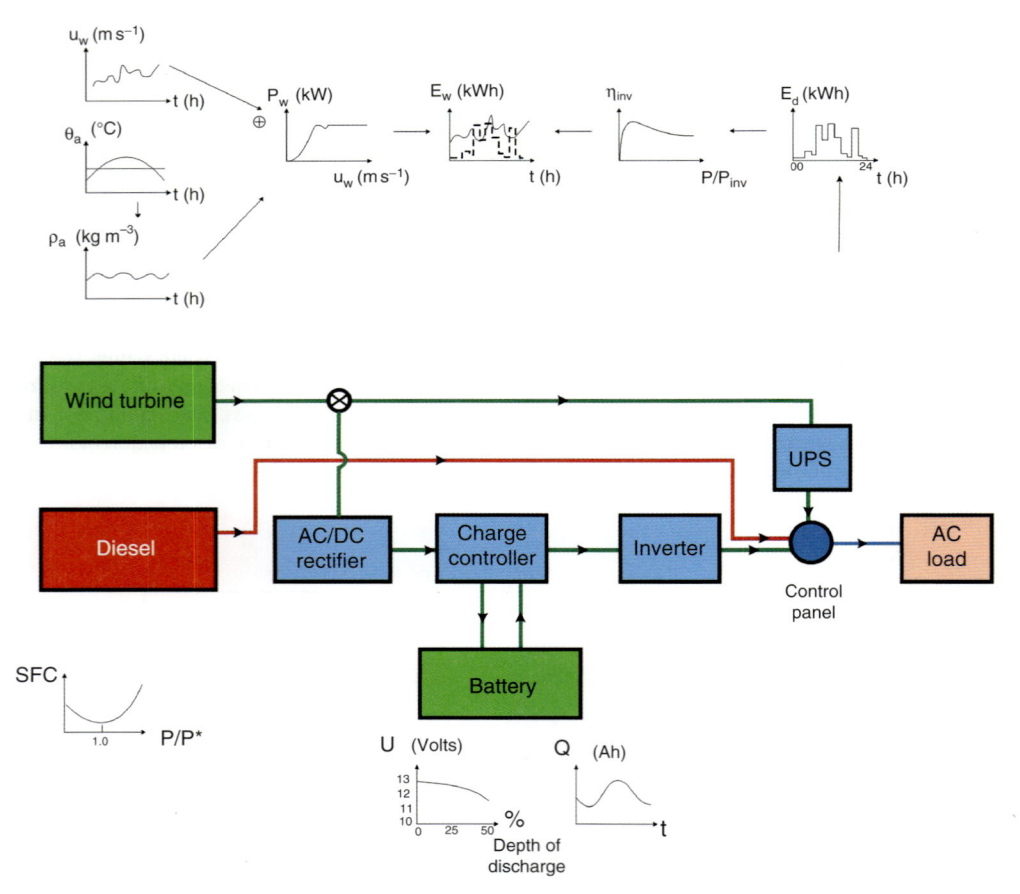

Figure 15 Typical wind–diesel hybrid power system configuration.

2. The power demand is higher than the wind turbine power output ($P_w < P_d$), for example, low wind speed, machine non-availability.
   a) In such situations, the energy deficit ($\Delta P = P_d - P_w$) is covered by the batteries via the battery charge controller and the DC/AC inverter, under the precondition that the corresponding battery depth of discharge DOD is lower than a given limit DOD_L, that is, $DOD < DOD_L$.
   b) If this precondition is not fulfilled (i.e., $DOD \approx DOD_L$), then the energy deficit is covered by the diesel generator at the expense of the existing oil reserves.
   c) In the case of no further oil reserves, the energy deficit ($\Delta P = P_d - P_w$) is covered by the batteries via the battery charge controller and the DC/AC inverter, violating the first-degree battery protection precondition, that is, accepting DOD values higher than DOD_L. However, if the battery's maximum permitted depth of discharge is exceeded, load rejection takes place.

Further to the sizing procedure presented in the wind stand-alone section, the rated power, P^*, of the engine should be capable of meeting the consumption peak load demand, P_p, increased by an appropriate safety coefficient, SF; hence,

$$P^* \geq P_p(1 + SF) \quad [9]$$

Therefore, close attention should be paid on selecting an appropriate SFC of the diesel engine (**Figure 16**) especially under partial loading ($P \neq P^*$) of the engine, in order to minimize the corresponding fuel consumption. It should be noted that for short periods at zero load, diesel generator fuel consumption is almost 30% of the corresponding fuel consumption at rated power. On top of this, it is recommended that diesel engine operation below 30% of full load for long periods be avoided, in order to prevent serious maintenance problems, like chemical corrosion and glazing.

Further, the maximum annual fuel consumption of the installation implies the theoretical case that the energy consumption is fulfilled solely by the diesel generator; hence, the corresponding annual fuel consumption is limited by

$$M_f \leq \frac{E_{tot}}{\eta_d \cdot H_u} \quad [10]$$

where η_d is the mean annual generator's electrical efficiency and H_u is the fuel's specific calorific value.

For the operation of a wind–diesel power system, there are two basic operational strategies possible to be adopted. The first strategy concerns the operation of the diesel engine on a continuous basis. In that case, the diesel fuel consumption is significant and the operational cost remains high, although one of the main purposes of installing a hybrid wind–diesel system is the reduction of operational cost. Furthermore, in this particular operational strategy, a minimum load on the diesel engine should be considered in order to minimize the respective fuel consumption (**Figure 16**). The second operating strategy concerns the operation of the diesel engine on an intermittent basis. In this case, the diesel engine operates only if the wind turbine and the energy storage system cannot fulfill the load demand. During the second operating strategy, limitations on the frequency of on/off cycling of the diesel engine as also the wear of the diesel generator caused by frequent switching should be considered.

Advanced numerical simulation models can be applied to specific load demand profiles and the corresponding wind potential of the area of the installation, for estimating the different size combinations of the wind–diesel hybrid power system. The final decision on which of the configurations will be installed is in most cases made on the basis of either the minimum installation cost or the minimum long-term energy production cost.

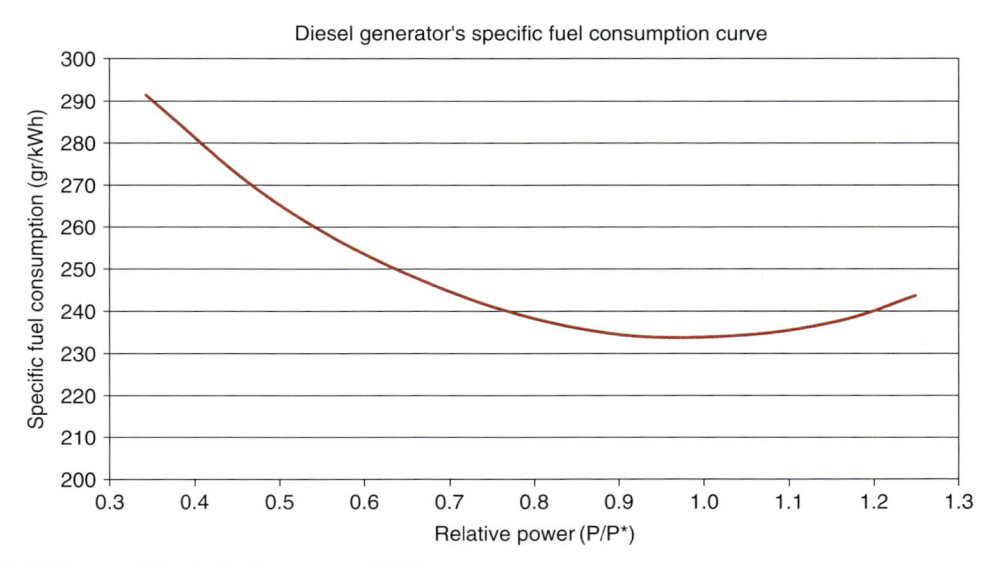

Figure 16 Typical SFC curve of diesel–electric generators (P/P^*).

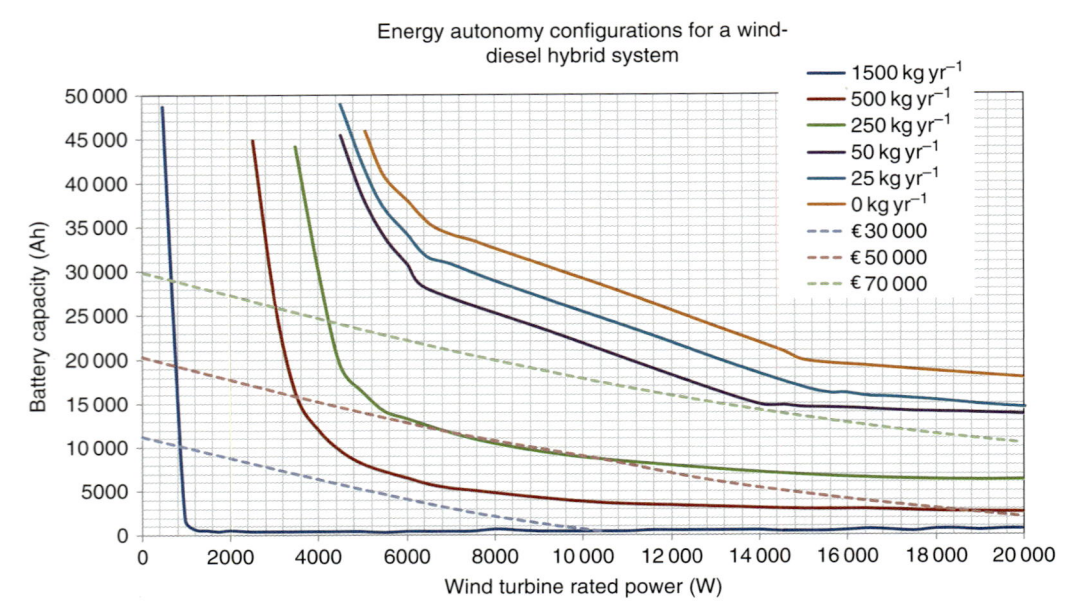

Figure 17 Energy autonomous configurations for a wind–diesel hybrid system in Kea island capable of satisfying the energy needs of a typical household.

The numerical code WIND-DIESEL developed by the SEA&ENVIPRO Lab is capable of estimating the appropriate configurations of a wind–diesel hybrid system. There are three governing parameters defined by the WIND-DIESEL algorithm: the rated power, P_o, of the wind turbine that should be used, the maximum necessary capacity, Q_{max}, of the storage system, and the annual fuel consumption, M_f. More specifically, given the M_f value – for each P_o and Q_{max} pair – the algorithm is executed for all the selected time periods (e.g., for 1 month, 6 months, 1 year or even for many years) and emphasis is laid on obtaining zero-load rejection operation. For every (P_o, Q_{max}, M_f) combination ensuring the energy autonomy of the remote system, energy production and demand balance details are available along with the corresponding time-dependent battery depth of discharge and the time evolution of diesel oil consumption.

The algorithm was applied to a typical household of 4750 kWh annual energy demand and 3.5 kW annual peak load [29]. The corresponding wind–diesel system was sized for being installed in a small Greek island (Kea) which possesses low wind potential as compared to the wind potential of most of the Aegean Sea islands. The mean annual wind speed in the island is 5.6 m s^{-1}, and the maximum calm spells appearing during a 3 year measurement period are 158 h.

The results of the WIND-DIESEL algorithm application are presented in **Figure 17** for various annual diesel oil consumption levels. More precisely, each curve corresponds to a given diesel oil annual consumption, whereas the x-axis describes the wind turbine's rated power and the y-axis, the corresponding battery capacity. According to the results provided, there is a considerable battery capacity reduction by accepting a minimum (25 kg yr^{-1}) diesel oil consumption, representing ~1% of the annual fuel consumption of diesel-only systems. A significant reduction in battery capacity is also come upon by accepting 250 kg yr^{-1} diesel oil consumption.

The optimum configuration is subsequently predicted on the basis of the minimum long-term cost. In **Figure 17**, the constant-initial cost curves are drawn without including the annual diesel oil consumption (dotted lines). If one examines the long-term cost of the configuration, then the optimum diesel oil contribution can be realized in order to minimize the system's life cycle cost (**Figure 18**).

2.19.5.3 Stand-Alone Wind–Photovoltaic Power Systems

Wind-driven stand-alone systems have proved to be a reliable energy solution, capable of satisfying the electrification needs of numerous remote consumers around the globe, especially in cases where the local wind energy potential is medium to high. Even so, where local conditions are not as favorable, oversizing of the wind turbine and the excessive energy storage capacity required discourage consumers from proceeding with RES installations [48]. On the other hand, there are several areas on our planet where one may encounter both abundant availability of solar energy and high or medium-high wind energy potential, the combination of which may substantially reduce the energy storage requirements of the traditional wind-based stand-alone systems. Solar and wind energy availability vary greatly over time and therefore normally cannot match the time variation of the load demand if operating independently. In this context, both photovoltaic and wind energy stand-alone systems require oversized storage capacity in order to fulfill the energy demand of remote consumers. The complementary nature of wind and solar (**Figure 19**) can smooth out the variation in the energy production of the system leading to a significant decrement of the energy storage requirements.

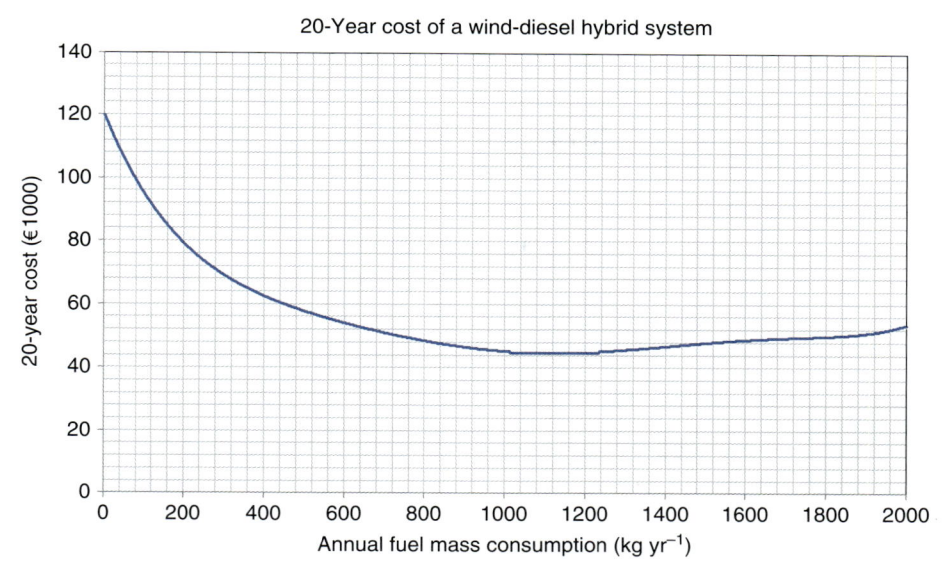

Figure 18 The minimum 20 year cost of a wind–diesel hybrid system installed in Kea island.

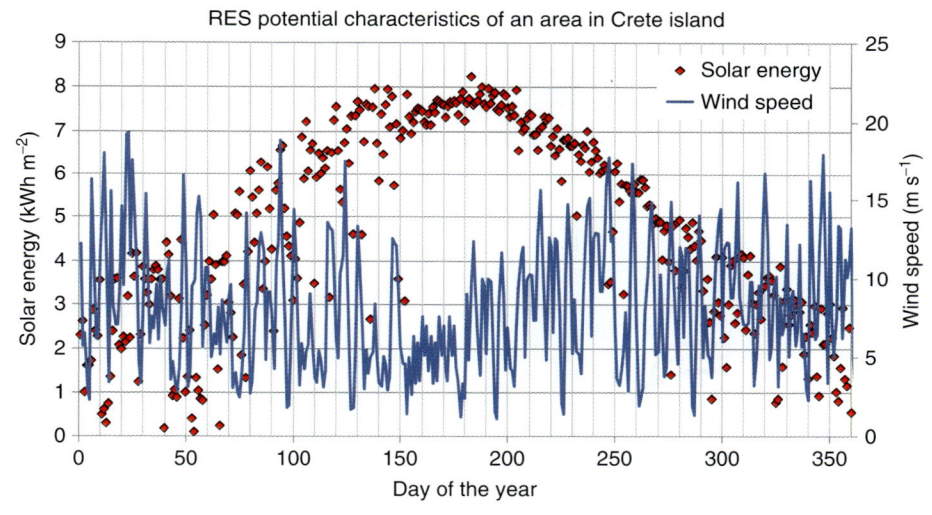

Figure 19 Solar energy and mean wind speed variation in Crete island.

A typical wind–PV hybrid system (**Figure 20**) consists of a small wind turbine, a photovoltaic generator, and an appropriate storage system along with the corresponding electronic equipment. More precisely, it involves

- a wind converter of rated power P_o and a given power curve $P = P_w(u_w)$ for standard-day conditions;
- a photovoltaic array of z panels (with a maximum/peak power P^+ of each panel) properly connected to feed the charge controller to the required voltage;
- a lead-acid battery storage system for h_o hours of autonomy, or, equivalently, with a total capacity of Q_{max}, operation voltage U, and maximum discharge capacity Q_{min} (or an equivalent maximum depth of discharge DOD_L);
- an AC/DC rectifier of P_r kW and operation voltage values U_{AC}/U_{DC};
- a DC/DC charge controller of rated power P_c, charge rate R_{ch}, and charging voltage U_{CC};
- a UPS of P_{UPS} kW, frequency 50 Hz, autonomy time $\Delta' t$ and operation voltage 230/400 V (or 60 Hz, 120/208 V in the United States) (The utilization of this device is optional, and it is used to protect the installation from any unexpected electricity production fluctuations owing to the stochastic behavior of wind); and
- a DC/AC inverter of maximum power P_{inv} capable of meeting the consumption peak load demand, frequency 50 Hz, and operational voltage 230/400 V (or 60 Hz, 120/208 V in the United States).

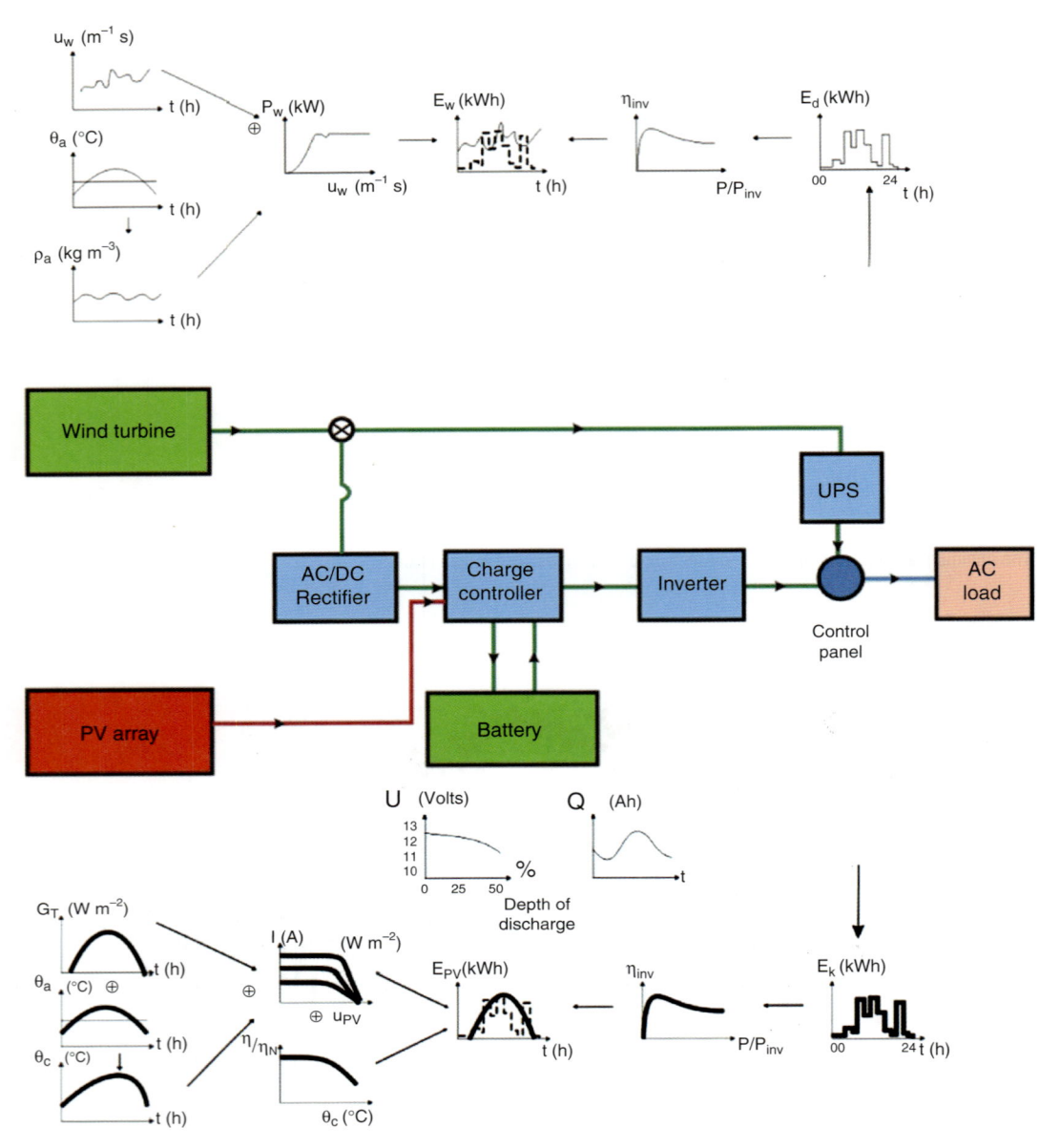

Figure 20 Typical wind–photovoltaic hybrid system configuration.

During the long-term operation of a stand-alone wind–PV hybrid system the following situations may arise:

1. The power demand, P_d, of the consumption is less than the power output, P_w, of the wind turbine ($P_w > P_d$). In that case, the energy surplus ($\Delta P = P_w - P_d$) is stored via the rectifier and the battery charge controller along with the energy production of the photovoltaic generator, P_{PV}. If the battery is fully charged ($Q = Q_{max}$), the residual energy is forwarded to low-priority loads.
2. The power demand is more than the power output of the wind turbine ($P_w < P_d$) but less than the sum of the powers of the photovoltaic station and the wind converter, that is, $P_w + P_{PV} > P_d$. In that case, the extra load demand is covered by the photovoltaic station via the DC/AC inverter. Any energy surplus from the photovoltaic station is stored in the battery via the charge controller. If the battery is fully charged ($Q = Q_{max}$), the residual energy is forwarded again to low-priority loads.
3. The power demand is more than the combined power output of the two renewable stations, that is, $P_w + P_{PV} < P_d$, where $P_w + P_{PV} \neq 0$. In such situations, the energy deficit ($\Delta P = P_d - (P_w + P_{PV})$) is covered by the batteries via the charge controller and the DC/AC inverter under the condition $Q > Q_{min}$. During this operational condition, special emphasis is laid on the management plan for the three electricity production subsystems.
4. There is no renewable energy production (e.g., low wind speed or machine not available, and zero solar irradiance), that is, $P_w + P_{PV} = 0$. In that case, all the energy demand is covered by the energy storage subsystem under the condition $Q > Q_{min}$.

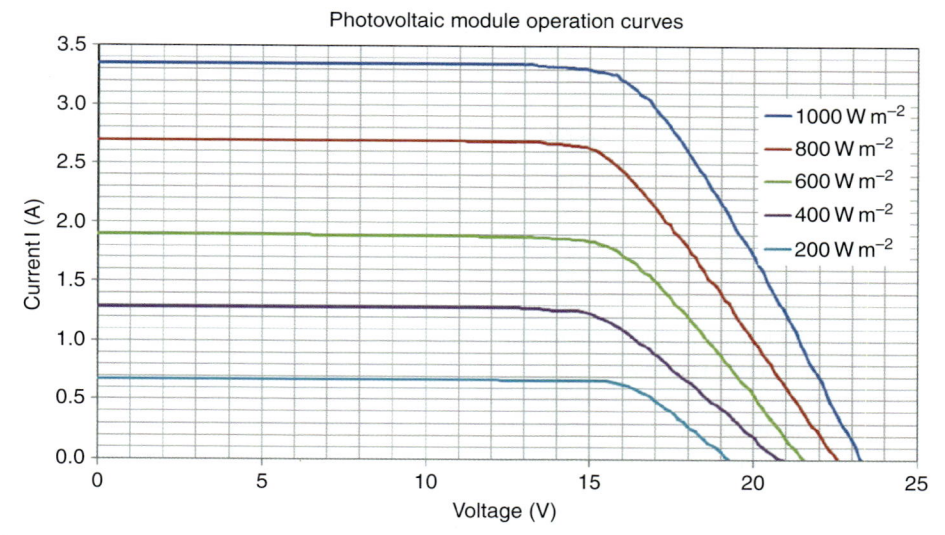

Figure 21 Operation curves of a photovoltaic module for different solar radiation values.

5. In cases (3) and (4) above, when the battery capacity is near the bottom limit, an electricity demand management plan should be applied; otherwise the load would be rejected.

In order to maximize the energy security of the system, a diesel engine could be added to act as a backup energy source in the extreme case that no renewable energy production is available and at the same time no energy is available in the storage system.

The sizing procedure of a wind–PV hybrid system is much more complicated than the above-mentioned stand-alone systems, as one has to match the stochastic wind generation and the fluctuating PV generation with the time distribution of load demand. Generally, the PV systems comprise an array of PV modules that produce electricity, taking advantage of the existing solar radiation, according to the PV operational curves (**Figure 21**). The number, z, of PV panels is bounded as follows:

$$\frac{E_{tot}}{8760 \ CF_{PV}} \leq z \, P^+ \leq \frac{E_{tot}}{8760 \ CF_{PV} \ \eta^*} \quad [11]$$

According to the charge controller voltage, U_{cc}, and the photovoltaic panels' operation voltage, U_{PV}, the necessary number of photovoltaic panels, z_2, connected in series is estimated as:

$$z_2 = \frac{U_{cc}}{U_{PV}} \quad [12]$$

Therefore, 'z_1' parallel strings of panels are required for the installation:

$$z_1 = \frac{z}{z_2} \quad [13]$$

Note that P^+ is the nominal power of the module, CF_{PV} is the photovoltaic installation's capacity factor, and η^* is the corresponding energy transformation coefficient, given that the PV production is not rectified.

In order to investigate the potential configurations of stand-alone wind–PV hybrid power systems, a more detailed sizing procedure should be followed. More precisely, given that analytical data of the operational characteristics exist, integrated computational algorithms could be used for the estimation of the most appropriate system configuration to be chosen. The analytical system sizing can considerably increase the stand-alone system's reliability and decrease the installation cost and, furthermore, the long-term energy production cost. The main inputs required for an analytical sizing procedure are

- detailed wind speed, u_w, measurements at hub height over a given time period (e.g., 1 year);
- detailed solar radiation, G, measurements over a given time period (e.g., 1 year) usually at a horizontal plane;
- ambient temperature, θ_a, and pressure data for the entire period analyzed;
- operational characteristics of the wind turbine (at standard-day conditions);
- operational characteristics (current, voltage) of the PV modules selected;
- operational characteristics of all the other electronic devices of the installation; and
- the electricity consumption profile on an hourly basis, being also dependent on the period of the year analyzed (winter, summer, or other).

An example will be presented based on the research of Kaldellis et al. [31], which strengthens the necessity of the analytical hybrid system dimension estimation in order to guarantee energy autonomy of a typical remote consumer. In this study, the numerical algorithm WT-PV, developed by SEA&ENVIPRO Lab, was used. This algorithm estimates the combination of the required wind turbine size, P_o; the number of photovoltaic panels, z, needed; and the corresponding battery capacity, Q_{max}, that will guarantee system energy autonomy for a given period of time. WT-PV is based on the following steps:

1. For the region analyzed, the wind turbine rated power, P_o, is selected, taking values from a specific numerical range defined by the user.
2. Accordingly, the number, z, of PV panels, each with a peak power P^*, is determined, based on the respective operational characteristics.
3. A battery capacity is selected, starting from a minimum value, while a maximum battery capacity limit also exists. Battery capacity range can vary according to the user's definitions. For every time point of a given time period, the wind energy, P_w, produced by the wind turbine and the energy yield, P_{PV}, of the photovoltaic generator are estimated, taking into account the existing wind speed, the available solar radiation, the ambient temperature and pressure, the selected wind turbine power curve, and the power curve of the photovoltaic panels (see **Figure 21**).
4. The wind energy production is compared with the consumer's energy demand, P_d. If an energy surplus occurs ($P_w > P_d$), the energy surplus along with the energy produced by the PV generator is stored in the battery system and a new time point is analyzed. Otherwise, the algorithm proceeds to the next step.
5. If ($P_w < P_d$), the energy deficit ($P_d - P_w$) is covered by the photovoltaic generator production. Any energy surplus is stored to the batteries and a new time point is analyzed. If this is not the case, the algorithm proceeds to the next step.
6. The energy deficit ($P_d - P_w - P_{PV}$) is finally covered by the energy storage system, if the batteries are not near the lower capacity permitted limit ($Q > Q_{min}$). Accordingly, the algorithm is repeated from step (4). In case the battery is practically empty, the battery size is increased by a given quantity, provided the maximum battery capacity limit is not exceeded. Then the complete analysis is repeated from step (3). If the maximum battery size is reached, the number of photovoltaic panels is increased and the algorithm proceeds to step (2). In case the maximum available number of photovoltaic panels is reached, a new wind turbine rated power is selected and the algorithm restarts.

After the analysis is completed, the distribution $Q_{max} = Q_{max}(P_o, z)$ is predicted, taking into account that every set of Q_{max}, P_o, and z guarantees the energy autonomy of the remote consumer for the entire period analyzed. The optimum configuration may be subsequently predicted on the basis of an appropriate criterion, for example, the minimum initial cost.

A case study in the island of Zakynthos in Greece presented by Zafirakis et al. [49] is selected for the implementation of the above algorithm. The wind–PV hybrid system should be able to cover the electricity needs of a typical remote consumer with a given consumption profile based on his seasonal electricity needs. In this study, the peak power demand of the remote consumer does not exceed 3.5 kW, whereas the annual energy consumption reaches ~4750 kWh. The configuration was designed to be installed in Zakynthos island, which possesses medium solar energy potential (1500 kWh m^{-2} yr^{-1}) and medium wind potential with mean annual wind speed values reaching 6 m s^{-1}. **Figure 22** presents the different configurations that are capable of guaranteeing 100% energy autonomy totally based on renewable energy sources for 1 year of operation. Scenarios of wind–battery and PV–battery were also included by the authors for comparison. According to their results, a stand-alone PV system would require at least 1250 Ah storage capacity combined with more than 10 kW of PV installation. On the other hand, the wind stand-alone system requires significantly higher battery capacities, up to 6000 Ah, for the same wind turbine size (15 kW). The combination of both renewable energy sources could decrease the storage system requirements as well as the necessary size of the wind turbine and the photovoltaic installation.

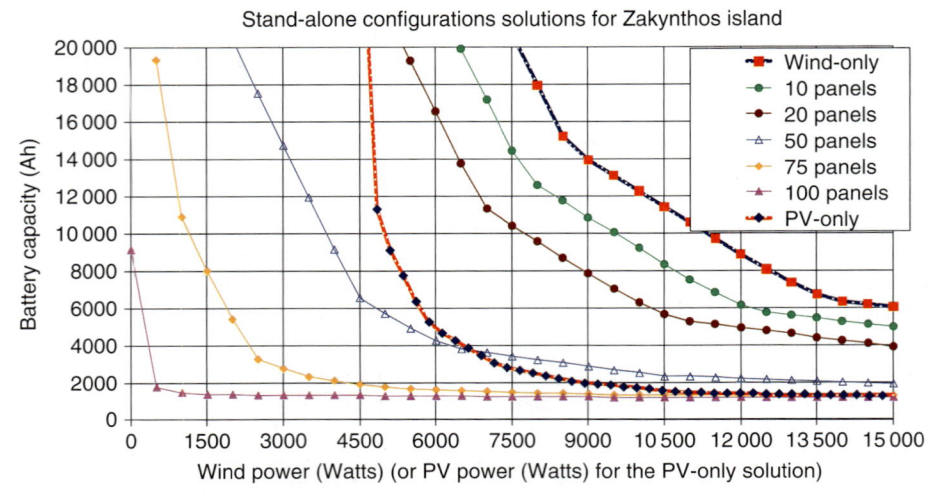

Figure 22 Variation of a wind–PV hybrid system dimensions in Zakynthos island.

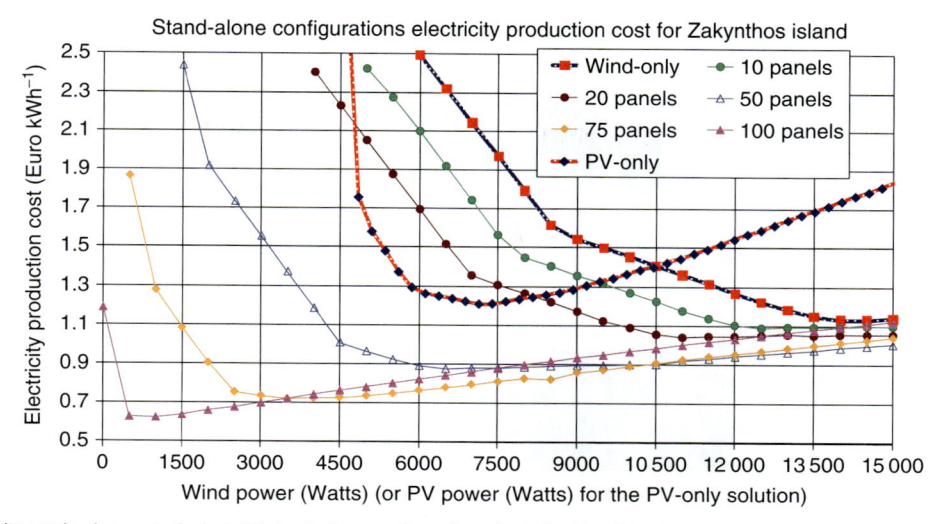

Figure 23 Electricity production cost of wind–PV stand-alone configurations for Zakynthos island.

As already mentioned, selection of the most appropriate configuration is normally decided on an economic basis: either the minimization of the initial installation cost or the optimization of the electricity production cost. **Figure 23** presents the electricity production cost for the different configurations of **Figure 22**. According to **Figure 23**, the minimum electricity production cost ranges between 0.6 € kWh^{-1} for a 500 W wind turbine and 5 kW of PV, and 1.2 € kWh^{-1} for a PV-only installation of 7 kW. It is also important to note that for high wind turbine rated power (15 kW) the electricity production cost presents very narrow variations converging at about 1.1 € kWh^{-1}.

2.19.5.4 Stand-Alone Wind–Hydro Power Systems

Complementarity of renewable energy sources can also be exploited in wind–hydro power systems, which are based on the exploitation of both wind potential and hydraulic power in order to enhance the reliability, energy quality, and stand-alone system performance. In addition, the water storage capability of the hydroelectric system can significantly limit the intermittence of wind power generation. Thus, a stand-alone wind–hydro power system does not essentially refer to the independent production of electricity by a hydro power installation or a wind turbine, both of which supply energy to a remote consumer. The wind–hydro concept mainly refers to the integration of a wind power installation with a pumped hydro storage (PHS) system that will be able to absorb the residual wind energy during low-power demand periods and return it for consumption when wind power cannot satisfy the demand. The implementation of wind power generation with PHS is targeting mainly the range of isolated communities in remote islands with no connection to any mainland grid rather than single consumers as indicated for the systems described in the previous sections.

The integration of wind power with PHS has been investigated for at least 20 years by numerous researchers [37, 46, 50, 51]. Most of the cases analyzed refer to isolated islands with the target of minimizing the conventional fuel energy consumption and eliminating the negative environmental impacts. Combined wind–hydro energy stations can contribute to the maximum RES penetration into the load demand, which, according to research results, can even exceed 90%.

A typical wind–hydro power system capable of fulfilling the energy needs of an isolated community is presented in **Figure 24**. More precisely, the hybrid system consists of

- one or more wind turbines,
- a small hydroelectric power plant,
- a water pump station, and
- two or more water reservoirs at elevations h_1 and h_2 ($h_1 > h_2$) working in a closed circuit along with the corresponding pipelines.

The hybrid wind–hydro power plant is usually supplemented by an existing autonomous power station (APS) which usually comprises conventional internal combustion engines. The main objective of the wind–hydro station is the fulfillment of the energy demand by increasing the renewable energy source absorption and reducing the operation time of the local APS.

The sizing procedure of the wind–hydro power system includes sizing of the wind turbine and the hydro turbine, as well as the determination of the exact location, volume, and geometry of the water reservoirs along with the determination of the rated power and operational range of the water pumps and the water piping system dimensions (diameter, length).

More precisely, the rated power of the water pumps may be determined by the maximum power of the wind turbines, as the water pump must have the capability to absorb the maximum power output of the wind turbines, whereas in the case of large-scale systems, the rated power of the pump depends on the frequency distribution of the wind park's energy surplus; that is,

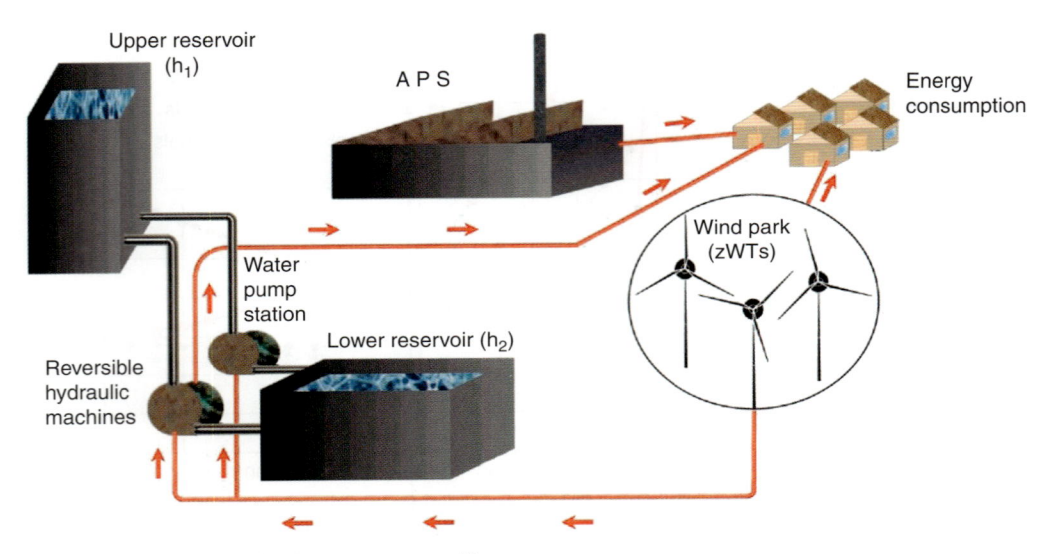

Figure 24 Combined wind–hydro installation for remote communities.

$$P_{pump} = \frac{\rho_w \, g \, H \, \dot{V}}{\eta_p \, \eta_{el}} \quad [14]$$

where P_{pump} is the power required by the water pumps; H the pump head; $\dot{V}$ the volume flow rate; η_p the pump efficiency; η_{el} the electrical efficiency of the system; ρ_w the density of the water; and g the acceleration due to gravity. The static head, H, of the pump must satisfy the expression

$$H \geq (h_1 - h_2) + \delta H_f = (h_1 - h_2) + K_p \dot{V}^2 \quad [15]$$

where δH_f is the total hydraulic losses, both lengthwise and local, when the water reservoir is used for energy storage and K_p is the friction losses factor.

It should be noted that H and η_p depend on the operational characteristics of the selected pump.

The nominal power of the hydro installation results from the precondition that it covers the peak power demand of the system each time examined, with an optional future increase (of 20%). The exit power is given as

$$P_h = \rho_w \, g \, H' \, \dot{V}' \, \eta_H \, \eta'_{el} \quad [16]$$

where $\dot{V}'$ is the flow rate of the turbine; H' the hydro turbine head, η_H the turbine efficiency, and η'_{el} the electrical efficiency of the system.

In addition, the following equation is also valid:

$$H' \leq (h_1 - h_2) - \delta H'_f = (h_1 - h_2) - K_H \dot{V}'^2 \quad [17]$$

where h is the hydrostatic head and $\delta H_f'$ is the total hydraulic losses, both lengthwise and local, when the water circuit is used for energy production.

Note that H' and η_H depend on the operational characteristics of the hydro turbine selected.

The dimensions of the upper water reservoir are defined by the available hydrostatic head, which depends on the relative elevation between the upper and the lower water reservoirs, and by the required levels of energy autonomy for the system. For example, by selecting d_0 days of energy autonomy, the useful volume V_o of the water reservoir is given as

$$V_o = \frac{E_{tot} \, 24 d_0}{\Delta t \, \eta_H \, \eta_{el} \, \rho_w \, g \, H'} = V_{max} - V_{min} \quad [18]$$

where E_{tot} is the total energy demand for the time duration of analysis, Δt, in hours (e.g., 8760 h for 1 year); and V_{max} and V_{min} are the maximum and minimum storage capacity, respectively, of the upper water reservoir.

During a long-term energy balance analysis of a wind–hydro power system operation, the following operational situations may arise:

1. The wind power produced is in excess of the energy demand of the system.
   a) In that case, the energy surplus is stored through operation of the water pumping system in the upper reservoir.

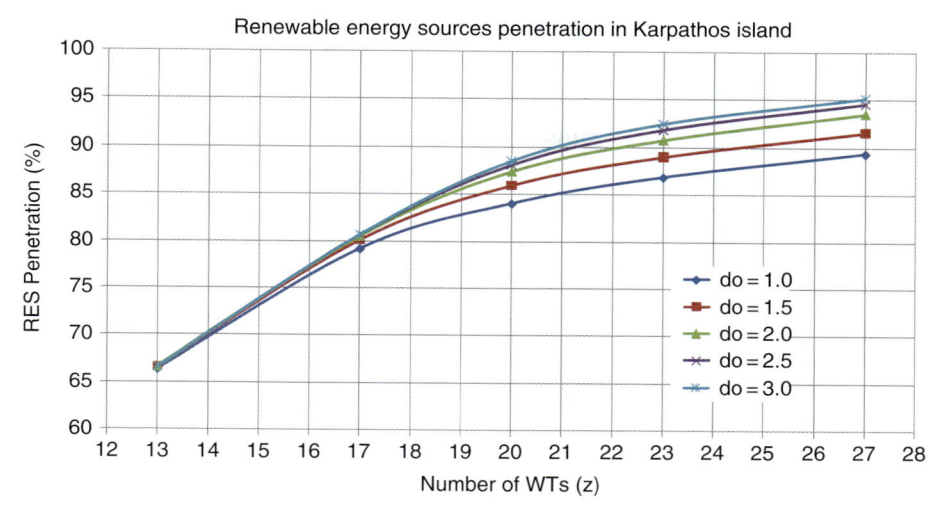

Figure 25 Renewable energy sources penetration capability using the wind–hydro solution in the autonomous electrical system of Karpathos island.

    b) In case the upper reservoir is full, the energy surplus is forwarded to other alternative uses, such as a water desalination plant.
2. The electrical power demand is higher than the wind park output.
    a) In that case, the hydro turbines cover the power deficit.
    b) In case the upper reservoir is almost empty, the internal combustion engines of the APS take over the power deficit, under a scheduled operational plan.

For estimating the optimum wind–hydro configuration, advanced numerical algorithms should be used, to analytically simulate the operation of different system size combinations. By applying an analytical simulation procedure, Kaldellis and Kavadias [52] presented interesting results regarding the renewable energy possibilities in the electrification of remote islands. The study, which is presented here, concerned a medium-sized Aegean Sea island (Karpathos), and the basic scope was the maximization of RES penetration. The annual energy production of the local APS of the island was estimated at 24 400 MWh and the peak-load demand at ~6500 kW, whereas the corresponding minimum value was 1400 kW. The island has a very high wind potential, as the long-term annual mean wind speed approaches 9.6 m s^{-1}, at 10 m. According to their results, remarkable renewable energy penetration can be achieved (**Figure 25**) by increasing the number of wind turbines used and the size of the water reservoirs selected through the parameter d_o which represents the number of days of energy storage autonomy.

Another interesting optimization approach for the economy enhancement of large wind–hydro installations concerns a planned hydro power production under a pattern of guaranteed energy by the hydro power system on a daily basis during the peak load demand hours. In this way, high energy-purchase prices can be realized by selling power to the local autonomous grid during the peak load demand hours [46]. Of course, in case the water stored in the upper reservoir is not enough for the fulfillment of the condition of guaranteed energy delivered to the local grid, the water pump absorbs the required energy from the grid during low-demand periods when the energy purchased price from the local grid is low.

2.19.5.5 Stand-Alone Wind–Hydrogen Power Systems

As already mentioned in Section 2.19.2, the first wind turbine installed in Denmark in 1891 was generating DC, which was used for electrolysis to produce hydrogen. The hydrogen produced was used for gas lighting and later on for autogenous welding [3, 53]. Since then wind energy was scarcely used for hydrogen production, and only during the last few decades did wind–hydrogen stand-alone systems become a reality. In this context, such configurations, when in stand-alone system mode, exploit the energy surplus of the wind turbine to produce hydrogen, provided of course that the electricity demand of the consumption side has been satisfied. Hydrogen as an energy carrier can be stored to overcome the daily and seasonal discrepancies between energy source availability and demand [54]. In cases of load deficit or no available wind, the hydrogen is fed to a fuel cell device to produce electricity and satisfy the demand.

There are several issues that should be taken into consideration when using wind energy for the production of hydrogen. More precisely, direct coupling of an electrolyzer with a wind turbine denotes intermittent operation and highly variable power output, which could cause the electrolyzer to operate at very low power rate resulting in the mixing of H_2 and O_2, which at such load levels permeate through the electrolyzer. Also, intermittent power makes the electrolyzer operate at temperatures lower than the respective nominal, as some amount of time is required for the electrolyzer to reach its normal operating temperature [55]. These problems in stand-alone power systems can be eliminated by the use of either a complementary renewable power source or a diesel generator, which may fill the power gaps during the electrolyzer's

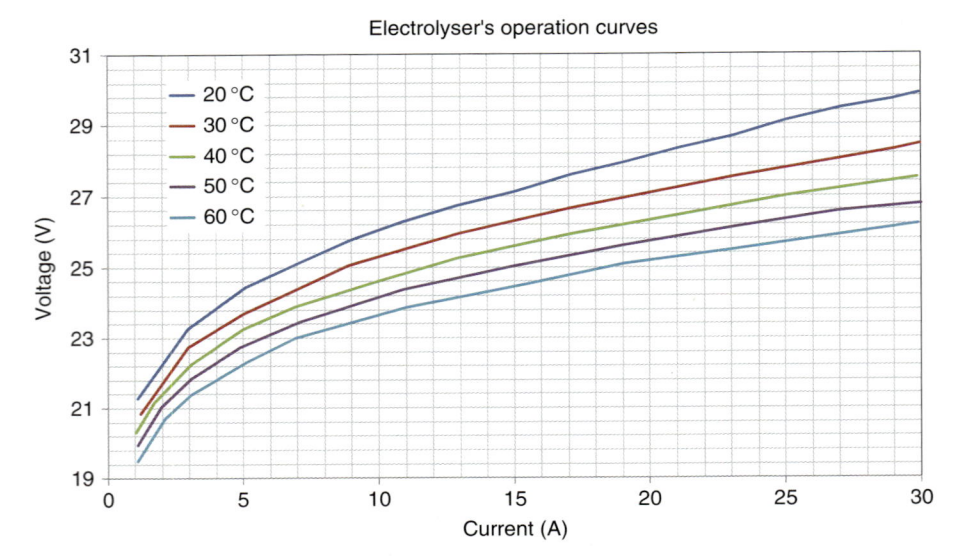

Figure 26 Operational characteristics of electrolyzers for different power levels and temperatures, based on Reference [55].

operation [56]. In this case, an extended economic analysis should be undertaken in order for the system to be proved not only energy-efficient but also cost-effective (**Figure 26**).

The use of an electrolyzer–fuel cell set as a storage option for wind stand-alone systems is still in its initial stage, although both electrolyzer and fuel cell technologies have achieved considerable progress during the last decades. The main drawback of such configurations is the low energy efficiency of the charge–discharge cycle (round-trip efficiency), which is estimated to be between 30% and 40%. The use of advanced electrolyzers can raise the efficiency even up to 60%, but, on the other hand, increased purchase cost should be taken into consideration.

A very interesting and viable application of wind–hydrogen stand-alone systems could be in configurations where a bulk energy storage system is necessary in order to absorb the rejected wind energy in remote electricity grids, similar to the case of wind–hydro power applications. Islands where usually weak electrical grids exist often possess significantly high renewable energy potential. However, the local autonomous electrical networks in most cases are unable to absorb the renewable energy produced. The other barriers against renewable energy penetration in islands are caused mainly by the significant difference between energy production and demand. As a result, significant amounts of renewable energy are rejected by the local grids. Furthermore, one should not neglect the cost of electricity production in remote electrical grids, where in most cases the electricity production cost could even be 4 times the corresponding selling price. By storing the excess wind energy and using it during peak load demands, that is, when there is no wind available, renewable energy penetration limits may be bypassed and the disturbance of the local grid stability may be avoided. The use of the stored energy at peak demand can also improve the operation of the autonomous power stations and reduce their operational cost.

A typical wind–hydrogen configuration capable of fulfilling the energy needs of an isolated community is presented in **Figure 27**. More precisely, the hybrid system consists of

- one or more wind turbines;
- a water purification unit to improve the quality of the water used;
- a water storage tank to ensure that the process has adequate water in storage in case the water supply system is interrupted;
- an electrolyte solution (in alkaline systems);
- a hydrogen generation unit consisting of an electrolysis stack, a gas purification module, a dryer, and a heat removal system;
- a hydrogen storage medium (It should be noted that in order to fill the hydrogen tank, a compressor may be required if the electrolyzer is not designed to provide high pressure [57]);
- a fuel cell electricity generation unit; and
- a power conditioning and control unit.

During the operation of a wind–hydrogen energy production installation, the following operational situations may arise:

1. The wind power produced is in excess of the energy demand of the system.
   a) In that case, the hydrogen production unit absorbs the energy surplus to produce and store hydrogen.
   b) In case the available wind energy is more than the hydrogen production unit's power capacity or less than the minimum power required, the surplus is transferred to low-priority loads.

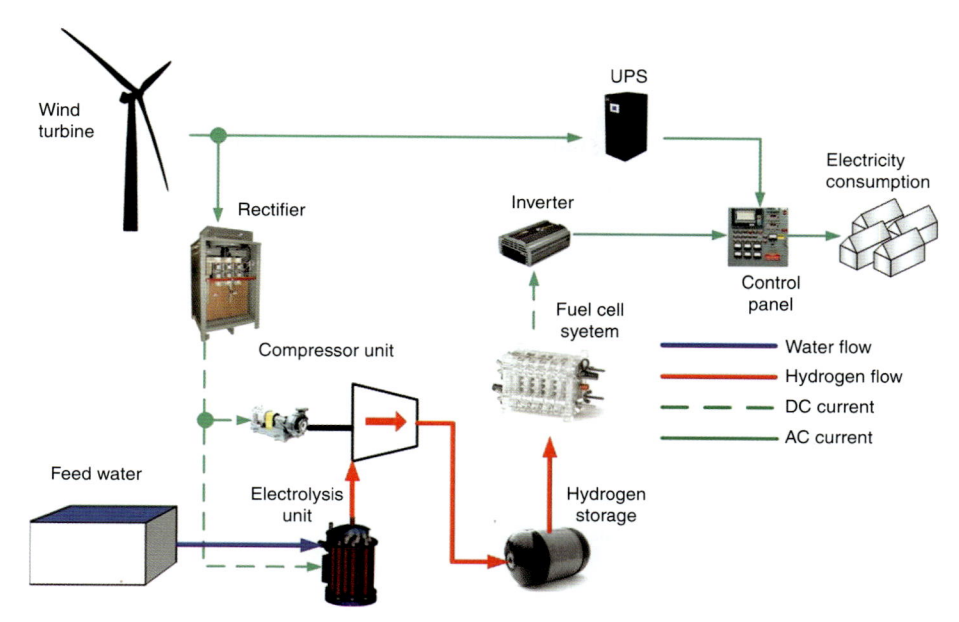

Figure 27 Integrated wind–hydrogen stand-alone installation.

2. The electrical power demand is more than the wind park output.
   a) In that case, the fuel cell unit covers the power deficit.
   b) In case there is not enough stored hydrogen, the internal combustion engines of the APS cover the power deficit, under a scheduled operation plan.

An alternative operation mode of a wind–hydrogen stand-alone system was suggested by Ntziachristos et al. [58]. In their study on a hybrid wind–fuel-cell power station, they consider that the electrolyzer should always remain in operation, and in cases where the wind turbine is not in operation, an internal loop should provide the electrolyzer with electrical power at standby levels from the fuel cell unit in order to avoid intermittent operation. In addition, in such a case, the wind turbine's electricity production is primarily supplied to the electrolyzer for producing and storing hydrogen. The analysis was based on a case study for the Karpathos island in Greece. Karpathos Island is a medium-size island in Greece with an autonomous electricity grid and possesses excellent wind potential. The simulation procedure developed by Ntziachristos et al. [58] introduced a level of hybridization, which indicates the ratio of wind energy delivered directly to the local grid to the energy delivered to the grid from the fuel cell. Given that the fuel cell provides constant power to the grid, the level of hybridization also indicates the variation over the constant power delivered to the grid. According to the results of their study, depending on the wind turbine selected and the preferred hybridization ratio, different electrolyzer rates and storage tank capacities can be realized.

In an attempt to define the energy production cost of a wind–hydrogen power system, Kavadias et al. [59] investigated the option of installing electrolyzers in order to absorb the wind energy rejected by a remote local electricity network in the island of Crete in Greece. Crete island is of great importance, as it has the largest autonomous electrical network in Greece. Although the island possesses excellent wind potential and faces substantial energy demand fulfillment, wind energy cannot be fully exploited owing to the local electrical grid instability barriers [60]. By an analysis made by Kaldellis et al. [60], it was estimated that in a 25 MW wind park almost 10% of the annual production was rejected leading to an average income loss of 25 000 € MW^{-1} for the wind park owners on the island [61]. According to their results, an optimum configuration could be achieved on the basis of minimum hydrogen production cost, which depends on the wind energy purchase price (**Figure 28**).

2.19.6 Energy Storage in Wind Stand-Alone Energy Systems

In long-term operation, dependence on the wind turbine energy production leads to the question of security of supply (firm power). Because of the stochastic nature of wind, independent and firm power cannot be realized by means of wind turbines alone. It requires a holistic supply concept which includes at least an energy storage system. All efforts in striving for an autonomous energy system with the aid of renewable energy sources always end up with a requirement for energy storage. The search for cost-effective energy storage is a theme pervading the whole range of these technologies. To exaggerate, one might say that as soon as an economically viable solution for storing energy has been found, all energy problems concerning the utilization of renewable energy sources can be solved [3].

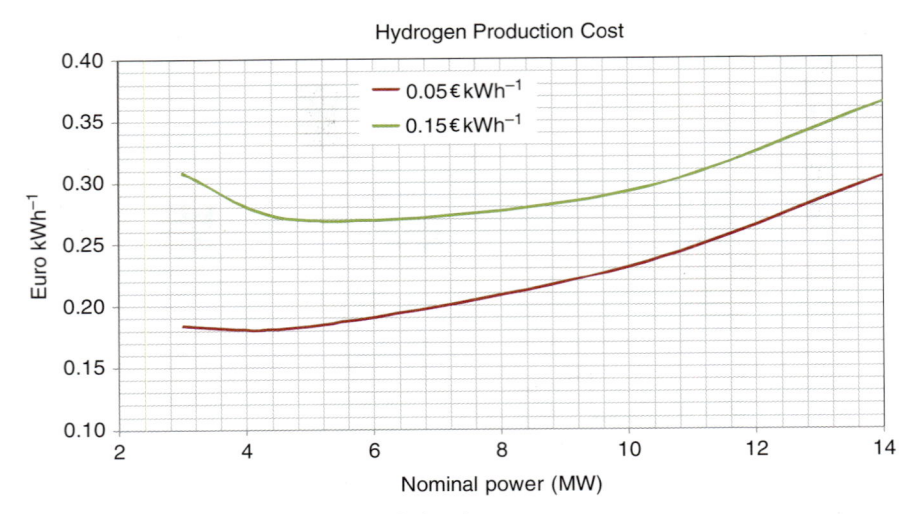

Figure 28 Hydrogen production cost for different electrolysis installation sizes.

The adoption of energy storage in stand-alone wind-based energy systems improves the reliability of energy supply and can contribute to the exploitation of the otherwise-wasted portion of renewable energy. The main drawback of energy storage systems is the high initial cost and in some cases the increased losses during a charge--discharge operation cycle. But it should be noted that maximum exploitation of renewable energy sources across a wide range of stand-alone energy system applications is possible only via the utilization of energy storage systems.

A typical energy storage system configuration comprises an energy source, which in the case of stand-alone systems involves renewable energy (e.g., wind); power conversion components, which include the necessary energy source interface and the main power conversion system; control devices; and an energy storage medium. The electricity generated by the renewable energy machine, which could be either AC or DC, passes through the necessary conversion stages to be stored in the appropriate form. In cases of energy deficit, the required amount of energy is drawn from the storage medium to be converted to the appropriate form of electricity requested by the load demand.

The energy flow of a typical energy storage system is presented in **Figure 29**. The input energy delivered to the energy storage system during its charging phase gets reduced owing to distribution and conversion losses. Distribution losses occur during the transfer of energy from the original energy source to the storage system, whereas conversion losses, which are the most important in majority of the cases, derive from the conversion of electrical energy to the form of energy required to charge the storage system. During the discharging phase, similar losses occur when the energy is drawn from the storage medium and is converted to electricity to fulfill the load requirements. Minor additional losses include self-discharge or idling losses that occur during standby or off-duty

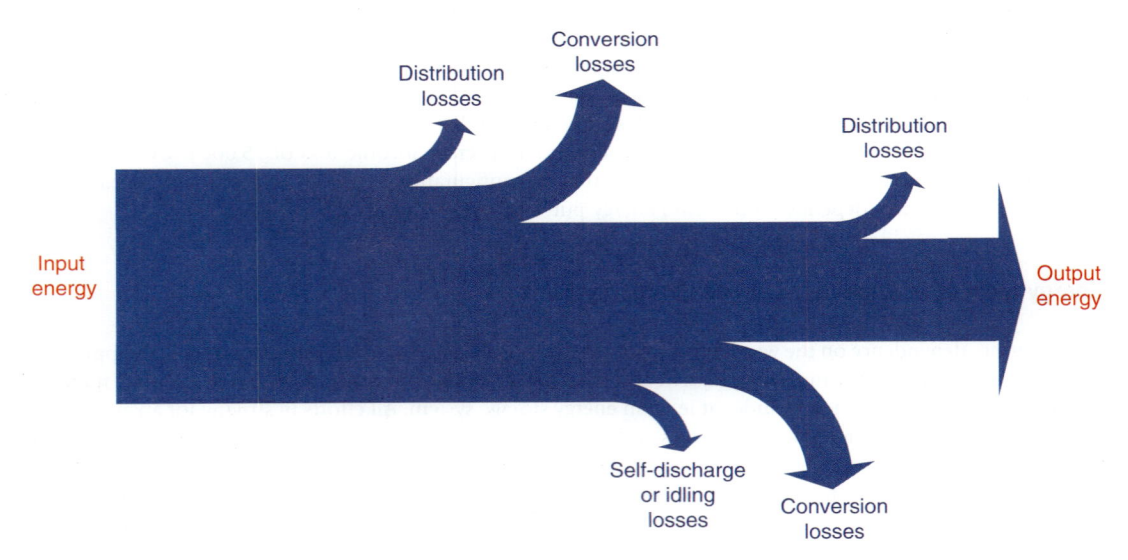

Figure 29 Sankey diagram of a typical energy storage system [62].

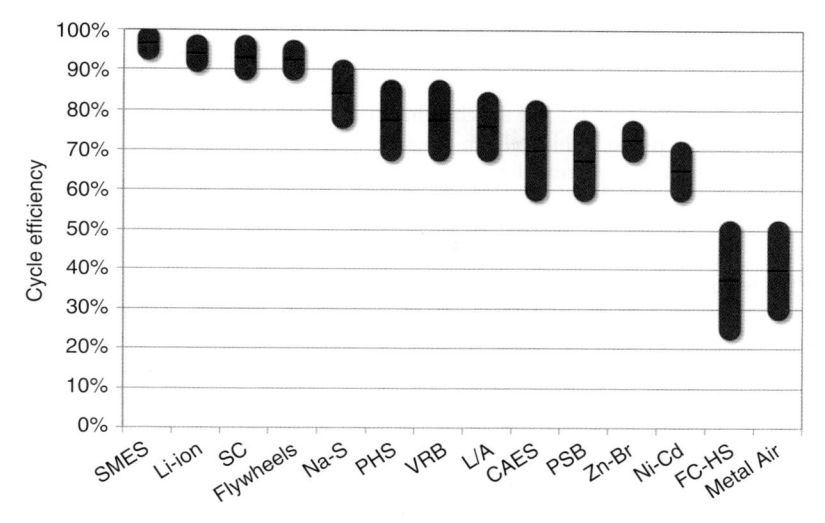

Figure 30 Cycling efficiency of different energy storage systems [63].

mode of the system. The efficiency of a charge–discharge cycle is defined as the ratio of the storage system energy output to the energy input to the storage system.

Accordingly, **Figure 30** presents the energy efficiency of the charging–discharging cycle of typical energy storage systems. According to **Figure 30**, flywheels and electrical energy storage systems, along with Na-S and Li-ion batteries, exceed 80% efficiency rates whereas fuel cell hydrogen storage systems (FC-HS) and metal–air batteries drop below 50%. The majority of the storage system technologies present efficiency rates between 60% and 80%.

2.19.6.1 Design Parameters of Energy Storage Systems

The power rating of an energy storage system is one of the main characteristics of the system. The power rating usually results from the maximum power requirements of the electrical load on the consumption side during discharging and the most frequently appearing excess power on the input side during charging. Accordingly, the size of the storage system is determined by the load demand and the energy source current and voltage requirements. The power rating influences the energy storage capacity, which is determined by the power and autonomy period requirements as well as by the system's efficiency and maximum depth of discharge.

Critical parameters of an energy storage system are also the discharge time and reaction time. The discharge time can be thought of as a dependent variable interrelated with the available storage capacity and the system power rating. The reaction time is inherent to the system, and short-reaction time energy storage systems can provide electricity instantly, whereas long-reaction time storage systems can only adjust to scheduled generation patterns that allow for a time interval between start-up and electricity production.

As mentioned before, self-discharge or idling losses are considered as minor energy losses in an energy storage system. At the same time, however, self-discharge or idling losses determine the maximum storage duration and thus delimit the system's application range. There are cases in which additional energy is required to compensate for self-discharge losses or sustain certain conditions of operation required for some storage systems (e.g., temperature level or vacuum requirements). Moreover, aging mechanisms should also be taken into account, as they invoke long-term gradual degradation reducing the system service period expectancy.

During the selection of the energy storage system for integration into a stand-alone power installation, the energy and power density should also be taken into consideration, as the space to be occupied by the system may in certain cases be extremely large or the required volume may not be available. Specific system boundaries are critical, and may be limited to storage media only or expanded so as to include power conversion systems and source/load interfaces.

2.19.6.2 Short Description of Energy Storage Technologies

The energy storage systems are classified according to the form in which energy is stored. Therefore, the main categories are mechanical, chemical, and electrical storage systems. The category of mechanical energy storage includes the PHS systems, the compressed air energy storage (CAES) systems, and the flywheels. In the category of chemical energy storage systems one may consider batteries, which in turn include lead–acid, nickel–cadmium, sodium–sulfur, metal–air, and lithium-ion batteries. Chemical storage also includes flow batteries (vanadium redox, polysulfide–bromine, and zinc–bromine batteries) as well as FC–HS systems. Finally, the category of electrical energy storage includes the superconducting magnetic energy storage (SMES) and the supercapacitor energy storage systems.

PHS is one of the most widely applicable bulk energy storage system, used in a wide range of installations all over the word (more than 100 GW have been installed worldwide). PHS may be coupled with wind turbines establishing the above-described wind–hydro power systems. In a PHS, the energy to be stored is exploited by a water pump used to pump water up an elevation to where the upper reservoir exists and this is considered the charging process. During the discharging process, water is released from the upper reservoir to an appropriate hydro turbine which operates connected to an electric generator. The cycle efficiency of a typical PHS ranges between 65% and 77%, whereas the main drawback of the corresponding systems is the high investment cost. The existence of at least two reservoirs at different elevations is also essential for feasible projects. PHS is able to take up load within a few minutes and is characterized by a high rate of extracted energy.

CAES systems are also used for bulk energy storage. During the charging process, the energy to be stored is used to pressurize air into an underground cavern, whereas during the discharging process the required amount of air is released from the cavern, heated using natural gas, and then supplied in the form of gases to a gas turbine where expansion takes place as in a typical Brayton–Joule cycle. The main benefit of the CAES is the separation of the compression and generation stages. Given that during charging-discharging cycle in a CAES the generation of 1 kWh of electricity requires ~0.75 kWh of electricity for the compressor and 4500 kJ of fuel for combustion, the overall efficiency of CAES is estimated to be on the order of 50%. The feasibility of CAES installation depends on the availability of a cavern [86]; therefore, favorable sites and geological formations for underground storage are necessary. The main advantages of CAES are that it has 2–3 times faster ramp rate than conventional units, its heat range at low capacity is stable, and it has considerably lower emissions than conventional gas turbines.

Flywheels are used mainly to ensure short-duration power quality and to provide a reliable option for UPS applications. In a flywheel energy storage system, the energy is stored as kinetic energy by causing a disk or rotor to spin on its axis. During discharging, that is, when power is required, the flywheel takes advantage of the rotor's inertia and the stored kinetic energy is converted to electricity. Modern flywheels consist of a rim attached to a shaft (rotating mass), which is supported by bearings and is connected to a motor/generator. Flywheels are characterized by high power density, relatively low maintenance needs, high cycling rate, deep discharges, and high self-discharge rate.

Regarding chemical energy storage, batteries are considered the most common and representative technology. They are the most widely adopted storage technique used in many RES-based applications. Different battery types exist; each one has its own special characteristics, over a wide range of applications. The most mature battery types are the lead–acid and nickel–cadmium batteries. Lead–acid batteries are characterized by their considerable self-discharge rate, low maintenance requirements, low energy density, limited service period, low depth of discharge, and considerable environmental impacts. Nickel–cadmium batteries are characterized by their higher energy density and self-discharge, deep discharge rate, longer service period, high capital cost, low efficiency rates, and quite severe environmental impacts. More advanced battery technologies include sodium–sulfur, metal–air, and lithium-ion batteries. For sodium–sulfur batteries, an operating temperature of 300 °C is required, meaning that heat supply is necessary. On the other hand, sodium–sulfur batteries have no self-discharge, and efficiency and depth of discharge are quite high. Lithium-ion batteries have high energy density, a considerable number of charge–discharge cycles, and deep discharge rates. On the other hand, the main drawback of the technology is the high capital cost and the required protection circuits to maintain voltage and current within safety limits. Finally, metal–air batteries are characterized by high energy density, low system performance, short service period, low self-discharge rate, and very low system cost.

Flow batteries store energy by means of a reversible chemical reaction. The energy is stored in two liquid electrolyte solutions. The energy capacity and the rated power of the system are independent of one another. Energy capacity depends on the quantity of electrolytes used. Flow batteries are used in a number of large-scale and stand-alone RES installations. Different technologies of flow batteries exists (vanadium redox, polysulfide–bromine, zinc–bromine) which are characterized by the electrolytes used. The efficiency of flow batteries ranges between 60% and 80%, with future prospects ensuring high cycling capacity and deep discharge rates. Finally, the significant environmental impacts should also be considered as a drawback of the technology.

Production of hydrogen is one of the ideal methods for the absorption of intermittent RES such as wind energy. In FC–HS systems, the renewable energy is converted to fuel (hydrogen), which is stored in appropriate storage tanks. The storage capacity depends only on the amount of the hydrogen that need to be stored and is theoretically independent of the fuel cell's nominal power. During the discharging procedure, hydrogen is released from the storage tank and is fed to the fuel cell unit, which then generates electricity. The main drawback of the FC–HS systems is the low charge–discharge cycle efficiency estimated to be between 30% and 40%, including the losses during both the electrolysis to produce hydrogen and the storage stage. The advantages of the technology, on the other hand, include the low energy cost, the high energy density, and the negligible self-discharge rate.

The category of electrical energy storage includes SMES and supercapacitors. SMES store energy in the magnetic field produced when DC flows through a superconducting coil. Significant amounts of energy is required to keep the system within the operating temperature range of 50–77 K. Supercapacitors' operation is based on the same operational principle as that of conventional capacitors where energy storage occurs in an existing electric field. Both these energy storage systems are destined for power quality applications supporting the short fluctuations of RES energy production rather than for storing residual energy.

Recapitulating, for the selection of the most appropriate energy storage system for a wind-based stand-alone system, one should take into consideration numerous characteristics among which are the power rating, required storage capacity, discharge time, self-discharge rating, mass and volume energy and power density, service period, cycle efficiency, maximum depth of discharge rate, response time of the storage system, and last, but not least, energy and power cost. Figure 31 presents a classification of different energy storage systems in terms of energy capacity, rated power, and discharge time. Pumped hydro,

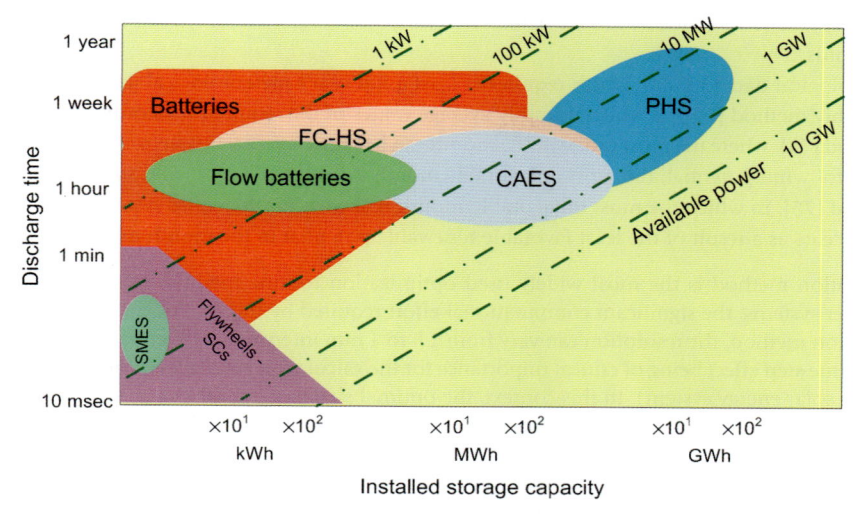

Figure 31 Energy capacity, discharge time, and power ratings for different energy storage solutions [64].

compressed air, and fuel cell hydrogen systems are ideal for applications of commodity storage, rapid reserve, and area control/frequency responsive reserve. On the other hand, flywheels, supercapacitors, and superconducting magnetic systems are suitable mainly for power quality/reliability and transmission system stability applications. Typical batteries can be used in a wide range of applications from power quality improvement to energy management. Flow batteries are appropriate for transmission and distribution deferral.

2.19.7 Design, Simulation, and Evaluation Software Tools for Wind-Based Hybrid Energy Systems

The future success of wind-based hybrid energy systems relies on continuous research, development, and demonstration of RES technologies, and is based on improvement in their operation performance, cost reduction, and improvement in their reliability. In order to determine the optimum configuration, different combinations of components should be considered, based on a number of factors, for example, the specific area's renewable energy potential, the load demand requirements, and the subjective preference factor of the designer or the user which may lead to favoring a particular system not necessarily constituting the optimum solution design.

The criteria used for the optimization of wind stand-alone hybrid systems are the same as the ones used for the optimization of any renewable energy-based hybrid system. The system designer should best balance power reliability and system cost requirements with the intermittent characteristics of renewable energy, compelling the investigation of the system's reliability during the design process. In this context, the most common method used for the power reliability analysis of hybrid systems is the 'loss of power supply probability (LOPSP)' [65], in which the probability of insufficient power supply (i.e., the probability of the system's maximum power output not satisfying the load demand) is recorded for a given period of time. The 'loss of load probability (LOLP)' model [11, 66] is also widely used, in which the probability that instantaneous power demand will exceed the respective power supply is estimated for the time period analyzed. Similarly, 'loss of load hours (LOLH)' [67] represents the number of load failures in which the load demand exceeds the power supply, based on simulations on an hourly basis.

Regarding the system cost analysis, several economic criteria can be used to determine the economic performance of hybrid energy systems. The most commonly used criterion is the 'net present value (NPV)' [21, 68, 69], which is defined as the total present value of a time series of cash flows including the initial cost of the system, the replacement cost of major components of the installation, the maintenance and operation costs, and finally the revenues (estimated as the avoided expenses by the use of RES). Further, the 'internal rate of return (IRR)' [21, 70] also constitutes a criterion that can be used for the evaluation of the economic performance of hybrid energy systems. More precisely, IRR is the discount rate that dictates NPV equal to zero during a given time period. Besides, on top of that, one may also use more simplified economic criteria that also provide an indication of a hybrid system's economic performance, such as the payback period and the economic efficiency [34, 71].

In this context, different optimization techniques have been developed in order to define the renewable-based electrification system that will guarantee the lowest energy production cost with the maximum exploitation of the system's capabilities, although, as already mentioned, system power reliability requirements should also be considered in the optimization methods applied. At this point, what should also be underlined is the important role of the meteorological data sets – used as time series – in such commonly used simulation approaches. More specifically, there are several methods presented by researchers on the basis of the available meteorological data sets, which include

- typical meteorological year' [72], which includes a dataset of hourly values selected for specific months from different years from a long period of records;
- long period meteorological data [33, 73], which requires at least a full year's meteorological data to be available;
- yearly average monthly method [74], in which monthly average values of the required meteorological parameters are used;
- worst months method [74], where the most unfavorable month can be chosen for each system component; for example, the most unfavorable month for wind potential, the most unfavorable month for solar radiation, and so on; and
- worst month method [75], in which the most unfavorable month is chosen for the entire system dimensions; that is, when the largest system size occurs as a result of the least favorable renewable potential in the month used.

The time series simulation method is the most widely used optimization routine method. Given the computational power of contemporary computer systems, the significant computational effort required by the specific method is no longer a drawback. In the time series simulation method, the resolution can vary from 1 h to 1 min intervals – or even lower – depending on the depth of the analysis, with the time step effect being of critical importance for the calculation results (see, for example, Reference [76] for the sizing of a stand-alone solar energy system). In this context, the optimal sizing of hybrid energy systems can be obtained through linear programing, probabilistic approach, iterative techniques, dynamic programing, and multiobjective optimization techniques [68, 77, 78].

A wide range of software tools have been developed to analyze the integration of renewable energy into different energy systems [79]. The list can include more than 70 software tools, with many more being able to adjust or be programed so as to be used as optimization tools for the design of hybrid energy systems. Nevertheless, this section will focus only on a few software tools that are both freely available to users and have been widely used in research papers.

The Hybrid Optimization Model for Electric Renewables (HOMER) software was developed by the US National Renewable Energy Laboratory [80–82]. HOMER is a computer model that can be used for the design of micropower systems and facilitates the comparison of power generation technologies across a wide range of applications. The software is capable of modeling a power system's physical behavior and its lifecycle cost over its lifetime. The user can compare many different design options based on their technical and economic characteristics. HOMER can model off-grid and grid-connected micropower systems serving electric and thermal loads, and including any combination of PV modules, wind turbines, small hydro, biomass power, reciprocating-engine generators, microturbines, fuel cells, batteries, and hydrogen storage. The required inputs of the software include load demand, hybrid system components, available resources to be exploited, economic indices, generator control dispatch strategy (load following, cycle charging), possible operational constraints, and finally the optimization variables used to build the set of all possible system configurations. After the data input procedure, HOMER simulates the operation of the system by making energy balance calculations on an hourly basis for 1 year. For each hour, the electric load is compared to the energy the system can supply and HOMER decides how to operate the generators and whether to charge or discharge the storage medium. If the system meets the load for the entire year, HOMER estimates the lifecycle cost of the system, accounting for the capital, replacement, operation and maintenance, fuel, and interest costs. The main advantage of HOMER is that it includes an optimization module that automatically finds the combination of components that can serve the load at the lowest lifecycle cost. The main disadvantage of HOMER is that it is mainly an economic model dedicated to system selection and pre-sizing, and cannot be used for system design requirements.

Hybrid2 software package is a combined probabilistic/time series computer model that helps the designer in sizing hybrid power systems and selecting operating options on the basis of overall system performance and economics [5, 77, 78, 83]. The program uses time series data, which include site-specific conditions and load profiles. The user is able to consider a number of system configurations and operating strategies in order to optimize the system design. Two different simulation models are used in the program: the logistical models used for long-term performance predictions and component sizing, and the dynamic models used for component design and assessment of system stability. Hybrid2 uses a time series simulation analysis over intervals typically ranging from 10 min to 1 h. The basic inputs of the program include load demand, site and resources data, power system characteristics including the bus system and system components, the base case which will be used for comparison purposes, and the costs/economic parameters of the system. The main advantage of Hybrid2 is that it is mainly a technical model dedicated to system design, so it can simulate some important technical constraints, including bus voltage levels, intrahour performance of components, and complex diesel generator dispatch strategies. The weakness of Hybrid2 is that it does not include optimization and sensitivity analysis modules.

Finally, Hybrid Optimization by Genetic Algorithms (HOGA) is a program developed by the electrical engineering department of University of Zaragoza in Spain [84, 85]. The optimization of the hybrid system is achieved through the minimization of the total system cost for the period analyzed, based on net present cost calculations. The multiobjective optimization feature of the program is achieved by additional variables that may also be considered, such as carbon dioxide emissions or LOLP. The program can be used – apart from the hybrid energy systems that generate electricity – to also examine the performance of hybrid systems that produce hydrogen or energy applied to water pumping loads. The simulation is carried out using 1 h intervals during which all parameters remain constant. The program allows surplus energy management, which includes the options of either selling the energy to the local electricity grid or producing hydrogen in an electrolyzer and storing it in tanks.

Table 1 summarizes the basic characteristics of the different tools that can be used for simulation or/and optimization of hybrid energy systems.

Table 1 Basic characteristics of hybrid system simulation tools

HOMER	Hybrid2	HOGA
National Renewable Energy Laboratory, HOMER Energy LLC	Renewable Energy Research Laboratory, University of Massachusetts	Electric Engineering Department, University of Zaragoza
• Free to download	• Free to download	• Free to download
• Simulation	• Simulation	• Simulation
• Optimization	• Optimization	• Optimization
• Multiple RES analysis capability	• Multiple RES analysis capability	• Multiple RES analysis capability
• Economical optimization	• Control strategies	• Multiobjective optimization
• Control strategies		• Control strategies

Thus, as it may be concluded, users nowadays have the advantage of designing optimum wind stand-alone hybrid energy system configurations with the help of a wide range of free software tools and commercially available integrated programs, and the elaborate research and development on stand-alone applications carried out continuously will certainly result in more reliable and cost-effective electrification systems.

References

[1] Takada M and Fracchia S (2007) *A Review of Energy in National MDG Reports*. New York: United Nations Development Programme.
[2] Legros G, Havet I, Bruce N, et al. (2009) The Energy Access Situation in Developing Countries: A Review Focusing on the Least Developed Countries and Sub-Saharan Africa. United Nations Development Programme and World Health Organization.
[3] Hau E (2006) *Wind Turbines: Fundamentals, Technologies, Application, Economics*. Berlin, Heidelberg: Springer Verlag.
[4] Lundsager P and Risø F (2001) *Isolated Systems with Wind Power: Main Report, 1256*. Roskilde, Denmark: Risø National Laboratory.
[5] Ackermann T (2005) *Wind Power in Power Systems*. Chichester, UK: Wiley.
[6] Burton T, Sharpe D, Jenkins N, and Bossanyi E (2001) *Wind Energy Handbook*. West Sussex, UK: Wiley.
[7] Caralis G and Zervos A (2007) Analysis of wind power penetration in autonomous greek Islands. *Wind Engineering* 31: 487–502.
[8] Salas V, Olias E, Rascon M, et al. (2000) Hybrid powering system for stand-alone remote telecom applications. *Proceedings of the 22nd International Telecommunications Energy Conference, INTELEC*, Phoenix, AZ, USA, pp. 311–316. 10–14 September.
[9] Kaldellis J and Kondili E (2007) The water shortage problem in the Aegean archipelago islands: Cost-effective desalination prospects. *Desalination* 216: 123–138.
[10] Spyrou ID and Anagnostopoulos JS (2010) Design study of a stand-alone desalination system powered by renewable energy sources and a pumped storage unit. *Desalination* 257: 137–149.
[11] Hadj Arab A, Chenlo F, and Benghanem M (2004) Loss-of-load probability of photovoltaic water pumping systems. *Solar Energy* 76: 713–723.
[12] Al Suleimani Z and Rao NR (2000) Wind-powered electric water-pumping system installed in a remote location. *Applied Energy* 65: 339–347.
[13] Twidell J (1987) *A Guide to Small Wind Energy Conversion Systems*. Cambridge: Cambridge University Press.
[14] Braña IB (2010) Historical Background of the Wind Power. http://isaacbrana.wordpress.com/2010/06/28/historical-background-of-the-wind-power
[15] Johnson GL (2006) *Wind Energy Systems*. Manhattan, KS. Englewood Cliffs, NJ: Prentice Hall.
[16] Honneff H (1932) *Windkraftwerke*. Brunswick: Fried. Vieweg & Sohn.
[17] Putnam PC (1944) Wind Turbine. US Patent 2,360,791.
[18] Putnam PC (1974) *Power from the Wind*. New York: Van Nostrand Reinhold Inc.
[19] Meyer NI (2007) Learning from wind energy policy in the EU: Lessons from Denmark, Sweden and Spain. *European Environment* 17: 347–362.
[20] American Wind Energy Association (AWEA) (2009) *Small Wind Turbine Global Market Study*. Washington, DC: AWEA.
[21] Kaldellis JK (2005) *Wind Energy Management*. Athens: Stamoulis Ed.
[22] Wood D and Freere P (2010) Stand-alone wind energy systems. In: Kaldellis JK (ed.) *Stand-Alone and Hybrid Wind Energy Systems*, pp. 165–215. Cambridge: Woodhead Publishing Ltd.
[23] Ekren O, Ekren BY, and Ozerdem B (2009) Break-even analysis and size optimization of a PV/wind hybrid energy conversion system with battery storage – A case study. *Applied Energy* 86: 1043–1054.
[24] Nema P, Nema RK, and Rangnekar S (2009) A current and future state of art development of hybrid energy system using wind and PV-solar: A review. *Renewable and Sustainable Energy Reviews* 13: 2096–2103.
[25] Urban Green Energy Inc. http://www.urbangreenenergy.com/ (accessed January 2011).
[26] Aeolos Wind Turbine LLC. http://www.windturbinestar.com/ (accessed December 2010).
[27] Seaforth Energy Inc. http://seaforthenergy.com/ (accessed December 2010).
[28] Vlachou D, Messaritakis G, and Kaldellis JK (1999) Presentation and energy production analysis of commercial wind turbines. *Proceedings of European Wind Energy Conference and Exhibition*, pp. 476–480. Nice, France.
[29] Kaldellis J and Vlachos G (2006) Optimum sizing of an autonomous wind–diesel hybrid system for various representative wind-potential cases. *Applied Energy* 83: 113–132.
[30] Kaldellis JK and Tsesmelis M (2002) Integrated energy balance analysis of a stand-alone wind power system for various typical Aegean Sea regions. *Wind Energy* 5: 1–17.
[31] Kaldellis JK, Kavadias KA, and Zafirakis D (2009) Integrated electrification solution for remote islands based on wind-PV hybrid system. *Proceedings of European Wind Energy Conference and Exhibition*, Marseille, France.
[32] Kaldellis JK (2010) Overview of stand-alone and hybrid wind energy systems. In: Kaldellis JK (ed.) *Stand-alone and Hybrid Wind Energy Systems*, pp. 3–28. Cambridge: Woodhead Publishing Ltd.
[33] Kaldellis JK (2002) Optimum autonomous wind–power system sizing for remote consumers, using long-term wind speed data. *Applied Energy* 71: 215–233.
[34] Kaldellis JK and Kavadias K (2007) Cost-benefit analysis of remote hybrid wind-diesel power stations: Case study Aegean Sea islands. *Energy Policy* 35: 1525–1538.
[35] McGowan JG, Manwell JF, and Connors SR (1988) Wind/diesel energy systems: Review of design options and recent developments. *Solar Energy* 41: 561–575.

[36] Kaldellis JK, Kapsali M, and Kavadias K (2010) Energy balance analysis of wind-based pumped hydro storage systems in remote island electrical networks. *Applied Energy* 87: 2427–2437.
[37] Kaldellis JK, Kavadias KA, and Christinakis E (2001) Evaluation of the wind-hydro energy solution for remote islands. *Energy Conversion and Management* 42: 1105–1120.
[38] Castronuovo E and Lopes J (2004) Optimal operation and hydro storage sizing of a wind-hydro power plant. *International Journal of Electrical Power & Energy Systems* 26: 771–778.
[39] Anagnostopoulos J and Papantonis D (2007) Pumping station design for a pumped-storage wind-hydro power plant. *Energy Conversion and Management* 48: 3009–3017.
[40] Balamurugan P, Ashok S, and Jose TL (2011) An optimal hybrid wind-biomass gasifier system for rural areas. *Energy Sources, Part A: Recovery, Utilization, and Environmental Effects* 33: 823–832.
[41] Pérez-Navarro A, Alfonso D, Álvarez C, *et al.* (2010) Hybrid biomass-wind power plant for reliable energy generation. *Renewable Energy* 35: 1436–1443.
[42] Kavadias KA, Zafirakis D, Rozakeas K, and Kaldellis JK (2008) Optimum sizing of a hydrogen production installation based on renewable energy surplus. *Proceedings of the World Renewable Energy Congress X and Exhibition*, Glasgow, Scotland.
[43] Garcia R and Weisser D (2006) A wind–diesel system with hydrogen storage: Joint optimisation of design and dispatch. *Renewable Energy* 31: 2296–2320.
[44] Wood DH (2001) An improved determination of the optimum tower height for a small wind turbine. *Wind Engineering* 25: 191–196.
[45] Lemstrom B, Rakkolainen J, and Peltola E (1999) A wind farm's impact on the quality of electricity in a weak network. *Proceedings of the European Wind Energy Conference: Wind Energy for the Next Millennium*, pp. 747–749. Nice, France, 1–5 March.
[46] Kapsali M and Kaldellis JK (2010) Combining hydro and variable wind power generation by means of pumped-storage under economically viable terms. *Applied Energy* 87: 3475–3485.
[47] Kaldellis JK (2003) An integrated feasibility analysis of a stand-alone wind power system, including no-energy fulfillment cost. *Wind Energy* 6: 355–364.
[48] Notton G, Muselli M, Poggi P, and Louche A (2001) Decentralized wind energy systems providing small electrical loads in remote areas. *International Journal of Energy Research* 25: 141–164.
[49] Zafirakis DP, Kavadias KA, and Kaldellis JK (2010) Optimization of energy autonomous wind-photovoltaic hybrid systems. *Proceedings of the World Renewable Energy Congress (WRECXI)*. Abu Dhabi, United Emirates, 25–30 September.
[50] Papaefthymiou SV, Karamanou EG, Papathanassiou SA, and Papadopoulos MP (2010) A wind-hydro-pumped storage station leading to high RES penetration in the autonomous island system of Ikaria. *IEEE Transactions on Sustainable Energy* 1: 163–172.
[51] Vlachou D, Christinakis E, Kavadias K, and Kaldellis J (1999) Optimum wind-hydro energy station operation, using an advanced fluid flow analysis code. *Proceedings of 3rd National Congress on Computational Mechanics*, Volos, Greece. pp. 811–820.
[52] Kaldellis JK and Kavadias KA (2001) Optimal wind-hydro solution for Aegean Sea islands' electricity-demand fulfilment. *Applied Energy* 70: 333–354.
[53] The Poul la Cour Museum. http://www.poullacour.dk/engelsk/museet.htm (accessed October 2010).
[54] Bernalagustin J and Dufolopez R (2008) Hourly energy management for grid-connected wind–hydrogen systems. *International Journal of Hydrogen Energy* 33: 6401–6413.
[55] Kauranen P, Lund P, and Vanhanen J (1994) Development of a self-sufficient solar-hydrogen energy system. *International Journal of Hydrogen Energy* 19: 99–106.
[56] Muljadi E, Wang C, and Nehrir MH (2004) Parallel operation of wind turbine, fuel cell, and diesel generation sources. *IEEE Power Engineering Society General Meeting*, Denver, CO, USA, pp.1927–1932.
[57] Sherif S and Barbir F (2005) Wind energy and the hydrogen economy – Review of the technology. *Solar Energy* 78: 647–660.
[58] Ntziachristos L, Kouridis C, Samaras Z, and Pattas K (2005) A wind-power fuel-cell hybrid system study on the non-interconnected Aegean islands grid. *Renewable Energy* 30: 1471–1487.
[59] Kavadias KA, Kondili EM, and Kaldellis JK (2006) Renewable energy based hydrogen production methods: An economic and energy efficiency comparison. *Proceedings of the IXth World Renewable Energy Congress*. Florence, Italy, August.
[60] Kaldellis JK, Kavadias KA, Papantonis DE, and Stavrakakis GS (2006) Maximizing wind generated electricity with hydro storage: Case study Crete. *Wind Engineering* 30: 73–92.
[61] Kaldellis JK, Kavadias KA, Filios A, and Garofallakis S (2004) Income loss due to wind energy rejected by the Crete island electrical network-the present situation. *Applied Energy* 79: 127–144.
[62] Zafirakis DP (2010) Overview of energy storage technologies for renewable energy systems. In: Kaldellis JK (ed.) *Stand-Alone and Hybrid Wind Energy Systems*, pp. 29–80. Cambridge: Woodhead Publishing Ltd.
[63] Kaldellis J, Zafirakis D, and Kavadias K (2009) Techno-economic comparison of energy storage systems for island autonomous electrical networks. *Renewable and Sustainable Energy Reviews* 13: 378–392.
[64] Kaldellis J and Zafirakis D (2007) Optimum energy storage techniques for the improvement of renewable energy sources-based electricity generation economic efficiency. *Energy* 32: 2295–2305.
[65] Abouzahr I and Ramakumar R (1991) Loss of power supply probability of stand-alone photovoltaic systems: A closed form solution approach. *Energy Conversion, IEEE Transactions* 6: 1–11.
[66] Celik AN (2007) Effect of different load profiles on the loss-of-load probability of stand-alone photovoltaic systems. *Renewable Energy* 32: 2096–2115.
[67] Shrestha GB and Goel L (1998) A study on optimal sizing of stand-alone photovoltaic stations. *Energy Conversion, IEEE Transactions* 13: 373–378.
[68] Deshmukh MK and Deshmukh SS (2008) Modeling of hybrid renewable energy systems. *Renewable and Sustainable Energy Reviews* 12: 235–249.
[69] Bakos GC and Soursos M (2002) Techno-economic assessment of a stand-alone PV/hybrid installation for low-cost electrification of a tourist resort in Greece. *Applied Energy* 73: 183–193.
[70] Short W, Packey DJ, and Holt T (2005) *A Manual for the Economic Evaluation of Energy Efficiency and Renewable Energy Technologies*. Honolulu, Hawaii: University Press of the Pacific.
[71] Kaldellis JK (2010) Feasibility assessment for stand-alone and HEW systems. In: Kaldellis JK (ed.) *Stand-Alone and Hybrid Wind Energy Systems*, pp. 102–161. Cambridge: Woodhead Publishing Ltd.
[72] Yang H and Lu L (2004) Study on typical meteorological years and their effect on building energy and renewable energy simulations. *ASHRAE Transactions* 110: 424–431.
[73] Koutroulis E, Kolokotsa D, Potirakis A, and Kalaitzakis K (2006) Methodology for optimal sizing of stand-alone photovoltaic/wind-generator systems using genetic algorithms. *Solar Energy* 80: 1072–1088.
[74] Protogeropoulos C, Brinkworth BJ, and Marshall RH (1997) Sizing and techno-economical optimization for hybrid solar photovoltaic/wind power systems with battery storage. *International Journal of Energy Research* 21: 465–479.
[75] Morgan TR, Marshall RH, and Brinkworth BJ (1997) ARES – A refined simulation program for the sizing and optimisation of autonomous hybrid energy systems. *Solar Energy* 59: 205–215.
[76] Notton G, Muselli M, Poggi P, and Louche A (1996) Autonomous photovoltaic systems: Influences of some parameters on the sizing: Simulation time step, input and output power profile. *Renewable Energy* 7: 353–369.
[77] Zhou W, Lou C, Li Z, *et al.* (2010) Current status of research on optimum sizing of stand-alone hybrid solar–wind power generation systems. *Applied Energy* 87: 380–389.
[78] Kondili E (2010) Design and performance optimisation. In: Kaldellis JK (ed.) *Stand-alone and Hybrid Wind Energy Systems*, pp. 81–101. Cambridge: Woodhead Publishing Ltd.
[79] Connolly D, Lund H, Mathiesen BV, and Leahy M (2010) A review of computer tools for analysing the integration of renewable energy into various energy systems. *Applied Energy* 87: 1059–1082.
[80] HOMER Energy. http://www.homerenergy.com/ (accessed December 2010).

[81]   Lambert T, Gilman P, and Lilienthal P (2006) Micropower system modeling with HOMER. In: Farret FA and Simoes MG (eds) *Integration of Alternative Sources of Energy*, pp. 379–418. New Jersey, USA: John Wiley & Sons, Inc.
[82]   Georgilakis PS (2005) State-of-the-art of decision support systems for the choice of renewable energy sources for energy supply in isolated regions. *International Journal of Distributed Energy Resources* 2: 129–150.
[83]   RERL – Research, Hybrid Power. http://www.ceere.org/rerl/ (accessed December 2010).
[84]   HOGA Software. http://www.unizar.es/rdufo/hoga-eng.htm (accessed January 2011).
[85]   Bernal-Agustín JL and Dufo-López R (2005) Simulation and optimization of stand-alone hybrid renewable energy systems. *Renewable and Sustainable Energy Reviews* 13: 2111–2118.
[86]   Denholm P and Kulcinski GL (2004) Life cycle energy requirements and greenhouse gas emissions from large scale energy storage systems. *Energy Conversion and Management* 45: 2153–2172.

Further Reading

Bansal AK, Gupta RA, and Kumar R (2011) Optimization of hybrid PV/wind energy system using Meta Particle Swarm Optimization (MPSO). *Proceedings of India International Conference on Power Electronics, IICPE*. January, New Delhi, India.
Belfkira R, Zhang L, and Barakat G (2011) Optimal sizing study of hybrid wind/PV/diesel power generation unit. *Solar Energy* 85: 100–110.
Calderón M, Calderón AJ, Ramiro A, et al. (2011) Evaluation of a hybrid photovoltaic-wind system with hydrogen storage performance using exergy analysis. *International Journal of Hydrogen Energy* 36: 5751–5762.
European Wind Energy Association (EWEA) (2009) Wind Energy – The Facts: A Guide to the Technology, Economics and Future of Wind Power. London; Sterling, VA: Earthscan.
Gipe P (1995) *Wind Energy Comes of Age*. John Wiley and Sons.
Gipe P (2009) *Wind Energy Basics: A Guide to Home- and Community-Scale Wind Energy Systems*. White River Junction, VT: Chelsea Green Publishing.
Kaldellis JK (2010) *Stand-Alone and Hybrid Wind Energy Systems: Technology, Energy Storage and Applications*. Cambridge: Woodhead Publishing Limited.
Kathirvel C and Porkumaran K (2010) Analysis and design of hybrid wind/diesel system with energy storage for rural application. *Proceedings of the 9th International Power and Energy Conference, IPEC*, pp. 250–255. October, Singapore.
Liu G, Rasul MG, Amanullah MTO, and Khan MMK (2011) Feasibility study of stand-alone PV-wind-biomass hybrid energy system in Australia. *Proceedings of the Asia-Pacific Power and Energy Engineering Conference, APPEEC*. March, Wuhan, China.
Ozaki Y, Miyatake M, and Iwaki D (2010) Power control of a stand-alone photovoltaic/wind/energy storage hybrid generation system with maximum power point tracker. *International Conference on Electrical Machines and Systems, ICEMS*, pp. 607–611. October, Incheon, South Korea.
Roy PC, Majumder A, and Chakraborty N (2010) Optimization of a stand-alone solar PV-wind-DG hybrid system for distributed power generation at sagar Island. *AIP Conference Proceedings*, pp. 260–265. Conference ICMOS 2010: International conference on modeling, optimization, and computing, West Bengal, India, October.
Stiebler M (2008) *Wind Energy Systems for Electric Power Generation*. Berlin: Springer Verlag.

2.20 Wind Power Industry and Markets

PE Morthorst, Technical University of Denmark, Roskilde, Denmark

© 2012 Elsevier Ltd.

2.20.1	Global Market Development	657
2.20.2	Trends in the Development of Wind Turbines	659
2.20.3	Main Drivers behind the Wind Power Development	660
2.20.4	Market Development in Europe	662
2.20.4.1	Germany	662
2.20.4.2	Spain	663
2.20.4.3	Rest of Europe	664
2.20.5	Development of Wind Power in North America	665
2.20.5.1	United States	665
2.20.6	Wind Power Development in Asia	666
2.20.6.1	China	666
2.20.7	Offshore Wind Power Development	666
2.20.8	Wind Turbine Manufacturers	667
References		669

2.20.1 Global Market Development

Within the last 15–20 years, wind power has on a global scale developed incredibly fast. In 1990, total installed capacity of wind power in the world amounted to approximately 2 GW – by the end of 2009, this capacity has increased to 158 GW equaling an annual growth rate of almost 25%. Although, on a global scale wind power accounts for only approximately 2% of total electricity supply, this small fraction is increasing rapidly.

As shown in **Figure 1**, wind power has experienced a fairly steady but continued rapid capacity development (left part). The right part of **Figure 1** shows the capacity development in the early years, from 1983 to 1995, and already from the late 1980s a strong development is taking place.

The growth in installed global wind power capacity is shown in **Figure 2**. Except for 1 year, 2004, the annual absolute growth has increased for every year. For quite an impressive time period, the annual percentage growth rates have exceeded 30%. In 2008, the growth equaled almost 29%, and in 2009, it was 31%, despite a financial crisis.

On a global scale, the three main regions regarding wind power development are Europe, North America, and Asia, comprising approximately 97.2% of total installed capacity. The rest of the world only has smaller amounts of wind power installed, that is, Latin America has 0.8% of world capacity, the Pacific has 1.4%, and finally, Africa and Middle East has 0.5%.

For a long period, Europe was dominating the wind power scene. At the beginning of the century, Germany and Spain were unrivaled in wind power expansion, but in recent years countries outside Europe have moved fast. This applies especially for the United States and China, where the latter in just a few years ranks third in terms of installed wind power capacity.

This becomes clear from **Figure 3**, where wind power installed in Asia in 2009 amounted to 14.6 GW, significantly above North America with 10.9 GW and Europe with 10.5 GW installed wind power capacity. Thus, the European share has decreased strongly from 67% of total world installed capacity in 2003 to 28% in 2009. However, with regard to cumulative installed capacity, Europe is still in the lead with a little more than 48% of total installed wind turbine capacity, while approximately 24% was installed in North America and approximately 25% in Asia [1].

Figure 4 shows the top 10 countries' distribution of the global installed wind power capacity by end 2009. Four countries, the United States, Germany, China, and Spain, are dominant covering approximately two-thirds of the cumulative installed capacity worldwide. Following these four, we find a large group of countries with smaller contributions, although some of them are developing quite fast.

Observe that all top 10 countries are from the above-mentioned three major regions (the most important countries will be treated in more detail in the following sections). The other regions of the world – Latin America, the Pacific, and Africa and Middle East – have not yet entered the 'take off' stage. In Latin America, Brazil, Mexico, and Chile have done well within the last couple of years, while other countries only contribute irregularly. In Africa, mainly the North African countries like Egypt and Morocco are in a steady growth. Finally, in the Pacific region, both Australia and New Zealand have experienced growth in 2009 (400 and 170 MW installed capacity, respectively); however, the development in recent years has not been stable.

658 Wind Power Industry and Markets

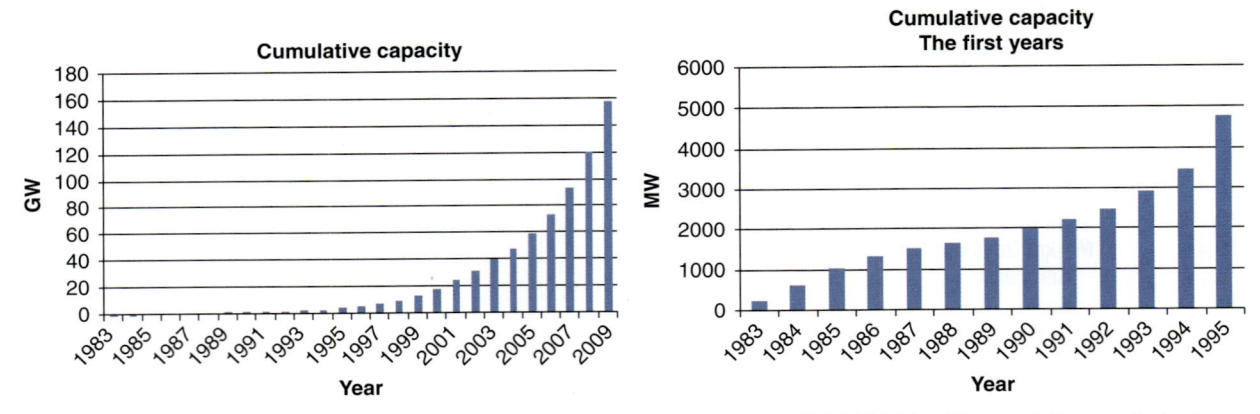

Figure 1 Development of the global wind power market. (Left) Cumulative installed capacity. (Right) Highlight of the cumulative capacity development 1983–95. Source: GWEC (2010) http://www.ewea.org [1]; BTM consult ApS – A part of NAVIGANT (2010) *World Market Update 2009*, March [2].

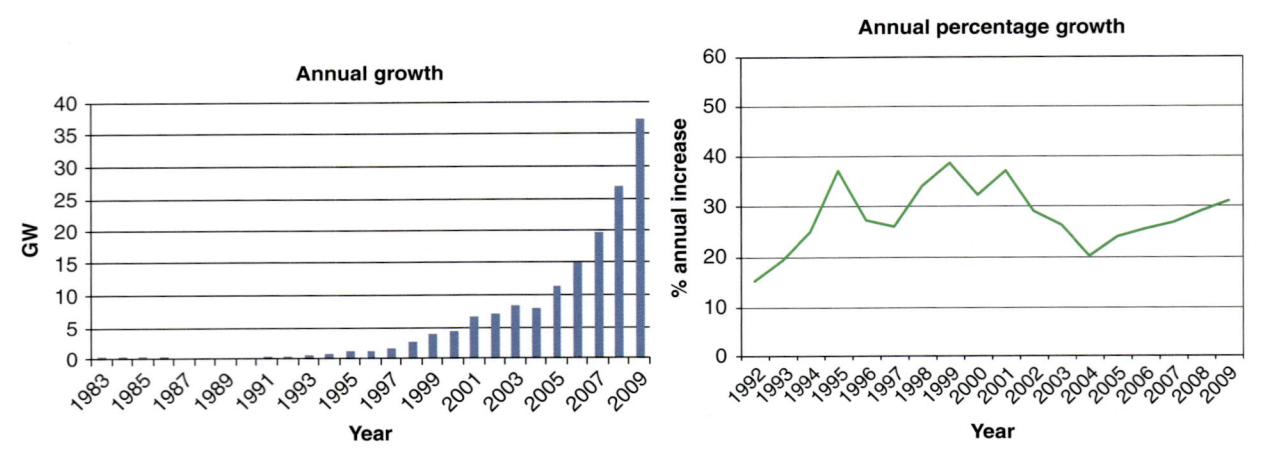

Figure 2 Growth in global annual installed wind power capacity. (Left) Absolute annual growth. (Right) Percentage annual growth. Source: GWEC (2010) http://www.ewea.org [1].

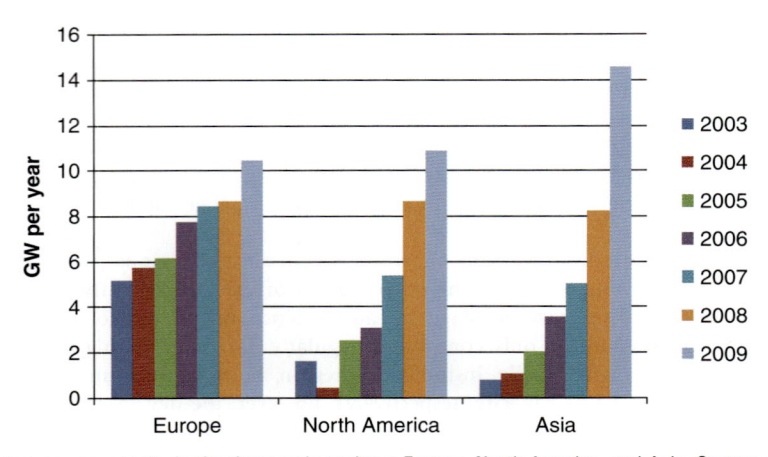

Figure 3 Annual installed wind power capacity in the three main regions: Europe, North America, and Asia. Source: GWEC (2010) http://www.ewea.org [1].

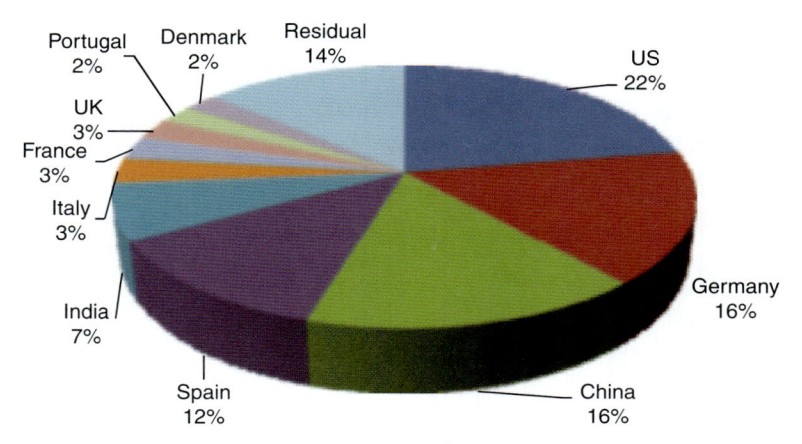

Figure 4 Top 10 countries' distribution of global installed capacity. Source: GWEC (2010) http://www.ewea.org [1].

2.20.2 Trends in the Development of Wind Turbines

In general, three major trends have dominated the development of grid-connected wind turbines in recent years:

1. The turbines have grown larger and taller – thus the average size of turbines sold at the market place has increased substantially.
2. The efficiency of the turbines' production has increased steadily.
3. In general, the investment costs per kilowatt have decreased, although recent years have shown a discrepancy from this trend.

Figure 5 shows the development of the average size of wind turbines sold each year for a number of the most important wind power countries. As illustrated in Figure 5, the annual average size has increased significantly within the last 10–15 years, from approximately 200 kW in 1990 to more than 2 MW in the United Kingdom and Denmark in 2008, with Germany, Spain, and the United States lagging only a little behind. But as shown, there is quite a difference between some of the countries. In India and China, the average installed size in 2008 was approximately 1 MW, significantly below the level of the United Kingdom and Denmark of 2256 and 2277 kW, respectively. The unstable picture for Denmark in recent years mainly reflects a fairly small number of new turbines being installed and in some years being dominated by offshore installations.

In 2008, turbines of the megawatt-class (i.e., above 1 MW) had a market share of more than 95%, leaving less than 5% for the smaller machines. Within the MW-segment turbines with capacities of 2.5 MW and up are getting increasingly important, even for on-land sitings. These large turbines had a share of 6% of the market in 2008, compared to only 0.3% at the end of 2003.

The wind regime at the chosen site, the hub height of the turbines, and the efficiency of production mainly determine power production from the turbines. Thus, increasing the height of the turbines has by itself yielded a higher power production. Similarly, the methods for measuring and evaluating the wind speed at a given site have improved substantially in recent years and thus improved the siting of new turbines. In spite of this, the fast development of wind power capacity in countries such as Germany and Denmark implies that most of the good wind sites by now are taken and, therefore, new on-land turbine capacity has to be erected at sites with a marginally lower average wind speed. To this though should be added that the replacement of older and smaller turbines with new ones is getting increasingly important, especially in countries that have taken part in the wind power development for a long time as is the case for Germany and Denmark.

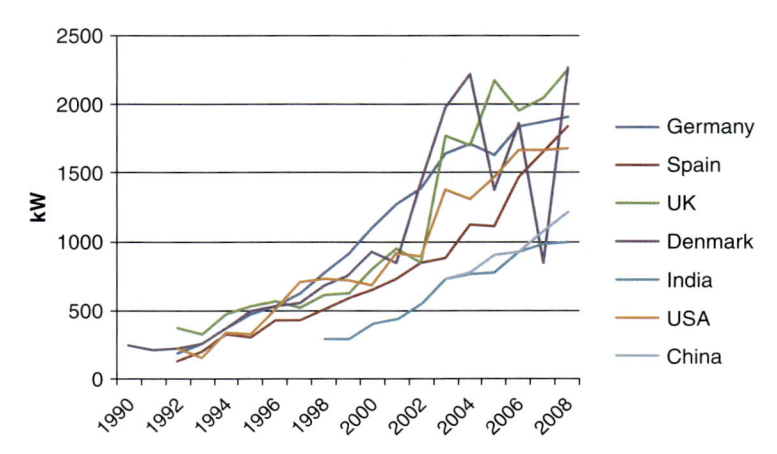

Figure 5 Development of the average wind turbine size sold in different countries. Source: BTM consult ApS – A part of NAVIGANT (2009) *World Market Update 2008*, March [3].

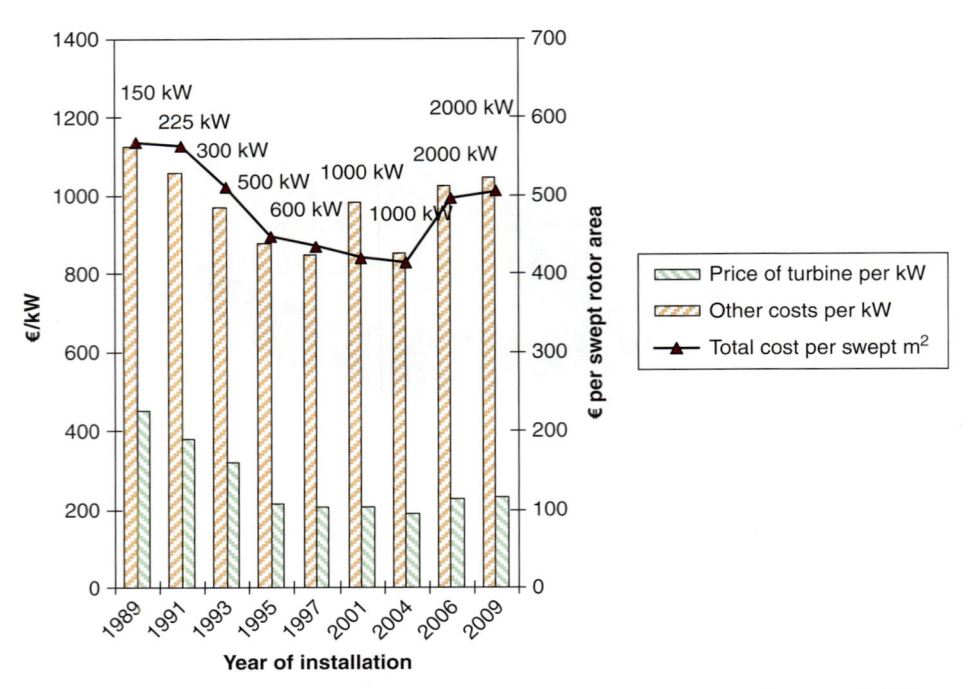

Figure 6 The development of investment costs exemplified by the case of Denmark for the time period from 1989 to 2009. Right axis: Investment costs divided by swept rotor area (€ m^{-2} in constant 2009 €). Left axis: Wind turbine costs and other costs per kW rated power (€ kW^{-1} in constant 2009 €).

The development of electricity production efficiency owing to better equipment design measured as annual energy production per swept rotor area (kWh m^{-2}) at a specific reference site has correspondingly improved significantly over recent years. Taking into account all the three mentioned issues of improved equipment efficiency, improved turbine siting, and higher hub height, the overall efficiency has increased by more than 2% annually over the last 15 years.

Figure 6 shows how investment costs have developed over the years, exemplified by the case of Denmark for the time period from 1987 to 2009. The data reflect turbines installed in the particular year shown (all costs are converted to 2009 prices) and all costs at the right axis are calculated per swept rotor area, while those at the left axis are calculated per kilowatt of rated capacity.

The number of square meters the rotor of the turbine is covering – swept rotor area – is a good proxy for the turbines' power production and therefore this measure is a relevant index for the development in costs per kWh. As shown in the figure, there has been a substantial decline in costs per unit swept rotor area in the considered period except from 2006 to 2009. Thus, from the late 1990s until 2004, the overall investments per unit swept rotor area have declined by more than 2% per annum during the period analyzed, corresponding to a total reduction in cost of almost 30% over these 15 years. But this trend was broken in 2006 where total investment costs rose by approximately 20% compared to 2004, mainly induced by a strong increase in demand for wind turbines combined with severe supply constraints [4].

Looking at the cost per rated capacity (per kW), the same decline is found in the period 1989 to 2004 with the 1000 kW machine in 2001 as the exception. The reason has to be found in the dimensioning of this specific turbine. With higher hub heights and larger rotor diameters, the turbine is equipped with a relatively smaller generator although it produces more electricity. This is particularly important to be aware of when analyzing turbines constructed to be used in low and medium wind areas, where the rotor diameter is dimensioned to be considerably larger compared to the rated capacity. As shown in **Figure 6**, the cost per kW installed also rose by 20% in 2006 compared to 2004, while the cost almost remained constant from 2006 to 2009. At the beginning of 2010, it seems that the cost has declined slightly compared to 2009; however, at present this cannot be documented by sampled data [5].

Also, the share of other costs as a percentage of total costs has in general decreased. In 1989, almost 29% of total investment costs were related to costs other than the turbine itself. By 1997, this share had declined to approximately 20%. The trend toward lower auxiliary costs continues for the last vintage of turbines shown (2000 kW), where other costs amount to approximately 18% of total costs. But from 2004 to 2006, other costs rose almost in parallel with the cost of the turbine itself and have stayed at this level in 2009.

2.20.3 Main Drivers behind the Wind Power Development

The reasons for the global success of wind power are many fold. Seen from a governmental viewpoint, some of the benefits are as follows [6]:

- Improved security of energy supply
- Enhanced competitive edge in the renewable energies technology industries

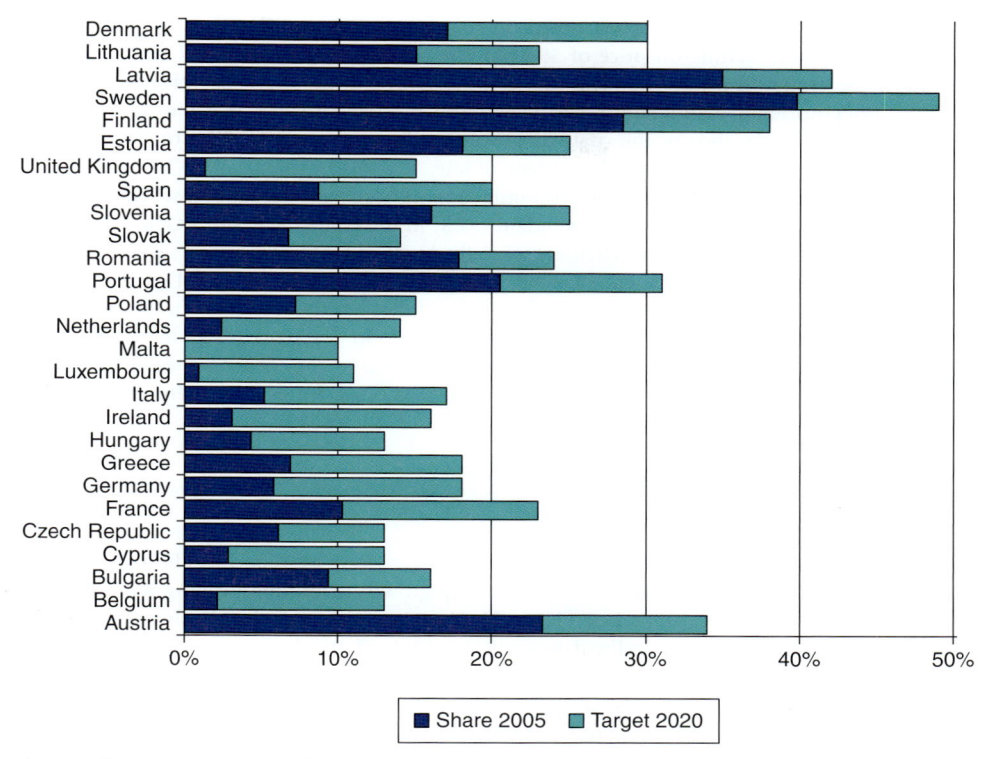

Figure 7 National renewable energy targets as % of final energy consumption.

- Mitigation of greenhouse gas emissions by power sector
- Mitigation of regional and local pollutant emissions
- Improved economic and social prospects especially for rural and isolated areas.

Thus, as part of their energy policy, a number of countries have established long-term targets for renewables, and thus implicitly for wind power as part of the renewable portfolio. As an example, European Union (EU) has set the mandatory target for renewable energy sources that by 2020 20% of final energy demand in EU has to be supplied by renewable technologies as hydro power, wind power, solar, and biomass. This EU renewable target has to be implemented mainly by national initiatives (the European Trading System for CO_2 allowances will be part of the regulatory framework) and is distributed on member states as shown in **Figure 7**. The mandates for the share of renewable sources by 2020 vary significantly for the individual member states from an increase of 13% to a total of 30% for Denmark to an increase of only 6.9% to a total of 13% for the Czech Republic.

However, only at sites with relatively high wind speeds, wind turbines are at present economically competitive to conventional power production on purely economic grounds. **Figure 8** shows the costs of wind power production in

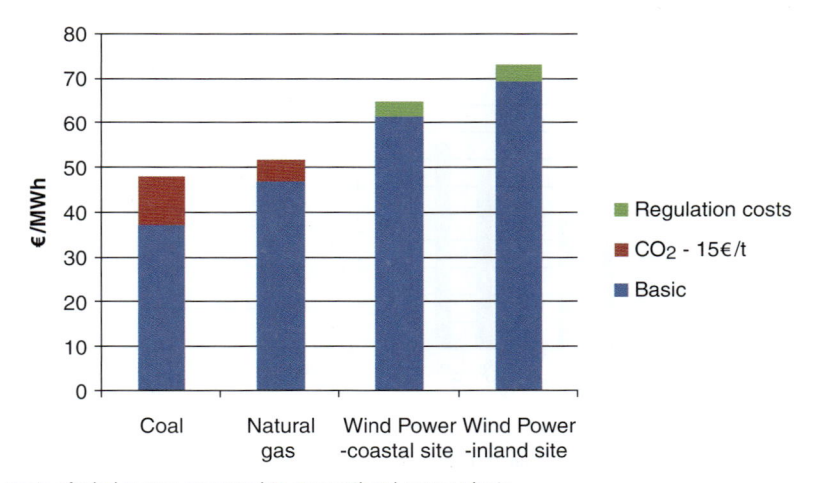

Figure 8 The production costs of wind power compared to conventional power plants.

comparison with costs of conventional power plants based on coal or natural gas. The analysis is performed on fuel prices from the international markets and a crude oil price of 59 $ bbl^{-1} in 2010 (constant terms) is assumed. The price of natural gas is assumed to follow the crude oil price. The price of CO$_2$ is assumed to be 15 €t^{-1} as observed by 2010 and basically covers the cost of fuels, operation and maintenance, and leveling of investment costs. It is based on cost from IEA [7] and assumptions from OECD/IEA [8]). As shown, the costs of power production based on coal or natural gas are significantly lower than the costs of wind power production independent of site.

Thus, to attract investors wind power is dependent on economic support from national support schemes based on feed-in tariffs, green certificates (alternative to the renewable portfolio standard (RPS) in the United States or ROCs in the United Kingdom) or investment subsidies. Most countries apply support schemes especially designed for their own and specific purposes. In EU, feed-in tariffs have been highly effective in the deployment of wind power in Germany, Spain, and Denmark. According to the EU Commission [4], the most effective scheme in general is the feed-in tariff that has the lowest risk as perceived by investors. In the United States, the production tax credit (PTC) and the Renewable Portfolio Standard (RPS) have proved to be efficient in the deployment of wind power. Nevertheless, the effectiveness of the support system depends heavily on the specific design of the scheme. Thus, other schemes might prove to be effective in particular cases, for example, tendering in the development of offshore wind farms.

2.20.4 Market Development in Europe

Right from the start of the wind power revival, European countries have done well, and by the end of 2009, total installed capacity amounted to 76 GW. During the 1990s there was a strong growth in Europe peaking with annual growth rates of cumulative capacity of 40–50% at the late 1990s (see **Figure 9**). However, although the absolute growth persistently is kept at a high level, the annual growth rates have declined severely, leveling off at a little more than 15% of annual growth in cumulative capacity.

This development is mainly the consequence of European policies. Thus, at present the development is dominated by a few countries, especially Germany and Spain; however, quite a number of new countries are entering the wind power scene. This applies especially for Italy, France, and the United Kingdom, which all are experiencing rapid expansions.

Quite a number of different instruments are presently used in the Member States in supporting the development of renewable energy sources. Quota obligations with tradable green certificates, feed-in tariffs, tender procedures, and tax measures are the most discussed schemes, dominating the national support systems at the moment. At present, most support schemes are based on a national entity and trade across the borders explicitly of green power is limited.

In the following the development of wind power in the most important European countries will be described.

2.20.4.1 Germany

By the end of 2009 wind power in Germany covered approximately 9% of the country's power consumption and accounted for approximately 34% of total installed wind power capacity in Europe making Germany the number one country in this area. However, the dominance of Germany is weakening. The German share of new annual installed capacity in Europe has gradually fallen from 48% in 1999 to 18% in 2009. The development of annual installed capacity in Germany is shown in **Figure 10**.

Together with Denmark, Germany was one of the first movers on the development of wind power in Europe. Already at the end of the 1980s, a rapid development was initiated in Germany, especially in the Northern part of the country with good wind conditions, driven by favorable feed-in tariffs for wind produced power. As shown in **Figure 10**, in the early 1990s Germany had

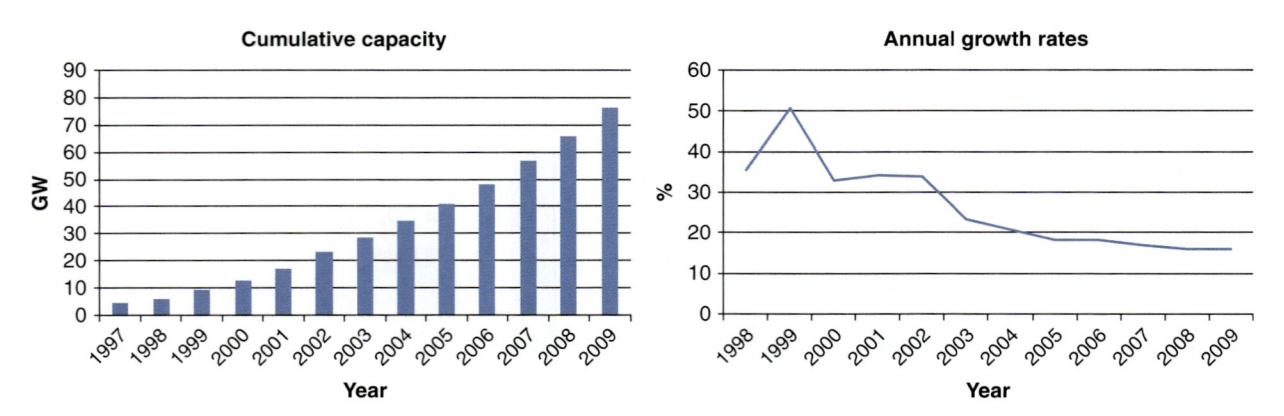

Figure 9 Development of wind power capacity in Europe. (Left) Total cumulative capacity. (Right) Annual growth rates of cumulative capacity. Source: GWEC (2010) http://www.ewea.org [1]; BTM consult ApS – A part of NAVIGANT (2010) *World Market Update 2009*, March [2].

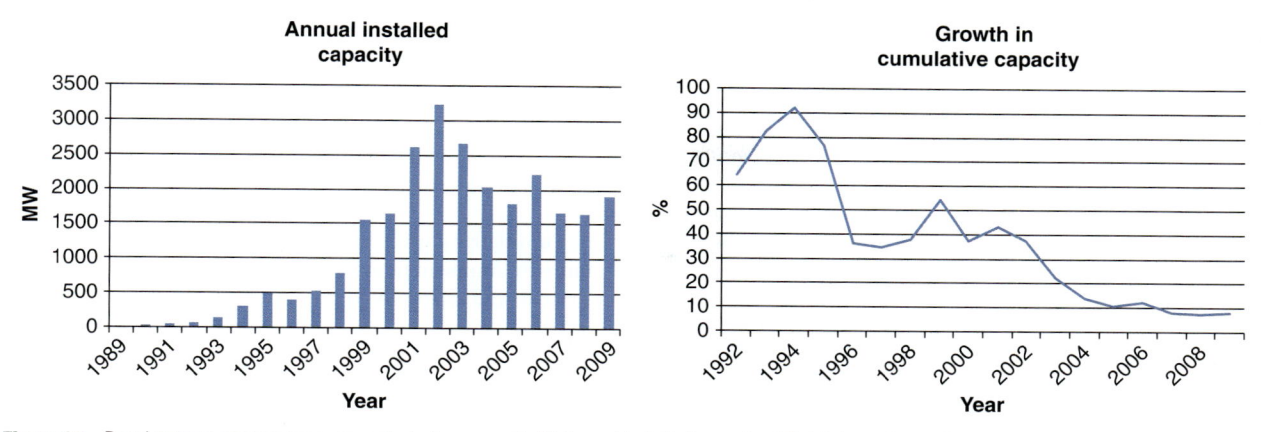

Figure 10 Development of wind power capacity in Germany. (Left) Annual installed capacity. (Right) Annual growth rates of cumulative capacity. Source: GWEC (2010) http://www.ewea.org [1]; BTM consult ApS – A part of NAVIGANT (2010) *World Market Update 2009*, March [2].

some years with very strong growth in cumulative capacity, 70–90% increase per year, followed by a stable time period with cumulative capacity growth rates of approximately 40% per year.

For many years, Germany has very successfully continued a policy of favorable feed-in tariffs, gradually decreasing the tariffs as wind power technology has economically matured. However, although tariffs are still at a high level in Germany, growth rates of cumulative capacity have gradually declined. For the last 5–6 years, the annual installed capacity has stagnated at approximately 1500–1700 MW, resulting in a growth rate of cumulative capacity below 10% per year. A major reason for this is that new available sites for on-land turbines are becoming scarcer. Thus, by now Germany is increasingly looking into the possibilities of offshore wind power development (see Section 2.20.7).

2.20.4.2 Spain

In Spain, wind power covers approximately 15% of the country's electricity consumption. Spain is the number two country in Europe accounting for a share of approximately 26% of total cumulative wind power capacity by 2009. But as for Germany also, the pace in the Spanish development is declining. In 1999, approximately 28% of the new capacity in Europe was installed in Spain; by 2009, this share has fallen to approximately 23%. However, Spain is still the country in Europe with the largest installation of new capacity amounting to almost 2500 MW in 2009 (see **Figure 11**).

The main driver in Spain has been a favorable feed-in tariff combined with a multitude of good wind sites in a large part of the country. Historically, problems of getting access to the electricity grid and slow administrative procedures have been a limitation to development in Spain. However, in recent years this seems to have improved [2]. Some uncertainty around the future level of the feed-in tariff has implied a more unstable development of wind power in Spain than seen in Germany and this uncertainty seems to persist for the future.

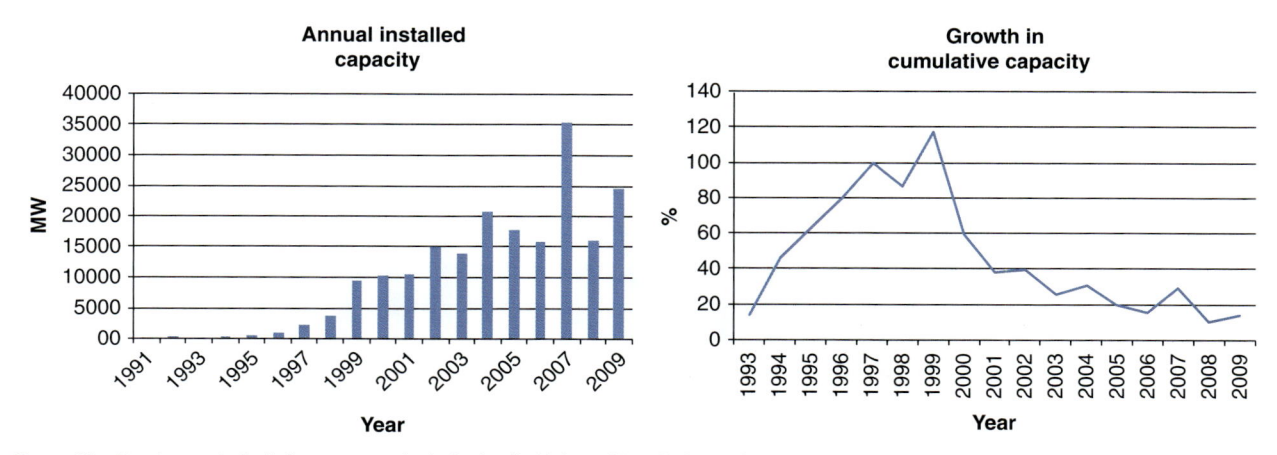

Figure 11 Development of wind power capacity in Spain. (Left) Annual installed capacity. (Right) Annual growth rates of cumulative capacity. Source: GWEC (2010) http://www.ewea.org [1]; BTM consult ApS – A part of NAVIGANT (2010) *World Market Update 2009*, March [2].

2.20.4.3 Rest of Europe

There is quite a distance from the dominating two wind power countries in Europe, Germany, and Spain, to the next level of countries. While Germany and Spain accounts for 34% and 25% of total installed capacity in Europe, respectively, the following countries account for less than 6% each. However, a group of rapid moving countries consists of Italy, France, the United Kingdom, and Portugal. The countries' share of total installed wind power capacity in Europe by the end of 2009 is shown in **Figure 12**.

The growth in cumulative wind power capacity in selected European countries is shown in **Figure 13**. As shown, quite a difference exists between fast growing countries and slow growing ones.

Italy is experiencing a strong growth for the time being, increasing cumulative capacity by 37% in 2008 and 30% in 2009. The country now has installed 4.8 GW and ranges as number three country in Europe in terms of cumulative wind power capacity. The development in Italy is driven by a well-working green certificate system, and especially in the Southern part of the country, a large number of good windy sites exist. At the end of 2009, a little more than 2% of power consumption in Italy was covered by wind power [2].

A strong development of wind power is also going on in France. In 2008, cumulative capacity increased by 39% and by 32% in 2009. The development in France is driven by the country's commitment to the EU renewable targets where wind power is expected to contribute significantly. A fairly high feed-in tariff is implemented in France, which of course is the major reason for the success.

The *United Kingdom* has taken the lead in offshore development of wind power. Forty-three percent of total installed offshore capacity was established in the UK waters by the end of 2009. However, on-land installations are still dominating in the UK and

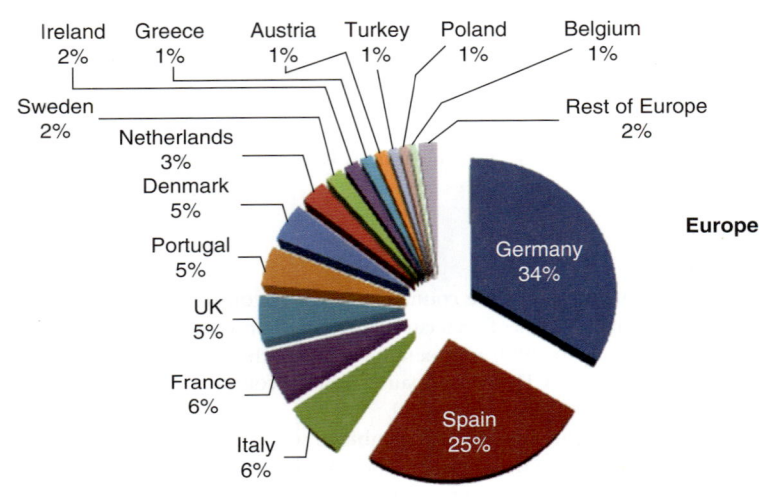

Figure 12 Share of total installed wind power capacity in Europe, 2009. Source: GWEC (2010) http://www.ewea.org [1].

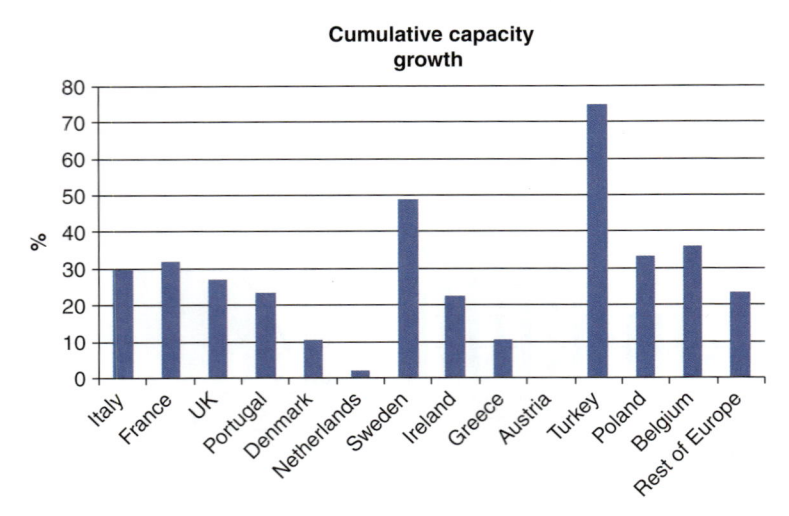

Figure 13 Growth in cumulative wind power capacity in Europe in 2009 (excluding Germany and Spain).

more than 80% of total installed capacity is land turbines. Also in the United Kingdom, the growth of cumulative capacity is strong amounting to 35% in 2008 and 36% in 2009. The EU target for renewables is driving the Government's actions and commits the UK to cover 15% of final energy consumption with renewable energy production by 2020; by now the contribution is approx. 4%. A system of Renewable Obligation Certificates (ROCs) is being utilized in the UK to promote renewable energy technologies [2].

In *Portugal* the EU renewable target is an important driver as well. The target for Portugal is a 32% coverage of final energy consumption by 2020, starting with approx. 21% by 2005. The national target is 5 GW by 2010 and at present this target seems not to be fulfilled. Growth rates are still high in Portugal reaching 33% in 2008 and 24% in 2009 in cumulative capacity.

Denmark back in the 1980s and 1990s was the frontrunner in the development of wind power. But the Danish development was stalled after year 2000, mainly because the fixed feed-in tariff was replaced with a feed-in premium at a lower level. In recent years the premium has been increased so on-land installations of wind turbines are slowly starting again. Denmark is worldwide number two in establishing offshore, holding 31% of total offshore installations only by-passed by the United Kingdom.

Among other established countries Sweden is developing pretty fast. Newcomers such as Poland and Turkey have large potentials for siting wind turbines and by now seem to be growing fast, although they still have small amounts of wind power installed.

2.20.5 Development of Wind Power in North America

The North American region consists of the United States and Canada, where the United States is clearly dominating covering approximately 91% of total installed wind power capacity. By the end of 2009, approximately 3.3 GW was installed in Canada, where the growth of cumulative capacity in 2008 was 28% and in 2009 an astonishing 40%. In the following, the United States will be treated in more detail.

2.20.5.1 United States

A little more than 35 GW of wind power in total was installed in the United States by the end of 2009, which makes it the largest wind power country in the world, followed by Germany and China. Approximately 22% of the world's wind power capacity was established in the United States by the end of 2009. A veritable boom has appeared in the United States in recent years; the growth in cumulative wind power capacity was in 2008 at astonishing 50% followed by a growth in 2009 of 39%. The development of annual installed capacity in the United States is shown in **Figure 14**.

As Denmark, the United States was one of the early movers within the development of new wind power. Already in the early 1980s, the United States had a strong development of wind power especially driven by a tax rebate scheme. But the tax scheme was abandoned in the mid-1980s and thereby the installation of wind power was halted (see **Figure 14**).

In general, the US policy is a combination of federal and State initiatives. Federal energy policies are complemented by State policies, where the State policies are often found to be designed in a variety of different ways. One of the important federal policies is the PTC. The PTC has had a significant influence on the development of wind power. At the same time, it has been subject to a stop-and-go policy, the decisions on PTC delaying the deployment of wind power and creating a significant uncertainty for the industry. The importance of the stop-and-go policy for wind power is clearly illustrated in **Figure 14**, most of the discontinuities caused by delayed PTC decisons [9].

Texas is the leading state in terms of wind power capacity, followed by Indiana and Iowa. In 2009, these three states accounted for 41% of new installed capacity in the United States [2]. At the state level, the use of a renewable portfolio standard (RPS) scheme is one of the more popular policy instruments.

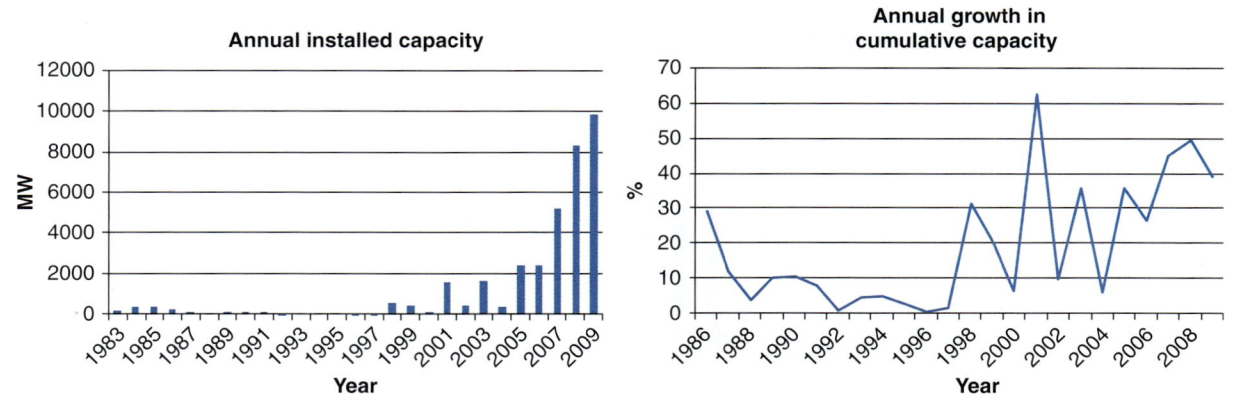

Figure 14 Development of wind power capacity in the United States. (Left) Annual installed capacity. (Right) Annual growth rates of cumulative capacity. Source: GWEC (2010) http://www.ewea.org [1]; BTM consult ApS – A part of NAVIGANT (2010) *World Market Update 2009*, March [2].

2.20.6 Wind Power Development in Asia

The Asian region is dominated by China and India, where China holds a share of Asian cumulative installed capacity of 65%, while India has a share of 28%. Japan has at present a share of 5% and is developing slowly. Finally, countries like Taiwan and South Korea have less than 1% of the Asian installed wind power capacity.

Today, India holds an installed capacity of 10.9 GW and is developing at a stable rate. In 2008, the growth rate of cumulative capacity was 23%, and in 2009, it was 13%. In the following, the Chinese development will be described in more detail.

2.20.6.1 China

China is clearly a newcomer to the wind power field, but nevertheless a newcomer that moves incredibly fast. By the end of 2009, China had in total installed 25.1 GW of wind power, making China the third ranking country in the world in terms of cumulative installed capacity, very close to Germany with a total capacity of 25.8 GW but still a way to go to reach the US level of installed capacity of 35.1 GW. The development of annual installed capacity in China is shown in **Figure 15**.

With regard to China, fast means really fast; both in 2008 and 2009, the total installed capacity was more than doubled compared to the previous year. Thus, the Chinese share of world installed wind power capacity went from 2% in 2005 to almost 16% by the end of 2009. By 2009, 35% of the world's new established capacity was located in China compared to only 5% in 2005. Combining this with the recent development in the United States, this clearly indicates that the European dominance is broken, that new trends are pointing to a fast development in Chinese and US markets.

The wind power development in China actually started back in the mid-1990s. For almost 10 years the development was fairly slow, the installed capacity being below 100 MW per year. But in 2005, the Renewable Energy Law was approved and this signaled the take-off for wind power in China. Thus, in 2005 the growth rate in cumulative capacity reached 65% and since then China has more than doubled cumulative capacity each year. In 2009 approximately 13 GW of new capacity was installed, making China the world's number one in terms of annual wind power installations.

The Chinese development is regulated by long-term plans and targets. The Renewable Energy Law in 2005 was an important achievement and since then a number of new laws was put in place, regarding feed-in tariffs and access to the grid. In 2008, the Renewable Energy development plan for the 11th 5-year period was approved, stating targets for wind power development in China. The target for 2010 of 10 GW was already fulfilled in 2008, and during 2009, the Chinese Government launched a new long-term target of 100 GW by 2020. If the pace of wind turbine installation is kept at the present level in China, this target will be fulfilled in due time before 2020 [2, 10].

2.20.7 Offshore Wind Power Development

In a number of countries, offshore turbines are playing an increasingly important role in the development of wind power, particularly in the north-western part of Europe. Partly this can be explained by on-land sitings being limited in number and that the utilization of these sites to a certain extent is exposed to opposition from the local population. This is seen in relation to an unexpected high level of energy production from offshore turbines compared to on-land sitings (based on the experiences gained until now) and has paved the way for huge interest in offshore development.

As for onshore turbines, the wind regime, where the offshore turbines are sited determining the production of power, is the single most important factor for the cost per generated unit of power. In general, the wind regime offshore is characterized by high

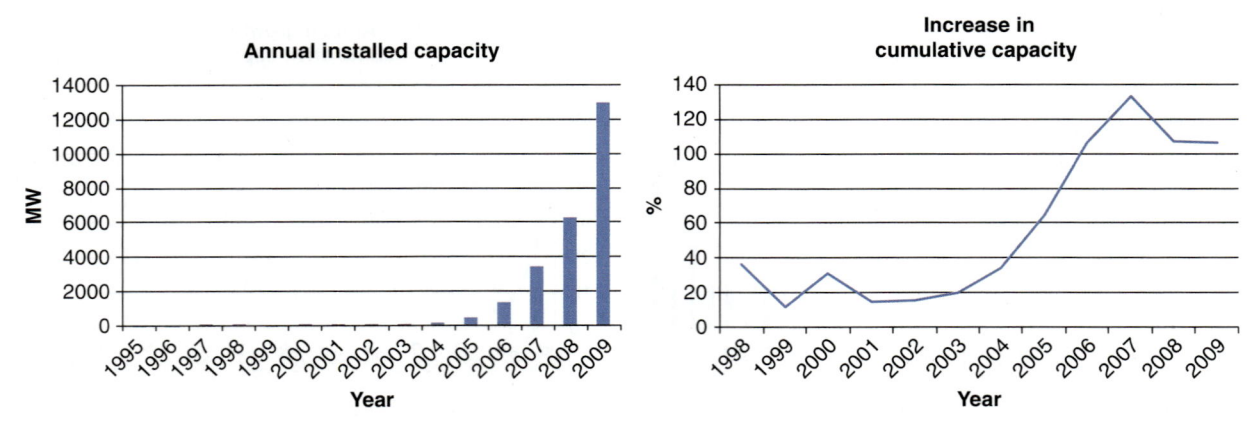

Figure 15 Development of wind power capacity in China. (Left) Annual installed capacity. (Right) Annual growth rates of cumulative capacity. Source: GWEC (2010) http://www.ewea.org [1]; BTM consult ApS – A part of NAVIGANT (2010) *World Market Update 2009*, March [2].

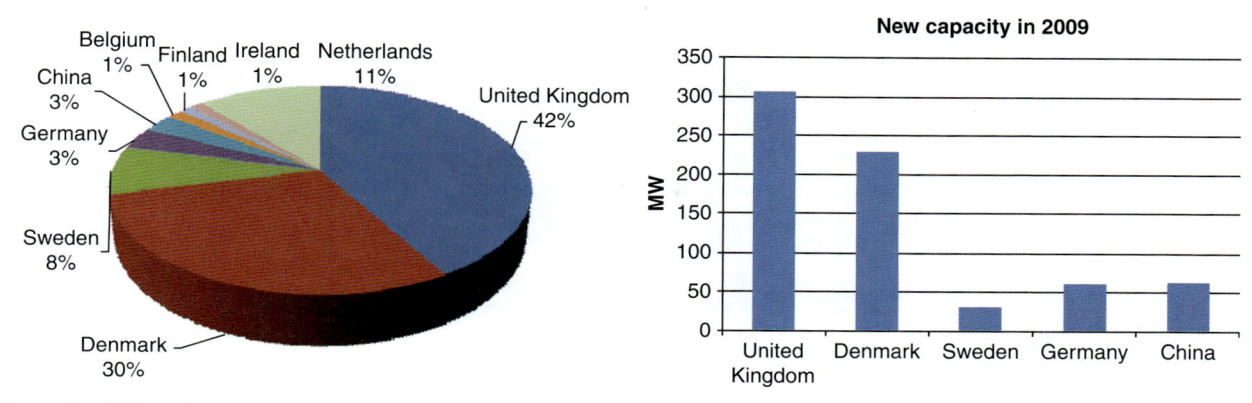

Figure 16 Offshore development. (Left) Distribution of total installed capacity by the end of 2009. (Right) New installed capacity in 2009. Source: BTM consult ApS – A part of NAVIGANT (2010) *World Market Update 2009*, March [2].

average wind speeds and more stability than onshore wind. At the Danish Horns Reef wind farm, a wind speed corresponding to a utilization time of more than 4200 h yr^{-1} was measured (adjusted to a normal wind year), thus giving a capacity factor close to 50%, which is comparable to many smaller conventional power plants. For most offshore wind farms, a utilization time of more than 3000 h yr^{-1} is to be expected, significantly higher than for onshore sited turbines and, therefore, to a certain extent compensating for the additional costs of offshore plants.

At present, more than 30 offshore wind farms with a total installed capacity of a little more than 2 GW are in operation with a few exceptions, all located in the northern part of Europe. The largest installation is in British waters where almost 900 MW are located corresponding to 43% of total offshore capacity. In Denmark, a little more than 600 MW are installed corresponding to 31% of total offshore capacity, followed by the Netherlands (12%) and Sweden (8%) [11]. The offshore development is shown in **Figure 16**.

Denmark was the first country to examine the possibilities in offshore wind power, and already at the beginning of the 1990s, the wind farm Vindeby consisting of 11 machines of 450 kW was established. This was followed by several small offshore wind farms; among these is Middelgrunden with a capacity of 40 MW located just outside Copenhagen. The large Horn Reef offshore wind farm consisting of 80 machines of 2 MW was established in 2002. The Danish Government is by now pursuing a tendering procedure in promoting offshore development. The Anholt wind farm with a capacity of 400 MW was approved in 2010 and is expected to be on line by 2012. Then it will be the world largest offshore wind farm. In Denmark, it is expected that by 2020 wind power supplies will be 50% of total electricity consumption.

The offshore development in the United Kingdom started back in 2000, where the Blyth cluster of two 2 MW machines was erected. The first real offshore wind farm was the North Hoyle in 2003 consisting of 30 turbines of 2 MW. Since then, quite a large number of wind farms of 60–100 MW have been established in British waters. The United Kingdom has a large potential for offshore wind both at West and East shores. The utilization of this potential is regulated by the Crown Estate, and a number of rounds for offshore exploitation have been launched. Renewable obligation certificates (ROCs) are being used to support the development of renewables in the United Kingdom. Offshore wind power is receiving 1.5–2 ROCs per MWh produced compared to the normal of 1 ROC for on-land wind. In the United Kingdom, 13 projects were awarded 32 GW at the beginning of 2010 in the Crown Estates Round 3 [9].

Although Germany had a hesitating start of offshore wind power development, in 2009 the Alpha Ventus project consisting of 10 turbines of 6 MW was finalized. By 2009, the legislation for offshore wind farms was also improved significantly in Germany, an improved feed-in tariff specifically for offshore came in place and grid companies were committed to establish and pay for the offshore transmission cable connecting the wind farm to land, which accounts for 15–20% of the total costs. A huge number of offshore wind farms reaching a capacity of up to 10 GW or more are by now approved by the German authorities. These wind farms typically have a size of 400 MW each.

Thus, although offshore wind power at present do not account for more than 1.3% of total installed wind power capacity, a strong development in offshore is expected. In a number of countries, offshore wind power projects are in the planning and implementation phase, as mentioned especially in Germany, the United Kingdom, and Denmark.

2.20.8 Wind Turbine Manufacturers

Thus, the pattern of growth in wind power is changing. While the absolute annual installed capacity in the last couple of years has remained almost at a constant level in Germany, Spain (Spain experienced a strong growth in 2007, but has since shown a somewhat uneven growth), and India, the installed capacity in the United States and especially China has boomed. Of course, these changing market perspectives are of utmost importance for the wind turbine manufacturers, the 'old' well-established European companies establishing subsidiaries in Asia and the United States, facing a still stronger competition from low-cost Asian manufacturers.

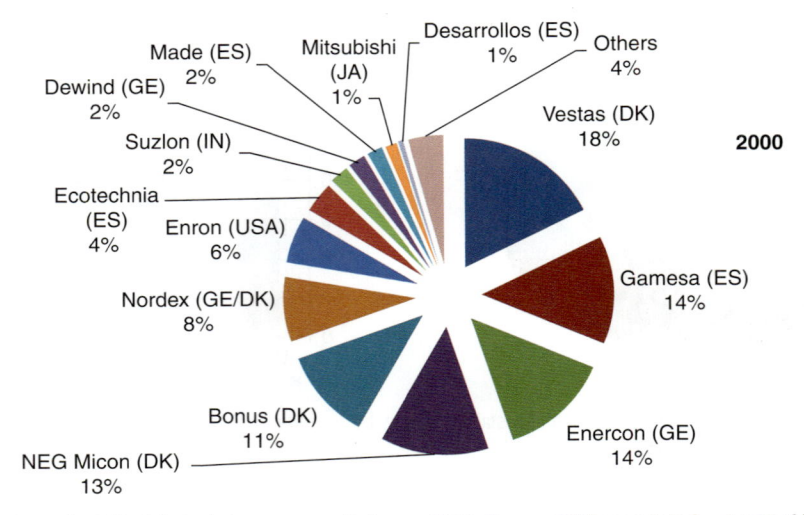

Figure 17 Manufacturers share of total installed wind power capacity in year 2000. Source: BTM consult ApS – A part of NAVIGANT (2001) *World Market Update 2000*, March.

Looking at manufacturers by the year 2000, Europe had a dominating share (**Figure 17**). Of the 13 largest manufacturers, 10 manufacturers were located in Europe, supplying approximately 87% of the installed capacity [12]. Observe that all European manufacturers were located in the three countries where most wind turbines were erected as well, namely Germany, Spain, and Denmark. Thus, there seems to be a close correlation between markets and local/national industrial development.

By 2009 the picture had changed significantly. Europe still has a strong position with a market share of 42%, but especially the United States and China have gained and by now have market shares of 15% and 27%, respectively.

Vestas still is the largest supplier with a market share of 13% in 2009, followed by GE Wind with a marginally lower market share of almost 13%. However, a number of company merges have taken place in the period from 2000 to 2009. Vestas and NEG-Micon were merged in 2004 under the Vestas name (a total market share of 31%), and taking this into account, the company has lost significant market shares. Bonus was bought by the German company Siemens, and continued under this name. Enron is now GE Wind, Made was overtaken, Ecotechnia was acquired by Alstom in 1997 and now has the name Alstom Wind (Alstom Wind is too small to enter the figure and accounted as others). However, the largest difference is to be found in the numerous new Chinese manufacturers that have entered the market in recent years. **Figure 18** shows only the largest Chinese manufacturers, but in 2009, more than 20 Chinese companies were producing wind turbines to the domestic market [8].

The Danish company 'Vestas' started its production of wind turbines back in 1979, where the first 55 kW machine was erected; a machine that actually got very popular not only in Denmark but also in the United States. As mentioned, Vestas is today the market leader with a market share of 13% and a delivery of 4766 MW in 2009 – this is five times as much as in year 2000. Vestas produces a broad range of turbines, ranging from 850 kW to 3 MW, all of a conventional three-bladed gear-box design. A new large turbine,

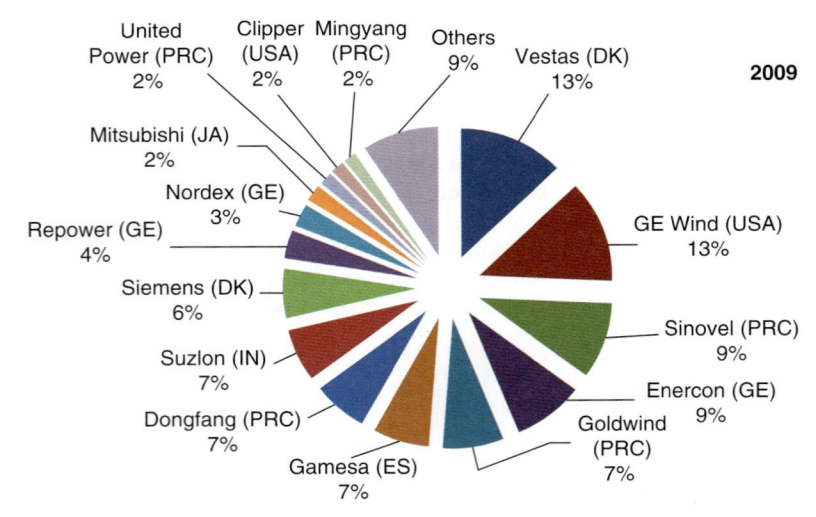

Figure 18 Manufacturers share of total installed wind power capacity by year 2009. Source: BTM consult ApS – A part of NAVIGANT (2010) *World Market Update 2009*, March [2].

presumably of 6 MW size, has been announced by the company to be on the way. Vestas is a truly international company supplying almost all countries of the world. Vestas has a headquarters in Denmark and subsidiaries in Spain, the United States, and China. By 2009, approximately 58% of the production was delivered in Europe, 27% in the United States, and 14% in Asia. The major part of Vestas' production is supplied for on-land projects; however, the 3 MW turbines are quite popular for offshore projects as well.

The US company 'GE Wind' is the second largest supplier with a 2009 market share of 13% and a delivery of 4741 MW. GE has a very strong position in the US market where it has a market share of more than 45%, and therefore, the booming American market has been a significant driver for GE. But also at the Canadian market, GE is one of the largest suppliers. GE is present at a number of markets in Europe but has no dominating position outside North America. GE has a product line consisting of conventional three-bladed gear-box machines ranging from 1.5 to 2.5 MW. Especially, the 1.5 model has been very popular and a large number of these turbines have been erected.

The Chinese company 'Sinovel' became the third largest supplier in 2009 with a market share of 9% and a delivery of 3510 MW. The company is a real newcomer, growing rapidly in recent years taking advantage of the booming wind power market in China. Sinovel produces a 1.5 MW machine with different rotor diameters and a pitch-regulated 3 MW machine all of conventional design. The company has a market share of 25% in China in 2009 and only a small export, mainly to India [2].

As Vestas the German company 'Enercon' is one of the pioneers within wind power and in 1992 their first gear-less turbine was erected. Thus, Enercon is *the* manufacturer of direct-drive gear-less turbines and by the end of 2009 the company held fourth position with a market share of 9% and an installation of 3221 MW this year. Enercon has a market share of more than 62% in Germany, but has also high market shares in other European countries such as Portugal, Italy, France, and Sweden. Outside Europe, Enercon is especially doing well in Canada. Enercon has a product line ranging from 1.8 to 6 MW all direct-drive gear-less machines.

Chinese 'Goldwind' holds a 20% share of the Chinese market but for the time being is mainly a domestic supplier. Spanish 'Gamesa' dominates the Spanish market with a share of 36% and is doing well in Italy and France. 'Siemens' – German owned with production facilities mainly located in Denmark – is an undisputable number one in offshore wind power, only rivaled by Vestas.

At present, manufacturers are split with regard to two technological trends: a trend toward producing very large turbines and one toward direct-drive gear-less machines. Among the manufacturers, Repower and Enercon are supplying 6 MW turbines, Bard has a 5 MW one, and Siemens has a very popular 3.6 MW machine. Vestas has announced a 6 MW machine to be on the way and American Clipper is building a 10 MW prototype in the United Kingdom [2].

The competition between the direct-drive gear-less concept and the traditional gear-based concept is still going on. As mentioned, German Enercon is a main driver in developing the direct-drive concept, but also Chinese Goldwind is producing a 1.5 MW direct-drive machine that has been sold in large numbers in China in 2009. Siemens launched a 3 MW direct-drive turbine with permanent magnets in autumn 2009. Although, the majority of turbines are conventional ones, the direct-drive concept seems increasingly to attract interest among manufacturers.

References

[1] GWEC (2010) http://www.ewea.org (Brussels, accessed March 2010).
[2] BTM-Consult (2010) *World Market Update 2009*, March.
[3] BTM-Consult (2009) *World Market Update 2008*, March.
[4] EWEA (2009) *Wind Energy the Facts*. Earthscan, Brussels.
[5] Nielsen P, Lemming J, Morthorst PE, et al. (2010) *Vindmøllers Økonomi (The Economics of Wind Turbines)*. Aalborg, Denmark: EMD.
[6] EU Commission (2005) Communication from the Commission. The support of electricity from renewable energy sources.
[7] IEA (2008) Recabs-model. *Developed in the IEA Implementing Agreement on Renewable Energy Technology Deployment.* http://recabs.iea-retd.org/energy_calculator (Paris, accessed March 2010).
[8] OECD/IEA (2008) *World Energy Outlook 2007.* Paris, France: OECD and International Energy Agency.
[9] Risø Energy Report (2006) Renewable energy for power and transport. *Risø*, November.
[10] BTM-Consult (2008) "Made in China", Chinese wind power market assessment 2008–2012, *Ringkjoebing*, November.
[11] BTM-Consult (2010b) Offshore report 2010. November.
[12] BTM-Consult (2001) *World Market Update 2000*, March.

2.21 Trends, Prospects, and R&D Directions in Wind Turbine Technology

JK Kaldellis and DP Zafirakis, Technological Education Institute of Piraeus, Athens, Greece

© 2012 Elsevier Ltd. All rights reserved.

2.21.1	Brief Description of Wind Power Time Evolution	671
2.21.2	The Current Wind Turbine Concept	675
2.21.3	Size Evolution of Wind Turbines	676
2.21.4	Pitch versus Stall and Active-Stall Wind Turbines	679
2.21.5	Direct-Drive versus Gearbox	680
2.21.6	Blade Design and Construction	682
2.21.7	Innovative Concepts	685
2.21.8	Environmental Impact Reduction	687
2.21.9	Offshore Wind Parks	688
2.21.10	Vertical-Axis Wind Turbines	693
2.21.11	Small Wind Turbines	696
2.21.12	Building-Integrated Wind Turbines	699
2.21.13	Wind Energy Cost Time Evolution	702
2.21.14	Research in the Wind Energy Sector	706
2.21.15	Wind Energy Technological Problems and R&D Directions	709
2.21.16	Financial Support of Wind Energy Research Efforts	710
2.21.16.1	1998–2002 (FP5)	710
2.21.16.2	2002–06 (FP6)	711
2.21.16.3	2007–Today (FP7)	711
2.21.17	Conclusions	712
References		720
Further Reading		723
Relevant Websites		724

Glossary

Capacity factor The capacity factor of a wind turbine refers to the ratio of the actual energy production of the machine for a given time period to the respective potential energy production of the same machine if it had operated at its rated power for the entire time period.

Embodied energy The energy consumed throughout the various life cycle stages of a system, for example, a wind turbine, equally well restricted to a single stage such as manufacturing. Embodied energy amounts are usually compared with the useful energy amounts produced by the system in order to investigate whether they can be compensated by the latter.

Feed-in tariff A policy mechanism developed for the support of renewable energy technologies, through the award of a certain payment per kilowatt hour for electricity produced by a renewable resource and fed into the grid. Feed-in tariffs may vary on the basis of technology, geographical location, and installation size.

Framework programs Framework programs for research and technological development, also abbreviated as FPs on the basis of Framework Programmes alone, comprise funding programs that have been created by the European Union so as to support and encourage research in various sectors, including also wind energy.

Pitch control In pitch-controlled machines, the angle of the blades is adjusted through signaling and the use of a pitch actuator, so as to capture the energy from the wind in the most efficient way.

Power (aerodynamic) coefficient A measure of the wind turbine rotor's ability to exploit the available kinetic energy of wind. Its maximum theoretical value corresponds to the Betz limit, being equal to 16/27.

R&D The term is used to describe research and development, and refers to creative work undertaken on a systematic basis in order to increase the stock of knowledge and the use of this stock of knowledge to devise new applications.

Stall control In stall-controlled machines, the angle of the blades is fixed, while the blades are designed so that they can increasingly stall the angle of attack with the increase of wind speed.

Tip speed ratio The ratio of the linear speed at the tip of the blade to the wind speed upstream of the rotor.

2.21.1 Brief Description of Wind Power Time Evolution

Wind energy development counts thousands of years, that is, from the starting point of the very first vertical-axis wind machines operating on the basis of drag forces, up until the current time, during which wind turbines under development have reached the scale of tens of MW (**Figure 1**).

Constant evolution of the wind power concept throughout this period may be reflected in the most straightforward way by the fact that we are now arguably entering the time of fourth-generation wind power machines (**Figure 2**) [1]. From the early times of wind power exploitation, when the first vertical-axis windmills were used for grinding, to the times that electricity power generation lies on the rotation of huge epoxy-based blades reinforced with carbon fiber and the exploitation of offshore potential, humankind has encountered numerous types of wind machines and designs, which have always found an important place in the puzzle of technological development.

It was in fact centuries ago when the technology of wind energy made its first actual steps – although simpler wind devices date back thousands of years – with the vertical-axis windmills found at the Persian–Afghan borders around 200 BC and the horizontal-axis windmills of the Netherlands and the Mediterranean following much later (AD 1300–1875) (**Figure 3**) [2–4]. Further evolution and perfection of these systems was performed in the United States during the nineteenth century, when over six million small machines were used for water pumping between 1850 and 1970 (**Figure 4**).

Figure 1 Wind power evolution: From the very first vertical-axis machines to large-scale contemporary wind turbines.

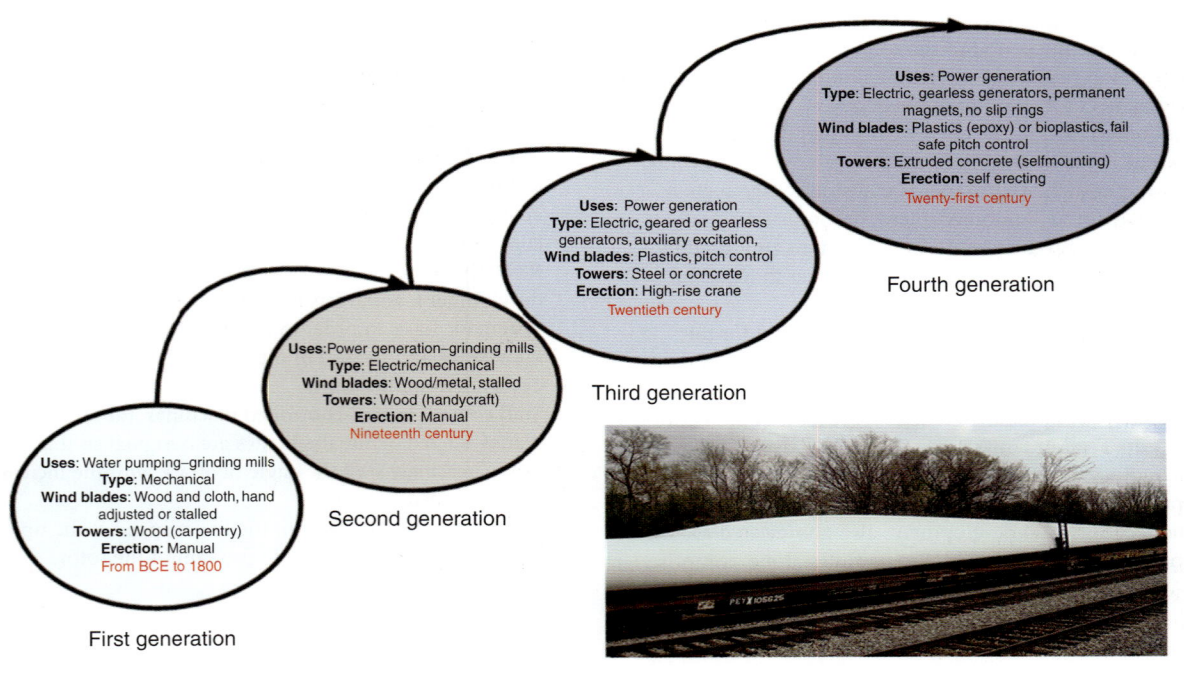

Figure 2 Wind power evolution: From the first to the fourth generation of wind power machines.

Figure 3 The vertical-axis grain machines of the Persians and the horizontal-axis windmills of the Netherlands.

Figure 4 From water pumping to the California outbreak.

On the other hand, the first 'large' wind machine to generate electricity (a low-speed and high-solidity wind turbine of 12 kW) was installed in Cleveland, Ohio, in 1888, while during the late stages of World War I, the use of 25 kW machines throughout Denmark was widespread. Much later, the first wind turbine feeding a local grid was installed in 1931 in the USSR in Balaklava, with the electricity generated being fed into a small grid that was supplied by a 20 MW steam power station. Further development of wind generators in the United States was inspired by the design of airplane propellers and monoplane wings, while subsequent efforts in Denmark, France, Germany, and the United Kingdom during the period between 1935 and 1970 showed that large-scale wind turbines could work. Note that during this period, emphasis was mainly given to the development of horizontal-axis wind machines (i.e., the shaft of rotation is parallel to the ground) operating on the top of adequately high towers and using a small number of blades (normally two or three).

Meanwhile, it was in 1931 that Georges Darrieus invented the vertical-axis wind turbine known as the 'eggbeater' windmill, introducing a new power generation concept for wind machines (**Figure 5**). European developments continued after World War II. In Denmark, the Gedser mill 200 kW three-bladed upwind rotor wind turbine operated successfully until the early 1960s [5], while in Germany, a series of advanced horizontal-axis designs were developed, with both of the aforementioned concepts dictating the future horizontal-axis design approaches later emerging in the 1970s.

One of the most important milestones of wind energy history coincides with the US government involvement in wind energy R&D after the oil crisis of 1973 [6–8]. Following this, in the years between 1973 and 1986, the commercial wind turbine market evolved from domestic and agricultural (1–25 kW) to utility-interconnected wind farm applications (50–600 kW). In this context, the first large-scale wind energy penetration outbreak was encountered in California [9], where over 16 000 machines ranging from 20 to 350 kW (a total of 1.7 GW) were installed between 1981 and 1990, as a result of the incentives (such as the federal investment and energy credits) given by the US government (**Figure 4**). In northern Europe, wind farm installations increased steadily through the 1980s and 1990s (**Figure 6**), with the higher cost of electricity and the excellent wind resources leading to the creation of a small but stable market.

After 1990, most market activity shifted to Europe [10], with the last 20 years bringing wind energy to the front line of the global scene, with major players from all world regions. Nevertheless, both the revival of interest in the United States and the recent dynamic introduction of the Chinese in the wind energy sector have much altered the up-to-now wind energy market situation.

In summary, during these past 20 years, the wind energy sector has met tremendous growth, not only in terms of market share but also in terms of technological developments, with the latest achievements bringing about the era of offshore wind power

Figure 5 Aspects of Darrieus vertical-axis wind machines.

Figure 6 Danish stamp of 1989 and a present-day offshore wind farm.

generation (**Figure 6**) [11]. At this point, it should be noted that important advancements met in the field comprise the result of constant and unceasing research efforts, aiming at the development of innovative clean energy technologies.

In fact, according to the latest figures, systematic efforts recorded throughout this period of growth correspond to a galloping global wind power capacity that recently managed to exceed 200 GW (**Figure 7**) and that is, according to market experts, anticipated to reach 450 GW by 2015 [12]. As already implied (**Figure 7**), the cumulative installed wind power is

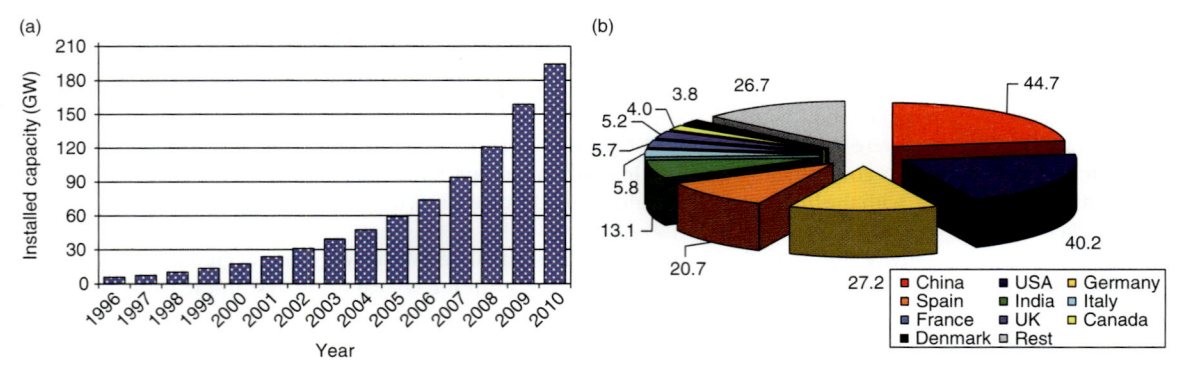

Figure 7 (a) Time evolution of installed wind power and (b) 2010 cumulative wind capacity distribution.

nowadays mainly concentrated in the European Union, the United States, China, and India, while what should also be noted is that there is aremarkable activity recently recorded in offshore installations, with contemporary machines now reaching or even exceeding 5 MW.

2.21.2 The Current Wind Turbine Concept

Being the result of strong competition among different design schools, techniques and manufacturers from all around the world, the vast majority of today's wind turbines comprise the following main parts [13] (**Figure 8**):

A 'rotor' of diameter D, using three relatively thin blades placed upstream of the tower and rotating on the basis of a horizontal axis that is almost parallel to both the ground and the wind direction. Rotational speed of the rotor n_R is kept relatively low in order to limit development of strong centrifugal stresses upon the blades [14], while it is the rotor that at the same time determines the power of wind to be exploited P_w (see also eqn [1]):

$$P_w = 0.5 \cdot \rho \cdot \frac{\pi \cdot D^2}{4} \cdot V^3 \qquad [1]$$

where ρ is the air density passing through the rotor and V is the vertical to the rotor component of wind speed upstream of the rotor (normally at a distance approximately equal to the rotor diameter D).

A 'tower', being normally of solid geometry and determined by a height H that is related to the rotor diameter (usually $H \approx D$). It should be noted that the tower height is configured by the need to both avoid the ground effect [15] and exploit higher wind speeds appearing at greater heights [16]. Increasing the tower height implies an overall structural cost increase, including the need for stronger foundations due to the increase of forces and torque transferred to the base of the machine as well. At the same time, towers

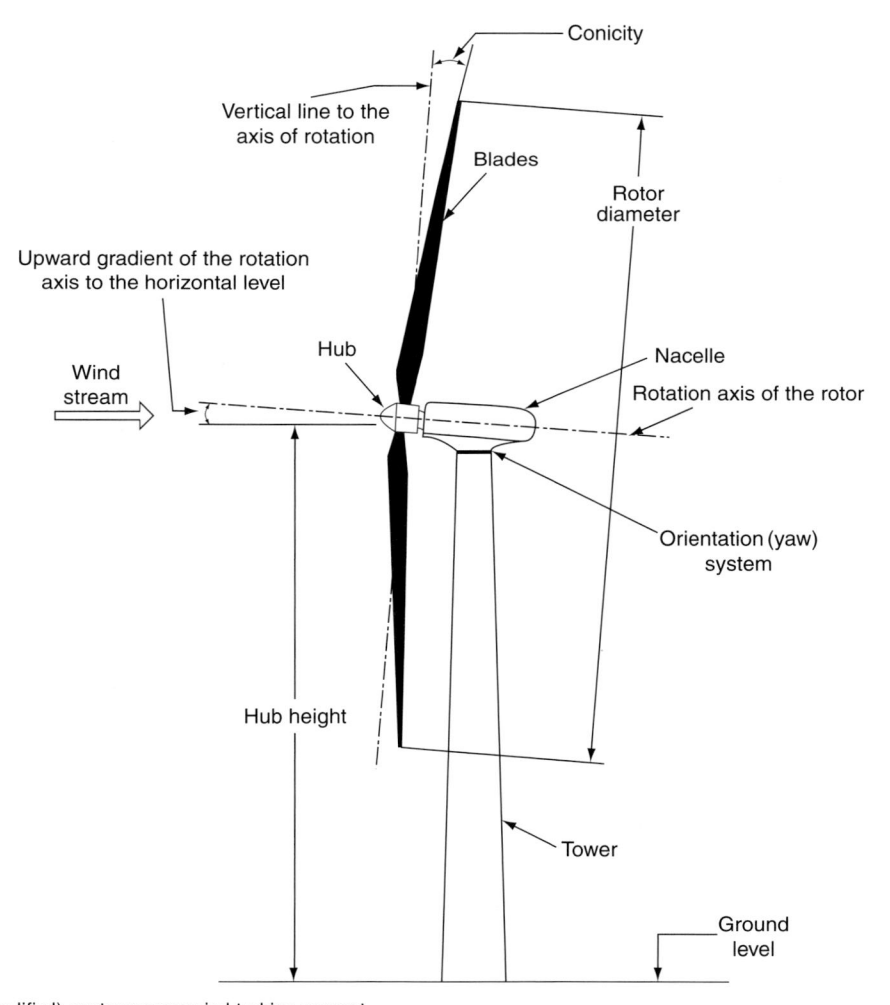

Figure 8 Typical (simplified) contemporary wind turbine concept.

of contemporary wind machines also come with more degrees of freedom in order to avoid excessive loading in the case of rather high wind speeds.

A 'nacelle' that is directed toward the wind with the help of a 'yaw mechanism' [17] and includes the equipment components necessary to convert the mechanical power of the low-speed primary shaft (i.e., the rotational speed of the rotor) to electrical energy satisfying the requirements of consumption. In this regard, there are two established concepts (see Section 2.21.5) to be considered.

In the first case, a gearbox is used in order to achieve increased rotational speed of the secondary axis n_G, which is directly connected to the electrical generator, in comparison with the low rotational speed of the primary axis n_R, based on the gearbox ratio i:

$$n_G = i \cdot n_R \qquad [2]$$

At the same time, the electrical generator (either synchronous or induction machine) converts the mechanical energy of the secondary axis to electrical energy of a given voltage and frequency f (e.g., 50 or 60 Hz depending on the consumption requirements), on the basis of the following equation:

$$f = \frac{p \cdot n_G}{60} \qquad [3]$$

where p is the number of pairs of poles of the electrical generator.

The second design option uses no gearbox and is actually based on the exploitation of the primary shaft mechanical energy with the use of a variable-speed electrical generator, which, according to eqn [3], produces electrical energy of variable frequency. Following this, the AC current is rectified (via an appropriate rectifier) and is then transformed again into AC of defined characteristics (frequency, voltage, etc.) with the use of an inverter.

The nacelle also includes a series of electronic and electrical support subsystems, the mechanical brakes, and the hydraulic circuits, all together ensuring safe and smooth operation of the machine. Finally, the overall installation is also supported by a number of monitoring instruments (e.g., for measuring wind speed and determining wind direction, for measuring air temperature, etc.) as well as the foundation structure of the machines, of which only a minor part is visible.

2.21.3 Size Evolution of Wind Turbines

Wind turbine technology has since 1980 encountered a constant size evolution that transformed the sector of small-scale turbines of tens of Watts to the sector of MW machines. During this time of evolution, the need for upscaling along with the urgency to exploit economies of scale managed to overcome every technological barrier appearing, resulting in the construction of rotors that nowadays even exceed 120 m. The main drivers behind this unceasing trend of size increase concerned the need to exploit higher winds at higher altitudes, maximize area exploitation, and minimize system operational costs per unit power. Size evolution is summarized in **Figures 9–11**, where the time evolution of the rotor diameter along with the evolution of hub height and nacelle mass in relation to the former provides an overview of swept area, height, and mass increase of wind turbines over time [18].

More precisely, according to **Figure 9**, rotor diameter may be determined by an almost exponential trend that, however, results in a typical S-shaped curve due to the stagnation of size development lately met in contemporary wind turbines at the level of 3 MW rated power. Following the trend of rotor diameter increase, the increase of the nacelle mass is also analogous, which, on the other hand, seems to become lighter per unit swept area of the rotor (i.e., from 14.6 to 13.4 kg m^{-2}) (**Figure 10**). The results are similar when considering hub height, with current numbers well exceeding 100 m (**Figure 11**), although it seems that there is now a trend toward shorter machines (hub height to rotor diameter below 1.0) that is partly justified by offshore developments (where taller towers do not make up for the need to build stronger foundations). In addition, according to the characteristics (thickness) of the

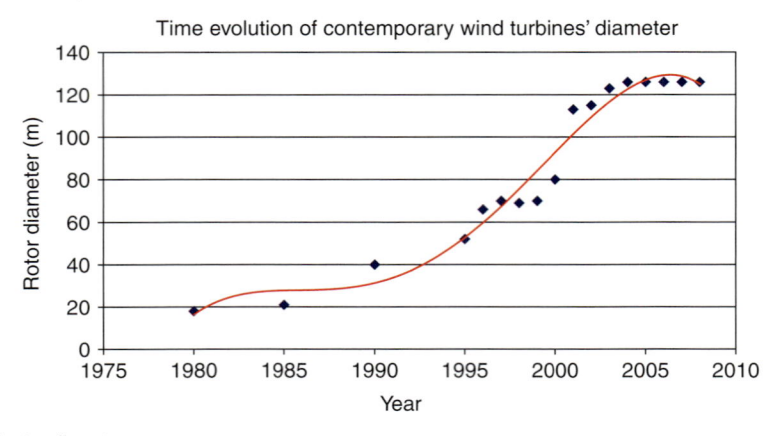

Figure 9 Time evolution of rotor diameter.

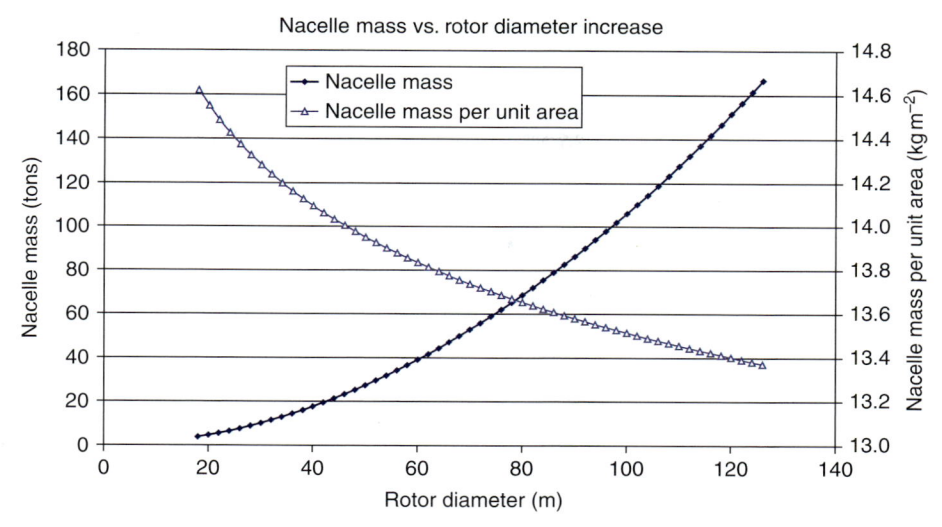

Figure 10 Relation between nacelle mass and rotor diameter.

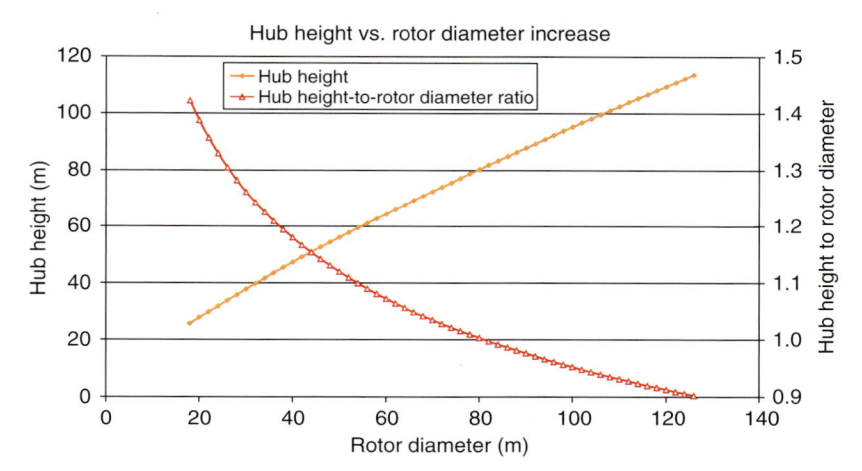

Figure 11 Relation between hub height and rotor diameter.

atmospheric boundary layer, wind speed increase at heights greater than 120 m is not as appreciable and, thus, there is no actual energy gain with further increase of the tower height.

What is also interesting to note in terms of structure is that size increase has in general brought about a downgrade of manufacturing energy requirements in the area of 2–3 MWh per kW of rated power (**Figure 12**), which is actually a key factor for the overall life-cycle energy performance of contemporary wind turbines [19–21].

Furthermore, although it cannot be attributed to upscaling of the machines alone, the fact that the mean annual worldwide capacity factor presents an increasing trend (**Figure 13**), among others (e.g., better wind resource assessment and better siting), also reflects the ability of larger machines to exploit the available wind potential more efficiently (**Figure 14**) [22].

Meanwhile, although stagnation has been recently noted in the wind energy industry around the scale of 2–3 MW machines, manufacturers are still increasing the size of commercial models. Note that a similar situation was encountered during the end of the 1990s as well, see **Figure 9**, with significant technological improvements of that period eventually pushing commercial machines to exceed the limit of 1 MW. As a result, according to the latest market data, the largest commercial wind turbine is at the moment the Enercon E-126, with a rated power of 7.5 MW [23], while one may also encounter the Repower 6 M model of 6 plus MW [24]. In this context, in **Figure 15**, the 10 giants of wind energy industry are gathered in order to obtain a first idea of current commercial sizes (2010–11), although it should be noted that models under development at the moment correspond to wind machines that may start from 7 MW (e.g., Vestas V164) and even reach up to 10 MW (e.g., Sway project, Clipper Windpower and American Superconductor).

There have been strong arguments during recent years that the current horizontal-axis concept is at its peak, with certain studies predicting a stagnation point around 5 MW [25]. The response to this question of whether the horizontal-axis concept has indeed little to give in the following years – as a result of both structural limitations and increased costs associated with the shift to 10 MW

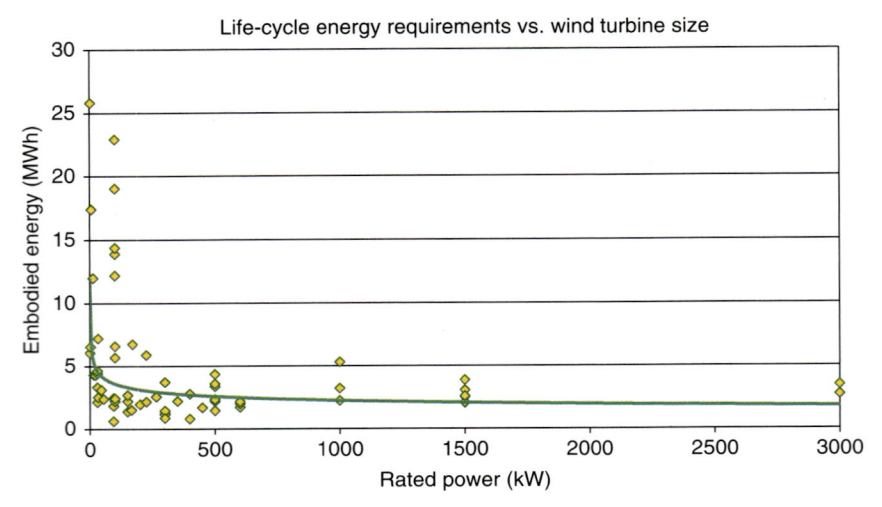

Figure 12 Manufacturing energy requirements of wind turbines in relation to their rated power.

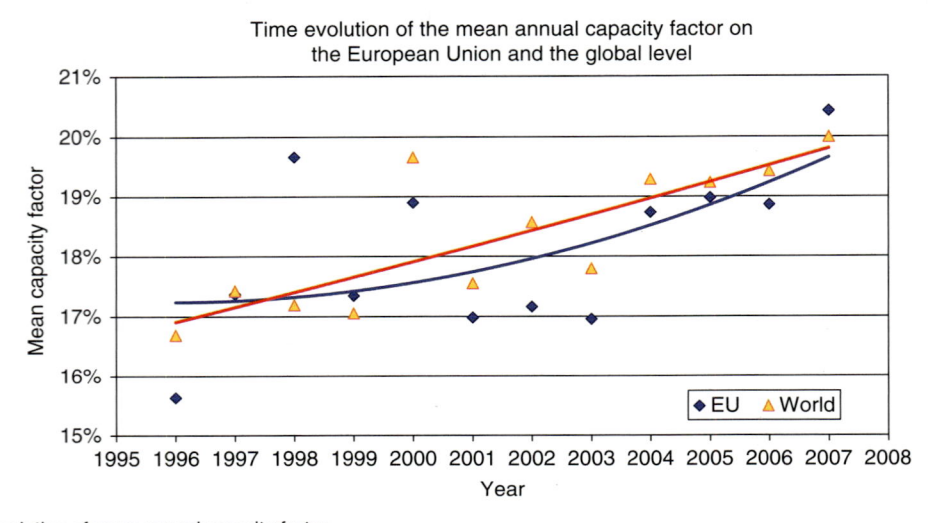

Figure 13 Time evolution of mean annual capacity factor.

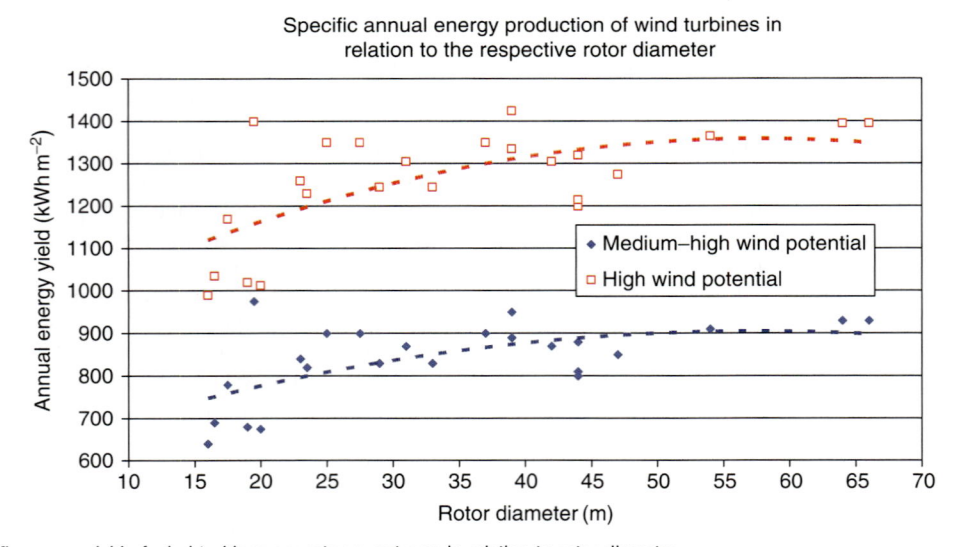

Figure 14 Specific energy yield of wind turbines per rotor swept area in relation to rotor diameter.

	WT	MW	Rotor (m)
Vestas	V112	3	112
GE	2.5xl	2.5	100
Gamesa	G128	4.5	128
Enercon	E-126	7.5	127
Suzlon	S88	2.1	88
Siemens	SWT-3.6-107	3.6	107
Sinovel	SL3000/113	3	113
Acciona	AW-119/3000	3	119
Nordex	N100	2.5	100
REpower	6M	6.15	126

Figure 15 The 10 commercial wind turbine giants of the present day (2011).

plus machines – is expected by the results of the UPWIND project [26], aiming at the development of 20 MW wind turbines, addressing all issues involved in such an outstanding effort.

In conclusion, it is the present day that the current concept of wind turbines faces the greatest challenge in more than 30 years, during which constant size increase led to the establishment of a tremendously growing industry that allowed wind energy to dominate. On the other hand, what must be noted is that even if proceeding with the *status quo* of commercial wind turbines, achieving power outputs in the order of 10 MW, future progress of wind power is still thought to be rather encouraging.

2.21.4 Pitch versus Stall and Active-Stall Wind Turbines

Unless the power production of a wind machine is regulated at high wind speeds, the occurring overloading may even cause failure of certain components or of the entire structure. Power regulation is applied with the use of two main concept mechanisms, that is, stall control and pitch control [27].

In the first case, power regulation is achieved through the exploitation of the stall phenomenon (**Figure 16(a)**) and the aerodynamic design of the rotor blades itself. More precisely, once a certain threshold of wind speed is exceeded, the airfoil angle

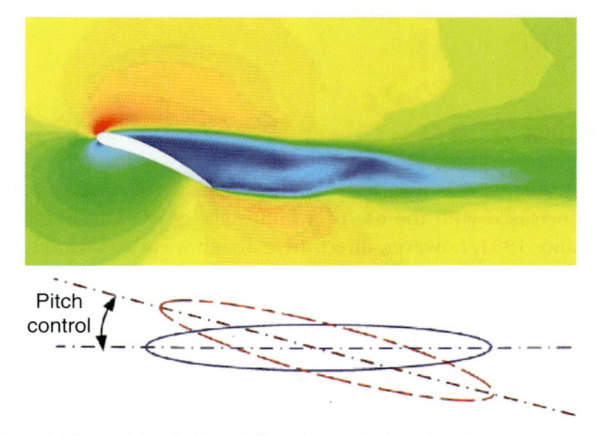

Figure 16 Wind flow over an airfoil when stalling and illustration of the pitch-control mechanism.

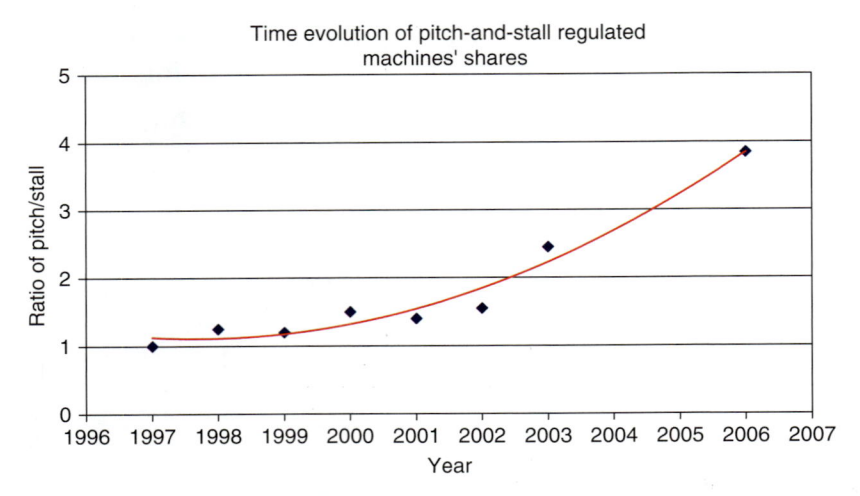

Figure 17 Gradual dominance of pitch-control over stall-control regulation.

of attack is increased and the lift force previously occurring upon the blades is now reduced due to a progressive and not abrupt passive stalling. In the second case, pitch-control regulation is based on the rotation of blades along their longitudinal axis in order to ensure power regulation within the desired limits (**Figure 16(b)**). More specifically, through electronic control, power output of the machine is controlled several times per second and blade angle changed to either obtain maximum power for a given wind speed or reduce power output after the point that rated power has been obtained.

A third option that has emerged during recent years, and is mostly applied to machines in the scale of MW, is the active stall-control concept [28]. In this case, pitchable blades are used by the machine, which are, however, operated in a somewhat different way than in the classic pitch-control design. More specifically, although at low wind speeds blade control is similar to the case of the classic pitch-control operation, the situation becomes different when rated power is exceeded. At that point, electronic controls decide to increase the angle of attack, which in turn leads to stalling, which is opposite to the case of pitch control, where reduction of the angle of attack is performed so as to reduce power output at the levels required. An immediate advantage of this solution is that by ensuring active stall in wind speeds above rated power, deep stall – as in the classic stall-control option – is avoided, thus allowing for greater wind energy exploitation.

Considering also the interaction between power regulation and rotational speed of the machine, there are actually three common options currently used in power regulation, that is, constant speed of the rotor and fixed blades using stall regulation (e.g., NM 1000/60), constant speed of the rotor and pitchable blades using pitch/active-stall regulation (e.g., WindMaster 750/48 and Vestas V82), and, finally, variable speed of the rotor and pitchable blades using pitch regulation (e.g., Enercon E126), with the latter concept being the one that has dominated in large MW-scale machines (**Figure 17**). The opposite trend was noted during the 1980s, when stall control found itself to be the dominant solution, with the respective three-bladed fixed-speed machines (Danish concept) actually comprising the only option during that time.

Between the two, due to the fact that the pitch fixed speed solution was never successful, many of the manufacturers decided to introduce only some level of variability to begin with, with systems such as OptiSlip and Flexi-slip allowing for a maximum slip in the area of 10–17% [29]. In the following years, attributes of variable speed such as considerable flexibility and high quality of power offered to the grid were much appreciated, although high costs compared with relatively small energy gains always comprised a barrier for total acceptance of the concept.

2.21.5 Direct-Drive versus Gearbox

Up until 1990, contemporary wind turbine models were based on the classical drivetrain concept, according to which the rotor (or the primary shaft) speed has to be increased with the use of a multistage gearbox in order to allow operation of the electrical generator at high rotational speeds. Since 1991, however, direct-drive design was also introduced (with the generator being directly coupled to the rotor), providing an alternative option for wind turbine manufacturers. Despite the breakthrough characteristics of the direct-drive design, however, the dominance of geared machines in terms of commercial use is still evident, since the only company that has, up to now, supported the specific solution is Enercon. In fact, according to the latest official data concerning the time period between 2001 and 2008, the market share of gearless machines reached only 15% [30], with the rest of the delivered machines corresponding to the classical geared concept (**Figures 18** and **19**).

During recent years, great interest has been demonstrated in the R&D of direct-drive concepts, much stimulated by the shift of wind power technology to offshore applications, with less complex direct-drive configurations implying significantly lower

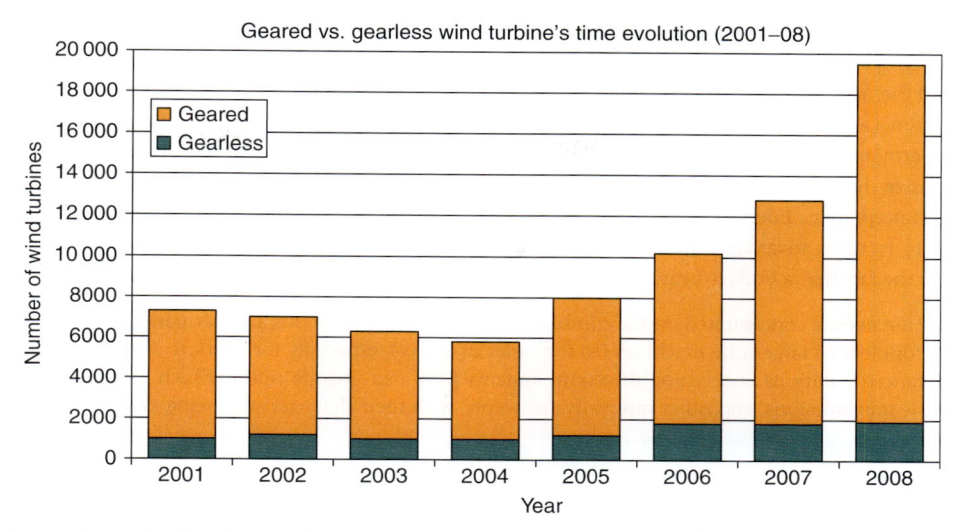

Figure 18 Market share of geared and gearless machines (number of wind turbines).

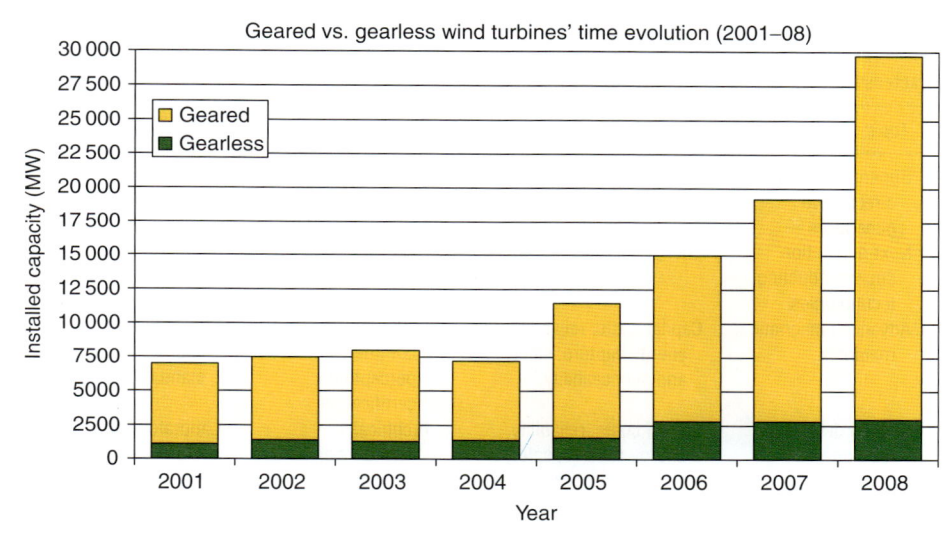

Figure 19 Market share of geared and gearless machines (delivered capacity).

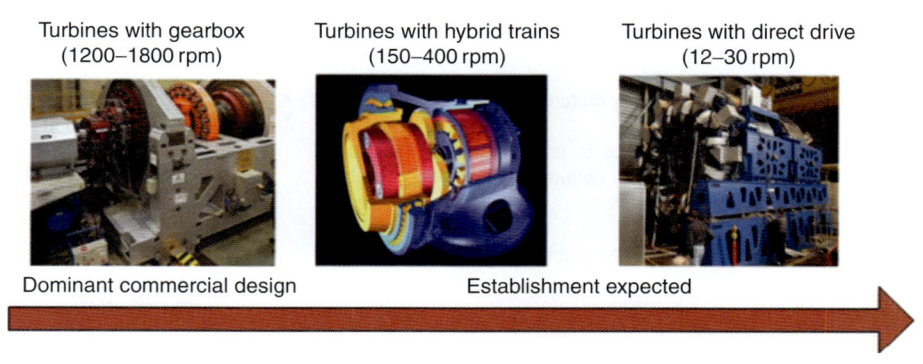

Figure 20 Current wind turbine drivetrain concepts.

maintenance and operation requirements, which are of primary importance when it comes to offshore wind parks. One should also take into account the so-called hybrid solutions, which manage to combine the two above-mentioned edges through the incorporation of a low gear ratio gearbox and a permanent magnet generator.

In summary, current drivetrain options [31] (**Figure 20**) include the following three solutions.

- 'The classical geared concept', with high gear ratios allowing for generator speeds in the order of 1200–1800 rpm. Its main benefits are the reduced size of electrical generators used and the up-to-now lower purchase costs, and its main drawbacks are the inherent energy losses and the need for considerable maintenance needs [32].
- 'The hybrid solution' (e.g., Multibrid [33]), in which the common synchronous electrical generator met in the direct-drive design is replaced by a permanent magnet generator that eliminates excitation losses. A single- or two-stage gearbox is also incorporated in order to downsize the need for the huge generators required in large-scale direct-drive machines [34].
- 'The direct-drive concept' (e.g., Enercon machines), with the introduction of low-speed generators that are directly connected to the machine rotor [31]. Its main advantages are the higher efficiency and the minimization of maintenance requirements, and its main disadvantages are the fact that a bulkier/heavier system should be considered, which also comes along with higher purchase costs.

Current R&D efforts are mainly concentrated on the combination of direct-drive systems and permanent magnet generators, destined to support the development of large-scale machines (in the order of 5 MW), especially for offshore applications. On the other hand, next-generation advanced solutions concerning drivetrain systems [35] also include options such as superconductive drivetrains, continuously variable transmissions, and other innovative concepts, with their characteristics being synopsized in Table 1.

2.21.6 Blade Design and Construction

Possibly the most important component of a wind machine, that is, its rotor blades, is the result of elaborate design on the basis of multiple tests carried out (Figure 21) [36], aiming at maximum exploitation of the available wind energy potential. Because the

Table 1 Main characteristics of next-generation drivetrains

	Topic	Benefits	Barriers	Pathways
Superconducting drivetrains	Superconducting direct-drive generators	Capital costs, reliability, energy capture, supply chain security	Technical, perception, scaling	Subcomponent reliability testing, demonstration project deployment, engage independent third parties
	Next-generation superconducting technologies	Energy capture	Technical	Laboratory testing
Permanent magnet generators	Advanced magnetic materials	Capital costs, reliability, energy capture, safety and serviceability	Technical, commercial, perception, certification	Materials science research, trade-off analysis, cost/benefit analysis, IEC standards development
	System design and topology	Capital costs, reliability, energy capture, safety and serviceability	Technical, commercial, certification	Laboratory research, cost/benefit analysis, IEC standards development
	Power electronics	Capital costs, reliability, performance	Technical, perception, commercial	Laboratory research, workforce education and training, cost/benefit analysis
	Diagnostics and maintenance	Reliability	Reliability, operator training, certification	Reliability research, workforce education and training, IEC standards development
Variable trains	Frictional contact drives	Capital costs, reliability, energy capture	Technical, scalability, materials	Cost/benefit analysis, design and modeling tools, demonstration projects, component development and testing
	Fluid drives	Capital costs, reliability, energy capture, energy storage	Technical, scalability, materials, perception	Cost/benefit analysis, design and modeling tools, component development and testing, demonstration projects
Innovative concepts	Uptower DC generator	Reliability, grid benefits	Technical	Feasibility studies, equipment survey
	Ground-level generators	Reliability	Technical	Feasibility studies
	Rim-drive turbines	Reliability	Technical	Feasibility studies
	Tandem generators	Availability, scalability	Commercial	Feasibility studies
	Complete uptower gearbox reparability	Reliability	Technical	Feasibility studies
	Other innovative drivetrains	Capital costs, reliability	Technical, perception	Design studies

Figure 21 Aspects of full-scale tests for evaluation of blade performance.

power output of a wind turbine is found to be analogous to the swept area of the rotor (or the square of the rotor diameter), blade manufacturers try to meet the challenge of creating larger and larger wind turbine blades that may ensure higher power output per unit machine. In this case, it was only recently [37] that LM Wind Power (former LM Glasfiber) announced the construction of a 73.5 m blade (equivalent to a 24-storey building) for the Alstom 6 MW offshore wind turbines, demonstrating advancements made in the specific sector during recent years.

Higher energy output requiring larger blades also comes with the drawback of increased weight and loads that affect the entire machine structure. As a result, efforts concerning the evolution of blade design are more focused on weight reduction, with the use of lighter materials being the research subject of many blade evolution projects during the past (e.g., WindPACT, the NREL-sponsored Turbine Rotor Design Study, the Sandia-sponsored Blade System Design Studies, etc.), with emphasis given on the development of jointed blade designs and the introduction of carbon fiber composites [38–41].

Meanwhile, according to Hau [42], there are five basic blade designs that must be considered, at least in terms of material used:

- Fiberglass/polyester: These comprise old-design heavy blades (in the order of 2–3 kg m^{-2} of swept area; see **Figure 22**), mainly used in older Danish machines, with built-in aerodynamic spoilers, being suitable for comparatively low tip speed ratios.
- Laminated fiberglass/polyester: Mostly used in the past, destined to serve small- to medium-scale wind turbines and medium to high tip speed ratios, with a specific weight ranging from 1.5 to 2.5 kg m^{-2}.
- Fiberglass/epoxy: With the use of epoxy resin, construction of lighter blades that are mostly used in large-scale machines has become possible, also supporting reduction of the specific weight, even under 1 kg m^{-2} for the smallest of machines.
- Wood epoxy: Such blades when introduced provided a temporary solution that was much lighter than the older fiberglass/polyester. Nevertheless, with the use of more advanced composites accordingly, the specific solution is not as common nowadays.
- Fiberglass/carbon: With the introduction of carbon fibers, extremely lightweight blades gave an answer to the challenge of developing very large-scale machines, employing rotors of more than 80 m. In this regard, many of today's companies use carbon

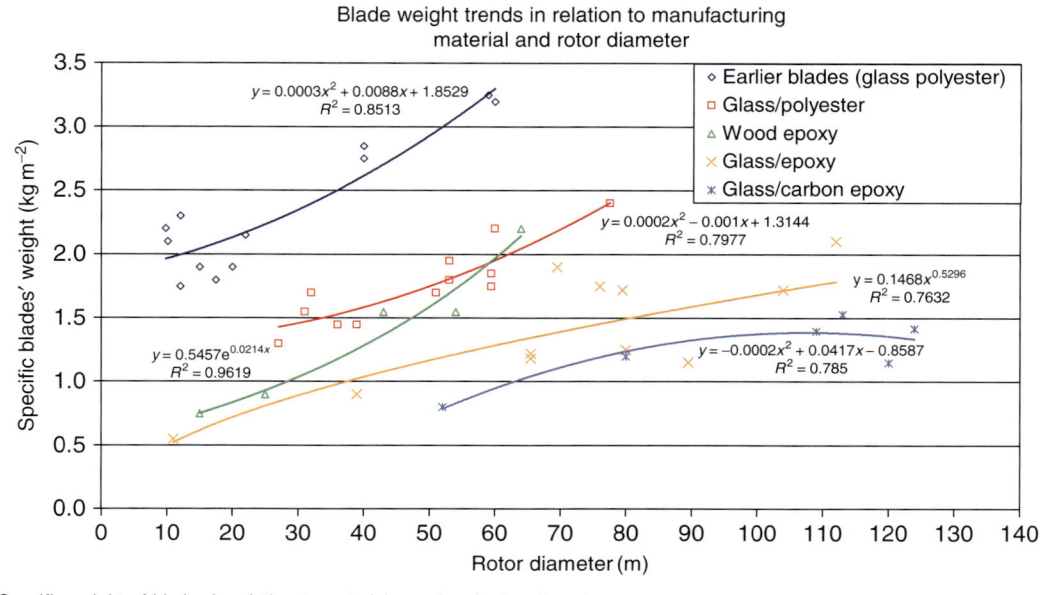

Figure 22 Specific weight of blades in relation to materials used and rotor diameter.

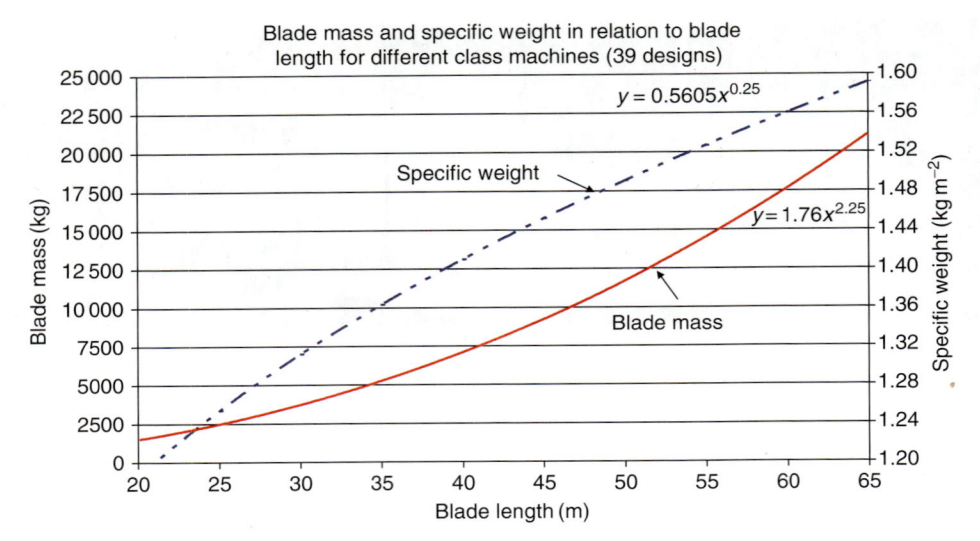

Figure 23 Blade mass and specific weight of blades in relation to blade length.

fiber, normally at a given proportion of 750–1000 kg MW^{-1}, while the weight reduction achieved is supposed to counterbalance increased costs, especially when considering extremely long blades.

Further investigation of weight trends may be obtained from the Energy Research Centre of the Netherlands (ECN) [43], where several machines are compared, with the results designating a power trend with the blade mass being analogous to the radius square (a power factor around 2 is to be expected; see **Figure 23**), whereas specific weight is found to vary between 1.2 and 1.6 kg m^{-2}. Gradual employment of lighter materials may be reflected by the results of **Figure 24**, where different period curves illustrate advancements made in the field, with weight difference being more and more pronounced as the blade length increases.

The issue of number of blades employed seems to have been solved long ago, with three-bladed machines being – as already seen – the almost exclusive option in contemporary wind turbines. The comparatively higher power coefficient of three-bladed machines, although not ensuring *a priori* sufficient energy yield to outweigh the cost of an extra blade, is also accompanied by other positive attributes. More precisely, operation of one- and two-bladed machines at higher tip speeds also implies higher levels of aerodynamic noise to consider. Furthermore, asymmetry introduced in terms of aerodynamics from the one- and two-bladed machines entails higher loading, which requires more complex components to be introduced in the machine (e.g., teeter hinge), while, finally, visual asymmetry is also a matter of concern, with three-bladed machines being more easily adapted to inhabited environments. Nevertheless, if the costs of facing additional loads – as a result of higher rotational speeds – become comparable to

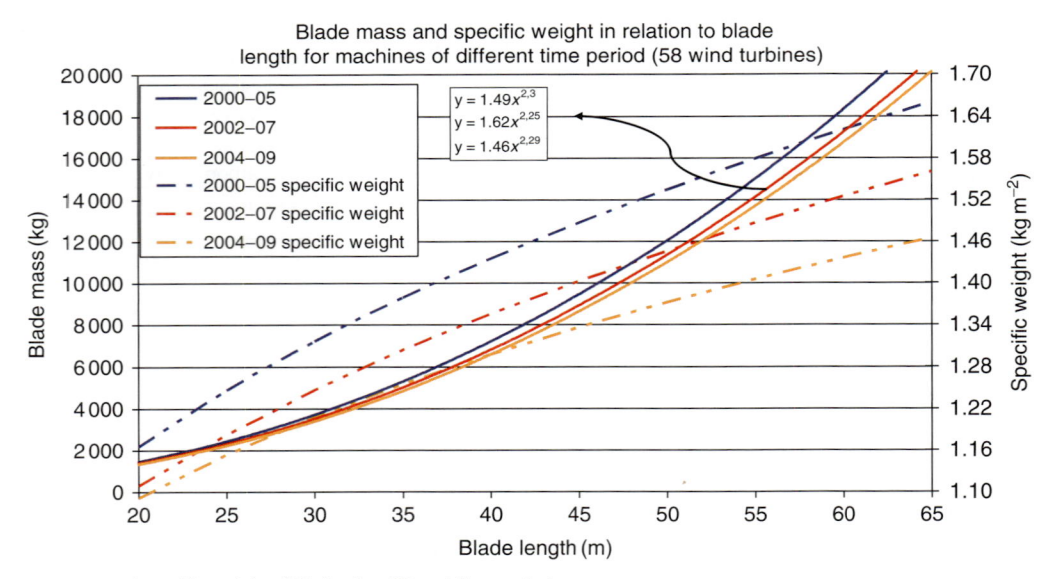

Figure 24 Blade mass and specific weight of blades for different time periods.

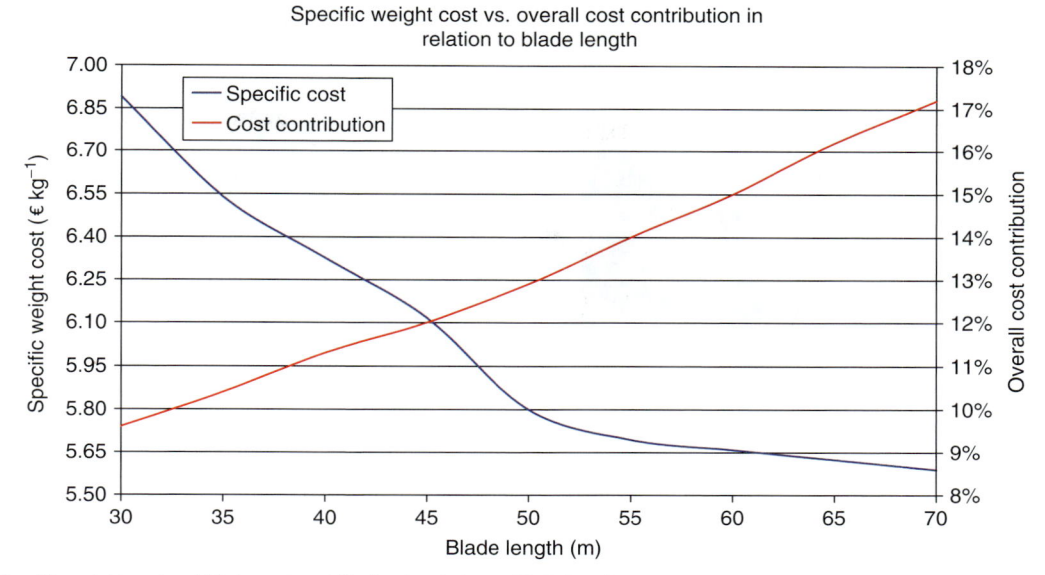

Figure 25 Specific weight cost and blade cost contribution in relation to blade length.

the cost of an extra blade, two-bladed machine applications may actually find their place in the wind energy market (e.g., in offshore applications where noise may not comprise such a problem and the potentially easier assembly of a two-blade rotor may prove more cost-effective [44]).

At the same time, economies of scale seem to apply in the blade industry as well (**Figure 25**), with larger blades ensuring some level of cost reduction [45], although this can be quite sensitive and much depends on the mix of materials to be used. On the other hand, gradual reduction of this cost was not found to be analogous to the overall cost reduction of wind turbines, with the contribution share of rotor blades found to increase with the size increase of the machines.

Nevertheless, this trend is expected to change in the years to come, since the diffusion to offshore wind machines will signal a shift of major costs to other components such as foundations. In fact, according to experts, it is this trend that will also allow for carbon fiber to be largely adopted in new wind turbine giants.

At the same time, R&D in the field is ongoing, with the latest efforts being carried out by the Wind Energy Department of Sandia Laboratories, where exploration of a 100 m blade, potentially for a 13.2 MW offshore machine, comprises the latest challenge.

2.21.7 Innovative Concepts

Although the three-bladed horizontal axis is by far the most common wind turbine concept, new design concepts constantly emerging demonstrate the ongoing research interest in the wind power field. More precisely, innovative designs presently being examined include the following:

- *Magenn Air Rotor System (MARS)*: MARS [46] is a tethered wind turbine that is lighter than air and rotates around a horizontal axis in order to produce electrical energy (**Figure 26**). MARS is elevated with the use of helium, which allows the machine to ascend to very high altitudes (up to 300 m), where exploitation of high wind speeds is possible. Furthermore, MARS may operate within the broad range of speeds from 2 up to 28 m s^{-1}, while one of its main advantages is its ability to remain mobile and be

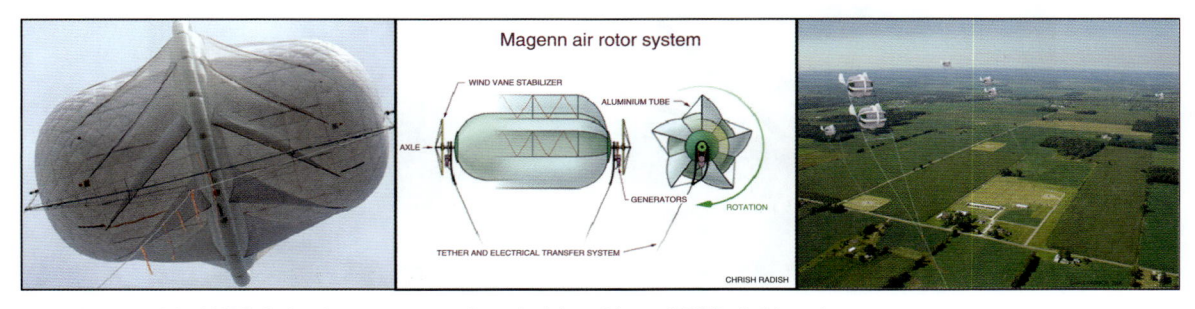

Figure 26 Aspects of the MARS design (prototype, operation principle and future MARS wind farms).

Figure 27 Aspects of the Maglev design (1 GW machine conceptualized and Maglev machine with guide vanes).

non-site-specific (i.e., at such high altitudes high-quality wind potential is *a priori* given, thus eliminating the need to seek for 'good' sites). According to its manufacturers, initial targets of MARS include mini-grid applications (e.g., small island regions), rapid deployment in areas where electricity is urgently required (taking advantage of its mobility), and other off-grid applications, with a 100 kW MARS being the first commercial size expected.

- *Maglev*: The specific vertical-axis concept [47] uses full-permanent magnets to almost eliminate friction through levitation of the blades above their base (**Figure 27**). According to its designers, the concept is able to provide enormous turbines in the order of 1 GW, requiring an area of almost 100 acres, while at the same time the machine is able to start operating at wind speeds of only $1.5\,\mathrm{m\,s^{-1}}$. At the moment, some first efforts to provide the first industrial product have been recorded in China, where developer Zhongke Hengyuan Energy Technology has invested a total of US$55 million so as to build a massive Maglev turbine of 1 GW.
- *Kite Gen*: The Kite Gen design [48–50] is based on the configuration of a carousel of tethered kites (**Figure 28**) centrally operated by a control system with two distinct operational phases. More precisely, when each of the kites pulls (i.e., when energy can be generated by the system), the control unit, which is attached on a vertical-axis rotor that is connected to an electrical drive, makes the drive act as a generator. However, when the kites need to be dragged (when no energy generation is available), the electric drive acts as a motor, with the proportion of energy required for dragging supposed to be minor. In use, according to rough estimations [50], the employment of 100 kites (total area of $500\,\mathrm{m}^2$), on a 1500 m radius carousel at an average wind speed of $12\,\mathrm{m\,s^{-1}}$, may even achieve a power output in the order of 1 GW.

In addition to the medium- and large-scale innovative designs targeted at the production of novel machines with power output from hundreds of kW to hundreds of MW, small-scale wind turbine concepts are also developed, with the rebirth of the specific market encouraging the development of several patents. Two examples of such concepts that have managed to go commercially are presented here, that is, aeroturbines and Windpods.

- *Aeroturbines*: The turbines [51] comprise small-scale vertical-axis machines destined to satisfy urban applications. Among their unique features are the modular/stackable cage that allows almost any kind of installation (horizontally, vertically, or diagonally) and the helical rotor (**Figure 29**), with available models reaching up to 2.5 kW of rated power.
- *Windpods*: These are also vertical-axis micro-turbines [52], basing their operation on three different sections, each with blade positions offset 60° from the next one (**Figure 29**). Commercial modules reach 500 W, with the design's main advantages being its modularity and building applicability.

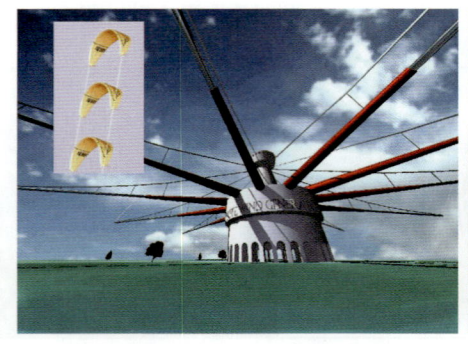

Figure 28 Carousel and small-scale prototype configurations for the Kite Gen concept.

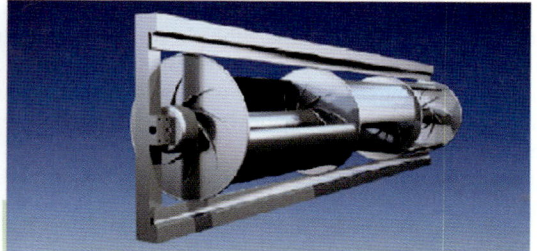

Figure 29 Aspect of the aeroturbine and the Windpod designs.

Figure 30 Diffuser-augmented wind turbines (DAWTs): From the early Vortec design to the recent FloDesign and WindTamer machines.

Finally, one of the most popular concepts that drew much attention during the past was the so-called diffuser-augmented wind turbine [53, 54]. Such wind turbines mainly evolved during the mid-1990s under Vortec, although the concept was much older; nevertheless, the specific type never managed to establish itself in the wind energy market. Such machines had a diffuser placed upstream of the rotor (**Figure 30**) in order to augment power output through achieving wind speed increase without increasing hub height, and claimed augmentation that was, however, never validated. The additional weight put upon the machine along with increased costs in order to provide sufficient support condemned the specific solution quite early on, although there are still some investing efforts, aiming at the rebirth of such wind turbines [55, 56].

2.21.8 Environmental Impact Reduction

The considerable increase of both installed wind power capacity and contemporary wind turbine size, and the need to operate wind farms in areas that are close to available electricity grids and are determined by sufficient infrastructure, have raised issues of social acceptance, as a result of impacts caused to the environment and local societies by the operation of wind farms. In this regard, although it is a common true that any type of impact caused by the operation of a wind farm is by far less important and more restricted (normally within a relatively limited area of some square kilometers in the vicinity of the wind farm location) than that caused by the majority of power stations (nuclear, thermal power, large hydropower, etc.), much attention has been given during the recent years to limit (if not to eliminate) the environmental impacts of wind energy [57]. What must be noted, however, is that with the current levels of social acceptability [58, 59] and appreciation of social benefits deriving from the operation of wind farms, installation of wind farms may well keep up with the up-to-now progress, allowing for integration of wind energy in all areas of the globe.

Among the most important environmental impacts caused by the operation of a single or more wind turbines is noise production (especially aerodynamic noise since mechanical noise has already been much limited on the basis of past efforts) [60]. As a result, emphasis is currently given on both the advanced design of blades in order to reduce noise produced and the optimum siting of the machines in an area of given characteristics (see Section 2.21.16). Special attention has also been given during recent years to the operational mode of the machines (e.g., reduction of the rotor rotational speed and variation of the angle of attack) in order to avoid annoyance. Finally, a significant part of the current research efforts has been concentrated on the noise propagation through and upon water [61], as a result of the growth met in offshore applications.

Moreover, one of the most important issues determining levels of social acceptability of wind turbines is also their aesthetic adaptation. Taking into account the extreme size of contemporary wind turbines (with the blade tip height above the ground even approaching 200 m), it becomes apparent that adaptation concerns have become critical. For this purpose, there are various calculation and photorealistic models currently developed [62], aiming at the minimization of the visual impact.

In addition to the above, one of the issues that has long since been considered as a negative attribute of wind energy is the impact of wind turbines on birds. For this purpose, there are serious attempts carried out nowadays so as to interpret behavior of birds in a given area and also record the paths of migratory populations [63], using suitable systems that are able to monitor and record the courses followed by birds and thus eliminate the already reduced fatalities [64].

As far as the rest of the wind energy environmental impacts are concerned, it must be noted that land occupation has considerably improved over the course of time, with the use of higher and larger-scale machines both offering greater power output per square area and allowing for land activities to occur even next to the wind turbine foundations. Besides, the gradual shift toward offshore applications has also much contributed to the amelioration of the land use impact. Local issues such as shadow flicker and interference with telecommunication signals can be thought of as resolved, especially if practices and regulations already available are properly applied.

Finally, special emphasis has been given during the past 20 years to the issue of communication with local societies as well as to the development of integrated strategies that may assess impacts and better comprehend the factors that configure the behavior of local inhabitants [65, 66]. One should also consider the involvement of various types of scientists, originating from different subject areas such as communication, sociology, psychology, biology, and strategic planning. Interaction of all these different experts then focuses on comprehending the opinion of the local societies, as well as determines the benefits accruing from the operation of wind energy in relation to the avoided costs deriving from the operation of alternative, usually conventional power sources. In addition, considerable effort should also be spent in the development of strategies that will allow the approach of local inhabitants and help them to both overcome their worries and become active participants in the development of new wind energy applications [67].

What should always be taken into account is that during every stage of developing a new wind park, all parties involved should acknowledge and appreciate the fact that wind energy comprises a sustainable energy solution that has the ability to sufficiently support the energy needs of contemporary societies.

2.21.9 Offshore Wind Parks

The future of wind energy is gradually heading seawards, with the following decade expected to be determined by the establishment of offshore wind farms as the next generation of wind power. Although the first offshore wind park was actually built in 1991, there were only seven additional farms installed up until 2001, resulting in a total of almost 100 MW capacity, which did not live up to the expectations of an impressive start. Nevertheless, following this infancy period, the offshore concept managed to develop rapidly during the next decade, that is, from 2001 to 2011, leading to a total of almost 2.4 GW installed capacity worldwide [68]. Distribution of cumulative installed capacity on the basis of the most recent official data may be obtained from **Figure 31**, where the leading role of the United Kingdom and Denmark may be noted, together holding approximately 72% of the overall capacity. Furthermore, the number of in-operation offshore wind farms corresponding to the above-mentioned overall capacity is 42 (**Figure 32**), with their majority encountered – as expected – in the UK (11) and Denmark (11) [69]. Despite the progress met, however, in the offshore field during recent years, one should not disregard the fact that, at the moment, offshore wind farms represent only a very small percentage of the global wind power capacity, in the order of 1–1.5%.

Although not in its infancy period, offshore wind power may be still thought of as an immature technology [70], and exploration of prospects and technological trends [71] is of primary importance for determining its ability to compete with conventional onshore wind farms. The evaluation of available offshore wind energy potential and mapping of the most suitable regions is the first step toward the promotion of the offshore concept. Relative to this, based on the results of the European Environment Agency report on the evaluation of the European offshore wind energy potential [72], the available as well as the restricted (i.e., when considering restricted areas such as Natura 2000) and the economically feasible wind energy potential are depicted in **Figure 33**, for a time horizon of up to 2030. As one may see, the available offshore potential is quite high, reaching almost 30 000 TWh yr^{-1}, although

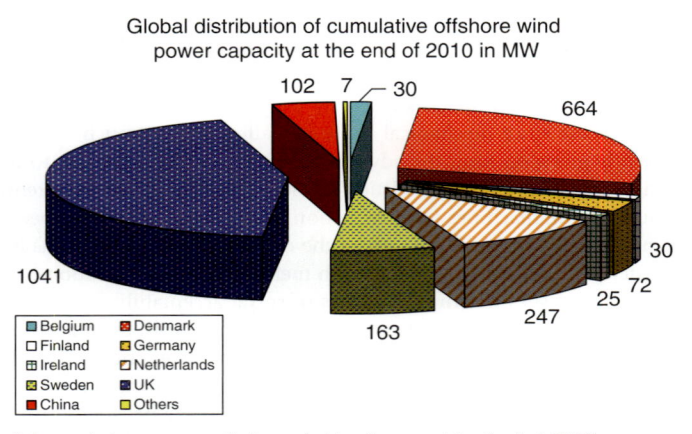

Figure 31 Distribution of global offshore wind power capacity in market-leading countries (end of 2010).

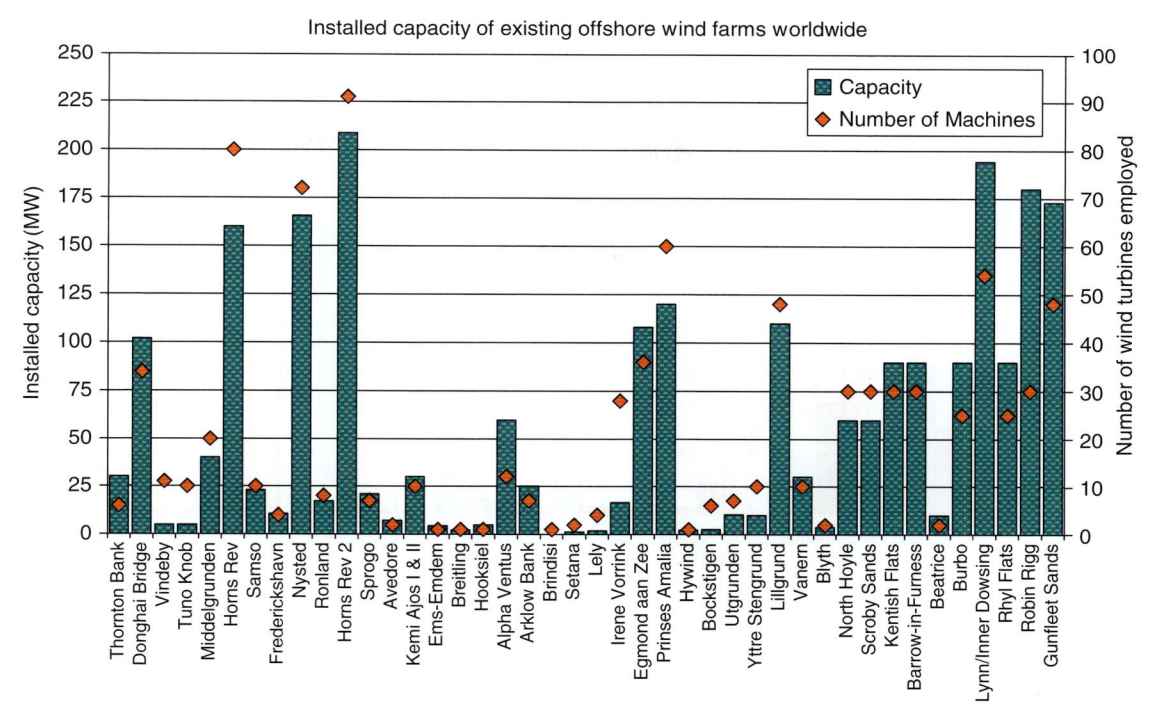

Figure 32 Main characteristics of in-operation offshore wind farms (end of 2010).

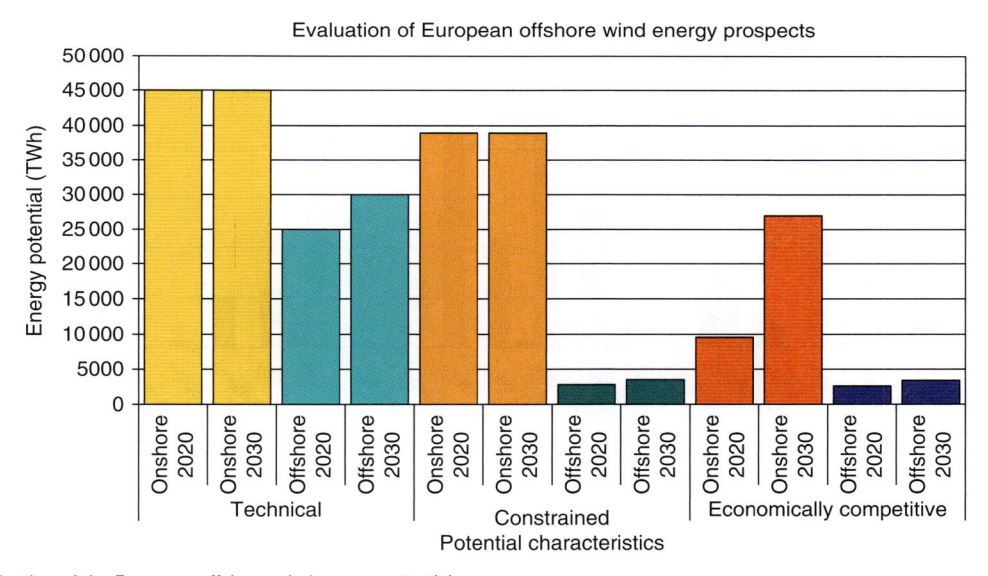

Figure 33 Evaluation of the European offshore wind energy potential.

what is estimated as economically feasible is eventually much less, that is, 3400 TWh$_e$, covering, in rough numbers, around 80% of that time's EU electricity demand (i.e., much less modest than the European Wind Energy Association (EWEA) target, aiming at approximately 600 TWh$_e$ of production by 2030) [73].

Similar results have also been published for the United States, where, although no offshore wind parks are still in operation, remarkable offshore wind power penetration could be stimulated in the years to come. More precisely, according to the figures provided by certain studies [68], there is an offshore wind power potential – in an area of less than 50 nautical miles from shore, which is also determined by mean annual wind speeds that are greater than 7 m s^{-1} – that well exceeds 4 TW or is almost 4 times the installed electrical capacity of the country (**Figure 34**).

Considering the above, new installations that are either in the stage of permission, or already approved, and under construction may be obtained from **Figure 35**, where the concentration of offshore wind farms in the European territory in the years to come

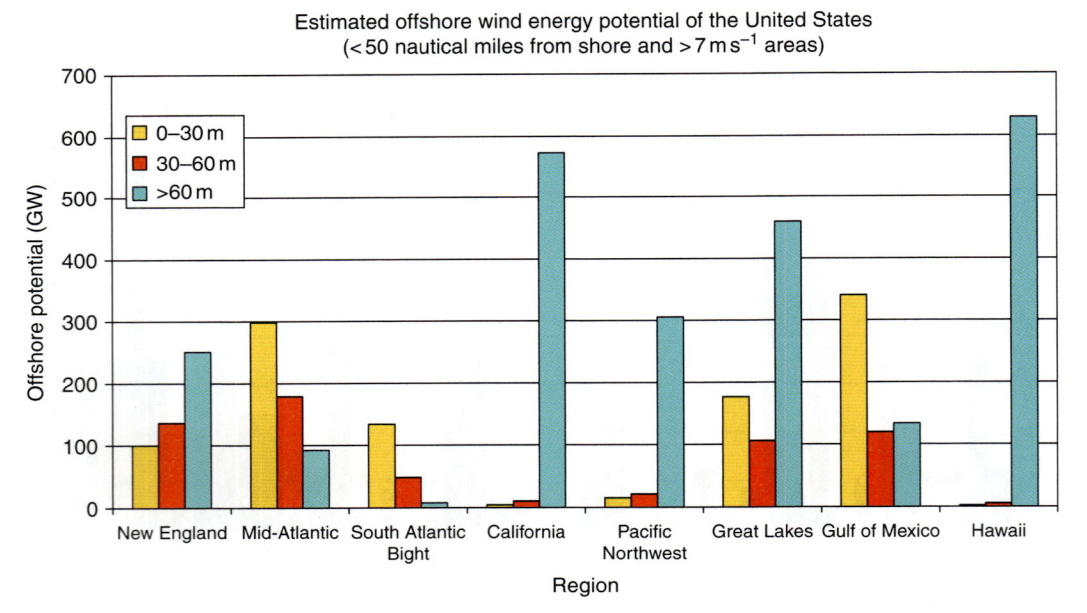

Figure 34 Evaluation of the US offshore wind energy potential.

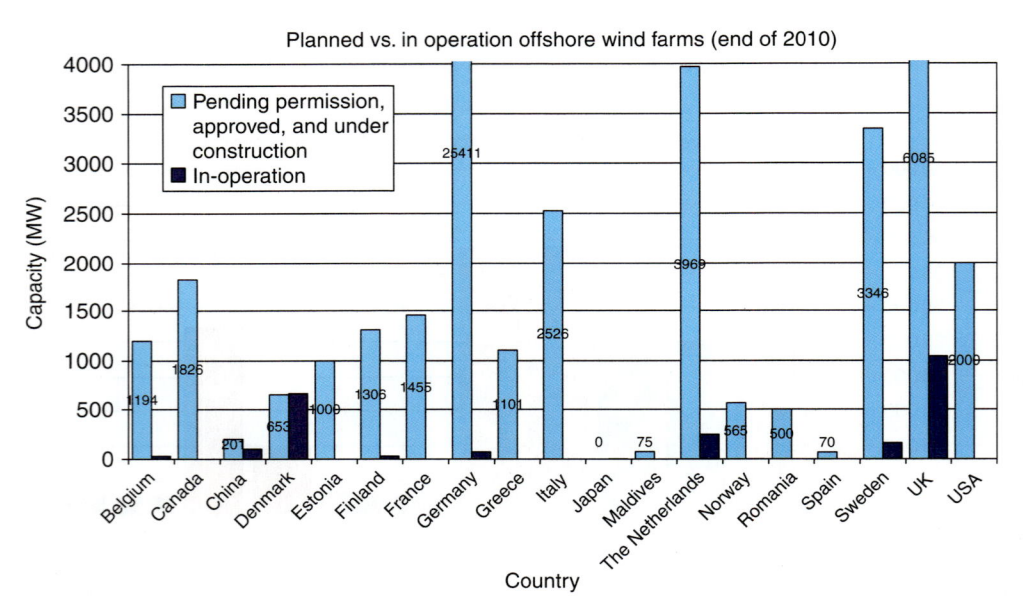

Figure 35 Under development/pending permission vs. in-operation offshore wind farms.

becomes evident. In fact, there is a remarkable integration of offshore wind farms to be expected in Germany (> 25 GW) and the United Kingdom (> 6 GW), followed by the Netherlands (~4 GW), Sweden (> 3.4 GW), and Italy (> 2.5 GW), while, despite its outstanding offshore wind energy potential, the US investors have only announced a total of 2 GW. As a result, it seems that the target set by the EWEA, pushing for a total of 40 GW by 2020 and 150 GW by 2030 for the European region (which along with onshore wind park developments aspire to lead to the remarkable installed capacity of 400 GW by 2030), could actually be rather realistic [74] (**Figure 36**).

Apart from the excellent opportunities in terms of available wind energy potential and the ambitious targets set at least at the European level, offshore wind energy is faced with many technological challenges such as the configuration of the most appropriate support structures for the safer and most cost-effective installation and operation of new offshore wind machines. At this point, it should be noted that according to current trends, contemporary offshore wind machines suggest very large-scale wind turbines (in the order of 5 MW; see **Table 2**) that advance installation and operation requirements to a whole new level. Up to now, support structures have been based on the concepts of monopole and gravity base, as well as on jackets and tripods. In order for deeper sea migration to be accomplished, however, investing in floating concepts is thought to be imperative (**Figure 37**).

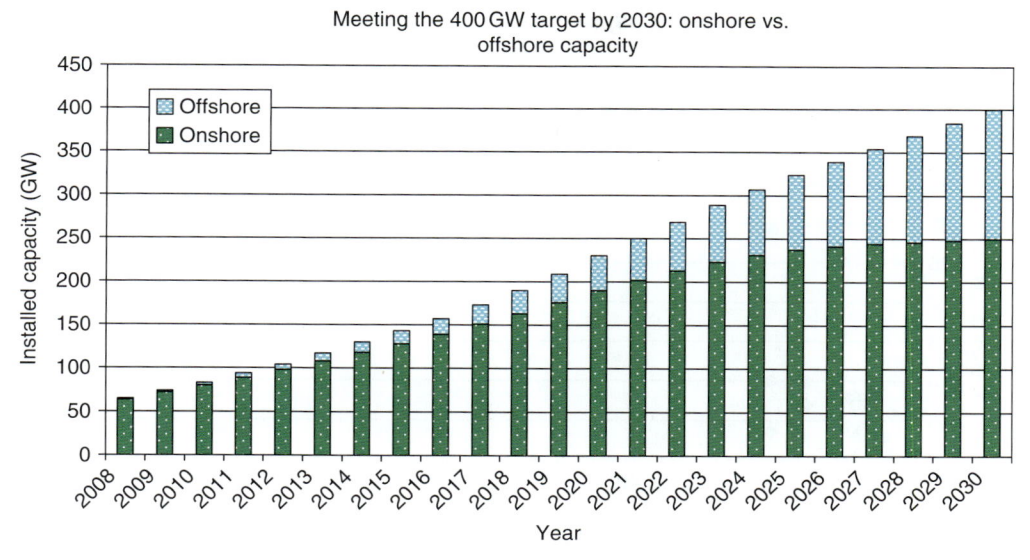

Figure 36 European targets concerning onshore and offshore wind energy installations.

Table 2 Commercial offshore wind turbines

Turbine manufacturer	Turbine model	Rated power (MW)	Date available	Offshore operating status
Siemens	SWT2.0	2.0	2000	Commercially inactive
Vestas	V80	2.0	2000	Commercially inactive
General Electric	GE 3.6	3.6	2003	Commercially inactive
Siemens	SWT2.3	2.3	2003	Commercial
Vestas	V90	3.0	2004	Commercial
Siemens	SWT3.6	3.6	2005	Commercial
REpower	5 M	5.0	2005	45 m water depth demonstration; Commercial at Alpha Ventus, Thornton Bank
Multibid	M5000	5.0	2005	Onshore 2005; Commercial at Alpha Ventus, 2009
Sinovel	SL3000	3.0	2009	First Chinese offshore project; 102 MW installed
BARD	BARD	5.0	2010	Installations at BARD Offshore 1 project; began in March 2010
General Electric	GE 4.0/110	4.1	2012	Commercial sales announced; no prototype experience

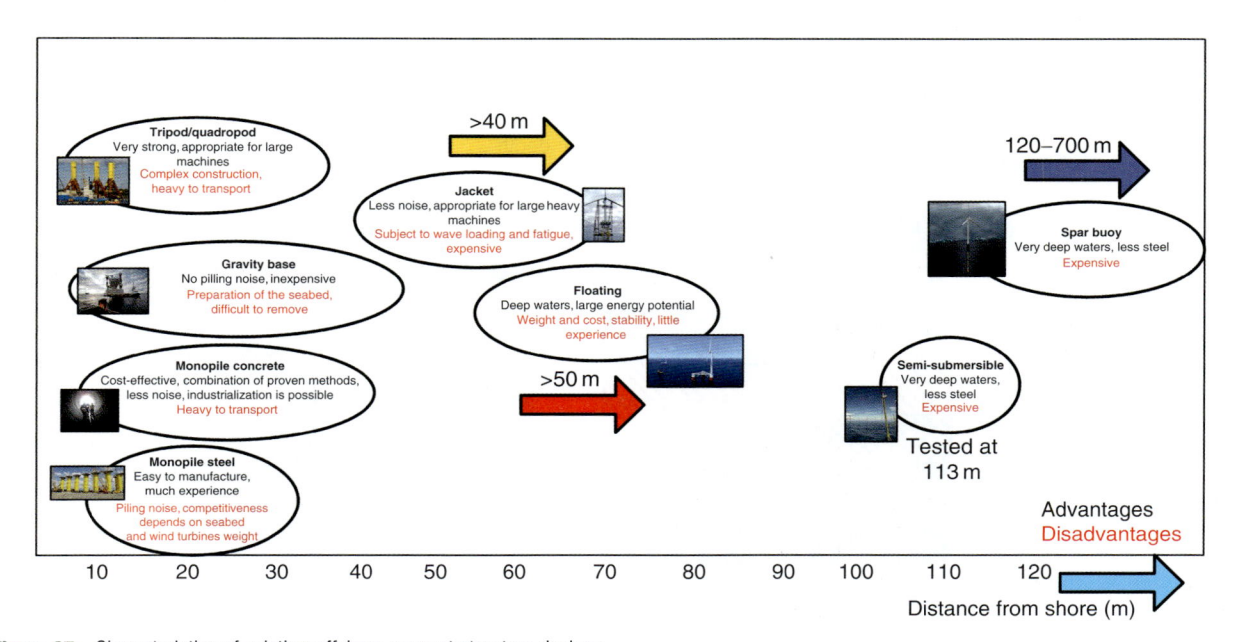

Figure 37 Characteristics of existing offshore support structure designs.

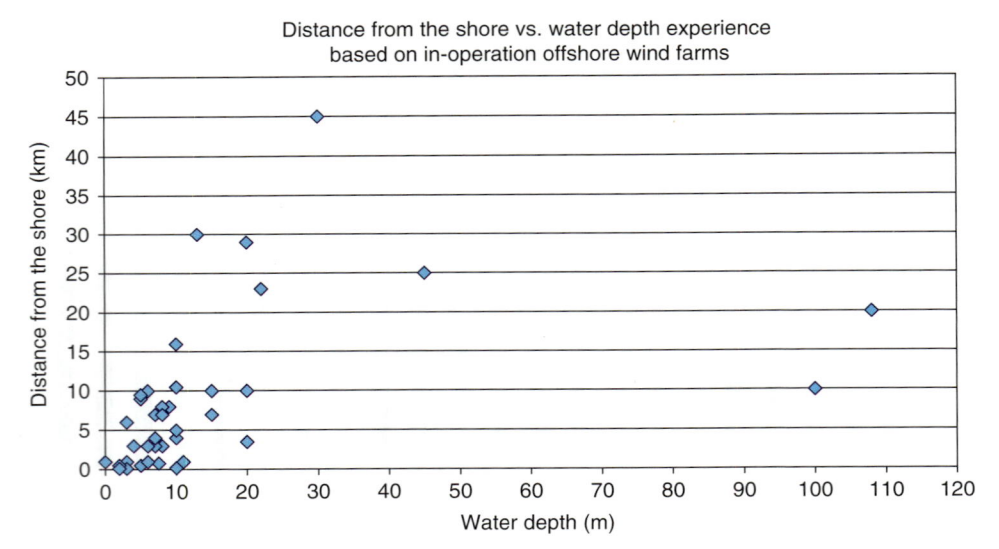

Figure 38 Operational depths and distances from shore for existing offshore applications.

More specifically, up to now, both inadequate support structures and the need to operate as close as possible to the shore (so as to minimize grid connection costs) have restricted installation area to the 20 × 20 rectangular (i.e., 20 km distance from the shore and 20 m depth; see **Figure 38**), which in order to be overcome will need both more advanced support structures and other cost components' cost reduction (**Figures 39** and **40**). For this to happen, however, sufficient time needs to be given to the offshore technology to establish itself and thus proceed to a gradual smoothing of specific costs (**Figure 41** [73]), which at the moment tend to increase, exactly due to the fact that new farms need to go both further and deeper.

Nevertheless, apart from the support structure advancements, the concept of offshore wind energy encompasses several other R&D directions that also need to be mentioned, with the main components being wind turbines, grid infrastructure, installation and assembly, and operation and maintenance.

First of all, the operation of wind turbines at sea poses a completely different design than that of onshore machines, with additional requirements to consider. As a result, there are considerable efforts carried out in issues such as developing larger machines (even 10 MW) and higher tip speeds along with improved electrical equipment that will ameliorate grid connection problems.

Furthermore, electricity infrastructure may need to both alter and advance, due to the requirements that will be posed by the large-scale deployment of offshore parks. High-voltage direct current (HVDC) transmission, which will probably progress alongside the offshore concept, and modification/strengthening as well as extension and interconnection [74] of existing electricity grids so as to absorb the available offshore wind energy yield should certainly be expected. In addition, facilitating large-scale penetration of offshore wind power requires all the hidden needs deriving from the actual birth of a new specialized industry to support offshore wind power (e.g., advanced logistics) [75], while adjustment to the unique operational features of these wind farms assumes advancements in the monitoring field as well [76], in both procedures and equipment (e.g., helicopters, platforms, optimization of maintenance plans, etc.).

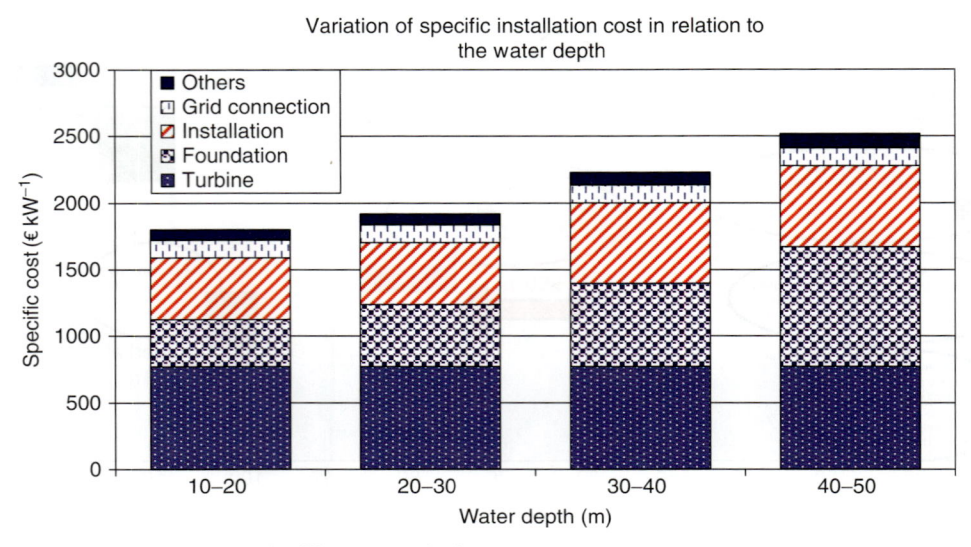

Figure 39 Specific cost of offshore wind parks for different water depths.

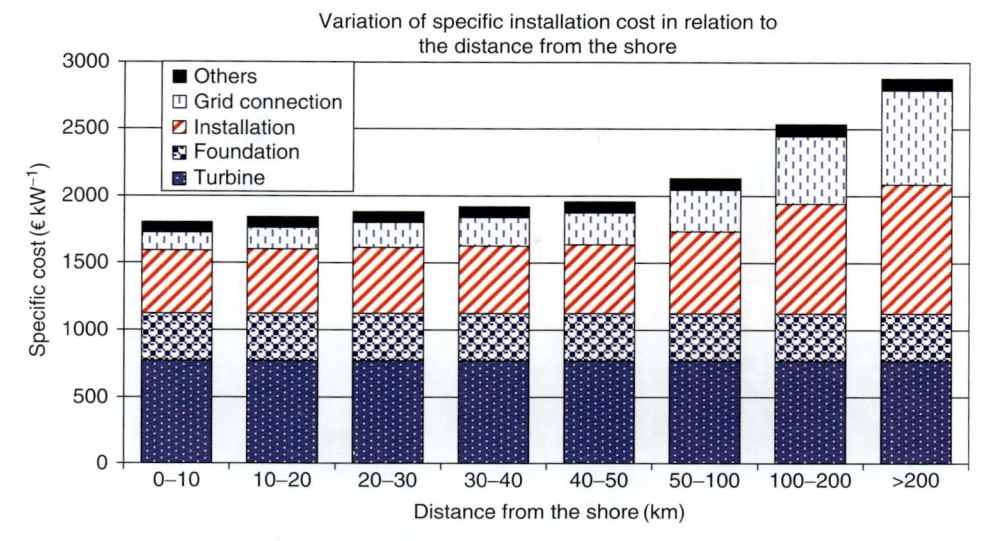

Figure 40 Specific cost of offshore wind parks for different distances from the shore.

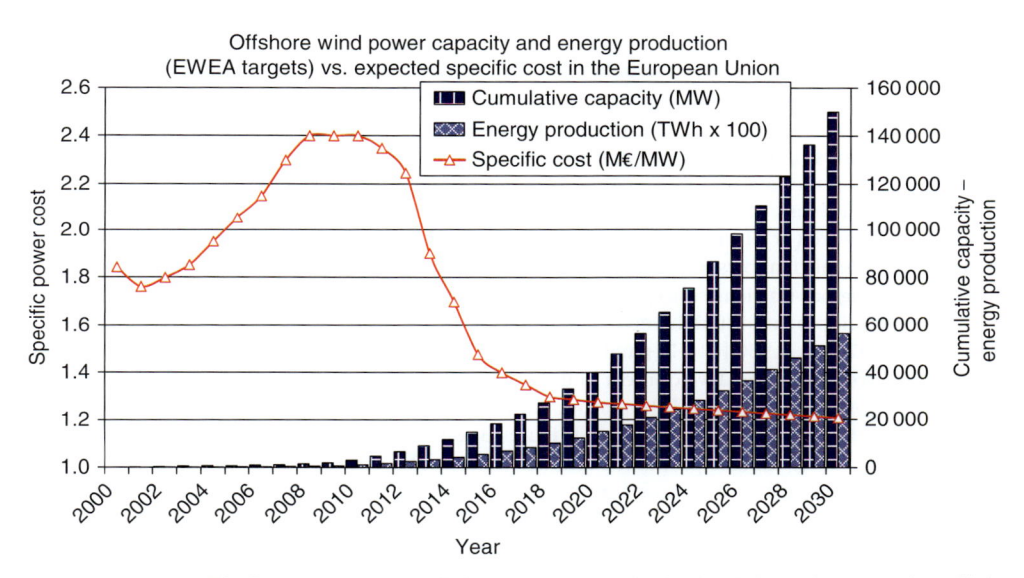

Figure 41 Future targets concerning EU offshore wind park installations and energy production in relation to the expected specific investment cost.

In conclusion, offshore wind energy comprises a rather promising technology that is expected to succeed the gradually and, after all, inevitably stagnating onshore concept, in order for both immediate and future ambitious targets of the wind energy industry to be accomplished. For this to happen, however, efforts in the R&D field need to be constant and equally intense in all directions involved in the promotion of offshore wind power.

2.21.10 Vertical-Axis Wind Turbines

Although the vertical-axis design was actually the first concept of wind power exploitation, establishment of the various types emerging over time never managed to support a solid market structure that would allow large-scale deployment of similar machines. However, recent progress in the field of small wind turbines [77] provides excellent grounds for the revival of the almost abandoned vertical-axis machines, while of great interest are recent efforts seeking to put the vertical-axis concept on the map of multi-MW machines.

There are two main types of vertical-axis machines that should be considered, that is, the Savonius type [78] and the Darrieus type [79]. The Savonius machine (**Figure 42**), comprising a wind turbine of two half drums driven by drag forces, was invented by S.J. Savonius in 1929. Such machines normally operate at a maximum power coefficient of 20% and are thus not suitable for

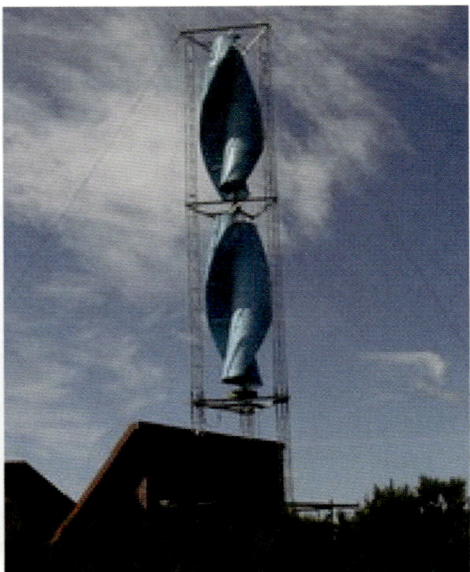

Figure 42 Examples of the original and the spiral-shaped Savonius type.

high-power applications, although they can prove rather effective in water pumping and other low-power applications. More modern Savonius designs suggest the introduction of spiral-shaped blades, which produce a torque performance that is more favorable during the whole rotation cycle [80], and are also determined by less vibrations to consider.

The Darrieus machine, comprising a wind turbine that is driven by lift forces and that may achieve a maximum power coefficient in the order of 40%, is based on the rotation of two or more aerofoil-shaped blades attached to a vertical axis. It was invented in 1931 by George Jeans Mary Darrieus and comes with two main design concepts, that is, the eggbeater or curved-bladed machine (**Figure 43**) and the straight-bladed (or Giromill or Cycloturbine) machine, with the latter supporting both fixed- and variable-pitch blades (introduction of variable pitch allows for the management of the low starting torque inherent characteristic). Actually, it was because of the fact that the original Darrieus concept suffered from severe drawbacks such as strong vibrations and relatively high noise levels that led to the development of straightened blades later on, with considerable efforts carried out in the United Kingdom during the period between 1970 and 1980 [81]. In parallel, considerable research efforts were also undertaken in the United States and Canada that eventually resulted in the development of the 4.2 MW Eole C machine installed in Canada, while one should also underline the research work of Sandia National Laboratories, further promoting the vertical-axis concept at this time [82].

It was also during this time that the simpler H-rotor type (**Figure 43**) established itself against more complex straight-blade designs that required feathering mechanisms (variable-geometry machines) to control overspeeding of the rotor, while in the following years, passive stall regulation was designated as the most appropriate solution for power control of such machines [78]. Meanwhile, experimental efforts to evaluate the performance of the H-rotor type led to very interesting results [83–87], designating the ability of such machines to compete not only with the original Darrieus concepts but also with horizontal-axis machines (**Table 3**).

Figure 43 Examples of the original Darrieus (eggbeater) and the H-rotor machines.

Table 3 Experimental results of different studies on H-rotor vertical-axis wind turbines

Power coefficient C_{pmax}	Tip speed ratio λ (at C_{pmax})	Rated power (kW)	Country	Year
0.40	3.8	100	Great Britain	1989
0.38	4.3	-	USA	1980
0.39	5.5	2–4	USA	1979
0.38	4.4	14	Japan	1984
0.43	3	1	USA	1979

Neglecting some abstract efforts from that point on, the concept of vertical-axis machines was, in the following years, more or less abandoned, with the vast development of more efficient horizontal-axis machines leaving no space for R&D in the field of the former for a period of almost 30 years. Nevertheless, the constant transformation of wind power and the designation of new needs during recent years are now calling for the forgotten attributes of vertical-axis machines. In this context, the ability of vertical-axis machines to constantly face the wind without any steering along with the lower levels of noise production – as a result of their operation at lower tip speed ratios – is now welcome in the small-scale wind turbine industry (**Figure 44**). Vertical-axis machines are destined to serve built environment applications [88, 89], where both turbulent wind and limitation of noise along with the simpler structures required (e.g. Savonius type) favor the above-mentioned attributes.

As certain groups argue during the time being, it is likely that horizontal-axis machines will peak in the next few years, largely due to blade limitations and their effects on the overall machine structure. As a result, there may be actual room for vertical-axis machines to proceed to utility-scale machines of 10 MW and beyond, with the first prototypes of H-rotor machines already being underway [90]. Besides, past experience has demonstrated the ability of the concept to reach the multi-MW level long ago (e.g., the Canadian Eole C of 4.2 MW in the 1980s already mentioned; see **Figure 44**).

Finally, of great interest are the recent research efforts in the field of offshore developments (**Figure 45**), where developers of UK concepts such as Aerogenerator X (10 MW) and Nova (9 MW) claim that the specific models are capable of producing the same power output as horizontal-axis machines of double to triple their size [91].

In summary, although not as evident, there are signs at the moment that the vertical-axis concept may find its place in the broad wind energy market by actually covering the two extreme edges, that is, small-scale machines destined to serve built environment applications and large-scale multi-MW machines exceeding the expected capacity limits of horizontal-axis machines. For this to occur,

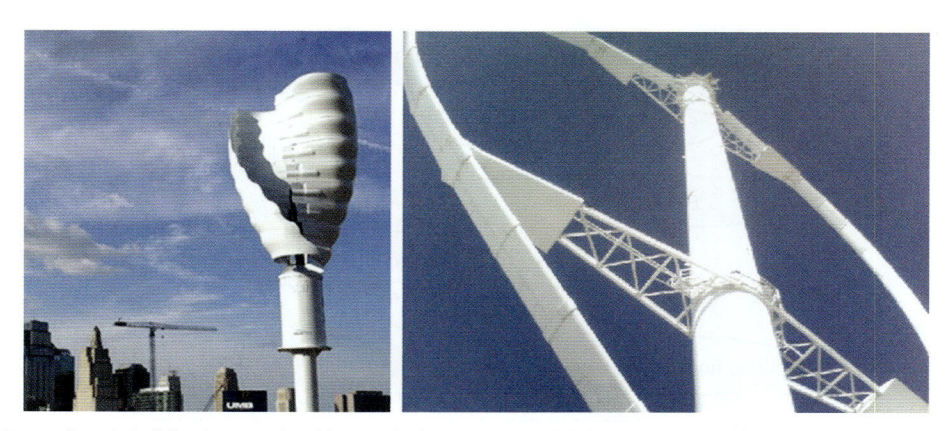

Figure 44 From the small-scale building-integrated turbines to the large-scale multi-MW machines (Eole-C 4.2 MW at Quebec).

Figure 45 Multi-MW vertical-axis offshore concepts (Aerogenerator X and Nova).

however, considerable research efforts are required in order to integrate and adapt some of the experience gained during this 30-year period in the field of horizontal-axis machines to the field of vertical-axis wind turbines and also develop existing concepts even further.

2.21.11 Small Wind Turbines

Small wind turbines were for a long time period considered as the best example of wind potential exploitation all around the planet, used in several areas for water pumping and electricity generation and in many other applications. However, ever since emphasis has been given to medium- and large-scale applications in order to take advantage of the so-called economies of scale, this has much restricted the evolution of small-size machines.

Due to the rebirth of distributed generation patterns as well as to the fact that during recent years integration of renewable energy sources (RES) in urban environments has actually become a reality, a growing interest has been recently recorded in the field of small-scale wind turbines. Both on-grid and off-grid applications (**Figure 46**), which include building integration, mini wind farms, and single turbine installations for the first and wind-battery plus wind-based hybrid systems for the second, have established a niche market that aspires to go even further. Common applications include installation on sailboats and remote houses, farms, water pumping, desalination systems, distributed generation, street lighting, building-integrated machines, and so on.

In contrast to large-scale wind turbines, small wind turbines are much simpler machines and are usually divided into three main categories in terms of power scaling, that is, micro wind, small wind, and small–medium wind, corresponding to the power scales of 0–1 or 1.5 kW, 1 or 1.5–10 kW, and 10–100 kW, respectively, although different classification may also encompass the class of pico wind (< 1 kW), micro wind (1–7 kW), mini wind (7–50 kW), and small wind (50–100 kW), with the respective application range given in **Figure 46**. In this regard, it is estimated that, at this time, the specific sector has a production line of over 500 wind turbine models [92], among which the majority are three-bladed machines featuring a generator – included in the hub – and a tail (**Figure 47**), although in the category of micro wind one may also encounter several vertical-axis models, mostly integrated in building structures (**Figure 47**).

According to the latest official data, the number of active manufacturers in the field nowadays is found to exceed 250, with the majority (almost 40%) of them found in the United States (**Figure 48**), where one may also meet the biggest national market. More specifically, the sector of small wind turbines in the United States (**Figure 49**) has during a decade's time managed to put in operation a total of more than 55 000 machines yielding a total of more than 70 MW capacity (2009 data) [93]. In addition, the progress seen in the UK market is analogous (**Figure 49**), where, according to the latest estimates [94], the number of operating

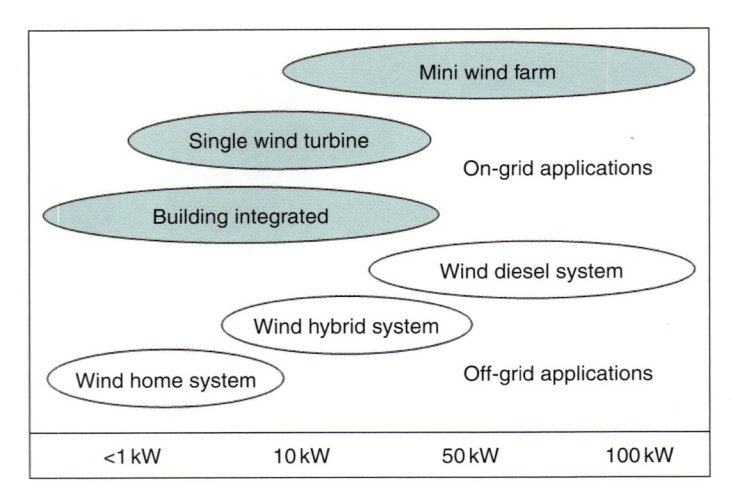

Figure 46 Range of applications for small scale wind turbines.

Figure 47 Examples of applications for small horizontal- and vertical-axis wind machines.

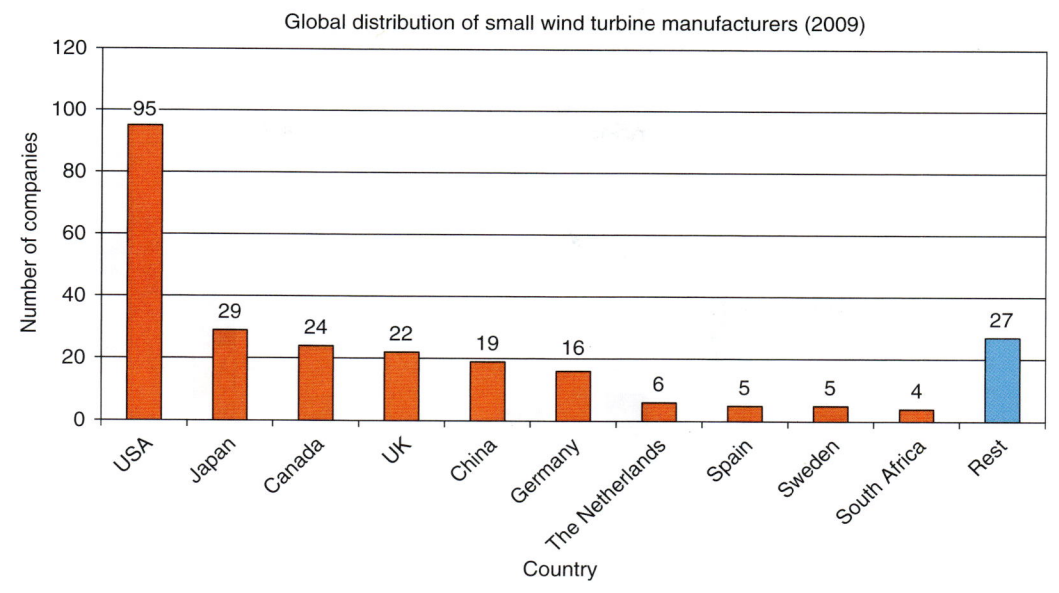

Figure 48 Distribution of small wind turbine manufacturers around the globe.

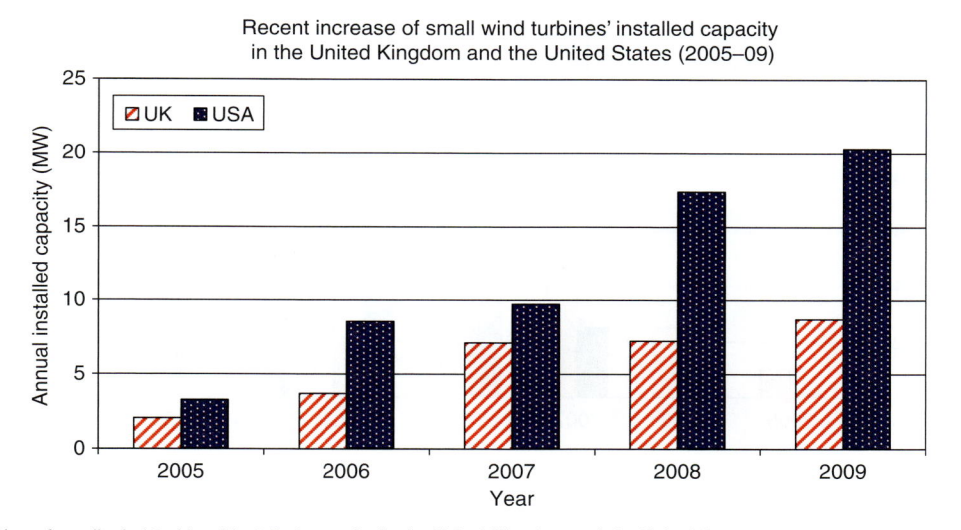

Figure 49 Evolution of small wind turbines' installed capacity in the United Kingdom and the United States.

machines is expected to exceed 20 000 in 2011, with the total installed capacity reaching 43 MW at the end of 2011 and anticipated to skyrocket to 1.3 GW by 2020.

Contribution shares of different power scale machines in these two countries may be obtained from **Figure 50**, where large-scale deployment of machines up to 10 kW summing up to MWs of installed capacity reflects the considerable market integration of micro and small wind turbines. Furthermore, based on the results of **Figure 51**, one may also obtain – as an example – the ratio between off-grid and on-grid applications as well as the ratio between horizontal- and vertical-axis wind turbines employed in the United Kingdom. Note that the gradual increase of interest toward on-grid applications encountered in the United Kingdom (**Figure 51**) is also valid for the rest of the world, at least in terms of installed capacity (**Table 4**), although at the same time, the number of off-grid machines in 2009 was triple that of on-grid machines. Finally, what is interesting to note is that although they are still found under the shadow of horizontal-axis machines, vertical-axis wind turbines have gradually taken their place in the market (**Figure 51**), especially since urban integration of on-grid small wind machines came along.

Economies of scale, however, in the case of small wind turbines, are still thought to comprise a major obstacle to the diffusion of small wind turbines, with the current specific costs being at least double (or even 6 times) that of large-scale machines (**Figure 52**). Besides, the results of past studies based on European experience [95] are also analogous, where the determination of the specific cost P_r (€ kW^{-1}) of small wind turbines may be provided with the use of the following semi-empirical equation, with N_o being the rated power of the machine:

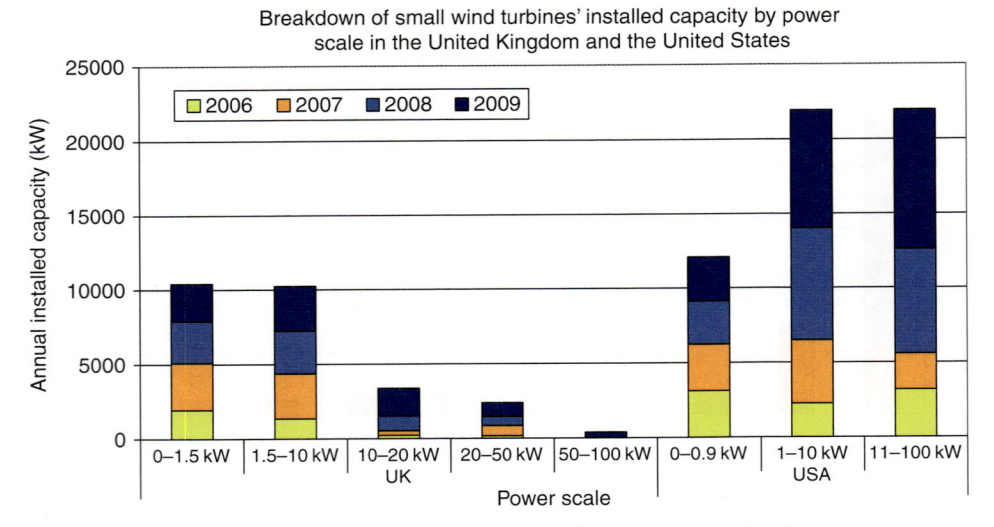

Figure 50 Contribution shares of different scale-small wind turbines in the United Kingdom and the United States.

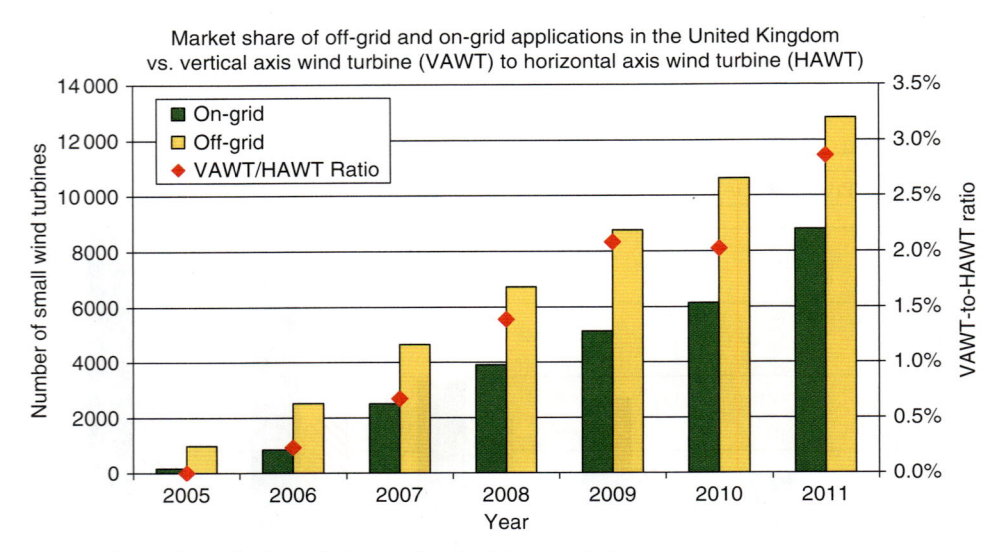

Figure 51 Market shares of on-grid vs. off-grid applications and horizontal- vs. vertical-axis machines.

Table 4 Global sales of small wind turbines for the year 2009

	Units	Capacity (kW)
Off-grid machines	15 500	7 600
On-grid machines	5 200	34 400
Total	20 700	42 000

$$P_r = \frac{a}{b + N_o^x} + c \quad (N_o \leq 100 \text{ kW}) \qquad [4]$$

considering that $a = 8.7 \times 10^5$ (€ kW^{-1}), $b = 621$, $x = 2.05$, and $c = 700$ (€ kW^{-1}).

In addition, reliability is also a matter of major concern for the emerging sector of small wind turbines, with development of performance and safety standards being a prerequisite for further development. Up to now, it is only the United States and the United Kingdom that have developed the certification schemes [96, 97] necessary for the sector to be further established in the near future.

Of critical importance when it comes to small wind turbines are certain design parameters. In particular, noise reduction is of major concern to small wind turbine manufacturers, especially since such machines are gradually adopted in the built and urban

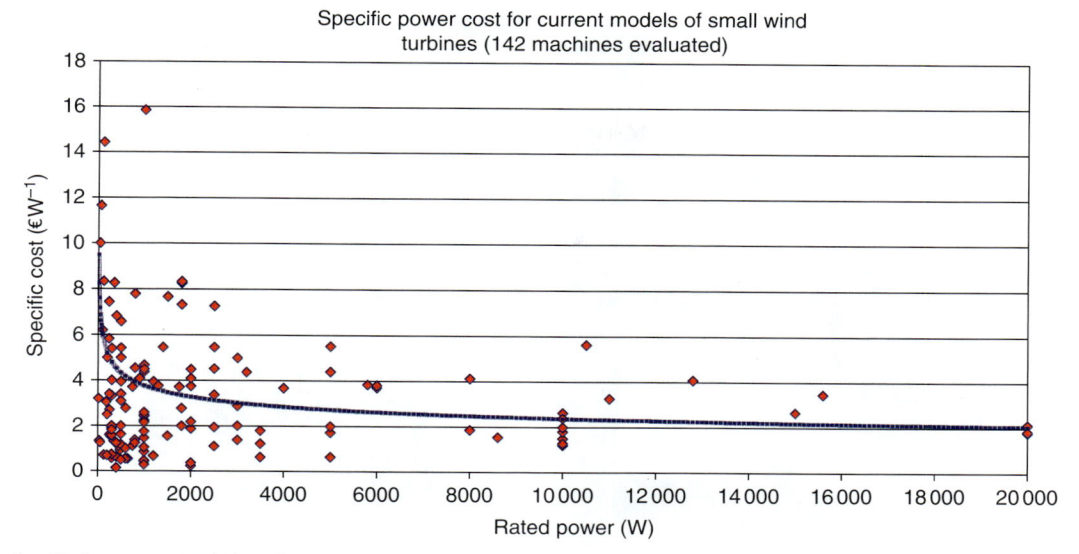

Figure 52 Specific investment cost of small wind turbines.

environment. For this purpose, investigation of airfoil shape, tip speed, and angle of attack as well as application of pitch instead of furling systems are among the first priorities, not disregarding, however, the fact that achieving noise reduction may in certain cases turn out to the expense of power performance, which is already low enough in most of the cases (aerodynamic coefficient in the order of 10–25% is common for small wind turbine machines).

An additional challenge for the sector to develop rapidly is the need for manufacturers to provide models that may be both aesthetical and easily adapted in the urban environment, where interaction with the more complex wind resources as a result of building structures should also be further investigated [98]. In the case of more isolated off-grid systems, collaboration of small wind turbine systems with other stand-alone system components (e.g., storage systems) should also be further elaborated, with emphasis given in achieving optimum operation conditions and minimum size of such configurations [99–101]. Similar needs appear, however, in the case of on-grid machines as well, where improvement of the interface between these machines and the grid is of primary importance.

Overall, the main R&D directions currently identified in the field of small wind turbines include investigation of active pitch controls for high wind speeds, vibration isolators to dampen sound, advanced blade design, self-protection mechanisms for extreme winds, dual-mode models (both on- and off-grid), software development, and inverters fitted into the nacelle.

2.21.12 Building-Integrated Wind Turbines

The interest recently demonstrated in the field of small-scale wind machines is directly relevant to the efforts undertaken in order to integrate wind energy into urban environments and, more precisely, into building structures [102, 103]. Thus, apart from proceeding to the fourth generation of wind energy machines, we are also proceeding to the third shift of wind power siting/topology, that is, from the single standing wind turbines of the early days to the establishment of onshore wind farms (first shift) that were accordingly transferred offshore (second shift) – the installation of small-scale wind turbines on rooftops and facades (**Figures 53** and **54**) being underway suggests the third shift.

Figure 53 Examples of vertical- and horizontal-axis rooftop wind turbines.

Figure 54 Examples of facade wind turbines.

The introduction of building-integrated wind power comes with certain benefits and drawbacks to be considered. On the one hand, exploitation of building heights and onsite energy generation implies an absence of big towers required to capture high wind speeds and minimum transmission losses, as well as contribution to the configuration of zero-energy buildings. But, on the other hand, drawbacks may be quite severe, especially if taking into account the building environment as a whole and not just referring to freely exposed buildings in which relatively high performance may be expected. More precisely, urban wind profile is a quite variable parameter that is strongly affected by the buildings' layout, the presence of street canyons, and the high roughness of the area [98, 104], which in most cases turns out to discourage rather than encourage installation of building-integrated wind machines. More precisely, the complexity of the layout and the stack of obstacles and structures being present pose characteristics of high turbulence to the available wind potential [105], which much restrict the smooth operation of a wind machine, even at the rooftops where the available flow tends to separate into streams. Furthermore, additional concerns of building integration include, as expected, noise emission during operation of the machines, which in many cases forces wind machines to be stopped during nighttime in order to avoid annoyance of local residents, as well as vibration concerns, especially in the case that relatively big machines are placed upon rooftops and high wind turbine stresses could be channeled to the building structure.

What is certainly detrimental is the actual poor performance of the machines, which has greatly discouraged further opening of the market so far. The combination of low wind speeds, along with the absence of siting experience and appropriate standards that may at some level respond to the complexity of urban environments, has up to now led to the depreciation of the concept, which in many cases serves as a symbol of environmental awareness, rather than a substantial power source that meets the needs of consumption.

To date, there are three major monitoring and evaluation efforts that have been carried out concerning the performance of building-integrated wind machines: two of them in the European Union (the WINEUR project and the Warwick Wind Trials) [106–110] and the third in the United States (Massachusetts) [111]. Results of all three are rather disappointing and lead to the common conclusion that unless manufacturers realize that the current technology is still in the stage of development, adverse effects may also hurt the credibility of larger-scale applications. To better illustrate the results of monitoring and performance evaluation efforts, some insight is given in the following points:

- The average capacity factor of monitored machines (19) was 4% (Massachusetts).
- On average, installers tend to overestimate energy production by a scale factor of 3–4 (Massachusetts).
- Apart from the apparent factor of poor wind potential, the disappointing performance of machines may also be attributed to inverter synchronization and standby time (Massachusetts).
- The average capacity factor of monitored machines (26) was 4.15%, excluding the time that machines were switched off (e.g., due to residents' annoyance about noise) and ranged from 0.29% to 16.54% (Warwick Trials).
- The wind potential of most locations was adequately described by Weibull, with the shape factor being around 1.6 (Warwick Trials).
- The minimum recommended average wind speed of the installation site should be 5.5 m s^{-1} (WINEUR), considering also that the rated power of most wind machines is found in the area of 12 m s^{-1} (**Figure 55**).
- The mast or building roof should be almost 50% higher than the surrounding objects, and ideally the wind turbine should be installed at the center of the roof (WINEUR).

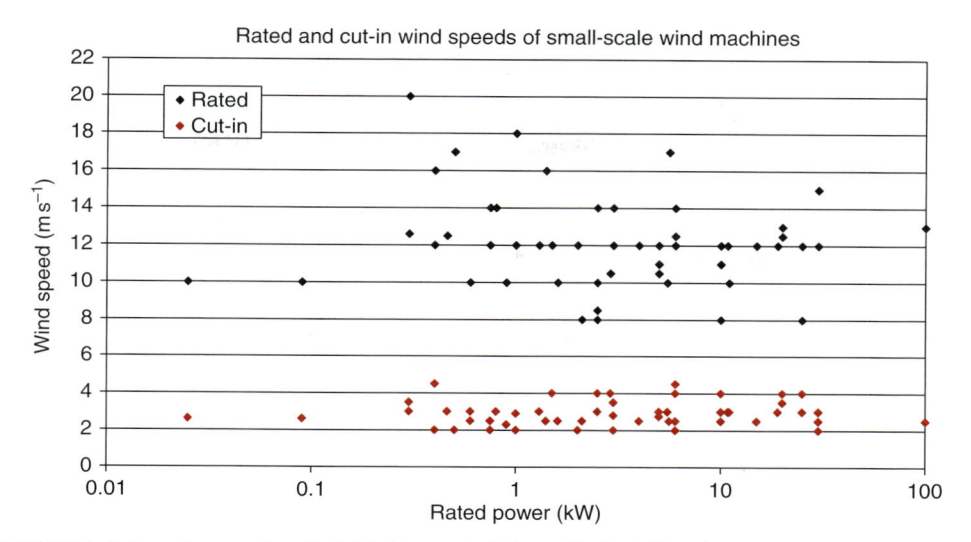

Figure 55 Cut-in and rated wind speed range of small wind turbines potentially used in the built environment.

Considering the above, the challenges faced in order to provide a reliable output and commercialize the concept of building-integrated wind machines become evident. Satisfying installation requirement restrictions on the one hand (see **Table 5**) and seeking maximum energy yield on the other hand suggests major contradictions that in order to be overcome require considerable effort in every aspect of the problem. Factors to consider, including architecture design (e.g., tilted facades may facilitate increased wind speed at the rooftop), wind turbine standards and reliability, and advanced siting procedures (e.g., use of computational fluid dynamics (CFD) and simulation methods; see **Figure 56**), should not be, however, restricted to a case-by-case approach, but should also proceed to the configuration of general standards that may satisfy a large diffusion of wind energy in the built environment. In the recent literature, one may find several interesting research efforts that try to simulate the complex flow field around a building-integrated wind turbine using advanced computational tools or systematic experimental measurements

Table 5 Summary of planning guidelines suggested by the UK government for the installation of micro wind turbines

Rooftop mounted turbines	Stand-alone turbines

Wind turbines on normal buildings permitted if:
    < 3 m above ridge (including the blade) and diameter of blades < 2 m
    Internal noise < 30 dB
    External noise < 40 dB
    'Garden' noise < 40 dB
    Up to four turbines on buildings > 15 m (as with antennas)
    Vibration < 0.5 mm s^{-1}
No rooftop-mounted turbines will be permitted on buildings in conservation areas or world heritage sites
	Wind turbines on normal buildings permitted if:
	    < 11 m (including the blade) and diameter of blades < 2 m
	    At least 12 m from a boundary
	    Internal noise < 30 dB
	    External noise < 40 dB
	    'Garden' noise < 40 dB
	    Vibration < 0.5 mm s^{-1}
	Stand-alone turbines will be permitted beside buildings in conservation areas or in world heritage sites as normal except in front of principal elevation

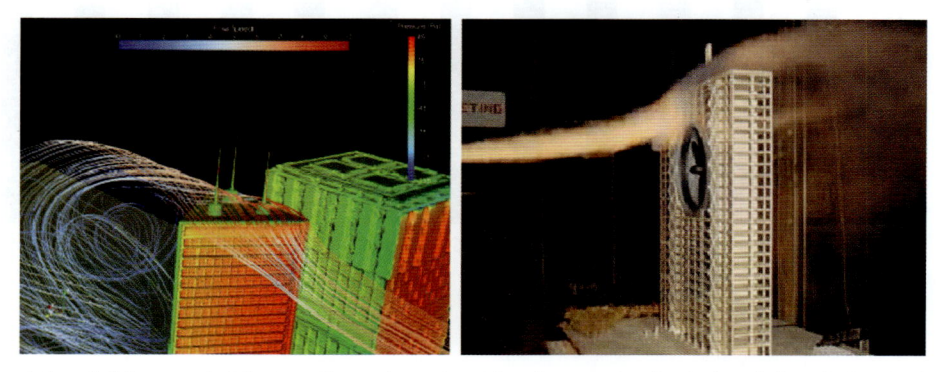

Figure 56 CFD simulation of airflow on a building's rooftop and experimental performance test for the installation of a facade wind turbine.

[112, 113], since it is a common belief that the energy yield of a similar installation may be considerably improved in the case that one knows the site flow field in detail.

In addition, certain policies supporting the installation of building-integrated wind turbines – already considered by several countries [114, 115] – are expected to further stimulate efficient energy performance of such machines. Nevertheless, what must be made clear is that building-integrated wind turbines cannot be thought of as 'plug and play' devices, as the case may be for photovoltaics and solar collectors, contrariwise, their adaptation requires detailed study of all the parameters involved [116].

2.21.13 Wind Energy Cost Time Evolution

As far as costs are concerned, wind energy has already come a long way, transforming from an extremely high cost energy solution to an energy alternative that now competes with conventional power technologies on equal terms. Among the main trends dominating the market of wind energy over the years, one should emphasize on the significant long-term reduction of the specific investment cost per kW (turnkey cost) of installed wind power capacity [117]. More precisely, although starting from a remarkable 3500 € kW^{-1} during the mid-1980s, it has during the past few years stabilized in the order of 1200 € kW^{-1}, that is, between 1000 and 1400 € kW^{-1} [118], depending also on the area of study (**Figures 57(a)** and **57(b)**). At this point, it is important to mention that during the beginning of the previous decade the first installation cost of wind turbines presented a minimum just below 1000 € kW^{-1}.

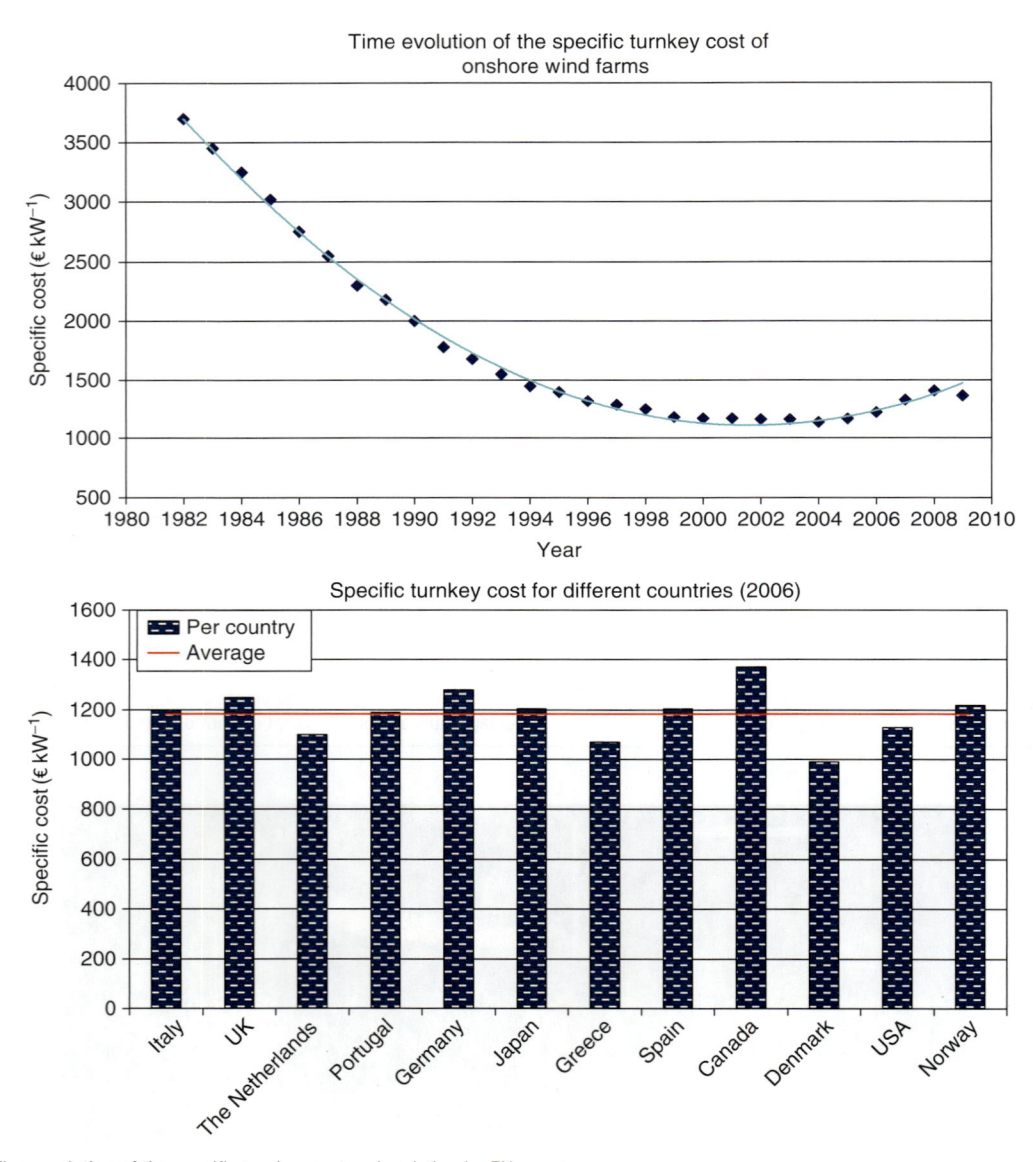

Figure 57 Time evolution of the specific turnkey cost and variation by EU country.

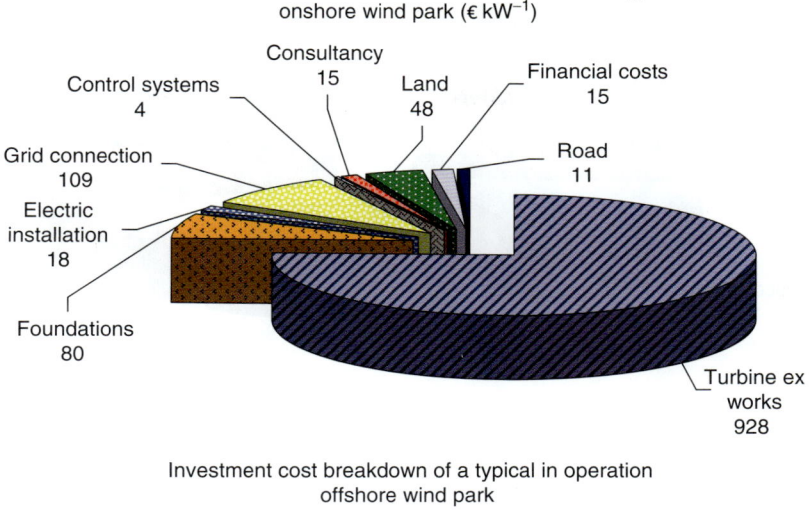

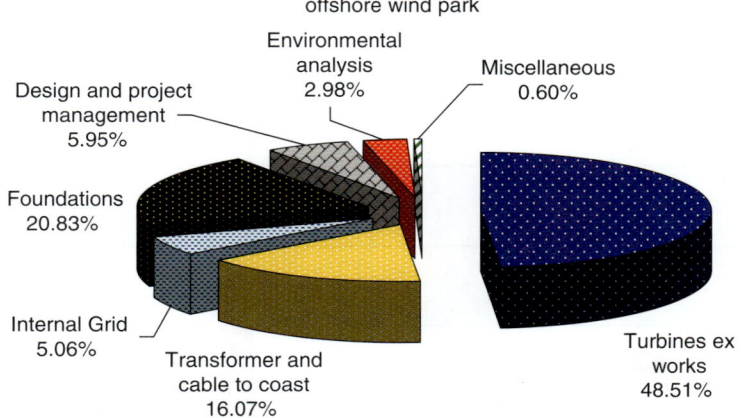

Figure 58 Breakdown of the investment cost of onshore and offshore wind parks.

However, during the following years, the market trend has changed and the turnkey cost values slightly increased, eventually approaching the current values.

Considering the above, some rough numbers may also be given in terms of investment cost breakdown, noting also the difference between onshore and offshore applications. More specifically, the turbine component being critical in onshore projects (~930 €kW^{-1}) (**Figure 58(a)**) drops to a typical 48% in offshore plants (**Figure 58(b)**), while foundation requirements increase by more than 4 times and grid connection offshore is increased by more than 150 €kW^{-1}. Overall, the total specific investment cost of offshore applications is found to be higher by more than 40% for most of the plants in operation and may increase to or even exceed 3000 €kW^{-1} for installations that are under construction [119, 120] in deeper waters and well away from the shore. Besides, based on the experience of in-operation offshore parks, employment of more turbines implies relatively lower turnkey costs. In any given case, maintenance and operation (M&O) costs (**Figure 59**), including insurance, regular maintenance, repairs, spare parts, administration, land rent, and others [121–123], are also considerable for wind power installations, although the introduction of more efficient machines and the reduction of downtime hours constantly decrease the M&O requirements, which are now in the order of 1.2–1.5 c€ kWh^{-1}. These values should be compared with the 3–4 c€ kWh^{-1} of the first (e.g., 55 kW) wind turbines, while special attention is paid in order to obtain values less than 1 c€ kWh^{-1} in the entire lifetime of a machine.

Wind energy production cost is found to be comparable with that of conventional fossil-fueled generation methods [124], even without internalizing the externalities, especially in areas with high wind potential and good infrastructure. As a result, the clear advantage of wind power in the economic field as well becomes evident (**Figure 60**), with estimations concerning the near-future electricity generation cost of onshore and offshore wind parks supporting values between 50 and 80 € MWh^{-1} and between 75 and 120 € MWh^{-1}, respectively [125–127].

Of great importance for the remarkable growth of the wind energy market has been the implementation of various support mechanisms [128], including price- and quantity-driven instruments such as feed-in-tariffs, investment and production tax incentives for the first, and quota along with tradable green certificates and tendering systems for the second. At this

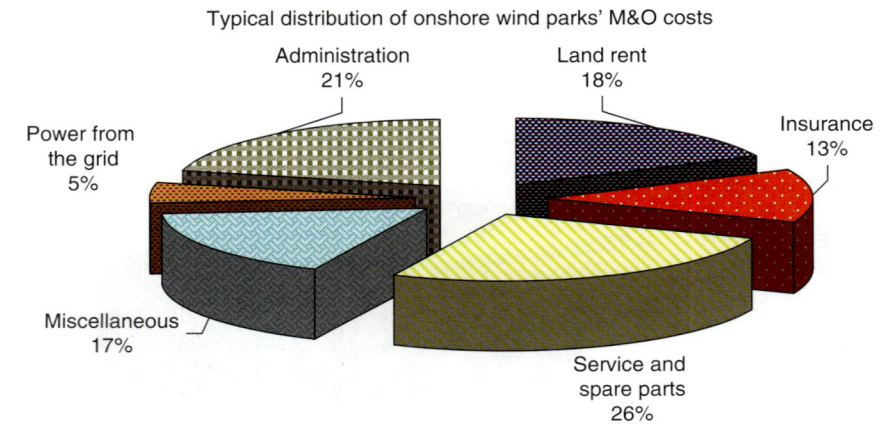

Figure 59 Breakdown of the maintenance and operation cost for onshore wind parks.

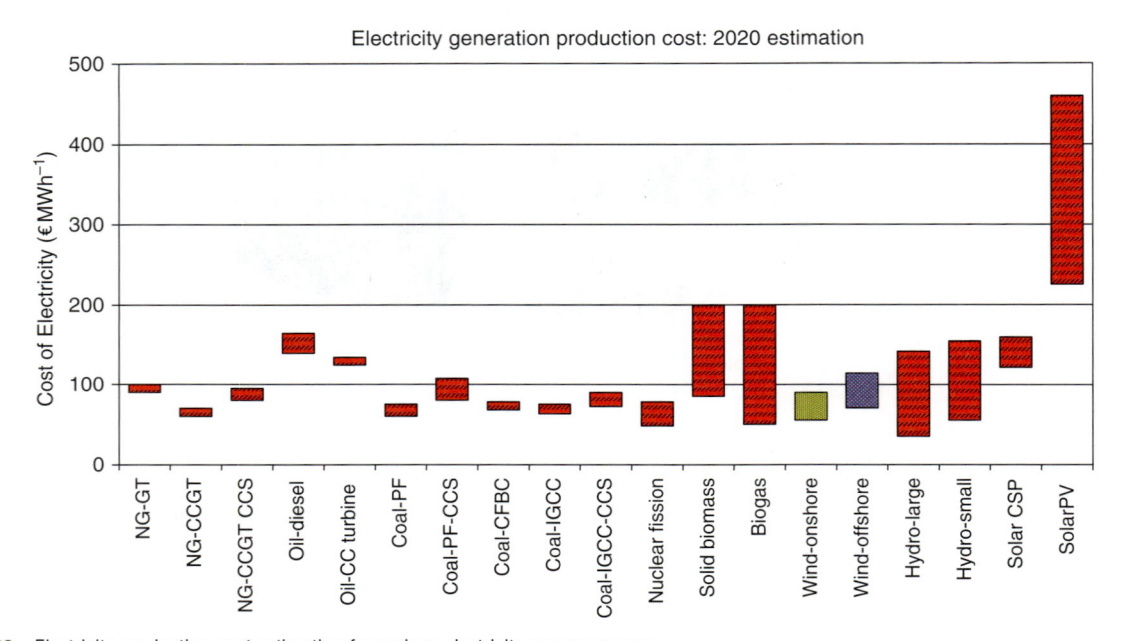

Figure 60 Electricity production cost estimation for various electricity power sources.

point, one should underline the effectiveness of most of these measures and especially the feed-in-tariff mechanism [129], which, since being adopted by the majority of leading countries worldwide (Germany, the United States, China, Denmark, Spain, India, etc.) [130], has led to the remarkable growth of wind energy generation (**Figures 61(a)–61(c)**). Keep in mind that in most cases the financial support provided by the society (state) is directly compensated by the benefits accruing from the operation of wind parks, also considering the avoidance of social costs deriving from thermal power stations.

Finally, one should also emphasize on the employment opportunities [131] offered by the expansion of the wind energy market at a global level. Approximately 100 000 plus 50 000 is the number of people employed directly and indirectly in the wind energy field of Europe, while another 85 000 correspond to the 100 manufacturing plants operating in the United States. These include employment posts in manufacturing companies, in promotion, utilities, engineering, and R&D (direct employment), or employment in companies providing services or producing components for wind turbines (indirect relation). Note that according to rough estimations [132], among the leading countries on the basis of the people employed per MW installed ratio (**Figure 62**), Denmark, Belgium, and Finland employ more than seven persons, while in terms of absolute numbers, Germany currently employs 38 000 people [133]. Taking into consideration the continuous growth of new wind power installations, it is reasonable to expect a remarkable increase of employment in the sector in the near future.

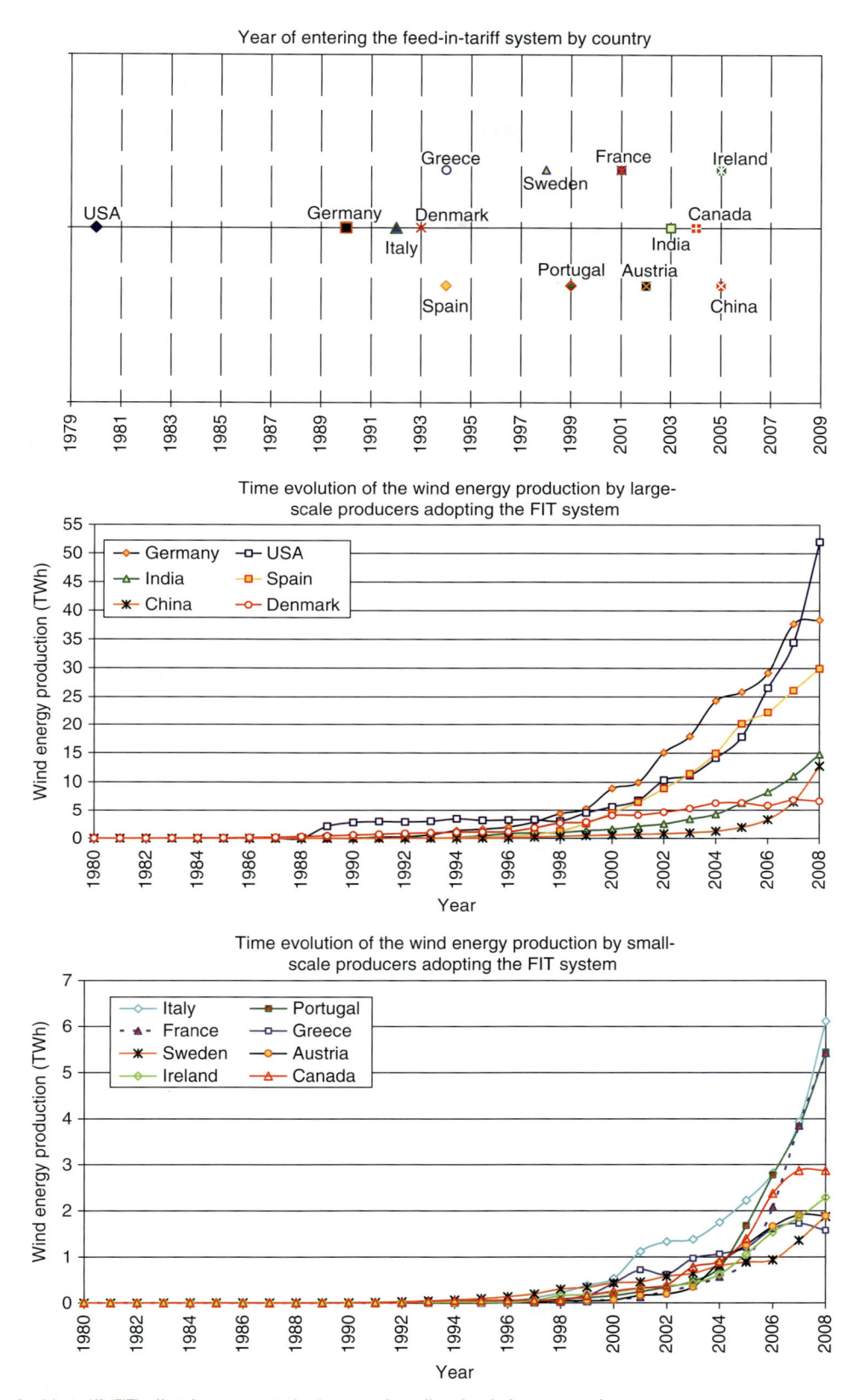

Figure 61 The feed-in-tariff (FIT) effect for representative large- and small-scale wind energy producers.

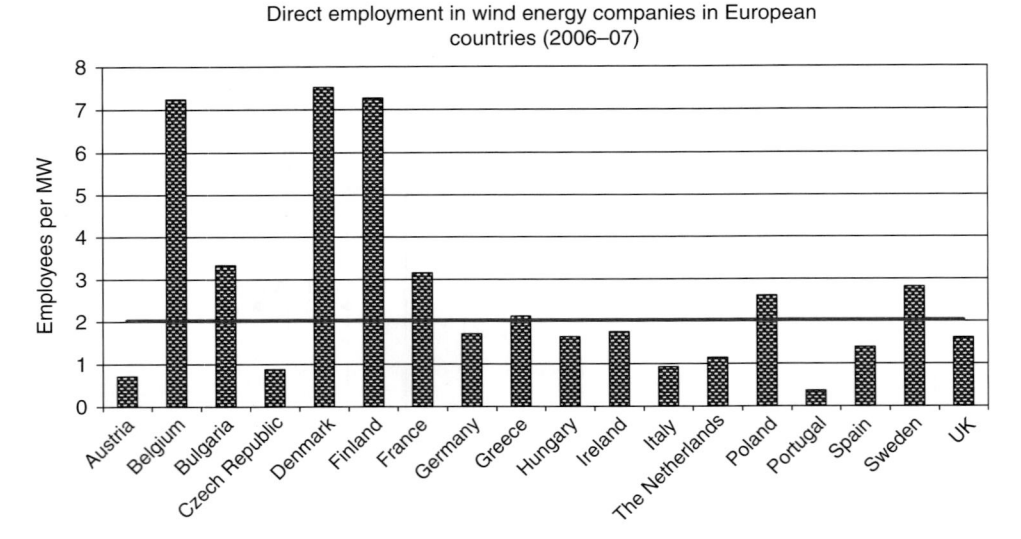

Figure 62 Employment status in the wind energy sector by EU country.

2.21.14 Research in the Wind Energy Sector

The evolution and development of wind turbines during the past 50 years has been based on the systematic and consistent research efforts of thousands of scientists and engineers, absorbing at the same time considerable funds and budgets in the order of billions of Euros. The development of contemporary wind turbines in the course of time [134–136] may be reflected by the gradual upscaling of machines, based on the rationale for better land exploitation, presence of scale economies, reduced M&O requirements, and past funding development programs [2] pushing toward the development of large-scale and more efficient machines. Recently, the shift to offshore applications calls for multi-MW solutions – already offered by some of the manufacturers (even at the levels of 7 MW) – that absorb substantial financial budgets, while designs of machines that will exceed the nominal power of 10 MW are already underway.

It is important to mention that in the first years of R&D (beginning of the 1980s), research institutes and universities created more knowledge than the wind power industry could actually handle. After that initial period of over-knowledge, however, market-driven upscaling of machines and offshore applications seem to pose more questions than the researchers can solve with the current knowledge. As a result, future research has the responsibility of addressing numerous and constantly emerging needs and problems in order for this unceasingly evolving technology to continue growing.

It was immediately after the oil crisis of the mid-1970s that wind energy was considered to be one of the most promising energy resources that could contribute to the reduction of the world economy dependence on fossil fuels. During this time, efforts to develop effective machines were based on two different but complementary groups. The first group was based on governmental programs that focused on developing large-scale wind turbines (multi-MW ones) [137], while the second one was supported by individuals and entrepreneurs building small turbines, starting from 15 to 50 kW. According to the results of the efforts at that time, a common conclusion was drawn, that is, that designing efficient and reliable wind machines was a quite difficult and complicated task that required, among other things, significant financial support. Among the most important research areas then designated, wind modeling, resource assessment, aerodynamics, and structural dynamics may be thought of as the most important ones.

Furthermore, in order to demonstrate the applicability of wind energy technology, a number of megawatt-size demonstration programs were implemented, starting from the beginning of the 1980s. These first demonstration projects of megawatt-class machines encountered in the United States, Germany, Denmark, and Sweden presented, however, some serious problems, mainly due to material fatigue. Nevertheless, performance evaluation of these early prototype machines provided useful information that was later exploited in the subsequent development efforts. Thus, in the late 1980s, quite reliable wind turbines of up to 300 kW were constructed and offered to the market. Following this, it was in the beginning of the 1990s that erection of the first offshore wind parks was achieved [138].

In the course of time, the average number of turbines in each wind farm grew along with the size of the individual machines. As a consequence, the penetration of wind-produced electricity in the local electrical grids was rather important in some areas. This resulted in a pressing need to improve the knowledge of power quality and better understand the interaction with weak (remote) grids [139], while, at the same time, the magnitude of the international trade in wind turbines along with the need for further market development dictated new standardization and design codes [140].

Intensive research activity encountered in the wind energy sector may be reflected by a series of data, such as the increased number of patent applications [141] concerning wind energy machines (**Figure 63**), especially in countries where the industry of wind energy is

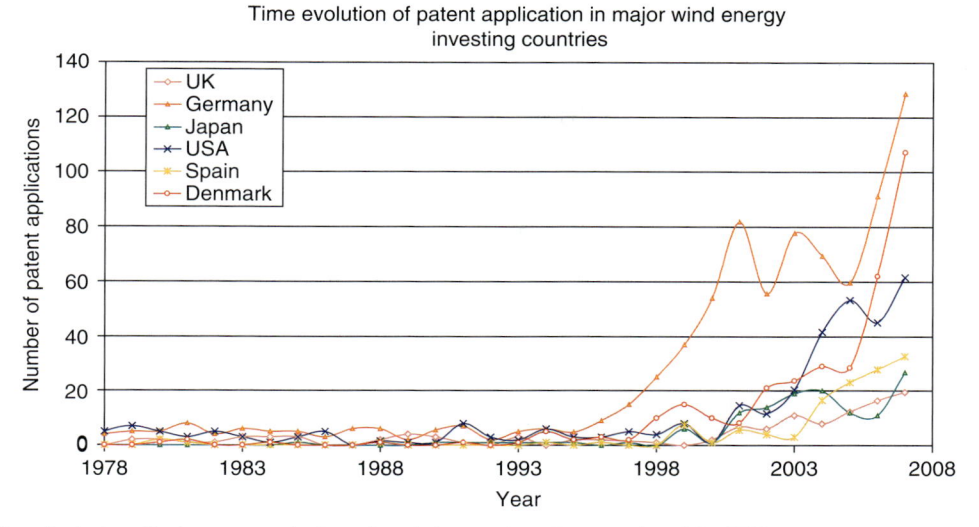

Figure 63 Number of patent applications per year in the major wind energy investing countries of the OECD.

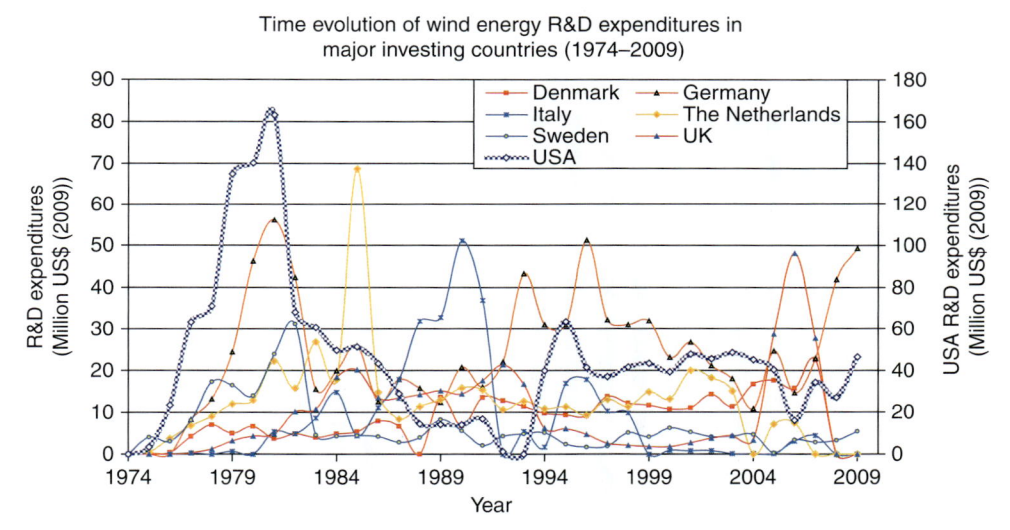

Figure 64 Annual R&D expenditures of major wind energy spenders of the OECD.

present. Similarly, in **Figure 64**, one may obtain the R&D expenditures in the field of wind energy for the most active countries during the past 25 years (1974–2009) [141]. Based on the data available, the remarkable contribution of the United States and Germany becomes evident, while the constant presence of Denmark throughout the period investigated is also of major importance.

Furthermore, the overall wind energy R&D expenditures for the Organisation for Economic Cooperation and Development (OECD) countries during this 25-year period are summarized in **Figure 65**, where the significant contribution of the United States and Germany is reflected on the basis of expenditures exceeding US$1.6 billion and US$0.8 billion invested, respectively. In addition, the considerable R&D expenditures of the Netherlands should also be recorded, while at the same time it should be noted that this specific country does not undertake any significant endogenous wind energy industrial activities. Furthermore, what is also noticeable is the fact that Spain has invested less than US$200 million, although local wind energy manufacturers currently hold approximately 25% of the global wind energy market, which clearly shows the relatively late involvement of the country in the wind energy sector (spending €8.7 million per year on average since 1998) [142].

Finally, in **Figure 66**, a breakdown of R&D expenditures per type of energy technology is also presented for OECD countries and for the same period of investigation (1974–2009). According to the data appearing in the figure, the limited funding of the wind energy sector is designated, with the specific expenditures found in certain cases, to remain much below the expenditures destined to support nuclear energy and conventional (thermal) power generation.

It must be noted that concerning the European Union, it was at the Barcelona European Council (2002) that the Heads of States agreed that research and technological development investment must be increased with the aim of reaching 3% of gross domestic

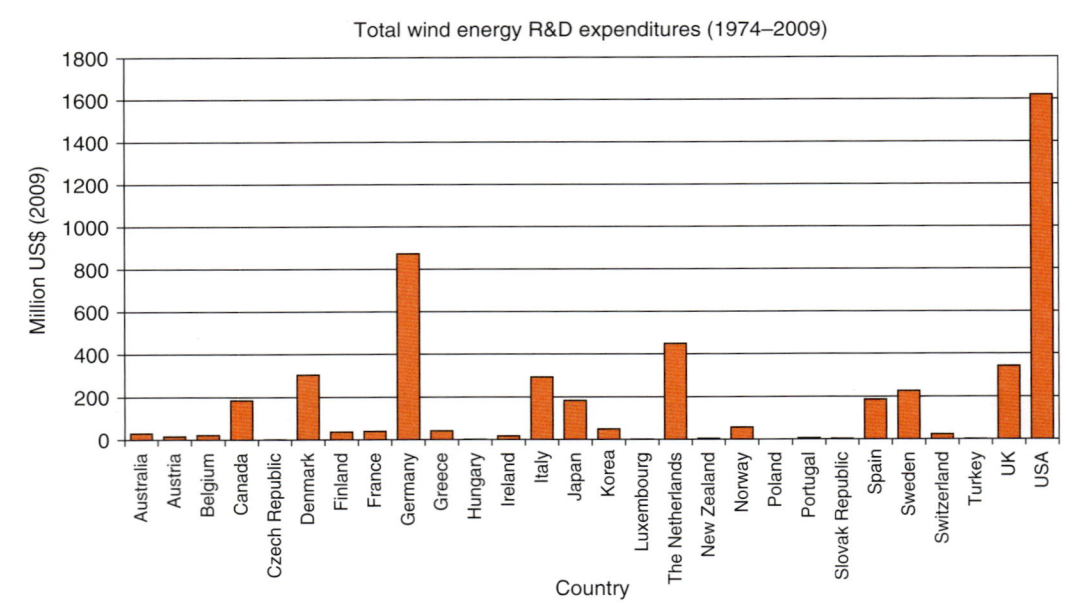

Figure 65 Total, 25-year period wind energy R&D expenditures of the OECD countries.

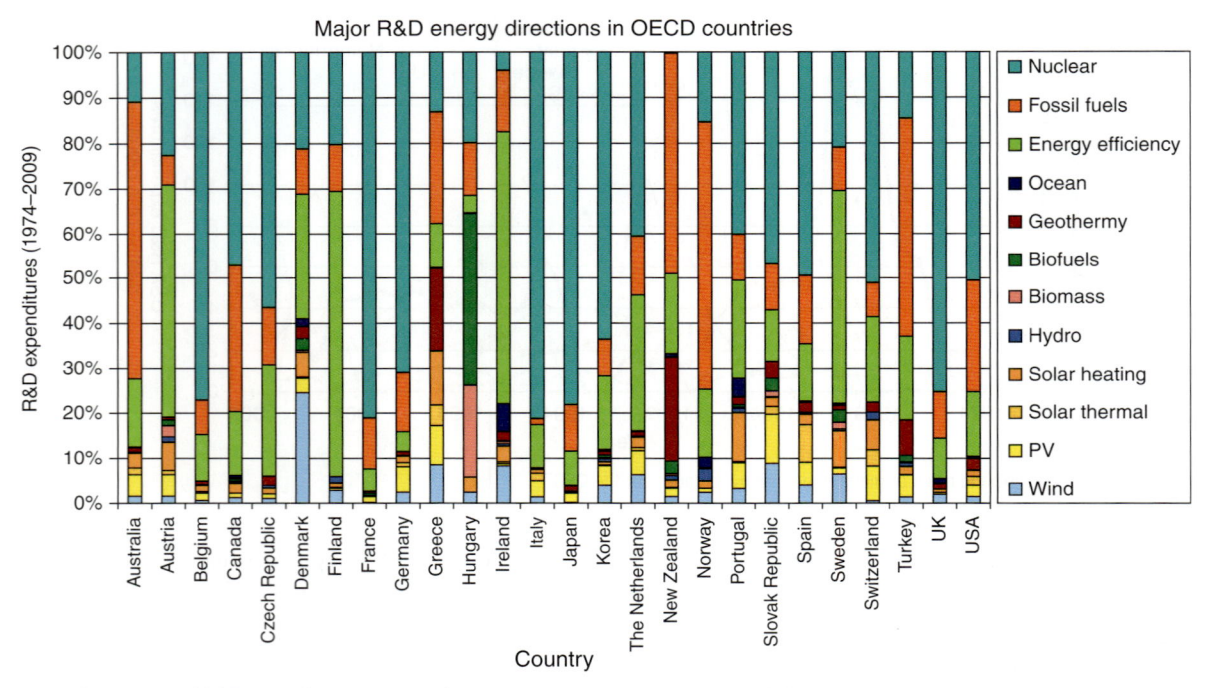

Figure 66 Breakdown of R&D expenditures per type of power generation technology for the OECD countries during the period from 1974 to 2009.

product (GDP) by 2010. Considering this, wind energy R&D investment would have to represent an average of €0.43 billion per year, where the expected public annual support would approach €0.15 billion per year.

Historically, R&D funding for wind energy has been a relatively small fraction of the funding for conventional energy technologies. In contrast, the corresponding funding by the European Union for nuclear energy research was more than 3 times greater than the entire budget dedicated for all the renewable energy resources. To be more accurate, for a long time period, the wind energy sector has received only 1% of the energy research funding in the International Energy Agency (IEA) member countries, in comparison with 58% given to the nuclear power sector during the same period.

Finally, EU funding efforts during FP5 and FP6 have been mainly concentrated on three main aspects, namely, large-size wind turbines, integration and management of wind power, and wind farm development and management. Unfortunately, the current EU R&D efforts cannot be characterized as sufficient to respond to the energy challenges faced by the European Union.

2.21.15 Wind Energy Technological Problems and R&D Directions

Up till now, the policy framework of the European Union was of critical importance for the promotion of RES and wind energy in particular. New targets set a call for 20% coverage of the final energy consumption by RES by 2020, while in terms of electricity consumption, wind energy is expected to contribute 14–17%. Moreover, according to long-term plans [143], 400 GW (250 GW onshore and 150 GW offshore) of wind power in the European Union and 20% of the US electricity demand covered by wind by 2030 [144], along with China requesting 150 GW installed by 2020 [145], set the scene for wind power prospects and challenge the target of 1000 GW globally by 2030. One should also note that in order for the aforementioned goals to be realized, R&D targets set must be put forward by the wind energy industry [146], with the main directions and actions to be taken including the following:

- New wind turbines need to reduce their overall costs
  - Large-scale turbines of 10–20 MW going offshore (R&D programs for prototypes already initiated). The market-driven upscaling and offshore applications require better understanding of extreme environmental conditions, safety, power performance, and noise, which will allow for the advantage of scale economies to be exploited as expected [147]. In addition, improved methods for predicting three-dimensional aerodynamic behavior and aeroelastic stability are essential for the reliable upscaling of contemporary wind turbines, avoiding any stability problems. In addition to this, reduction of the wake effect between the successive wind turbines of a wind park reduces the load upon the machines, ameliorates the energy performance of the installation, and optimizes the land use.
  - Improved design and reliability of components (testing facilities to assess efficiency and reliability of wind turbines, more efficient use of materials, flexible structures, and control advancements). The development of international standards will be essential for the successful deployment of wind energy throughout the world. In addition, finding viable concepts and improving the design of direct-driven generators will contribute to constructing more efficient and lighter machines. Furthermore, it is also important to find combined solutions for generation and transmission of electricity from low-voltage alternating current (LVAC) to high voltage alternating current (HVAC) or direct current (HVDC). In addition, condition monitoring of vulnerable components such as blade bearings and generators could reduce operational and maintenance cost. New concepts may also include highly flexible downwind machines and diffuser-augmented turbines.
  - Development of innovative logistics (cross-industrial programs). Intelligent material utilization and development of new materials that can also take part in a more environmentally friendly recycling process will definitely increase the value of similar installations [148].
- Deeper waters and larger turbines for offshore
  - Development and industrialization of support structures for sea installations, both fixed and floating (structure concepts to be developed and tested at different depths and under different conditions), is to be considered in the current direction, while, overall, developing large, highly reliable, silent, and 'invisible' wind turbines for offshore applications in both shallow and deep waters are among the top R&D priorities.
- Achieve grid integration for even greater wind energy penetration
  - The introduction of large-scale energy storage systems [149] and HVAC–HVDC interconnections (offshore farms connected with more than one grid, long distance HVDC, and R&D of energy storage systems) [150]. Effective storage of electricity (even at the wind park location) could enhance the value and reduce the uncertainty of wind-generated electricity through the leveling out of delivered power. This fact is much more important when large-scale penetration of wind power in the local electrical grid is attempted. In addition, development of tools and modeling and controlling energy supply to the nearby electrical grid is essential to the large-scale contribution of wind energy in electricity consumption. Among the technological advancements supporting the significant penetration of wind power in an electrical grid, one may include automatic load flow controls, adaptive loads, and demand-side management [151]. Extensive use of high-capacity power electronic devices in national networks of HVDC links is also a prerequisite. Finally, the ability to correct grid faults or deficiencies and to support the local grid stability is also a matter of concern. On the other side, stand-alone wind-based installations [152] also need further improvements, mainly due to the extreme value and importance of electricity production in remote locations where grid connection is not feasible. Finally, achieving the optimum collaboration between wind turbines and other power sources in integrated hybrid power stations [101] is also essential in small grids or autonomous installations.
- Resource assessment and spatial planning
  - More sophisticated assessment of wind resources (high-quality measurements and databases for wind data as well as short-term wind speed forecasting with the use of neural networks). Sites with high-quality wind potential are crucial for the economic utilization of wind energy. As a result, scarcity of such sites encountered in the course of time requires improved site assessment and siting [153], which in turn need better models and measurement inputs. Better measurements to predict extreme wind, wave, and ice situations will eventually result in lighter and more reliable machines, while it is also valid that the value of wind energy will be further increased if reliable prediction of the expected power output can be made for time periods between 6 and 48 h in advance [154].

- Spatial planning through social and environmental considerations (development of planning tools and methodologies). At this point, it is important to underline that finding suitable sites where there is also general social acceptance for building new wind parks has become more and more complicated. Thus, public attitude toward wind energy, as well as the influence from the visual impact and competitive use of landscape by different interest groups, has to be seriously investigated during the spatial planning procedure [155]. Also, it is essential to better understand the noise production and propagation mechanisms over large distances. Improved knowledge and methods for predicting noise propagation should be validated on the basis of actual measurements, while special attention should be paid to the offshore parks' noise impact, due to the different noise propagation patterns upon the water surface. Finally, interaction between wildlife and wind turbines must be better understood, especially as far as bird mortality is concerned. For this purpose, better understanding of the existing data and the behavior of different species is required.

In summary, the R&D areas of major importance in the mid-term time frame – based on incremental improvements – include offshore technology, wind potential forecasting techniques, grid integration, public attitude, and visual impact. For the long-term time frame, it is of vital importance to conduct research that shall lead to 'out of the box' solutions, in order to make wind turbines interact harmonically with other energy sources. Finally, it is believed that one of the critical factors that may enhance the possibility of achieving a contribution of wind energy above 20% is the adequate development of energy storage techniques, offering the opportunity for both the recovery of otherwise lost wind energy amounts and the provision of high-quality power output.

2.21.16 Financial Support of Wind Energy Research Efforts

Considering the vast development of wind energy and the broad expansion of the respective applications, new needs and pressing problems constantly appearing require the creation of new knowledge to allow for further advancements in the field. We list here the main research activities noted in the sector of wind energy during the last decade. Research carried out on the basis of state funding initiatives (e.g., the European Union) is summarized first, while, following this, attention is given to research efforts supported by the wind energy industry, as these are stated by the companies of the sector.

Promotion of wind energy was already one of the priorities set out by the European (Lisbon) strategy, aiming to support the sustainable economic growth with more and better jobs and greater social cohesion by 2010. Unfortunately, energy research funding in the European Union has decreased dramatically and is currently at the level of 25% of the respective 1980 levels. In addition, according to the EU FP7, EU nuclear energy research funding approaches €0.55 billion per year (54% of the total amount) for the 2007–11 period, while non-nuclear energy research under the same period is expected to receive almost €0.46 billion per year (46% of the total amount), equally divided between RES-related and energy efficiency topics.

Using the official historical data, wind energy received €25 million under FP5 and €32 million under FP6; thus, one may expect an amount equal to 3% of the total FP7 energy research budget. Among the most important research efforts included in the last three framework programs (FPs), one may find the following projects organized in chronological order [156].

2.21.16.1 1998–2002 (FP5)

Between 1998 and 2002, the European Union funded a number of smaller projects that dealt with a great variety of topics. The European Commission's FP5 for R&D funded demonstration projects (short- to medium-term impact) and research projects with medium- to long-term impact on the market.

The 23 funded research projects can be divided into the following categories:

2.21.16.1.1 Wind turbines (total budget approximately €9.3 million, EU contribution approximately €5 million)

There are five R&D projects in this category, aimed at investigating larger wind turbines on complex terrain and offshore installations, taking into account the experience from the first offshore wind parks. Also, effort has been spent on investigating new wind turbine concepts for non-grid-connected power systems.

2.21.16.1.2 Blades and rotors (total budget approximately €18 million, EU contribution approximately €10.4 million)

In this category, there are a total of seven R&D projects investigating the blades and rotors of wind turbines. Taking into account that the blades are among the most critical components of a wind turbine, effort has been spent on investigating the aerodynamic properties of the blades, using experimental data in order to improve the energy efficiency and reduce the aerodynamic noise. Besides, improvement of the dynamic behavior of the blades (including the hub), on the basis of new materials and the overall weight reduction, was among the targets of the R&D programs.

2.21.16.1.3 Wind resources forecasting and mapping (total budget approximately €7.8 million, EU contribution approximately €4 million)

This category comprises three R&D projects investigating the quality of wind resources in order to maximize the wind energy production by the selection of the most appropriate sites and improving power production forecasting and scheduling preventive action to protect wind turbines from excessive wind loads.

2.21.16.1.4 Wind farm development and management (total budget approximately €4 million, EU contribution approximately €2.3 million)

This category comprises three R&D projects aiming to improve the management, monitoring, and surveillance of wind farms and to provide recommendations on how to best set up new installations.

2.21.16.1.5 Integration of wind power (total budget approximately €11.9 million, EU contribution approximately €5.9 million)

Six R&D projects are investigating the optimum way of integrating wind power in existing electrical grids. Problems may appear in cases that wind is to provide a high share of overall electrical power supply.

Note that projects included in FP5 are also presented in Appendix A.

2.21.16.2 2002–06 (FP6)

Based on the above projects of FP5, larger projects were funded between 2002 and 2006 in the context of FP6, which brought together a great number of participants and addressed more ambitious challenges. A perfect example of this approach is the UPWIND project, which aims at making very large wind turbines (mainly for offshore applications), bringing together more than 40 leading organizations in the wind energy field, receiving at the same time a record EU contribution of more than €14 million.

More specifically, FP6 funded 16 research projects (Appendix B), with the total EU contribution equal to approximately €42.7 million. Interesting R&D efforts are focused on the following:

- ✓ Next generation design tool for optimization of wind farm topology and operation (TOPFARM)
- ✓ Integrated Wind Turbine Design (UPWIND)
- ✓ Prediction of Waves, Wakes and Offshore Wind (POWWOW)
- ✓ Self Installing Wind Turbine (SIWT)
- ✓ Development of a new principle 3 MW direct drive generator and wind turbine (NEWGEN 3 MW)
- ✓ Hogsara island demonstration project (HISP)
- ✓ South-East Europe Wind Energy Exploitation – Research and demonstration of wind energy utilization in complex terrain and under specific local wind systems (SEEWIND)
- ✓ Wind Energy Technology Platform Secretariat (WINDSEC)
- ✓ Decision Support for Large Scale Integration of Wind Power (SUPWIND)
- ✓ European Wind Integration Study (EWIS)
- ✓ Action Plan for high-priority renewable energy initiatives in Southern and Eastern Mediterranean area (REMAP)
- ✓ Wind on the Grid: An integrated approach (WINDGRID)
- ✓ Grid Architecture for Wind Power Production with Energy Storage through load shifting in Refrigerated Warehouses (NIGHT WIND)
- ✓ Dissemination Strategy on Electricity Balancing for Large Scale Integration of Renewable Energy (DESIRE)
- ✓ Distant offshore wind farms with no visual impact in deepwater (DOWNVIND)
- ✓ Standardization of Ice Forces on Offshore Structures Design (STANDICE).

2.21.16.3 2007–Today (FP7)

Since 2007, the European Union has concentrated on the funding frame of FP7. Financial support was mainly directed toward improvement of the reliability of wind turbines, wind predictability, and the integration of offshore wind parks in the existing electrical grids, while wave energy is also included in the corresponding R&D efforts. More specifically, FP7 has up to now funded 10 research projects (Appendix C), with the total EU contribution being equal to approximately €43.8 million. Interesting R&D efforts are focused on the following:

- ✓ Off-shore Renewable Energy Conversion platforms – Coordination Action (ORECCA)
- ✓ Marine Renewable Integrated Application Platform (MARINA PLATFORM)
- ✓ High Power, high Reliability offshore wind technology (HIPRWIND)
- ✓ Future Deep Sea Wind Turbine Technologies (DEEPWIND)
- ✓ Northern Seas Wind Index Database (NORSEWIND)
- ✓ Reliability focused research on optimizing Wind Energy systems design, operation and maintenance: Tools, proof of concepts, guidelines & methodologies for a new generation (RELIAWIND)
- ✓ Multi-scale data assimilation, advanced wind modeling and forecasting with emphasis to extreme weather situations for a secure large-scale wind power integration (SAFEWIND)
- ✓ Pilot Demonstration of Eleven 7 MW-Class WEC at Estinnes in Belgium (7 MW-WEC-BY-11)
- ✓ PROcedures for TESTing and measuring wind energy systems (PROTEST)
- ✓ High Altitude Wind Energy (HAWE).

All these R&D efforts, absorbing more than €0.11 billion, strongly contribute to improving the knowledge of wind energy exploitation and to manufacturing more efficient and environmentally friendly wind turbines. However, there is still a long way to go in order to obtain the final target of covering 20% of the planet electricity consumption on the basis of wind power systems.

At the same time, remarkable R&D efforts that are more targeted at the real application problems have been made by the leading companies of the sector. However, collecting and analyzing the available information concerning private R&D investments for the wind power sector is far from straightforward, while data from several manufacturers are not available in the open literature. According to the most recent data available for 2006 from some wind turbine manufacturers, the total amount spent approaches €0.2 billion, while the ratio of R&D expenditure to net sales varies significantly between 0.5% and 3.5%.

Subsequently, there are only certain details of the R&D efforts of the major wind turbine manufacturers to be found in the open literature. In July 2010, Vestas announced that it is going to support two large R&D projects. The first attempts to create more cost-effective deep water foundations for large offshore wind turbines. The goal of this project is to be able to design, construct, and build cost-effective deep water jacket foundations for very large wind turbines located far offshore in water depths of up to 70 m. The second project is to develop an Intelligent Energy Management System that will introduce energy storage into a wind power plant as an optional component for enhanced power generation control. In addition, the Danish National Advanced Technology Foundation has announced that it will support these two projects with approximately US$8.8 million, while the total projects cost is expected to be US$17.7 million to US$19.3 million.

Gamesa, the largest wind turbine manufacturer in Spain and one of the biggest on the planet, employs more than 600 people in its R&D departments (Gamesa has seven R&D centers located in Spain, the United States, China, and India and will open another three during 2011 in Brazil, Singapore, and the United Kingdom). Gamesa's current R&D projects include the 'Azimuth Offshore Wind Energy 2020 Project' aiming to develop a turbine of 15 MW using 100% Spanish technology. Also, 'Windlider 2015' is aimed at researching key technologies for designing large wind turbines by 2015. Furthermore, 'Sustainenerg' seeks to use proprietary technology for centralized storage of tens to hundreds of MWh. Additionally, 'Cars4grid' aims to test the viability of managing millions of batteries in electric and hybrid cars as a giant decentralized virtual battery with capacity of almost 6 GWh in Spain alone. Finally, company participation in 'Upwind' and 'ReliaWind' EU projects has already been presented.

Acciona is another Spanish wind turbine manufacturer that undertakes remarkable R&D activities in the wind power sector. More precisely, Acciona is developing (AW-3000) a line of 3 MW land-based turbines investigating the idea (on top of other innovations) of creating blades in sections, which facilitates their transportation and could be put together on the wind farm site. Another project focuses on using wind power to split water into hydrogen and oxygen in an electrolyzer. The hydrogen can then be used in fuel cells. Also, in the 'Eolia' R&D project (total budget €38.9 million, Acciona Group contribution of €18.4 million), efforts are being spent to develop the proper technology for implementing deepwater offshore wind parks (over 40 m depth). In this project, offshore desalination is included. Besides, the 'Composite Material R&D Project' funded (€2.5 million) by the government of Navarre and the Spanish Ministry of Science and Innovation is developing the appropriate industrial process for manufacturing 37.5 m wind turbine blades, taking into account, among other things, the workplace health and safety as well as the environmental behavior on a life-cycle basis. Additionally, the overall objective of the EMERGE project (total budget €9.2 million) is a development of the technology required to extend and lead the construction of deepwater (over 60 m depths) offshore wind farms. Finally, the company participates in the 'Marina' EU project (Acciona contribution €1.8 million) already presented.

From the indicative information presented above, it is absolutely clear that the wind energy sector has during recent years appreciated a remarkable financial support in order to create more efficient and reliable electricity generation machines. Acknowledging the effectiveness and results of all these funding efforts during this golden age of wind power along with the fact that new, pressing needs constantly emerge (e.g., development of machines that are bigger, more efficient, more environmentally friendly and socially accepted, etc.), the continuation of financial support in the R&D section of wind energy is more than imperative.

2.21.17 Conclusions

Based on the detailed investigation of long-term wind energy trends, what may be concluded is that wind power technology has up to now demonstrated a constantly evolving character, leading to the fourth-generation wind turbines currently emerging and the offshore diffusion of wind farms all around the globe. At the same time, the adaptation of the technology in urban environments and the rebirth of small-scale wind machines reflect the wide range of applications supported by the wind energy industry. A wide range that finds itself expanding rather than shrinking, with innovative concepts now supporting developments from building-integrated micro-turbines up to wind-driven giants of 1 GW. Within the context of unceasing development, efforts undertaken at the micro-level must also be underlined, with the evolution of each component comprising a wind turbine (e.g., blades, gearbox, control mechanisms, etc.) being the result of elaborate research and interaction among many different engineering fields. Besides, in parallel with engineering efforts, the contribution of other non-engineering sciences in the promotion of wind energy and the solution of peripheral problems through time should also be taken into account when considering wind energy evolution.

During this course of growth, financial support was of course one of the key issues. As may be easily concluded, funding and investment directed toward the development of wind energy has certainly paid off, with only limited resource exploitation leading to the creation of an established technology. However, what must be underlined is that for new challenges to be overcome, wind energy should in the future appreciate sufficient support that will allow it to take the next step, that is, to achieve a great contribution to every aspect of the energy demand of contemporary societies.

Appendix A Wind Energy Projects Funded by FP5 (1998–2002)

Wind Turbines

Research and Development of a 5 MW Wind Turbine

Project acronym: 5 MW WIND TURBINE
EC contribution: €1.76 million (50% of total budget)
Duration: 36 months

Development of a MW Scale Wind Turbine for High Wind Complex Terrain Sites

Project acronym: MEGAWIND
EC contribution: €2.0 million (56% of total budget)
Duration: 36 months

Recommendations for Design of Offshore Wind Turbines

Project acronym: RECOFF
EC contribution: €0.8 million (50% of total budget)
Duration: 36 months

Exploring New Concepts for Small and Medium-Sized Wind Mills with Improved Performance

Project acronym: EXPLOREWIND
EC contribution: €0.34 million (50% of total budget)
Duration: 24 months

Blades and Rotors

Wind Turbine Rotor Blades for Enhanced Aeroelastic Stability and Fatigue Life Using Passively Damped Composites

Project acronym: DAMPBLADE
EC contribution: €1.14 million (57% of total budget)
Duration: 36 months

Wind Turbine Blade Aerodynamics and Aeroelastics: Closing Knowledge Gaps

Project acronym: KNOW-BLADE
EC contribution: €1.0 million (65% of total budget)
Duration: 36 months

Model Rotor Experiments Under Controlled Conditions

Project acronym: MEXICO
EC contribution: €1.5 million (65% of total budget)
Duration: 36 months

Reliable Optimal Use of Materials for Wind Turbine Rotor Blades

Project acronym: OPTIMAT BLADES
EC contribution: €2.4 million (54% of total budget)
Duration: 52 months

Silent Rotors by Acoustic Optimization

Project acronym: SIROCCO
EC contribution: €1.7 million (45% of total budget)
Duration: 36 months

Aerolastic Stability and Control of Large Wind Turbines

Project acronym: STABCON
EC contribution: €1.9 million (52% of total budget)
Duration: 48 months

Innovative Composite Hub for Wind Turbines

Project acronym: COMHUB
EC contribution: €0.785 million (56% of total budget)
Duration: 36 months

Wind Resources Forecasting and Mapping

Development of a Next Generation Wind Resource Forecasting System for the Large-Scale Integration of Onshore and Offshore Wind Farms

Project acronym: ANEMOS
EC contribution: €2.5 million (46% of total budget)
Duration: 42 months

A High Resolution Numerical Wind Energy Model for On- and Offshore Forecasting Using Ensemble Predictions

Project acronym: HONEYMOON
EC contribution: €0.89 million (75% of total budget)
Duration: 24 months

Wind Energy Mapping Using Synthetic Aperture Radar

Project acronym: WEMSAR
EC contribution: €0.6 million (50% of total budget)
Duration: 36 months

Wind Farms

Advanced Management and Surveillance of Wind Farms

Project acronym: CLEVERFARM
EC contribution: €0.5 million (60% of total budget)
Duration: 36 months

Efficient Development of Offshore Wind Farms

Project acronym: ENDOW
EC contribution: €0.7 million (58% of total budget)
Duration: 36 months

Condition Monitoring for Offshore Wind Farms

Project acronym: CONMOW
EC contribution: €1.0 million (54% of total budget)
Duration: 48 months

Integration of Wind Power

Wind Energy Network

Project acronym: WIND ENERGY NETWORK
EC contribution: €0.4 million (61% of total budget)
Duration: 42 months

Towards High Penetration and Firm Power from Wind Energy

Project acronym: FIRMWIND
EC contribution: €0.46 million (53% of total budget)
Duration: 36 months

More Advanced Control Advice for Secure Operation of Isolated Power Systems with Increased Renewable Energy Penetration and Storage

Project acronym: MORE CARE
EC contribution: €0.9 million (60% of total budget)
Duration: 36 months

Wind Power Integration in a Liberalized Electricity Market

Project acronym: WILMAR
EC contribution: €1.4 million (43% of total budget)
Duration: 36 months

Cluster Pilot Project for the Integration of RES Into European Energy Sectors Using Hydrogen

Project acronym: RES2H2
EC contribution: €2.5 million (47% of total budget)
Duration: 60 months

Solar and Wind Technology Excellence, Knowledge Exchange and Twinning Actions Romanian Centre

Project acronym: RO-SWEET
EC contribution: €0.35 million (89% of total budget)
Duration: 36 months

Appendix B Wind Energy Projects Funded by FP6 (2002–06)

Next generation design tool for optimization of wind farm topology and operation

Project acronym: TOPFARM
EC contribution: €1.7 million
Duration: December 2007 to December 2010 (36 months)

Abstract: The TOPFARM project addresses optimization of wind farm topology and control strategy as based on detailed aeroelastic modeling of loads and power production in a coherent manner. The outcome of the TOPFARM project is a toolbox consisting of advanced dynamic wake load models, power production models, cost models, and control strategy models, and the synthesis of these models into an optimization tool.

European Wind Integration Study

Project acronym: EWIS
EC contribution: €4.0 million
Duration: June 2007 to October 2009 (28 months)

Abstract: The project aims to work with all the relevant stakeholders, especially representatives of wind generation developers. The study will use results from detailed network and market models of the European transmission system for scenarios representing immediate and longer-term needs. The recommendations will be aimed at developing, where possible and appropriate, common European solutions to wind integration challenges.

South-East Europe Wind Energy Exploitation – Research and Demonstration of Wind Energy Utilization in Complex Terrain and Under Specific Local Wind Systems

Project acronym: SEEWIND
EC contribution: €3.7 million
Duration: May 2007 to May 2010 (36 months)

Abstract: The aim of the project is the performance of investigations at different locations in south-east Europe, relating to the mountainous and complex structure of terrain, the characterization of local wind systems like 'Bora', and the more efficient and reliable operation of large-scale wind turbines under this conditions.

Wind Energy Technology Platform Secretariat

Project acronym: WINDSEC
EC contribution: €0.67 million
Duration: March 2007 to March 2010 (36 months)

Abstract: The wind energy sector has proposed and developed a technology platform for wind energy, with the support and encouragement of the member states, the wind industry, the European Parliament, and the European Commission. WindSec, the Platform Secretariat, will optimize the activities of the technology platform, and develop its infrastructure.

Action Plan for High-Priority Renewable Energy Initiatives in Southern and Eastern Mediterranean Area

Project acronym: REMAP
EC contribution: €0.39 million
Duration: January 2007 to December 2008 (24 months)

Abstract: The objectives of the REMAP project are to work with key stakeholders in order to achieve the following objectives: (1) compilation of a solar and wind energy resource atlas for the southern and eastern Mediterranean area; (2) identifying and prioritizing potential demonstration sites for wind and concentrated solar projects in Algeria, Tunisia, Jordan, and Turkey; (3) recording a set of commitments to be made by major stakeholders to push forward a few wind and concentrated solar thermal energy projects in the region; and (4) proposing a credible financing scheme for the identified priority renewable demonstration projects in the region.

Self Installing Wind Turbine

Project acronym: SIWT
EC contribution: €1.5 million
Duration: January 2007 to January 2009 (24 months)

Abstract: The project plans to demonstrate to the offshore wind industry the realization of a novel offshore wind turbine concept using a suction pile foundation. The subject concept allows installation of the complete wind turbine, substructure, and suction pile foundation offshore in one piece. The concept is virtually independent of the water depth as floating equipment is utilized. This allows offshore wind parks to be installed in deeper waters out of sight from the coastline.

Wind on the Grid: An Integrated Approach

Project acronym: WINDGRID
EC contribution: €1.69 million
Duration: December 2006 to December 2009 (36 months)

Abstract: Wind on the Grid is a project focused on preparation of the European electricity network for the large-scale integration of wind farms through the design, development, and validation of new tools and devices for its planning, control, and operation in a competitive market.

Decision Support for Large Scale Integration of Wind Power

Project acronym: SUPWIND
EC contribution: €1.17 million
Duration: October 2006 to July 2009 (36 months)

Abstract: The project has the following objectives: (1) To demonstrate the applicability of decision support tools based on stochastic analysis and programming for operational management of grids and power plants; (2) to demonstrate the applicability of strategic analysis tools for decision support for long-term management of grids; and (3) to provide detailed analysis of improved coordination mechanisms between grid operators, power plant operators, and power exchanges.

Development of a New Principle 3 MW Direct Drive Generator and Wind Turbine

Project acronym: NEWGEN 3 MW
EC contribution: €2.0 million
Duration: September 2006 to March 2010 (42 months)

Abstract: The new direct-drive generator – the NewGen – has the potential to reduce the weight and thus the cost of the generator installation by 70%. This is mainly achieved by applying a novel mechanical solution, which drastically reduces the stiffness requirements and therefore permits a larger diameter of the generator. In this way, both the amount of electrically active material and the amount of construction material are reduced. Thus, the total wind turbine cost will decrease by roughly 20%.

Grid Architecture for Wind Power Production with Energy Storage through Load Shifting in Refrigerated Warehouses

Project acronym: NIGHT WIND
EC contribution: €0.72 million
Duration: July 2006 to June 2008 (24 months)

Abstract: The NIGHT WIND project proposes to design grid architectures for wind power production combined with energy storage means of load management of refrigerated warehouses (cold stores). Refrigerated warehouses are constant power users, day and night.

Integrated Wind Turbine Design

Project acronym: UPWIND
EC contribution: €14.56 million
Duration: March 2006 to February 2011 (60 months)

Abstract: UPWIND looks toward wind power tomorrow, toward the design of very large turbines (8–10 MW) standing in wind farms of several hundred megawatts, both on- and offshore. It will develop the accurate, verified tools, and component concepts the industry needs to design and manufacture this new breed of turbine. It will focus on design tools for the complete range of turbine components. It will address the aerodynamic, aeroelastic, structural, and material design of rotors. Critical analysis of drivetrain components will be carried out in the search for breakthrough solutions.

Prediction of Waves, Wakes and Offshore Wind

Project acronym: POWWOW
EC contribution: €1.05 million
Duration: October 2005 to September 2008 (36 months)

Abstract: Currently, a good number of research projects are underway on the European and national level in the fields of short-term forecasting of wind power, offshore wind and wave resource prediction, and offshore wakes in large wind farms. The purpose of this action is to coordinate the activities in these related fields, to spread the knowledge gained from these projects among the partners and colleagues, and to start the work on some roadmaps for the future.

Dissemination Strategy on Electricity Balancing for large Scale Integration of Renewable Energy

Project acronym: DESIRE
EC contribution: €1.2 million
Duration: June 2005 to May 2007 (24 months)

Abstract: DESIRE will disseminate practices that will integrate fluctuating renewable electricity supplies, such as wind power, into electricity systems using combined heat and power. This will allow an increase in pan-European trade in electricity, improve the economic competitiveness of both combined heat and power production (CHP) and wind power, and allow the proportion of renewable electricity that can be absorbed by the system to increase.

Distant Offshore Wind Farms with No Visual Impact in Deepwater

Project acronym: DOWNVIND
EC contribution: €6.0 million
Duration: September 2004 to September 2009 (60 months)

Abstract: The R&D program will conduct research into the factors of environmental, electrical, operations and maintenance and wind turbine substructure pertinent to the installation and operation of large-capacity wind farms offshore in deepwater. The Demonstrator Project will install two 5 MW wind turbine generators (WTGs) in deep water near the Beatrice Alpha oil production platform in the Moray Firth, offshore north-east Scotland, then monitor their operation for an extended period to gather data on the WTG and substructure performance.

Standardization of Ice Forces on Offshore Structures Design

Project acronym: STANDICE
EC contribution: €0.24 million
Duration: June 2004 to December 2007 (43 months)

Abstract: The main objective of this project is to contribute to the development of an international standard for the design of marine structures such as offshore wind energy converters (OWECs) against ice loads with special emphasis on European subarctic ice conditions. To achieve this objective, the project will take advantage of an international standardization effort.

Hogsara Island Demonstration Project

Project acronym: HISP
EC contribution: €1.7 million
Duration: April 2004 to July 2007 (39 months)

Abstract: The objective of the project is to gain experience and to build up a track record of a small wind farm with multi-megawatt wind turbines built on an island, to demonstrate high availability, and to verify the low-cost foundation design with as little alteration on the nature and inhabitants of the islands as possible. The electrical conversion system will be designed for a cluster of turbines in order to minimize the number of components and to optimize costs, thus contributing to the objectives mentioned.

Appendix C Wind Energy Projects Funded by FP7 (Since 2007)

Off-Shore Renewable Energy Conversion Platforms – Coordination Action

Project acronym: ORECCA
EC contribution: €1.6 million
Duration: March 2010 to August 2011 (18 months)

Abstract: The objectives of the projects are to create a framework for knowledge sharing and to develop a research roadmap for activities in the context of offshore renewable energy (RE). In particular, the project will stimulate collaboration in research activities leading toward innovative, cost-efficient, and environmentally benign offshore RE conversion platforms for wind, wave, and other ocean energy resources, for their combined use, as well as for the complementary uses.

Marine Renewable Integrated Application Platform

Project acronym: MARINA PLATFORM
EC contribution: €8.7 million
Duration: January 2010 to June 2014 (54 months)

Abstract: MARINA is a European project dedicated to bringing offshore renewable energy applications closer to the market by creating new infrastructures for both offshore wind and ocean energy converters. It addresses the need for creating a cost-efficient technology development basis to kick-start growth of the nascent European marine renewable energy (MRE) industry in the deep offshore.

Multi-Scale Data Assimilation, Advanced Wind Modeling and Forecasting with Emphasis to Extreme Weather Situations for a Secure Large-Scale Wind Power Integration

Project acronym: SAFEWIND
EC contribution: €3.99 million
Duration: September 2008 to August 2012 (48 months)

Abstract: The aim of this project is to substantially improve wind power predictability in challenging or extreme situations and at different temporal and spatial scales. Going beyond this, wind predictability is considered as a system design parameter linked to the resource assessment phase, where the aim is to take optimal decisions for the installation of a new wind farm.

Pilot Demonstration of Eleven 7 MW-Class WEC at Estinnes in Belgium

Project acronym: 7 MW-WEC-BY-11
EC contribution: €3.27 million
Duration: August 2008 to August 2012 (48 months)

Abstract: This action focuses on demonstrating the development of a cost-effective, large-scale, high-capacity wind park using new state-of-the-art multi-megawatt turbines coupled with innovative technology used to stabilize the grid. A key objective of the '7-MW-WEC-by-11' project is to introduce a new power class of large-scale wind energy converters, the 7 MW WEC, into the market. The new 7 MW WEC will be designed and demonstrated at a large scale: 11 such WECs will be demonstrated in a 77 MW wind park close to Estinnes (Belgium).

Northern Seas Wind Index Database

Project acronym: NORSEWIND
EC contribution: €3.95 million
Duration: August 2008 to August 2012 (48 months)

Abstract: NORSEWIND is a program designed to provide a wind resource map covering the Baltic, Irish, and North Sea areas. The project will acquire highly accurate, cost-effective, physical data using a combination of traditional meteorological masts, ground-based remote sensing instruments (LiDAR and SoDAR), and satellite-acquired synthetic aperture radar (SAR) winds. The resultant wind map will be the first stop for all potential developers in the regions being examined, and as such represents an important step forward in quantifying the quality of the wind resource available offshore.

PROcedures for TESTing and Measuring Wind Energy Systems

Project acronym: PROTEST
EC contribution: €1.98 million
Duration: March 2008 to December 2010 (30 months)

Abstract: The objective of this pre-normative project is to set up a methodology that enables better specification of design loads for the mechanical components. The design loads will be specified at the interconnection points where the component can be isolated from the entire wind turbine structure (for gearboxes, for instance, the interconnection points are the shafts and the attachments to the nacelle frame). The focus will be on developing guidelines for measuring load spectra at the interconnection points during prototype measurements and to compare them with the initial design loads.

Reliability Focused Research on Optimizing Wind Energy Systems Design, Operation and Maintenance: Tools, Proof of Concepts, Guidelines & Methodologies for a New Generation

Project acronym: RELIAWIND
EC contribution: €5.18 million
Duration: March 2008 to March 2011 (36 months)

Abstract: The RELIAWIND consortium, for the first time in the European wind energy sector, and based on successful experiences from other sectors (e.g., aeronautics) will jointly and scientifically study the impact of reliability, changing the paradigm of how wind turbines are designed, operated, and maintained. This will lead to a new generation of offshore (and onshore) wind energy systems that will hit the market in 2015.

Future Deep Sea Wind Turbine Technologies

Project acronym: DEEPWIND
EC contribution: €2.99 million
Duration: October 2010 to October 2014 (48 months)

Abstract: The objectives of this project for new wind turbines are (1) to explore the technologies needed for development of a new and simple floating offshore concept with a vertical-axis rotor and a floating and rotating foundation, (2) to develop calculation and design tools for development and evaluation of very large wind turbines based on this concept, and (3) to evaluate the overall concept with floating offshore horizontal-axis wind turbines.

High Altitude Wind Energy

Project acronym: HAWE
EC contribution: €1.92 million
Duration: October 2010 to April 2014 (42 months)

Abstract: The aim of this project is to develop a wind power system capable of harnessing the energy potential of high-altitude wind (actually wind towers mainly use low-altitude wind, which is slow and intermittent and means that most wind farms operate at only 25–35% of their capacity) through R&D in technology fields such as materials, aerodynamics, and control.

High Power, High Reliability Offshore Wind Technology

Project acronym: HIPRWIND
EC contribution: €11.0 million
Duration: November 2010 to November 2015 (60 months)

Abstract: The aim of the HIPRWIND project is to develop and test new solutions for very large offshore wind turbines at an industrial scale. The project addresses critical issues such as extreme reliability, remote maintenance, and grid integration, with particular emphasis on floating wind turbines, where weight and size limitations of onshore designs can be overcome.

References

[1] Grob GR (2011) Wind Power Evolution. International Sustainable Energy Organization for Renewable Energy and Energy Efficiency. http://www.uniseo.org/documents/ (accessed June 2011).
[2] Fleming PD and Probert SD (1984) The evolution of wind-turbines: An historical review. *Applied Energy* 18: 163–177.
[3] Musgrove P (2010) *Wind Power*, 1st edn. Cambridge: Cambridge University Press.
[4] Pasqualetti MJ, Righter R, and Gipe P (2004) History of wind energy. In: Cleveland C (ed.) *Encyclopedia of Energy*, pp. 419–433. San Diego, CA: Academic Press.
[5] Meyer NI (1995) Danish wind power development. *Energy for Sustainable Development* 2: 18–25.
[6] Carmoy D (1978) The USA faces the energy challenge. *Energy Policy* 6: 36–52.
[7] Thomas RL and Robbins WH (1980) Large wind-turbine projects in the United States wind energy program. *Wind Engineering and Industrial Aerodynamics* 5: 323–335.
[8] Gipe P (1991) Wind energy comes of age California and Denmark. *Energy Policy* 19: 756–767.
[9] Righter RW (1996) Pioneering in wind energy: The California experience. *Renewable Energy* 9: 781–784.
[10] Ackermann T and Söder L (2002) An overview of wind energy-status 2002. *Renewable and Sustainable Energy Reviews* 6: 67–127.
[11] Esteban MD, Diez JJ, López JS, and Negro V (2011) Why offshore wind energy? *Renewable Energy* 36: 444–450.
[12] Global Wind Energy Council (GWEC) (2010) Global Wind Report. http://www.gwec.net/ (accessed June 2011).
[13] Kaldellis JK (2005) *Wind Energy Management*, 2nd edn. Athens, Greece: Stamoulis.

[14] Ronold KO and Larsen GC (2000) Reliability-based design of wind-turbine rotor blades against failure in ultimate loading. *Engineering Structures* 22: 565–574.
[15] Ahmed MR and Sharma SD (2005) An investigation on the aerodynamics of a symmetrical airfoil in ground effect. *Experimental Thermal and Fluid Science* 29: 633–647.
[16] Tar K (2008) Some statistical characteristics of monthly average wind speed at various heights. *Renewable and Sustainable Energy Reviews* 12: 1712–1724.
[17] Gasch R and Twele J (2002) *Wind Power Plants. Fundamentals, Design, Construction and Operation*, 1st edn. Berlin, Germany: Solarpraxis AG; London, UK: James & James Science Publishers Ltd.
[18] Gardner P, Garrad A, Hansen LF, et al. (2009) Wind Energy the Facts, Part I: Technology. http://www.wind-energy-the-facts.org/documents/download/Chapter1.pdf (accessed June 2007).
[19] Lenzen M and Munksgaard J (2002) Energy and CO_2 life-cycle analyses of wind turbines-review and applications. *Renewable Energy* 26: 339–362.
[20] Crawford RH (2009) Life cycle energy and greenhouse emissions analysis of wind turbines and the effect of size on energy yield. *Renewable and Sustainable Energy Reviews* 13: 2653–2660.
[21] Tremeac B and Meunier F (2009) Life cycle analysis of 4.5MW and 250W wind turbines. *Renewable and Sustainable Energy Reviews* 13: 2104–2110.
[22] Kaldellis JK and Vlachou. DS (2002) Analyzing the historical evolution of contemporary wind turbines. In: *Global Windpower Conference*. Paris, France, 2–5 April 2002.
[23] ENERCON (2011) Wind Turbines, E126/7.5MW. http://www.enercon.de/en-en/66.htm (accessed June 2011).
[24] Repower Systems (2011) Products, Wind Turbines, 6M. http://www.repower.de/produkte/windenergieanlagen/6M/?L=1 (accessed June 2011).
[25] Li N (2008) Size matters: Installed maximal unit size predicts market life cycles of electricity generation technologies and systems. *Energy Policy* 36: 2212–2225.
[26] UPWIND (2011) Finding Solutions for Very Large Wind Turbines. http://www.upwind.eu/ (accessed June 2011).
[27] Ragheb M (2009) Control of Wind Turbines. University of Illinois at Urbana-Champaign. https://netfiles.uiuc.edu/mragheb/www/NPRE%20475%20Wind%20Power%20Systems/Control%20of%20Wind%20Turbines.pdf (accessed June 2011).
[28] Spruce CJ (2004) Power control of active stall wind turbines. In: *European Wind Energy Conference 2004*. London, UK, 22–25 November 2002.
[29] Khadraoui MR and Elleuch M (2008) Comparison between OptiSlip and Fixed Speed wind energy conversion systems. In: *5th International Multi-Conference on Systems, Signals and Devices*. Amman, Jordan, 8–10 August 2008.
[30] Urban A (2010) With or without gearbox? Drive train development for wind turbines. In: *Technologie-Workshop "Windenergie – Quo Vadis?"* Vienna, Austria.
[31] Polinder H, van der Pijl FFA, de Vilder G, and Tavner PJ (2006) Comparison of direct-drive and geared generator concepts for wind turbines. *IEEE Transactions of Energy Conversion* 21: 725–733.
[32] Musial W, McNiff B, and Butterfield S (2007) Improving wind turbine gearbox reliability. In: *European Wind Energy Conference 2007*. Milan, Italy, 7–10 May 2007.
[33] Siegfriedsen S and Bohmeke G (1998) Multibrid technology – A significant step to multi-megawatt wind turbines. *Wind Energy* 1: 89–100.
[34] Li H, Chen Z, and Polinder H (2009) Optimization of multibrid permanent-magnet wind generator systems. *IEEE Transactions of Energy Conversion* 24: 82–92.
[35] US Department of Energy (2010) Advanced Wind Turbine Drivetrain Concepts: Workshop Report. http://www.nrel.gov/docs/fy11osti/50043.pdf (accessed June 2011).
[36] Busmann HG, Kensche C, Berg-Pollack A, et al. (2007) Fraunhofer-Center für Windenergie und Meerestechnik, Testing of Rotor Blades. *DEWI Magazin* 30: 5–9.
[37] LM Wind Power, Press Release (2011) LM Wind Power Marks Global Wind Day with Some 'Big' News. June 15. http://www.lmwindpower.com/ (accessed June 2011).
[38] Griffin DA (2000) *Advanced Research Turbine (ART) Aerodynamic Design of ART-2B Rotor Blades*. National Renewable Energy Laboratory. http://www.nrel.gov/docs/fy00osti/28473.pdf (accessed June 2011).
[39] Griffin DA (2009) *Blade System Design Study, Part II: Final Project Report (GEC)*. Sandia National Laboratories, SAND2009-0686. http://prod.sandia.gov/techlib/access-control.cgi/2009/090686.pdf (accessed June 2011).
[40] Griffin DA (2001) *WindPACT Turbine Design Scaling Studies Technical Area 1-Composite Blades for 80- to 120-Meter Rotor*. National Renewable Energy Laboratory. http://www.nrel.gov/docs/fy01osti/29492.pdf (accessed June 2011).
[41] Griffin DA (2001) *WindPACT Turbine Design Scaling Studies Technical Area 2: Turbine, Rotor, and Blade Logistics*. National Renewable Energy Laboratory. http://www.nrel.gov/docs/fy01osti/29439.pdf (accessed June 2011).
[42] Hau E (2006) *Wind Turbines: Fundamentals, Technologies, Application, Economics*, 2nd edn. Berlin; Heidelberg, Germany: Springer-Verlag.
[43] Engels W, Obdam T, and Savenije F (2009) Current Developments in Wind – 2009. Going to Great Lengths to Improve Wind Energy. Energy Research Centre of the Netherlands (ECN). http://www.ecn.nl/docs/library/report/2009/e09096.pdf (accessed June 2011).
[44] Manwell JF, McGowan JG, and Rogers AL (2002) *Wind Energy Explained: Theory, Design and Application*, 1st edn. New York: John Wiley & Sons.
[45] Sandia National Laboratories (2003) *Cost Study for Large Wind Turbine Blades: WindPACT Blade System Design Studies*. ftp://ftp.ecs.umass.edu/pub/rerl/outgoing/MIE_697W/Readings/WindPact/WindPact31428.pdf (accessed June 2011).
[46] MAGENN (2011) Technology. http://www.magenn.com/technology.php (accessed June 2011).
[47] Maglev Wind Turbine (2011) http://magturbine.com/ (accessed June 2011).
[48] Argatov I, Rautakorpi P, and Silvennoinen R (2009) Estimation of the mechanical energy output of the kite wind generator. *Renewable Energy* 34: 1525–1532.
[49] Argatov I and Silvennoinen R (2010) Energy conversion efficiency of the pumping kite wind generator. *Renewable Energy* 35: 1052–1060.
[50] Canale M, Fagiano L, and Milanese M (2009) KiteGen: A revolution in wind energy generation. *Energy* 34: 355–361.
[51] Aerotecture International Inc. Products. Available at: http://www.aerotecture.com/ (accessed 15 July 2011).
[52] Windpods Technology. Available at: http://www.windpods.com/technology.html (accessed 15 July 2011).
[53] Badawy MTS and Aly ME (2000) *Theoretical Demonstration of Diffuser Augmented Wind Turbine Performance*. World Renewable Energy Congress VI, pp. 2300–2303.
[54] Fletcher CAJ (1981) Computational analysis of diffuser-augmented wind turbines. *Energy Conversion and Management* 21: 175–183.
[55] FloDesign (2011) FloDesign Wind Turbine. http://www.flodesign.org/ (accessed June 2011).
[56] ARISTA Power (2011) WindTamer 8.0 GT. http://aristapower.com/wind/our-systems/windtamer-8-0-gt/ (accessed June 2011).
[57] Morrison ML and Sinclair K (2004) Wind energy technology, environmental impacts of. In: *Encyclopedia of Energy* 6: 435–448.
[58] European Commission, Special Eurobarometer (2006) Attitudes Towards Energy. http://ec.europa.eu/public_opinion/index_en.htm (accessed June 2011).
[59] European Commission, Special Eurobarometer (2007) Energy Technologies: Knowledge, Perception, Measures. http://ec.europa.eu/public_opinion/index_en.htm (accessed June 2011).
[60] Björkman M (2004) Long time measurements of noise from wind turbines. *Sound and Vibration* 277: 567–572.
[61] Bailey H, Senior B, Simmons D, et al. (2010) Assessing underwater noise levels during pile-driving at an offshore windfarm and its potential effects on marine mammals. *Marine Pollution Bulletin* 60: 888–897.
[62] Bishop ID and Stock C (2010) Using collaborative virtual environments to plan wind energy installations. *Renewable Energy* 35: 2348–2355.
[63] Desholm M (2009) Avian sensitivity to mortality: Prioritising migratory bird species for assessment at proposed wind farms. *Environmental Management* 90: 2672–2679.
[64] Bright J, Langston R, Bullman R, et al. (2008) Map of bird sensitivities to wind farms in Scotland: A tool to aid planning and conservation. *Biological Conservation* 141: 2342–2356.
[65] Josimović B and Pucar M (2010) The strategic environmental impact assessment of electric wind energy plants: Case study 'Bavanište' (Serbia). *Renewable Energy* 35: 1509–1519.
[66] Jolivet E and Heiskanen E (2010) Blowing against the wind – An exploratory application of actor network theory to the analysis of local controversies and participation processes in wind energy. *Energy Policy* 38: 6746–6754.
[67] Gross C (2007) Community perspectives of wind energy in Australia: The application of a justice and community fairness framework to increase social acceptance. *Energy Policy* 35: 2727–2736.

[68] Musial W and Ram B (2010) Large-scale offshore wind power in the United States. *Assessment of Opportunities and Barriers, National Renewable Energy Laboratory*. http://www.nrel.gov/wind/pdfs/40745.pdf (accessed June 2011).
[69] 4C Offshore (2011) Global Offshore Wind Farms Database. http://www.4coffshore.com/windfarms/ (accessed June 2011).
[70] Smit T, Junginger M, and Smits R (2007) Technological learning in offshore wind energy: Different roles of the government. *Energy Policy* 35: 6431–6444.
[71] Markard J and Petersen R (2009) The offshore trend: Structural changes in the wind power sector. *Energy Policy* 37: 3545–3556.
[72] European Environmental Agency (2009) Europe's Onshore and Offshore Wind Energy Potential. An Assessment of Environmental and Economic Constraints. http://www.energy.eu/publications/a07.pdf (accessed June 2011).
[73] European Wind Energy Association (2009) Oceans of Opportunity. Harnessing Europe's Largest Domestic Energy Resource. http://www.ewea.org/fileadmin/ewea_documents/documents/publications/reports/Offshore_Report_2009.pdf (accessed June 2011).
[74] European Wind Energy Association (2009) Pure Power, Wind Energy Targets for 2020 and 2030. *A Report by the European Wind Energy Association*. http://www.ewea.org/fileadmin/ewea_documents/documents/publications/reports/Pure_Power_Full_Report.pdf (accessed June 2011).
[75] Scholz-Reiter B, Luten M, Heger J, and Schweizer A (2010) Planning and control of logistics for offshore wind farms. In: *12th WSEAS International Conference on Mathematical and Computational Methods in Science and Engineering*. Faro, Portugal, 3–5 November 2010.
[76] Hameed Z, Vatn J, and Heggset J (2001) Challenges in the reliability and maintainability data collection for offshore wind turbines. *Renewable Energy* 36: 2154–2165.
[77] Riegler H (2003) HAWT versus VAWT: Small VAWTs find a clear niche. *Refocus* 4: 44–46.
[78] Peace S (2004) Another approach to wind (cover story). *Mechanical Engineering* 126: 28–31.
[79] Darrieus GJM (1931) Turbine Having Its Rotating Shaft Transverse to the Flow of the Current. US Patent 1,835,018.
[80] Can K, Feng Z, and Xuejun M (2010) Comparison study of a vertical-axis spiral rotor and a conventional Savonius rotor. In: *Power and Energy Engineering Conference (APPEEC), 2010 Asia-Pacific*. Chengdu, China, 28–31 March 2010.
[81] Price TJ (2006) UK large-scale wind power programme from 1970 to 1990: The Carmarthen Bay experiments and the Musgrove vertical-axis turbines. *Wind Engineering* 30: 225–242.
[82] Sandia National Laboratories (2011) Vertical Axis Wind Turbine: The History of the DOE Program. http://windpower.sandia.gov/topical.htm (accessed June 2011).
[83] Morgan CA, Gardner P, Mays ID, and Anderson MB (1989) The demonstration of a stall regulated 100 kW vertical axis wind turbine. In: *1989 European Wind Energy Conference*. Glasgow, UK, 1–5 March 1989.
[84] Morcos VH and Abdel-Hafez OME (1996) Testing of an arrow-head vertical axis wind turbine model. *Renewable Energy* 7: 223–231.
[85] Migliore PG, Wolfe WP, and Fanucci JB (1980) Flow curvature effects on Darrieus turbine blade aerodynamics. *Energy* 4: 49–55.
[86] Ham ND, Soohoo P, Noll RB, and Drees HM (1979) Analytical and experimental evaluation of cycloturbine aerodynamic performance. In: *AIAA Terrestrial Energy Systems Conference*. Orlando, FL, USA, 4–6 June 1969.
[87] Eriksson S, Bernhoff H, and Leijon M (2008) Evaluation of different turbine concepts for wind power. *Renewable and Sustainable Energy Reviews* 12: 1419–1434.
[88] Sharpe T and Proven G (2010) Crossflex: Concept and early development of a true building integrated wind turbine. *Energy and Buildings* 42: 2365–2375.
[89] Müller G, Jentsch MF, and Stoddart E (2009) Vertical axis resistance type wind turbines for use in buildings. *Renewable Energy* 34: 1407–1412.
[90] Marsh G and Peace S (2005) Tilting at windmills: Utility-scale VAWTs: Towards 10 MW and beyond? *Refocus* 6: 37–42.
[91] Wind Power Ltd (2011) Aerogenerator X. http://www.windpower.ltd.uk/ (accessed June 2011).
[92] All Small Wind Turbines (2011) All the World's Small Wind Turbines in One Overview. http://www.allsmallwindturbines.com/ (accessed June 2011).
[93] American Wind Energy Association (AWEA) (2010) AWEA Small Wind Turbine Global Market Study. http://www.awea.org/learnabout/smallwind/upload/2010_AWEA_Small_Wind_Turbine_Global_Market_Study.pdf (accessed June 2011).
[94] RenewableUK (2011) Small wind systems. *UK Market Report*. http://www.bwea.com/small/index.html (accessed June 2011).
[95] Kaldellis JK and Kavadias KA (2007) Cost–benefit analysis of remote hybrid wind–diesel power stations: Case study Aegean Sea islands. *Energy Policy* 35: 1525–1538.
[96] American Wind Energy Association and Northwest Sustainable Energy for Economic Development (2003) *Permitting Small Wind Turbines – A Handbook*. http://www.rpdmohesr.com/uploads/custompages/awea_permitting_small_wind%2012.pdf (accessed June 2011).
[97] American Wind Energy Association (AWEA) (2009) AWEA Small Wind Turbine Performance and Safety Standard. http://www.awea.org/learnabout/smallwind/upload/AWEA_Small_Turbine_Standard_Adopted_Dec09.pdf (accessed June 2011).
[98] Walker SL (2011) Building mounted wind turbines and their suitability for the urban scale-A review of methods of estimating urban wind resource. *Energy and Buildings* 43: 1852–1862.
[99] Kaldellis JK (2002) Optimum autonomous wind–power system sizing for remote consumers, using long-term wind speed data. *Applied Energy* 71: 215–233.
[100] Kaldellis JK and Vlachos GTh (2006) Optimum sizing of an autonomous wind–diesel hybrid system for various representative wind-potential cases. *Applied Energy* 83: 113–132.
[101] Kaldellis JK (2010) *Stand-Alone and Hybrid Wind Energy Systems: Technology, Energy Storage and Applications*, 1st edn. Cambridge, UK: Woodhead Publishing.
[102] Bahaj AS, Myers L, and James PAB (2007) Urban energy generation: Influence of micro-wind turbine output on electricity consumption in buildings. *Energy and Buildings* 39: 154–165.
[103] Peacock AD, Jenkins D, Ahadzi M, et al. (2008) Micro wind turbines in the UK domestic sector. *Energy and Buildings* 40: 1324–1333.
[104] Ledo L, Kosasih PB, and Cooper P (2011) Roof mounting site analysis for micro-wind turbines. *Renewable Energy* 36: 1379–1391.
[105] Yassin MF (2011) Impact of roof shape and its height of building on air quality in urban street canyons. *Atmospheric Environment* 45: 5220–5229.
[106] Warwick Wind Trials (2011) Microwind – A Catalyst for Change in UK Energy Culture? http://www.warwickwindtrials.org.uk/index.html (accessed June 2011).
[107] WINEUR (2011) Wind Energy Integration in the Urban Environment. http://www.urbanwind.net/wineur.html (accessed June 2011).
[108] Syngellakis K and Robinson P (2006) Urban wind turbines: Development of the UK market. In: *European Wind Energy Conference 2006*. Athens, Greece, 27 February–2 March 2006.
[109] Cace J, Horst E, Syngellakis K, et al. (2007) Urban Wind Turbines: Guidelines for Small Wind Turbines in the Built Environment. http://www.urban-wind.org (accessed June 2011).
[110] Encraft (2008) Warwick Wind Trials Fourth Interim Report. http://www.warwickwindtrials.org.uk/resources (accessed June 2011).
[111] Shaw S (2008) Progress Report on Small Wind Energy Development Projects Receiving Funds from the Massachusetts Technology Collaborative (MTC). http://www.ualberta.ca/~mtyree/SWIEP/Docs/CadmusGroupReport20041408.pdf (accessed June 2011).
[112] Zhang A, Gao C, and Zhang L (2005) Numerical simulation of the wind field around different building arrangements. *Wind Engineering and Industrial Aerodynamics* 93: 891–904.
[113] Blocken B, Carmeliet J, and Stathopoulos T (2007) CFD evaluation of wind speed conditions in passages between parallel buildings – Effect of wall-function roughness modifications for the atmospheric boundary layer flow. *Wind Engineering and Industrial Aerodynamics* 95: 941–962.
[114] Heagle ALB, Naterer GF, and Pope K (2011) Small wind turbine energy policies for residential and small business usage in Ontario, Canada. *Energy Policy* 39: 1988–1999.
[115] American Wind Energy Association (AWEA) (2010) Policies to Promote Small Wind Turbines. A Menu for State and Local Governments. http://www.awea.org/learnabout/smallwind/upload/Policies_to_Promote_Small_Wind_Turbines.pdf (accessed June 2011).
[116] Marsh G (2008) No child's play? Making small wind pay. *Renewable Energy Focus* 9(5): 30–36.
[117] Junginger M, Faaij A, and Turkenburg WC (2005) Global experience curves for wind farms. *Energy Policy* 33: 133–150.
[118] Morthorst PE, Auer H, Garrad A, and Blanco I (2009) *Wind Energy the Facts, Part III: The Economics of Wind Power*. http://www.wind-energy-the-facts.org/documents/download/Chapter3.pdf (accessed June 2011).
[119] Department of Trade and Industry (2007) Study of the costs of offshore wind generation. *A Report to the Renewables Advisory Board (RAB) & DTI*. URN Number 07/779, UK.

[120] Garrad Hassan GL (2009) *UK Offshore Wind: Charting the Right Course. Scenarios for Offshore Capital Costs for the Next Five Years.* Garrad Hassan on behalf of the British Wind Energy Association, London, UK.
[121] Blanco MI (2009) The economics of wind energy. *Renewable and Sustainable Energy Reviews* 13: 1372–1382.
[122] Deutsches Windenergie-Institut (2002) Studie zur aktuellen kostensituation 2002 der Windenergienutzung in Deutschland. http://www.dewi.de (accessed March 2010).
[123] Kaldellis JK (2002) An integrated time-depending feasibility analysis model of wind energy applications in Greece. *Energy Policy* 30: 267–280.
[124] European Commission (2009) Future Fossil Fuel Electricity Generation in Europe: Options and Consequences. http://ec.europa.eu/dgs/jrc/downloads/jrc_reference_report_200907_fossil_fuel_electricity.pdf (accessed December 2010).
[125] European Commission, Strategic Energy Technologies Information System (SETIS) (2010) Production Cost of Electricity – 2020 Projection. http://setis.ec.europa.eu/newsroom-items-folder/production-cost-of-electricity-2020-projection (accessed December 2010).
[126] Royal Academy of Engineering (2004) The Cost of Generating Electricity. http://www.raeng.org.uk/news/publications/list/reports/Cost_Generation_Commentary.pdf (accessed December 2010).
[127] International Energy Agency (2010) Projected Costs of Generating Electricity. http://www.mit.edu/~jparsons/current%20downloads/Projected%20Costs%20of%20Electricity.pdf (accessed June 2011).
[128] Lewis JI and Wiser RH (2007) Fostering a renewable energy technology industry: An international comparison of wind industry policy support mechanisms. *Energy Policy* 35: 1844–1857.
[129] Butler L and Neuhoff K (2008) Comparison of feed-in tariff, quota and auction mechanisms to support wind power development. *Renewable Energy* 33: 1854–1867.
[130] Ragwitz M, Held A, Resch G, *et al.* (2007) Assessment and Optimization of Renewable Energy Support Schemes in the European Electricity Market (OPTRES), Intelligent Energy. http://ec.europa.eu/energy/renewables/studies/doc/renewables/2007_02_optres.pdf (accessed June 2011).
[131] Blanco MI and Rodrigues G (2009) Direct employment in the wind energy sector: An EU study. *Energy Policy* 37: 2847–2857.
[132] Wind Energy the Facts (2011) Employment in the Wind Energy Sector. http://www.wind-energy-the-facts.org/fr/part-3-economics-of-wind-power/chapter-7-employment/ (accessed June 2011).
[133] Lehr U, Nitsch J, Kratzat M, *et al.* (2008) Renewable energy and employment in Germany. *Energy Policy* 36: 108–117.
[134] Martínez A and Prats P (1999) Wind technology issues. *Renewable Energy* 61: 835–839.
[135] Şahin AD (2004) Progress and recent trends in wind energy. *Progress in Energy and Combustion Science* 30: 501–543.
[136] Herbert GM, Iniyan S, Sreevalsan E, and Rajapandian S (2007) A review of wind energy technologies. *Renewable and Sustainable Energy Reviews* 11: 1117–1145.
[137] Clarke A (1991) Wind energy progress and potential. *Energy Policy* 19: 742–755.
[138] Barthelmie RJ, Courtney MS, Højstrup J, and Larsen SE (1996) Meteorological aspects of offshore wind energy: Observations from the Vindeby wind farm. *Wind Engineering and Industrial Aerodynamics* 62: 191–211.
[139] Weisser D and Garcia RS (2005) Instantaneous wind energy penetration in isolated electricity grids: Concepts and review. *Renewable Energy* 30: 1299–1308.
[140] Stork CHJ, Butterfield CP, Holley W, *et al.* (1998) Wind conditions for wind turbine design proposals for revision of the IEC 1400-1 standard. *Wind Engineering and Industrial Aerodynamics* 74–76: 443–454.
[141] Organization for Economic Co-operation and Development (OECD) (2011) OECD StatExtracts. http://stats.oecd.org/index.aspx (accessed June 2011).
[142] Perez Y and Ramos-Real FJ (2009) The public promotion of wind energy in Spain from the transaction costs perspective 1986–2007. *Renewable and Sustainable Energy Reviews* 13: 1058–1066.
[143] Wind Energy the Facts (2010) Scenarios and Targets. http://www.wind-energy-the-facts.org/fr/scenarios-and-targets/scenarios-and-targets.html (accessed June 2011).
[144] American Wind Energy Association (AWEA) (2008) 20% Wind Energy by 2030. http://www.awea.org/pubs/factsheets/20percent_Wind_factsheet.pdf (accessed December 2010).
[145] Chinese Renewable Energy Industries Association (2010) China Wind Energy Outlook – 2010. http://www.greenpeace.org/raw/content/china/en/press/reports/wind-power-report-english-2010.pdf (accessed December).
[146] Dismukes JP, Miller LK, and Bers JA (2009) The industrial life cycle of wind energy electrical power generation: ARI methodology modeling of life cycle dynamics. *Technological Forecasting and Social change* 76: 178–191.
[147] Hopwood D (2011) Generation innovation. Part two: We continue our focus on cost reduction in wind energy, and ask some major innovators in the sector where we are heading for in the major markets. *Renewable Energy Focus* 12: 36–41.
[148] Larsen K (2009) Recycling wind. *Reinforced Plastics* 53: 20–23.
[149] Kaldellis JK and Zafirakis D (2007) Optimum energy storage techniques for the improvement of renewable energy sources-based electricity generation economic efficiency. *Energy* 32: 2295–2305.
[150] Gomis-Bellmunt O, Liang J, Ekanayake J, *et al.* (2011) Topologies of multiterminal HVDC-VSC transmission for large offshore wind farms. *Electric Power System Research* 81: 271–281.
[151] Moura PS and de Almeida AT (2010) The role of demand-side management in the grid integration of wind power. *Applied Energy* 87: 2581–2588.
[152] Kaldellis JK, Kondili E, and Filios A (2006) Sizing a hybrid wind-diesel stand-alone system on the basis of minimum long-term electricity production cost. *Applied Energy* 83: 1384–1403.
[153] van Haaren R and Fthenakis V (2011) GIS-based wind farm site selection using spatial multi-criteria analysis (SMCA): Evaluating the case for New York State. *Renewable and Sustainable Energy Reviews* 15: 3332–3340.
[154] Costa A, Crespo A, Navarro J, *et al.* (2008) A review on the young history of the wind power short-term prediction. *Renewable and Sustainable Energy Reviews* 12: 1725–1744.
[155] Simão A, Densham PJ, and Haklay M (2009) Web-based GIS for collaborative planning and public participation: An application to the strategic planning of wind farm sites. *Environmental Management* 90: 2027–2040.
[156] European Commission, Research and Innovation (2011) Wind, EU Support. http://ec.europa.eu/research/energy/eu/research/wind/support/index_en.htm (accessed June 2011).

Further Reading

Asmus P (2000) *Reaping the Wind: How Mechanical Wizards, Visionaries, and Profiteers Helped Shape Our Energy Future*, 1st edn. Washington, DC: Island Press.
Gipe P (1995) *Wind Energy Comes of Age*, 1st edn. New York: John Wiley & Sons.
Mathew S and Philip GS (2011) *Advances in Wind Energy Conversion Technology*, 1st edn. Berlin; Heidelberg; New York: Springer.
Stankovič S, Campbell N, and Harries A (2009) *Urban Wind Energy*, 1st edn. London, UK: Earthscan.
Twidell J and Gaudiosi G (2009) *Offshore Wind Power*, 1st edn. Brentwood, Essex, UK: Multi-Science Publications.
Wood D (2011) *Small Wind Turbines. Analysis, Design and Application*, 1st edn. Berlin; Heidelberg; New York: Springer (due August 2011).

Relevant Websites

http://www.acciona.com – Acciona.
http://www.dewi.de – DEWI GmbH.
http://www.ecn.nl – ECN: Energy Research Centre of the Netherlands.
http://www.enercon.de – Enercon.
http://ec.europa.eu – European Commission: Research & Innovation.
http://www.ewea.org – EWEA (The European Wind Energy Association).
http://www.gamesa.es – Gamesa.
http://www.ge-energy.com – GE Energy.
http://www.goldwindglobal.com – Goldwind.
http://www.ieawind.org – IEA Wind.
http://www.nordex-online.com – Nordex: We've got the power.
http://www.nrel.gov – NREL (National Renewable Energy Laboratory).
http://stats.oecd.org – OECD.StatExtracts.
http://www.repower.de – Repower Systems.
http://www.risoe.dk – Risø DTU: National Laboratory for Sustainable Energy.
http://windpower.sandia.gov – Sandia National Laboratories.
http://www.energy.siemens.com – Siemens.
http://www.suzlon.com – Suzlon: Powering a greener tomorrow.
http://www.vestas.com – Vestas.
http://www.wind-energy-the-facts.org – Wind Energy: The Facts

2.22 Special Wind Power Applications

E Kondili, Technological Education Institute of Piraeus, Athens, Greece

© 2012 Elsevier Ltd. All rights reserved.

2.22.1	Introduction – The Water Demand Problem	726
2.22.2	Desalination Processes and Plants	726
2.22.2.1	General Considerations	726
2.22.2.2	Membrane/RO Desalination Processes	728
2.22.3	Energy Requirements of Desalination Processes	729
2.22.3.1	General Issues	729
2.22.3.2	Utilizing RESs in Desalination	730
2.22.4	Integrated Systems of RES with Desalination Plants	732
2.22.5	RO–Wind Desalination	732
2.22.5.1	Basic Characteristics	732
2.22.5.2	Design Issues	733
2.22.5.3	Operational Issues – Technical Difficulties	734
2.22.6	Wind–RO Configuration Possibilities	734
2.22.6.1	Systems with Backup (Diesel/Grid)	734
2.22.6.2	Systems without Backup	734
2.22.6.3	Near-Constant Operating Conditions	734
2.22.6.4	Storage Devices	734
2.22.6.5	RO Unit Switching	734
2.22.6.6	Wind Turbine Derating	735
2.22.6.7	Variable Operating Conditions	735
2.22.7	Implementation of Projects	735
2.22.8	Implementation of Projects with Hybrid Energy Systems	735
2.22.9	Economic Considerations in RES-Based Desalination	736
2.22.9.1	Introductory Comments	736
2.22.9.2	Parameters Affecting Economics of Desalination	736
2.22.10	Examples of Wind-Based Desalination Applications – Case Studies	738
2.22.10.1	General Issues for the Case Studies Analysis	738
2.22.10.2	Libya	739
2.22.10.3	Morocco	739
2.22.10.4	Spain	739
2.22.10.5	Milos Island, Greece	739
2.22.11	Technological Developments and Future Trends in Hybrid Desalination Systems	740
2.22.12	Telecommunication Stations	740
2.22.12.1	General Considerations	740
2.22.13	The Wind Power-Based T/C Station	741
2.22.13.1	Configuration Options Overview	742
2.22.14	Applications of Wind Energy in T/C Stations	742
2.22.15	Wind Water Pumping Systems	742
2.22.16	Water Pumping System Applications	744
References		745
Further Reading		746

Glossary

Desalination The process of removing salt from saline water and producing fresh potable water

RES based desalination Desalination processes that cover their energy needs from Renewable Energy Sources.

Reverse osmosis This process involves the forced passage of water through a membrane against the natural osmotic pressure to separate ions.

Wind pumping The exploitation of wind power systems to pump water mechanically.

2.22.1 Introduction – The Water Demand Problem

Wind based desalination is the first of the special applications that are dealt with in this chapter. This topic is very crucial as today about 3 billion people around the world have no access to clean drinking water. Moreover, about 1.76 billion people live in areas already facing a high degree of water shortage [1]. Water shortage is one of the most critical global problems. As a result, various solutions for the security of water supply are investigated and desalination is considered as one of the most promising ones [2]. To that effect, much attention is being paid in research and technological development fields in desalination issues.

The specific objectives of this section are to analyze and describe the use of wind energy in desalination processes. More specifically, the main directions are

- to highlight the critical water shortage problems being faced by various areas of the planet;
- to focus on the energy aspects of desalination and emphasize the use of renewable energy sources (RESs) and, more specifically, wind energy in desalination processes and plants;
- to identify the critical parameters and provide guidelines for the successful design and operation of a wind-based desalination system;
- to provide an insight into the future prospects of wind-based desalination systems.

As a matter of fact, water is a valuable natural resource and access to freshwater is considered as a basic human right. Water shortage is considered as one of the most serious social and environmental problems to be faced in the next years in many areas of the planet. Water scarcity implies not only the lack of water in arid regions but also the mismatch between water supply and demand, a problem with very strong spatial and temporal characteristics. Even in cases of a positive total water balance, there may be periods of time or specific areas when and where water is not available.

The water shortage problem is being solved with various methods, depending on the specific case, such as the construction and operation of infrastructure projects like desalination plants, dams, and groundwater reservoirs. As almost 97% of the water on earth is seawater, desalination, that is, the removal of salt from the virtually unlimited supply of seawater or brackish water, is considered as a very promising method to meet the water demand and it is today widely applied in areas with limited water resources. Wind energy is used for solving the water shortage problem because of the fact that desalination is an energy-intensive process and RES, more specifically wind energy, is a very promising solution for supplying energy to these units.

2.22.2 Desalination Processes and Plants

2.22.2.1 General Considerations

Desalination is the process of removing salt from saline water and producing fresh potable water. Seawater desalination separates saline water into two streams: a freshwater stream containing a low concentration of dissolved salts and a concentrated brine stream.

A large number of desalination plants have been installed throughout the world, the majority of which can be found in the Middle East and the Caribbean islands, with very good prospects for the coming years in China. Desalination is still considered more expensive than other methods, mainly due to its intensive use of energy, but this picture is continuously changing as R&D efforts and technological advancements have reduced the cost of the produced freshwater. Today desalination has proved to be more reliable and an economically cheaper solution in various cases, compared with other solutions such as dam construction or transportation of water by marine vessels.

The new amount added each year to total desalination capacity is shown in **Figure 1**. Demand in desalination capacity is predicted to grow rapidly and is taking place not only in the Middle East, led by the Gulf Cooperation Council countries, but also in other countries led by Algeria, Australia, and Spain. New markets are opening in China, India, and the United States [3].

The currently available desalination technologies can be categorized as follows:

1. Phase change processes that involve heating the feed (seawater or brackish water) to 'boiling point' at the operating pressure to produce 'steam' and condensing the steam in a condenser unit to produce freshwater. Applications of this principle include solar distillation (SD), multieffect distillation (MED), multistage flash distillation (MSF), mechanical vapor compression (MVC), and thermal vapor compression (TVC).
2. Nonphase change processes that involve separation of dissolved salts from the feed water by mechanical or chemical/electrical means using a membrane barrier between the feed (seawater or brackish water) and the product (potable water). Applications of this principle include electrodialysis (ED) and reverse osmosis (RO).
3. Hybrid processes that involve a combination of phase change and separation techniques (as in the case of nonphase change processes) in a single unit or in sequential steps to produce pure or potable water. Examples include membrane distillation (MD) and RO combined with MSF or MED processes. The most common desalination processes being implemented today are distillation and membrane processes (**Figure 2**), each accounting for about half of the installed global desalination capacity.

Today, most of the R&D efforts and the technological innovations are oriented toward membrane processes and, more specifically, toward RO processes. As in any type of separation, the critical issue in water desalination is the high energy demand. Many countries in the world that lack freshwater sources are also deficient in energy sources, making the problem even more difficult to solve. With

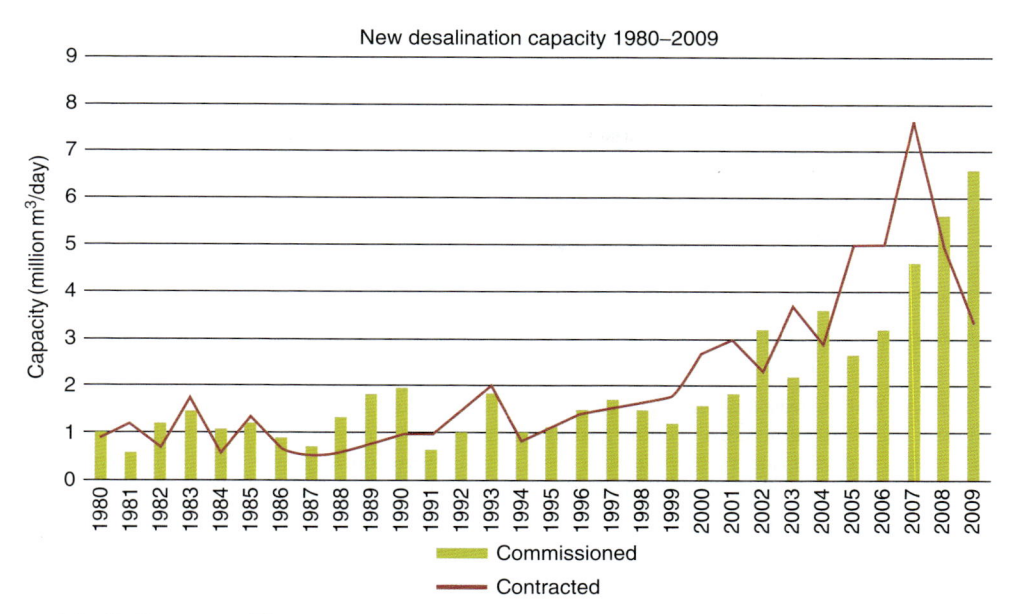

Figure 1 New annual desalination capacity [3].

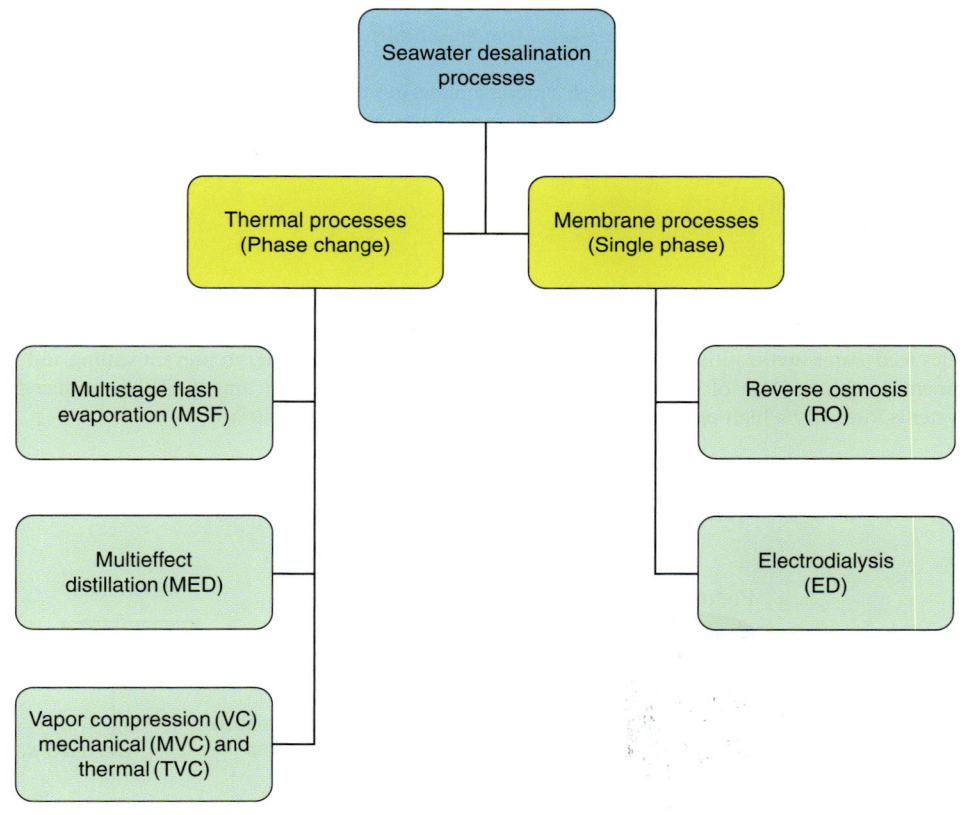

Figure 2 Main classification of desalination processes [4].

the world's freshwater demand increasing, much research has been directed at addressing the challenges in using renewable and environmentally friendly energy to meet the power needs for desalination plants.

Typically, desalination processes are powered by energy derived from combustion of fossil fuels, which contribute to acid rain and climate change by releasing greenhouse gases (GHGs) as well as several other harmful emissions. Therefore, the environmental impacts of the energy use in desalination plants are also a very significant problem that needs to be considered. **Table 1** presents the

Table 1 World population, desalination capacity, oil requirements, and GHG emissions over the past five decades [5]

Year	World population (billions)	World desalination capacity (million m^3 day^{-1})	Oil required (million metric tons day^{-1})	GHG emissions (tons CO$_2$ day^{-1})[a]
1960	3.1	0.12	0.00	0.36
1970	3.8	0.72	0.02	2.16
1980	4.5	4.4	0.12	13.2
1990	5.3	13	0.36	39
2000	6	23	0.63	69
2008	6.8	52	1.42	156

[a] Basis: 1 m^3 of water generated from a desalination plant using fossil fuel (oil) contributes to 3 tons CO$_2$.

world population growth with increased desalination capacity and the oil requirements to produce freshwater through desalination technologies and associated GHG emissions over the past five decades.

Therefore, it is necessary to develop alternatives to replace conventional energy sources used in the desalination process with renewable ones and reduce the energy requirements for desalination by developing innovative low-cost, low-energy technologies and processes.

The driving forces for such an increase are the rising water shortage and the technology-driven cost reductions. Although desalination has been considered as a very expensive water supply method, the technological advancements (mainly focused on improved energy utilization) have allowed it to really become a competitive method against other water supply approaches.

2.22.2.2 Membrane/RO Desalination Processes

Most new desalination plants now use membrane technologies. Membrane processes have considerable advantages in desalting water and are now being widely applied in this market. More specifically, the most widely applied membrane process, RO, represents more than 88% of membrane processes [6].

RO process involves the forced passage of water through a membrane against the natural osmotic pressure to separate water and ions. In these high pressures, the water molecules can pass through the membranes and the salts are left behind as a briny concentrate.

A typical RO system consists of four major subsystems (**Figure 3**):

- pretreatment system,
- high-pressure pump,
- membrane modules, and
- posttreatment system.

Feed water pretreatment is a critical factor in the operation of an RO system due to membrane sensitivity to fouling. Pretreatment commonly includes feed water sterilization, filtration, and addition of chemicals in order to prevent scaling and biofouling.

The posttreatment system consists of sterilization, stabilization, and mineral enrichment of the produced freshwater. The pretreated feed water is forced by a high-pressure pump to flow across the membrane surface.

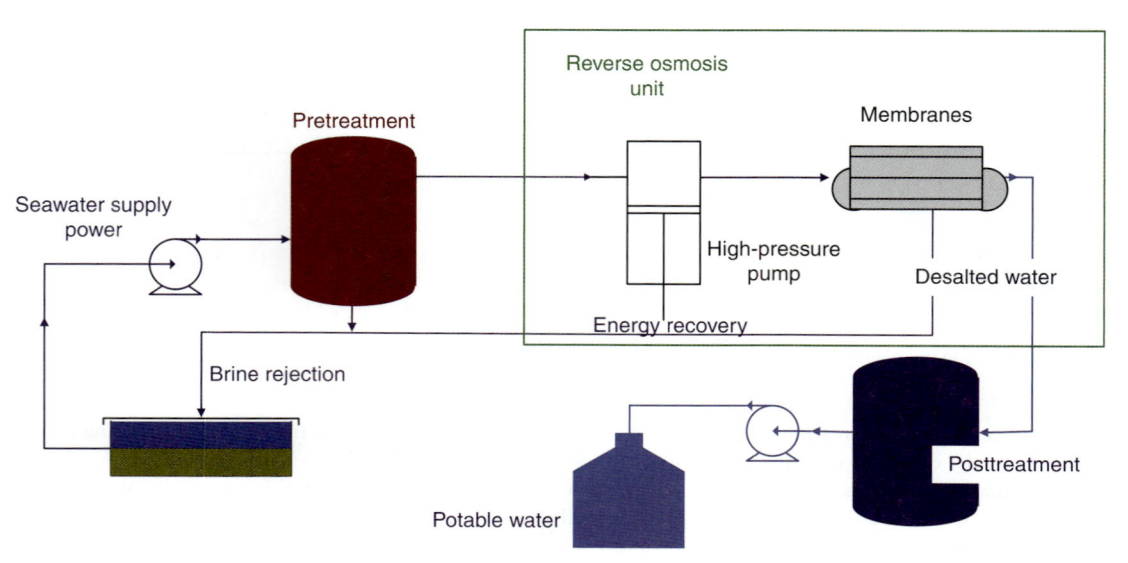

Figure 3 Typical RO unit flow sheet.

RO operating pressure varies from 17 to 27 bar for brackish water and from 55 to 82 bar for seawater. Part of the feed water passes through the membranes, removing from it the majority of the dissolved solids resulting in the so-called product or permeate water. The remaining water together with the rejected salts emerges from the membrane modules at high pressure as a concentrated reject stream (brine).

In large plants, the reject brine pressure energy is recovered by a turbine, recovering from 20% up to 40% of the consumed energy. In fact this is one of the most significant issues in RO technological development and innovation. The energy saving, that is, the percentage of the mechanical energy that can be recovered pressurizing the feed water, and the water recovery ratio – the ratio of the desalinated water output volume to the seawater input volume used to produce it – are the critical parameters in the RO process.

RO processes have been characterized by a significant reduction in energy consumption. Apart from its need for an elaborate pretreatment plant, the RO process has many advantages such as the following:

- The modular structure of the process makes it flexible enough to handle different plant capacities.
- The process is conducted at ambient temperature, which minimizes corrosion hazard.
- There is an embedded potential of water–power cogeneration and coupling with energy recovery systems.
- The rate of development in RO technology is high compared with other desalination processes and this fact promises for more cost reduction of desalted water produced by RO in the near future.
- Desalination by RO results in high salt rejection (up to 99%) and high recovery ratios (up to 40%).
- Seawater RO (SWRO) can produce potable water with salt content of about 500 ppm.

The energy issues of desalination processes and plants are discussed in the following sections of the chapter.

2.22.3 Energy Requirements of Desalination Processes

2.22.3.1 General Issues

All desalination processes use energy, which is the largest cost component in the operation of a desalination plant and offers the greatest potential for further efficiency improvement and cost reduction. In fact, energy consumption is considered as the main reason that desalination has not yet been widely applied. The share of energy in overall cost varies with the plant, its operation parameters, and location, as shown in **Figures** 4 and 5 for thermal and membrane processes, respectively.

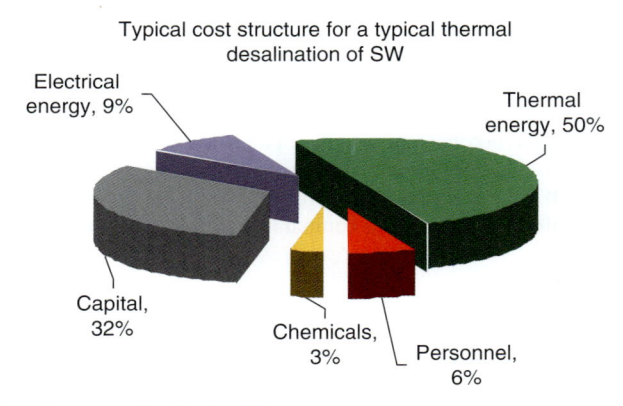

Figure 4 Typical cost structure of thermal seawater desalination [6].

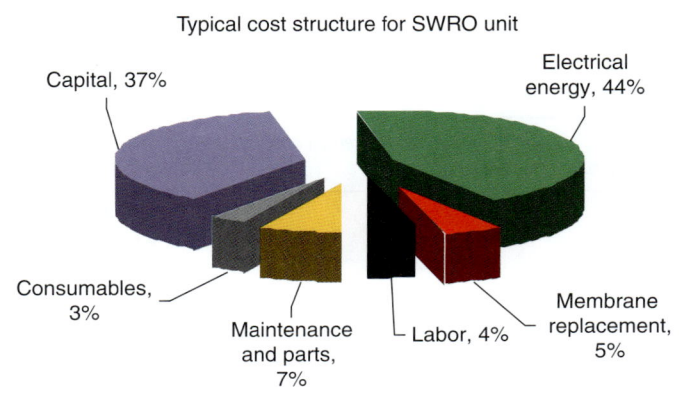

Figure 5 Typical cost structure of SWRO desalination [6].

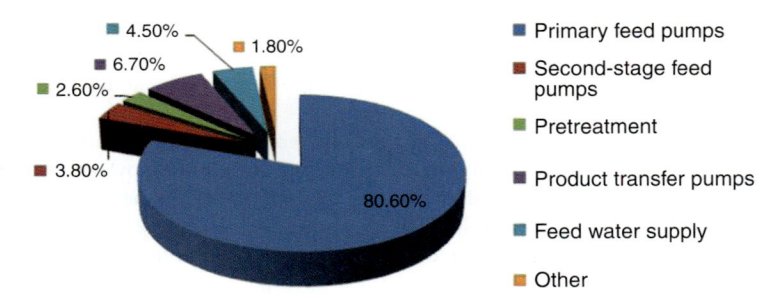

Figure 6 Distribution of power usage in an RO plant [7].

Therefore, it is necessary to develop alternatives to replace conventional energy sources used in the desalination process with renewable ones and reduce the energy requirements for desalination by developing innovative low-cost, low-energy technologies and processes. There are various possible combinations of RESs with well-established desalination technologies with different suitability and cost requirements of such desalination processes for domestic, small-scale, and large-scale applications.

Furthermore, the distribution of power usage in a two-stage SWRO system is shown in **Figure 6**. More than 80% of the power is required for the primary feed pumps [7].

In any desalination process, the energy consumption depends on a variety of factors, including

- seawater salinity,
- the technology being used,
- the ability of the system for energy recovery,
- the temperature of operation for membrane processes,
- performance ratio,
- heat losses, and
- temperature difference for thermal processes.

In **Table 2** the major power requirements of desalination processes are shown [6, 8].

The development of RO and more recently the improvements in energy recovery devices have changed that situation. With energy consumption on Mediterranean SWRO plants down to $3\,kWh\,m^{-3}$, seawater desalination is now feasible for many communities. In practice, much higher energy is required by the currently available desalination technologies.

In countries making significant desalination investments, energy policies and energy investment planning should possibly be revised to provide the right incentives for appropriate desalination processes and to decide whether cogeneration of water and power is a suitable option under particular circumstances. This has become more significant for reasons ranging from integration of policies, the demand for water growing at a different rate than the demand for power, and seasonal variations between power and water demands [9, 10].

However, thermal processes (MSF, MED) operating with steam supplied by the exhaust and steam bleeding from backpressure or extraction steam turbines are economically attractive and comparable with RO energy cost [11].

2.22.3.2 Utilizing RESs in Desalination

The use of RESs for the operation of desalination plants is a feasible and environmentally compatible solution in areas with significant RES potential. The main driving forces for applying RES in desalination plants are

- the continuous technological advancements in RES systems and their cost reduction;
- the seasonal variability in water (and energy) demand, usually occurring in areas with high renewable energy availability, for example, islands;

Table 2 Power requirements of various desalination processes [6, 8]

Process	Gain output ratio	Electrical energy consumption $(kWh\,m^{-3})$	Thermal energy consumption $(kWh\,m^{-3})$
MSF	8–12	3.25–3.75	6.75–9.75
MED	8–12	2.5–2.9	4.5–6.5
MED-TVC	8–14	2.0–2.5	6.5–12
MVC	N/A	9.5–17	N/A
BWRO	N/A	1.0–2.5	N/A
SWRO	N/A	4.5–8.5	N/A

N/A, not available.

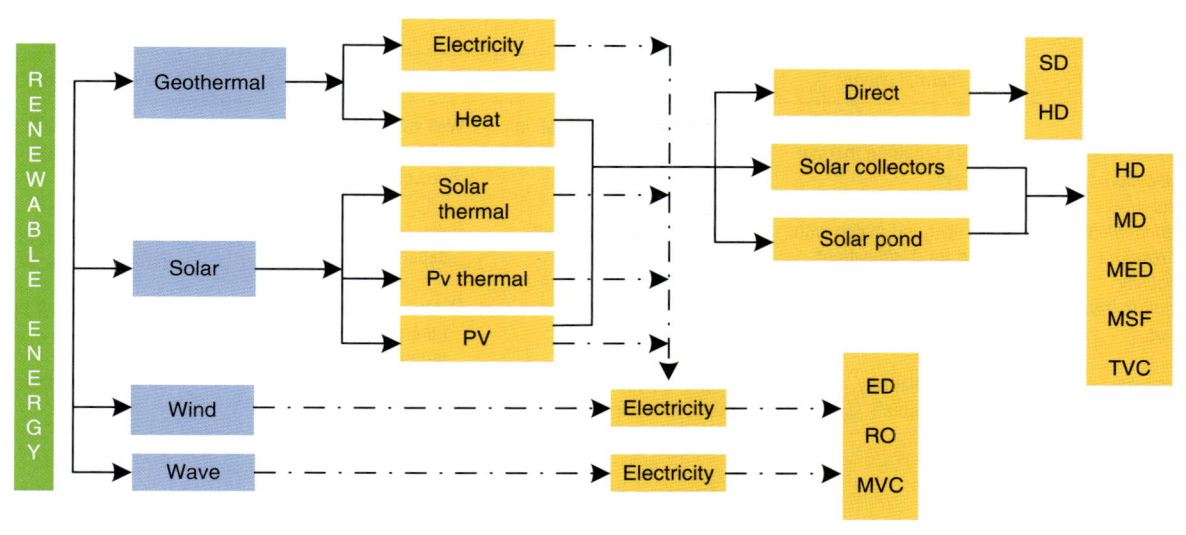

Figure 7 Possible combinations of RESs with desalination processes [5].

- the limited availability of a conventional energy supply in remote areas;
- the technological advancements being achieved in desalination systems;
- the limitation of environmental impacts of conventional desalination systems; and
- the relative ease of the plant's operation and maintenance compared with conventional energy ones.

To that end, a lot of research and development work has been carried out and the problem of the optimal configuration/combination of an RES energy source with a desalination plant attracts the interest of many researchers and construction and engineering companies.

Figure 7 shows potential pathways by which common RESs can be utilized to drive the different desalination processes. Each pathway involves different technologies, each with its own yield and efficiency.

The best coupling of RES to desalination systems is a complicated and interesting problem and its solution is not always obvious and unique. In fact, this is a major decision-making issue, part of the wider problem of infrastructure planning. Various criteria should be taken into account, including among others

- the renewable energy availability,
- the investment and operational cost and the availability of financial resources,
- the system's efficiency,
- the availability of operational personnel,
- the suitability of the system to the characteristics of the location, and
- the possibility for future increase of the system capacity

Matching renewable energies with desalination units, however, requires a number of important factors to be considered. Not all the combinations of RES-driven desalination systems are practicable, as many of these possible combinations may not be viable under certain circumstances. The optimum or just simple specific technology combination must be studied in connection with various local parameters such as geographical conditions, topography of the site, capacity and type of energy available at low cost, availability of local infrastructures (including electricity grid), plant size, and feed water salinity.

More specifically, the factors to be considered for selecting desalination process suitable for a particular application include the following:

- the amount of freshwater required in a particular application (i.e., the plant's capacity) combined with the applicability of the various desalination processes;
- the seawater treatment requirements, that is, the feed water's salinity;
- the technical infrastructure of the area (e.g., road access, network) and the local regulations concerning the land use and the land area required, or that could be made available, for the installation of the integrated energy and desalination unit;
- the remoteness of the area and the availability of grid electricity;
- the suitability and effectiveness of the process with respect to energy consumption;
- the capital cost of the equipment;
- robustness criteria and simplicity of operation;
- low maintenance, compact size, and easy transportation to site;

Table 3 Evaluation of various RESs in desalination applications [12]

Criterion	Solar thermal energy	PV	Wind energy	Geothermal energy
Suitability for powering desalination plants	Well suited for desalination plants requiring thermal power[a]	Well suited for desalination plants requiring electrical power[a]	Well suited for desalination plants requiring electrical power[a]	Well suited for desalination plants requiring thermal power[a]
Site requirements and resource availability	Typically good match with need for desalination[a]	Typically good match with need for desalination[a]	Resources are location dependent[b]	Resources are limited to certain location[c]
Continuity of power output	Output is intermittent (energy storage required)[c]	Output is intermittent (energy storage required)[c]	Output is intermittent (energy storage required)[c]	Continuous power output[a]
Predictability of power output	Output is relatively unpredictable[b]	Output is relatively unpredictable[b]	Output is very stochastic/ fluctuates[c]	Output is predictable[a]

[a] Excellent compliance with criterion.
[b] Good compliance with criterion.
[c] Poor compliance with criterion.

- acceptance and support by the local community; and
- organization at local level with relatively simple training.

Table 3 evaluates the combinations of desalination and RES according to certain energy-related criteria.

2.22.4 Integrated Systems of RES with Desalination Plants

Desalination using renewable energy is undergoing a rapid development nowadays. The most likely market for coupling renewable energy with desalination is small communities in remote locations where there is no power grid connection or where energy is expensive. In the context of the utilization of the more established RESs, that is, the sun (thermal and photovoltaic (PV)) and the wind, stand-alone desalination systems have been widely discussed. Even if one focuses on one particular renewable source and a specific desalination method, there may still be many options available in terms of the final system configuration.

There is very strong research interest in this specific area. Many research teams work in specific technical issues or in integration and optimization aspects of the combination between RES and desalination. However, as far as implementation is concerned, many small-scale and rather experimental projects have been installed but there is no serious experience from industrial-scale projects. The Red-Dead project, aiming at linking the Red Sea with the Dead Sea, might be the first large-scale renewable energy-driven desalination scheme. It would have a potential of producing up to 850 million $m^3\ yr^{-1}$ of potable water.

2.22.5 RO–Wind Desalination
2.22.5.1 Basic Characteristics

Desalination systems driven by wind power are the most frequent renewable energy desalination plants (**Figure 8**). Wind-powered desalination represents one of the most promising renewable energy options for desalination, especially in coastal areas with high availability of wind energy resources. In fact, after solar energy, wind energy is the most widely used RES for low-capacity desalination plants. The two most common approaches for wind-powered desalination systems include connecting both the wind turbines and the desalination system to the grid and direct coupling of the wind turbines with the desalination system.

Also a primary concern with the use of wind energy for desalination is that wind speed is very variable. Another option is likely to be a stand-alone system at remote locations which have no electricity grid. In this case, the desalination system may be affected by power variations and interruptions caused by the wind. Hence, the stand-alone wind desalination systems are often hybrid systems combined with another type of RES (e.g., solar) or a backup system such as batteries or diesel generators. For stand-alone wind energy-driven desalination units, the reported cost of freshwater produced ranges from 1.5 to 3.5 € m^{-3} [9].

More specifically, wind energy can be used efficiently on condition that the average wind velocity is above 5 m s^{-1}. This makes wind-powered desalination a particularly interesting option for windy islands, both for the solution of their energy supply problem and for the operation of seawater desalination plants.

The main design variables that affect the design of a wind–RO system are

- the water demand and, therefore, the RO plant's capacity,
- the location where the wind turbine and the desalination plant will be installed (required siting, altitude, etc.),
- the feed water salinity,
- the wind speed distribution,

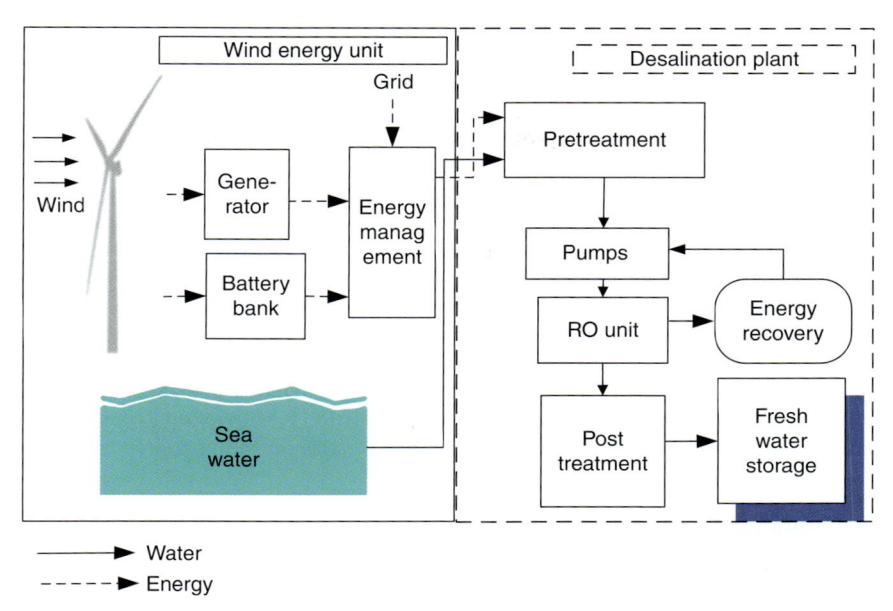

Figure 8 Structure of a wind-based RO desalination plant [13].

- the configuration of the energy system,
- the water storage capacity,
- the available power distribution,
- the feed water source, that is, seawater, brackish water,
- desalination unit energy consumption,
- the salt rejection,
- the forecasted environmental impacts,
- the operating pressure, and
- the permeate flux, in terms of both overall product rate and specific rate (per unit membrane area).

Desalination plants using membrane technologies are available in a wide range of capacities. As far as the recommended RES–desalination combinations are concerned, it is considered that wind desalination is suitable for a wide spectrum of desalination capacities (50–2000 m³ day⁻¹), resulting in a cost of desalinated water of 1.5–4 € m⁻³ [14].

Recent developments in wind turbine technology imply that wind power can now be regarded as a reliable and cost-effective power source for many areas of the world. Wind turbines may be classified depending on their nominal power 'N_o' as very small ($N_o < 10$ kW), small ($N_o < 100$ kW), medium sized ($N_o < 1.0$ MW), and large ($N_o > 1.0$ MW). All are based on mature technologies and they are commercially available except for the very large power systems (> 5 MW), which still require several adjustments.

2.22.5.2 Design Issues

The basic assumptions for the required calculations concerning the energy efficiency of the wind turbines with or without an energy storage system may be considered as below.

For a wind turbine with a nominal power of N_o kW, we expect an energy production 'E' in the order of magnitude of '$E = CF \times N_o \times 8760$' kWh yr⁻¹. Note that the installation capacity factor 'CF' usually varies between 20% and 30%. Depending on the type of desalination plant, the required amount of energy per cubic meter of potable water will also be given. Therefore, we may have a series of alternatives concerning the installed power of the wind turbine and the combined capacity of the desalination plant. Many other parameters should be taken into account in this design issue, such as the possible losses of an energy storage system and the availability of a water storage system [15].

The variable nature of wind power is not a problem as far as water availability is concerned, because water can be stored inexpensively. With a plant that is dimensioned according to the local wind conditions, water becomes available any time. However, the serious problem of this type of installations is that variable wind power may cause operational problems in the system's operation and this is one of the most critical issues to be resolved in the design and implementation of an RES–wind-based desalination project.

One common way of storing the surplus energy is by using batteries [10] or water pumping systems. Storage size should be considered in the design stage. In addition, capital and maintenance costs should carefully be assessed.

2.22.5.3 Operational Issues – Technical Difficulties

RESs are characterized by intermittent and variable intensity, whereas desalination processes are designed for continuous steady-state operation. One of the problems of utilizing wind power in process applications is the variable nature of the resource. While the wind is relatively predictable, it is seldom constant and there will be periods of calm spells.

The storage of wind energy in the form of electrical power is really practical only when small amounts are involved. Storage batteries increase the total investment cost; therefore, running a process of any magnitude on stored electrical energy is not a practical proposition.

However, if the product of the process can be stored inexpensively, then it may be practical to oversize the process equipment to allow for downtime. Water can be stored for long periods of time without deterioration and the storage vessels are relatively cheap.

Variable power input forces the desalination plant to operate in nonoptimal conditions, which may cause operational problems. To avoid the fluctuations inherent in renewable energies, different energy storage systems may be used. The only areas that would require some careful design would be the relative sizes of the wind turbine and the RO plant and the cut-in and cut-out criteria for the RO plant to avoid excessive start-up and shutdown cycles.

For the operation of a wind-powered desalination plant, it is most important to have a plant that is insensitive to repeated start-up and shutdown cycles caused by sometimes rapidly changing wind conditions. RO is, with regard to pretreatment, membrane fouling, after-treatment, and efficiency of the high-pressure pumps, a process that is rather sensitive to a stop and start operation.

2.22.6 Wind–RO Configuration Possibilities

Different wind-powered RO systems found in the literature have been classified, also taking into account some of the points previously discussed [16]:

- the existence of an alternative electrical supply (weak grid or diesel generator);
- the matching of the available wind energy to the load; and
- the operational characteristics of RO membranes.

2.22.6.1 Systems with Backup (Diesel/Grid)

In these systems, an additional energy source is provided (a diesel-powered generator or even the local grid) so that the power supplied to the RO is constant. The backup generation complements the power production from the wind turbine to match the RO unit power consumption. The main benefit of these systems, as in any hybrid wind–diesel configuration, is fuel savings, which may increase the generator availability and reduce overall energy costs. On the other hand, problems such as fuel shortages, diesel generator maintenance, and interruptions or power cuts in the supply may lead to unavailability of the RO system as it cannot be powered by the wind turbine alone for a long period of time including calm spells.

2.22.6.2 Systems without Backup

Systems without an external energy source can be divided into two categories, with emphasis on the RO unit operation: systems which run under approximately constant operating conditions and those that experience variable operational conditions.

2.22.6.3 Near-Constant Operating Conditions

This first type of operation can be implemented by three different means: on/off switching of the RO units, usage of storage devices, and derating the wind turbine. In all three cases, an attempt is made to supply the individual RO modules with approximately constant power.

2.22.6.4 Storage Devices

In this strategy, storage devices are employed to accumulate energy surplus during periods when the power generated by the wind turbine is greater than the load demand from the desalination unit. This surplus would then be used later when the generated power is insufficient to meet the load demand. One common way of storing the surplus energy is by using batteries. In this case, the relation between operational pressure, storage sizing, and average wind speed should be considered in the design stage. In addition, capital and maintenance costs should be carefully assessed. A disadvantage of this approach to the system design is the rating of the energy storage system, as this can make it economically unattractive at higher power levels due to the sizing of the battery bank.

2.22.6.5 RO Unit Switching

This strategy is based on the use of a higher power wind turbine connected with multiple smaller RO units. The power control is achieved by switching the units on and off so as to match the demand to the total power generated instantaneously by the turbine. There is no limitation concerning the system power rating, and this approach is feasible up to power levels of hundreds of kilowatts.

Although frequent cycling of RO units is not usually recommended, this problem can be overcome by implementing different types of configurations. Higher power wind turbines operating at near-constant speed connected to many equally smaller RO units switching on/off (load management) may be employed. To smooth out the fluctuations, short-term energy storage (a flywheel in this instance) may be used.

2.22.6.6 Wind Turbine Derating

This approach consists of making use of the flat end of a pitch-controlled wind turbine power curve to operate the RO unit at approximately constant power. An implication of this configuration is that, as the turbine rated power is only achieved at high wind speeds, it would have to be derated by changing the settings of the pitching mechanism. This will cause the generated power to be flattened at lower wind speeds and consequently to have lower values. Therefore, the original rating of the turbine rotor should be considerably higher than the RO unit rated power, making the system more expensive.

2.22.6.7 Variable Operating Conditions

In contrast to systems that operate under constant conditions, another operational strategy is based on the establishment and imposition of certain operational limits. This means that, based on the input power to the RO unit (flow times pressure), a control strategy is determined which imposes a fixed operating point on the system that lies within the allowed region (i.e., the operational window of the RO unit).

By doing this, an attempt is made to operate the system autonomously over a wider power range, without the need to use a backup unit or storage device. The overall effect is to reduce capital and operating costs. One aspect that should be emphasized is that very little is known about the consequences of variable operation of RO membranes. It is recognized that mechanical fatigue can occur and that the lifetime of the RO elements may be shortened and performance impaired.

2.22.7 Implementation of Projects

The practical experience regarding wind-powered RO systems has been with relatively low-capacity systems. There have been a number of attempts to combine wind energy with RO. A number of plants have actually been operated. However, most of them are of small size, mainly for research purposes, as previously mentioned.

Therefore, not many conclusions have been reached in terms of expertise and know-how. It is still difficult to control the usage of wind in a cost-effective way. Coupling of a variable energy supply system, as mentioned earlier, to a desalination unit requires either power or demand management, and there is not much experience on it. However, the prospects of this combination are high mainly due to the low cost of wind energy. The operational experience from early demonstration units is expected to contribute to improved designs, and a large number of commercial systems are expected to be implemented.

A number of units have been designed and tested; however, most of them are in the demonstration and experimental scale [17–19]. As early as 1982, a small system was set at Ile du Planier, France: a 4 kW turbine coupled with a 0.5 $m^3\,h^{-1}$ RO desalination unit. The system was designed to operate via direct coupling or batteries.

Another case where wind energy has been combined with RO is that at the Island of Drenec in France, in 1990. The wind turbine in this case was rated at 10 kW and was used to drive an SWRO unit.

More recently, some R&D projects have been carried out, such as the wind desalination system built at Drepanon on a cement plant, near Patras, Greece. The project, including a 35 kW wind turbine, was initiated in 1992 and was completed in 1995. The project called for full design and construction of the wind generator turbine (blades, etc.) plus installation of two RO units with a production capacity of 5 and 22 $m^3\,day^{-1}$. Unfortunately, since 1995, operational results have been poor due to the low wind regime.

A very interesting experiment has been carried out at a test facility in Lastours, France, where a 5 kW wind turbine provides energy to a number of batteries (1500 Ah, 24 V) and via an inverter to an RO unit with a nominal power of 1.8 kW. Furthermore, great work on wind RO systems has been carried out by the Instituto Tecnologico de Canarias (ITC) in several projects such as AERODESA, SDAWES, and AEROGEDESA.

An energy optimization model which simulates hourly power production from RESs has been applied using the wind and solar radiation conditions for Eritrea, East Africa, for the computation of the hourly water production for a two-stage SWRO system with a capacity of 35 $m^3\,day^{-1}$. According to the results obtained, specific energy consumption is about 2.33 kWh m^{-3}, which is a lower value than that achieved in most of the previous designs. The use of a booster pump, energy recovery turbine, and an appropriate membrane allows the specific energy consumption to be decreased by about 70% compared with less efficient designs without these features. The energy recovery turbine results in a reduction in the water cost of about 41%. The results show that a wind-powered system is the least expensive and a PV-powered system the most expensive, with water costs of about 0.50 and 1.00 $ m^{-3}, respectively. By international standards, for example, in China, these values are considered economically feasible [1].

2.22.8 Implementation of Projects with Hybrid Energy Systems

Due to the intermittent production of wind energy, suitable combinations of other RESs can be employed to provide smooth operating conditions. Autonomous hybrid systems are independent and incorporate more than one power source.

Wind generator/PV energy combination can drive the desalination process round the clock with a battery bank system. Diesel generators are mainly used as backup systems; however, fuel transportation to remote areas poses the same difficulties as water transportation. RES penetration depends only on the economic feasibility and the proper sizing of the components to avoid oversizing and ensure quality and continuity of supply. One important application is the use of PVs and wind generator to drive RO desalination units.

As has already been mentioned, each desalination system has specific problems when it is connected to a variable power system. RO has to deal with the sensitivity of the membranes regarding fouling, scaling, as well as unpredictable phenomena due to start–stop cycles and partial load operation during periods of oscillating power supply.

Several RO units with intermittent or infrequent operation have to replace their membranes very often. On the other hand, units including storage backup system like a battery bank increase the system's initial cost and, in difficult climatic conditions, the maintenance requirements.

As stated earlier, most of the plants constructed to date have been either as research or demonstration projects. With the end of the project, most of the systems stop their operation due to limited budget and staff unavailability.

General Electricity Company of Libya (GECOL) and a consulting consortium of experts are managing the implementation of an experimental research facility for SWRO desalination powered from RESs (SWRO-RES) in the Mediterranean Sea off the coast of Libya. The nominal production of the plant will be 300 $m^3 day^{-1}$ for the supply of a village with potable water. Both wind energy conversion (WEC) and PV power generation will be integrated into a grid-connected power supply for an RO desalination plant with power recovery by pressure exchange. The facility design is flexible for the integration of diesel generator and electrochemical storage as power supply alternatives as well as brackish water reverse osmosis (BWRO). The wide range of feasible plant configurations will allow for extension of the scope of research to off-grid stand-alone performance analysis of such hybrid systems.

While the expected nominal power load for the operation of the RO desalination system is 70 kW (net power after recovery), the solar PV system is designed for 50 kW_p and the WEC for 200 kW nominal output. The design aims at a reduction of the annual nonrenewable energy consumption to about 40%. The economic analysis of the integrated renewable energy systems predicts levelized water cost (LWC) of the integration of grid and wind energy with RO 1.8 € m^{-3} and for grid and PVs with RO 1.9 € m^{-3} compared with 1.3 € m^{-3} for operation of the plant only from the grid [20, 21].

2.22.9 Economic Considerations in RES-Based Desalination

2.22.9.1 Introductory Comments

Various efforts have been made to develop tools for the design, economic evaluation, and the determination of the main parameters for RES-based desalination plants. Estimating the capital and production costs of desalination systems is very difficult due to many reasons such as the following:

- the varying energy, material, and labor costs per geographic area;
- the type of the desalination process (design, size, etc.); and
- the salinity of the feed water.

There are many references [21–31] and research and development works analyzing design and financial issues of these units and reaching various conclusions concerning the optimal decision under specific circumstances. As a general rule, an SWRO unit has low capital cost and significant maintenance cost due to the high cost of the membrane replacement. The cost of the energy used to drive the plant is also significant.

As described in the previous sections of this chapter, a number of parameters affect decision making on the design of such a plant. This also applies in the financial evaluation of the units; that is, a number of parameters and their complex interactions affect the produced freshwater cost. A conclusion of all the efforts being made on this issue is that there is no specific and generally applicable tool for determining the cost of such units. All the parameters, being technical, environmental, and social, are very site specific.

In this context, the contribution of this chapter to those that need to develop and evaluate an RES-based desalination plant and to the researchers of the field could be seen in two directions:

- to enumerate (exhaustively) the parameters and factors that should definitely be taken into account in such a work;
- to provide examples of real case studies with specific design and cost.

2.22.9.2 Parameters Affecting Economics of Desalination

The economics of a wind-powered desalination system differ from conventional plant economics as it is almost entirely based on the fixed costs of the system. Certainly there are no fuel costs as they are replaced by the wind turbine.

In fact it should be mentioned at this point that a detailed financial analysis leading to the estimation of precise financial indices should be carried out in case private investments are attempted. It is expected that this type of project implementation will prevail in many countries in the next years, and in some places (e.g., Cyprus) significant experience on that has already been built.

In this case, the investor will possibly undertake the capital and – for some years at least – the operational cost of the project expecting to benefit from the selling of water, either in the free market or in the municipality it belongs to (e.g., the case of a Greek island desalination plant [13]). It is expected that many such private investments will take place in the next years, especially in areas with water shortage and financial activities in the field of tourism.

Desalination costs per unit of produced water for different desalination processes with RESs and different feed sources are shown in **Tables 4** and **5**.

Table 6 makes a synthesis of the most critical parameters and choices that affect the feasibility and financial attractiveness of an RES-based desalination project (e.g., wind-based desalination plant).

More specifically, for the case of wind–RO desalination, the factors that are taken into account in water production cost are shown in **Table 7**.

Table 4 Desalination water costs for various combinations of desalination processes with RES [5]

Water type	Desalination system powered by RES	Water cost (€ m^{-3})
Brackish water	Conventional energy + RO, ED	0–1
Brackish water	Photovoltaic energy + RO	5–6
Brackish water	Photovoltaic energy + ED	4.5–6
Brackish water	Wind + RO	2–3.5
Brackish water	Wind + ED	2–3
Brackish water	Geothermal + MED	2
Seawater	Conv. energy + RO, ED, MSF, MED, VC	1–3
Seawater	Photovoltaic energy + RO	3–5.5
Seawater	Wind + RO	2.5–5.5
Seawater	Wind + VC	4–5.5
Seawater	Solar thermal + MED	2.5–5.5
Seawater	Geothermal + MED	3.5–5

Table 5 Investment and operation costs for desalination processes with capacities in the range 200–40 000 m^3 day^{-1} [5]

Capacity (m^3 day^{-1})	Costs	MVC	RO	MED	MED–TVC
200	Cost/unit ($ m^{-3})	3.8	3.25		3.3
	Investment (M$)	0.75	0.5		0.5
600	Cost/unit ($ m^{-3})	2.65	2.35		2.25
	Investment (M$)	1.7	1.1		1
1200	Cost/unit ($ m^{-3})	2.25	2.15	1.6	1.85
	Investment (M$)	3.2	2	2.3	1.65
2000	Cost/unit ($ m^{-3})		2	0.825	1.8
	Investment (M$)		3	3.25	2.5
3000	Cost/unit ($ m^{-3})		1.85	0.65	1.7
	Investment (M$)		4.2	4.85	3.3
20 000	Cost/unit ($ m^{-3})			1.24	1.55
	Investment (M$)			35	35
30 000–40 000	Cost/unit ($ m^{-3})			1.31	
	Investment (M$)			67	

Table 6 Parameters affecting economics of wind-based desalination plants

Parameters affecting economics of RES-based desalination plants	Comments
The desalination technology (thermal, RO)	In general, RO units have lower investment cost but high operation and maintenance costs
Plant's capacity	Large capacity units are more expensive but the water unit cost is lower
The climatic conditions and the characteristics of wind turbines	They define the size of the wind farm required for a given annual production of freshwater
The energy requirement of the desalination plant	This is determined by the water supply salt concentration and the coupling of the energy and the desalination system
The feed water salinity	BWRO is generally cheaper than SWRO
The location where the wind turbine and the desalination plant will be installed	Required siting, altitude, infrastructure preparation costs
The configuration of the energy system	Main design decision determining the operation and the cost of the unit
The water storage capacity	Design parameter determining the operation of the unit
The available power distribution (e.g., the wind speed distribution)	It affects the size, the configuration, and, therefore, the investment cost

Table 7 Cost items of a wind-based desalination plant

Investment cost
    Cost of land
    Cost of wind turbine
    Cost of energy storage systems
    Cost of the RO plant components
Annual operating cost
    Manpower cost
    Chemicals cost
    Electricity cost
    Maintenance and spares cost
    Membrane replacement

2.22.10 Examples of Wind-Based Desalination Applications – Case Studies

2.22.10.1 General Issues for the Case Studies Analysis

The experience from the design and operation of a number of selected desalination systems powered by wind energy that have been installed and operating in various locations around the world is described in review research works [32, 33].

It is interesting to mention that cost analysis of a wind-assisted RO system for desalinating brackish groundwater in Jordan has been conducted and the authors stated that it would cost less to desalinate brackish water with a wind-assisted RO system than with a conventional diesel-powered system [34].

Forstmeier et al. [35] demonstrated that the costs of a wind-powered RO desalination system are in line with what is expected for a conventional desalination system, proving to be particularly cost-competitive in areas with good wind resources and that have high costs of energy.

In all these studies, results obtained were theoretical and not verified by experimental data. At the same time, the implementation of several wind-powered RO desalination system prototypes has been reported.

A prototype wind-powered RO desalination system was later constructed and tested on Coconut Island off the northern coast of Oahu, Hawaii, for brackish water desalination [32]. The system has four major subsystems: a multivaned windmill/pump, a flow/pressure stabilizer, an RO module, and a control mechanism. The authors showed that at an average wind speed of $5\,m\,s^{-1}$, brackish feed water at a total dissolved solids concentration of $3000\,mg\,l^{-1}$ and at a flow rate of $13\,l\,min^{-1}$ could be processed. The average rejection rate and recovery ratio were 97% and 20%, respectively. Energy efficiency equal to 35% was shown to be comparable to the typical energy efficiency of well-operated multivaned windmills.

Miranda and Infield [15] developed a system with a 2.2 kW wind turbine generator powering a variable-flow RO desalination unit. Operation at variable flow allows the uncertainty and variability of the wind to be accommodated without the need for energy storage. Batteries, which are common in stand-alone systems, are avoided and water production is dependent on the instantaneous wind speed.

A prototype of a fully autonomous wind-powered desalination system has been installed on the island of Gran Canaria in the Canarian Archipelago [36]. The system consists of a wind farm, made up of two wind turbines and a flywheel, which supplies the energy needs of a group of eight RO modules throughout the complete desalination process (from the pumping of seawater to the storage of the product water), as well as the energy requirements of the control subsystems. The authors concluded that this system can be applied to seawater desalination, both on a small and large scale, in coastal regions with scarcity of water for domestic and/or agricultural use but with adequate resources.

In the following section, some case studies from real plants are presented. They are all different types of plants installed in different areas, with each having its own technical characteristics.

2.22.10.2 Libya

A demonstration plant has been designed in Libya (Integrated Power and Water Point) that will supply up to 300 m^3 day^{-1} of water and 240 kW electricity to a village [20, 25]. For the 60 kW RO power demand, a 275 kW wind turbine is integrated with a 300 kW diesel plant. The process simulation for desalination of seawater with 4.3% salinity under nominal operating conditions yields 57% recovery rate at a specific energy consumption of 4.8 kWh m^{-3} (pumping included). The power demand at nominal output of 300 m^3 day^{-1} is 60 kW, based on the calculation of 300.0 m^3 day^{-1} × 4.8 kWh m^{-3}/24 h day^{-1} = 60 kW.

The resulting cost of water is 2.24 € m^{-3}. In the specific plant, detailed measurements have been taken in order to make reliable calculations of the costs.

2.22.10.3 Morocco

Morocco is characterized by a semiarid climate [28]. The obligation to use other nonconventional water resources such as desalinated water or wastewater reuse becomes a necessity. In addition, Morocco has a large potential of wind energy sources that could be used in seawater desalination.

In the following, the cost of desalinated water is calculated for three towns in the south of Morocco, using the method of LWC. The cost was estimated for two seawater desalination processes: RO and MVC powered by wind turbines. Electric connection to the grid is available, so that the grid can be used to power the plant when RESs are not available. This alternative is then compared with the baseline which consists of the grid-only configuration.

The desalination processes studied in this chapter were designed to produce 1200 m^3 day^{-1} of water, the daily consumption of almost 10 000 inhabitant-equivalent. Depending on the wind potential of a given region, the installed power of wind turbines will be chosen in order to deliver an annual energy production equivalent to the annual energy consumption of the desalination system.

The baseline water cost per cubic meter was evaluated at €0.91 for the RO. It is interesting to notice the cost breakdown structure for a wind-based desalination unit, as has been given for the plant in Morocco. In these two cases being referred, this breakdown for an RO unit is as follows:

- 37.5% desalination investment cost,
- 31.6% wind turbine cost,
- 24.2% operation and maintenance of desalination unit cost, and
- 6.7% operation and maintenance of wind turbine cost.

The sum adds up to an LWC of almost 0.85 € m^{-3}.

2.22.10.4 Spain

For a given wind farm capacity (with a particular type of wind turbine) and a given wind regime, there exists, from an economical point of view, an optimum nominal production capacity for each plant that needs to be specified in each case under consideration [36, 37]. In this context, a wind farm with a nominal power of 460 kW and a wind regime (in the area of Pozo Izquierdo, proposed for its installation in Gran Canaria) with an annual average speed of 7.9 m s^{-1} and 10 m above ground level would give rise to an optimum number of RO plants of 11, each with a capacity of 100 m^3 day^{-1}. However, for technical and economical reasons, the decision was made to use eight RO plants, each with a capacity of 25 m^3 day^{-1}.

The water cost of a wind BWRO unit (large system, about 250 m^3 day^{-1}) is of the order of 2 € m^{-3}. The implemented project in Tenerife, Spain, included a 200 kW wind turbine, which would operate on an average wind velocity of 7.5 m s^{-1}, with an expected yearly energy yield around 600 MWh. This amount of energy is capable of producing over 200 m^3 day^{-1} of water.

2.22.10.5 Milos Island, Greece

A wind-based desalination unit has recently been installed in a Greek island called Milos belonging to the Cyclades complex [13]. The plant (**Figure 9**) has been in operation since summer 2007 and has a capacity of 3000 m^3 day^{-1}. At the moment, it produces 2000 m^3 day^{-1} of potable water. This is a private investment that has been subsidized by the state. The water is sold to the municipality of Milos, in a continuous effort to solve the water shortage problem, especially during the summer months. The contract that has been signed between the private company and Milos municipality refers to a selling price of almost 1.8 € m^{-3}.

The entire plant includes

- the desalination unit,
- a wind turbine of 600 kW,

Figure 9 Milos wind-based desalination plant.

- the storage tanks (capacity 3000 m^3), and
- the remote control system.

Before the installation of the unit, water was transported from Athens at a very high cost and rather poor quality [13]. The implementation of this novel project has improved the quality of life of the island in many respects. The siting of the unit in a very touristic island such as Milos could be a major problem, mainly because of the visual and noise disturbance. Therefore, the unit has been located on a hill that is not visible from most island villages.

2.22.11 Technological Developments and Future Trends in Hybrid Desalination Systems

Although present desalination technologies and various forms of RESs are well developed, there is scope for improvements in efficiency, reliability, simplicity, and investment costs in each one of these technologies. Therefore, a lot of research efforts should be directed toward improving and enhancing the presently utilized technologies. It is also important that new technologies be investigated.

There is definitely a wide scope for research and development in the coupling between desalination and RES. Serious progress in the field will take place in case industrial-scale projects are implemented, something that has not happened yet.

The following examples indicate the trends in R&D activities:

- Energy consumption in all desalination processes is much higher than the thermodynamic minimum requirement. Energy cost is the major component of the operating cost of a desalination plant. Research under this topic is focused on reduction in energy consumption and the use of alternative energy sources.
- Development of high-flux membranes and introduction of energy recovery devices have greatly reduced overall energy consumption, resulting in a currently possible energy consumption of even below 2 kWh m^{-3}.
- Coupling of desalination processes with RESs.

A significant contribution in the design and operation of these systems would be twofold:

- The development of a tool for the selection and design of the appropriate energy and desalination system, including its configuration. The parameters that should be taken into account in this decision include the desalination plant capacity, energy availability, infrastructure available, investment and operational costs, and operation and maintenance capabilities in this specific site.
- The development of a tool for the optimal operational planning of the coupled desalination–energy system mainly determining optimal size, the storage capacity, and the detailed operation of the system, that is, which hours per day the system will operate to produce water for the consumption, or to be stored, and which hours the energy system will operate to supply energy to the consumption, to the storage, or to the desalination unit [38, 39].

In addition to all the references already cited, many other contributions are mentioned at the end of this document in order to facilitate further reading.

2.22.12 Telecommunication Stations

2.22.12.1 General Considerations

The telecommunication (T/C) sector has experienced a rapid growth over the past years in the developed world. As the need for connectivity continues to grow extensively, more T/C equipments such as cellular base stations and satellite communication devices need to be installed in urban as well as in remote locations. The majority of T/C stations cover their electrification needs by large and robust electrical networks supported by fossil fuel-fired power stations. However, there are several cases wherein T/C stations are located far away from the electrical grid. Furthermore, in many developing countries and remote areas, there is no grid connection.

This insufficient infrastructure has hindered the up-to-now establishment of T/C networks in these regions. Certainly, cost-effective operation of the T/C equipment (i.e., remote T/C stations) becomes critical in order to satisfy local demand. The use of electrification alternatives such as diesel power generation, comprising a common power supply option for the existing remote T/C stations, entails considerable life cycle costs and aggravation of the local environment. In this context, the use of RES may replace costly and heavily polluting diesel engines [40].

Among the alternatives of electricity generation for T/C stations, T/C providers themselves [41] identify wind energy as an energy solution of minimum operating expenses and negligible environmental footprint, suitable for coastal locations or hilly areas with appreciable wind potential. Small-sized wind turbines may even be adjusted on the relay mast (**Figure 10**) as a supplementary to the diesel option energy solution, while wind-based stand-alone systems occupy comparatively larger wind turbines. These are installed near the mast area and are able to minimize the fuel consumption of diesel generators used for backup supply only.

In any given case, however, a battery bank of the appropriate capacity is also necessary; while depending on the local area characteristics, reduction of the battery bank size may be achieved through the incorporation of a PV array. Introducing PV power to the system may complement wind energy generation while also eliminating oversizing of storage and further reducing oil fuel consumption, especially during the summer months, that is, when the air-conditioning needs of the station increase [43].

2.22.13 The Wind Power-Based T/C Station

Small wind turbines can be used cost-effectively to power such T/C sites. Wind power, coupled with an appropriately designed energy system, can secure constant power supply, which is crucial for telecom services, and reduce the need for ongoing maintenance such as fuel and equipment transportation. Reliable energy supply and significant cost savings increase wind power competitiveness and turn it into the best energy choice for telecom and network operators.

The main benefits from the exploitation of RES in general and wind energy – more specifically – in T/C stations are the following:

- The very small need for maintenance. This is very important as the T/C stations are in remote regions.
- The easy and simple installation.
- The high-energy output thus implying a cost-effective operation.
- In some cases, there is no need for a tower as the wind turbines may be attached to the existing T/C towers.

Nowadays, many engineering and manufacturing companies have been active in the area of design, manufacturing, and installation of wind turbines for T/C applications, suggesting that various types of wind turbines are providing a range of alternative solutions to specific implementation projects suitable for these types of applications [42, 44, 45].

In fact, the suggested wind turbines exhibit properties that make them very attractive for these applications, such as

Figure 10 Wind turbine in a T/C station [42].

- variable pitch blades,
- aluminum alloy castings,
- upgraded electronic systems and wiring for improved reliability over standard models, and
- externally regulated controller designed for rugged environments.

The critical point of such an application is the very high reliability that is required, a feature that must be taken into account very seriously in the design of the system. Various configurations are implemented for stand-alone or grid-connected systems and they are summarized below. The configuration to be chosen depends on the application characteristics and requirements and the infrastructure available.

2.22.13.1 Configuration Options Overview

In the stand-alone systems (off-grid), there is the option of connection to the battery bank using a charge controller. In this case, connection is suitable in sites that include a large battery bank and where a diesel generator charges batteries every few hours (noncontinuous diesel generator operation). The power generated by the turbines charges the batteries and reduces diesel generator costs.

There is the option for wind turbine only or hybrid wind and PV. The hybrid system benefits from complementary energy cycles from each technology (day/night, summer/winter, etc.). Again, there is the option of connecting the hybrid system to the battery bank using charge controllers.

There is also the option of connecting the wind turbine directly to the consumption using an inverter. In this case, connection is suitable in sites that include a diesel generator working on a continuous basis and small back up battery bank. The power generated by the turbine/s reduces the required diesel generator output level and thus reduces generator costs.

In this context, various researchers have been investigating different interesting issues in this area, such as the design and the feasibility of specific RES and hybrid energy sources in T/C stations [40, 43, 46]. The problems under consideration usually are the modules to be included, that is, the system configuration itself and the determination of the optimum size of each system component, in order to satisfy a selected optimization criterion, for example, the minimum cost. Usually, the results obtained indicate that properly sized hybrid power stations appear to be one of the most attractive energy solutions for the support of remote T/C stations, providing increased levels of reliability and presenting low maintenance needs.

2.22.14 Applications of Wind Energy in T/C Stations

Energy efficiency programs run by T/C companies, for example, in Portugal, use wind micro-generating systems countrywide, reducing fuel consumption and emissions by a considerable 15–20%, while in other cases the employment of higher power output wind turbines minimizes oil use and its impacts. For example, three very remote base stations were installed in Kenya in 2005, based on pilot wind–diesel hybrid energy systems. The systems consisted of a 7.5 kW turbine on a 24 m tower, sealed batteries, and an inverter, with the results obtained showing excellent reliability and diesel fuel savings of 70–95%. Other examples include the similar but comparatively larger wind-diesel installation located at Osmussaar, Estonia, comprising a 30 kW wind turbine, two ordinary diesel generator sets of 32 kW each, and a battery bank of 250 Ah, while another two wind–PV systems may be found in Turkey, with the system incorporating two wind turbines of 5 kW each, PV panels of 4 kW_p, and an appropriate battery bank system [43].

The majority of the mobile T/C cell stations in the developing world rely on diesel generators for their power. However, wind power could soon be challenging the diesel generators and power the cell stations with renewable green energy.

Over 99% of cell sites worldwide are deployed with diesel generators as a backup or as the primary source of electrical power. But the operating expense involved in keeping the diesel fuel flowing can be prohibitive, especially in light of increasingly remote base station sites and rising theft of diesel fuel and generators.

As diesel generators are favored for their low capital cost, the price of diesel has risen and the cost of solar panels and wind turbines has dropped. Economists estimate that the return on investment (ROI) will flip in favor of renewable green energy by 2014.

By 2015, an installed base of 1.9 million mobile telecom sites will be candidates for green power upgrades or retrofits, with a compelling ROI driving operators to choose solar and wind power [47].

2.22.15 Wind Water Pumping Systems

Wind energy is used very frequently for pumping of water. Wind water pumping embraces a number of potential applications [43], including domestic water supply, community water supply, cattle watering, and irrigation. Wind water pumping systems may belong to the following categories as far as the exploitation of wind energy is concerned:

- to use wind energy to supply shaft power that is used in a direct manner to pump water or
- to use wind energy to generate electricity to drive an electrical pump.

The former shows higher efficiency at low wind velocities, whereas electric wind systems show better efficiency at high wind velocities. The electro-wind pumping systems present greater annual efficiency concerning the water pumped. Efficiencies about 10–15% are achieved in the electro-wind pumping compared with efficiencies of 5% or 6% from a mechanical water pumping system of the same rotor diameter [48].

In fact, there are two types of wind power systems to pump water mechanically, namely

- the piston pump system that converts rotary wind power to vertical motion using a piston pump to lift water and
- the airlift pump system that uses wind power to charge a compressor that pumps air to lift water.

The design of the system to be chosen depends on the specific energy needs and various other parameters, such as the type of application, the battery storage system, and the wind available on the site [49].

In electrical water pumping, a wind turbine, generally a fast running one, drives an electric generator which feeds an electric motor connected to a pump. This solution is valuable when aquifers are deep under the soil surface and when the wind mean speed is higher than 5 or 6 m s^{-1} [50].

Erecting a wind-driven generator away from the water source, at an elevated place where the wind rate is higher, can increase the power output by 30% or more. To achieve good results in water delivery, it is preferable to have a battery for storage of electricity. The battery stores energy when the wind speed is higher and gives it back when the wind has low velocity. In that case the generator is an alternator and the current must be rectified.

In practice, the pumps used are chosen in such a manner that their manometric heads are equal to 1.5 or 2 times the height of elevation [50].

In the general case, the electrical systems have the added advantage that the turbine can be located on a site with a better wind profile and not necessarily on the site where the water is pumped. Wind electrical systems for water pumping are more expensive because, generally speaking, they require five components to convert the wind energy into electrical energy (wind generator, rectifier, charge controller, batteries, and inverter). A less expensive system can be obtained by connecting the electric pump to the generator with a controlled converter, which provides safe operating conditions for both the wind generator and the electric pump [48].

This method reduces the number of components and allows the power storage in the battery bank to be replaced by a water storage tank. A storage tank is most feasible where the morphology of the land allows locating the tank at a convenient height that permits distribution of the water gravitationally. Low-power wind turbines generally operate in isolated systems and frequently the energy is stored in battery banks.

One of the most crucial issues of these systems is that they need to be very efficient, that is, they need to maximize the quantity of pumped water per unit of electricity or work being produced. This consideration affects the design of the pumps employed. Many researchers have investigated various aspects of wind-based water pumping and have dealt with the analysis, design, and control of these systems.

Several wind water pumping installations may be encountered in remote areas (e.g., in isolated farms, see **Figure 11**), where infrastructure is poor and water supply is used to cover additional needs, on top of domestic ones. Actually, the importance of serving the water needs of remote communities is well illustrated by the fact that even though there is increasing water consumption in both the domestic and the industrial sector, agriculture – especially in the developing countries – is still the dominant water user, absorbing almost three-quarters of the global water resources. More specifically, the use of freshwater is distributed as follows [51].

- 70% for irrigation,
- 22% for industry, and
- 8% for domestic use.

Figure 11 Wind water pumping system in a remote area.

In this context, the use of wind pumps throughout the developing world remains very valuable and has led to the development of small-scale markets for multibladed and low-rated speed wind turbines.

For successful wind pumping, the availability of adequate wind and water resources is essential.

On the other hand, grounded on the complementarity between increased water needs and high solar potential available during the summer months, a shift is noted during the recent years to the PV pumping concept, encouraged also by the gradual cost reduction of contemporary PV modules. Nevertheless, the possibility of wind-based hybrid energy systems incorporating PV power as well is also an option. A similar pilot hybrid energy system is operated by the Soft Energy Applications & Environmental Protection Laboratory in Greece (**Figure 12**), where a 2 kW wind turbine along with 610 W$_p$ of PV power and an appropriate lead acid battery bank are able to elevate water quantity of 23 m^3 day^{-1} from a ground depth of 30 m [52].

Wind pumping is economically feasible at very moderate average wind speeds of 3 m s^{-1} and above. In some conditions, average wind speeds of 2.5 m s^{-1} are sufficient for cattle watering and domestic water supply applications. Such wind speeds can be found in so many regions of developing countries that solely on the basis of wind resources the potential for wind pumping is enormous, probably tens of millions of wind pumps. Water resources could be the bottleneck; wind pumps, however, are especially suited for pumping water from wells with low recharge rates.

2.22.16 Water Pumping System Applications

Wind pumping systems are used for a variety of applications: for community or domestic water supply, animal husbandry, irrigation and drainage, fish ponds, and salt pans. Pumping heads vary from very low (<3 m), to low (<10 m), to medium (10–30 m), to deep (30–100 m), and in exceptional cases up to 200 m. Pumping requirements may vary from a few cubic meters per day for private domestic water supply to a few hundred cubic meters per day for drainage.

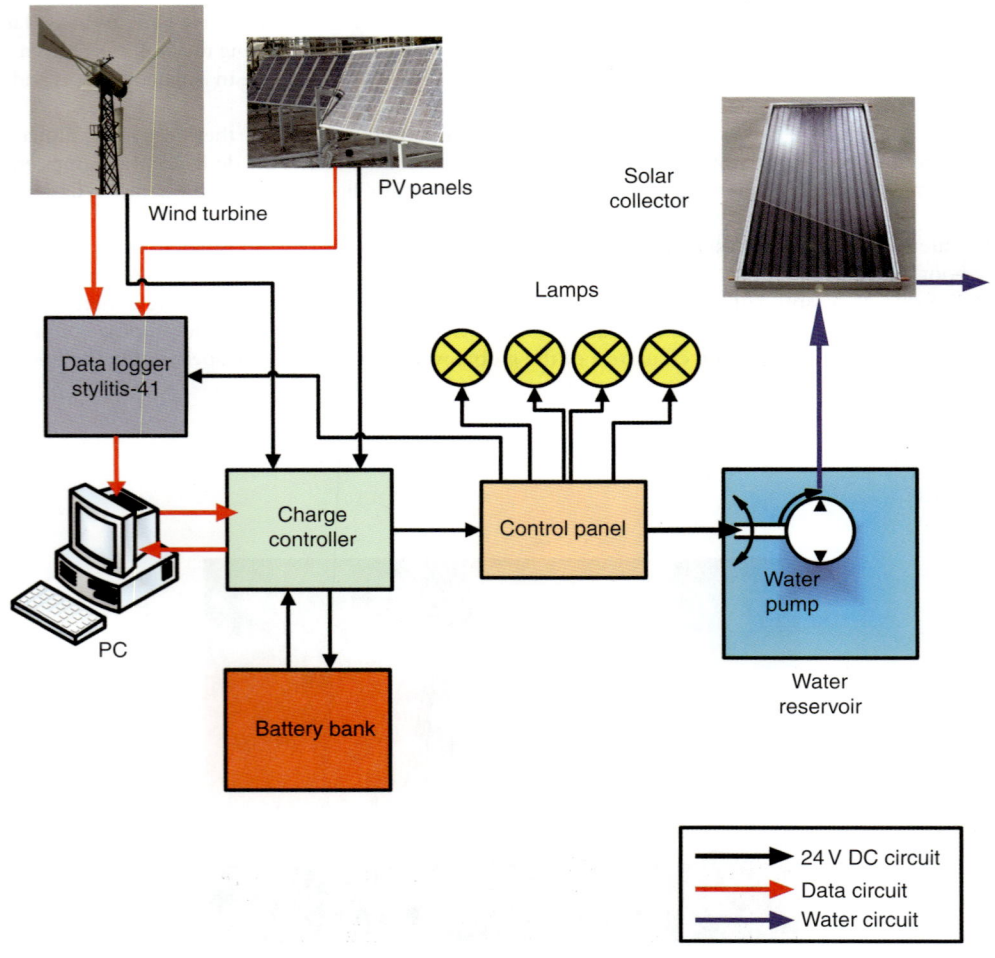

Figure 12 Experimental hybrid wind-based stand-alone unit in the Soft Energy Applications & Environmental Protection Laboratory [52].

These requirements are mainly met by mechanical wind pumps, having a pure mechanical transmission. It should be noted that other transmissions are also used. In Northern Brazil, wind pumps are manufactured with a pneumatic transmission, using compressed air. These machines are installed in very remote sites.

Mechanical wind pumps can be subdivided into three types. The majority of these machines have diameters between 2 and 4 m and seldom exceed 8 m.

1. Classical multibladed wind pumps driving piston pump with the main manufacturers in Australia, South Africa, the United States, and Argentina. This design was developed from before the turn of the century up to the 1930s. These machines are quite heavy, include a reduction gearbox, are complicated to install, and are quite costly. On the other hand, their reliability is high, they have a long lifetime, and maintenance is reasonably simple, provided spare parts are available. It is estimated that between half a million and a million are still operational, especially in Argentina for cattle watering.

    This classical multiblade is also referred to as the first-generation wind pump and has also been more or less copied by a number of manufacturers in developing countries, in general without attaining the high quality of production of the traditional manufacturers.

2. Second-generation machines. Most of these machines were developed after 1975, for example, by ITDG (UK), Gaviotas (Colombia), CAAMS (China), CWD (The Netherlands), BHEL (Kenya), and Oasis (France). Most of these machines were developed for local production. These modern light-weight wind pumps (also driving piston pumps) are characterized by the use of standard materials (angle iron, ball bearings, pipes, steel plates, etc.) and the absence of castings and reduction gear boxes.

    Usually their rotors have fewer blades than the classical wind pump and so rotate faster. As a gearbox is also omitted, the pump speeds are higher, which can lead to detrimental pump loads and shorter lifetimes if the machine has not been designed adequately.

3. Low-cost wind pumps. This type has an investment cost which is a fraction of that for a comparable first- or second-generation wind pump. Low cost is attained by the simplicity of the product, the low manufacturing cost, and the use of cheap local materials. For example, a lathe is not necessary for production.

Maintenance can be considerable, but it can all be carried out locally. The application is usually restricted to low heads (salt pans in Cape Verde and Thailand, low-head irrigation in Peru). Various research projects have been carried out in order to determine the optimal design and operating conditions of such systems [53, 54].

References

[1] Gilau AM and Small MJ (2008) Designing cost-effective seawater reverse osmosis system under optimal energy options. *Renewable Energy* 33: 617–630.
[2] Kondili E (2010) Hybrid wind energy systems for desalination. In: Kaldellis JK (ed.) *Stand-Alone and Hybrid Wind Energy Systems: Technology, Energy Storage and Applications*, ch. 15. Woodhead Publishing, UK. ISBN 1-84569-527-5, ISBN-13: 978-1-84569-527-9.
[3] New contracted desalination capacity, Global Water Intelligence, Oxford, UK. http://www.globalwaterintel.com/ (accessed March 2011).
[4] Al-Karaghouli A, Renne D, and Kazmerski LL (2009) Solar and wind opportunities for water desalination in the Arab regions. *Renewable and Sustainable Energy Reviews* 13(9): 2397–2407.
[5] Gude VG, Nirmalakhandan N, and Deng S (2010) Renewable and sustainable approaches for desalination. *Renewable and Sustainable Energy Reviews* 14: 2641–2654.
[6] Eltawil MA, Yhengming Y, and Zuan L (2009) A review of renewable energy technologies integrated with desalination systems. *Renewable and Sustainable Energy Reviews* 13(9): 2245–2262.
[7] Subramani A, Badruzzaman M, and Oppenheimer J (2011) Energy minimisation strategies and renewable energy minimization for desalination: A Review. *Water Research* 45: 1907–1920.
[8] Miller JE (2004) *Review of Water Resources and Desalination Technologies*. Albuquerque, NM: Sandia National Laboratories, http://www.sandia.gov/water/docs/MillerSAND2003_0800.pdf, p. 49.
[9] Kaldellis JK, Kavadias KA, and Kondili E (2004) Renewable energy desalination plants for the Greek islands-technical and economic considerations. *Desalination* 170(2): 187–203.
[10] Kaldellis JK, Kondili E, and Kavadias KA (2005) Energy and clean water coproduction in remote islands to face the intermittent character of wind energy. *International Journal of Global Energy Issues* 25(3–4): 298–312.
[11] Vlachos G and Kaldellis JK (2004) Application of a gas-turbine exhausted gases to Brackish water desalination. A techno-economic evaluation. *Applied Thermal Engineering* 24(17–18): 2487–2500.
[12] Papapetrou M, Wieghaus M, and Biercamp C (2011) Roadmap for the development of desalination powered by renewable energy. http://www.prodes-project.org/fileadmin/Files/ProDes_Road_map_on_line_version.pdf (accessed March 2011).
[13] Kondili E and Kaldellis JK (2008) Wind energy based desalination processes and plants. In: Sayigh A (ed.) *Proceedings, Xth World Renewable Energy Congress (WREC X)*, July 2008, pp. 2120–2128 Glasgow, UK.
[14] Mathioulakis E, Belessiotis V, and Delyannis E (2007) Desalination by using alternative energy: Review and state-of-the-art. *Desalination* 203(1–3): 346–365.
[15] Miranda MS and Infield D (2003) A wind-powered seawater reverse-osmosis system without batteries. *Desalination* 153(1–3): 9–16.
[16] Papapetrou M and Epp C (2007) Autonomous desalination units based on renewable energy systems – A review of representative installations worldwide. In: Rizzuti L, Ettouney HM, and Cipollina A (eds) *Solar Desalination for the 21st Century: A Review of Modern Technologies and Researches on Desalination Coupled to Renewable Energies*. The Netherlands: Springer, ISBN-978-1-4020-5506-5, Book chapter.
[17] Tzen E, Theofilloyianakos D, and Kologios Z (2008) Autonomous reverse osmosis units driven by RE sources, experiences and lessons learned. *Desalination* 221(1–3): 29–36.
[18] Tzen E, Epp C, and Papapetrou M Co-ordination action for autonomous desalination units based on RE systems. In: *Desalination Units Powered by Renewable Energy Systems. Opportunities and Challenges*, http://www.adu-res.org/PDF/ADU_RES_509093_D1_3_EN.pdf (accessed in March 2011).
[19] Kershman SA, Rheinländer J, and Gabler H (2003) Seawater reverse osmosis powered from renewable energy sources – Hybrid wind/photovoltaic/grid power supply for small-scale desalination in Libya. *Desalination* 153(1–3): 17–23.

[20] Kershman SA, Rheinlander J, Neumann T, and Goebeld O (2005) Hybrid wind/PV and conventional power for desalination in Libya – GECOL's facility for medium and small scale research at Ras Ejder. *Desalination* 183(1–3): 1–12.
[21] Agashichev SP (2004) Analysis of integrated co-generative schemes including MSF, RO and power generating systems (present value of expenses and 'levelised' cost of water). *Desalination* 164(3): 281–302.
[22] Atikol U and Aybar HS (2005) Estimation of water production cost in the feasibility analysis of RO systems. *Desalination* 184: 253–258.
[23] Ekren O, Ekren BY, and Ozerdem B (2009) Break-even analysis and size optimization of a PV/wind hybrid energy conversion system with battery storage – A case study. *Applied Energy* 86(7–8): 1043–1054.
[24] Fiorenza G, Sharma VK, and Braccio G (2003) Techno-economic evaluation of a solar powered water desalination plant. *Energy Conversion and Management* 44: 2217–2240.
[25] Rheinländer J (2007) De-central water and power supply integrating renewable energy – Technical and economic performance prediction. In: Rizzuti L, Ettouney HM, and Cipollina A (eds) *Solar Desalination for the 21st Century: A Review of Modern Technologies and Researches on Desalination Coupled to Renewable Energies*. pp. 111–126. The Netherlands: Springer, ISBN 978-1-4020-5506-5.
[26] Saheb-Koussa D, Haddadi M, and Belhamel M (2009) Economic and technical study of a hybrid system (wind–photovoltaic–diesel) for rural electrification in Algeria. *Applied Energy* 86(7–8): 1024–1030.
[27] Warfel CG, Manwell JF, and McGowan JG (1988) Techno-economic study of autonomous wind driven reverse osmosis desalination systems. *Solar & Wind Technology* 5(5): 549–561.
[28] Zejli D and Elmidaoui A (2007) Moroccan potentialities of renewable energy sources for water desalination. Rizzuti L, Ettouney HM, and Cipollina A (eds) *Solar Desalination for the 21st Century: A Review of Modern Technologies and Researches on Desalination Coupled to Renewable Energies*. pp. 127–138. The Netherlands: Springer, ISBN 978-1-4020-5506-5.
[29] Zervos A and Assimacopoulos D (2000) Estimating the cost of water produced by RES powered desalination systems. *Mediterranean Conference on Renewable Energy Sources for Water Production*, Santorini, Greece, September 2000.
[30] Kaldellis JK, Kavadias K, and Vlachou D (2000) Improving the economic viability of desalination plants. *Mediterranean Conference on Policies and Strategies for Desalination and Renewable Energies*, Santorini, Greece, September 2000.
[31] Kaldellis JK and Kondili E (2007) The water shortage problem in Aegean Archipelago Islands. Cost-effective desalination prospects. *Desalination Journal* 216: 123–128.
[32] Charcosset C (2009) A review of membrane processes and renewable energies for desalination. *Desalination* 245: 214–231.
[33] Papapetrou M and Papadakis G (2009) *Operating RE/Desalination Units, Seawater Desalination*. Berlin: Springer.
[34] Habali SM and Saleh IA (1994) Design of a stand-alone brackish water desalination wind energy system for Jordan. *Solar Energy* 52(6): 525–532.
[35] Forstmeier M, Mannerheim F, D'Amato SM, et al. (2007) Feasibility study on wind-powered desalination. *Desalination* 203(1–3): 463–470.
[36] Carta JA, Gonzhlezb J, and Subiela V (2004) The SDAWES project: An ambitious R&D prototype for wind powered desalination. *Desalination* 161(1): 33–48.
[37] García-Rodríguez L (2002) Seawater desalination driven by renewable energies: A review. *Desalination* 143(2): 103–113.
[38] Kondili E and Kaldellis JK (2010) Optimization methods and tools for sustainable water resources management. Experiences and trends. Invited Paper, WREC XI, Abu Dhabi, UAE, September 2010.
[39] Kondili E, Kaldellis JK, and Tiligadas D (2010) Wind-based combined electricity and clean water production for remote islands. *Proceedings, WREC XI*, Abu Dhabi, UAE.
[40] Kaldellis JK, Ninou I, and Zafirakis D (2011) Minimum long-term cost solution for remote telecommunication stations on the basis of photovoltaic-based hybrid power systems. *Energy Policy*, 39(5): May 2011, pp. 2512–2527.
[41] http://www.motorola.com (accessed March 2011).
[42] The Most-Used Wind Turbines for Telecommunication Sites, http://www.windenergy.com/commercial/telecommunications.htm (accessed March 2011).
[43] Kaldellis JK (2010) Applications of stand-alone and hybrid energy systems. In: Kaldellis JK (ed.) *Stand-Alone and Hybrid Wind Energy Systems: Technology, Energy Storage and Applications*, ch. 1.5. Woodhead Publishing, ISBN 1-84569-527-5, ISBN-13: 978-1-84569-527-9.
[44] Telecommunications, http://www.globalwindgroup.com/services/telecommunication-solutions (accessed March 2011).
[45] Telecommunication stations, http://www.china-windturbine.com/telecommunication-stations.htm (accessed March 2011).
[46] Kaldellis JK (2010) Optimum hybrid photovoltaic-based solution for remote telecommunication stations. *Renewable Energy* 35(10): 2307–2315.
[47] Wind and solar could power telecommunications in developing world, http://www.tomorrowisgreener.com/wind-and-solar-could-power-telecommunications-in-developing-world/ (accessed March 2011).
[48] Lara DD, Merino GG, Pavez BJ, and Tapia JA (2011) Efficiency assessment of a wind pumping system. *Energy Conversion and Management* 52: 795–803.
[49] Jaramillo OA, Rodriguez-Hernandez O, and Fuentes-Toledo A (2010) Hybrid wind hydropower systems. In: Kaldellis JK (ed.) *Stand-Alone and Hybrid Wind Energy Systems: Technology, Energy Storage and Applications*, ch. 9. Woodhead Publishing, ISBN 1-84569-527-5, ISBN-13: 978-1-84569-527-9.
[50] Gourieres D *Wind Power Plants, Theory and Design*. Pergamon Press, ISBN 0-08-029966.
[51] World Water Assessment Programme for development, capacity building and the environment. http://www.unesco.org/water/wwap (accessed March 2011).
[52] Kaldellis JK, Spyropoulos GC, Kavadias KA, and Koronaki IP (2009) Experimental validation of autonomous PV-based water pumping system optimum sizing. *Renewable Energy Journal* 34: 1106–1113.
[53] Ramos JS and Ramos HM (2009) Sustainable application of renewable sources in water pumping systems: Optimized energy system configuration. *Energy Policy* 37: 633–643.
[54] Smulders Paul T and Jan de Jongh I (1994) Wind water pumping: Status, prospects and barriers. *Renewable Energy* 5(Pt I): 587–594.

Further Reading

ALTENER Programme (2002) Renewable energy driven desalination systems – REDDES. Technical analysis of existing RES desalination schemes. Stylianos Loupasis. http://www.nad.gr/readsa/files/TechnodatabaseREDDES.PDF (accessed March 2011)

Ekren BY and Ekren O (2009) Simulation based size optimization of a PV/wind hybrid energy conversion system with battery storage under various load and auxiliary energy conditions. *Applied Energy* 86(9): 1387–1394.

Fritzmann C, Löwenberg J, Wintgens T, and Melin T (2007) State-of-the-art of reverse osmosis desalination. *Desalination* 216(1–3): 1–76.

Garcia-Rodriguez L, Romero-Ternero V, and Gomez-Camacho C (2001) Economic analysis of wind-powered desalination. *Desalination* 137: 259–265.

Hamed OA (2005) Overview of hybrid desalination systems – Current status and future prospects. *Desalination* 186(1–3): 207–214.

Kamal I (2008) Myth and reality of the hybrid desalination process. *Desalination* 230(1–3): 269–280.

Kim YM, Kim SJ, Kim YS, et al. (2009) Overview of systems engineering approaches for a large-scale seawater desalination plant with a reverse osmosis network. *Desalination* 238(1–3): 312–332.

NREL, Wind Energy/Desalination System (2005) wwww.nrel.gov/wind/pdfs/39485.pdf (accessed February 2011).

Schiffler M (2004) Perspectives and challenges for desalination in the 21st century. *Desalination* 165: 1–9.

Tzen E, Theofilloyianakos D, and Kologios Z (2008) Autonomous reverse osmosis units driven by RE sources, experiences and lessons learned. *Desalination* 221(1–3): 29–36.

Continuous and unlimited operation of telecom sites, http://www.tswind.com/index.php/telecom.html (accessed March 2011).

Kondili E (2010) Design and performance optimization of stand-alone and hybrid wind energy systems. In: Kaldellis JK (ed.) *Stand-Alone and Hybrid Wind Energy Systems: Technology, Energy Storage and Applications*, ch. 3. Woodhead Publishing, UK, ISBN 1 84569 527 5, ISBN-13: 978 1 84569 527 9.